THE RUMINANT ANIMAL

DIGESTIVE PHYSIOLOGY
AND NUTRITION

THE RUMINANT ANIMAL

DIGESTIVE PHYSIOLOGY AND NUTRITION

D. C. Church, Editor

A Reston Book
PRENTICE HALL, Englewood Cliffs, New Jersey 07632

Library of Congress Cataloging-in-Publication Data

The Ruminant animal.

"A Reston book."
Includes bibliographies and index.
    1. Ruminants—Physiology.   2. Ruminants—Feeding and
feeds.   3. Animal nutrition.   4. Digestion.
I. Church, D. C.
SF768.2.R8R86   1988   636.2'08923   87-11346
ISBN 0-8359-6782-4

Previously published as *Digestive Physiology and
Nutrition of Ruminants*, 2nd ed., Vol. I, 1969, 1976,
and Vol. II, 1971, 1979, D. C. Church et al.,
O&B Books, Inc.

Printed in the United States of America

10 9 8 7 6 5 4 3 2 1

ISBN 0-8359-6782-4   025

Prentice-Hall International (UK) Limited, *London*
Prentice-Hall of Australia Pty. Limited, *Sydney*
Prentice-Hall Canada Inc., *Toronto*
Prentice-Hall Hispanoamericana, S.A., *Mexico*
Prentice-Hall of India Private Limited, *New Delhi*
Prentice-Hall of Japan, Inc., *Tokyo*
Prentice-Hall of Southeast Asia Pte. Ltd., *Singapore*
Editora Prentice-Hall do Brasil, Ltda., *Rio de Janeiro*

CONTENTS

1 The Classification and Importance of Ruminant Animals   1

    Prof. Emeritus D. C. Church, Ph.D. Dept. of Animal Science, Oregon State Univ.,
    Corvallis, OR 97330

Part I. Digestive Physiology

2 Anatomy of the Gastro-Intestinal Tract   14

    Prof. R. R. Hofmann, Dr. med. vet., Dept. of Comparative Anatomy, Institut
    für Veterinär-Anatomie, Justus-Liebig-Universität, 6300 Giessen, Federal Republic of
    Germany

3 Growth and Development of the Ruminant Digestive System   44

    Prof. Sidney J. Lyford, Jr., Ph.D., Dept. of Veterinary and Animal Sciences, Univ. of
    Massachusetts, Amherst, MA 01003

4 Motility of the Gastro-Intestinal Tract   64

    Prof. Y. Ruckebusch, DVM, Dr. Sci., Dept. Physiologie-Pharmacodynamie-Thérapeutique,
    Ecole Nationale Vetérinaire, 31076 Toulouse, France

5 Ingestion of Feed and Water   108

    Prof. J. G. Welch, Ph.D. and A. P. Hooper, Ph.D., Dept. of Animal Sciences, Univ. of
    Vermont, Burlington, VT 05405

6 Salivary Function and Production   117

    Prof. D. C. Church

7 Microbiology of the Rumen and Intestine   125

    M. T. Yokoyama, Ph. D. and K. A. Johnson, Ph. D., Dept. of Animal Science, Michigan
    State Univ., East Lansing, MI 48824

8 Ruminal Fermentation   145

    Prof. F. N. Owens, Ph.D., Dept. of Animal Science, Oklahoma State Univ., Stillwater,
    OK 74078 and A. L. Goetsch, Ph.D., Dept. of Animal Science, Univ. of Arkansas,
    Fayetville, AK 72701

9 Digestion, Absorption and Excretion in Ruminants   172

    N. R. Merchen, Ph.D., Dept. of Animal Sciences, Univ. of Illinois, Urbana, IL 61801

Part II. Nutrient Consumption, Metabolism and Requirements

10   Appetite, Palatability and Control of Feed Intake   202

        W. L. Grovum, Ph.D., Dept. of Biomedical Sciences Univ. of Guelph, Guelph, Ont.,
        Canada NIG 2W1

11   Water and Its Functions, Regulation and Comparative Use by Ruminant Livestock   217

        Victor R. Squires, Ph.D., Dean, Faculty of Natural Resources, Roseworthy Agricultural
        College, Roseworthy, SA 5371, Australia

12   Protein Metabolism of Ruminant Animals   227

        Prof. Fred N. Owens, Ph.D., Dept. of Animal Science, Oklahoma State Univ., Stillwater,
        OK 74078 and Richard Zinn, Ph.D., Agricultural Experiment Station, Univ. of California,
        El Centro, CA 92243

13   Energy Metabolism   250

        C. L. Ferrell, Ph.D., USDA, ARS, Roman L. Hruska, US Meat Animal Res. Center, Clay
        Center, NB 68933

14   Carbohydrate Nutrition of Ruminants   269

        G. C. Fahey, Jr., Ph.D., and L. L. Berger, Ph.D., Dept. of Animal Sciences, Univ. of
        Illinois, Urbana, IL 61801

15   Lipids in Ruminant Nutrition   298

        Prof. F. M. Byers, Ph.D. and Prof. G. T. Schelling, Ph.D., Dept. of Animal Science,
        Texas A&M Univ., College Station, TX 77843

16   Vitamins in Ruminant Nutrition   313

        Prof. J. Tal Huber, Ph.D., Dept. of Animal Science, Univ. of Arizona, Tucson, AZ 85721

17   Macro Elements for Ruminants   326

        Ron Kincaid, Ph.D., Dept. of Animal Science, Washington State Univ., Pullman,
        WA 99164

18   The Trace Elements   342

        Prof. J. K. Miller, Ph.D. and Nancy Ramsey, M.S., Dept. of Animal Science, Univ. of
        Tennessee, Knoxville, TN 37901 and F. C. Madsen, Ph.D., Nutribasics Co., Highland,
        IL 62249

19   Digestion, Metabolism and Nutrient Needs in Preruminants   401

        Profs. Sidney J. Lyford, Jr., and J. Tal Huber

20   Nutrient Needs During Critical Periods of the Life Cycle   421
        Effect of Nutrition on Fertility, Reproduction and Lactation

        Prof. David J. Schingoethe, Ph.D., Dept. of Dairy Science, South Dakota State Univ.,
        Brookings, SD 57007

        Nutrition in Growth   437

        Profs. F. M. Byers and G. T. Schelling

21   Nutrient Needs of Ruminants versus Monogastric Species   448

        Prof. David J. Schingoethe

Part III. Nutritionally Related Problems

22   Effect of Environmental Stress on Nutrient Needs   456

> Prof. B. A. Young, Ph.D., Dept. of Animal Science, Univ. of Alberta, Edmonton, Albt., Canada T6G 2P5

23   Nutritional Problems Related to the Gastro-Intestinal Tract

Bloat   468

> Prof. H. W. Essig, Ph.D., Dept. of Animal Science, Mississippi State Univ., Mississippi State, MS 39762

Acidosis   474

> Gerald B. Huntington, Ph.D., USDA, ARS, Ruminant Nutrition Laboratory, Beltsville, MD 20705

Nitrate and Urea Toxicities   480

> Prof. Royce J. Emerick, Ph.D., Station Biochem. Sec., Dept. of Chemistry, South Dakota State Univ., Brookings, SD 57007

Acute Pulmonary Edema and Interstitial Emphysema in Cattle   485

> Prof. J. R. Carlson, Ph.D., Dept. of Animal Science, Washington State Univ., Pullman, WA 99164

24   Metabolic Problems Related to Nutrition,   493
Milk Fever, Ketosis and the Fat Cow Syndrome

> Prof. L. H. Schultz, Ph.D., Dept. of Dairy Science, Univ. of Wisconsin, Madison, WI 53706

Grass Tetany   511

> H. F. Mayland, Ph.D., USDA, ARS, Snake River Conservation Res. Center, Kimberly, ID 83341

Urinary Calculi   523

> Prof. Royce J. Emerick

25   Therapeutic Nutrition   532

> Prof. J. H. Ternouth, MVS, Ph.D., Dept. of Animal production, Univ. of Queensland, St. Lucia, Brisbane, Qld. 4067, Australia

Subject Matter Index   543

PREFACE

This book for all practical purposes, brings together in one volume the series, Digestive Physiology and Nutrition of Ruminants, whose first volume originally appeared in 1969. Many things have changed in the intervening years.

The subject of digestive physiology and nutrition of ruminants is a fascinating field dealing with most interesting animals. As extensive research continues on a world-wide scale, we are gradually accumulating more and more data with which to better understand these animals. We thus strive towards more complete understanding and because of continued readers' interest have pursued the publication of this volume by way of facilitating the dissemination of this ever growing body of knowledge.

The Ruminant Animal represents a compilation of up-to-date information on major topics related to nutrient requirements and nutrient metabolism. You will note that each chapter has been newly illustrated and assimilates recent research citations. Due to the ever increasing amount of recent research and the pub-

lisher's concern for lengthiness, older references have by necessity been dropped from this volume.

The editor might also point out that a book written by multiple authors has both advantages and disadvantages. If the editor selects the right co-author, it can result in a chapter with more authoritative writing on any particular topic because it is easier to write about a topic on which you are well versed and have done extensive research. On the other hand, not all great researchers are good writers. Another disadvantage of multiple authorships is that coverage of the total topic is less likely to be as cohesive as if one or two individuals had done all the writing. Conversely, as a field of knowledge expands, it also becomes more specialized and eventually becomes too much for one or two individuals to do it justice.

We would also like to take this opportunity to thank the countless individuals both past and present, without whose time, vision and energies, this volume would not have been possible.

D. C. Church

THE RUMINANT ANIMAL

DIGESTIVE PHYSIOLOGY
AND NUTRITION

1 THE CLASSIFICATION AND IMPORTANCE OF RUMINANT ANIMALS

by D. C. Church

INTRODUCTION

Ruminant animals can be a fascinating topic of study for any person having a personal, commercial or professional interest in animals. There are many different species found in a diverse range of body size, shapes and colors, and they are distributed over a wide variety of climatic and vegetative zones. In size they range from the very small Mouse Deer (*Hyemoschus* or *Tragulus*) which may weigh from 2 to 5 kg and have a shoulder height of 200 to 350 mm, to the Giraffes, which may attain a shoulder height of 3.5 m and, in some instances, an overall height of about 6 m and a weight of about 1.9 metric tons (males). Most species, of course, fall between these extremes. The tremendous diversity in these animals makes them an extremely interesting topic for the casual reader, animal lover, livestock producer or professional animal scientist. Thus, this book is dedicated towards a better understanding of ruminant animals, both wild and domestic, in our modern world.

Ruminant animals are classified in the subclass referred to as ungulates (hooved mammals) and in the order *Arteriodactyla* (even-toed) and the suborder, ruminantia. The word, ruminant, comes from the Latin word, *ruminare,* which means to chew over again; thus, ruminants are cud-chewing, even-toed, hooved mammals.

Of the various herbivorous species of animals, ruminants are by far the most important in terms of the numbers of mammals existing today, either domestic, feral (domesticated animals which have returned to the wild state) or wild. Although fossil remains are less complete than might be desired, existing evidence indicates that the number of species increased considerably during the Tertiary period of prehistoric times, a period coinciding with the development and spread of grasses and related vegetation. During the post-Oligocene period, ruminants were the dominant herbivores. Simpson (1) gives some estimates of the number of extinct and living genera of herbivorous animals derived from fossil finds. For the *Artiodactyla,* he estimated that 333 genera are extinct and 86 living, as compared to 1,932 extinct and 932 living genera for all mammals. He further estimated that about 180 genera of ruminants are extinct and that 68 genera have survived to this time. Only a few primitive ruminants (*Traguilade*) have survived. Domesticated ruminants, represented by only a few genera, undoubtedly outnumber all of the wild ruminants at the present time.

Fossil records are, without doubt, far from complete. Thus, the geographical distribution of ruminants in prehistoric times is not as well documented as one might wish, but ruminant fossils have been found on all current land masses except Australia and Antartica. In recent geological times it is certainly true in the western hemisphere that a larger variety and more total numbers lived in temperate climates. In contrast, at the present time, in Africa many more diverse species exist in semitropical and tropical regions than in other areas. Whether the diversity in Africa is caused by the climate and geography or to geological phenomena that allowed existing species to survive ice invasions, continental drift and separation, or other drastic climatic changes or events in times past is an unresolved question. Certainly, the mountain ranges of southern Europe and Asia, the Mediterranean Sea, or surrounding deserts would be formidable barriers for many species to overcome following a period of ice invasion or extreme cold in the northern areas of Europe and Asia.

Existing species inhabit climates varying from arctic (yak, caribou, musk ox, mountain goats and sheep, etc.) to wet and dry tropical climates (primarily African species), and from swampy environments (moose, water buffalo, swamp deer, water bucks) to deserts (antelope, sheep, various African and Asian species). Consequently, the dietary habits or food preferences vary from those ruminants such as the caribou which consumes arctic lichens to the giraffe's predilection for the leaves of the thorny acacia tree. The moose, for example, is a heavy consumer of aquatic plants and has been reported to feed in water up to 3 m in depth. Antelope species, most deer, goats, sheep and many other species prefer browse (woody plants) or forbes to grasses. Animals such as the water buffalo do well on coarse reeds and grasses that would not sustain many domestic cattle. The American bison and domestic cattle, as well as many other species, prefer grasses. However, data (for species on which it is available) demonstrate that ruminants will consume a varied diet if they have the opportunity to do so. As pointed out in Ch. 2, the nature of the stomach and other parts of the gastro-intestinal tract have an important effect on the type of diet that a given species can utilize well.

The geneticist might say that this natural preference for certain plant types is the outcome of evolution, resulting from development of the animal in a given environment. Pressure of other species for a plant type or over-population of an animal species might also have been factors. Undoubtedly, unknown physiological differences are also involved, but comparative data are inadequate to establish this point on most wild species and, for that matter, even on domestic species.

CLASSIFICATION OF SPECIES

For the benefit of readers interested in classification, animals are classed into smaller and smaller groups in the following manner.

Kingdom—Animal
　Phylum—Cordata (with a backbone)
　　Class—Mammals (produce milk)
　　　Subclass—Ungulata (hooved animals)
　　　　Order—Artiodactyla (even-toed)
　　　　　Suborder—Ruminantia (true ruminants) and
　　　　　　Tylopoda (even-toed with fleshy pads
　　　　　　rather than true hooves)
　　　　　Family or Suborder
　　　　　　Genus and Subgenus
　　　　　　　Species and Subspecies

With regard to classification, it should be pointed out that there are differences of

opinion among taxonomic authorities. In some cases there is no agreement as to what the genus should be or on what constitutes a true species and there is even less agreement on subspecies. In the usual terminology, species are differentiated from another similar animal if they do not interbreed or, if they do, a fertile offspring is not produced. A good example is the mule, a hybrid between the horse (*Equas cabalus*) and the ass (*Equas asinus*); mules are infertile in almost all instances.

In the case of domestic cattle, European and Zebu cattle will interbreed and produce fertile offspring, thus they should probably be classed in one species. Non-humped cattle vary tremendously in size, color, color patterns, presence or absence of horns and shape and size of horns. For example, horns may vary from none in the polled breeds to the huge, upsweeping horns of the Ankole breed found in Africa. Honacki et al (2) state that all cattle are *Bos taurus,* but other writers such as Walker et al (3) list Zebu cattle as *Bos indicus.* The same problems arise when classifying domestic sheep and goats. With wild species, subspecies may be named because of differences in size, coat color, color pattern of the coat, size and shape of horns and, possibly, geographical distribution. For further information on this topic the writer would recommend the book of Mochi and Carter (4) which presents descriptions in the form of silhouettes accompanied by some written text.

A listing of existing ruminant and pseudo-ruminant species is given in Table 1-1, essentially as described by Honacki et al. In the table the various animals are listed alphabetically by families and alphabetically by genus and species within families in order to facilitate finding a given animal.

In this classification, ruminant animals are divided into three families: Cervidae, with 14 genera and 37 species; Giraffidae, with 2 genera and 2 species; and Bovidae, with 45 genera and 126 species. Cervidae are deer and related animals which carry antlers (sometimes on both sexes), comprised of solid bone, which are shed and renewed annually. The Musk Deer is an exception because it has no antlers, but enlarged canine teeth which form tusks. The Muntjacs have tusks and antlers and Tufted deer have tusks and small antlers. Giraffidae are characterized by having

Table 1-1. Taxonomic classification of ruminants and pseudoruminants.

Pseudoruminants—Cud-chewing animals which have stomachs with three compartments and other minor differences from true ruminants

    Family: Tragulidae. Mouse Deer or Chevrotains

      Hyemoschus aquaticus. Water Chevrotain. Sierra Leone to Gabon to Zaire and Uganda.

      Tragulus javanicus. Small Malayan Chevrotain or Mouse Deer. S.E. Asia.

      T. meminna. Indian Chevrotain. Sri Lanka, India, Nepal.

      T. napu. Large Malayan Chevrotain. S.E. Asia, Philippines, Sumatra.

  Suborder: Tylopoda. Even-toed, but have feet which resemble pads more than hooves; 3 compartmented stomach.

    Family: Camelidae. Camels and Llamas and their relatives

      Camelus bactrianus. Bactrian (two-humped) camel. Some still exist in the wild form in the Gobi Desert. Produces fertile hybrids with dromedarius.

      C. dromedarius. Arabian Camel or Dromedary. Arabia, N. Africa.

      Lama glama. Llama. Domesticated. Multiple purpose animal. Western and southern South America.

      L. guanicoe. Guanaco (wild form). Southern and western S. America.

      L. pacos. Alpaca (domesticated). Wool production. Peru, Bolivia.

      Vicugna vicugna. Vicuña. Western S. America.

True Ruminants (Pecora)

  Suborder: Ruminantia. Even-toed, hooved true ruminants.

    Family: Cervidae. Deer and Allied species

      Alces alces. European Elk, American Moose. At least 5 subspecies have been identified. Northern Europe, Asia, Alaska, Canada, USA.

      Blastocerus dichotomus. South American Marsh Deer. C. Brazil to Paraguay and N. Argentina.

      Capreolus capreolus. European Roe Buck. Europe, Asia.

      Cervus albirostris. Thorold's or White-Lipped Deer. Tibet and N. China.

      C. axis. Axis Deer or Chital. India, Sri Lanka, Nepal

      †*C. dama.* Fallow Deer. Europe, near east, formerly N. Africa.

      †*C. duvauceli.* Barasingha or Swamp Deer. N. and C. India, S.W. Nepal.

      †*C. elaphus.* Red Deer, American Elk, Wapiti, etc. 10-12 subspecies have been described. Forest moorland and alpine habitats of Europe, Caucasus and C. Asia to China, USSR, N. Africa and N. America. In the USA, three elk subspecies are present—Rocky Mountain, Roosevelt and Tule Elk.

      C. eldi. Thamin or Eld's Deer. S.E. Asia.

      †*C. nippon.* Sika Deer. China, Siberia, S.E. Asia.

      †*C. porcinus.* Hog Deer. India, China, Indonesia.

      C. schomburgki. Schomburgk's Deer. S.E. Asia. Probably extinct.

      C. timorensis. Rusa. Indonesia.

      C. unicolor. Sambar. Philippines, Indonesia, India, S.E. Asia.

      Elaphodus cephalophus. West China Tufted Deer. China, Burma.

      Elaphurus davidianus. Pere David's Deer. China. Now only in captivity.

      Hippocamelus antisensis. Peruvian Guemal, Taruga, Andean Deer. Andes Mtn. from Ecuador to N.W. Argentina.

      H. bisulcus. Chilean Guemal or Huemul. Andes Mtn. of S. Chile and S. Argentina.

      Hydropotes inermis. Chinese Water Deer. China, Korea.

      Mazama americana. Red Brocket. S. Mexico to N. Argentina.

      M. chunyi. Brocket Deer. Bolivian Andes, S. Peru.

      M. gouazoubira. Brocket Deer. Central and northern S. America.

      M. rufina. Brown Brocket Deer. Venezuela and nearby countries.

      Moschus berezovski. Musk Deer. S.W. China, Vietnam.

      M. chryogaster. Musk Deer. India, Nepal, S.E. China.

      †*M. moschiferus.* Musk Deer. E. Siberia, N. China.

      M. sifanicus. Musk Deer. Tibetan plateau.

      Muntiacus crinifrons. Hariy-Fronted or Black Muntjac. China. Rare or extinct.

      M. feai. Tenasserim Muntjac. Thailand, Burma. Rare.

      M. muntjak. Javan Muntjac. Indonesia, Sri Lanka, India, China.

      M. reevesi. Muntjac or Barking Deer. S. China.

      M. rooseveltorum. Muntjac. S.E. Asia.

      †*Odocoileus hemionus.* Mule and Black-tailed Deer (different subspecies). West of Rocky Mountains, Alaska to Baja, CA, and Sonora.

      †*O. virginianus.* White-tailed Deer. At least three subspecies—Virginia and Florida White-tailed and Key Deer. Some writers list as many as 5 other *Odocoileus* species.

      Ozotoceros bezoarticus. Pampas Deer. Plains of Brazil, Argentina, Paraguay, Uruguay, S. Bolivia.

      Pudu mephistophiles. Pudu. Andes of Colombia and Ecuador.

Table 1-1. Continued.

P. pudu. Pudu. S. Chile, S.W. Argentina.

Rangifer tarandus. Caribou, Reindeer. At least 12 subspecies have been described. Europe, N. Asia, Alaska, Canada. Domestic and wild.

Family: Giraffidae. Giraffes and Okapi.

Giraffa camelopardalis. Giraffe. 12 subspecies are found in C., E. and S. Africa.

Okapia johnstoni. Okapi. E.C. Zaire; perhaps adjacent areas.

Family: Bovidae. Ruminants with horns which are not shed.

Addax nasomaculatus. Adax. Nearly extinct in wild. Mauritania to Sudan; formerly Egypt to Tunisia.

†*Aepyceros melampus.* Impalla. South Africa to Zaire, Rwanda, Uganda and N.E. Kenya.

†*Alcelaphus buselaphus.* Hartebeests. Several subspecies. Senegal to W. Somalia to N. South Africa to S. Angola.

†*Ammodorcas clarkei.* Dibatag or Clark's Gazelle. E. Ethiopia, N. Somalia.

Ammotragus lervia. Barbary Sheep or Aoudad. N. Egypt to Morocco. Niger to Sudan.

Antidorcas marsupialis. Springbuck or Springbok. South Africa.

†*Antilocapra americana.* Pronghorn Antelope. Several subspecies. S. Alberta and Saskatchewan through W. USA to N. Mexico. Formerly classified in a separate family of **Antilocapra.**

Antilope cervicapra. Blackbuck or Indian Antelope. Pakistan and India.

†*Bison bison.* American Buffalo or Bison. Formerly N.W. and C. Canada, south through USA to N. Mexico. Several subspecies. Now in confinement or parks, only.

B. bonasus. European Bison or Wisent. Europe and W. USSR. Now captive only.

Bos frontalis. Gayal or Mithan. Pakistan, India to Malay Peninsula. Some writers claim it is a domesticated form of the Guar.

†*B. grunniens.* Yak. N. China, India, Tibet. Domesticated in Central Asia.

†*B. guarus.* Guar or Sladang. India, Indochina. Some writers put it in the same species as frontalis.

B. indicus. Domestic Humped Cattle or Zebu. Some writers state that this species evolved from the wild Malayan Banteng. Others state that it was developed from *B. primigenius namadicus,* an eastern variety of this species. Origin in mideast.

**B. javanicus.* Banteng. Burma, Thailand, Malaysia, Indonesia.

**B. sauveli.* Kouprey or Forest Ox. Kampuchea. Some writers believe it to be a hybrid between the Guar and other species.

B. taurus. Domestic cattle. Some writers state the *B. t.* cattle evolved from *B. primigenius,* the great ox or Auroch of Europe and *B. longifrons,* a smaller type found on the British Iles. Origin probably in mideast. The last wild form of *B. primigenius* (captive) died in 1627. Some writers lump both *B. taurus* and *B. indicus* under *B. taurus.*

Boselaphus tragocamelus. Nilgai or Bluebuck. India to Indochina. Widespread as domesticated or feral animals in S.E. Asia, S. Europe, N. Africa, N. Australia and E. South America.

†*Bubalus depressicornis.* Anoa or Dwarf Water Buffalo. Celebes Islands.

**B. mindorensis.* Tamarou. Mindoro Island in the Philippines.

†*B. quarlesi.* Mountain Anoa. Mountains in the Celebes.

Budorcas taxicolor. Takin. At least 3 subspecies. Mountains of S.E. Asia.

Capra angorensus. Domesticated mohair-producing goats (Angora) which appear to have originated in Turkey. Some writers do not list it as a separate species from *C. h. h.*

C. caucasica. Caucasian Tur. W. Caucasus Mtn. (USSR).

C. cylindrincornis. Tur. USSR, E. Caucasus Mtn.

†*C. falconeri.* Astor Markhor and Cabul Markor. India, Kashmir.

C. hircus aegarus. Persian or Grecian Ibex. Several subspecies are found in the mountains from the Caucasus to Baluchistan. This species is believed to be the ancestor of domestic goats.

C. hircus hircus. Domesticated goats used for milk production. Origin probably in Greece, Turkey and other near eastern areas.

†*C. ibex.* Ibex. Several subspecies. C. Europe, Afghanistan and Kashmir to Mongolia and C. China; N. Ethiopia to Syria and Arabia.

†*C. pyrenaica.* Spanish Ibex or Tur. Pyrenees Mtn. of Spain and Portugal.

Capricornis crispus. Serow. Japan, Taiwan.

**C. sumatraensis.* Serow. Indochina, S.E. Asia.

Cephalophus adersi. Duiker. Tanzania, Zanzibar.

C. callipygus. Peter's Duiker. Central Africa.

C. dorsalis. Gray's Duiker. Central Africa.

**C. jentinki.* Duiker. Liberia, W. Ivory Coast.

C. leucogaster. Gaboon Duiker. S. Cameroun south to Congo River, east to E. Zaire.

C. maxwelli. Maxwell's Blue Duiker. Senegal and Gambia to Nigeria.

C. moticolo. Equatorial Blue Duiker. Nigeria to Gabon, Kenya to South Africa to Angola, Zanzibar.

C. natalensis. Duiker. Central Africa.

C. niger. Black-fronted Duiker. Guinea to Nigeria, west of Niger river.

C. nigrifrons. Duiker. Cameroun, Gabon, and east to Kenya.

Table 1-1. Continued.

C. ogilbyi. Duiker. Western Africa.

C. rufilatus. Duiker. Senegal to S.W. Sudan and N.E. Uganda south to Cameroun.

C. spadix. Abbott's Duiker. Tanzania at higher elevations.

C. sylvicultor. Light-backed Duiker. Central Africa.

C. weynsi. Weyn's Duiker. Zaire, Uganda, Rwanda and W. Kenya.

C. zebra. Striped-backed or Zebra Duiker. Sierra Leone, Liberia, Ivory Coast.

Connochaetes gnou. White-tailed Wildebeest or Gnu. Now found only in semidomesticated state in Transvaal and the Orange Free State.

C. taurinus. Brindled and White-beared Wildebeest. S. Angola, Namibia, N. South Africa, Botswana, C. Mozambique and E. Zambia to Tanzania and S.E. and S.C. Kenya.

†*Damaliscus dorcas.* Bontebok. South Africa; now only in captivity.

D. hunteri. Hunter's Hartebeest. Somalia to N. Kenya.

D. lunatus. Hartebeest. Subspecies referred to as Senegal Hartebeest, Topi, Tiang or Sassaby. Central to southern Africa.

Dorcatragus megalotis. Beira. Somalia and E. Ethiopia.

Gazella cuvieri. Edmi or Atlas Gazelle. Morocco, N. Algeria, C. Tunisia.

†*G. dama.* Addra Gazelle. Deserts of N. Africa.

†*G. dorcas.* Dorcas Gazelle. Deserts of N. Africa.

G. gazella. Arabian Gazelle. Syria, Sinai to Arabia.

G. granti. Grant's Gazelle. S. Sudan and N.E. Uganda, Somalia to N. Tanzania.

G. leptoceros. Loder's Gazelle. Deserts of N. Africa.

G. rufifrons. Red-fronted Gazelle. Subsaharan areas of N. Africa.

G. rufina. Red Gazelle. Algeria. Thought to be extinct.

G. soemmerringi. Soemmerring's Gazelle. Ethiopia, Somalia, Sudan.

G. spekei. Speke's Gazelle. Somalia, E. Ethiopia.

†*G. subgutturosa.* Goitered Gazelle. Iran and Arabia to S. Gobi Desert.

G. thomsoni. Thomson's Gazelle. S. Sudan to N. Tanzania.

Hemitragus hylocrinus. Nilgiri Tahr. Mtn. of S. India.

H. jayakari. Arabian Tahr. Oman, S.E. Arabia.

H. jemlahicus. Tahr, Himalayan Tahr. Himalayas from Kashmir to Tibet.

Hippotragus equinus. Roan Antelope. Senegal to Ethiopia, Sudan to South Africa.

H. leucophaeus. Bluebok. South Africa.

†*H. niger.* Sable Antelope. Central Africa.

Kobus ellipsiprymnus. Common Waterbuck. Senegal to Somalia to N. South Africa to Angola.

K. kob. White-eared, Buffon's or Uganda Kob. Central and W. Africa.

K. leche. Lechwe. Central Africa.

K. megaceros. Nile Lechwe. S. Sudan, W. Ethiopia.

K. vardoni. Puku. Central Africa.

Litocranius walleri. Gerenuk or Waller's Gazelle. Somalia to Kenya, N.E. Tanzania and E. Ethiopia.

Madoqua guentheri. Long-snouted Dik-Dik. Somalia, Ethiopia, Tanzania.

M. kirki. Kirk's Dik-Dik. Eastern and S.W. Africa.

M. piacentini. Dik-Dik. E. Somalia.

M. saltiana. Phillip's Dik-Dik. Somalia, Ethiopia, Sudan.

Nemorhaedus goral. Goral. N. India and Burma to S.E. Siberia, south to Thailand.

Neotragus batesi. Pygmy Antelope. S. Nigeria to Gabon, N.E. Zaire to W. Uganda.

†*N. moschatus.* Pygmy Antelope. N. South Africa to Kenya.

N. pygmaeus. Pygmy Antelope. Sierra Leone to Ghana.

Oreamnos americanus. Rocky Mountain Goat. Alaska south through Idaho, Colorado, Washington.

Oreotragus oreotragus. Klipspringer. South Africa.

Oryx dammah. White Oryx. Deserts of N. Africa.

O. gazella. Gemsbok and Beisa Oryx. C. and S.W. Africa.

O. leucoryx. Arabian Oryx. S.E. Arabian Peninusla; formerly Iraq.

Ourebia ourebi. Uasin Gishu Oribi. E. and C. Africa.

Ovibos moschatus. Barren Ground, Hudson Bay and White-fronted Muskox. Arctic tundras of N. America, Greenland.

†*Ovix ammon.* Argali or Marco Polo's Sheep. Mtn. of C. and E. USSR east to W. China, south to Nepal.

O. aries. Domestic sheep. Origin in Turkey, Iran or other mideast areas. Some writers say that *O. ammon* is the source, others that *O. musimon* or *O. vignei* are ancestors.

O. canadensis. Rocky Mountain Sheep or Bighorn Sheep. Rocky Mtn. of Alberta and British Columbia south into western states of USA.

O. canadensis nelsoni. Desert Bighorn. Nevada and California south to Mexico.

O. dalli. Dall's or White Sheep. Alaska and Yukon area.

O. dalli stonei. Stone's Sheep. N. British Columbia, Yukon.

O. musimon. Mouflon. Originally restricted to islands of Sardinia and Corsica. Widely introduced into Europe.

Table 1-1. Continued

O. nivicola. Siberian Argali. Mtn. of Siberia and E. USSR.

*O. *vignei.* Asiatic Mouflon, Red Sheep, Urial or Shapu. Mtn. of southern and western USSR, Iran, Afganistan, Kashmir, Pakistan and Baluchistan.

Pantholops hodgsoni. Chiru or Tibetan Antelope. Tibet, S.W. China, N. India.

Pelea capreolus. Rhebok. South Africa.

Procapra gutturosa. Zeren or Mongolian Gazelle. Mongolia.

P. picticaudata. Goa or Tibetan Gazelle. Tibetan Plateau.

P. przewalskii. Przewalski's Gazelle. S. Mongolia, N.W. China.

Pseudois nayaur. Bharal or Blue Sheep. Tibet, Nepal.

Raphicerus campestris. Steinbok. Angola to South Africa to S. Kenya.

R. melanotis. Grysbok. South Africa.

R. Sharpei. Sharpe's Grysbok. South Africa to Tanzania and S.E. Zaire.

Redunca arundinum. Reedbuck. South Africa to Gabon and Zaire; Tanzania, Zambia, Mozambique.

R. fulvorufula. Mountain Reedbuck. C. and S. Africa.

R. redunca. Behor Reedbuck. Senegal to C. Ethiopia, south to E. Zaire and S.W. Tanzania.

†*Rupicapra rupicapra.* Chamois. Mtn. of S. Europe and Asia Minor.

†*Saiga tatarica.* Saiga. N. Caucasus to Mongolia.

Sigmoceros lichtensteini. Lichtenstein's Hartebeest. Central Africa.

Sylvicapra grimmia. Red Hartebeest. Subsaharan Africa.

Syncerus caffer. Cape Buffalo. Senegal to S. Ethiopia to South Africa.

Tetracerus quadricornis. Chousingha or Four-Horned Antelope. India, Nepal.

Tragelaphus angasi. Nyala. South Africa.

T. buxtoni. Mountain Nyala. Ethiopia.

T. eurycerus. Bongo. Central Africa.

T. imberbis. Lesser Kudu. Tanzania, Ethiopia, Somalia, S.E. Sudan.

T. oryx. Eland. Central and S. Africa.

T. scriptus. Bushbuck or Harnessed Antelope. S. Mauritania to Ethiopia and S. Somalia to South Africa.

T. spekei. Sitatunga. Gambia to S.W. Ethiopia, south to Angola, Namibia and South Africa.

T. strepsiceros. Greater Kudu. Somalia and Ethiopia to N. South Africa, west to Namibia and S.E. Zaire and other C. African areas.

*Endangered species. † One or more subspecies are classed as endangered.

short horns covered with hair-bearing skin. Bovidae—the antelopes, goat-antelopes, musk oxen, takins, goats, sheep, cattle, bison and buffalo—characteristically have horns which grow over a bony core and which are never shed. The pronghorn antelope (*Antilocapra americana*) was formerly put in the family Antilocapridae, but is classed in Bovidae by Honacki et al. In its case, it has horns which carry a prong which grows over a bony core, but the outer sheath is shed and renewed each year.

Tragulidae (2 genera, 4 species), the mouse deer or chevrotains, are small primitive species similar to the Pecora (true ruminants) in not having upper incisor teeth and in chewing their cud, but different in that the stomach has only three compartments and, for males, in having tusk-like canine teeth. Walker et al (3) state that they are probably more closely related to Camelidae and Suidae (pigs) than to Cervidae.

The Camelidae (3 genera, 6 species), camels and camelids (llama and related species), are animals which walk on broad fleshy pads and have two toes on each foot. They are generally classed as pseudoruminants because the stomach has only three compartments as opposed to four compartments in true ruminants. They differ also in that they have two upper incisor teeth whereas true ruminants have none. Vicugna are unique in the Artiodactyla in that they have ever-growing lower incisors with enamel on only one side. None of these species have horns and they all run with a pacing gait—i.e., by moving the front and rear legs on one side forward in unison.

It should be noted that a number of species are classed as "endangered". Those so listed up through 1982 are identified in Table 1-1. Further information on this topic may be found in Honacki et al (2), the Convention on International Trade in Endangered Species of Wild Fauna and Flora (CITES) or The Federal Register. Hopefully, this list will not grow and, also, that many of those on the list will be protected and helped to survive in this crowded world.

7

IMPORTANCE OF RUMINANTS IN WORLD AGRICULTURE

Based on a strictly utilitarian viewpoint, ruminant animals are highly important to the human race because these herbivorous species are capable of harvesting vegetation of one type or another from lands that will not support economic crop production. The importance of ruminant animals (and other herbivorous species) is, perhaps, more properly emphasized when we look at the total world land area. Approximately one-third of the earth's surface is land—about 34 billion acres (13.7 billion hectares) or a little more than 53 million square miles. Of this, about 3-4% is utilized for urban and industrial purposes, while about 10% is under cultivation. Non-productive lands comprise about 15% of the earth's land area. These lands, which are termed non-productive because plant photosynthetic activity is relatively unimportant, include the very high mountain areas, barren deserts and land areas covered by glaciers or permanent snow. Forest lands, some of which may be utilized by grazing animals, cover 28-30% of the land. The land remaining, which includes 40% or more of the total area, is comprised of rangeland, which is more suitable for grazing than cultivation. Rangelands include natural grasslands, savannas, shrublands, most deserts, tundra, alpine communities, coastal marshes and wet meadows. Thus, it is obvious that productivity of products useful to humans from a large majority of the earth's surface would be reduced greatly if grazing animals are not available to utilize the vegetation to some degree.

Ruminant animals have been hunted by humans, possibly for as long as 750,000 years. Domesticated ruminant animals have had an important place in human society and agriculture for many centuries. Archeological findings show that sheep have been domesticated for at least 11,000 years, goats for about 9,000 years and cattle for 8,500 years. The rather "sudden" appearance of domestic animals presumably occurred more or less in conjunction with the development of cultivated crops following the last severe ice age (5).

One example from the recent past of the extreme dependence of some societies on ruminants is the many nomadic American Indian tribes which depended on the bison,

Figure 1-1. Hunting may be either a means of providing food or primarily a form of recreation. In this instance the hunter has bagged a nice elk. Courtesy of the Oregon Dept. of Fish and Wildlife, Portland, OR.

elk, deer and other species. These species yielded meat, clothing, shelter, weapons and utensils which were the staff of life to most tribes. Today, the Masai tribes in East Africa are almost as dependent upon their domestic cattle which provide meat, milk and blood to drink, as well as various artifacts of use to these primitive people.

In our modern world, humans are dependent upon ruminant animals for substantial quantities of food, animal feed and many industrial items. Recent estimates of world inventories of domestic animals indicate about 1 billion head of cattle and buffalo and 650 million head of sheep (Table 1-2). Data do not seem to be available on goats.

Cattle are spread world-wide except in arctic areas where reindeer and yaks are utilized by some societies. Buffalo are utilized more heavily in wet tropical areas in Asia and, to a lesser extent, in Africa. As the climate

8

Table 1-2. Food and fiber production from ruminant animals in 1983.[a]

Item	Production metric tons x 10³		Per capita consumption, kg/year	
	USA	World	USA	World
Beef and veal	10,564	40,960	49.1	16.2
Lamb, mutton & goat	165	4,677	0.8	2.2
Poultry	7,185	23,205	29.8	14.5
Pork	6,495	37,339	30.2	23.8*
Wool	53[+]	2,455[+]		
Mohair	4.3			
Milk	140,000	394,000		
Cheese (cattle)	2,164			

	Animal inventories, 1983 x 10³
Cattle and buffalo	999,554
Sheep	656,905
Swine	401,000

[a]Anonymous (6)
*Does not include any African countries except South Africa nor any countries in Africa or Asia which consume little, if any, pork.
[+]Grease basis

grows drier, relatively more sheep, goats and camels are found in Eurasian and African countries. Llamas and alpacas are found in relatively large numbers only in some of the central South American countries. No other ruminant species have been truly domesticated by man.

Estimates of world production of meat, wool and milk are shown in Table 1-2. Assuming that these values are more or less accurate, ruminant meat sources account for about 44% of the total red meat and poultry supply. An unknown amount is available from wild species hunted for food. In addition to the meat, large quantities of milk, cheese and milk by-products are used in all of the developed countries. Milk production in most tropical and/or undeveloped countries is low and much of it is from goats, sheep (Fig. 1-2), buffalo or camels.

Wool, mohair and leather are used for many different products, with clothing and various fabrics being one of the more important uses. Many by-products from slaughter houses are of importance. Such products include fats which find uses in a wide variety of foods, soaps and industrial chemicals.

Figure 1-2. Modern facilities used for milking sheep or goats. This particular installation is in Oman. Courtesy of C.W. Fox.

Intestines are used for sausage casings and surgical sutures, for example, and a wide variety of pharmaceutical products are prepared from blood, liver, adrenal glands, pancreas and other glands and tissues. Animal by-products originating from slaughter or rendering plants, such as meat meal, bone meal, etc., are used extensively in animal feeds.

During the period of time in which ruminants have been domesticated, they have been used to harvest vegetation or have been fed high fiber feeds which are unusable as a food source for humans. Only in recent times, i.e., during the past 75 years or so, have edible grains been used to any degree as feed for ruminants, and then only in the highly industrial countries. This may or may not be a lasting trend because so many factors affect the relative prices of grains and meat or milk. In the undeveloped countries, grains are normally used in very moderate amounts and then are more apt to be fed to milk producing animals rather than those intended primarily for slaughter. The big advantage of ruminant animals is, of course, that they can eat and digest vegetation high in cellulose and other fibrous carbohydrates which many animals cannot utilize as a major source of their diet.

In addition to being used as a source of meat, milk or fiber, some species still serve an important place in undeveloped countries—particularly in Asia and Africa—as a source of power. Cattle, buffalo and camels are used to pull vehicles, carry loads or to provide power for grinding fodders or grains, pumping water

9

Figure 1-3. Cattle providing the power to operate a machine to chop fodder in India. Similar arrangements are used to grind feed or food, pump water, express juices from sugar cane, etc. Photo courtesy of F. Mattioli, FAO, Rome, Italy.

Figure 1-4. Asian buffalo being used to haul carts during the sugar cane harvest on the island of Negros, Philippine Islands. Photo courtesy of G. De Sabatino, FAO, Rome, Italy.

10

Figure 1-5. Zebu type cattle being used to pull a plough in Ethiopia. Photo courtesy of M.C. Comte, FAO, Rome, Italy.

Figure 1-6. A camel caravan being used to transport reeds along the road near Maradi, southern Niger. Photo courtesy of F. Mattioli, FAO, Rome, Italy.

Figure 1-7. Cattle being used to haul carts in the interior of Kampuchea. Photo courtesy of H. Page, FAO, Rome, Italy.

and other similar tasks (Fig. 1-3 through 1-7). The relative price increase in fossil fuels since 1974 has made it difficult for many of the undeveloped countries to pay the costs associated with mechanization with fossil-fueled machines. At the current time, this situation does not seem likely to change.

Ruminant animals also provide recreation for many people in different countries. Recreation may range from bull fights to rodeos to hunting. In some areas hunting may be a means to basically provide food; in others, it is more of a sport, although food provided is not without its uses, particularly since it comes from animals harvested from lands that may not be used by domestic species. Some of the wild species are being used to a limited extent for "game ranching". Other species, especially the red deer, are being grown for a source of meat and antlers; the latter bring a high price for various medicinal uses in most Asiatic countries. The profitability of such ventures is uncertain at this time, at least on a large scale basis.

In most societies the better quality meat typically comes from surplus male animals, often slaughtered at an early age. This trend

is still in evidence in Europe where veal and young kid goats are commonly an important item on the meat menu. The remainder of the meat (in most countries) is normally from animals which have lived out their usefulness as draft animals or those used for milk production. Cooking methods in use to tenderize meat from old, tough carcasses reflect this fact in most areas of the world.

WHAT ABOUT THE FUTURE?

What does the future hold for ruminant animals? The writer is not blessed with any ability to foresee the future, but perhaps a few comments are in order. Assuming that the world population of humans continues to increase, it is highly probable that many of the wild species will be more and more restricted in suitable habitats. This will, inevitably, lead to a reduction in numbers and, probably, extinction of some of the endangered species and subspecies. Others will very likely exist in significant numbers only in parks and zoos.

With respect to domestic ruminants, their relative importance as a food resource will be

12

Figure 1-8. A rodeo cowboy roping a calf in competition. Courtesy of the Professional Rodeo Cowboys Association.

possible that demand as well as supply will be lower in future years.

From a more optimistic point of view, it is likely that ruminant animals will be a major factor in animal agriculture for many years because of the large areas of non-arable land on the globe. Future research should result in developments in genetics, physiology, nutrition, management and disease control which will allow either increased levels of production or more efficient production. Continued research and improved application of research findings offer many possibilities for future improvements through a better understanding of these animals. We should not try to make our domestic ruminants into a large "chicken", but to improve the wonderfully

Figure 1-9. Bull riding in a professional rodeo, one of several ways in which cattle are used in recreational and professional sports. Courtesy of the Professional Rodeo Cowboys Association.

dependent upon surplus feed grains and other sources of feed that, at this time, are used indirectly as human food. If, as some writers suggest, more food will be produced in the future by conversion of wastes to food by microorganisms, feed sources traditionally used for ruminants may be less available. Unless genetic engineering of plants leads to the development of plants which can grow and produce food where they now cannot, it should be expected that less and less feed grain will be used for ruminants in the developed countries and that a higher proportion of that available will be used by swine and poultry which are far more efficient in converting high quality feed to human food. In addition, at the present time there is a trend by many health professionals to recommend less consumption of red meat; thus, it is

Figure 1-10. Elk antlers collected from the National Elk Refuge near Jackson, WY. Antlers are sold at auction, with the bulk of them going to the orient. Courtesy of John Wilbrecht, National Elk Refuge.

complex symbiotic system of microbes and animal biology that has already reached a high level of development.

Figure 1-11. A llama outfitted with a back pack to be used by hikers in Central Oregon. Courtesy of Llamas & More, Bend, Oregon.

Literature Cited

1. Simpson, G.G. 1945. Bull. Amer. Museum of Natural History. 85:1-350.
2. Honacki, J.H., K.E. Kinman and J.W. Koeppl (eds.). 1982. Mammal Species of the World. Allen Press, Inc. and The Assoc. of Systematics Collections, Lawrence, KS, USA.
3. Walker, E.P. et al (ed.). 1975. Mammals of the World, Vol. II, 3rd Ed. The Johns Hopkins Univ. Press, Baltimore, MD.
4. Mochi, U. and T.D. Carter. 1971. Hoofed Mammals of the World. 2nd Ed. Chas. Scribner's Sons, New York, NY.
5. Zeuner, F.E. 1974. In: Animal Agriculture. Cole, H.H. and M. Ronning (eds.). W.H. Freeman and Co., San Francisco.
6. Anonymous. 1984. Livestock and Poultry Situation. Foreign Agr. Circ., Foreign Agr. Serv., USDA, Washington, DC.

by R. R. Hofmann

INTRODUCTION

It has become a customary assumption, even amongst veterinarians, that the digestive system of ruminants derives its peculiarity from the four-chambered stomach, while most other portions of the gastro-intestinal tract are considered similar to those of other mammals or, at least, other herbivores.

This view cannot be upheld any longer, as will be seen; because literally *all* portions of the tract show some degree of specialization and adaptation typical for ruminants. Even more than that, they exhibit anatomical variations which are the results of evolutionary trends in favor of a specific food selectivity. This permits us to classify them as one of several *morphophysiological feeding types* (Fig. 2-1). Species which evolved early adapted to their food plants before the grasses developed and spread on earth are termed **concentrate selectors** (the term "browser" is too narrow and misleading). Animals in this group select plants or plant parts rich in easily digestible and highly nutritious plant cell contents like starch, plant protein, fat and oil (i.e., concentrate). These types have a very limited capacity to digest cell wall (i.e., fiber,

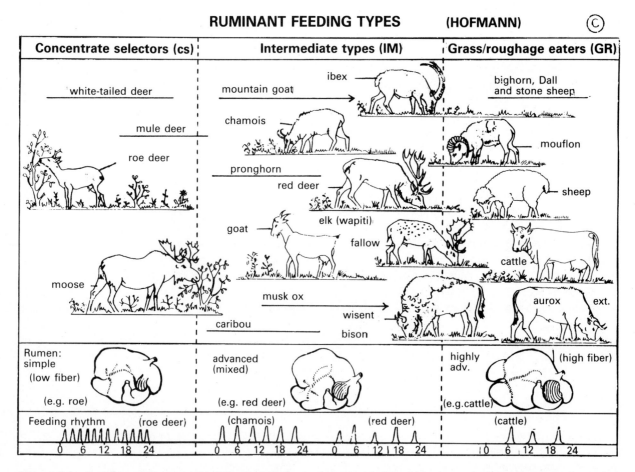

Figure 2-1. Position of European and North American ruminant species within the evolutionary system of morphophysiological feeding type. The further the baseline of a species extends to the right, the greater its ability to digest fiber in the rumen, which has concurrently advanced. Selection for plant cell content implies shorter feeding intervals as the simple rumen of CS has fewer food passage delay structures than that of GR.

All figures in Chapter 2 are © by R. R. Hofmann.

cellulose). Typical examples in Europe and Asia are roe deer and in North America its relatives, white-tailed and mule deer; in South America, the mazama and pudu; and in Africa, duikers, dikdiks, kudus and giraffes.

Ruminants which evolved later depend on grasses and other fibrous plant material, although they still can cope more or less with rapidly fermenting cell contents. Cattle, domestic and wild sheep and many grass savannah antelope species of Africa as well as the American and European bison belong to this advanced feeding type ("grass and roughage eater"). There is a heterogenous third group, which we termed "intermediate, mixed feeders", as they show adaptations to the one or the other extreme. Some of them are highly variable and flexible within one year or vegetation period, like the arctic caribou or the alpine chamois. The best known representatives of this regionally and seasonally adaptable, opportunistic feeding type are the red deer of Europe and Asia and their larger phenotype, the North American elk (Wapiti). Amongst the long domesticated species, only the goat is intermediate, with a great preference for cell contents and a fair though limited capacity to digest cellulose. This text will frequently refer to these three feeding types, hence abbreviations will be used: CS for concentrate selectors, IM for intermediate mixed feeders and GR for grass and roughage eaters.

The anatomical terminology used in this chapter conforms to the Nomina anatomica veterinaria. The division of the tract follows that logically dictated by development and function into (a) head portion with connected glands, (b) foregut portion (esophagus and stomach), (c) midgut portion (small intestine with connected glands) and (d) hindgut portion (large intestine and anus).

THE HEAD AND ASSOCIATED GLANDS

Prehensile Organs

The initial portion of the digestive system shows a remarkable diversification in ruminants. This is especially true for its prehensile organs consisting of lips, tongue, lower incisor teeth and the dental pad in front of the hard palate which reflect an important feature of ruminant nutrition, i.e., their food selectivity. In the ox, being a lately evolved non-selective

GR, this portion of the system with its cornified rigidity differs greatly from that of sheep (selective grazer), goat (highly selective mixed feeder) or from CS like roe and white-tailed deer, as well as giraffes with their almost artistic way of food prehension. This action is followed by sorting out and transporting plant material caudally, which is achieved by contraction of labial and buccal muscles in conjunction with the counter-pressure system of tongue against hard palate, and by the presence of large buccal papillae of varying length and density. Mastication and insalivation again are processes different in ruminants as compared with other herbivores. Yet they are specialized according to ruminant feeding type. Rumination differs greatly between CS and GR as the former feed and ruminate much more frequently. There are striking differences in the development of the salivary glands, as will be shown (Fig. 2-2). Similarly, the structure of the cheek teeth, the lever-type construction of the mandible as well as size, arrangement and attachment of the masticatory muscles have been shown to be specialized and typical for each of the three main feeding groups.

Oral Cavity

The oral cavity is lined by a heavy, frequently cornified cutaneous mucous membrane which is partly exteriorized onto the rigid upper lip in the characteristic nasolabial plate of bovine animals, where it is underlain by heavy serous glands. The mouth is bound rostrally by more or less mobile lips (labium mandibulare/maxillare) containing the orbicularis oris muscle and, especially in selective species with prehensile lips, several well-developed facial muscles of the nasolabial group. The mucous labial glands are dispersed between the muscle fibers which empty these glands on contraction. While GR have short lips and a small mouth opening, CS have a large mouth opening (e.g., fruit eaters). The cheeks provide the lateral boundary of the oral cavity. Their muscular core is derived from the vertically arranged buccinator muscle which contains many or fewer lobules of the dorsal and middle buccal glands. The ventral buccal gland borders the lower edge of this important muscle which empties the buccal vestibule after ingested food has been ground with lateral occlusion.

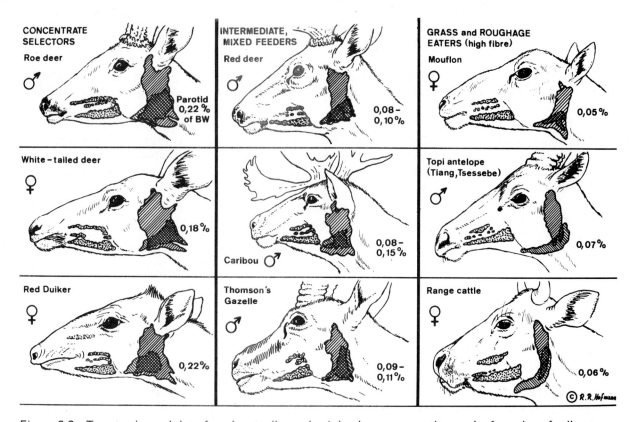

Figure 2-2. Topography and size of ruminant salivary glands in nine representative species from three feeding types.

parotid ⬤ mandibular ⬤ overlap ⬤ buccal

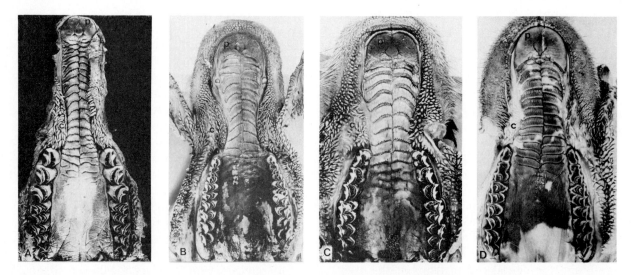

Figure 2-3. Ventral (lower) aspect of ruminant hard palates in situ, buccal mucosa deflected. A = moose (CS), B = red deer (IM), C = fallow deer (IM), D = mouflon sheep (GR); c = cheek papillae; p = dental pad with central incisive papilla.

In CS the compact ventral buccal gland produces a serous secretion, but in GR it is a mucous gland of remarkable dimensions and weight. Its many openings lead into the vestibulum buccale, which is bound medially by the cheek teeth and which also receives, in all ruminants, the parotid saliva via the parotid duct with its terminal papilla parotidea. Labial and buccal papillae, especially dense in the interalveolar area between incisors and premolars, are directed towards the pharynx; they are more delicate and numerous in CS. The dorsal wall or roof of the oral cavity is provided by the hard palate which, due to evolutionary suppression of upper incisor development, begins rostrally with the dental pad. This is a heavily cornified counterpart for the lower incisors and the apex of the tongue used in grasping food plants.

The rigid pad is demarcated centro-caudally by the incisive papilla. Its circular groove receives the incisive ducts, delicate connections both with the nasal cavity and Jacobson's organ (a sex pheromone detecting tubular organ of smell). The surface relief of the heavily cornified, frequently pigmented hard palate is almost species-specific, but certainly showing a characteristic pattern in ruminants belonging to the same feeding type (Fig. 2-3). The number of palatine ridges decreases in ruminants which are selecting for plant cell content, but these forb, fruit and foliage-eating species have much more and longer papillae arising from the caudal edge of these ridges. Moose or giraffe have a fimbriated palate, the ox delicately serrated and the sheep almost smooth rugae. The latter diminish and finally disappear caudally, i.e., the molar region of the hard palate is smooth with minute openings of numerous mucous palatine glands or lymph follicles and it shows no clear demarcation against the soft palate. The entire hard palate mucosa rests upon a resilient layer of venous plexuses. This arrangement promotes rapid backflow into the maxillary and jugular veins during feeding and rumination. The dorsum of the tongue then exerts the main pressure force.

The Tongue

The tongue (Fig. 2-4) fills most of the space of the oral cavity proper between the mandibular arch of teeth. Non-selective roughage eaters like the ox and the water buffalo have a plump, piston-like tongue; foliage selectors like giraffe and moose have a slender, pointed tongue. Other selective species are in between. The ratio between torus linguae (the elevated back portion) and the free apex (controlled by the wide lingual frenulum) is different in GR and CS, but even more typical for these contrasting groups which feed differently, is the distribution and size of both mechanical and taste papillae. The mucous membrane of the tongue is thin and delicate on the lower aspect and firm, thick and cornified on the dorsal, but less so on the lateral surfaces. The stratified squamous epithelium forms densely packed delicate filiform papillae. On the torus of grass-eating species we find thick, blunt conical or flattened lenticular papillae, some of which grow irregularly large, e.g., in the goat and in impala antelopes (IM). Fungiform and vallate papillae, which are characterized histologically by the presence of taste buds with gustatory receptors (VII and IX cranial nerve) and by serous rinsing glands, are as a rule less numerous in CS than in GR. Fungiform papillae are distributed over most of the tongue. Vallate papillae are restricted to the caudolateral area which is transitory between torus and root of the tongue but cranial to the lingual tonsil. There are regularly more tastebuds per vallate papilla in GR than in CS (20) which points to the primary selection by olfactory means in CS and taste avoidance in GR. In the ox, there are 8-17 vallate papillae on each side, 18-24 in sheep, 12-18 in the goat.

The sublingual floor of the oral cavity, between incisor teeth and frenulum, is covered by a smooth but cornified epithelium. The sublingual caruncle with the paired mouth of the mandibular and major sublingual duct, an almost constant source of mixed saliva flow, has a typical shape in each ruminant species (Fig. 2-5). It is more inconspicuous in GR.

Salivary Glands

The salivary glands are highly variable according to feeding type (Fig. 2-2 and Fig. 6-1, Ch. 6). CS have up to 0.3% of their body weight as parotid saliva-producing tissue, while GR have only one-fourth or one-fifth of that, e.g., sheep 0.05%. Their physiological importance as transport liquid (minor) and

18

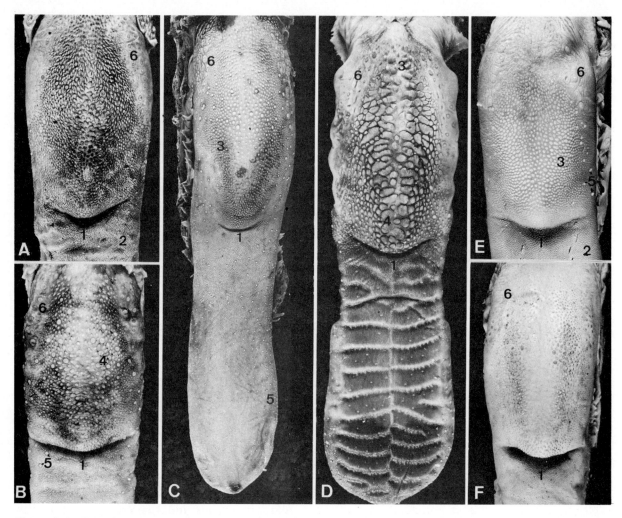

Figure 2-4. Dorsal aspect of the ruminant tongue. A = Greater Kudu (CS), torus only; B = Muntjak (CS), torus only; C = Red Deer (IM); D = Impala (IM); preserved in situ with impressions of the palatine ridges; E = Ox (GR), torus only; F = Pere David's Deer (GR), torus only. 1 = fossa lingae; 2 = filiform papillae; 3 = conical papillae; 4 = lenticular papillae; 5 = fungiform papillae; 6 = circumvallate pap.

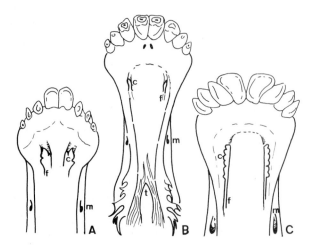

Figure 2-5. Dorsal aspect of the sublingual floor of the lower jaw with incisors I1-I4 of mouflon sheep (A), fallow deer (B) and red deer (C) (19); c = sublingual caruncle with openings of the mandibular and sublingual salivary glands (concealed); f = caruncular fold; m = foramen mentale; t = frenulum.

fermentation buffer fluid (major) may be added to by rinsing functions for nutrients which are released and become soluble in the oral cavity during mastication associated with eating and also during ruminatory mastication. Especially, the serous parotid saliva may wash soluble ingesta down the ventricular groove into the abomasum, thus by-passing ruminal fermentation.

The parotid gland is found in the retromandibular depression along the caudal border of the masseter, below the base of the ear and the temperomandibular joint. In CS it is both wide and thick, has a pre- and post-auricular process and conceals most of the mandibular gland. Its neck process surrounds the linguofacial and maxillary veins while its dorsocranial border covers part or most of the parotid lymph node. The distinctly lobulated gland forms a parotid duct arising from the deep face of the gland at its ventrocranial angle. In most ruminant species it follows the facial blood vessels curving around the masseter and finally it pierces the buccal muscle. It opens on the parotid papilla in the vestibulum buccale opposite one of the molar teeth (M_2 in ox, M_1 in sheep and goat). The parotid is covered by a wide (in CS ventrally widening) muscle tape, the depressor of the ear. The mandibular gland, a mixed/seromucous gland, is larger than the parotid only in non-selective GR. It is proportionally smaller in CS and many IM, where most of it is covered by the parotid. It extends from the wings of the atlas to the region of the rostral masseter border, where it touches its fellow from the other side and the mandibular lymph node. Its topographic situation is more complicated than that of the parotid. It is related medially to the common carotid artery and its branches, to cranial (V, X) and sympathetic nerves, while the external jugular and the maxillary vein, the facial nerve and the linguofacial artery touch it laterally. The mandibular duct arises from the gland rostrally. It crosses the digastricus and runs along the inner surface of the mylohyoideus.

All ruminants have a seromucous sublingual gland which is proportionally smaller in GR than in CS. Its ventro-rostral portion, the monostomatic sublingual gland, extends from the incisive portion of the mandible more or less caudal. Its duct joins that of the mandi-

bular gland to end upon the sublingual caruncle. The dorso-caudal portion is a narrow band of glandular lobules each of which detaches a small duct. They all open next to a row of papillae on the groove-like floor of the lateral sublingual recess.

Pharynx and Larynx

The pharynx (Fig. 2-6) is the short caudal continuation of the oral cavity leading into the esophageal vestibule. Its initial isthmus portion or oropharynx is bound dorsally by the soft palate (velum palatinum) and ventrally by the root of the tongue. The relatively long and thick glandular velum is raised during initial swallowing and regurgitation, helping to form a bolus for chewing or swallowing (rumination, remastication). According to Dougherty et al (1) most of the eructated fermentation gas from the rumen is forced into the larynx, trachae and lungs after closure of the mouth and the intrapharyngeal opening. This variable opening, formed by the archlike free caudal edge of the soft palate and the palatopharyngeal arches, i.e., mucosal folds along the lateral and caudal wall of the pharynx, connects the nasal cavity with the laryngeal opening during normal breathing. It is constricted and almost closed by the elevation of the soft palate (spanner and elevator muscles, arising from the petrous temporal bone) and the contraction of the pharyngeal constrictors, flat skeletal muscles with reflectory action during swallowing. The oropharynx is caudally followed by the laryngopharynx. The epiglottic and arytenoid portion of the larynx project from below into this room and through the intrapharyngeal opening. Liquids pass on either side of the larynx into the collateral piriform recesses which finally lead onto the pharyngoesophageal junction and into the esophagus. Solid plant material passes the laryngeal opening safely because a complicated action of tongue and hyoid muscles and joints shortens and tilts the pharynx when the animal swallows. The elastic cartilage of the epiglottis is then passively reverted to cover the laryngeal entrance. The tonsils, which surround the mucosal area of the digestive and the nasal pharynx, have no immediate physiological relationship to digestive processes.

20

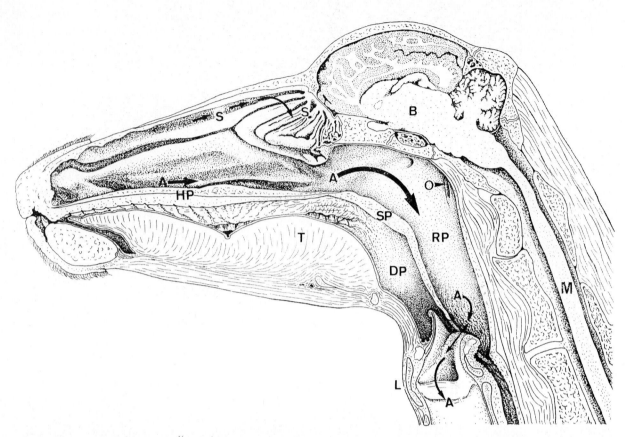

Figure 2.6. Longitudinal section through a red deer head, oral cavity and pharynx. A and arrows = airflow (nasal cavity, respiratory pharynx = RP; laryngeal entrance); B = brain stem; DP = digestive pharynx; HP = hard palate; L = laryngeal bulge (thyroid cartilage); M = spinal chord; O = pharyngeal opening of auditory tube; S and arrows = nasal duct of smell and olfactory region of the nasal cavity (ethmoid); SP = soft palate.

Teeth and Masticatory Muscles

The masticatory apparatus of ruminants, comprised of the jaws, teeth and masticatory muscles supported by tongue, lips and cheeks, shows a high and specific degree of development. As was shown by Stöckmann (15), mandibular shape is adapted to food preference. Irrespective of body size, GR offer larger surfaces for masticatory muscle attachment, and Kiplel (10) has shown that IM with a preference for grasses have bigger masticatory muscles than CS. Moreover, CS exhibit an early osseous fusion of their mandibular symphysis which remains flexible (syndesmosis) in GR. Both incisors and cheek teeth of CS are more delicately built than those of GR, but are more firmly attached to their sockets. The formula for the permanent dentition of the ruminants is 2 (I 0/4 C 0/0 P 3/3 M 3/3); i.e., 32 teeth.

In all ruminant species, incisors are absent from the upper jaw. The canines are present only in several cervid species (Fig. 2-7). The antagonistic function to the lower incisors is taken over by the dental pad made of fibrous connective tissue covered by heavily cornified epithelium. The canines of the lower jaw have moved into the row of lower incisors. They function like fourth incisors and are also termed corner incisors. Comparatively, the dentition formula of the elk (Wapiti, *Cervus elaphus*) would be 2 (I 0/3 C 1/1 P 3/3 M 3/3). The incisors of GR have a wide, shovel-shaped and asymmetrical crown; those of CS have a chisel-shaped narrower crown. Their lingual surface is concave and may act together with the tongue during food prehension (pulling or plucking). The narrow neck of the incisor teeth is well distinguished from the crown. The neck continues into the root which is covered by annually increasing layers of cementum. These can be made visible with histological techniques for reliable ageing of free-ranging ruminants.

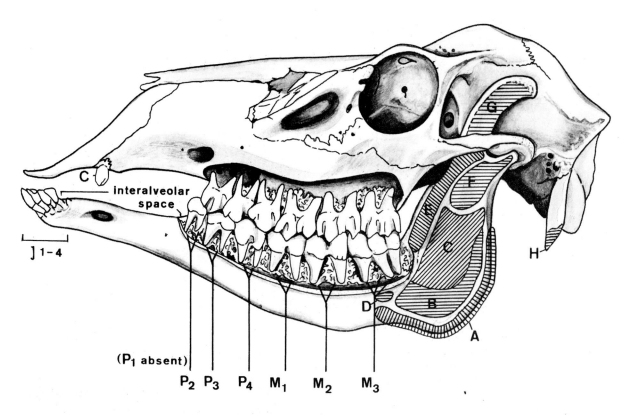

Figure 2-7. Skull of a female red deer (*Cervus elaphus*) with cheek teeth alveoli laterally opened; lateral insertion surfaces of the masticatory muscles marked according to Kiplel (10): A = superficial masseter portions; B, C, D = deep masseter portions; E, F = zygomandibular portions; G = temporal muscle; H = digastric muscle. I = Incisors, P = premolars, M = molars.

While the incisors are of the haplodont type, the cheek teeth of ruminants are high columns (hypsodont) with all three tooth substances alternating on the occlusal surface, thus forming high, sharp ridges of enamel with half-moon-shaped depressions (selenodont) in between. These teeth grow initially in length, then form short roots and are later on, in the course of steady wear, advanced from their sockets. M_1 (the fourth cheek tooth) takes the greatest pressure and is worn down first. Steady wear and final loss of the teeth are an important factor in limiting the life span of a ruminant. There are great individual variations in tooth wear within one species, some of them related to feeding habits (e.g., intake of sand), some to food composition and some to the hardness of the tooth constituents. Enamel has been found to vary considerably in hardness and thus in resistance to wear. The premolars increase in length rostrocaudally, but all are single component teeth. The molars are composed of

two strong components each, and M_3 has an additional third one. The premolars do not form true infundibula, but sharp ridges. The molar teeth have one infundibulum per component. This repeating alternation of softer and harder tooth substances (the enamel being the hardest and most resistant to wear) provides the ruminant animal with highly effective tools for crushing and grinding plant structures during initial mastication and rumination.

The cheek teeth of the upper and lower jaw, both forming a solid row, fit into each other perfectly. With the exception of the third molars, each upper cheek tooth is in interdigitating contact with two lower cheek teeth. No lower jaw of any individual can fit the upper jaw of another individual. This is mainly due to individual tooth wear grinding tracks gradually effected during the sideways swing of the mandible. Any ruminant's mandible with its two rows of cheek teeth is narrower than the maxillary cheek teeth rows, i.e., the distance between the latter is much wider. At centric occlusion there is little contact between upper and lower cheek teeth; they are anisognathous. Lateral occlusion is achieved always only on one side during grinding actions of the masseter and pterygoid muscles facilitated by incongruent temperomandibular joints. Thus, in less technical terminology, ruminants can chew with their molar teeth only on one side of the mouth at a given time.

Effective mastication is a vital precondition for ruminant digestion as it reduces plant material to a small particulate size which permits ruminal and intestinal microorganisms to attack structural carbohydrates. As ruminants differ both in their digestive strategies and their morphophysiological adaptation to forage, they use their masticatory apparatus in different ways. GR like cattle or bison, which graze over long periods, chew initially very briefly, but have long rumination periods to reduce particulate size for the better facilitation of microbial fermentation. CS apply an intensive initial chewing of dicot plant material (puncture crushing) which releases much cell content. They show a pattern of short intermediate rumination periods which alternate with short feeding periods, several times a day.

Young ruminants have a deciduous dentition much of which has erupted before birth, and in CS more so than in GR. The former usually begin to take in herbaceous food in their first week of life. The formula for the deciduous dentition of ruminants is 2 (Di 0/4 Dc 0/0 Dp 3/3) = 20. After gradual replacement, the permanent dentition of an ox is established by about 34 months; in ruminants with a shorter life span this occurs much earlier (e.g., roe deer 14 months, goat 17-20 months).

THE ESOPHAGUS AND STOMACH

The foregut is a term derived from embryology and includes the esophagus and stomach. The paramount importance of the quadrolocular (four compartmented) stomach for ruminant digestive physiology and nutrition demands a detailed description of the functional anatomy of each portion and of their morphophysiological interrelations.

Esophagus

The esophagus is the connecting tube between pharynx and rumino-reticulum and mediates between areas of differing pressure. In the ruminant it is used regularly in both directions and is subject, to a certain extent, to the animal's voluntary control. It is composed of two concentric membraneous tubes, the inner mucosa and the outer muscular tunic. The mucous membrane is cutaneous and non-glandular, i.e., lined by a stratified squamous epithelium. This mucosal tube rests on a loose submucosal layer permitting considerable distension or the formation of longitudinal folds. The muscular tunic with its sphincter-like connections to the caudal pharyngeal muscles is of the skeletal (striated) type throughout its length and even somewhat beyond the cardia.

There are two portions of the esophagus. The cervical part extends from the cricoid cartilage to the cranial thoracic inlet. It is attached to the neighboring structures by an elastic adventitia and follows the curve of the neck. It is in a dorsal position to the trachea initially, but lies mostly left to it along the neck. On entering the thoracic aperture, where its diameter is smallest, it gains a position dorsal to the trachea again. Throughout the length of the thoracic part, the esophagus keeps a position between the two pleural sacs of the lung, i.e., in the mediastinum. Caudal to the tracheal bifurcation, the steadily widening esophagus is related dorsally to the caudal mediastinal lymph node which embeds the dorsal vagal trunk. During disease conditions, this long lymph node may enlarge and subsequently cause ill effects on the vagus and its gastro-intestinal supply area, or it may impede esophageal passage. Finally, the esophagus opens into the stomach at the junction of rumen and reticulum. Topographically, the esophagus ends within the esophageal hiatus of the diaphragm which is, in most ruminants, at about the 8th intercostal space.

The flexures of the esophagus are S-shaped in the normal standing position but are almost deleted during the grazing posture with the head lowered. The physiologically important processes of eructation and rumination depend on alternating constriction and relaxation of the so-called cranial and caudal esophageal sphincters. The former is provided by the caudal pharyngeal constrictor muscles,

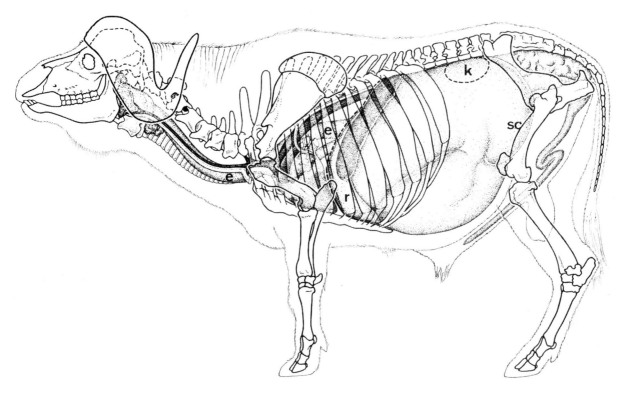

Figure 2-8. Abdominal topography (left side) of a GR, the African buffalo; diaphragm midline interrupted. Rumen extends into pelvic inlet; e = esophagus; k = left kidney; r = reticulum; sc = dorsocaudal blindsac. From Hofmann (3).

the latter by circular esophageal musculature in connection with the cardiac muscular loop of the stomach entrance. The reversed funnel shape of the final portion of the esophagus and its situation in a location with lower or negative pressures (between the pleural sacs), facilitate the cranial transport of both gasses and cud boli with the help of antiperistaltic actions of the esophageal musculature.

The Stomach

The quadrolocular stomach of ruminants shows the highest stage of evolutionary development of all mammals (Fig. 2-8). All four compartments—reticulum, rumen, omasum and abomasum—are derived from the embryonic equivalent of a simple stomach. Hence, the esophagus and its typical epithelium terminate at the cardia. There are, however, no cardiac glands at this point as the first three stomach compartments (in functional sequence: reticulum, rumen, omasum) are lined with non-glandular mucous membrane. Only the fourth compartment, the abomasum, is lined with glandular mucosa.

The forestomach compartments (reticulum, rumen, omasum) function to store and delay passage of ingested food. They are the sites of anaerobic microbial fermentation of plant material and of absorption, mainly of the fermentation products. These functions are documented by their considerable capacity and a differentiated mucosal surface enlargement. This is added to by structures related to more mechanical functions. They all result in anatomical characteristics typical of each compartment which are varied in adaptation to different feeding habits and strategies. The glandular compartment, in contrast, is similar to and performs comparably with simple stomachs, yet exhibits specific structures which, as in the forestomach compartments, correlate to their function.

Stomach Size and Capacity

In all ruminant species the rumen is the most capacious of the four compartments (Fig. 2-9) and is followed, in most cases, by the abomasum. The omasum is third in size only in highly developed, late evolved

24

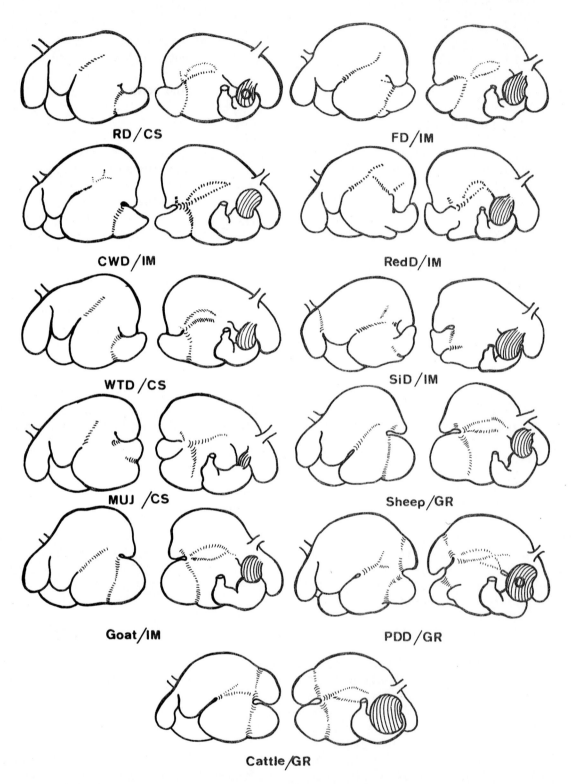

Figure 2-9. Ruminant stomach shape and proportions in *Cervidae* vs domestic *Bovidae* (irrespective of actual size). CS = concentrate selector; IM = intermediate; GR = grass and roughage eater. RD = roe deer; CWD = Chinese water deer; WTD = white-tailed deer; MUJ = muntjak; FD = fallow deer; Red D = Red deer/elk; SiD = Sika deer; PDD = Pere David's deer. Note three blindsacs in muntjak and cervus-species and relative size of omasum (o): smallest in MUJ; largest in cattle. From Hofmann (5).

non-selective grazers (with maximal fiber digestion) as in all true bovine species like *Bos taurus, Bos indicus, Bubalus bubalis,* Yak, etc. However, in the majority of species the omasum is the smallest of the four, as they have (unlike bovine animals) a rather large reticulum which, in a few "ancient" ruminant species, can be even larger than the abomasum.

During the suckling period the abomasum is the largest stomach compartment (see Ch. 3). As milk is the sole source of nutrients for CS during a much shorter period than for GR, the postnatal changes of relative capacity and proportional size of the four compartments occur at different rates. In the bovine stomach the abomasum has still at least half of the capacity of the ruminoreticulum when a calf is 8 weeks old. In CS like roe or white-tailed deer, this is achieved after about two weeks as fawns begin consuming herbaceous food much earlier than GR. In fully grown ruminants the ratio between ruminoreticulum and omasum is variable due to the seasonal enlargement or reduction of the fermentation chamber and thus can be anything between 1:7 and 1:15. In grass-fed bovine animals it is about 1:9.

The actual capacity of the ruminant stomach has, in most cases, been overrated when measurements were taken after water infusion followed by unnatural distension. Even large cattle breeds rarely have a capacity of the ruminoreticulum exceeding 100 ℓ and medium-sized races 60-80 ℓ. The bovine abomasum, which is probably never completely filled, can take 5-8 ℓ but not 20, as some textbooks state. Of the small domestic ruminants, sheep (GR) have usually a greater ruminoreticular capacity than goats (IM), although on free range the latter can enlarge or reduce this capacity remarkably. Hence, a ruminoreticular capacity range from 9-18 ℓ appears realistic, while their abomasum rarely exceeds 2 ℓ. While grass eating species can utilize this capacity to fill when forage is of poor, fibrous quality, they do not utilize more than 60-70% when forage is easily digestible and rich in cell contents. This is the rule in concentrate selectors.

Topographic Relations in Abdomen

As with relative capacity, the position of the four stomach compartments in the abdomen is characteristic for ruminants belonging to the same feeding type. In GR the maximally subdivided and voluminous rumen occupies all of the two left quarters of the abdominal cavity. It is attached to the dorsal wall, rests upon the abdominal floor, and extends into the pelvic inlet (Fig. 2-8). After long food intake periods or during contractions of the dorsal ruminal sac, the ventral ruminal sac extends also into the right ventral quarter of the cavity. In CS the simpler and relatively smaller rumen with its short dorsocaudal blindsac does not usually extend into the pelvic inlet (Fig. 2-10). This permits a physiological dislocation of jejunal coils and the cecum to the left dorsal quarter (paralumbar fossa). The reticulum occupies a cranial and median position, moulding the cupola of the diaphragm and resting upon the xiphoid cartilage when relaxed. During its biphasic contractions the reticulum moves dorsal towards the cardia along the diaphragm. Because it is connected by a muscular ligament to the fundus abomasi, the latter is pulled to the left and dorsally during reticular contractions. This is the physiological reason for abomasal displacements, i.e., then the abomasum does not return to its normal

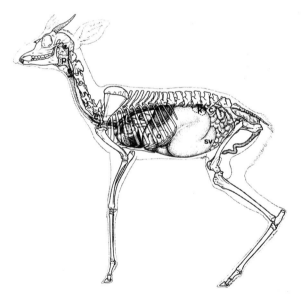

Figure 2-10. Abdominal topography (left side) of a CS, Guenther's Dik-dik; small rumen remains considerably cranial from pelvic inlet, shows s-shape, main blindsac ventral (sv); cecum (c) and jejunum also on left side; e = esophagus; k = left kidney; o = omasum (on right side); p = parotid gland; r = reticulum. From Hofmann (3).

oblique ventral position between the reticulum and rumen. The omasum is always situated to the right of the median plane (Fig. 2-13B) and moulds itself deeply onto the visceral surface of the liver. It reaches the ventral abdominal wall below the right costal arch only in bovine ruminants which have a highly developed, large omasum. Both omasum and abomasum are attached to the liver by the lesser omentum.

Stomach Gross Anatomy

The rumen is divided externally into several portions by grooves (Fig. 2-9) in which blood vessels and lymph nodes and some adipose tissue are found. A left and a right longitudinal groove run along the parietal and visceral surface, respectively. These grooves join each other as the cranial and caudal grooves to form a more or less complete ring which externally divides this big fermentation chamber into the dorsal and ventral ruminal sacs. A distinct accessory groove detaches from and rejoins the right longitudinal groove, providing the dorsal boundary of the insula ruminis. Coronary grooves demarcate the ruminal blind sacs, both of them situated caudal to the main ruminal sacs, i.e., saccus caecus caudodorsalis and s.c. caudoventralis. In many ruminant species the dorsal coronary groove is incomplete while the ventral coronary groove forms a complete ring. There is another groove which demarcates the cranially projecting atrium ruminis (or cranial sac) against the reticulum, termed sulcus ruminoreticularis. The cranial projection of the ventral ruminal sac (below the cranial groove) is termed recessus ruminis. The dorsal and ventral curvatures of the rumen fit tightly onto the dorsal and ventral wall of the abdominal cavity, while the cranial surface of the reticulum reflects the concave cupola of the diaphragm.

The omasum has an almost spherical or ovoid shape. It has a dorsolateral curvature directed towards the liver and a shorter, flattened base. Its cranial pole shows a distinct constriction next to the reticulum called collum omasi. The caudal pole has a less conspicuous circular constriction (sulcus omasoabomasicus).

The abomasum is pear-shaped with the wide, initial portion (fundus) next to the omasum. It narrows gradually, becoming the pyloric part which is tube-shaped. The abomasum is curved and thus one can distinguish a greater and a lesser curvature which provide attachment to the greater and lesser omentum.

The outer surface of all four stomach compartments is coated by visceral serosa with the exception of an area of variable size on the dorsal ruminal sac. In GR, especially in bovine species, there is a relatively large area of fibrous attachment to the sublumbar muscles and the diaphragm, which in CS is restricted to the splenic and pancreatic attachment areas next to the diaphragmatic pillars. Hence, selective ruminants with high fermentation rates and relatively small ruminoreticula can contract their unattached dorsal ruminal sac more effectively than GR and, thus, are less likely to develop bloat (3).

All four stomach compartments have a relatively thin wall comprised from outside inward of serous membrane, muscular tunic and mucous membrane. The muscular tunic is always two-layered, but the muscle fibers are differently arranged in the four compartments. The reticulum and rumen, which embryologically have developed from the fundic portion of the simple stomach primordium, contain also internal oblique fibers.

The omasum and abomasum muscles are made up of a longitudinal and a circular layer only. The distribution of the three gastric muscular layers is shown in Fig. 2-11. The ruminal pillars and the ruminoreticular fold are infoldings (duplications) of the internal oblique fiber layer. The lips of the reticular portion of the ventricular (or reticular) groove and their commissure around the reticulo-omasal opening are formations of the cardiac loop of the internal oblique muscle fibers (Fig. 2-12). The floor of the groove as well as the outer layer of reticulum and ventral ruminal sac are derived from the circular layer.

Interior Surfaces of the Compartments (Mucosal Relief)

Due to the size of the four thin-walled compartments, any study of their spatial relationship and the flow of ingesta through them can be meaningful only if carried out in situ. The opened-up rumen and reticulum reveal their morphophysiological unity which has led to the use of the term ruminoreticulum (Fig. 2-13).

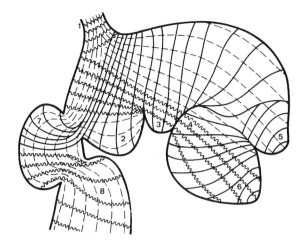

Figure 2-11. The muscle layers of the ruminant stomach, redrawn from Pernkopf, 1930, and Langer, 1973. Solid lines: internal oblique fibers (ruminal pillars, lips of reticular groove, omasal pillar); broken lines: longitudinal fibers; wave lines: circular fibers. At any given place, there are only two muscle layers in the stomach wall. 1 = cardia; 2 = reticulum; 3 = atrium ruminis (cranial sac); 4 = recessus ruminis; 5 = dorsocaudal; 6 = ventricaudal blindsac; 7 = omasum; 8 = abomasum (fundus).

The cardia opens above their junction and the ruminoreticular fold is more an overflow connection than a separation wall because the ruminoreticular opening provides a permanent communication, in the first place between the atrium ruminis and the fundus reticuli. This gastric opening, like all others, is relatively narrower in GR than in CS, i.e., the former have a more effective food passage delay mechanism than the latter. The ruminal grooves on the outside correspond to the ruminal pillars on the inside which more or less demarcate subdivisions of this huge fermentation chamber. Cranial, longitudinal and caudal pillars together form an almost complete circle which surrounds the ostium intraruminale (Fig. 2-13B) where the dorsal and ventral ruminal sac are joined. The coronary pillars, especially the ventral one, partially separate the caudal blindsac from the ventral sac, allowing further delay in digesta for microbial action.

The mucosal relief with considerable surface enlargements is characteristic for each of the four stomach compartments. Due to its physiological importance, the mucosa of each

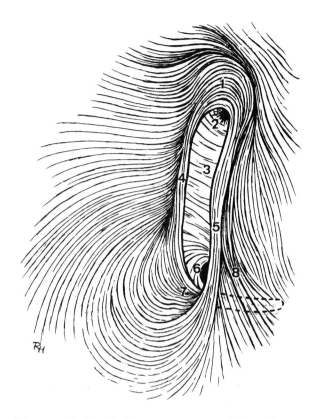

Figure 2-12. Muscle fiber arrangement of the reticular groove. 1 = cardiac muscular loop of the internal oblique fibers; 2 = cardia; 3 = transverse fibers of the circular muscle layer (floor of the groove); 4 = left lip; 5 = right lip of the groove; 6 = reticulo-omasal opening; 7 = distal commissure of the oblique fibers, detaching omasal pillar (dotted outlines); 8 = fibers detached to join ruminoreticular fold. From Hofmann (3).

of them has to be discussed in detail. The three forestomach portions are lined by a specialized stratified squamous epithelium which is not an extension or continuation of the esophageal epithelium. Hence, these portions are characterized by a non-glandular cutaneous mucous membrane which cornifies heavily where mechanical, protective functions are dominating. This epithelium has an important transport function (mainly absorption) in relation to the microbial activities of fiber and starch degradation, but also with regard to water balance, N and mineral metabolism. This forestomach mucosa terminates abruptly at the omasoabomasal opening on the vela abomasica. The glandular abomasal mucosa is covered by a simple columnar

28

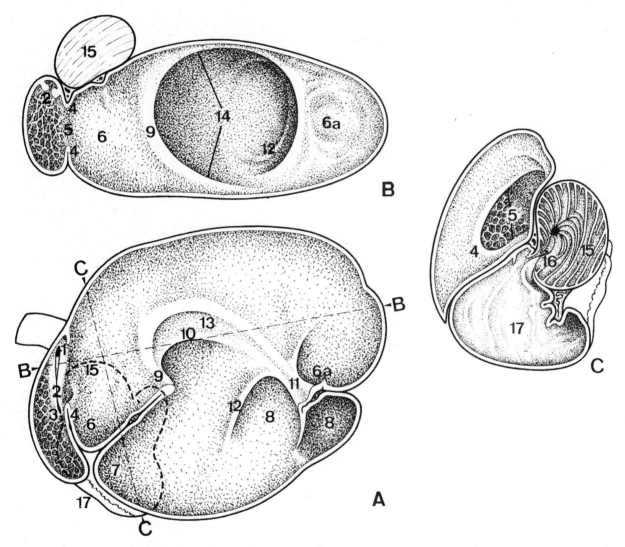

Figure 2-13. Spatial relationship and internal structural arrangement of the ruminant stomach in general; A = longitudinal section, left view; B = horizontal section (in A: B-B), dorsal view; C = transverse section (in A: C-C), caudal view. 1 = cardia; 2 = reticular groove; 3 = reticulo-omasal opening; 4 = ruminoreticular fold; 5 = ruminoreticular opening; 6 = main absorption area of atrium; 6a = main absorption area of dorsocaudal blindsac; 7 = ruminal recess (ventral sac); 8 = ventrocaudal blindsac; 9 = cranial pillar; 10 = right longitudinal pillar; 11 = caudal pillar; 12 = ventral coronary pillar; 13 = insula ruminis; 14 = intraruminal opening (connecting dorsal and ventral sac); 15 = omasum (in A outline, in C interlaminar recesses); 16 = omasal groove; 17 = abomasum (fundus). Modified from Hofmann (3).

epithelium which is typical for the remaining parts of the gastro-intestinal tract.

Ruminal Mucosa

The mucosal surface relief of the rumen is characterized by ruminal papillae which can be defined as organs of absorption. Their distribution, size and number are closely related to feeding habits, forage availability and

digestibility. Thus, to a certain extent, the papillae may be variable.

The division of ruminants into three morphophysiological feeding types is primarily based on the evolutionary adaptation of the digestive system, especially the forestomach. Its typical features are genetically fixed but may be varied considerably under different feeding conditions, resulting in acute and usually temporary or seasonal adaptations. Concentrate selectors (CS) exhibit evenly distributed ruminal papillae (Fig. 2-14). There is no area free of papillae, and even the pillars are more or less papillated. However, there are differences in number and size of papillae within the rumen. The physiologically important surface enlargement factor (SEF) can be calculated as 2 x papillary surface + basal surface over basal surface. The representative sampling of rumen mucosa from only four defined ruminal regions (8) provides indicative data on the nutritional status of a ruminant, especially on free range. Changes of the ruminal papillation and thus the SEF in response to nutritional changes require an adaptation period of two to three weeks. Repair periods are similar. Adaptive seasonal changes of the ruminal mucosa are most pronounced in ruminants of the intermediate feeding type (IM) like goats, red deer/elk or impala antelopes. Changes occur, particularly on the mucosa of the dorsal wall

of the dorsal ruminal sac (Fig. 2-15). Increasing proportions of butyric and also propionic acid set free by ruminal bacteria increase the ruminal blood flow which stimulates mucosal mitoses, resulting in vascular budding and epithelial cell proliferation. Finally, ruminal papillae grow in size and number or they regress when cellulysis based on fibrous forage results in a very high proportion of acetic acid but very little butyric and propionic, as is the case during winter or dry season periods.

The rumen mucosal pattern of all GR is characterized by an uneven distribution of papillae (Fig. 2-16). It reflects the stratification of ingesta and the regional differences of microbial activity which is greater in the mid-level area with its many niches in the vicinity of the ruminal pillars. The latter, as well as the dorsal ruminal wall, are usually devoid of papillae. In general, GR have a relatively smaller mucosal surface enlargement by ruminal papillae than CS or IM. Absorptive ruminal papillae (Fig. 2-17) have a thin-layered

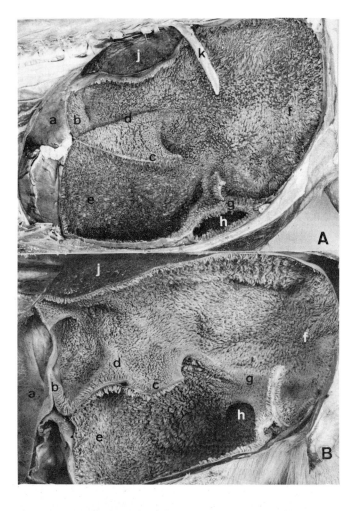

Figure 2-14. Internal ruminal relief of concentrate selectors (even distribution of absorptive papillae). A = Harvey's duiker; B = roe deer; a = reticulum; b = ruminoreticular fold; c = cranial pillar (cut surface); d = atrium; e = ruminal recess; f = caudodorsal blindsac; g = caudal pillar; h = caudoventral blindsac; j = spleen; k = 13th rib. Both animals preserved standing, stomach in situ. From Hofmann and Schnorr (7).

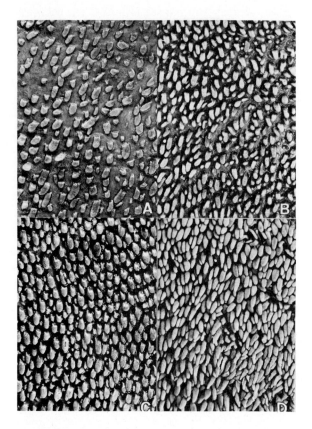

Figure 2-15. Seasonal changes in rumen papillation induced by changes in forage quality (free-ranging impala antelopes) as seen in homologue regions of the rumen dorsal wall; enl. 2,5-2,9. A = peak of dry season, minimal SEF (early March); B = 3 weeks after onset of rainy season (mid-April); C = 5 weeks after onset of rains (end of April); D = climax of rainy season (May), predominant selection of leaves, maximal SEF. From Hofmann (3) and Hofmann and Schnorr (7).

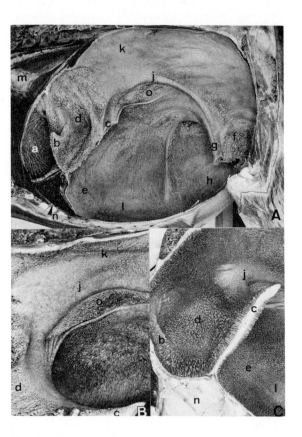

Figure 2-16. Internal ruminal relief of grass and roughage eaters (uneven distribution of absorptive papillar, mainly about midlevel). A = Coke's hartebeest; B = Bohor reedbuck; C = dom. goat; a-h = as in Fig. 2-14; i = accessory pillar; k = unpapillated mucosa, dorsal wall, 1 = and ventral wall; m = esophagus; n = abomasum; o = ruminal islet. In situ-preparations. From Hofmann and Schnorr (7).

epithelial coat, the superficial cells of which are transformed into swollen, bursting "balloon cells". The connective tissue core of each papilla contains a densely arranged but variable system of parallel venules on the broad surfaces and capillaries at the edges, all of which is supplied by one central or two marginal arterioles or both (Fig. 2-17). Molecules which have passed through the epithelial barrier layer of a papilla by diffusion finally reach the venules which transport all absorbed material via the ruminal veins and hepatic portal vein into the liver.

In all ruminants the papillae are most numerous and longest in the atrium ruminis (cranial sac), followed by the floor of the dorso-caudal blindsac. Both areas have the highest SEF, irrespective of feeding type.

Under adverse feeding conditions (Fig. 2-18), the ruminal papillae revert to a rounded, thin filiform shape which was found in all fetal rumens (perinatal phase). Such "hunger papillae" may become parakeratotic and clump together in groups.

The ruminoreticular fold (Fig. 2-13A, C), a stomach wall duplication, carries absorptive papillar on its ruminal (caudal) apsect but reticular crests on its cranial face. In a number of CS, the ruminal papillae continue well over the edge onto the reticular side of the fold. In several GR this fold, with its strong, iris-like muscular bundles, resembles a pillar; its free edge has no or merely rudimentary papillae and a heavily cornified epithelium.

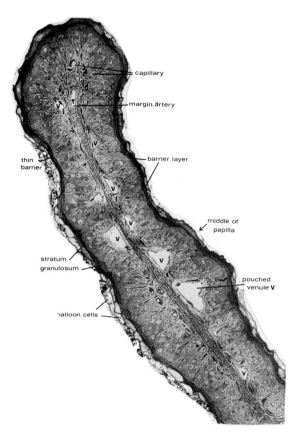

Figure 2-17. Microstructure of an absorptive ruminal papilla (atrium, Oribi, semithin transverse section, enl. 97 x); few epithelial cell layers with denser barrier, superficial balloon cells with ruminal bacteria; extensive vascular system (mainly venules with fenestrated endothelium, i.e., absorptive type). From Hofmann (3).

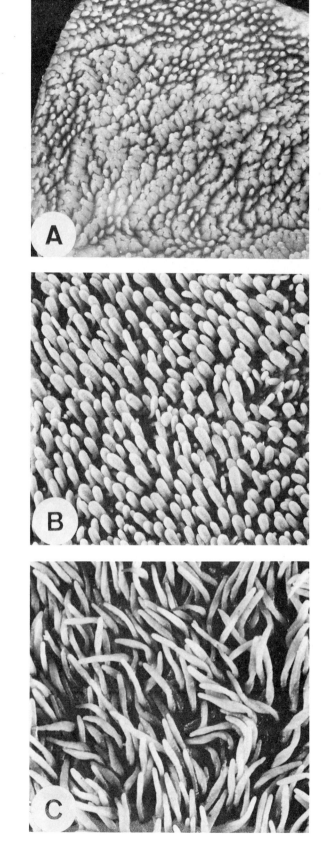

Figure 2-18. Filiform ruminal papillae (oval or circular cross section) are indicative of unstimulated ruminal blood flow/lack of butyric and propionic acid. A = atrium papillae of a one-day old goat kid (IM); B = dorsal wall papillae, roe deer CS (winter); C = atrium papillae, Bohor reedbuck GR (drought), "hunger papillae".

32

Reticular Mucosa

The typical mucosal pattern of the drop-shaped reticulum (Fig. 2-19) has caused both its Latin and its English name, honeycomb. The mucosa is arranged in intersecting crests which separate cellulae reticuli. These are deep and subdivided by secondary and/or tertiary, etc. crests in GR, but they are shallow and rarely subdivided in CS. In the latter group the sides, i.e., the low crests and bottom of the cellulae, are studded with spiky cornified papillae which interdigitate on contraction. The primary mucosal crests contain a specific muscular layer which takes its origins from the mucosal covering of the left

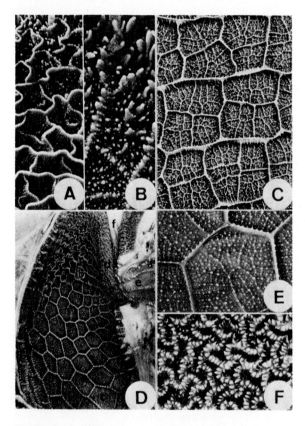

Figure 2-19. Mucosal relief of the reticulum. Transition from papillae into reticular crests in A = zebu bull (GR), B = steenbok (IM). Subdivided deep cellulae in GR (Topi antelope) = C; undivided, low, spiky cellulae in CS (Lesser Kudu) = E and contracted to hold back larger food particles (roe deer, CS) = F; right reticular wall of a goat (IM) in situ = D; a = reticular papillae; b = small cellulae; c = large cellulae, fundus reticuli; d = left lip of reticular groove; e = reticulo-omasal opening exposed, note clawlike papillae; f = groove. From Hofmann and Schnorr (7).

lip of the reticular groove. The contraction of this musculature constricts the entrances of the cellulae, resulting in the temporary retention of coarse food particles. The biggest cellulae reticuli are found in the ventrally situated wide fundus of this compartment, the smallest toward the cardia. At this level the crests become transformed into papillae. Hence, the dorsal portion of the reticular mucosa consists of papillae which blend, through the ostium ruminoreticulare, into those of the atrium ruminis (cranial sac).

Ventricular Groove

The right wall of the reticulum carries the reticular portion of the ventricular groove (Sulcus ventriculi, pars reticularis; Fig. 2-20). It connects the cardia with the reticulo-omasal opening, being the most important section of a shunt or shortcut which permits liquids to circumvent the ruminoreticulum. Its very short continuation (omasal groove) is based on the omasal canal along the basis omasi which leads, through the omaso-abomasal opening, onto the lesser curvature of the abomasum.

The reticular groove consists of two more or less bulging lips which are slightly twisted, reflecting the course of the cardiac muscular loop, i.e., they surround both the cardia and the reticulo-omasal orifice whose size they can regulate (Fig. 2-12). Closure of the lips, which is not restricted to the milk sucking period, is effected by contraction of the internal oblique fibers which straighten and shorten the lips and by the more externally situated circular fibers which bring the lips closer together. This action results in the formation of a tube with a slitlike lumen (Fig. 2-13B) and is triggered by a reflex involving cranial and caudal esophageal sphincters in alternating actions. The term "esophageal groove" is based on an outdated morphophysiological concept and should be abolished. It can be assumed that all adult ruminants are capable of activating their ventricular groove. The different morphophysiological adaptations for food prehension and oral breakdown, including salivation of selective species, appears to involve the ventricular groove regularly when plant cell contents are released as soluble nutrients in the oral cavity. Recently, Schenk-Saber et al (14) were able to show in adult goats and sheep highly

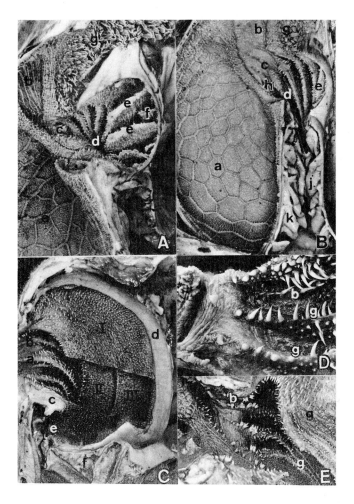

Figure 2-20. Mucosal relief of the omasum (A, B, C in situ). A = small omasum of a gerenuk (CS), dorsolateral view; B = very small omasum of a klipspringer (CS); a = reticular mucosa; b = reticular groove; c = reticulo-omasal opening (exposed); d = omasal canal; e = omasal laminae; f = omasal folds (without muscle tissue); g = ruminal papillae (atrium); h = clawlike papillae; j = abomasum; k = spiral folds. C = middle sized omasum of a goat (IM); a = reticulo-omasal opening (exposed); b = clawlike papillae on the origins of the laminae omasi; c = omasal pillar (longitud. section surface); d = omasal curvature; I, II, III = laminae of diff. size orders; e = velum abomasicum; f = abomasal mucosa. D, E = clawlike papillae (straining and filtration apparatus) in the reticulo-omasal opening: D = in an oribi (GR); E = in a zebu bull (GR); g = laminae omasi I. From Hofmann and Schnorr (7).

developed afferent nerve endings in the reticular mucosa close to the left lip of the groove. These nerve fibers are found either next to the basal lamina/basal cell layer of the stratified squamous epithelium or they penetrate to the stratum granulosum. They have club-, button- or arrowhead-shaped endings. They must be considered as receptors of great physiological importance in the regulation of food passage and food intake.

Omasal Anatomy

The ostium reticulo-omasicum (Fig. 2-13; 2-21) has been considered by physiologists working on sheep and cattle (GR) as the bottleneck for the outflow from the ruminoreticulum, hence, for food passage. This, in turn, limits new food intake. The structure of the ostium, however, differs in ruminants of various feeding types. There are strong indications that at least ruminants of the CS and IM feeding types can regulate the size of this orifice, thus permitting at times the rapid

passage also of larger fibrous particles which they cannot break down sufficiently in their rumen.

The floor of the reticular groove usually carries longitudinal folds or short papillae. In the reticulo-omasal orifice, they increase in size and form a weir-basket sieve-like mechanism primarily in those species which select dicotyledonous plants for their cell contents (Fig. 2-20). In grass-eaters these unguiculiform papillae are shorter and fewer and may not pose a major mechanical obstacle to food particles. They do, however, demarcate the beginning of the primary omasal leaves or laminae which diverge from this opening in all types of ruminants.

The ventrocentral space in the omasum, which is bound ventrally by the omasal pillar, dorsally and dorsolaterally by the free edges of the laminae, is termed the omasal canal. It has a wide entrance portion next to the reticulo-omasal orifice (Fig. 2-20B, C) and it receives radiating interlaminar recesses. These

34

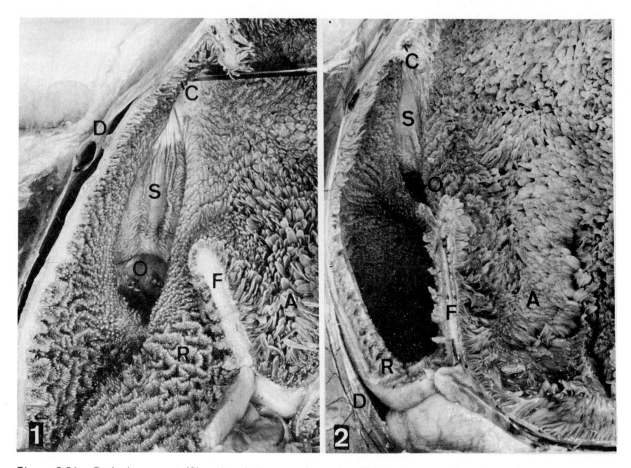

Figure 2-21. Reticular groove (S) and reticulo-omasal opening (O) in situ; 1 = Grant's gazelle, groove relaxed, ostium wide-open; 2 = Oribi, groove half-contracted, ostium half open. A = atrium ruminis; C = cardia; D = diaphragm; F = rumino-reticular fold; R = reticular mucosa, half contracted wall. From Hofmann (3).

interspaces between adjacent laminae omasi of different orders and sizes (best seen on omasal cross sections, Fig. 2-22) are slowly passed by the small particle of ingesta whose water and mineral contents are absorbed by the broad laminar surfaces.

The omasal laminae, which are of 3 or 4 orders in GR but only of 1-2 in CS (Fig. 2-22), contain a central muscular layer only in laminae of the 1st order. These and all smaller laminae are furnished with a distinct muscularis mucosae layer at each mucosal surface, i.e., there are two muscle layers but three in the primary leaflets. All GR, especially bovines with a very large omasum, have evolved a considerable omasal mucosa surface enlargement and thus have gained an additional absorptive capacity (in sheep ca. 10% of the rumen, in the ox much more). The omasal mucosa (Fig. 2-23) carries an absorptive stratified squamous epithelium quite

Figure 2-22. Transverse sections of the omasum (schematic) of 1 = CS; 2 = IM; 3 = GR; C = omasal canal; s = omasal groove; r = interlaminar recesses.

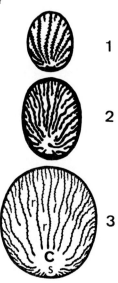

1

2

3

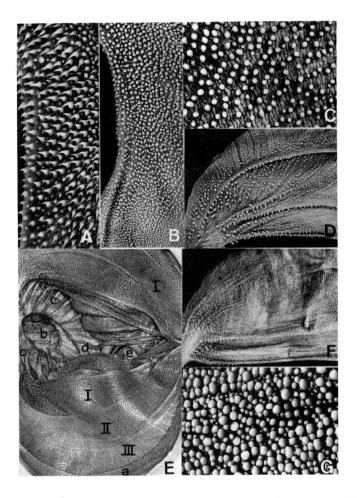

Figure 2-23. Mucosal relief of the omasum, variations of feeding types: A, B = claw-like papillae on narrow laminae of CS (A = grey duiker; B = roe deer); C = blunt, wart-like horn papillae and interpapillary absorptive mucosa in GR (Topi); D = papillated longitudinal crests (Lesser Kudu, CS); E = omasum of a GR (Topi) opened from omasal curvature, halves reflected; I-III = omasal laminae of diff. size orders; a = non-muscular mucosal fold; b = reticulo-omasal opening; c = initial "stalks" of laminae I in omasal canal; d = omasal groove; e = omaso-abomasal opening; note regular distribution of blunt papillae omasi. F = lamina I of a GR (Uganda kob) with very few papillae, soft absorptive mucosa. G = extremely dense, heavily cornified "cobble stone" papillae on lamina I of eland antelope (IM/CS), almost no absorptive interpapillary mucosa. From Hofmann and Schnorr (7).

comparable to that of the ruminal papillae and similarly well vascularized. The omasal horn papillae are spaced out and blunt in GR but densely arranged and long (claw-like or spiky) in CS. The cutaneous mucous membrane of the omasum terminates upon two asymmetrical mucosal folds which arise from the omaso-abomasal opening. Their omasal portion is the continuation of two folds flanking the sulcus omasi. Their abomasal portion made of glandular mucosa is reflected more or less onto the omasal side. These folds, which may close the ostium omaso-abomasicum more or less but never completely, are termed vela abomasica. They lack a sphincter muscle.

Abomasal Mucosa

The abomasum has a glandular gastric mucosa comparable to that of other mammals. It is, in general, thinner in GR than in CS. There is no significant region containing cardiac glands. The wide initial portion of the abomasum is the region of the proper gastric glands. These contain a much higher proportion of HCl-producing parietal cells per surface area in CS. The mucosa (Fig. 2-24) of the fundus and corpus abomasi is arranged in permanent spiral folds, which are relatively high in GR and lower in CS. They decrease in height toward the pyloric part of the organ. Two of these folds arise from the vela abomasica and run parallel along the lesser curvature of the abomasum. They flank the sulcus abomasi, the final portion of the ventricular or gastric groove. The tube-shaped terminal portion of the abomasum is lined by relatively thick pyloric glandular mucosa which also coats a fat bulge called torus pyloricus. It augments the constricting action of the sphincter pylori muscle against the duodenum.

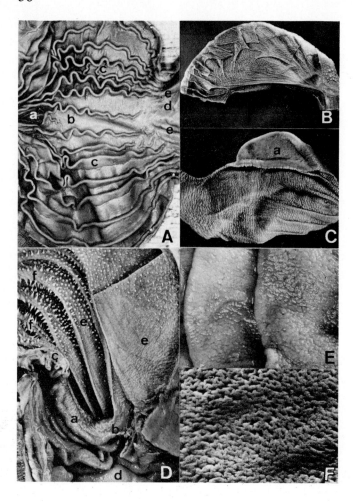

Figure 2-24. Mucosal relief of the abomasum. A = fundus region of a steenbok (IM/CS) opened from major curvature, halves reflected; a = omaso-abomasal opening, flanked by the vela abomasica; b = abomasal groove (end of ventricular groove); d, e = pyloric mucosa. B, C = omasal side of vela (B = gnu, GR; C = kob, GR; showing glandular mucosa at a). D = velum abomasicum (a) in situ in a Thomson's gazelle (IM) showing abrupt change from cutaneous omasal into glandular abomasal mucosa; c = omasal pillar; e, f = omasal laminae with spiky papillae. E = fundic glandular mucosa, spiral folds (Thomson's gazelle, IM). F = pyloric glandular mucosa, gastric pits (reticulated giraffe, CS). From Hofmann and Schnorr (7).

Stomach Blood and Nerve Supply (Fig. 2-25)

The blood supply for the ruminant stomach is from the celiac artery which often originates by a common trunk with the cranial mesenteric artery from the aorta, still within or near the hiatus aorticus of the diaphragm. The celiac artery of ruminants forms six major branches instead of three as in monogastric mammals: a small phrenic, the hepatic (for liver and abomasum), several small pancreatic, the splenic which detaches the right ruminal artery (main arterial supply of the rumen on both sides), the left ruminal artery which detaches the reticular (for the reticulum on either side) and the left gastric artery which supplies the remaining portions of reticulum, omasum, abomasum and omentum. These arteries form extensive anastomoses. The veins, which are equipped with valves, run parallel to the arteries, embedded in fat in the gastric grooves and mesenteries. There is a dense muscular, submucosal and mucosal network of blood vessels in the stomach wall. The latter is best developed in prime areas of absorption (rumen, omasum) and shows an extreme level of differentiation within the absorptive ruminal papillae. All venous blood from the ruminant stomach is carried into the hepatic portal vein.

The efferent nerve supply of the ruminant stomach comes from the dorsal and ventral vagal trunks which have accompanied the esophagus through its hiatus. The dorsal vagal trunk, however, has many more branches and a wider distribution (due to the ruminoreticular development) than in monogastric mammals. There are ten branches of the dorsal vagal trunk and seven of the ventral. They follow the gastric grooves and curvatures, usually along the course of the blood vessels. The sympathetic nerves are derived from the celiac plexus which contains a number of celiac ganglia. The terminal neurons of the gastric nerve supply are found in several layers in the intramural system.

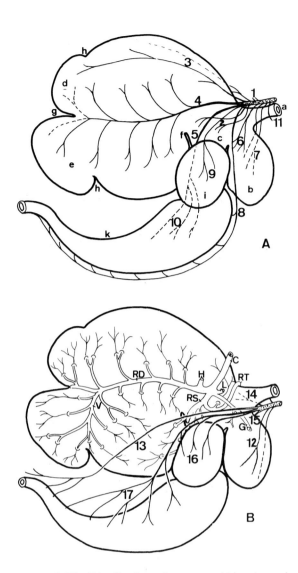

Figure 2-25. Distribution of nerves and blood vessels on the right side of the ruminant stomach, schematic (modified). A = dorsal vagus trunk (D), B = ventral vagus trunk and arteries; rumen nerves, blood vessels any lymph nodes are lodged in the grooves, those of the other compartments in the mesenteries (omenta). For designation of the vagal branches (1-11 in A, 11-17 in B) refer to Hofmann and Schnorr (7). Arteries: C = celiac, G = left gastric, H = hepatic, L = lienal, RD = right ruminal, RS = left ruminal, RT = reticular (supplies also atrium), V = right ventral coronary; a = esophagus, b = reticulum, c = atrium, d = dorsocaudal blindsac, e = ventrocaudal blindsac, f = cranial groove, g = caudal groove, h = coronary grooves, i = omasum, k = abomasum (lesser curvature).

Lymph Vessels and Nodes

The lymphatic vessels of the stomach originate at three levels: in the mucosa, muscular tunic and serous membrane. They all unite in a submucosal network, with densely placed valves. They then form afferent vessels which enter the gastric lymph nodes. Their efferent lymphatics unite near the celiac artery to form the gastric lymph trunk which finally opens into the lumbar cisterna chyli with or without joining the hepatic and intestinal trunks. Part of the lymph of the abomasum only is filtered in the hepatic lymph nodes (in bovines). There are up to 10 distinct groups of gastric lymph nodes in ruminants, most of them on the right aspect and situated in the grooves and along the curvatures next to blood vessels and nerves.

The Midgut

The intestine of ruminants is characterized by its considerable length, by a distal fermentation chamber and by a spiral colon attached to a mesenteric plate. This principal structural plan is modified in accordance with differences in feeding behavior and digestive strategies (Fig. 2-26).

Intestinal Length and Relative Size

Total intestinal length increases relative to body length with the increasing ability of a ruminant to digest fiber. Thus, sheep and cattle have a relatively longer intestine than selective deer species. In GR the ratio of body length to intestinal length is approximately 1:22-30, in intermediate mixed feeders, e.g., red deer, wapiti, impala antelopes or goats it is 1:15-20, but in CS it is 1:12-15, e.g., roe deer, white-tailed deer or muntjak. Physiologically more important is the ratio of small intestine to large intestine. Ruminants with a capacious, subdivided rumen well-suited for cellulolysis, i.e., GR, have a much shorter proportion of large intestine than those species which select for cell contents and readily digestible forage. Thus, CS show a ratio of 2.3-2.6:1, but GR a ratio of 3.7-4.2:1.

In this context the evolutionary development, especially of the cecum and the initial portion of the colon, has been regressive while the development of the rumen has been progressive with increasing fiber digestion. When one considers the ruminoreticulum according to its position in the digestive tract as a proximal fermentation chamber (PFC), then the wide and capacious portions of the large

38

Intestine: evolutionary + functional adaptation

Concentrate selector – LOW FIBRE (cell content)

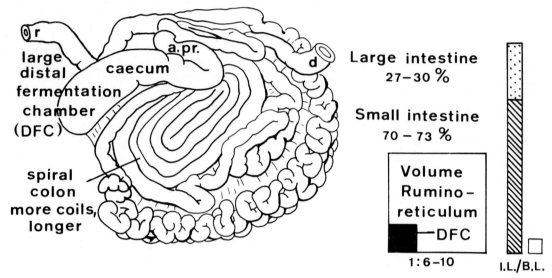

large distal fermentation chamber (DFC)

spiral colon more coils, longer

caecum

a.pr.

r

d

Large intestine 27–30 %

Small intestine 70 – 73 %

Volume Rumino-reticulum

DFC

1:6–10

I.L./B.L.

Intestine 12–15 x body length (BL)

Grass eater – HIGH FIBRE (cell wall)

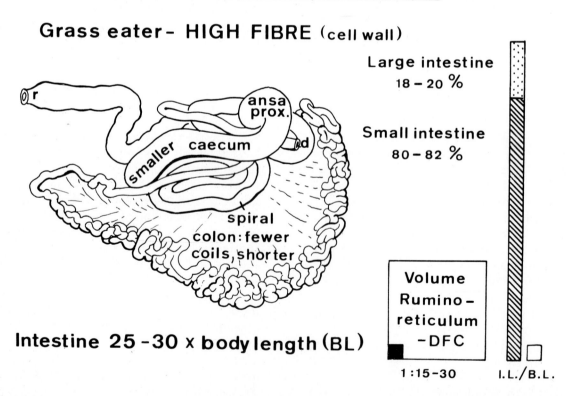

r

smaller caecum

ansa prox.

d

spiral colon: fewer coils, shorter

Large intestine 18 – 20 %

Small intestine 80 – 82 %

Volume Rumino-reticulum –DFC

1:15–30

I.L./B.L.

Intestine 25 –30 x body length (BL)

Figure 2-26. Anatomical differences of mid- and hindgut (duodenum = d to rectum = r) according to feeding type, schematic. From Hofmann (5) (data modified).

intestine (ceco-colon) represent the distal fermentation chamber (DFC). Although both portions are seasonally variable, there is a typical pattern, consistent with feeding type, to be observed. The ratio DFC:PFC is 1:6-10 in CS, 1:9-24 in IM and 1:15-30 in GR. This must be due to the fact that more unfermented food escapes from the rumen in ruminants selecting primarily for cell content and avoiding fiber. Hence, in selective species post-ruminal digestion and absorption is of considerable importance. This is reflected in anatomical variations facilitating physiological adaptations.

The ruminant intestine is confined to the supraomental recess to the right of the rumen. Its common mesenteric plate suspends it and, thus, restricts its movements. A considerable portion of the intestine is in an intrathoracic situation limited cranially by the lesser omentum, the omasum and the liver.

Description of Small Intestine

The duodenum forms a loop on the extreme right (Fig. 2-27). It begins at the pylorus as the cranial part with a sigmoid loop near the porta hepatis. Bile and pancreatic ducts enter the small intestine at that point (major duodenal papilla). The descending duodenum begins at the cranial flexure. It runs caudally and suspends both walls superficial and deep, of the greater omentum. At the level of the last lumbar vertebra or the tuber coxae, the duodenum forms a sharp caudal flexure and is continued by the ascending duodenum, which runs cranially, dorsomedial from the descending limb. It is connected to the descending colon by the duodenocolic fold. It finally forms the duodenojejunal flexure and is continued by the jejunum.

Being the longest portion of the small intestine, the jejunum is arranged in a great number of coils along the edge of the common mesenteric plate (Fig. 2-26) which carries the spiral colon. The most cranial jejunal coils fit into a deep niche provided by rumen, abomasum, omasum and pancreas. The ventral coils may reach (through the walls of the greater omentum) the ventral abdominal wall. This is so as a rule in CS or also in GR, if their ventral ruminal sac is contracted. The caudal jejunal coils are attached to a long extension of the mesenteric plate which

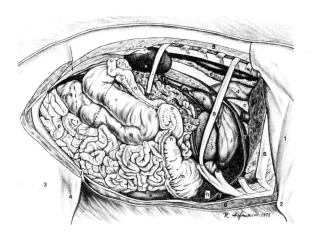

Figure 2-27. Abdominal topography of an adult roe buck, exposed from the right side; lung, diaphragm and liver partly removed. (In situ fixation, standing); a,b,c = lung; d = esophagus; e = caudal mediastinal lymph node; f = caudal vena cava, central portion removed; g = aorta; h = left portion of liver; i = reticulum; k = rumen; l = omasum; m = abomasum; n = pylorus; o = duodenum (cranial and descending portion, caudal flexure); p = jejunum; q = cecum; r = wide portion of ansa proximalis coli (q + r = distal fermentation chamber); s = pancreas; t = portal vein; u = greater omentum, mostly removed, permitting view into supraometal bursa; its caudal border/reflection line dotted; v = left kidney (right removed). 1 = triceps, 2 = elbow joint, 3 = quadriceps (partly removed, broken line), 4 = stifle joint, 5 = longissimus dorsi, 6 = pectoralis, 7 = diaphragm, 8 = 6th rib, 9 = 9th rib. From Hofmann and Geiger (17).

permits them to move outside the supraomental recess. In CS and IM with a relatively small rumen (Fig. 2-10), they regularly are found on the left side (paralumbar fossa) together with the cecum caudal to the dorsocaudal blindsac of the rumen.

The jejunum is continued by the relatively short ileum. It takes a straight caudocranial course ventral to the cecum to which it is connected by the ileocecal fold. It terminates at the cecocolic junction on entering the large intestine via the ileal orifice. The intestinal mucosa is elevated around this opening and contains numerous aggregate lymph nodules.

The muscular tunic of the small intestine is comprised of a thicker inner circular and a weaker outer longitudinal layer. The thickness of the muscular tunic varies in adaptation to forage quality. In CS it is weaker during winter (intake reduction). The mucosa can shift on the muscular tube through the loose connective tissue of the submucosal layer which permits the formation of temporary folds. The mucous membrane of the small intestine is characterized by the presence of intestinal villi. Their shape is tapelike, more rarely pointed or tonguelike. In several ruminant species the villi are fused at their base portions forming villous crests [visible on parallel surface sections as reticular structures, e.g., in roe deer (11)]. The mucosa embeds simple tubular crypts of Lieberkühn which extend down to the lamina muscularis mucosa. In their deep portions they are coiled in the small intestine but they are straight in the large intestine. The number of slime-producing goblet cells increases steadily from the duodenum to the central loop of the spiral colon (appr. 1:8). In general, the total glandular tissue proportion of the small intestine is up to 100% higher in CS than in grass-eating species. Brunner's submucosal glands are restricted to the cranial part of the duodenum in ruminants. In all species investigated (12) they disappear 5-10 mm beyond the major duodenal papilla. Whereas solitary lymph modules are found in all portions of the intestinal mucosa, there is a concentration into Peyer's patches (aggregate nodules) in the ileum which continue well into the cecal mucosa.

THE HINDGUT

The ceco-colon, like all other portions of the large intestine, is distinguished by the absence of villi, by semicircular mucosal folds, by an increasing proportion of goblet cells and by long tubular crypts of Lieberkühn. There is, however, a relative reduction of goblet cells and an increase in the density of submucosal and mucosal blood vessels in the ceco-colon (DFC) of several concentrate selectors (e.g., roe deer, dikdik) or IM (e.g., caribou, goat), indicative of rapid absorption of short-chain fatty acids.

The Cecum

The cecum (Fig. 2-26, 2-27) of all ruminants is a big blunt-tipped tube which is continued without external demarcation by the colon ascendens cranially from the ileocolic junction. The relative volume of the cecum decreases from CS over IM to GR, i.e., the relatively largest cecum is found in highly selective ruminants like giraffe, dikdik or roe deer.

The Colon

The initial portion of the colon is evenly wide and forms the first two limbs of the ansa proximalis coli, an S-shaped tube which narrows more or less abruptly before it continues as the spiral colon (Fig. 2-26). Its proportion of the entire intestinal length decreases from 18-20% in CS to 12-14% in GR, i.e., grass eating species have fewer and shorter spiral coils than ruminants selecting easily digestible forage with a high percentage of cell contents. The spiral colic loop has a lesser diameter than the proximal loops. Its coils may be raised into a flattened cone in species with a greater number of coils like goat, deer or moose. The spiral consists of centripetal turns, a central loop and centrifugal turns. In many ruminant species, but not in the bovines, the last centrifugal turn lies close to the jejunum and is separated from the spiral by the jejunal lymph nodes. It is in this portion of the spiral, that fecal pellets are formed. Dorsally, this end portion of the spiral colon is continued by the thin distal loop of the ascending colon. It lies medial to the proximal loop and close to the ascending duodenum. At the level of the last thoracic vertebra and cranial to the cranial mesenteric root it turns abruptly to the left. Its short continuation is the transverse colon which is related dorsally to the pancreas. The terminal portion, the descending colon, stays on the left side of the cranial mesenteric root in a high dorsal position. It is attached to the ascending duodenum. On its caudal course its mesentery gradually lengthens, resulting in a ventral curve termed colon sigmoideum. The longer mesentery permits wider excursions during rectal palpation in larger ruminants.

Finally, the descending colon is followed by the rectum which extends into the pelvic cavity. Its median mesorectum terminates at the blind ending of the rectogenital excavation of the peritoneal sac. The muscular tunic and the muscularis mucosae reach their maximal thickness in the retroperitoneal portion of the rectum. Subsequently, this musculature condenses to form the internal anal sphincter which is added to by the voluntary

external anal sphincter. The muscular wall of
the anal canal is joined by the inserting leva-
tor ani muscle. The mucosa of the anal canal
provides several longitudinal folds known as
columnae rectales. Thereafter, the glandular
intestinal mucosa abruptly changes into
cutaneous mucous membrane. This in turn is
demarcated against the skin of the anus by
the appearance of hairs.

Liver and Pancreas (Fig. 2-28)

Both liver and pancreas are derivates of the
midgut. Their excretory ducts enter the
cranial part of the duodenum upon the major
duodenal papilla or, as in bovine animals, the
accessory pancreatic duct terminates distal to
the papilla. The liver of ruminants (Fig. 2-28)
is a compact undivided gland which has been
dislocated, during pre- and postnatal development of the rumen, to the right side of the
diaphragmatic cupola. Its long axis is in a
vertical position but is horizontal in other
mammals. As a result of this dislocation, the
left lobe of the ruminant liver is in a ventral
position, the right lobe dorsal above the gall
bladder (which is absent in a number of
cervids and bovids). Its caudalmost portion
is the caudate process of the caudate lobe
which embeds the cranial pole of the right
kidney. The omasum leaves a deep impres-
sion on the left lobe which has a notch for
the falciform and round ligament. The caudal
vena cava runs almost vertically along the left
rounded border of the liver before it enters
the foramen venae cavae of the diaphragm.
Here it receives the hepatic veins. The right
border with its sharp edge follows more or
less the right costal arch. In CS it is more
often protruding from the thorax than in GR
as the liver is always heavier in the former
(1.9-2.3% of body weight vs 1.1-1.3%).

On the concave visceral surface of the liver,
at the base of the caudate lobe, is the porta
hepatis which is entered by the portal vein
and the hepatic artery but is left by the
hepatic duct. The latter is joined by the
cystic duct in those species which have a gall
bladder. The attachment line of the lesser
omentum runs obliquely from the esophageal
notch to the porta hepatis. The convex diaphragmatic surface provides the main attach-
ments: the triangular, falciform and coronary
ligaments (all of which are short serosa duplications), the fibrous area nuda and the caudal

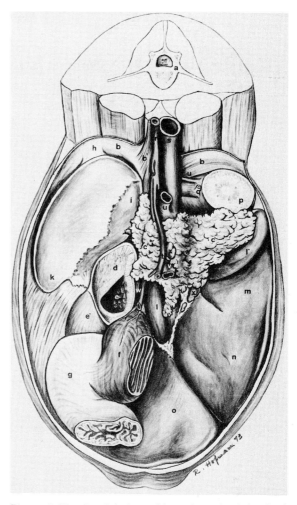

Figure 2-28. Caudal view of intrathoracic abdominal
organs of a roe deer in situ; rumen and intestine
mostly removed. a = 3rd lumbar vertebra; b = diaphragm; c = pancreas; d = atrium ruminis; e = ruminoreticular opening and reticulum; f = omasum; g =
abomasum, pyloric part removed; h = phrenico-lienal
fold; i = splenic attachment area with rumen; k =
spleen, distal pole; l,m,n,o = liver portions; p = cut
surface of right kidney; q = ureter; r = aorta; s =
caudal vena cava; t = cran. mesenteric artery; u =
renal vessels; v = portal vein; w = left gastric artery;
x = portal lymph nodes. From Hofmann and Geiger
(17).

vena cava. The ruminant liver has very little
interstitial connective tissue and there is no
macroscopic demarcation of the liver lobules.

Their principal structure adheres to the
common mammalian plan with hepatic trias,
sinusoids and central vein. The bile ductules
form a uniting network at the edges of the
coneshaped lobules and then form the

42

common hepatic duct. It leaves the liver via the porta and finally becomes the bile duct to the duodenum.

The pancreas (Fig. 2-27 and 2-28) is a light-colored lobulated gland which is closely related to the liver (incisura pancreatis). Its venous blood is directly drained into the portal vein which fills this incisura. The pancreas consists of a small body and two asymmetric lobes. Its shape is variable in different ruminant species, but it is always attached to the right wall of the atrium ruminis and to the left crus of the diaphragm. It may also extend to the area of adhesion of the spleen. The right lobe touches the omasum, before it accompanies the descending duodenum. It forms part of the aforementioned intrathoracic niche which lodges the cranial-most coils of the jejunum. The intralobular duct system of the excretory portion of the gland unites in bovine ruminants to form only the accessory pancreatic duct, which emerges from the right lobe. Most other ruminant species have the pancreatic duct which opens into the cranial part of the duodenum together with the bile duct. The pancreatic islets, which constitute the endocrine portion of the pancreas, have an uneven distribution but their microstructure is quite comparable to that of other herbivores.

Intestinal Blood, Lymph and Nerve Supply

The initial part of the duodenum, the liver and pancreas, receive their arterial blood supply from the celiac artery. Most of the duodenum and all other portions of the small intestine and most of the large intestine are supplied by the cranial mesenteric artery. The descending colon and most of the rectum are vascularized by the caudal mesenteric artery, the rectum also by the internal iliac arteries. With the exception of the end portion of the gut, the entire gastro-intestinal system, including the pancreas, drain their venous blood into the hepatic portal vein. This arrangement makes the liver the center of a specific portion of the circulatory system, facilitating storage, mobilization, transformation (e.g., gluconeogenesis) and metabolism of nutrients and their biochemical constituents. The hepatic veins, which leave the liver on its diaphragmatic side, carry the venous blood back to the main circulation (caudal vena cava). The autonomic nervous system provides the innervation for the intestines and the big glands. Sympathetic nerve fibers (retarding function) and parasympathetic (activating) fibers originate from, have synapses or pass through the celiac, cranial and caudal mesenteric and lumbar ganglia. They form, around the vascular trunks as mentioned above, extensive networks, termed cranial and caudal mesenteric plexus and cranial rectal plexus. Most of the parasympathetic fibers are derived from the vagus nerve. After several synapses, they terminate in the intestinal wall (intramural system). The lymph vessels of the intestines are most numerous in major regions of absorption. The intestinal lymph nodes of ruminants are numerous. They are situated in the respective mesenteries of each intestinal portion, but lymph from the duodenum passes also to the liver and pancreas (hepatic and pancreatico-duodenal lymph nodes).

SUMMARY

A condensed anatomical description is given of all portions of the digestive system relating to function, i.e., digestive physiology and feeding behavior. The common structural plan of the ruminant tract is treated consistently in a comparative way based on the concept of a flexible classification of all ruminant species being grouped into three morphophysiological feeding types: concentrate selectors, grass and roughage eaters and a transitory, opportunistic intermediate type of ruminant. All portions of the digestive system exhibit adaptive variations (more or less pronounced) which permit such a classification. It reflects primarily evolutionary process in response to vegetation changes in the tertiary period. Cattle, bison or buffalo show the most advanced ruminant system as they are non-selective and perfectly able to digest forage of poor quality, rich in cellulose. Focal points of anatomical diversion are the salivary glands, the three forestomach compartments and the ceco-colic (distal) fermentation chamber. They all clearly imply variations in digestive physiology, choice of feed or feeding management of the various ruminants which must not be treated as a homogenous group any longer.

Literature Cited and Further Reading

1. Dougherty, R.W., et al. 1962. Amer. J. Vet. Res. 26:213.
2. Habel, R.E. 1975. Guide to the Dissection of Domestic Ruminants. Cornell University, Ithaca, NY.
3. Hofmann, R.R. 1973. The Ruminant Stomach (Stomach Structure and Feeding Habits of East African Game Ruminants). Kenya Literature Bureau, Box 30222, Nairobi, Kenya.
4. Hofmann, R.R. 1983. In: Fibre in Human and Animal Nutrition, pp. 51-58. G. Wallace and L. Bell, eds. The Royal Society of New Zealand Bulletin 20.
5. Hofmann, R.R. 1985. In: Biology of Deer Production. P.F. Fennessy, K.R. Drew and P. Volz, eds. The Royal Society of N.Z. Bull. 22.
6. Hofmann, R.R. Undated. The Wild Ruminants (Comparative Functional Anatomy, Feeding Habits and Adaptation), Monograph in preparation.
7. Hofmann, R.R. and B. Schnorr. 1982. Die funktionelle Morphologie des Wiederkäuer-Magens (Schleimhaut und Versorgungsbahnen), Ferdinand Enke-Verlag, Stuttgart, 1-170.
8. Hofmann, R.R., A.S. Saber and M. Wehner. Undated. Rumen mucosal morphology as an index of nutritional status in wild and domestic ruminants. J. Wildl. Dis. (in press)
9. Kay, R.N.B., W. von Engelhardt and R.G. White. 1980. In: Digestive Physiology and Metabolism in Ruminants, pp. 743-761. Y. Ruckebusch and P. Thivend, eds. MTP Press Ltd., Lancaster, UK.
10. Kiplel, N.M. 1981. Comparative Studies of the Functional Anatomy of the Masticatory Muscles in Ruminants of the Intermediate Feeding Type, M. Sc. Thesis (Med. Vet.) Univ. Nairobi, Kenya.
11. Lackhoff, M. 1983. Vergleichende histologische und morphometrische Untersuchungen am Darm von Rehwild (Capreolus capreolus, Linné 1758) und Buschschliefer (Heterohyrax syriacus), Vet. Med. Diss., Univ. Giessen, Germany.
12. Meisel, H. Undated. Vergleichend-histologische Untersuchungen am Duodenum von Haus- und Wildwiederkäuern (in preparation).
13. Sack, W.O. (Transl.), R. Nickel, A. Schummer and E. Seiferle. 1973. The Viscera of the Domestic Mammals, Verlag Paul Parey, Berlin und Hamburg, Germany.
14. Schenk-Saber, B., B. Schnorr and K.D. Weyrauch. Undated. Afferente Nervenendigungen in der Vormagen-schleimhaut von Schaf und Ziege (Afferent nerve endings in the forestomach mucous membrane of the sheep and goat). Zschr. Mikrosk. Anat. Forschung (in press).
15. Stöckmann, W. 1979. Zool. Jb. Syst. 106:344.
16. Van Soest, P.J. 1982. Nutritional Ecology of the Ruminant. O & B Books, Inc., Corvallis, Oregon.
17. Hofmann, R.R. and G. Geiger. 1974. Zbl. Vet. Med., C, 3:63.
18. Langer, P. 1973. Gegenbaurs morph. Jahrb., Leipzig 119:633.
19. Saber, A.S. and R.R. Hofmann. 1984. Gegenbaurs morph. Jahrb., Leipzig 130:273.
20. Schmuck, U. 1986. Vergleichend-anatomische und-histologische Unkersuchungen an der zunge von 42 Wiederkäuer-Arten (Ruminantia). Vet. Med. Diss., Univ. Giessen, Germany.

3 GROWTH AND DEVELOPMENT OF THE RUMINANT DIGESTIVE SYSTEM

by Sidney J. Lyford, Jr.

INTRODUCTION

The development of the ruminant digestive system begins in very early stages of embryonic growth and progresses in formation, growth, and function to adulthood. The individual digestive organs develop at different rates with respect to each other and to total body growth during fetal and postnatal development. While the forestomach (rumen, reticulum and omasum) has the capability of rapid growth and metabolic development, the ruminant enters life as a simple stomached animal lacking the development or function of the forestomach compartments. Only a few weeks are required however, for the transition of the newborn from a dependent nursing neonatal to an independent weanling fully reliant on its environment for nutrition.

FETAL DEVELOPMENT

The origin of the ruminant stomach is from an enlargement of the primitive gut (stomach primordia) of the embryo. Examination of the 4-week-old embryo of cattle reveals a spindled-shaped stomach primordium with well defined dorsal and ventral curvatures similar to that found in simple stomached animals. The primordia of the four stomach compartments are present by the 6th week with the rumen and reticulum developing from the dorsal or greater curvature of the stomach primordia. The omasum and reticular groove develop from the cranial and the abomasum from the caudal portions of the ventral curvature. During the 8th week the reticular groove develops extensively and epithelial stratification of the esophagus and the forestomachs is initiated (1). In cattle, stratification begins at the terminal end of the esophagus and progresses to the reticular groove and adjacent areas of the forestomach, but may begin in the reticular groove of the domestic buffalo (*Bubalus bubalis*) (2). The simple columnar type cells characteristic of the adult abomasum begin to develop at this time.

In the 9-week-old bovine fetus the rumen sacs and pillars become apparent, the reticulum established with the omasum becoming a more distinctive nearly spherical compartment. The primordia of the omasal laminae are present as epithelial folds and the cardiac and pyloric regions of the abomasum have become well established with the abomasal folds in evidence. Fig. 3-1 illustrates the extent of differentiation and development of the stomach at a fetal age of about 10 weeks in cattle.

Fetal stomach differentiation occurs earlier in sheep and goats than in cattle (3, 4). Distinguishable areas for the stomach compartments are present in the 3rd week of embryonic development of sheep and with an easily identifiable stratified cuboidal epithelium observed at 7 weeks. Definite stomach pouches begin to develop by the 8th week. Clearly defined folded layers of cells indicative of the first four orders of the omasal laminae are present at 10 weeks and at 12 weeks the honeycomb-like surface structure (reticular ribs) of the reticulum has started to develop.

Figure 3-1. The stomach of a 11.5 cm bovine fetus Ca. 14 weeks old. A latex injected preparation with the fetal tissues digested away. Note the extent of development of the mucosal folds (rugae) of the abomasum and the laminae of the omasum. From Warner and Flatt (3). Courtesy H.E. Evans. Dept. Vet. Anatomy, Cornell University.

Initiation of rumen papillae development begins with the morphogenesis of the lamina propria and increases in the microvasculature of the capillary bed (5). This process, depicted in Fig. 3-2, begins as a capillary loop late in the 3rd mo. of gestation in the bovine fetus and proceeds by pushing up the lamina propria to create the papillae of the ruminal surface detectable microscopically by the 5th mo. Pronounced rumen papillae development was observed by Hofmann (6) in the late fetal stages of growth of several different species of African antelope. Papillary development was also apparent on the first order omasal leaves of some species and the rugae (folds) characteristic of the adult abomasum were observed in the fundic region as well. Keratinization of the rumen epithelium occurs earlier in fetal life in the domestic buffalo than in other ruminants studied (2).

GROWTH OF THE DIGESTIVE TRACT

All organs of the digestive tract, with the exception of the small intestine, increase in tissue weight from the time of first differentiation in the embryo to adulthood. During early fetal growth, forestomach development is greater than that of the abomasum in both sheep and cattle (Fig. 3-3). However, near birth the weight of the abomasum equals that

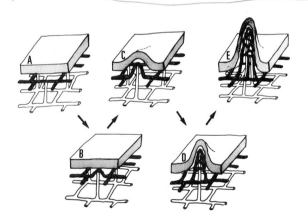

Figure 3-2. A diagrammatic representation of the relationship between the development of the ruminal microvasculature and the epithelial layer. A-E are at estimated gestation periods of (a) late 3 mo.; (b) early 4 mo.; (c) early 5 mo.; (d) 6 mo. and (e) early 8 mo. From Amasaki and Daigo (5). Courtesy H. Amasaki, Nippon Vet. and Zootech. College.

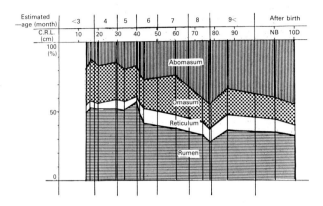

Figure 3-3. The relative weights of the ruminant stomach of the calf from the 3rd mo. of gestation to 10 d after birth. C.R.L.: crown rump length, NB: new born calf, 10D: 10 d old calf. From Amasaki et al (7). Courtesy H. Amasaki, Nippon Vet. and Zootech. College.

of the combined forestomachs in both species and comprises 70% of the total stomach weight in the newborn deer (Odocoileus virginianus) (8).

Total alimentary tract tissue comprises 2.4% of the body weight of the lamb fetus near birth but increase to 5.7% by 9 weeks of age and then decrease to 3.6% at maturity. The organs primarily responsible for the increase during the first few weeks of life are the forestomach and the small intestine. The forestomach of the lamb increases from 0.4 to 1.7% and the small intestine from 1.1 to 2.6% of body weight between birth and 9 weeks of age. The dramatic increase in the growth of the rumen and reticulum of the newborn with access to solid feeds is illustrated in Fig. 3-4 with the grazing lamb. The other digestive organs continue to increase in tissue weight, but at a slower rate.

Rapid increases in tissue weight of the small intestine of lambs has ceased by 8 or 9 weeks of age. Limited data suggest there may actually be a decrease in weight of the small intestine in the latter stages of growth in sheep, domestic buffalo (10) and cattle. The order of growth of the organs of the alimentary tract from birth to adulthood are: rumen rumen, reticulum, omasum, cecum, large intestine and rectum, small intestine, abomasum, and esophagus for sheep, cattle (11) and domestic buffalo (12).

The growth patterns of the digestive organs relative to each other differs little in the first

46

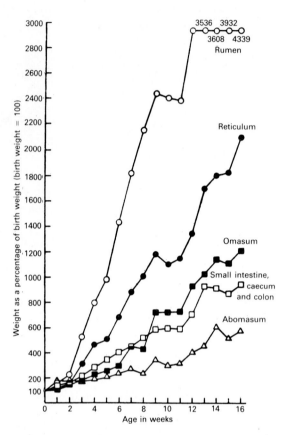

Figure 3-4. Digestive organ growth in lambs from birth to 16 weeks of age. Lambs nursing ewes on pasture. Wet tissue organ weights expressed as a percentage of that organ weight at birth. From Wardrop and Coombe (9).

2-4 weeks of life. Rapid growth of the fore-stomach begins at this time if the neonatal has been consuming solid food (Fig. 3-5). Coupled with the cessation in growth of the small intestines, the stomach becomes the dominant organ by 12-16 weeks of age (13). The influence of diet on the development of some digestive tract parameters of the calf is shown in Table 3-1.

Comparison of the growth patterns between cattle and the domestic buffalo suggests that ruminoreticular growth is more rapid in the buffalo (12, 15) but the small intestine may be less rapid than observed in cattle (*Bos taurus* and *B. indicus*). However, this effect may be due in part to the greater ruminoreticular and less omasal and large intestinal weight that water buffalo have when compared to cattle (10).

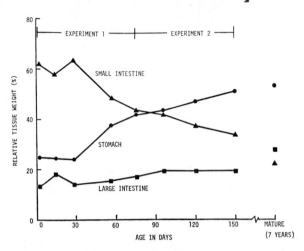

Figure 3-5. The relative growth of the digestive system of the growing lamb. Wet tissue organ weights expressed as a percentage of the total weight of the alimentary tract. Experiment 1 lambs nursing ewes on pasture and experiment 2 an average of lambs fed three different diets. From Oh et al (13).

The relative size and capacity of the digestive organs at different stages of growth and for different species and diets has been reviewed by Church (16). These data suggest the hind gut continues to be a signficant proportion of the alimentary tract into adulthood in both sheep and cattle, contributing from 11.1-25.0% of the wet tissue weight of the total tract of sheep and 9.2-16% of cattle.

The length of the small and large intestines increases rapidly in the later stages of fetal growth and in the first few weeks of postnatal life. Most of the increase in length occurs in the first 9 weeks. James et al (17) observed an average length of the small intestine in newborn calves weighing over 50 kg to be 11.9 m, ranging from 8.2 to 15.1 m. In 13 to 14-week-old calves weighing 140 kg the length of the small intestine varied between 29.3-42.7 m, the large intestine 4.9-6.5 m and the cecum 0.33-0.43 m. Total weights and weight per unit of length of the small intestine was greater for calves fed milk replacers containing non-milk proteins (18). In adult sheep and goat the lengths of the small and large intestine ranges from 18-35 m and 4-8 m and that of the adult bovine from 27-49 m and 6.5-14 m, respectively.

NORMAL STOMACH DEVELOPMENT

Ruminants born and raised in natural environments have access to vegetation from

Table 3-1. The growth of the digestive tract of the calf consuming rations high in either hay or grain.[a]

Item[b]	3 Weeks old Milk only	12 Weeks old	
		High hay	High concentrate
Concentrates, kg/d	- - - - -	0.45	2.27
Live body weight, kg	36.9	59.1	76.7
Empty body weight, kg	34.6	45.3	65.4
LBW increase due to Ruminoreticulum fill, %		49.4	19.2
Fresh tissue weight			
Ruminoreticulum, g	244	1,678	2,120
g/kg EBW	7.1	37.0	32.4
Omasum, g	54	397	410
Abomasum, g	239	405	555
Intestines, g	1,778	5,315	6,722
Contents - digesta			
Ruminoreticulum, g	750	10,900	7,700
g/kg EBW	22	241	118
Omasum, g	18	178	157
Abomasum, g	578	631	745
Alimentary tract, g	2,300	13,800	11,300
Volume, ℓ			
Ruminoreticulum	2.9	27.3	22.4
ml/kg EBW	83	603	343
Omasum	0.1	0.7	0.7
Abomasum	2.5	3.5	3.5

[a] Adapted from Stobo et al (14)
[b] LBW = live body weight, EBW = empty body weight, volume determined by water fill.

birth. Consumption of vegetation promotes rapid development of the forestomach in size and function. Wardrop (19) suggests the development of the grazing young can be divided into three phases: (a) 0-3 weeks of age, a non-ruminant phase; (b) 3-8 weeks of age, a transitional phase; and (c) 8 weeks of age onward, adult ruminants. However, the rate of forestomach development, even under grazing conditions, will depend on the levels of milk consumed by the neonatal with respect to its growth requirements and the availability and consumption of readily digestible feedstuffs.

Stomach Growth

The rumen in the newborn is small and flaccid with rudimentary papillae giving the rumen lining a texture similar to that of fine sandpaper in deer and calves with somewhat larger papillae in sheep and in several different species of African antelope (6). Papillae are the most developed at birth in the domestic Asiatic water buffalo with lengths up to 1.2 mm including the presence of some with the more mature tongue-like shape (2). The reticulum is a small elastic sac one-third the size of the rumen, with a differentiated polygonal surface structure (reticular ribs) that have rudimentary papillae on the floor and walls of the "rib" cells. The omasum is a small bulbous structure on the abomasum and in the deer about 2.5 cm long containing a number of laminae with rudimentary, conical papillae scattered on their surface, but the laminae of sheep omasum are smooth at birth. The omasum is relatively larger at birth in cattle and domestic buffalo than in deer or

48

sheep. The abomasum at birth is well developed and highly functional with the folds characteristic of the adult present in the fundic region (8). The differences between species in degree of stomach development at birth are relatively small and may be easily overshadowed by dietary considerations in the first few weeks of life. Fig. 3-6 depicts the calf stomach at birth and shows the relative proportions of the abomasum to the forestomach. Note the size of the reticulum and omasum compared to that of the rumen and abomasum.

Given access to pasture, the newborn ruminant will begin to graze in the first week or two of life, initiating forestomach growth. Small amounts of grass may be found in the ruminoreticulum of calves, deer and lambs at 2 weeks of age with considerable quantities present in the calf at 3 weeks. Short (8) observed that one-third of the total stomach contents of 2-week-old fawns consisted of sand and grass found in the ruminoreticulum. The majority of the contents consisted of milk curds in the abomasum.

By 4 weeks of age the rumen grows to 4-8 times its birth weight but still appears as an elastic sac without the thickness of walls characteristic of later stages of development. The rumen papillae are larger and more distinct and forage intake has aided in the development of the spaces between the laminae of the omasum (19). The abomasum has increased in size, tissue weight and in width of the abomasal folds. At this time in the deer, about 40% of the stomach contents are found in the abomasum and consist of milk curds and some vegetative matter (8).

By 8 weeks of age the body weight of nursing and grazing calves has doubled and that of lambs and fawns quadrupled. The maximum rate of growth of the rumen occurs during this period, and it approaches adult proportions with respect to the other digestive organs and to body weight. The rumen papillae are well developed, and in deer are about 4-5 mm long and 1 mm wide. The reticulum and omasum have increased in weight with the omasum growing in muscularity but with little change in the abomasum. About 80% of the stomach contents of the fawn are found in the ruminoreticulum with only 20% of the abomasal contents being milk curds (8). At this age young ruminants have become heavily dependent upon the products of rumen fermentation for maintenance and growth.

Maturing ruminants experience an increase in total stomach tissue weight commensurate with increased body weight. There is an increase in rumen capacity and a proliferation of the smooth musculature of the rumen, giving it a heavy, muscular appearance. The papillae in the cranial sac grow to about 10 mm long and 2 mm wide. The reticulum remains a pliable sac without the heavy musculature of the rumen and accounts for only 4-7% of the total stomach capacity and 6% of its volume. Hofmann (21) points out that the reticulum is third in size after the rumen and abomasum in most ruminants and only in a few species, such as the bovine, buffalo, gnu and giraffe, is the reticulum the smallest of the four compartments. The weight of the omasum continues to increase in relative proportion to the total tract up to 36-38 weeks of age (16). The capacity of the omasum to hold digesta or fluids increases very slowly with time (22), suggesting that the increased tissue weight is related to increased muscularity and continued growth of the omasal laminae (15). The weight of the abomasum continues to increase slowly after 4-8 weeks, most probably due to increased muscularity of the organ. The increase in stomach tissue weights from birth to 17 weeks for nursing, pasture-raised calves is depicted in Fig. 3-7

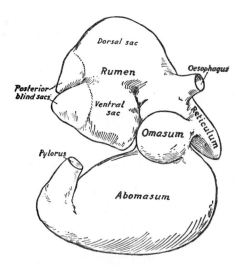

Figure 3-6. A diagram of the stomach of the newborn calf. Right view with the rumen raised. From Sisson and Grossman (20). Courtesy of W.B. Saunders Publishing Co.

and for lambs in Fig. 3-8. The relative success of the weaning process will depend upon the rate of forestomach development, the size of the ruminoreticulum, and the relative ease of fermentation of ingested feedstuffs.

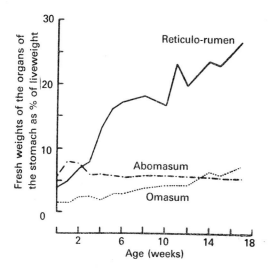

Figure 3-7. Growth of the stomach of calves from birth to 17 weeks of age. Calves fed milk replacer with access to pasture. Wet tissue organ weight expressed as a percentage of live weight. Adapted from Godfrey (23).

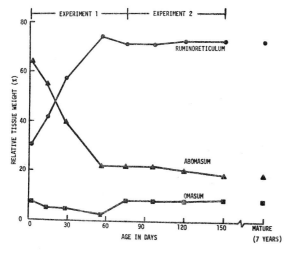

Figure 3-8. The relative change in the wet tissue organ weights of growing lambs expressed as a percentage of the total stomach. See Fig. 3-2 for rations. From Oh et al (13).

Comparative Development

Direct comparisons between species on the rate of forestomach development remains difficult due to variations in diet, rate of body growth and experimental conditions. In addition, Ruminantia include a wide spectrum of basic stomach structures ranging from the relatively simple system of saculations found in certain of the East African wild ruminants to the highly differentiated stomach of grass eaters like domesticated cattle (see Ch. 2). Stomach size is also related to body size and type of diet.

Table 3-2 presents the growth of the stomach from birth to maturity for nursing, free-ranging calves, lambs, fawns and for domestic buffalo calves which were fed different proportions of hay and concentrates with weaning after 6 weeks of age. These data suggest that the development of the ruminoreticulum with respect to body weight and relative stomach weight is essentially complete by 8 weeks of age. This information and that of Nangia (15) suggest very rapid development of mature stomach proportions in the domestic buffalo occurring as early as 4-6 weeks of age. The ruminoreticulum is a smaller proportion of the body weight in growing deer and sheep than cattle and buffalo, a difference that persists into adulthood. Comparisons between growing Asiatic water buffalo and cattle suggest greater relative size and development of the ruminoreticulum in the domestic buffalo (12, 22).

The fraction of total stomach tissue weight in the reticulum varies within a relatively small range during growth. Values for grazing lambs range from 8.3-10.7% (9), for grass-fed buffalo calves 9.0-12.0% (15), grazing fawns 5.6-9.1% (8) and young goats fed purified diets plus various fiber sources 9.2-11.7% (25).

The differences between species in the size of the omasum during growth and at maturity is pronounced when compared to both body size and relative proportion of the total stomach. At maturity it is about 0.5% of body weight in cattle and domestic buffalo but only 0.15-0.20% in deer, sheep and the goat. At this time it comprises from 20-24% of the total stomach tissue weight of cattle (11) and buffalo (15) and between 8% and 9% of that of deer and sheep. . Hofmann (21) has observed that the wild ruminant "concentrate

Table 3-2. Growth of the stomach of cattle, domestic buffalo, deer and sheep expressed as wet tissue wt, wet tissue weight/kg live wt and as a percentage of the total stomach.[a]

Age, weeks	Body weight, kg	Ruminoreticulum			Omasum			Abomasum			Ref.
		g	g/kg	%	g	g/kg	%	g	g/kg	%	
Cattle											
Birth	23.9	95	4.0	35	40	1.68	14	140	2.13	51	23
2	25.8	180	7.0	40	65	2.51	15	200	7.75	45	''
4	32.6	335	10.3	55	70	2.15	11	210	6.44	34	''
8	42.9	770	18.0	65	160	3.72	14	250	5.82	21	''
12	59.7	1,150	19.3	66	265	4.43	15	330	5.52	19	''
17	76.3	2,040	26.7	68	550	7.21	18	425	5.57	14	''
Adult	325.4	4,540	14.0	62	1,800	5.53	24	1,030	3.17	14	11
Domestic Buffalo											
3	34.0	439	12.9	65	54	1.59	8	180	5.29	27	22
6	38.7	553	14.3	68	60	1.55	7	206	5.32	25	''
9	44.7	875	19.6	71	133	2.98	11	223	4.99	18	''
12	45.7	1,084	23.7	71	183	4.00	12	258	5.65	17	''
15	56.7	1,348	23.8	71	270	4.76	14	286	5.04	15	''
Adult	347.6	7.000	20.3	70	1,800	5.18	18	1,200	3.45	12	10
Deer											
Birth	3.9	9	2.3	25	2	0.51	6	25	6.91	69	8
2	6.3	33	5.3	39	5	0.79	6	45	7.46	47	''
4	7.0	54	7.7	63	3	0.43	3	32	4.57	36	''
8	15.6	210	13.4	71	17	1.09	6	70	4.49	24	''
12	20.0	211	10.6	79	11	0.55	4	45	2.25	17	''
16	28.5	350	12.3	84	19	0.66	5	48	1.68	11	''
Adult	66.9	1,010	15.1	80	102	1.52	8	145	2.17	12	''
Sheep											
Birth	5.7	19	3.3	32	5	0.86	8	36	6.32	60	9
2	12.1	39	3.2	36	5	0.41	5	63	5.21	59	''
4	14.4	131	9.1	62	11	0.76	5	68	4.72	33	''
8	21.5	343	15.9	77	21	0.98	5	82	3.81	18	''
12	30.0	466	15.5	71	45	1.50	7	145	4.83	22	''
16	38.9	695	17.9	72	59	1.53	6	206	5.29	22	''
Adult	61.8	919	14.9	73	119	1.92	9	226	3.66	18	24

[a]Some data adapted from referenced sources for presentation here, particularly wt/kg live wt.

selectors" (with the most primitive ruminant stomach) have an omasum that is smaller and less well developed than that of the bulk and roughage eaters such as cattle and buffalo.

Compared to forestomach development the abomasum changes little after the first month of life, growing in tissue weight at the same rate as overall body growth during the next 15-17 weeks or longer. During this time it comprises about 0.5% of the body weight, dropping to 0.32-0.37% in cattle, domestic buffalo and sheep and 0.22% in deer at maturity.

At 10 weeks of age the average relative percentages of stomach compartments of young goats fed concentrates alone or with hay (after weaning at 5 weeks) were: rumen 64.6%, reticulum 9.7%, omasum 5.7% and the abomasum 20.0%. The organ weights per unit of body weight (g/kg) were 21.8, 3.2, 1.9 and 6.7, respectively (25). The omasal weight relative to body weight is small and appears to

Figure 3-9. Changes in the ovine stomach with age. Top row: at birth, 2 weeks and 4 weeks of age. Bottom row: 6 weeks, 8 weeks and the stomach of a fat lamb of unknown age. From Church (16).

be more similar to that of deer and sheep while that of the ruminoreticulum is closer to that of cattle. The dramatic increase in size of the stomach from birth to maturity is illustrated in Fig. 3-9.

Abdominal Position

The forestomachs are small in the newborn and are located near the anterior portion of the abdominal cavity with the rumen of newborn calves and lambs located half way between the dorsal and ventral surfaces and that of the newborn goat closer to the dorsal surface. In contrast, the abomasum is well developed, lying below the forestomachs and on the floor of the abdomen directly behind the diaphragm with its long axis running dorso-ventrally. When filled with digesta, it is located on the left side of the body and extends from the diaphragm to the rear or caudal third of the abdomen. The pyloric region lies to the right of the body midline and turns dorsally to the pylorus and duodenum.

The reticular groove lies in a dorso-ventral direction moving from this vertical position towards a horizontal one as the abomasum fills during a meal. It becomes fully horizontal in calves when the abomasum is full. Closure of the reticular groove and simultaneous dilation of the reticulo-omasal orifice and the omasal canal forms a conduit that

shunts milk being consumed past the forestomach directly to the abomasum (26).

The space required by the rumen increases rapidly with the consumption of solid feeds. Tamate (27) found the ventral sac reached to the bottom of the abdominal cavity and extended posteriorly and ventrally, almost reaching the pelvic inlet in 12-week-old calves consuming hay and concentrates. The rumen occupied the entire left side of the abdominal cavity. Expansion of the rumen may be more rapid in the young nursing goat with access to grass with extension to the pelvic inlet as early as 4 weeks of age. The rumen occupied three-fourths of the abdominal cavity by 6-9 weeks of age.

The reticulum develops more slowly than the rumen and by weaning time in the goat extends forward to the diaphragm wall. It is located toward the left of the body and in contact with the lower ends of the 6th and 7th intercostal spaces. The development of the omasum is very slow, enlarging only slightly by weaning and becoming a somewhat more noticeable pouch near the abomasum. The mature position of the omasum is on the right side of the body at the ventral ends of the 7th and 9th intercostal spaces. It is small in mature sheep, goats and the growing calf and is supported on the dorsal surface of the abomasum. However, in mature cattle the omasum is large, sinking to the abdominal

52

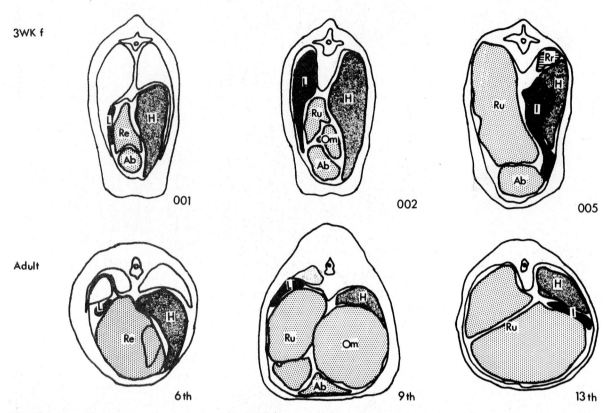

Figure 3-10. The abdominal position of the digestive organs of a 3-week old bovine calf and the adult. Views are cross sections at the 6th, 9th and 13th thoracic vertebrae. Letters refer to: H, liver; Ru, rumen; Re, reticulum; Om, omasum; Ab, abomasum; L, spleen; I, small and large intestine; Rr, right kidney; Rl, left kidney. From Amasaki et al (28). Courtesy of H. Amasaki, Nippon Vet. and Zootech. College.

floor, pushing the body of the abomasum to the midline and causing a right angle between the fundic and pyloric regions.

The abomasum moves caudally away from the diaphragm during the first 2-3 weeks of life as the reticulum enlarges. By 12 weeks it becomes confined between the abdominal floor and the ventral sac of the expanding rumen and moves toward the right side of the body cavity (27). The adult position of the abomasum is attained when the ruminant is consuming large quantities of solid feed. It may vary in position with the quantity of digesta contained within the organ and by the contractions of the reticulum and rumen due to a direct ligament attachment between these organs and the abomasum (21).

The relative positions of the digestive organs of the 3-week-old calf were recently studied by Amasaki et al (28) and are presented in Fig. 3-10. Note particularly the marked increase in space required by the

growing reticulum and omasum in the forward part of the abdominal cavity, the expansion of the rumen compartments to the rear and the changes in the position of the liver.

STOMACH VOLUME

Several methods have been used to measure stomach development in the growing ruminant. These include: (a) organ wet or dry tissue weight, (b) fat-free dried organ tissue weight, (c) water fill, the amount of water the exteriorized organ can hold under a slight pressure when submerged in water, (d) weighing the contained digesta at time of sacrifice, (e) emptying the ruminoreticulum through a fistula, and (f) dilution techniques with liquid markers. While each of the methods estimates the relative size and capacity of the organ, the accuracy of the estimate may be influenced by the wet tissue moisture and fat content, relative epithelial and muscle development, stretching when filled, feed intake prior to measurement, rate of digesta passage, and marker mixing and dilution.

Church et al (29) found rumen volume and organ dry tissue weights of nursing lambs raised with access to solid feeds to be highly correlated and suggested that tissue weight is satisfactory as a measure of development. Water fill results in much larger estimates of capacity than the more physiological estimates of digesta contained within the organ. Such estimates may exceed actual digesta volumes by 1.5-1.7 fold in cattle (3) with differences up to 3-4 fold observed in domestic buffalo (22). This method is particularly difficult with ruminants under 8 weeks of age because the rumen wall is thin and easily stretched (30).

Warner and Flatt (3) summarized bovine rumen volume data obtained under different conditions and some excerpts follow. As measured by water fill, the volume of the ruminoreticulum of the newborn calves weighing 36 kg was 44 ml/kg of empty body weight, 13 week-old calves weighing 94 kg was 300 ml/kg and that of cattle weighing an average of 542 kg varied between 230 and 360 ml/kg. The weight of ruminoreticular digesta from cattle obtained immediately after being fed a meal of excellent quality long hay was 33 kg for heifers weighing 201 kg and varied between 39-84 kg for mature cattle weighing between 510-653 kg.

Church (16) points out that the ruminoreticulum is usually not completely filled with digesta as it contains an appreciable quantity of gas. In addition it is restricted by its own size and by the adjacent organs and tissues on which it rests. Once excised for measurement, the stomach muscles and ligaments relax giving a different estimate of capacity. He suggests that the best measure of "physiological fill" would be the measurement of stomach contents of a normally fed animal. The data in Table 3-3 illustrate the increasing capacity with age as measured by stomach contents or water fill.

An allometric equation may be used to relate the parameters of digestive system growth to changes in body weight through the equation: $Y = aX^b$, where Y is the digestive system parameter such as wet tissue weight or organ capacity, X the body weight parameter and b the regression coefficient. This expression has been used to compare the relative rates of digestive organ development of domestic buffalo to zebu cattle (*Bos indicus*) (12) and to Friesian crossbred cattle (*B. taurus*) (10), to determine the effect of nutrition on digestive organ growth in Angus cattle (11) and to relate the effects of liquid vs solid feeds on the development of the rumen in the goat (33). Linear relationships between cumulative solid food intake and ruminoreticular growth have been reported for growing goats (25) and dairy calves 5-12 weeks of age (34).

Markers, particularly polyethylene glycol (PEG), have proven useful in measuring rumen volume in intact older animals, with good agreement obtained between measurements of fluid volume by using PEG compared to direct emptying through a rumen fistula (35). Egan et al (36) evaluated a double-marker system in sheep using ^{51}Cr-EDTA to estimate liquid phase volume and solid phase marker, a ^{103}Ru-labelled complex, and found good agreement with direct measurements. These and other markers used in older animals could be very useful in studying digestive system growth and dynamics in the developing ruminant. Accuracy of fluid volume estimates depends upon equilibration of the marker with the liquid phase of the organ contents, constant ruminoreticular volume over the period of measurement and penetration of the marker into all of the water space (37). Refer to Ch. 8 or to Van Soest (37) and Faichney (38) for use of markers in the measurement of volume, rates of digesta passage and digestion dynamics.

EPITHELIAL DEVELOPMENT

The tissues of the stomach consist of an outer layer of connective tissue covering an underlying layer of muscle with a distinctive separate inner epithelium. The muscles surrounding each organ serve to mix the digesta and to move it through the digestive tract. In young ruminants, increased muscularity occurs with the ingestion of solid feedstuffs and, in particular, coarse fibrous forages. The epithelium of the developed ruminant forestomach serves in the absorption and metabolism of minerals and the VFA. It also protects the underlying tissues from abrasion by the digesta and from microbial invasion. The

Table 3-3. Volume and contents of the ruminoreticulum or total stomach of growing ruminants.

Age, weeks	Body weight, kg	Dietary forage	Volume[a] ml	Volume[a] ml/kg	Contents ml	Contents ml/kg	Ref.
Calves							
Birth	42.4	Hay and grain	636	15.0			27
4	47.5	"	4,105	86.5			"
8	70.0	"	7,105	101.5			"
12	104.4	"	11,902	114.0			"
14	76.0	Pasture	16,900	222.4	7,100	93.4	31
Adult	313.2	Forage/concentrates			56,900	181.7	10
Zebu	340.4	Straw			63,700	187.1	12
Buffalo							
3	34.0	Grass	7,584	223.1	469	13.8	22
6	38.7	"	10,728	275.1	1,950	50.1	"
9	44.7	"	13,536	300.8	4,392	98.3	"
12	45.7	"	16,796	365.1	5,548	121.4	"
15	56.7	"	18,105	317.6	6,333	111.7	"
Adult	347.6	Straw			59,600	171.6	12
Sheep							
3	7.6	Grazing			83	10.9	32
6	10.5	"			538	51.2	"
9	27.7	"			2,043	73.7	"
16	38.3	"			3,960	103.4	9
29	53.2	"			4,796	90.2	"
47	61.8	"			4,286	69.4	"
Goats							
Birth	2.6	Milk only	70	26.9			33
2	4.7	"	140	29.8			"
5	4.8	Grazing	1,734	361.2			"
9	5.2	"	3,021	581.0			"
Deer (total stomach)							
Birth	3.9	Grazing	290	75.1	9	2.3	8
2	6.3	"	846	134.7	33	5.2	"
4	7.0	"	1,075	152.9	54	7.7	"
8	15.2	"	3,192	204.0	210	13.4	"
12	20.0	"	2,987	149.6	211	10.6	"
16	28.5	"	3,487	122.5	350	12.3	"
Mature	66.9	"	9,525	142.5	1,010	15.1	"

[a]Volume determined by water fill. Some data adapted from referenced sources, particularly volume per kg live weight.

epithelial surface is expanded considerably by the presence of large papillae containing a richly vascularized connective tissue core.

The lining of the forestomach is a keratinizing, non-glandular epithelium differing from other epithelia in several respects. Most importantly, the cells of the stratum basale contain large vesicles, numerous ribosomes, mitochondria and Glogi vesicles (Fig. 3-11) that function in the assimilation and metabolism of products absorbed from the forestomach. Several changes occur as the basal cells differentiate and pass to the lumenal surface of the epithelium (Fig. 3-12). Membrane bound mucous granules and aggregates of filaments form in the cells of the stratum

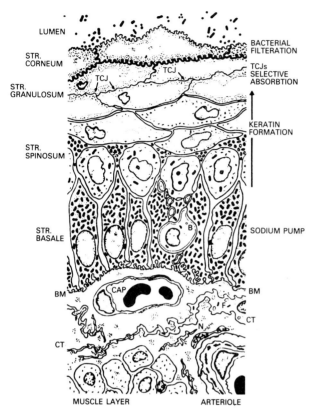

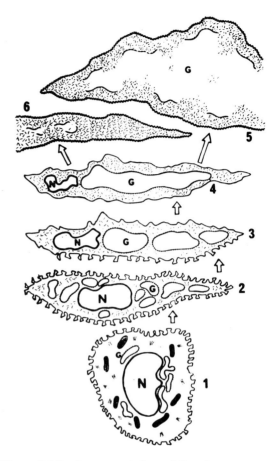

Figure 3-11. A diagrammatic cross section of the fully developed rumen wall depicting the types of cells and layers present. Details of the cell junctions are omitted. Letters refer to: B, branching cell; BM, basement membrane; CAP, capillary; CT, connective tissue; F, fibroblast; N, nerve trunk; TCJ, tight cell junction. From Steven and Marshall (39). Courtesy of D.H. Steven, University of Cambridge.

Figure 3-12. A representation of the changes occurring in basal cells during their passage to the epithelial lumen. Granule (G) and fibril accumulation with nuclear (N) degeneration occurs as cells pass to the epithelial lumen. Lack of complete nuclear degeneration with a thickening due to an accumulation of centrally placed granules produces parakeratotic cells. From Steven and Marshall (39). Courtesy of D.H. Steven, University of Cambridge.

spinosum (40). Signs of cellular degeneration and increased fibril formation occur in the stratum granulosum with the intercellular spaces present near the stratum spinosum which are lost by fusion of adjacent cell membranes near the stratum corneum. Separation of the tight cell junctions occurs during the process of transition to the stratum corneum.

The cells of the stratum corneum consist of a core of fine granular material surrounded by fibrils producing the characteristic horny cell type of forestomach epithelial surface including the presence of intercellular spaces (39). Microscopic examination of the stratum corneum reveals partially keratinized cells with fuzzy coated microvillus extensions strongly resembling the terminal cells of mucus-producing epithelia. It also contains relatively

large numbers of filaments and condensed material resembling the horny cells of keratinizing epithelia. The insoluble, non-reactive, durable character of keratins are modified under the saturated conditions of the rumen and these soft keratins are likely to be more permeable to water and water-soluble materials. The resulting surface is a complex system of keratinized cells that offer good protection from abrasion with mucosal cells that have less protective characteristics but good absorptive qualities (40).

Large numbers of microorganisms are found over the surface of the epithelium; in some cases they may be found in the intercellular spaces of the stratum corneum and occasionally may enter these outer horny cells (40, 41). No differences have been found in the ultrastructure of the epithelia from the rumen, reticulum or the omasum (40).

Histologically, rumen epithelium at birth has changed from the stratified cuboidal type found in the mid fetal-stages to a keratinized, stratified, squamous epithelium similar to but less developed than the adult. The stratum corneum is not developed, but in the rumen of the lamb there is an outer layer of flattened keratinized cells about three cell layers thick (19). These cells lack the conspicuous masses of fine granular material and the dense fibrils characteristic of the stratum corneum of the adult. The stratum basale is distinct but with a more densely packed cell structure than the adult. There is no distinct continuous stratum granulosum present (39).

FACTORS AFFECTING FORESTOMACH DEVELOPMENT

The effects of maternal nutrition on the growth and development of the fetal digestive tract have not been studied extensively. Limited research does suggest that the digestive tract weight is less severely depressed than total fetal weight when ewes were on a low plane of nutrition during the last half of pregnancy. Abomasal growth is depressed more than other organs of the digestive tract, a difference that persists after birth in lambs kept on a low plane of nutrition. This may contribute to their inefficient use of available milk supplies in early life. Lambs raised on an essential fatty acid-deficient diet gained less rapidly with restricted digestive organ growth similar to that observed on a low plane of nutrition (42).

Cessation of growth resulting from a low plane of nutrition reduces the weight of the digestive tract tissues. Murray et al (11) observed reductions in the tissue weights of all the digestive organs of 300-440 kg beef cattle when a period of active growth (0.8 kg/d) was followed by a 150-d period of maintenance (no growth). The small intestines decreased 32% in weight while the omasum, ruminoreticulum, large intestine and abomasum decreased by 18, 18, 7 and 15%. They cite (43) similar, though larger, reductions in 25-kg sheep held at maintenance for

a 50-d period with reductions in the respective organs of 45, 29, 27, 24 and 9%.

The normal growth and development of the ruminant stomach may be altered by feeds ingested, their physical form and the animal's nutritional status. Including or excluding concentrates or forages and the processing of forages may enhance or retard the rate of forestomach growth in size, muscle and epithelial development. However, little or no forestomach development occurs in the absence of solid food intake common to some feeding management programs (44) or with abundant supplies of milk under free-ranging conditions (31).

Initiation of Forestomach Growth

The data of Warner et al shown in Table 3-4 clearly illustrate the major effects of diet on stomach development in the dairy calf. The lack of forestomach development on all-milk diets contrasts sharply with the stimulatory effects of concentrates or hay. However, the increased forestomach capacity of hay-fed calves is due to stretching of the ruminoreticulum rather than increased tissue growth, while inclusion of hay with concentrates enhanced omasal growth. The inclusion of concentrates into roughage-based rations of calves (46), goats (25) and domestic buffalo (15) increases the rate of rumen epithelial formation and animal growth but retards the development of stomach size and musculature. Little papillary growth occurs in the rumen of calves fed milk exclusively for 16 weeks (ca. 2 mm long), while extensive papillary growth (ca. 10 mm long) was present when solid foods were included in the diet (45) (see Plate 3-1). Milk placed directly into the rumen or leaking into it may also initiate epithelial development of the forestomach (27).

Bulky non-fermentable materials such as nylon bristles, plastic sponges, plastic cubes, and wood shavings do not initiate epithelial development but do result in expansion and muscular growth of the rumen and reticulum. Salts of the VFA introduced directly into the rumen initiate papillary and total epithelial development but do not stimulate growth of muscle tissue. Na butyrate is the most effective, as measured by tissue weight and mitotic indices, followed by propionate and acetate (47). In fact, added levels of butyric acid to

Table 3-4. Dry fat-free tissue weights and capacity of the stomach organs of calves fed different diets to 13 weeks of age.[a]

Diet	Empty body weight, kg	Ruminoreticulum		Omasum		Abomasum	
		. . . . Weight fat-free tissue					
		g	g/kg	g	g/kg	g	g/kg
Newborn	35.4	20.9	0.59	6.1	0.17	25.7	0.73
13 weeks old							
Milk only	93.1	78.7	0.85	20.5	0.22	60.5	0.65
Concentrate	104.9	356.1	3.39	56.1	0.54	48.1	0.46
Hay	53.6	195.9	3.65	30.6	0.57	36.6	0.68
Hay + conc.	94.0	250.5	2.67	75.6	0.80	59.4	0.63
		. . . . Volume					
		ml	ml/kg	ml	ml/kg	ml	ml/kg
Newborn	35.4	1,559	44	102.5	1.1	2,105	59.5
13 weeks old							
Milk only	93.1	7,394	70	184.8	1.8	3,235	30.8
Concentrate	104.9	30,037	286	878.0	8.4	2,542	24.2
Hay	53.6	37,071	692	1,157.0	21.6	3,778	70.5
Hay + conc.	94.0	28,159	300	1,780.6	18.9	3,105	33.0

[a] Adapted from Warner et al (45). Volume determined by water fill. Volume and fat-free organ weight per unit of empty (ingesta free) body weight.

the rumen of mature sheep to simulate the sudden introduction of processed grains produced a marked proliferation of the epithelium as well (48). This response may be the result of an increased blood flow to the papillae (49) or of a slight inflammatory response caused by acid damage to the epithelium (50).

Using 3- to 4-week-old goats, Hamada (50) found 1,2-propanediol (propylene glycol) to be effective in stimulating rumen development whether administered directly into the ruminoreticulum or into the abomasum. This compound may be fermented in the rumen to produce propionic acid or be absorbed (51). It is also a metabolic intermediate in the conversion of lactate to glucose (52). The effectiveness of direct abomasal placement may be explained by the compound reaching ruminal tissues via the ruminal blood vessels, readily penetrating cellular boundaries to stimulate epithelial DNA synthesis and cell growth. When combined with an inert bulky

material (plastic cubes), both rumen epithelial and muscular growth were stimulated (50).

Development of the distinctive epithelial strata also occurs with access to solid food. Distinct keratinization of the stratum corneum occurs by 8 weeks of age in the domestic buffalo, becoming like that of the adult by 12-16 weeks. Very little development occurred when the calves were fed as preruminants for 12 weeks, but with rapid growth and some keratinization of the epithelium 4 weeks after the introduction of concentrates. However, 8 weeks were required for a definite stratum corneum to develop. The presence of lipid, glycogen and alkaline phosphatase was observed histochemically in the rumen epithelia of both milk only and concentrate-fed buffalo calves, but appeared in higher concentrations at an earlier age with concentrate supplementation (53). Earlier maturity is suggested in lambs with adult histological characteristics present by 11 weeks of

58

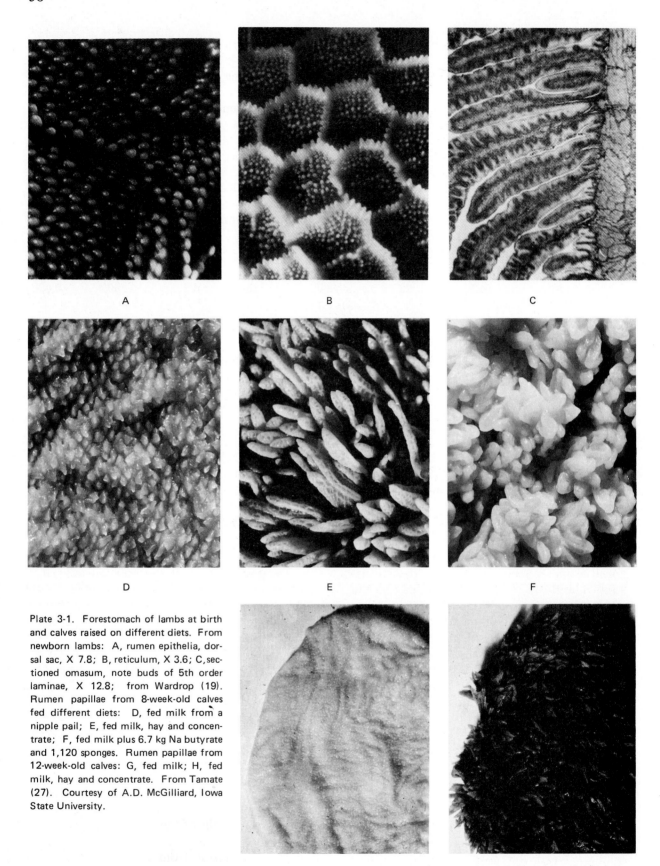

A

B

C

D

E

F

Plate 3-1. Forestomach of lambs at birth and calves raised on different diets. From newborn lambs: A, rumen epithelia, dorsal sac, X 7.8; B, reticulum, X 3.6; C, sectioned omasum, note buds of 5th order laminae, X 12.8; from Wardrop (19). Rumen papillae from 8-week-old calves fed different diets: D, fed milk from a nipple pail; E, fed milk, hay and concentrate; F, fed milk plus 6.7 kg Na butyrate and 1,120 sponges. Rumen papillae from 12-week-old calves: G, fed milk; H, fed milk, hay and concentrate. From Tamate (27). Courtesy of A.D. McGilliard, Iowa State University.

G

H

age (19). Some development also occurred in 7-week-old lambs fed milk exclusively with a well defined stratum corneum formed only 4 weeks after the introduction of hay.

Insulin has been shown to stimulate rumen epithelial cell proliferation (54), and this hormone plus others may act to control epithelial development and mediate the mitotic stimulation induced by the VFA. Butyrate was found to stimulate the release of insulin from sheep pancreas in vitro (55).

Dietary Influences

The degree of forestomach development of the free-ranging nursing young may be retarded or enhanced by the milk producing ability of the dam. Stewart (31) found very little increase in wet tissue weights, capacity of the ruminoreticulum, or papillary development in beef calves grazing with their dams up to weaning at 9 weeks of age. A high concentrate diet fed after weaning resulted in dramatic increases in all three parameters by 14 weeks of age. Calves left to nurse as well as graze during this period grew faster than those weaned at 9 weeks, but rumen tissue weights, rumen volume and papillae development were less.

Rapid adaptation to the introduction of solid food occurs in older preruminants. Singh and Yadava (56) found that 15-week-old preruminant bovine and buffalo calves developed rumen tissue weights, digestive contents and volume within 4 weeks after being switched to a diet of hay and concentrates equaling calves with access to these feeds from 3 weeks of age. However, marked reductions of rumen papillae, epithelial and muscle development occur when calves are switched from high concentrate to high forage rations. Complete removal of forage and concentrates from ruminant calves followed by a return to an all milk diet results in the disappearance of rumen papillae, regression of ruminoreticular muscle tissue and cessation of ruminoreticular and omasal growth.

Calves fed milk exclusively may be maintained in a preruminant state for extensive lengths of time. Thivend et al (44) found increases in ruminoreticulum growth consistent with body growth without the developmental changes observed with solid food intake, even with animals 7 months of age weighing up to 300 kg. The weight of the total tract and tract contents remained a constant proportion of body weight with the stomach a constant 35% of the total tract. The dressing percentage of the calves was similar to that of simple-stomached animals.

The presence of dietary fiber in a relatively coarse form may be required for normal rumen development and function (57, 58). McGavin and Morrill (57) observed marked changes of the rumen epithelium of 4- and 6-week-old calves fed either pelleted high- or low-fiber concentrates in contrast to calves also consuming long hay. Selected observations of papillae from the ventral floor of the antrium ruminis (cranial sac) are shown in Plate 3-2. Normal tongue-like papillae were present in the calves fed long hay (A, X 7) while those receiving the pelleted high-fiber concentrate (25% ground alfalfa added) varied much more in shape with a higher proportion rounded in form and with keratinization of their tips (B, X 19.2). In contrast, the low-fiber, pelleted concentrate resulted in small, nodular, cauliflower shaped papillae with narrow stalks, very dark color, heavily keratinized, and with hair-containing ingesta packed between them. Branching of the papillae was well developed (C, X 14.7; D, X 44.8). Histological examination of the papillae revealed parakeratosis with ingesta and bacteria also observed between the layers of the parakeratotic cells. Note the individual epithelial cells from a moderately keratinized papillae taken from the antrium ruminis (E, X 576) of a calf fed the pelleted, low-fiber diet in contrast to the heavy sloughing keratinization (F, X 170) found on papillae taken from the recessus ruminis, the first area of the rumen affected by decreasing fiber levels. These authors point out that the observed "clumping" on low-fiber rations is not the fusing of adjacent papillae but the branching of single papillae. It is this change in papillae morphology that produces the marked change in the ruminal surface, perhaps as a compensating mechanism to increase the surface area and absorptive capacity reduced by the thickened layers of parakeratotic cells.

Parakeratosis may be identified by incomplete keratinization. The nuclei are retained in the horny cells of the stratum corneum and the stratum granulosum is absent. This appears to result from both increased proliferation and outward migration of the

A

B

C

D

E

F

Plate 3-2. Scanning electron microscopy and histological examination of rumen papillae from 6 week old calves fed different diets. See text for description of photos. From McGavin and Morrill (57). Courtesy of M.D. McGavin, College of Veterinary Medicine, University of Tennessee and the Amer. J. Vet. Res.

epithelial cells of the stratum basale. In contrast, hyperkeratosis is characterized by excessive thickening of the stratum corneum and the stratum granulosum with a depressed outward migration of the cells of the stratum basale. The control mechanisms of epithelial hyperplasia are not well understood. However, the direct stimulation of the metabolism and increased mitotic indices of the rumen epithelial cells by higher VFA levels suggests the occurrence of adaptation by these tissues to ration changes (59). Thus, both rumen tissue and microbial adaptation becomes critical on low-fiber, high-concentrate diets if the incidence of parakeratosis and ruminitis-liver abscess complex are to be minimized.

Nocek et al (46) studied the effects of hay, concentrates and rumen N availability on epithelial and muscle development and function in calves (see Table 3-5 and Fig. 3-13). High-concentrate diets reduced VFA transport across the rumen epithelium while higher rumen degradable N levels increased acetate and proprionate transport in older calves. Rumen epithelial glutamic dehydrogenase and aspartate amino transferase activity also increased with age, suggesting an adaptation to higher rumen ammonia levels. Propionyl Co-A synthetase activity was higher with older calves (20 weeks) fed concentrates but total VFA transport was less than that of calves fed chopped hay.

Coarse fiber may also reduce the occurrence of penetration of the ruminal epithelium by animal and plant hairs which is enhanced by the accumulation of keratin and the embedding of the digestive mass between papillae. Penetrated hairs and other ruminal lesions observed on low or finely ground fiber diets provide potential sites for bacterial entry, thus contributing to occurrence of liver abscesses (see Ch. 23). The adverse effects of high-concentrate diets on rumen morphology are produced within a 4-week period and reversed within 2-4 weeks when cattle and sheep are returned to coarse roughage-containing diets.

The normal dark brownish color of the rumen epithelium that develops with age may arise from pigments produced from microbial metabolism of dietary materials. These pigments attach firmly to the keratinized layer resulting in a color similar to that of the

Table 3-5. Effect of ration physical form on rumen parameters in the growing calf.[a]

Item	Ground	Chopped	All concentrate
Contents, ℓ	20.8	16.6	9.4
Wet tissue wt, kg	2.5	2.0	3.4
Wet epithelial wt, kg	1.5	1.2	2.5
Wet muscle wt, kg	1.0	0.8	0.9
Wet muscle, %	40.8	42.3	25.7

[a]From Nocek et al (46)

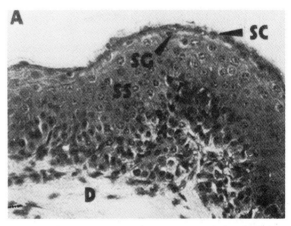
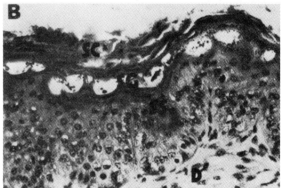

Figure 3-13. Light micrograph of rumen papillae epithelium from 20-week-old calves fed different diets. Grade 2 epithelium (A) was more prevalent on rations containing chopped or ground hay while grade 4 (B) occurred more frequently on all concentrate rations. Labeled are: SC, stratum corneum; SG, stratum granulosum; SS, stratum spinosum; and D, dermis. X 264. From Nocek et al (46). Courtesy of J.E. Nocek, Agway Inc., Syracuse, N.Y.

62

rumen contents. Minerals, particularly Fe, increased pigmentation when tested in purified diets (60).

SUMMARY

Normal forestomach development depends upon access and ingestion of fermentable materials (commonly solid foods) from birth and the entry of these materials into the ruminoreticulum. Rapid growth ensues with forestomach expansion, epithelial development and the start of rumination. The initial rate of forestomach development is also related to the need for supplemental energy. Insufficient nutrient supply from milk (or milk replacers) encourages solid food intake and hastens forestomach development. In approximately 8 weeks the stomach compartments reach their relative adult proportions. Growth of the stomach then continues at the rate of body growth until the animal reaches maturity.

Development may be accelerated by the introduction of grains or other readily fermentable substances into the rumen. No, or very little forestomach development takes place on all liquid diets, but very rapid growth occurs once solid food is introduced. The presence of VFA and bulk is required for normal growth in capacity, muscularity and epithelial formation. Diets without some long, fibrous materials may result in abnormal rumen papillae formation resulting in parakeratosis, a condition reversed with the introduction of coarse fibrous feedstuffs.

Literature Cited

1. Warner, E.D. 1958. Amer. J. Anat. 102:33.
2. Panchamukhi, B.G. and H.C. Srivastava. 1979. Zbl. Vet. C. Anat. Histol. Embryol. 8:97.
3. Warner, R.D. and W.P. Flatt. 1965. In: Physiology of Digestion in the Ruminant. Butterworths, London.
4. Ramrishna, V. and G.P. Tiwari. 1979. Acta Anat. 103:292.
5. Amasaki, H. and M. Daigo. 1984. Can. J. Animal Sci. 64:257.
6. Hofmann, R.R. 1969. Beiheft Nr. 10 zum Zentralblatt f. Vet. Med. Verlag Paul Parey. Berlin und Hamburg.
7. Amasaki, H., M. Daigo, S. Yamano and S. Kamiya. 1983. Bull. Nippon Vet. Zootech. Coll. 32:6.
8. Short, H.L. 1964. J. Wildl. Mgmt. 28:445.
9. Wardrop, I.D. and J.B. Coombe. 1960. J. Agr. Sci. 54:140.
10. Abdallah, O.Y., K.A. Shahin and M.G.A. Latif. 1982. Indian J. Animal Sci. 52:506.
11. Murray, D.M., N.M. Tulloh and W.H. Winter. 1977. J. Agr. Sci. 89:119.
12. Moran, J.B. and J.T. Wood. 1982. J. Agr. Sci. 98:493.
13. Oh, J.H., I.D. Hume and D.T. Torell. 1972. J. Animal Sci. 35:450.
14. Stobo, I.J.F., J.H. Roy and H.J. Gaston. 1966. Brit. J. Nutr. 20:171.
15. Nangia, O.P., N. Singh, J.P. Puri and S.L. Garg. 1982. Indian J. Animal Sci. 52:939.
16. Church, D.C. 1976. Digestive Physiology and Nutrition of Ruminants. Vol. 1, 2nd Ed. O & B Books, Inc., Corvallis, OR.
17. James, R.E., C.E. Polan and M.L. McGilliard. 1979. J. Dairy Sci. 62:1415.
18. Roy, J.B.H., et al. 1977. Brit. J. Nutr. 38:167.
19. Wardrop, I.D. 1961. J. Agr. Sci. 57:335.
20. Sisson, S. and J.D. Grossman. 1953. The Anatomy of Domestic Animals. 4th Ed. W.B. Saunders Co., Philadelphia, PA.
21. Hofmann, R.R. 1973. The Ruminant Stomach. East African Lit. Bureau, Nairobi, Kenya.
22. Singh, M., I.S. Yadava and A.R. Rao. 1973. J. Agr. Sci. 81:55.
23. Godfrey, N.W. 1961. J. Agr. Sci. 57:173.
24. Wallace, L.R. 1948. J. Agr. Sci. 38:244.
25. Hamada, T., S. Meada and K. Kameoka. 1976. J. Dairy Sci. 59:1110.
26. Dziuk, H.E. 1984. In: Dukes' Physiology of Domestic Animals. 10th Ed. Cornell Univ. Press, Ithaca, NY.
27. Tamate, H., A.D. McGilliard, N.L. Jacobson and R. Getty. 1962. J. Dairy Sci. 45:408.
28. Amasaki, H., M. Daigo, S. Yamano and S. Kamiya. 1981. Bull. Nippon Vit. Zootech. Coll. 30:29.
29. Church, D.C., G.D. Jessup, Jr. and R. Bogart. 1962. Amer. J. Vet. Res. 23:220.
30. Seip, D.R. and R.M.F.S. Sadleir. 1982. J. Wildl. Mgmt. 46:819.

63

31. Stewart, A.M. 1971. Rhod. J. Agr. Res. 9:53.
32. Walker, D.M. and G.J. Walker. 1961. J. Agr. Sci. 57:271.
33. Tamate, H. 1957. Tohoku J. Agr. Res. 8:65.
34. Hodgson, J. 1971. Animal Prod. 13:449.
35. Bauman, D.E., C.E. Davis, R.A. Frobish and D.S. Sachan. 1975. J. Dairy Sci. 54:928.
36. Egan, J.K., G.R. Pearce, P.T. Doyle and R. Thomas. 1983. Australian J. Agr. Res. 34:307.
37. Van Soest, P.J. 1982. Nutritional Ecology of the Ruminant. O & B Books, Inc., Corvallis, OR.
38. Faichney, G.J. 1975. In: Digestion and Metabolism in the Ruminant. Univ. of New England Publ., Unit, Armidale, NSW, Australia.
39. Steven, D.H. and A.B. Marshall. 1970. In: Physiology of Digestion and Metabolism in the Ruminant. Oriel Press, Newcastle upon Thyne, England.
40. Lavker, R., W. Chalupa and J.F. Dickey. 1969. J. Ultrastructure Res. 28:1.
41. Henrikson, R.C. 1970. J. Ultrastructure Res. 30:385.
42. Bruckner, G., K.K. Grunewald, R.E. Tucker and G.E. Mitchell, Jr. 1984. J. Animal Sci. 58:971.
43. Slezacek, O. 1976. Growth and Body Composition of Lambs. MS Thesis, Univ. New South Wales, Australia.
44. Thivend, P., R. Toullec and P. Guilloteau. 1980. In: Digestive Physiology and Metabolism in Ruminants. AVI Publ. Co., Inc. Westport, CN.
45. Warner, R.D., W.P. Flatt and J.K. Loosli. 1956. J. Agr. Food Chem. 4:788.
46. Nocek, J.E., C.W. Heald and C.E. Polan. 1984. J. Dairy Sci. 67:334.
47. Sakata, T. and H. Tamate. 1979. J. Dairy Sci. 62:49.
48. Sakata, T. and H. Tamate. 1978. J. Dairy Sci. 61:1109.
49. Thorlacius, S.O. 1972. Amer. J. Vet. Res. 33:247.
50. Hamada, T. 1975. J. Dairy Sci. 58:1352.
51. Clapperton, J.L. and J.W. Czerkawski. 1972. Brit. J. Nutr. 27:553.
52. Czerkawski, J.W. and G. Breckenridge. 1973. Brit. J. Nutr. 29:317.
53. Singh, N., et al. 1982. Indian J. Animal Sci. 52:490.
54. Sakata, T., K. Hikosaka, Y. Shiomura and H. Tamate. 1980. Brit. J. Nutr. 44:325.
55. Sasaki, Y., T.E.C. Weekes and J.B. Bruce. 1977. J. Endocrinol. 72:415.
56. Singh, M. and I.S. Yadava. 1971. Indian J. Animal Sci. 41:922.
57. McGavin, M.D. and J.L. Morrill. 1976. Amer. J. Vet. Res. 37:497.
58. Nocek, J.E. and E.M. Kesler. 1980. J. Dairy Sci. 63:254.
59. Fell, B.F. and T.E.C. Weekes. 1975. In: Digestion and Metabolism in the Ruminant. Univ. of New England Publ. Unit, Armidale, NSW, Australia.
60. Hamada, T., S. Maeda and K. Kameoka. 1970. J. Dairy Sci. 53:588.

4 MOTILITY OF THE GASTRO-INTESTINAL TRACT

by Y. Ruckebusch

INTRODUCTION

The physical breakdown of feed is a major function of the ruminant foregut, the section of the alimentary tract from the lips to the omaso-abomasal junction. The operation, which is continuous and effective, is achieved by two major processes: chewing during eating and rumination, and microbial fermentation favored by maceration and detrition in the reticulo-rumen.

The four-chambered stomach's motility patterns which allow the stomach to process low-energy plant materials and to regulate the passage of particles out of the reticulo-rumen have been described in detail in earlier books by Phillipson (13) and Church (3). How the extrinsic contractions of the reticulo-rumen are essential for mixing the contents, for eructation and for rumination, has been discussed recently by Reid (15) and Ulyatt (28). How the rate, form and amplitude of the contractions are the consequence of central nervous activity, reflexly modified by sensory inputs from the alimentary tract itself and related mechanisms, have been presented in a workshop, The Ruminant Stomach, edited by Ooms et al (11). This chapter will refer to these sources of informations and detailed aspects from Ph.D. theses (8, 14, 17, 18) as well.

Several other characteristic motions of the ruminant gastro-intestinal tract have been defined by the use of X-rays, electromyography and direct flow rate measurements. As long as the food consists only of milk (see Ch. 3), the reticular groove closes reflexly, hence the diversion of milk from the fermentation chamber (27); this phenomenon might persist in lactating cows to allow ruminal by-pass of about 20% of drinking water (31). In adult ruminants there is also a continuous sequence of some 14-18 migrating myoelectric complexes passing down the thin-walled small intestine each day and corresponding to an intermittent flow of 12.7-20.3 ℓ/d from the abomasum in sheep (20); this adaptive pattern is disrupted in the milk-fed preruminant as by feeding in monogastric species (5, 25). Finally, the study of the hindgut motility patterns has shown that the spiral colon, similar in the small and large ruminant species, is not the site of segmentary contractions in cattle, hence the production of dung which is not in pellet form (20).

The motor processes of postnatal adaptive changes and of breakdown of feed structure will be discussed in the following ten sections. It will be apparent that the knowledge of the multiple mechanisms and control systems involved in the regulation of motility and passage of digesta remains sketchy and that the significance of the most common signs of general disease, i.e., hypomotility and anorexia, is poorly understood.

RETICULAR [ESOPHAGEAL] GROOVE CLOSURE

The reticular groove, when fully contracted, is essentially a continuation of the esophagus as a tube which bypasses the reticulo-rumen. Observations of groove functions in fistulated animals have demonstrated that the reticular groove functions primarily in the young suckling ruminant to bypass milk from the esophagus to the omasum. Partial suture of the lips of the groove has no effect on regurgitation, disproving any role in rumination.

When young mammals suck their dams, a behavior pattern is evoked which is quite different from that seen during drinking to relieve thirst. Closure of the groove, a component of sucking behavior, ensures that milk is channeled directly to the abomasum, instead of entering the forestomach. A lamb normally loses its sucking behavior soon after being separated from its mother, but if it is trained to suck milk or other fluids from a bottle or pail, sucking can be retained well into adult life. When the sucking animal starts to eat solid food, the forestomach develops and assumes its function as a fermentation chamber.

Reflex Mechanisms

Closure of the groove is initiated by sucking or drinking as a reflex and is apparently not affected by temperature or gross composition of the milk. The typical posture assumed while drinking is not required for reflex closure and milk passes into the abomasum if the animal is accustomed to taking milk in the manner in which the fluid is given. If, in contrast, milk or water are given in a manner in which the animal normally quenches its thirst with water, the fluid passes mainly into the reticulo-rumen. Evidence for the reflex character of reticular groove contractions has been obtained in decerebrate preparations of young lambs and calves (27). The efferent limb of the reflex consists of cholinergic parasympathetic fibers distributed to the groove mainly in the dorsal abdominal vagus nerve. A release of vasoactive intestinal peptide (VIP), which opens the reticulo-omasal orifice, has recently been demonstrated. Both the reflex response of the reticular groove and its contraction upon peripheral stimulation of the vagus are annulled by intravenous administration of atropine. The introduction of water into the posterior mouth cavity or mechanical stimulation of this region are effective sensory stimuli in decerebrate (after intercollicular section) preparations. The majority of the afferent nerve fibers concerned in mediating these responses are contained in the cranial laryngeal nerves, because stimulation of their central ends evokes both swallowing and groove contraction. In conscious sheep the closure is a function of the route taken by the milk and does not occur if milk is introduced directly into the esophagus (Fig. 4-1).

The properties of the reflex demonstrable in decerebrate preparations are a summation of adequate stimuli, fatigue, reflex latency, after-discharge and inhibition. This inhibition is both peripheral and central. The peripheral inhibition appears to be an effect of adrenaline on the musculature of the esophageal groove, or its release after stimulation of the peripheral end of a splanchnic nerve. The central inhibition is produced by stimulation of the central end of an abomasal branch of the ventral abdominal vagus nerve or of the glossopharyngeal nerve. Abomasal stretch or distension inhibits the reflex contraction of the reticular groove; this effect is mediated by the abomasal branch of the ventral vagus

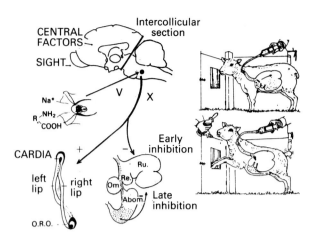

Figure 4-I. Diagram showing the afferent limb of the reflex closure of the reticular groove, i.e., the posterior mouth cavity. The vagal efferent fibers are at the same time inhibitory for the reticulo-ruminal movements and stimulatory for the lips of the groove. Late inhibition of the reticulo-rumen occurs when milk is clotted into the abomasum. On the right, milk directly introduced in the esophagus bypasses the mouth, i.e., the afferent limb of the reflex and falls into the rumen. The sight of a teat in an adult trained sheep may be sufficient to close the groove.

nerve, stimulation of which also produces inhibition.

Recent studies showed that the reticular groove contracts with two distinct movements; first, by shortening, the right and left lips become firmly opposed allowing direct passage of 30-40% of the volume of liquid towards the abomasum. Then, the closure of the groove can be complete if the lips are inverted, mainly the right lip. In this case, 75-90% of the ingested liquid is recovered in the abomasum. The direct passage of liquid during sucking in adult cattle is accompanied by transient and immediate inhibition of reticulo-ruminal contractions.

Inhibition of rumino-reticular contractions associated with closure of the reticular groove during sucking was first reported in an adult cow when licking salt. During the sucking of milk (or water), reticular contractions are inhibited in frequency. After sucking (or after introduction of fluid directly into the abomasum), reticular contractions are slower whereas ruminal and omasal contractions are more fully inhibited. It can be thus postulated that the inhibitory response to sucking has two phases: a cephalic phase dependent upon

66

the eagerness of sucking, which mainly influences the strength (inotropic) of the contractions of the forestomach, and an abomasal phase dependent on the degree of distension of the abomasum, which mainly affects the frequency (chronotropic) of contractions (9). Such results have been obtained in a 12-month-old bull fitted with a rumen cannula, while sucking 2-5 ℓ of milk from a watering can and when 2-5 ℓ of milk were introduced into the abomasum through the reticulo-omasal orifice. The inhibition of the cephalic phase is, therefore, mainly inotropic in nature while that of the abomasal phase is mainly chronotropic (Fig. 4-2).

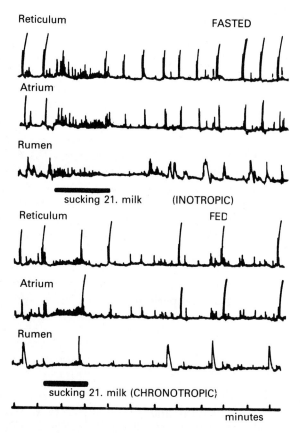

Figure 4-2. Inhibition of the reticulo-ruminal cyclic contractions to sucking 2 ℓ of warm milk in an adult bull at 45-min intervals as indicated by the bars. The cephalic phase (top) is inotropic since it is related to the amplitude. The abomasal phase, for sucking when the abomasum is already full by the first introduction of milk (bottom), is related to the frequency and is chronotropic. Small pressure fluctuations seen during sucking are associated with swallowing. Time in minutes. From Kay and Ruckebusch (9).

The increased excitability provoked by showing a nipple bottle is sufficient in a trained subject to double or triple the volume of liquid collected in the abomasum after administration into the lower esophagus. A complete closure of the groove takes place in lambs trained to drink small meals through a trough, similar to those drinking from a nipple bottle. Teasing with a bottle beyond swallowing also causes groove closure; if not teased, the groove does not close. X-ray studies of groove closure in lambs fed milk-replacers either individually or in groups show that poor sucking, low milk consumption and entry of milk into the rumen result in very poor performance by the lambs which demonstrate a non-specific unthriftiness similar to 'tail enders' often observed in flocks.

Manipulations of the Reflex

Calves are more apt to have milk in the reticulo-rumen than lambs, and bucket-fed animals are apt to have more milk or gruel in the rumen than nipple-fed animals. Apparently, the neural stimulation from drinking is not adequate to stimulate complete closure of the reticular groove when drinking from a bucket in relatively large amounts. However, a keen appetite for milk is stimulatory, regardless of age or various environmental factors. The reticular groove reflex is an all or none response in both fed calves or lambs. Cu salts in sheep and Na salts in calves will stimulate closure of the groove. The reflex has been studied (using polyethylene glycol 4,000 as a marker) in animals fitted with rumen fistulas, by measuring the proportion of ingested liquid food found in the rumen after a meal as compared to the total volume introduced directly through the fistula to determine the volume of ruminal liquid.

The reflex progressively disappears with age, although in calves receiving occasionally liquid food instead of milk, a very small proportion (<10%) of skim-milk, suspension of soybean meal and solution of fish protein concentrate is recovered in the rumen. In older calves (1 year) the proportion of water recovered in the rumen is much lower when water is withheld during the night than in the animals receiving it ad libitum.

The two reasons for manipulating this closure reflex in ruminants are (a) to avoid activation of the reflex from oropharyngeal origin in mature ruminants during oral dosing of medications, and (b) to activate the reflex in calves, thus avoiding the escape of milk into the rumen, e.g., when pharyngitis or oropharyngeal abcesses prevent the afferent arc of the reflex to be operative.

Intraruminal Drug Delivery. In adult sheep, to ascertain that the drug remains in the reticulo-rumen for a local action, three possibilities are at hand to prevent the activation of the reflex: injection of atropine, application of local anesthetics to the oral cavity and drug delivery into the thoracic esophagus via a gastric tube. The latter procedure is to be recommended for its simplicity and effectiveness. As shown by the peaks of blood concentration of meclofenamic acid, a single peak occurs at 2.5 h after esophageal dosing, instead of two peaks after oral dosing; the first due to the rumen bypass and the second due to ruminal release.

Teat Versus Bucket Feeding. When the xylose absorption test is applied to evaluate the degree of groove closure in sheep after Cu ions administration (10 ml of 10% CuSo$_4$), a detectable rise in xylose concentration occurs after D-xylose (0.5 g/kg BW) is administered via an esophageal tube but not via a rumen cannula. In calves, at the time of weaning, no rise in xylosemia is detectable when bucket-fed, even after a 24-h fast (food and water). Teat feeding always results in a marked increase of xylosemia within 60 min. The pH measurement of the chyme in the duodenum of calves shows a marked increase by 2 to 3 units due to saliva swallowed during teat feeding (Fig. 4-3), suggesting a closure of the esophageal groove, while there was only a tendency of increase in pH after bucket feeding. An almost complete closure must occur for teat feeding because duodenal pH values were very similar to those seen after a direct abomasal administration of Na bicarbonate (10 g). The buffering effect of saliva is demonstrated by an enhancement of duodenal alkalinization after pilocarpine also mimicked by the blockage of gastric acid secretion (Fig. 4-3).

A significant ruminal bypass of drinking water may also occur in lactating cows. When water is withheld for 4.5 and 9 h following feeding, 18% and 5% of drinking water was

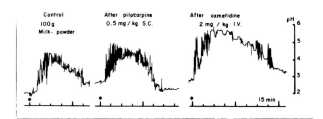

Figure 4-3. Changes in duodenal pH values of the chyme after sucking 1 ℓ of reconstituted milk powder (100 g) from a nipple in a calf fitted with a re-entrant cannula at the time of weaning. The transient increase in duodenal pH values indicate the closure of the groove with gastric delivery of less acidic chyme buffered by saliva. The response is enhanced after a previous (20 min) injection of pilocarpine which increases the salivary secretion or after blockage of gastric acid secretion with oxmetidine, an antihistaminic H$_2$ drug (11).

found to bypass the rumen in 8 rumen-fistulated Holstein cows (31). The fact that bypass of water was greatest when water was withheld for only 4.5 h vs 9 h was probably due to a greater fill of the rumen (31).

Activation of the Reticular Groove Reflex. The closure of the groove is accompanied by an inhibition of rumino-reticular contractions which is mimicked by L-DOPA (1 mg/kg) acting as a precursor of dopamine and suppressed by metoclopramide (0.2 mg/kg) pretreatment acting as a dopamine antagonist which also acts via the cholinergic system. A similar effect on reticulo-rumen contractions was found with domperidone which does not penetrate the CNS to the same extent as metoclopramide.

MOVEMENTS OF THE RETICULO-RUMEN

The orderly and synchronized movements of the reticulum and rumen aid in mixing newly ingested food with that already in the stomach, in regurgitation and eructation of gas and in moving food into the omasum. Motility of the reticulo-rumen is involved in the retention and mixing of the ingesta so that the contents can undergo a relatively slow process of microbial digestion, followed by absorption. Some of the contents must be regurgitated, re-insalivated, and re-swallowed, while large amounts of gas produced in the rumen must be eructated. Finally, the

68

contents must leave the reticulo-rumen in an orderly and controlled fashion through the omasum before they reach the abomasum. Such events are accomplished by coordinated cyclical contractions of the different chambers of the stomach occurring for the reticulum every 50 to 70 sec, i.e., 1,440 times a day.

These contractions (*extrinsic* contractions) are dependent on bursts of efferent (motor) nerve impulses travelling in the vagal nerves and are essential to the maintenance of fermentation as a vigorous and continuous process. In the absence of vagal nerves, the smooth muscle of the reticulo-rumen walls undergoes low amplitude contractions (*intrinsic* contractions) and stagnation with accumulation of feed and gas until the animal dies. That the paralysis is not by itself the immediate cause of death is indicated by the fact that animals survive for several months if fed through an abomasal fistula (12).

Most of the extrinsic activity can be divided into (a) **primary** contractions, sometimes referred to as the mixing cycle, and (b) **secondary** contractions, sometimes called eructative contractions. The fact that observations and measurements have been made by a variety of methods in different laboratories,

on different species and regimens, has resulted in some discrepancies. Also, motor activity may be influenced by eating, rumination, bloat, and by deprivation of food or water with the result that a wide variety of motor activity may occur; some of these may represent complete cycles and others may represent abbreviated cycles as shown in Table 4-1.

Primary Reticulo-Ruminal Contractions.
When reticulo-ruminal activity resumes after a period of rest or inhibition, recordings of pressure or electrical activity of the wall of the different compartments indicate that contractions are first initiated by the reticulum. That is the point at which the normal cycle begins. After an initial sharp contraction of the reticulum and the reticulo-ruminal fold during which the reticulum contracts to about half of its resting size, a second (and more powerful) contraction of the reticulum occurs. The wave of contraction passes caudally over the rumen, resulting in a lifting of the cranial sac due to contraction of the cranial pillars, contraction of the caudal and dorsal coronary pillars and compression of the dorsal sac of the rumen resulting, partially, from contraction of the longitudinal pillars

Table 4-1. Incidence (%) of pressure waves in the rumen of cows and sheep.

Activity	D[c]	DV	DSV	DVSV	Others	Primary (DV)	Modified primary (D)	Secondary (SV)
			a*				b**	
Cows[d]								
Feeding	1	27	5	56	11	55	4	41
Resting	10	35	25	22	8	41	25	34
Ruminating	22	28	37	6	7	25	43	32
Sheep[d]								
Feeding	0	45	1	46	8	65	1	34
Resting	2	48	4	39	7	64	4	32
Ruminating	4	48	13	30	6	57	12	31

*Total patterns analyzed under (a) = 5,998; **The analyses under (b) excludes the group "others" under (a).
[c]D, primary wave in dorsal sac; V, pressure in ventral sac; S, secondary wave in dorsal sac, which at its peak usually coincides with a sharp spike of pressure in the anterior and ventral sacs of the rumen and which accompanies eructation. Those under (a) represent the sequences of these changes and the incidence of which about 10% cannot be classified into the 4 main categories listed. Those under (b) indicate the incidence of primary waves (DV), modified primary in which the ventral sac shows no pressure change (D), and secondary waves (SV).
[d]From Phillipson (13).

(Fig. 4-4). The wave of contraction continues over the caudodorsal blind sac, ventral coronary pillar, ventral sac and caudoventral blind sac with some displacement ventrally of the cranial pillar.

It should be pointed out that these events result in a gradual wave of contraction followed by a wave of relaxation. As a matter of fact, some sacs may be dilating while others are contracting. For example, when the dorsal sacs are contracting in the primary cycle, the ventral sacs and the reticulum are dilating.

From the recent diagrammatic illustrations of cyclical contractions of the sheep's

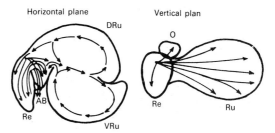

AB Abomasum, DRu Dorsal rumen, O Omasum, Re Reticulum, Ru Rumen, VRu Ventral rumen

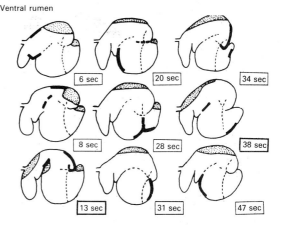

Figure 4-5. Movement of digesta in the reticulo-rumen as seen radiographycally in the horizontal and vertical planes. Top. Arrows indicate direction of movement. Main contraction sequences of the sheep's reticulo-rumen as indicated by X-radiography. Bottom. Time in seconds indicates the interval after the reticular movement and the contracting region of the reticulo-rumen wall is indicated as a heavy line. The gas bubble (stippled area) is brought over the cardiac orifice at 13 sec in the case of a primary contraction and during the secondary ruminal contraction at 38 sec. From Wyburn (32).

stomach by Wyburn (32) shown in Fig. 4-5, it is clear that the result of the cyclical activity is a flow of ingesta from the reticulum to the cranial sac, from the cranial sac into the dorsal sac; from the dorsal sac back through the cranial sac to the reticulum or into the ventral sac. Thus, the contractions result in a circulation of semisolid digesta and fluids within the reticulo-rumen. This sequence of events requires 30 to 50 sec to complete when the animal is resting (neither eating or ruminating or deeply asleep).

Secondary Ruminal Contractions

Those contractions occurring in the rumen may or may not occur after a primary

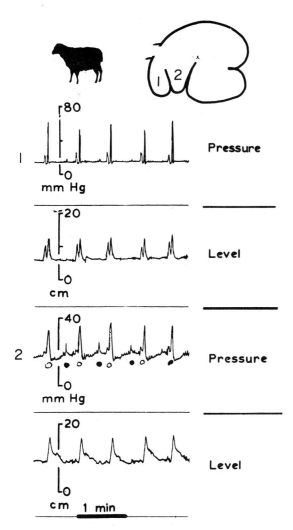

Figure 4-4. Comparison of simultaneous recordings of pressure and vertical displacement of the reticulum and the carnial sac of the rumen during primary (○) and secondary ruminal contractions (●) in sheep. From Reid and Cornwall (16).

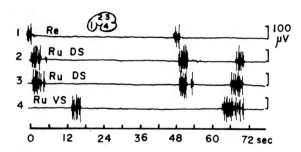

Figure 4-6. Reticulo-ruminal (Re-Ru) contraction as indicated by electromyography and lasting 48 sec. Another cycle, a secondary ruminal contraction, starts on the posterior ventral sac of the rumen (Ru-VS) and spreads forwards over the rumen dorsal sac (Ru-DS) in the sheep at rest. From Ruckebusch (20).

contraction. These contractions generally involve the dorsal coronary pillar, contraction of the caudodorsal blind sac and dorsal sac and relaxation of the caudoventral blind sac. At times only the dorsal sac is involved and requires about 30 sec to complete in cattle when associated with eructation. When evaluating ruminal contractions with electromyography (electrical activity in muscles) in sheep, secondary contractions originated in the ventral blind sac, either independently or immediately following a primary contraction (Fig. 4-6). The wave of contraction is seen to pass in a circular manner to the dorsal blind sac, dorsal sac and ventral sac and back to the ventral blind, with eructation occurring at the end of contraction of the dorsal sac. The time required to complete a cycle is related to the strength of contraction of the ventral blind sac.

In cattle, the effects of rumen fistulation on the motility patterns of the reticulum are not trivial, as shown in Table 4-2. They are probably related to the opening of the cannula because the rumen pressure is normally below atmospheric pressure (see Fig. 4-7). Six patterns of activity were identified in the cow when the fistula was tightly closed, or by electromyography (22).

Primary contractions involve the reticulum (R) and the rumen dorsal sac (D) or the dorsal and the ventral sacs (RDV). Figure 4-8 shows that the ventral blind sac (Vp) may also contract between a primary cycle and a secondary ruminal contraction involving the dorsal and ventral sacs. Similar sequential patterns of contractions have been presented for the sheep (see Table 4-1).

About 85% of the contractions in resting cattle fall in the patterns RD or RDV (45%) and RD,DV or RDV,DV (40%). Only 10% of the contractions involved the ventral blind sac (Vp). About 5% of the ruminal contractions were found represented by other patterns in which Vp replaced the main ventral sac contractions or was in addition to the main ventral sac contractions.

Species Comparisons

The reticular contractions of cattle and bison consist essentially of two separate pressure waves, whereas in sheep, goats and

Table 4-2. Effect of rumen fistulation on frequency and amplitude of reticular contractions.[a]

Treatment	Contractions per min	Amplitude, mm Hg
Resting		
Intact	1.2	18.2
Fistul.	1.4	5.9
Feeding		
Intact	2.0	22.1**
Fistul.	2.0	9.4
Ruminating		
Intact	1.1	10.4
Fistul.	1.1	10.9

[a]Data excerpted from ref. 3. **Statistically >9.4.

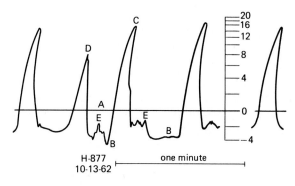

Figure 4-7. Rumen gas pressure of a fasting steer fed on long oat hay. A, atmospheric pressure; B, resting rumen pressure; C, primary rumen contraction; D, eructation contraction; E, deflection caused by movement of the steer. Scale is graduated in cm of water. Courtesy of H.W. Colvin, Univ. of California, Davis. From Church (3).

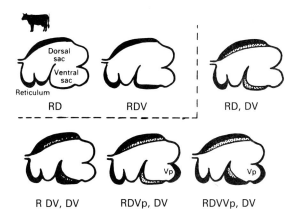

Figure 4-8. Primary (heavy lines) and secondary ruminal contractions (dotted lines) in the cow. Single or primary cycles comprise a contraction of the reticulum followed by the rumen dorsal sac (RD) or, in addition, of the ventral sac (RDV). The additional secondary ruminal contraction may occur after RD or RDV. Some contractions involved the ventral blind sac (Vp) after RD or RDV. From Ruckebusch and Kay (22).

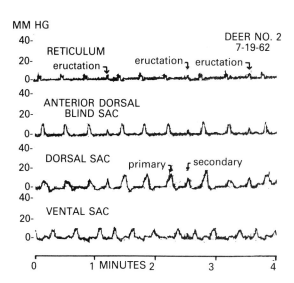

Figure 4-9. Typical pressure events recorded in the reticulo-rumen of deer when standing and resting. Courtesy of H.E. Dziuk, Univ. of Minnesota. From Church (3).

white-tailed deer (Fig. 4-9), the reticular contraction is more a biphasic one. Work from Dziuk's laboratory indicates that the motility patterns of the rumen in cattle and bison are similar, i.e., that the secondary contraction of the caudodorsal blind sac begins before dorsal sac contraction whereas in goats, sheep and white-tailed deer, these contractions are simultaneous. The rates of primary to secondary contractions are similar for the cow, bison, sheep and goat. Although the deer showed a higher frequency of cycles (about 2/min) and a higher ratio of primary to secondary contractions, the number of secondary contractions are about the same as in cattle. In the buffalo the numbers of total, primary and secondary contractions were less than in cattle; the interval between primary contractions being longer.

Of major interest are the studies of motility in llamas and guanacos (Fig. 4-10). If the first two compartments undergo cyclic motility and if like the reticulum of ruminants, the second compartment contractions lead the cycle of contractions, it appears that the first compartment contractions are multiple, often having 6-8 contractions before the next contraction of compartment 2. The intervals of these contractions are similar to those seen after vagotomy in sheep, suggesting a lower control from the central nervous system. Nevertheless, the rate in the cranial sac (1.8 per min) at rest increased to 4/min while feeding, and then decreased to ca. 1.4/min during rumination. During rumination the cranial sac shows extra contractions not preceded by contractions of the caudal sac. These are accompanied by regurgitation and a single cycle can include 3-4 regurgitations. Eructation occurs near the peak of caudodorsal and ventral sac contractions and is followed immediately by deglutition.

Effect of Feeding

Initially, a rather constant 1:2 rhythm between the primary and secondary contractions was described in the cow examined at rest. Later, it was found that a 1:1 rhythm occurred a majority of the time (74% of 400 animals); a 2:1 rhythm occurred in 16% of the cows, whereas a 1:2 rhythm occurred in 10% only (palpation and auscultation). Finally, four major patterns of contractions occur in the rumen of cattle as measured with pressure-sensitive recordings: R,D; R,DV; R,D,DV; and R,DV,DV. These patterns account for 90% of the changes observed (see Table 4-1).

In fact, the sight of food and then its ingestion stimulate the salivary secretions, especially the parotid glands and the nasolabial gland secretions which, in bovines, are salivary

72

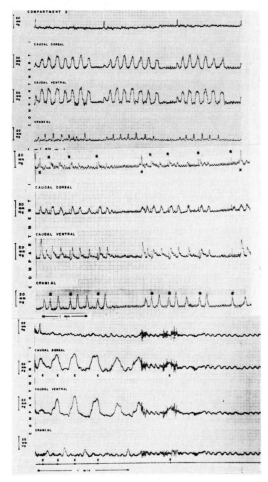

Figure 4-10. Pressure in the llama stomach. Top. Pressure event in compartments 1 and 2 in absence of feeding or rumination. Note rapid, single contraction of 2nd compartment at beginning of each cycle. This is followed by a series of contractions involving caudal and cranial sacs of compartment 1. Last caudal sac contraction is not followed by contraction of cranial sac. Middle. Pressure patterns during rumination. R=regurgitation, X=contraction of 2nd compartment. Bottom. Pattern shown during eructation (E). Note the erucatation occurs at peak of caudal sac contraction. Courtesy of C.E. Stevens. From Church (3).

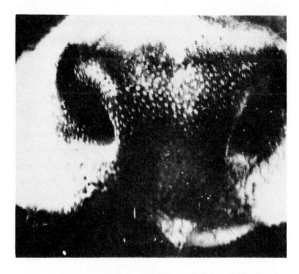

Figure 4-11. Increased rate of secretion of the bovine muzzle at the sight of food of great palatability. The basal rate of secretion, equal to 0.8 ml/min/cm^2, was increased threefold during food intake.

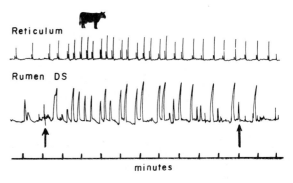

Figure 4-12. Stimulatory effects of feeding concentrates during 10 min in reticulo-ruminal contractions (frequency and amplitude) in cattle. From Ruckebusch and Kay (22).

in nature (Fig. 4-11). This is paralleled by an increase in the frequency and amplitude of the reticulo-ruminal contractions (Fig. 4-12). In sheep, after an overnight fast, the motility is characterized by (a) a low frequency of coordinated sequences with only 1 to 0.3 contractions/min; (b) a low proportion of secondary contractions—as few as 1 for every 5 primary contractions; (c) a low level of tonic activity;   (d) short, simple relatively weak

rumen contractions in which the ventral sac may not contract during primary sequences; and (e) the emergence of a characteristic form of both primary and secondary sequences (14). This marked decrease in amplitude of contractions as well as in frequency is reversed and an increase in frequency and amplitude of the reticulo-ruminal contractions occur as soon as the animal starts to eat (Fig. 4-13). This effect, characterized by contractions of the RD type, lasts only 5-10 min, after which the frequency of contractions is increased by about 30% for 1 or 2 h. Rumen motility in the feeding sheep is characterized by a high frequency of contractions—as many

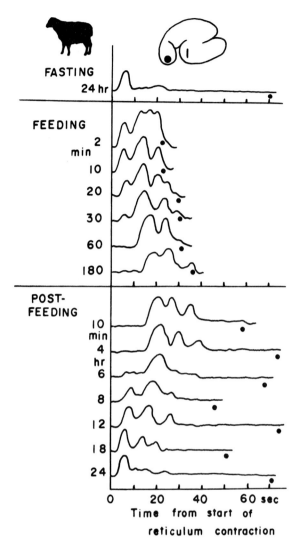

Figure 4-13. Changes in the form of the primary contractions of an exteriorization in the main ventral rumen of a fasted (24 h) sheep (1), during and after a 3-h period of feeding on hay. The tracings are taken from kymographic records made from one animal over a period of 28 h. The black dots indicate the start of the succeeding reticular contraction. From Reid (14).

as 3/min; a ratio of primary to secondary contractions of about 1:1; and a high level of tonic activity with the contractions of the ventral sac being prolonged and polyphasic during about 30 min. The distance separating the cranial from the caudal pillars increases from 10 cm to 18 cm within 90 min during eating. During sham-feeding the reticulum (Fig. 4-14) also exhibits a high rate of contractions in relation with the animal's drive for food (18).

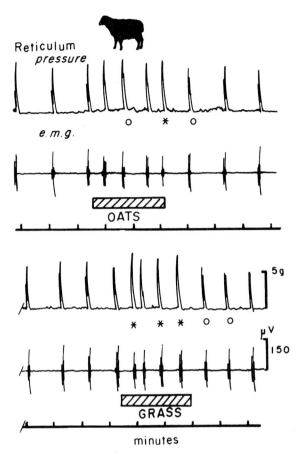

Figure 4-14. Increased rate of reticular contractions in sheep during sham feeding of oats or grass. Note that the biphasic contraction may be lost (*) and that the first phase of the contraction becomes preeminent for 2 or 3 minutes (o).

Effect of Diet

The effect of physical form of the feed has been studied by several authors. When cattle are fed oat hay in long form or ground through 1/4 or 3/32 in. hammermill screens, the finest grind results in a slower rate of contractions and a reduction in the amplitude of contractions. The amplitude of rumen contractions takes from 2 to 6 weeks to stabilize after animals are changed from one diet to another, the change from the 3/32 in. hay to long hay taking the longest time. With sheep grinding the hay also results in reduced rate and lower amplitude of rumen contractions. This phenomenon is also recorded for the reticular contractions in sheep receiving long hay or the same diet in the form of pellets. The amplitude of contractions is reduced but not the rate. However, the intervals separating the two phases of reticular contractions increase from 1.4 to 1.8 sec with the pellet form so that the duration of reticular contractions increases from 3.5 to 4.3 sec. During rumination the extra-contraction is more distinct from the biphasic contractions and the mean duration of the contractions is 7.3 sec instead of 6.6 sec (19). This suggests a more sluggish vago-vagal reflex by lower afferent inflow from a diet containing particles of small size and thus lower tactile stimulation of mechanoreceptors.

Experiments of intragastric nutrition in sheep (Table 4-3) showed that a rumen free of dietary debris maintains motility patterns which resembled those seen when eating pelleted grass, i.e., lower amplitude of contractions. According to Ørskov (12), the infused animals show the same frequency of primary ruminal contractions but a reduced frequency of secondary cycle contractions, both of reduced amplitude, and also show frequent periods of pseudorumination. The role of the texture of the digesta has thus been possibly over-estimated and the volatile fatty acids (VFA) produced by different diets may be at the origin of hypomotility via excitation of vagally innervated chemoreceptors. Reticular contractions are inhibited by acetic (90 mM),

propionic (50 mM) or butyric (37 mM) acids separately. The threshold at which the primary ruminal contractions are inhibited is only 33.5-29.3 and 21.1 mM for acetic, propionic or butyric acid, respectively, given as a mixture. This indicates a possible direct effect of the VFA on the musculature or the plexus neurons.

The effects of two diets (maize silage and long-grass hay) on alimentary behavior in the ovine and bovine species in stall-fed conditions are given in Table 4-4. These data suggest relatively few specific differences between these two species in confined and overfed animals.

Events Associated with Regurgitation

One of the primary differences in reticulo-ruminal motility between rumination and that of the resting phase or eating is the presence of an extra-reticular contraction (or triphasic) that occurs prior to the usual biphasic contraction (Fig. 4-15). This extra-reticular contractions occurs a few seconds prior to the usual reticular contraction. Usually, regurgitation of ingesta into the thoracic esophagus occurs during a drop in intrapleural pressure due to the contraction of the diaphragm at the end of the extra contraction. The

Table 4-3. Influence of intragastric infusion of nutrients on gastro-intestinal motility in sheep.[a]

	Forestomach contractions per hour		Migrating myoelectric complexes per day		
	Primary	Secondary	Duodenum	Jejunum	Ileum
Roughage (n = 6)	48.5	30.4	14.5	22.1	14.1
Intragastric infusion (n = 6)	47.2	21.6	13.9	18.4	12.3

[a]Data from Ørskov et al (12)

Table 4-4. Effect of the species and of the type of ruminant on the eating and ruminating behavior in stall-fed conditions.[a]

Animal	Wether*	Ewe†	Growing bull	Cow‡	Wether*	Ewe†	Goat†	Growing bull	Cow‡
Liveweight, kg	59	54	367	572	69	61	44	366	536
Feed (ad libitum)	Maize silage + urea				Long-grass hay				
Voluntary intake, g DM/kg $BW^{0.75}$	48	64	77	111	62	52	75	77	111
Eating time, min/d	237	213	368	341	261	281	293	294	350
Ruminating time, min/d	509	516	397	432	547	542	473	385	563
Number of meals/d	6.3	7.0	8.3	10.8	5.2	10.7	10.0	5.6	5.7
Duration of 1 ruminating cycle, sec.	52	66	55	52	45	65	----	54	54

[a]From Dulphy et al (7)
* Adult; † Adult, non-pregnant, non-lactating; ‡ Producing 9 kg milk daily

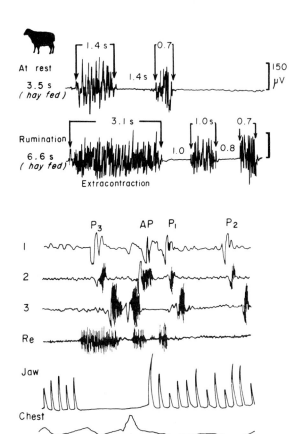

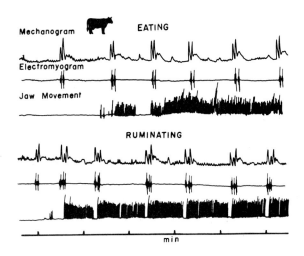

Figure 4-16. Pressure recordings, electrical activity and jaw movements detected by pressure changes in a balloon fixed on the halter of a cow starting to eat hay (above) or ruminating (below).

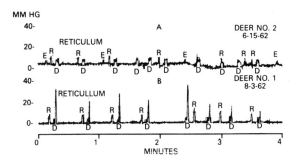

Figure 4-17. Pressure recordings in the reticulum of two deer (A & B), indicating regurgitation (R) occurring out-of-phase with respect to the reticulo-rumen cycle as indicated by the positions of reticular doublets (D) in deer A on the right side of the chart. E = eructation. Courtesy of H.E. Dziuk, Univ. of Minnesota. From reference 3.

Figure 4-15. Top. Electromyogram of the sheep reticulum wall showing the biphasic activity in the animal at rest and the superimposed extra-reticular contraction during regurgitation. Bottom. Events on the esophagus, reticulum, jaw and chest associated with regurgitation (arrow). The esophageal electromyograms are recorded from electrodes placed at an equal distance on the esophagus, near the glottis (1), at the entry of the chest (2), and close to the cardia (3), and the reticulum (Re). The regurgitation of digesta (AP) is followed by swallowing just the excess of liquid on two occasions (P_1 and P_2) and later of the bolus (P_3).

antiperistaltic wave of esophageal contraction is initiated at the onset of the first phase of reticular contraction. In sheep, goats and cattle, the first phase of the biphasic contraction following regurgitation and, to a lesser extent, the second reticular pressure change are of a very low amplitude or are absent (Fig. 4-16).

Pressure changes associated with secondary ventral sac contractions extend into the subsequent reticulo-ruminal cycle during rumination, with the terminal phases occurring during the regurgitation contraction of the reticulum. In the deer some regurgitation contractions occur out of phase with respect to the usual biphasic reticular contraction. These are illustrated in Fig. 4-17.

Ruminants, with open tracheal cannula which was presumed to prevent the formation of negative pressure in the chest, ruminated normally. Diversion of the regurgitated material by opening an esophageal cannula did not suppress the antiperistaltic wave travelling along the esophagus towards the buccal cavity. However, this caused the loss of masticatory

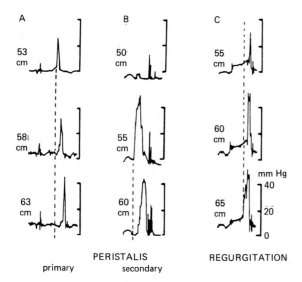

PERISTALIS
primary   secondary

REGURGITATION

Figure 4-18. A, primary peristalsis, the wave of positive pressure respresenting esophageal muscular contraction moves down the esophagus following deglutition at the velocity of 23 cm/sec. B, secondary peristalsis; peristaltic response to intraluminal balloon distension occurring in the distal esophagus and distal to the balloon. C, regurgitation; an initial plateau of positive pressure occurs simultaneously in all three leads without coincident respiratory change and terminates in a rapid retrograde peristaltic wave at a velocity of 42.5-53.8 cm/sec in sheep. From Winship (30).

movements and reduced by 50-70% the duration of the reticulo-ruminal cycle. Pressure changes recorded with tandem balloons are shown in Fig. 4-18. The bolus travelled cephalically in sheep at the mean rate of 120-170 cm/sec depending if the animal was standing or in sternal recumbency, and the liquid squeezed from the bolus returned to the reticulo-rumen at a mean rate of 35 cm/sec (30).

Events Associated with Eructation

The coordinated ruminal contraction and lower esophageal sphincter relaxation lead to eructation of the gases (mainly CO_2 and CH_4) produced as by-products of fermentation. Eructation in sheep most commonly occurs following a contraction of the rumen which spreads in a cranial direction over its dorsal sac as shown by electromyography (Fig. 4-19). Such contractions have been identified as displacing gas cranially towards the cardia from a caudal and dorsal position in the rumen, and

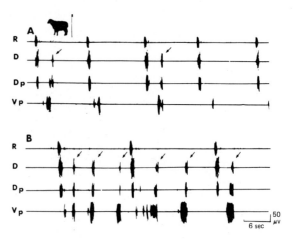

Figure 4-19. A, Normal reticulum contraction spreading backwards on the rumen and eructative sequence starting 18 sec later on the posterior ventral sac in sheep (arrow). B, The distension by air at a mean pressure of 10 cm H_2O is accompanied by an eructative sequence starting within 6 sec after the primary contraction and followed by other secondary contractions of the rumen (arrows) starting on the ventral sac. From Ruckebusch and Tomov (23).

they can be stimulated reflexly in decerebrate preparations by insufflation of gas into the rumen. Following each of these contractions, there is passage of gas into and along the esophagus, from which some may escape directly into the atmosphere, but most passes into the respiratory tract (6). Eructation may also occur in sheep at the time of regurgitation, but in cattle the secondary ruminal contractions are necessary for the alleviation of the excess gas.

Miscellaneous Factors

Many different pathophysiological situations or diseases will cause alteration or cessation of normal stomach motility cycles. One example of this type of alteration in reticular contractions is shown in Fig. 4-20. In this case the cow developed traumatic peritonitis (hardware disease) caused by a nail piercing the reticulum and irritating other tissues. Presumably, the resulting pain altered the normal reflex in an attempt to reduce further damage. During febrile episodes, ruminants suffering from infectious diseases also show an inhibition of gastric motility and a dose-dependent inhibition of reticulo-ruminal motility has been observed during endotoxin-induced fever. Among the several other

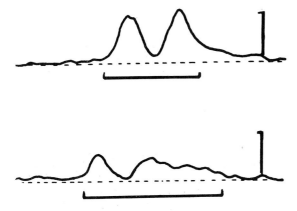

Figure 4-20. Reticular pressure patterns of (top) normal cow and (bottom) cow with spontaneous traumatic peritonitis caused by tissue damage from a nail in the reticulum. Note the prolonged second contraction. Courtesy of P. Holtenius. From Church (3).

possibilities which may reduce reticuloruminal movements, hypocalcemia and hyperglycemia are humoral factors commonly involved, acting at both a central and peripheral level. The distension of the abomasum and/or duodenal acidification represent other inhibitory factors which may be grouped under the term of duodenal braking mechanism, indicating a protective reflex against the overload of the postgastric area (11).

MOTOR ACTIVITY OF THE OMASUM

The omasum is a compact organ more developed in cattle than in sheep or goats. It contains numerous leaves of epithelium which originate from its greater curvature (see Ch. 2). Its motor functions have been studied by means of radiologic examination in sheep and goats. Manometric studies in sheep and cattle and electromyography in both species progressively gave understandable data on the functions of this organ in terms of cyclical contractions and transfer of digesta.

Cyclical Activity
With respect to motility, the sequence of contractions is the neck (which connects with the reticulum), the omasal canal and the body of the organ. Omasal contractions are relatively slow and prolonged (Fig. 4-21) when compared to reticular contraction, and there is considerable variability among animals in cattle, whereas contractions in sheep and

goats are more regular. Recently, evidence has been presented to show contractions of the leaves but without relation with the considerable changes in position and shape of the whole organ during a normal contractile cycle observed with radiographic studies.

In cattle, pressure recordings made between the leaves of the omasal body and in the omasal canal are quite different in character, with the body contractions being of much greater amplitude than those from other parts of the viscus (30-40 mm Hg). The body contractions are also of longer duration than the canal contractions and overlap into the next ruminal cycle. Another difference is that the canal contractions occur with each reticular cycle whereas the body contractions do not always occur, at times being absent for 2-5 cycles. Apparently, canal contractions force the more fluid components of the ingesta from the canal between the leaves of the omasal body and the contraction of the omasal body forces ingesta out of the intra-leaf space into the abomasum. Backflow of large volumes of ingesta from the omasum to the reticulum is also noted and seems to occur when the omasal body contracts with a concurrent high pressure in a distended abomasum.

In sheep with surgically placed wire electrodes and/or strain gauges, the contraction apparently starts on the oral and middle

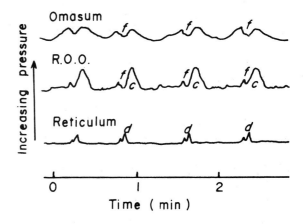

Figure 4-21. Pressure changes in the reticulum, reticulo-omasal orifice and the omasum of a cow at rest. The double contraction of the reticulum (d), the sudden fall in pressure in the omasum and reticulo-omasal orifice (f), and the powerful contraction of the orifice (c) are shown. Courtesy of C.C. Balch. From reference 3.

78

thirds of the organ. In fact, it originates at the omasal groove and proceeds to the right and then left surfaces and ceases at the onset of reticular contraction (Fig. 4-22). In the lower third of the ovine omasal body, the contractions are prolonged regardless of the reticular contraction and thus seem to behave as the whole omasal body in cattle. It is noteworthy too that the omasal leaves contract independently from the omasal body wall.

Reticulo-Omasal Orifice

Movements of the omasal orifice in relation to contractions of the reticulum, cranial pillar of the rumen, the omasum and abomasum were studied in cattle by means of small, lightly inflated balloons. During resting, eating and drinking, the orifice functions in a constant pattern. For the greater part of the reticulo-ruminal cycle of contraction, the orifice is loosely open but following the last reticular contraction, the orifice closes strongly. The end of the reticular contraction is accompanied by a marked fall in pressure in the neck of the omasum, followed by a marked rise of pressure in the omasum which coincides with the closure of the orifice (see Fig. 4-21). The transfer of digesta from the

reticulo-rumen most likely occurs at the end of the reticular contraction, coinciding with the fall in pressure in the omasum. Thus, the passage of digesta from the reticulo-rumen is relatively continuous and is largely controlled by the valve-like action of the omasum. It has also been observed that swallowing may be associated with monophasic contractions of the esophageal groove and the omasal orifice, a pattern reminiscent of that seen in the sucking lamb (27).

Measurement of the changes in diameter of the orifice in sheep by means of impedance electrodes shows that the orifice dilates strongly during the second phase of reticular contraction and also during the extra-reticular contraction associated with regurgitation. This is accompanied by flow of digesta into the omasum. Alternating opening and closing movements are seen at a frequency of 5-7/min (Fig. 4-23). These changes are independent of the contractions of the omasal leaves which

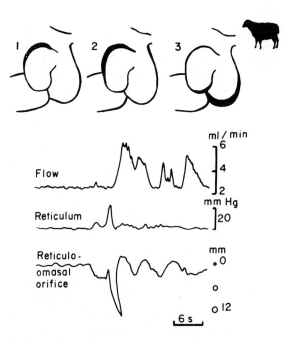

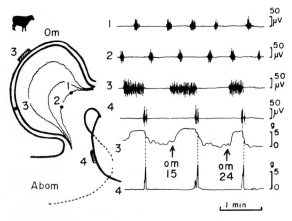

Figure 4-22. Origin of the cyclical motility of the ovine omasum. Top, contractions of an omasal leaf recorded from its free border are twice as frequent as those of the omasal greater curvature. Bottom, the contraction of the omasal body is blocked at the time of the contraction of the reticulum. The prolonged contraction of the omasal canal (OM-15), which begins 15 sec after the reticular contractions, spreads slowly over the omasal body. The one (OM-24) which begins later (24 sec) spreads more slowly (20).

Figure 4-23. Above, diagram showing the contraction of omasal body (1 and 2), which involves successively its oral and aboral parts. Only the area of the aboral part shows contractions not inhibited at the occurrence of the reticular contraction (3). Below, increased passage of digesta measured with a Doppler probe for 18 sec following the opening of the reticulo-omasal orifice, recorded from an impedance bridge, during the two phases of the contraction of the reticulum. From reference 20.

occur at 2-3/min and pass from the free border to the base and travel in an aboral (away from the mouth) direction.

Finally, the cyclic activity of the omasum involves the omasal groove and most of the omasal body, except for a small area near the abomasum. A rhythmical activity at 6-8 sec intervals, which begin after the reticular contraction, is recorded from the omasal canal near the reticulo-omasal orifice and is probably related to the spontaneous recurring closing and opening movements of this orifice (27). This activity fuses in a prolonged contraction which spreads over the omasal body to cease at the onset of reticular contraction in sheep. This strong relationship between the omasum and the reticulo-ruminal activity, an inhibitory-like effect of the reticulum on the omasum, has not been evidenced in cattle (22).

Transfer of Digesta

Only direct measurements of flow through the orifice in relation with the pressure oral to and aboral to the orifice can provide reliable data on the resulting variations in flow. In both sheep and cattle the flow is increased during feeding. In sheep the duration of omasal contractions are strongly reduced concurrently with an increase in the frequency of reticular contractions. More precisely, the duration of group discharges of the omasal body is reduced from 30 to 10 sec (see Fig. 4-24) when the frequency of contractions of the reticulum is doubled. The most simple explanation for this effect is that the transfer of digesta increased when the mean pressure in the reticulum is high and that of the omasal canal low. Accordingly, the passage of digesta starts during the second phase of reticulum contractions whereas the omasum is relaxed (Fig. 4-24). During eating, reticular contractions and associated omasal relaxations increase and thus the passage of digesta. Since in sheep, a period of rumination usually ends by two or three longer intervals between reticular contractions and subsequently prolonged contractions of the omasal body, it is possible that emptying of the material stored in the omasal body during rumination is enhanced during this period.

In cattle the body of the omasum gives rise to a rhythmic pattern of pressure change which is much slower than the reticulo-

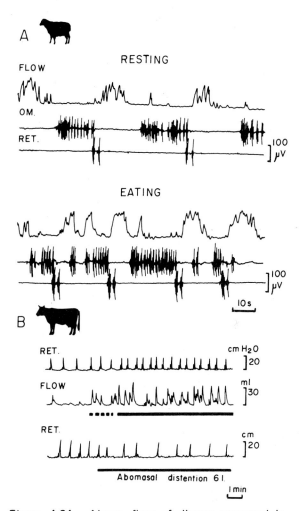

Figure 4-24. Above, flow of digesta measured in sheep through a Doppler probe placed behind the reticulo-omasal orifice. The contractions of the omasal body and reticulum are evaluated by electromyography. The flow, recorded just following the reticular contractions which have blocked the omasal body contractions, is increased during eating. Below, flow of digesta measured in a similar way in a cow with concomitant evaluation of the frequency and amplitude of reticular contractions. Teasing with oats increases the flow as well as eating concurrently with an increased rate of reticular contractions. From Ruckebusch and Kay (22).

ruminal cycle. It is thus likely that the transient pressure changes into the omasum are not determinant factors, as in sheep or goats, regulating intermittent flow of digesta at each reticulo-ruminal cycle of contraction.

Opening of the reticulo-omasal orifice especially during rumination and pressure changes in the reticulum brought about are probably the two main factors involved in the transfer of digesta. Figure 4-24 shows in a hay-fed cow that both teasing her with oats as appetizers and eating increase the flow rate of digesta through the reticulo-omasal orifice. In contrast, the distension of the abomasum obtained by rapid infusion of saline (6 ℓ) reduces the rate and amplitude of the reticular contractions and thus the outflow from the reticulo-rumen.

The effect of the muscular activity of the reticulum on the outflow of rumen digesta has been recently emphasized in the growing steer. Using disappearance of polyethylene glycol (PEG) as a basis of estimation of turnover rate of liquid rumen digesta, it was found that, if the liquid capacity of the forestomach increased with bodyweight, the turnover of digesta was related to the frequency of reticular contractions which in turn responds to variations in diet composition. In animals receiving a high-hay diet, the digesta flow is accelerated by 30% compared to the animals receiving pelleted straw and flaked maize supplemented with soybean meal. Indeed, the reticular myoelectric activity is likewise increased (and by nearly 300%) for measurements beween 3 and 7 h after feeding and thus the pressure gradient between the reticulum and the omasal canal as well as the duration of opening of the reticulo-omasal orifice (see Fig. 4-23).

DEVELOPMENT AND CONTROL OF MOTILITY

The functional development of the reticulo-rumen is of special interest because it corresponds to the development of plant growth in the Eocene period. The main contribution to evolutionary development was the formation of non-secretory diverticula of the primitive anterior stomach (fundus) to accommodate symbiotic bacteria capable of secreting cellulase to degrade the plant polysaccharide cellulose and produce substances utilized as sources of energy by the host animal. This development starts in the 6-week old embryo (see Ch. 3) and is accompanied by the differentiation of a **local nervous system**. The ganglia of the myenteric plexus are situated within the muscle coat and in the submucosa. They are connected by nerve strands to form a mesh more dense in the reticulum and

rumen dorsal sac than in the ventral sac or the abomasum (Fig. 4-25). Electrophysiological methods have revealed that this enteric nervous system (ENS) is the origin of an intramural reflex activity only influenced by the extrinsic nerves (Fig. 4-26) and modulated by gut hormones and neurotransmitters.

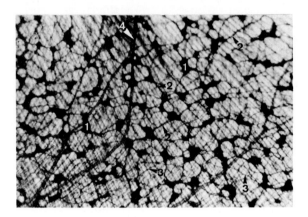

Figure 4-25. Auerbach's plexus after staining for cholinesterase (AchE) from the rumen dorsal sac in an ovine fetus (18 cm) (77 x). 1, ganglion. 2, interganglionic nerve bundles (internodal strands). 3. interlacing AchE + nervous network; and 4, branch of the dorsal vagal trunk. Courtesy of A. Weyns, Dept. Vet. Anatomy, Antwerp (11).

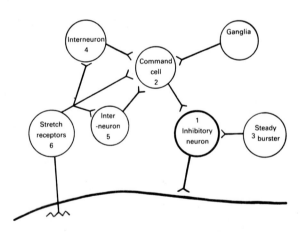

Figure 4-26. Example of smooth muscle cell response via the enteric nervous system. The activity of an inhibitory neuron (1) follows the activation by a command cell (2) or by a 'steady-burster' neuron rhythmically active (3) with acetylcholine as the neurotransmitter. The command cell (2) responds indirectly through interneurons (4 & 5) or directly to stretch receptors of the muscle cell (6). The command cell communicates with other ganglia within the plexus.

The other main contribution to evolutionary development is the formation for the reticulo-rumen, about equal in volume to the abomasum at birth, of **gastric centers** situated in the brain stem (1). The role of these centers is to allow a cyclical motion of the rumen as vago-vagal reflexes and to coordinate this cyclical activity with the process of regurgitation and eructation. Electrophysiological methods suggest that the outflow of the vagal motoneurons is strictly related to the afferent neural input. It is supposed that a neuronal network with types B and C interneurons constitutes a rate circuit of the cyclic movements. Another network with A interneurons is involved in the form and amplitude of these movements through early vagal discharges on the reticulum, and through later vagal discharges on the rumen. The rate circuit is inhibited by abomasal distension. The amplitude circuit is stimulated by reticular distension. As already shown, a strong net excitatory drive on the rate and amplitude circuits arises from the higher nervous centers, e.g., at the sight of food (Fig. 4-27). The functional development of this central nervous system (CNS) is arrested for the duration of the milk-fed period, that is the first 1-3 postnatal

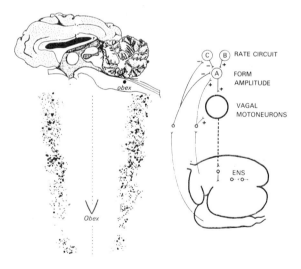

Figure 4-27. Gastric centers in the brain are indicated by a dot located near the obex under the cerebellum (top). The retrograde cellular degeneration (black dots) 16 d after rumenectomy in a milk-fed lamb suggests that the centers relative to the obex extend laterally and less caudally than rostrally. On the right, diagram of the functional organization of the gastric centers.

weeks during which the reticulo-rumen is held in functional stasis. However, the CNS control is operative and its effects are favored by the rapid postnatal growth of the reticulo-rumen which reduces the relative proportion (by weight) of the abomasum. At 2 weeks of age calves graze for about 3 h/d and by 7 weeks have attained almost adult grazing times and adult blood VFA levels. Restricting calves to a milk diet delays the development of the rumen, although suckling calves, within a week of birth, have pieces of hay and straw in the abomasum, when regurgitatory and masticatory movements of rumination become apparent.

The nervous mechanism controlling the motor events of rumination is so active in the 2-week-old calf that only slight stimulations, such as the presence of recording balloons or the suture of the wall after rumen ablation, are sufficient to produce frequent regurgitations (21). Rumen contractions in a calf as early as 4 d of age have been recorded and some calves may ruminate by 5 d of age (the majority do so by 28 d of age). The time spent ruminating increases rapidly in calves given hay and concentrates to average 5 h/d at 6-8 weeks of age (26).

Preruminant State

Transition to the ruminant method of digestion is largely dependent on the diet that a calf receives. The longer the period that a calf has access to a plentiful supply of milk, the less will be its urge to supplement its diet with other foods. Indeed, veal calves given ad libitum liquid diet and access to dry food consume only about 3 kg hay in a 3-month period. Given a limited quantity of liquid diet, calves will begin eating grass and, providing it is palatable, dry food at about 7 d of age.

Flatt et al (8) recorded changes in reticulo-rumen pressure in calves receiving either milk, hay, grain or grain + hay with polyvinyl plastic sponges or nylon bristles (Fig. 4-28). Primary and secondary ruminal contractions were recorded in the hay-fed calf at the age of 57 d and later (71 d) in the calves fed grain + hay (8). This is the first demonstration at our knowledge of a relationship between the capacity of the reticulo-rumen and its muscular activity.

82

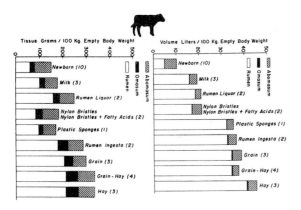

Figure 4-28. Effect of diet on dry tissue (and on the volume) of the stomach compartments of fistulated calves at slaughter. Figures in parentheses = number of calves per treatment. The consumption of solid feeds, such as rumen ingesta or hay and grain, consistently resulted in development of rumen papillae and a slight response to the administration of rumen liquor was noted, hence values of more than 250 g per 100 kg. From Flatt et al (8).

Studies of the development of rumen motility in calves by the fluoroscopic method showed an apparent developmental process of reticulo-ruminal motility. It was composed of feeble movement of the bottom of the reticulum at 2 weeks of age, feeble movement of the reticulum followed by slow movement of the rumen at 3 weeks of age and active biphasic contraction of the reticulum and strong movements of the rumen at 6 weeks of age.

Dietary influences on ruminal motion have been studied also in rumen-fistulated calves from 2 to 10 weeks of age which were fed a variety of different diets: milk; milk, hay and grain; milk + sponges; milk + VFA; or milk + sponges + VFA. Reticular and ruminal motility was arbitrarily divided into five stages of development with progressive development from no motility to well-defined reticular and ruminal contractions. In calves allowed milk and hay ad libitum, contractions of the rumen were recorded at 3-10 weeks of age, related to dry matter intake and VFA concentration in the rumen. In contrast, calves given milk did not show any stable ruminal contractions. The combination of milk, sponges and VFA allowed complete development at 3-5 weeks of age.

In calves receiving only milk by abomasal fistula, the effect of intraruminal infusions of a mixture of VFA and ammoniac solution was compared with that of indigestible plastic particles introduced by a rumen fistula. The plastic develops the ruminal musculature without stimulating the papillary growth; the friction of roughage acting probably on the muscular layer of the rumen through the mechanical stimulation of the reflexogenic areas (Fig. 4-29).

The VFA allow an important development of mucosal layer and growth of papillae: the association of plastic and VFA having a synergistic effect on the mucosal and the muscular layers. Ammonia represents a chemical stimulus for the development of the muscular layer and its papillae, however this stimulus is less effective than VFA.

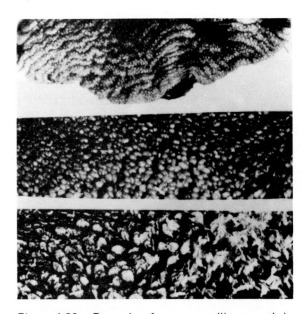

Figure 4-29. Example of rumen papillae growth in 3-week-old calves receiving either milk or milk substitutes (top), hay (middle) or silage (bottom). The considerable increase in thickness of the mucosa is due to the development of rumen papillae stimulated by the end-products of rumen fermentation rather than by the fibrous nature of the food. Excessive papillary development may lead to rumen parakeratosis, i.e., an increase in the length and width of the papillae, clumping of the papillae with rumen contents and encrusting of the tips of the papillae with dark keratinized material. This occurs with diets in which the hay has been pelleted (rather than wafered or given in long form), hence the lack of muscle tone. From Ruckebusch and Candau (21).

As shown in Fig. 4-29, only 3 weeks are necessary to modify the papillary growth. Comparisons of the digestive characteristics of 16-week-old calves fed concentrates or hay ad libitum (Table 4-5) show a higher weight gain concurrently with a higher concentration of VFA in the rumen and of glucose in the blood (26).

The motility of the concentrate-fed calves is reduced when compared to the hay-fed as is their time spent in rumination or the coordination between regurgitation and reticular contractions (Fig. 4-30). The role of chewing in the development of motility has been ascertained on milk-fed lambs and calves on which the rumen has been removed or separated from the reticulum. In the case of calves only milk-fed and the rumen removed, rumination occurs without regurgitation of solid material ("rumination à vide" or pseudorumination)

and can last for 4-5 h/d. The major effect of this behavior on calves with an isolated but innervated rumen is to trigger contractions on the dorsal sac of the rumen and even the ventral sac. In this case the duration of the cycle is increased by 20 to 50% (Fig. 4-31). The infusion of VFA at a concentration found in calves fed on concentrates reduced the time spent in "rumination à vide" (see section on rumination). Nevertheless, the development of motility patterns and associated behaviors like rumination accompanies the forestomach growth and capacity, as shown in lambs from 1 to 8 weeks after birth (Fig. 4-32).

Table 4-5. Comparison of certain characteristics of 16-week-old Ayrshire calves given concentrates or hay ad libitum.[a]

	Diet	
	Concentrates ad lib.	Hay ad lib.
Dry matter intake, kg/d	2.5	1.6
Digestibility of dry matter, %	81	58
Rumen total volatile fatty acids, meq/dl	11	5
Partition of rumen VFA, molar %		
Acetic	47	74
Propionic	31	19
Butyric	18	7
Valeric and higher	4	--
Rumen pH	5.9	7.4
Plasma total VFA, mg/dl	0.9	1.3
Blood glucose, mg/dl	93	56
N-retention, g/d	31	4
Live weight gain, kg/d	0.65	0.19

[a]From Stobo et al (26)

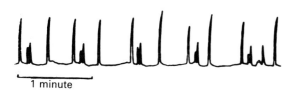

Figure 4-30. Pressure changes in the reticulum of the young calf showing that regurgitation (longest spikes) sometimes occurs without a followup of the usual biphasic reticular contraction. Courtesy of T. Asai. Excerpted from reference 3.

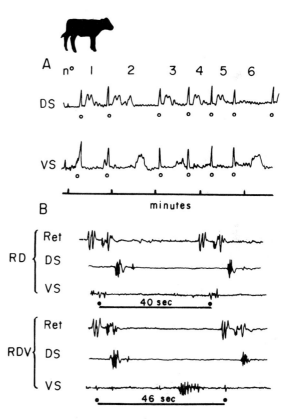

Figure 4-31. Effect of rumination without regurgitation of solid material on the rumen motility patterns of 3-wk-old fed calves in which the rumen is separated from the reticulum since 10 d. Above, ruminal (dorsal and ventral sac) pressure changes during 6 regurgitatory efforts indicated by dots (●). Cycles 1, 3, 4 and 5 only involve the dorsal sac. Cycles 2 and 6 involve the ventral sac. Below, electromyograms corresponding to a cycle without (RD) and with (RDV) ventral contractions. From Ruckebusch and Candau (21).

84

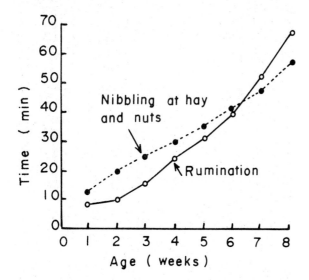

Figure 4-32. The amount of time spent in ruminating or nibbling at solid food during a 6-h period. Graph is based on pooled data from 9 lambs observed over a period of 8 weeks. Courtesy of D.B. Stephens. Excerpted from reference 3.

Intrinsic Versus Extrinsic Contractions

The extrinsic contractions of the forestomach are essential for mixing and for aboral propulsion of the contents. Their rate, form and amplitude are the consequence of central nervous system activity (CNS), reflexly modified by sensory inputs largely from the alimentary tract itself (*vagovagal reflex*). Any husbandry practices or clinical conditions which affect either the general level of CNS or the volume, texture and composition of the gut contents will modify extrinsic contractions and may lead to digestive dysfunctions.

The sectioning of one vagus nerve does not interfere with contraction because the contralateral rate circuit is still operating. Severing both vagi abolish the contractions as when a ruminant is simply anesthetized. However, after 1-2 weeks, large group discharges and generalized contractions in the reticulo-rumen develop in chronically vagotomized sheep (Fig. 4-33). This intrinsic activity is recorded as group discharges during the intervals of phasic contractions and their density is more important in the reticulum than in the rumen. The frequency of the discharge varies according to the ruminal volume; the group discharges are absent throughout the reticulo-rumen at volume below 0.5 to 3 ℓ in a 50-kg

sheep and reappear when the rumen volume is raised again above the volume threshold. The consistent relationship, after vagotomy, between either the frequency or the number of the series of discharges and the ruminal volume suggests a neural integrated activity at the myenteric plexus level, i.e., the enteric nervous system (ENS). Atropine (0.1 mg/kg) and hexamethonium (2 mg/kg), as well as cold (30° vs 37°C) or VFA, abolish this local activity. Warmed 0.2 M-acetic, propionic or butyric acids, buffered to pH 4.0, rapidly annul the group discharges over the whole reticulo-rumen. The inhibition is more rapid (3 min) for butyric and propionic acids than for acetic acid (7-17 min).

The functional organization of the gastric centers located in the medulla (dorsal vagal motor nucleus) may be simplified as follows. The vagus nerve conducts most of the afferent activity from the stomach to the gastric centers. The splanchnic nerve mediates part of the inhibitory effect of moderate abomasal distension on motility of the reticulo-rumen. The abomasum may have a net inhibitory influence on motility of the reticulo-rumen although it is not yet clear whether this accounts for part of the increased rate of reticulo-ruminal contractions arising from differentation.

The dorsal and ventral abdominal vagi nerves both contribute fibers to the right and the left cervical vagi with afferent fibers for the eructation and regurgitation reflexes

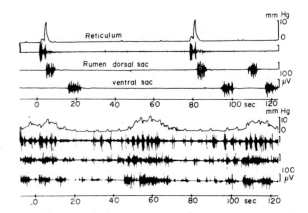

Figure 4-33. Extrinsic vs intrinsic motor activity of the reticulum (intraluminal pressure and electrical activity) and the dorsal (DS) and ventral sac (VS) of the rumen as seen 12 d after vagotomy. From Ruckebusch et al (24).

present mainly in the dorsal and ventral abdominal vagi, respectively. The mechanism controlling the frequency of contractions in different regions of the reticulo-rumen is unknown, except the suggestion of a medullary pattern generator together with types B and C interneurons to constitute a rate circuit (see Fig. 4-27).

The primary contractions continue when the reticulo-rumen of a conscious animal is emptied of digesta even though the stimulatory input into the center from the in-series tension receptors in those organs is probably markedly reduced (see Table 4-3). One must therefore postulate a strong net excitatory drive on the rate, form and amplitude circuits of gastric centers arising from within the higher nervous activity.

The role of the ENS in the reticulo-rumen is presumably similar to the regular discharges in the myenteric plexus of the small intestine, which occur every 6 sec and are abolished at 30°C. The afferent discharge in some reticulo-ruminal vagal fibers, which is phasic at intervals of 4-10 sec, resembles the slowly adapting mechanoreceptors located in the muscle layer and coincides with the intrinsic contractions recorded from strips of reticular and ruminal muscle. In the chronically vagotomized reticulo-rumen, this intrinsic activity consists of a rhythmic series of contractions, and each period of activity is separated by a quiescent period. The level of intrinsic reticulo-ruminal motility of chronically vagotomized sheep is regulated by the degree of reticulo-ruminal distension and, like the CNS-controlled motility of the vagus-intact sheep, it is inhibited by high concentrations of VFA. The regular fluctuations of the resting membrane potential, and hence of muscle excitability, which are seen as minute rhythms (or slow waves when the longitudinal muscle layer is well developed) may correspond to an inhibition of the ENS by subclinical hypocalcemia.

It is also of interest that inflation of the dorsal sac (above the level of the rumen fluid) produces a local increase in discharge frequency in vagotomized sheep. Figure 4-34 is presented as an attempt to represent the interactions between the CNS and the ENS and, thus, the possible causes of ruminal stasis, e.g., anesthesia for CNS, ground and pelleted diet for lack of excitatory inputs, abomasal

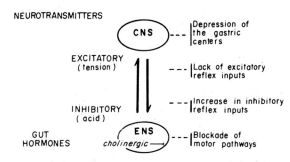

Figure 4-34. Schematic representation of the central (CNS) and the enteric nervous system (ENS) involved in the control of reticulo-ruminal movements. Causes of ruminal stasis are given on the right.

distension for inhibitory inputs and hypocalcemia for blockage of motor pathways.

RUMINATION

The phenomenon of "chewing the cud" or rechewing rumen contents ingested at some earlier time is one of the features most characteristic of ruminant animals. Rumination involves regurgitation of ingesta from the reticulo-rumen and remastication of the solids accompanied by re-insalivation and reswallowing of the bolus. The interest in feeding cattle solely on fibrous diets has reinforced attention on the degree of comminution obtained during eating and rumination, i.e., chewing efficiency and on the control mechanisms, i.e., the CNS response to peripheral stimulation of the reticulo-rumen (RR) by the ingesta.

Mechanics

Regurgitation of digesta is associated with an extra-reticular contraction that precedes the usual biphasic contraction. This contraction results in a marked increase in fluid pressures in the cardial area by lifting the floor of the reticulum about half the distance between its relaxed position and the cardia. Accompanying the reticular contraction, in most cases, is an inspiratory effort of greater volume than usual due to a sharp contraction of the diaphragm. The negative pressure developed in the trachea indicates that the glottis must be closed to create the negative pressure. The digesta regurgitated is largely derived from contents that were in the cavity of the relaxed reticulum. They are not necessarily the coarsest in the reticulo-rumen. The "traffic" in the esophagus is complex and must be taken into account when collecting boli for studying the process. Cephalad (upward) traffic includes the regurgitated digesta bolus and eructed gas if erucatation occurs. Caudad (downward) traffic includes excess regurgitated digesta swallowed immediately after the mount is filled (tail), intermediary swallows of partially-ruminated digesta, and the final swallow of fully-ruminated digesta. The effectiveness of chewing during ruminating is at least as great as chewing during eating, the coarsest particles (those obtained on a 4 mm sieve) being eliminated or much reduced in numbers (Fig. 4-35).

Movement of digesta from the distal portion of the esophagus to the mouth is accomplished by a rapid antiperistaltic contraction apparently possible due to the fact that esophageal muscle in ruminants is striated. Rapid contraction would also be facilitated by the physical nature of the regurgitated material, which is a semi-fluid or slurry. In contrast, normal swallowing is much slower. Opening of the cardia during regurgitation and its closure at the end of swallowing depend upon action of the same, but quantitatively different, esophageal muscle layers.

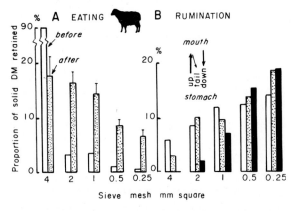

Figure 4-35. Comminution of feed during eating (A) and rumination (B) of chaffed luzerne in sheep with esophageal fistula. Percentage of particles of size indicated in the regurgitated material (up), that immediately swallowed (tail) and the masticated bolus (down). Courtesy of C.S.W. Reid (15).

Fate of Swallowed Ruminated Boli

Ruminated digesta, when returned to the RR, are retained there for a time; it does not immediately pass to the omasum. The ruminated bolus is deposited in the dorsal part of the cranial sac of the rumen. The next reticulum contraction then sweeps it caudally over the cranial pillar. Sometimes the remains of several boli can be seen clustered under the cranial pillar in the ventral rumen. Ruminated boli break up more readily than do boli swallowed during eating.

In the relatively liquid contents of the reticulum, particles of higher specific gravity tend to sink to the bottom while particles of lower specific gravity and coarser particles remain floating in the dorsal region of the organ. Thus, they do not flow out of the reticulum through the reticulo-omasal orifice (ROO) at the height of the second contraction phase.

Particulate matter that will pass through a 1 mm sieve is able to pass rapidly out of the rumen in sheep, whereas coarser material is retained. Comparison of particle size spectra in contents taken from the different compartments of the stomach indicates that the site of discrimination lies between the reticulum and the omasum, for reticular contents are similar to rumen contents and omasal to abomasal contents. This is true for all diets examined, whether dry or fresh, whether the animals are grazing or stall-fed. Selection of particles for passage does not appear to be by straining. According to Reid (15), the selection is more likely achieved by a combination of three factors: the dynamics of the contraction of the reticulum, the anatomical changes of the reticular lining during the contraction, and factors facilitating the presence of appropriate particles in the pole of the reticulum. When the reticulum is relaxed, the 'cells' of the mucosal honeycomb are open, the ridges separating them low; but when the reticulum contracts, the cells are greatly reduced in size and the ridges are raised and prominent. As the contraction continues a system of walls and gutters forms, radiating in towards the reticular groove and the reticulo-omasal orifice. The gutters appear to allow liquid to flow freely along their length. This hypothesis proposes that, during the vigorous contraction of the reticulum, particles along-side the lining are trapped in the honeycomb by inertia and then, when the contraction is reaching its peak, travel along the gutters to the groove and the orifice. Whether or not they pass through will then be determined by the degree of opening of the orifice and the pressure gradient across it.

Time Spent Ruminating

The urge to ruminate is rather strong and the time spent ruminating for a given animal and texture of food related to the amount of intake. For example, in a sheep eating 400-600 g of hay per 24 h, the time spent ruminating reaches 327-409 min, corresponding closely to the number of boli (327-373) chewed at the rate of 43-50 chews per min. If the hay intake is restricted to 200 g/24 h, the time spent ruminating averages 210 min/24 h, corresponding to 225 boli slowly chewed at 40 movements/min. In contrast, when the intake is increased fourfold (800 g), the time spent ruminating is doubled (451 min/24 h), corresponding to 404 boli chewed at the rate of 52 movements/min.

Data on sheep indicate that there may be many periods of rumination when animals were fed concentrate and hay. These periods may range from ca. 30 sec to 2 h, but half or more where shorter than 30 min. When fed 1X daily, sheep had from 9 to 18 rumination periods/d; when fed frequently, the number ranged from 12 to 35; mean values were on the order of 14 for those fed 1X and ca. 18 for those fed frequently. Other studies in sheep (see Ch. 5) indicate that sheep will spend about 8-9 h/d in rumination, the amount being affected by a number of different variables.

With dairy cows on a variety of different roughages, Balch and Campling (2) reported from 11 to 21 periods/d, and found mean values to be 15, 16 and 16 in heifers, pregnant cows and lactating cows, respectively, fed roughage or roughage and concentrates. In experiments where reticular contractions were measured (assuming that each extra contraction produced a bolus) the mean values during rumination were 448/d in cows fed ca. 10 lb of straw, 686 in cows fed 22 lb of hay; 635 in cows fed 21 lb of hay, 438 in those fed 29 lb of dried grass, and 109 in those fed 20 lb of concentrates (2).

A circadian distribution of the periods of ruminating in stall-fed animals is obvious and their occurrence at night is favored by drowsiness. Calves spend ca. 120 min during the day and ca. 180 min at night. Data from several sources indicate that cattle may spend from 35 to 80 min in ruminating time/kg of roughage consumed with 2/3 of them during night-time (3). Figure 4-36 illustrates the patterns of jaw movements in a cow during rumination and when asleep. Deep sleep episodes, during which motility ceases, occur frequently at the end of a period of rumination when the animal is recumbent (19). It is noteworthy that the overall activity of the reticulo-rumen is only slightly increased during rumination in the bison (as in the cow) compared to resting (Fig. 4-37). In fact, ruminating like resting are both postprandial behaviors in which drowsiness or even sleep and chewing the cud are intermingled (19).

The circadian pattern of both grazing and rumination is altered when it is necessary to adjust for climatic conditions, and to maintain grazing time and food intake. The

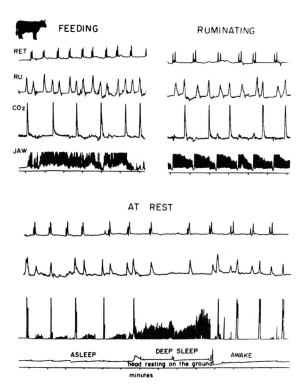

Figure 4-36. Reticulo-rumen motility patterns and eructation detected as peaks of CO_2 in the trachea in a cow during feeding, rumination and falling asleep when at rest. From Ruckebusch (19).

88

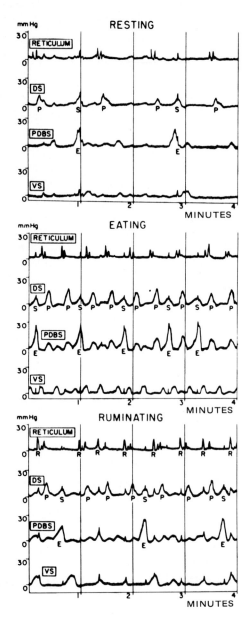

Figure 4-37. Reticulo-rumen activity of the bison while resting, eating and ruminating. Note the increased activity during eating, contractions occurring at 2-3X the rate while eating as while resting. Contractions during rumination are also accelerated, and the extra-reticular contraction associated with regurgitation is quite evident in the lower recording. Courtesy of H.E. Dziuk, Univ. of Minnesota. Excerpted from Church (3).

rumination time of sheep is significantly reduced as pasture availability declines, but in contrast with cattle, the ratio of eating time: ruminating time does not decrease when grazing on small plots. The decreased ratio observed in cattle is probably linked to their

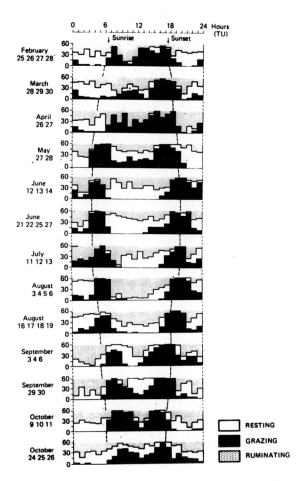

Figure 4-38. Circadian pattern of maintenance activities in sheep. Black area, grazing; dotted area, ruminating in Lacaune breed (Causses du Larzac) outside from March to November. From Leclerc (10).

reduced diet selection resulting in an intake of forage of lower digestibility and higher fiber contents. When cows are allowed to graze only on a small area (5,000 m²) after coming from a larger area (30,000 m²), the time spent grazing (25.9% of 24 h) decreases (30.5% on the larger area) but not rumination (22.9% vs 21.8%). Nevertheless, the circadian pattern of two major periods of grazing during daytime has a tendency to disappear and thus the subsequent periods of rumination. Finally, the time spent ruminating remains relatively constant in relation with the dry matter intake and is distributed throughout the year as a maintenance activity (Fig. 4-38).

Factors Influencing Rumination

All the factors stimulating or inhibiting rumination have not been clearly defined.

One sensory modality, tactile stimulation, appears appropriate to monitoring the physical breakdown of feed. Tactile stimulation of the reticular and ruminal epithelium is a powerful stimulus, and stimulation is still most effective when applied to the reticulo-rumen fold. According to Reid (15) the cranial-caudal pillar complex acts as a site for monitoring the amount and nature of the ruminal digesta and thus the duration of rumination.

Eating results in a sharp increase in the frequency and vigor of pillar contractions. The mean displacement of each radioopaque marker during contractions while eating was 75 mm. Changes in the separation of the markers were caused by respiratory or body movements, pillar contractions and by distension of the rumen accumulating feed as a baseline shift; a 60-min meal being associated with a 24% increase in the median distance between the pillars (Fig. 4-39). These observations suggest the receptors in the pillars are

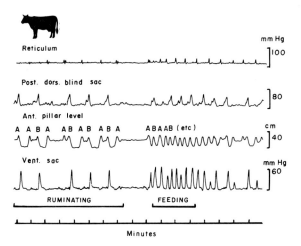

Figure 4-40. Cranial pillar contractions during rumination and feeding (cow). Incomplete A (primary) sequences occurred during rumination (the cranial pillar did not descend fully, and there is no ventral rumen pressure peak); in contrast, the B (secondary) sequences continue to be "normally" associated with a caudal dorsal blind sac contraction and a strong ventral rumen pressure wave. Normal "full" activity occurred during feeding, but there is reversion to the reduced activity after feeding stops. From Reid and Cornwall (16).

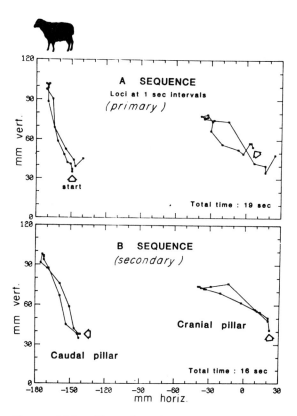

Figure 4-39. Two dimensional recordings (X-ray videofluoroscopy) of the displacement of the cranial and caudal pillars during a primary (A) sequence and a secondary (B) sequence of contractions (sheep). From Reid (15).

well-placed to monitor the ruminal digesta because they form a constriction lying across the bulk of the digesta and account for large displacement during each contraction sequence. Digesta texture (from tactile stimulation afforded by the movement of digesta over the pillar surfaces during contractions), digesta consistency (from the resistance offered to the contracting pillars), and rumen fill (from stretch of the pillar array), are three possible types of sensory information which can be derived from the pillars. Figure 4-40 shows that relative motion of the cranial pillar is completely different during rumination and feeding, thus suggesting a different effectiveness of stimulation of the pillars during the delay required for a fed animal to start to ruminate. Since the lag period following ingestion occurs during a time when tactile stimulation is high at first but decreases to a lower level, it is possible that the reduction of sensory information to central control centers is a prerequisite to initiate the ruminating behavior (15).

By feeding long- vs short-chopped grass silage to sheep (not to cattle), it has been found that the particles in the rumen were longer and more interwoven. As a result the separation and mechanical breakdown of the particles is more difficult, so that transfer of small particles from the dorsal sac into the ventral sac of the rumen and backflow into the cranial sac and reticulum is delayed. Therefore, during the period after food intake, not enough solid food particles are present to stimulate the reflexogenic area for rumination (Fig. 4-41). Consequently, and especially with the long grass silage, the beginning of the rumination activity following a main meal is delayed (longer latency time) and it presents a large number of pseudorumination boli, especially for the first rumination periods during the day. The delayed and less efficient mechanical breakdown of the particles by the pseudorumination activity is a partial explanation of the underlying physiological basis for the lower voluntary intake of long- vs short-chopped grass silage (11).

Mechanisms and Significance

Rumination is centrally mediated as demonstrated by stimulation of the gastric centers and the anterior hypothalamic area (1). Reflex rumination is also induced frequently in dairy cows during milking as they become drowsy. Conditioned reflexes have been obtained in goats by the association of a series of flashes with gentle stroking of the reticular wall (18). However, a high number of associations is required to obtain instantaneous regurgitation at the time of a reticular

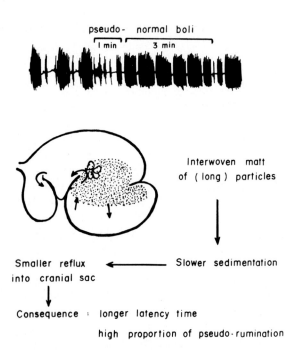

Figure 4-41. Pseudorumination as observed in sheep fed long chopped grass silages. The lack of stimulation of reflexogenic areas because of the accumulation of the solid contents behind the cranial pillar is at the origin of the absence of rumination at the end of a main meal and then of numerous pseudoruminations. From reference 11.

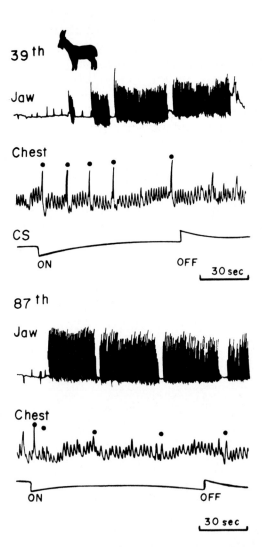

Figure 4-42. Conditioned rumination in the goat. Inspiratory efforts (o) were followed by the regurgitation within 15 sec after the emission of the conditioned stimulus (CS) for 39 associations. The latency was shorter and regurgitation was seen immediately at the emission of the light for 87 associations. From Ruckebusch (18).

contraction (Fig. 4-42). Repetitive intravenous injection of very low doses of adrenaline (3 µg/kg) evokes in both sheep and in cattle an intense salivation followed *only* in sheep by regurgitation. The induced rumination results from the activation of the "gastric centers" by the increased afferent input from the reticular wall stimulated by adrenaline. After 20 to 30 trials, some animals just start to ruminate as soon as a control injection of saline was performed (unpublished observations). The role of an inhibitory opioid-system pathway in the control of rumination in sheep has recently been evidenced on the basis that opiate antagonists like naloxone not only stimulate ruminal motility, but also adrenaline-induced rumination even in animals fed on pellets.

When ruminating behavior cannot be expressed, a very irregular pattern of chewing behavior is brought about to mimic the natural process. For example, in calves with an isolated rumen and fed via an abomasal cannula, pseudorumination occurred as a behavioral drive (Fig. 4-43). The high percentage

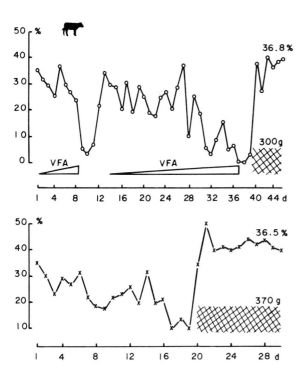

Figure 4-43. Opposite effects of volatile fatty acids infusion in the isolated rumen and its mechanical stimulation by plastic shavings on pseudorumination (% per 24 h) in two 10-d-old calves. From Ruckebusch and Candau (21).

of pseudorumination was reduced by ruminal infusion of increasing amounts of VFA but enhanced by tactile stimulation by indigestible particles of the isolated rumen wall (21), thus suggesting opposite influences on the behavioral development of rumination during the postnatal adaptation to solid food.

Theories on Development of Rumination

Some of the theories which have been put forward to explain rumination are as follows:

(a) The *predator theory* states that the ruminant is an animal subject to attack by predators (large carnivores) and therefore it has to eat rapidly without adequate chewing. To compensate for this it rechews the food thoroughly when it rests in a safe place. The tacit assumption that the resting ruminant is safer from attack than when it is grazing is unwarranted. A wakeful active flock or herd are safer from predators when they are grazing because of their readiness to respond on instructions from their own senses. Although the theory is not convincing, it must be remembered that drowsiness and rumination are associated and that deep sleep occurs in the recumbent animal at the end of a period of rumination.

(b) Another possibility which has been put forward is the increased *passage of reticulo-rumen contents* into the omasum. The extra-reticular contraction, the increased motility, the possible function of the reticular groove in swallowing remasticated food or the supply of finely-divided ingesta could be evoked. However, rechewed food is not passed directly via the reticular groove into the omaso-abomasum (15) and the disappearance of material from the reticulo-rumen may be increased during eating but not rumination.

(c) That the most important function of rumination is to *break down material* in the rumen which otherwise would remain, occupy useful space and hinder food intake and that rumination is mainly responsible for the disintegration of coarse material in the rumen, is fairly obvious. Many experiments of grinding food, restriction of chewing by means of a muzzle or morphine administration indicated that the rate at which roughage can be broken down is related to the voluntary intake of that roughage and the effect of communion of food is to accelerate emptying of the rumen, thus permitting greater feed intake.

Adequate preliminary chewing when the food is first eaten could be a simpler and biologically more reasonable method of ensuring the breakdown of ingesta for free passage in the gut (as in equids) without requiring a special mechanism. Indeed, food is masticated to a finer state by animals that have had their rumen surgically removed. It might be expected, also, that stimulation increases digestibility, particularly in the case of coarse fodder where bacterial attack will be facilitated by increasing the surface area of the food and by removing physical barriers to the release of nutrients. On the other hand, if rumination results in a greater intake and outflow of food from the rumen at a low energy cost, the loss of digestibility will be unimportant when compared with the effect upon the total availability of nutrients. When one considers that the ruminating animal is recumbent, drowsy and chewing material which has been softened and partly broken down in the rumen, the development of rumination appears as an elegant process to maximize the intake of fibrous diets.

ERUCTATION

Eructation is the mechanism whereby the ruminant animal belches the large quantities of gas produced in the forestomach as a result of microbial fermentation. During periods of peak gas production (30 min to 2 h after feeding), gas production may reach high values. Steers fed on alfalfa green chop produced 12-27 ℓ/min by means of 3-17 eructations/min.

Eructation is associated with secondary rumen contractions for the most part in cattle. In sheep, radiographic studies showed that the biphasic contractions of the reticulum clear the cardial area of much of the ingesta. The cranial pillar remains in a contracted state, acting as a dam restraining the ingesta from filling the reticulum. These events allow rumen gas to be forced into the cardial area.

The sequence of events involved in eructation has been described by Rousseau (17). As shown in Fig. 4-44, eructation occurs in association with different forms of esophageal activity: a filling phase, an eructation contraction and a secondary or clearing contraction. The clearing contraction is the term recently

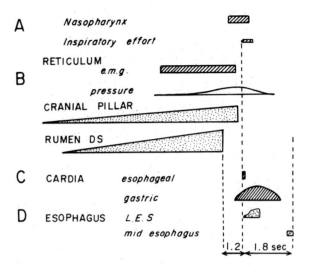

Figure 4-44. Sequence of events involved in eructation. A corresponds to the closure of the nasopharynx with slight inspiratory effort occurring 1.2 sec after the secondary contraction of the rumen dorsal sac and at the time of a simultaneous increase in pressure by the reticulum and the cranial pillar (B). The esophageal and gastric components of the LES open the cardia (C). Response in the mid-esophagus occurred 1.8 sec after the LES response (D). From Rousseau (17).

applied to caudally progressing esophageal contractions, which happen independently of buccopharyngeal movements of swallowing.

Measurement

In cows equipped with face masks and tracheal cannulas, Dougherty et al (6) found that 3-7X as much gas was expelled through the trachea as through the face mask; from 0.5-33% of eructated gas escaped by mouth or nose, the remainder being respired from the trachea.

Eructation is a silent process in ruminants as contrasted to belching in some humans. This, no doubt, is a protective mechanism which would help these animals avoid predators during quiet periods or rumination while at rest (3). The amount of gas expelled can be easily collected by inserting a tube into the upper part of the trachea (Fig. 4-45).

Eructated gases enter the trachea at pressures approximating those occurring in the esophagus during the expulsive phase of eructation and penetrate deeply into the lungs. Elevation in systemic arterial CO_2 values occur with eructation of this gas. That this

93

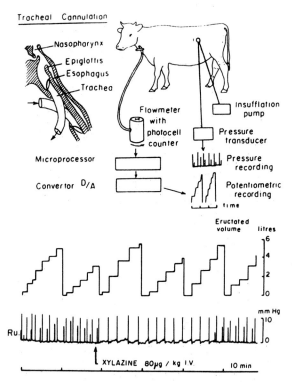

Figure 4-45. Measurement of gas expulsion in cattle fitted with a tracheal tube and rumen cannula. An X siliastic tube is inserted in the trachea and gas (N_2 + CO_2) is maintained in the rumen just above the resting pressure by insufflation. The volume of gas expelled at each secondary contraction is recorded via a flowmeter with a zero-setting at 10-min intervals. The tracings show that eructation was not impaired during blockage of the primary ruminal contractions by the intravenous injection of a low dose of xylazine (Rompun) (11).

increase in arterial CO_2 is not due to the reflex activation of pulmonary arteriovenous shunts is indicated by the fact that arterial levels greatly exceed the CO_2 content of simultaneously collected venous blood samples (6).

That the pulmonary system provides a route of absorption of eructated gas is further substantiated by the finding that various gases, including CO_2, CO, H_2S, and O_2, after being placed in the rumen, are more readily capable of causing changes either in blood gas levels or in the physiologic activity of the animal when the trachea is patent and capable of receiving these gases during eructation (6).

Inflation of the rumen with gas stimulates the eructation reflex and eructation is inhibited when an area around the cardia is covered with ingesta, water, foam or mineral oil. Dougherty's work indicates that, in sheep, the area around the cardia is kept free of ingesta by strong contractions of the reticulo-ruminal fold and the cranial pillar. In cattle too, the cranial pillar may assume the major role in clearing the cardia.

Comparison of the eructation and rumination mechanisms indicates that they are stimulated in different ways. Eructation is stimulated by gas pressure in the rumen, whereas rumination is stimulated by tactile and chemical means.

Insufflation of the rumen with gas increases the incidence of secondary rumen contractions in conscious sheep and the occurrence of reticular contractions has an inhibitory effect on secondary ruminal contractions, especially those of the ventral sac and the ventral blind sac (23). The increase in resting intraruminal pressure results in a linear increase in primary contraction frequency at pressures below 10 cm H_2O. Resting intraruminal pressures exceeding 10 cm H_2O has a suppressing effect on primary contraction frequency which is greater when the insufflating gas contains no CO_2 than when CO_2 is present. Secondary contraction frequency is found to increase linearly with all gases and pressure levels tested.

Species Differences

The fact that both central and peripheral mechanisms are involved in eructation suggests possible species differences in their interplay. Comparison of the effects on rumen distension of opiate antagonists like naloxone methylnaloxone (which did not cross the blood brain-barrier) and of neuroleptanalgesics (like xylazine or detomidine) shows that (a) belching is linked to the occurrence of secondary ruminal contractions (the lower their frequency, the lower the volume eructated) in cattle. In contrast, belching also occurs during primary cycles of reticulo-ruminal contractions in sheep, hence a higher volume of gas eructated during rumination (Fig. 4-46). (b) The enhancement by increased intraruminal pressures concerns both primary and secondary cycles without changes in the ratio in cattle. Ruminal distension in sheep evokes an increase in its own frequency with a ratio of 1:2 towards 1:3. (c) Peripheral inhibition of

94

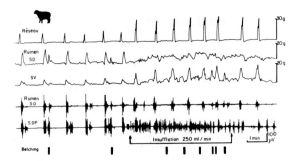

Figure 4-46. Motor effects of an acute distension of the rumen by air in sheep. Recordings are from strain-gauge force transducer on the rumen dorsal (SD) and ventral sac (SV) and electrodes on the rumen dorsal sac (SD) and blind sac (SDP). Note the increase in reticulo-rumen cycles and that belching occurs at the time of the reticular contractions concomitant with those of the ventral sac. The electrical activity of the rumen dorsal blind sac is continuous.

motility is a major factor of bloating in cattle as indicated by the suppression of primary cycles of contractions by opiates or neuroleptics without causing bloating. Accordingly, methylnaloxone is as efficient as naloxone in the alleviation of bloat in cattle. In contrast, in sheep, central inhibition of motility is also involved, hence bloating after treatment with opiates or xylazine which block the primary reticulo-ruminal cycles. Accordingly, naloxone is more efficient than methylnaloxone in alleviation of free-gas bloat.

However, in both species, relief of free-gas bloat by passing a nasogastric tube through the lower esophageal sphincter (LES), incriminates this structure as a factor involved in the elimination of ruminal gas and where adrenergic, cholinergic, serotonergic and possibly substance P receptors are present. The specific role of the LES tone is also assessed by the absence of any improvement in bloating when the frequency and amplitude of reticulo-ruminal contractions are stimulated by cholinergic agents like carbachol, bethanechol or pilocarpine. Conversely, during hypomotility induced by hypocalcemia, the volume of gas expelled can be increased by treatment with 5-HT$_2$ antagonists without major changes in the magnitude of contractions (11).

Control of the LES

The unitary activity of sensory vagal neurons, which was recorded from the nodose ganglion of anesthetized sheep and originating from the lower esophageal sphincter (LES), belongs to the slow adapting type of receptors. Numerous mechanoreceptors, which are localized in the LES, show a spontaneous activity consisting of tonic discharge due to a slight longitudinal tension and are inhibited before the passage of the bolus. The absence of the inhibition of the LES without motility changes leads to transient free-gas bloating as seen 60 min postprandially in cattle receiving alfalfa tops. Frothy bloat, which is a major cause of death of stocker cattle grazed on winter wheat pastures, is not accompanied by major changes in ruminal motility. Because the cardiac orifice contracts in a tetanic manner when exposed to the wheat pasture rumen fluid, it is possible that the musculature associated with the LES might contract spasmodically and hamper eructation following exposure to certain compounds of rumen ingesta origin.

On the other hand, because esophageal pressures are a means of indirect estimation of pleural pressure, the pleural pressure could be one of the factors influencing the LES pressure. Increase in pleural pressure, e.g., in pneumonia, may result in an increase of LES pressure. Such mechanism could be involved in chronic tympany, frequently observed in animals suffering from pneumonia.

Relaxation of the LES by 5-HT$_2$ antagonists has been observed during ruminal distension in both sheep and cattle. The insufflation of N$_2$ in the rumen slightly increases its cyclical activity, hence the increased volume of eructated gas from 3.7 to 6.2 ℓ/10 min. After pretreatment with ritanserin (0.1 mg/kg BW), the volume of eructated gas is further increased from 10 to 30 min after its injection. In this case the volume of each bolus of gas expelled is increased rather than the rate of eructation. Similar effects were observed after administration of other 5-HT$_2$ antagonists, suggesting that 5-HT$_2$ receptors play a major direct or indirect role in the control of LES pressure. Another possibility of action may be the blockage of substance P, the companion peptide of 5-HT.

Finally, the necessary elimination of gas in ruminants allows a varied assortment of gases to be presented to the lungs, absorbed into the blood and appear in the milk. Several aspects of the motor patterns of the LES, which seem to be impaired in both induced or natural bloat, are poorly known.

ABOMASAL MOTOR ACTIVITY

In terms of motility, the abomasum has been largely ignored in both preruminant and ruminant stages. This is so despite its role of paramount importance during the digestion of milk or milk substitute diets in young animals, and in the adult when gastric emptying is the prerequisite for the passage of solids out the reticulo-rumen and a shorter retention time of ruminal contents.

Receptive Relaxation

At least during the first 3-4 months of life, calves given milk or milk substitute diets ad libitum have little desire to eat dry food, provided that the milk substitute has been formulated to supply sufficient of all essential nutrients during this period. In one study the daily intake of concentrates and hay was 0.11 and 0.08 kg, respectively. Calves have been reared to about 350 kg live weight as preruminant animals on diets based on milk protein. When non-milk proteins are used above 80 kg, a depression in appetite limits the weight that can be achieved with a high efficiency of food conversion.

Coagulation of milk occurs within 3-4 min after ingestion, forming a clot of casein together with the entrapped fat so that only whey containing lactose and whey protein pass into the duodenum. The motor activity of the abomasum consists (during about 50% of the recording time) of contractions at a frequency of 4 to 6/min which are detected on the antrum as spike bursts superimposed on permanent slow waves and as only spike bursts on the fundus (5). In addition, there are periods of inactivity when migrating motor complexes (MMC) are generated at the gastroduodenal junction (20).

True pressure variations are difficult to assess from the abomasum without a number of suitable manometers, and often implanted strain gauges or electrodes are used to record the force generated by alimentary tract muscle as a substitute for pressure measurement. A notable advance was achieved when large restrictive electrodes were replaced by

fine wires which could be sewn into the gut wall, and employed to record electromyograms (EMG) from multiple sites. Although recording flow and intragastric volume changes in the abomasum is difficult because of reflux, absorption, secretion and non-linear flow, it appears that milk intake is accompanied by an immediate gastric relaxation as an inhibition of the activity of the fundic part of the stomach. This relaxation is prolonged during about one hour on the greater curvature, whereas the antral pump becomes very active (Fig. 4-47). According to observations made in other species, the fundus relaxation is elicited by a low degree of antral distension as a vago-vagal relaxatory reflex. This relaxation

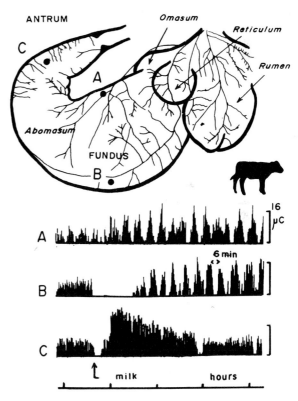

Figure 4-47. Relative size of the different parts of the stomach in the newborn calf (top) and effects of milk-feeding on the motility recorded as the electromyogram integrated at 20-sec intervals of the fundic and antral parts of the abomasum 5 d later. Note the reduction of the activity along the greater curvature at the sight and ingestion of milk. This indication of a relaxation of the fundus persisted during about 1 h, whereas the antrum exhibited the controlled force necessary to the delivery of chyme to the duodenum. From Dardillat and Ruckebusch (5).

96

is different from the reflex adrenergic inhibition of gastric motility also elicited from the gastric antrum for a high degree of distension.

Gastric Emptying

In conscious, minimally restrained calves fitted with a permanent cannula (so that the abomasum can be washed clean for the introduction of a test meal and using phenol red as a non-absorbable marker to determine abomasal volume), the basic pattern of emptying is exponential in character for most of the period of evacuation as it is in other species.

The introduction of additional re-entrant duodenal cannulas, 5 cm from the pylorus, provides a preparation whereby it is possible to infuse the duodenum via the distal cannula, and to collect the abomasal effluent from the proximal arm of the cannula. The following points were confirmed: (a) on infusion into the duodenum, isotonic solutions of NaCl and $NaHCO_3$ increase abomasal emptying, bicarbonate being the more effective stimulus; (b) dilute HCl inhibits emptying; (c) hypertonic solutions, including disaccharides and monosaccharides, inhibit gastric emptying; (d) ammonium chloride, urea, lactose and acetic acid have little effect on abomasal emptying.

Simultaneous recording of abomasal electromyogram and measurement of gastric emptying showed a causal association between the administration of gastrin and reduction in gastric emptying. Gastrin appears to exert its effects directly on mechanisms governing motility and not indirectly, for example, by stimulation of acid secretion. This is suggested by the rapid onset of effects, the close temporal association between the inhibition of motility and gastrin infusions as well as the rapid return of electrical activity and resumption of gastric emptying. In contrast, the late inhibition of gastric motility and emptying due to duodenal acidification, which persists after sectioning of the vagus and splanchnic nerves, seems related to the release of somatostatin..

The hierarchical order of factors affecting gastric outflow is: distension of the abomasum > osmolality > pH of the chyme > products (fat and protein) entering the duodenum. *Distension* is the main intragastric stimulus for emptying the abomasum. The volume of gushes of digesta through the pylorus is the result of the antral pump, with a positive correlation between stroke volume and gastric volume. The periodicity of the antral gushes is relatively constant and closely related to the antral contractions (25). The pattern of emptying is a function of the presence or not of the migrating motor complexes (MMCs) initiated at the gastroduodenal junction—the disruption of the MMC pattern occurring only for large meals (Fig. 4-48). During the first 4 weeks of life, milk diets with polyethylene glycol as a whey marker are evacuated within 3 h. Thus, the initial phase of gastric digestion

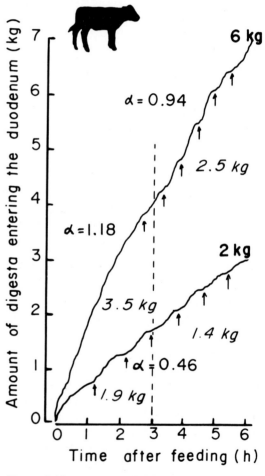

Figure 4-48. Amount of chyme delivered to the duodenum in the milk-fed calf after a small (2 kg) and large (6 kg) meal. The flow is stopped (↑) when the motor activity of the antrum shows periods of inactivity at the initiation of MMC at hourly intervals. This cyclical activity is not disrupted by a small meal, hence the 6 steps (arrows) during the outflow of 3.3 kg in 6 h. In contrast, the MMC pattern is disrupted, hence the continuous outflow of 3.5 kg during the first 3 h for the large meal. From Sissons (25).

is dominated by distension and the constant fractional rate of emptying with increased volume appears to be a property of the stomach, the differences that later occur being a function of variation in response to duodenal receptors.

After distension of the abomasum, *osmolality and pH* of the chyme in the duodenum appear to be the important factors in controlling gastric emptying in the calf. At 300 mosmoles/kg, duodenal infusions with isotonic NaCl over a pH range of 2.0 to 12.0 do not alter the high level of gastric emptying. Adopting the test meal techniques used in man, it was shown that hypertonic solutions of NaCl, glucose and $NaHCO_3$ inhibit emptying as well as gastric acid production. Whereas duodenal infusions of NaCl solution adjusted to pH 8 to 12 with NaOH do not modify the motility and the rate of gastric emptying of this pH range, the gastric electromyogram and emptying are inhibited during the duodenal (but not abomasal) infusion of fluid of low pH. It is noteworthy that duodenal acidification strongly stimulates locally the duodenal motor activity which thus may stop indirectly the gastric outflow like at the onset of an MMC. Accordingly, acidified milk substitutes (pH 4.3 to 5.5) have been introduced with the intention of improving keeping quality so that ad libitum systems of group feeding can be used. The introduction of acidified saline into the abomasum down to pH 2 did not affect gastric emptying, acid, or pepsinogen secretion compared with a saline meal. Abomasal acid secretion was inhibited only at pH 1.2 as was gastric EMG, with minor effects on gastric emptying; duodenal motility was not increased. This finding is in contrast to the effect of acidity in the duodenum, when abomasal emptying, motility and acid secretion are all reduced significantly, suggesting a relatively minor direct role of duodenal acidification in the calf.

Motor Patterns

The usual procedure adopted for obtaining information on the gastric functions has involved the use of animals prepared with fistulas and re-entrant cannulas allowing the collection (and return) of all digesta flowing from the exit cannula (Fig. 4-49) as well as the rate of passage of stained particles. Continuous gastric secretion in adult ruminants

Figure 4-49. Upper. Steer with abomasal (lower) and intestinal cannulas. This type of cannula allows samples to be taken readily, yet does not interfere greatly with digesta passage if implaced properly. Photo courtesy of C.O. Little. Lower. A cow with a re-entrant cannula. This type may tend to restrict digesta passage, but is more useful for arriving at quantitative estimates of digesta passage (3).

was confirmed using sheep fitted with fundic pouches and with both antral and fundic pouches. Secretion from fundic pouches is continuous and is reduced in volume and acidity, as is pepsin output, by resection of the antral pouches. Teasing with food and feeding stimulates fundic acid and pepsin secretion in animals with antral pouches before and after antrectomy. Interestingly, antrectomy reduces the total acid output of the fundic pouches and may be followed by an increased food intake. All the studies on

98

the outflow of digesta from the ovine abomasum measured with markers like chromic
oxide-impregnated paper have shown a direct
relationship between abomasal volume and
outflow, with the level of food intake and the
motility index of the gastric body. For example, the calculated mean slope for flow
(ml/h) and volume (ml) were 0.33 ± 0.07 and
0.34 ± 0.05 (g/d food intake of a pelleted diet
containing 50% barley straw). The duodenal
flow and abomasal motility for a similar level
of food intake decreases as the particle sizes
decrease from 6.5 to 1.4 mm because of the
increased rumination and quantity of saliva
caused by diets with 6.5 mm particle size.

The increased motor activity resulting in a
higher abomasal outflow for high level of
food intake or large particle size has been
assessed by the measurement of the patterns
of contractions by electromyography and
strain-gauge force transducers in relation with
the flow rate evaluated by magnetic flowmeter on the duodenal bulb (see Fig. 4-54).
In both cattle and sheep, 70-80% of the antral
slow waves (5-6/mn) are superimposed with
spike bursts. In cattle, half of them pass
aborally to the duodenal bulb which is also
the site of retrograde contractions starting at
the level of the entrance of the bile duct. In
sheep, nearly all the contractions start nearby
the pylorus at short intervals (50-70 sec) and
are propagated aborally corresponding to a
bolus of chyme of 5-6 ml.

However, continuous recording of motility
patterns of the antrum showed the existence
of 15 to 18 periods of antral inactivity and
absence of flow per 24 h, each of them lasting
5 to 10 min. Fig. 4-50 (corresponding to the
mechanical activity of the gastroduodenal
junction) shows that periodic antral inhibition
coincides with the development of a series of
contractions on the gastroduodenal junction
and lasts during the subsequent period of
quiescence. These series of contractions are
transformed on the duodenum in a phase of
regular spiking activity (RSA) which is preceded by a phase of irregular spiking activity
(ISA) and followed by a phase of no spiking
activity (NSA), propagated along the whole
small intestine, hence the terms of migrating
myoelectric complex (MMC) (see Fig. 4-54).
The RSA phase is also termed activity front.
Thus, the delivery of contents through the
pylorus in the adult ruminant is continuous
but rhythmic due to an inhibition at the time

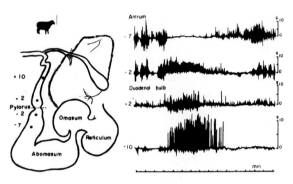

Figure 4-50. Mechanical activity of the gastroduodenal junction in sheep recorded by curved strain-
gauge force transducers fixed on the antrum, 7 and 2
cm before the pylorus, and on the proximal duodenum, at 2 and 10 cm beyond the pylorus. Contractions *in series,* which lasted approximately 4 min on
the duodenal bulb and the pyloric antrum, occurred
almost synchronously with an inhibition of the more
distal part of the antrum. The contractions *in series*
of the duodenal bulb were propagated aborally at a
mean velocity of 8-10 cm per min (11).

of the occurrence of RSA-NSA phases of the
migrating myoelectric complexes on the junction. Stimulation of duodenal motor activity,
via distension, acid and serotonin release
which increase the frequency of RSA-NSA
phases, results in the inhibition of antral
motor activity and delayed gastric emptying.

Functional Disturbances

In both the preruminant and adult states,
the transpyloric outflow occurs as gushes with
periods of no activity and no flow. Abomasal
overfill causes increased rate of abomasal
emptying by reduction of the duration of the
NSA phases. Increased osmolality of the
abomasal contents decreases abomasal emptying and also allows the accumulation of acid
which furthers the inhibition. An important
malfunction which then occurs is the *disposition of gas* (or air) in the abomasum which
accumulates in the abomasal body above the
fluid contents and is voided by eructation.
Excessive air taken as the calf sucks from a
bottle may accumulate in the antrum to prevent liquid efflux.

Some proteins affect the depth of the
villi and growth of enterocytes, which may
in turn affect 5-HT production sufficiently
to influence alimentary tract motility, especially atony by *duodenal ulceration*. Gastric

perforations are located near the pylorus in 2/3 of calves (3-12 mo-old) and 2/3 in the fundic part of the abomasum in more than 1-yr-old animals. The process of ulceration in calves and subsequent antral dysrhythmia and rumen tympany are favored by cold during the winter period (unpublished observations).

Adult sheep, when infected with *Ostertagia circumcincta,* show regression of abomasal mucosa and reduced motility which may be due to the *hypergastrinemia* coincident with the parasitism of the antrum because gastrin levels fall with effective anthelmintic treatment.

There is much suggestive evidence that duodenal infection is at the origin of changes in gut motility, hence abomasal distension. The distension of the abomasum in adult cattle leads to *atony* and displacement to the right side. The pathophysiology of this condition shows a direct causal relationship of abomasal motility with VFA in excess, possibly via a direct action on smooth muscle cells.

Among the excitatory and inhibitory factors regulating gastro-intestinal smooth muscle movements and thus gastric emptying, the cholinergic neurotransmitter increases antral peristalsis and relaxes the pyloric sphincter like the vasoactive intestinal polypeptide (VIP). The duodenal hormones, secretin, cholecystokinin (CCK) and gastric inhibitory polypeptide (GIP), as well as somatostatin (SRIF), have opposite effects. Another neurotransmitter, 5-hydroxytryptamine (5-HT) and its co-release peptide substance P (SP), have powerful stimulant effects on both the antrum and duodenum. Thyrotropin-releasing factor (TRF) and corticotropin releasing factor (CRF) and some endogenous opioid peptides (EOP) first discovered in the brain and subsequently in the gut have similar effects. This dual localization of peptides has given rise to the concept of a *brain-gut axis.* Because some peptides like VIP, SRIF, SP and EOP are secreted down the vagus to the gut, the concept that the vagus nerve is the *peptidergic highway* connecting the brain and the gut has been proposed. Recently, it has been shown that at least three peptides of the brain-gut axis (CCK, TRF and SRIF), which all impair gastric emptying and decrease food intake in sheep (unpublished observations) have opposing central and peripheral actions in the regulation of gastric function. Sympathetic pathways have been proposed to explain how the central action is relayed to the stomach. On this basis, motor disturbances of the abomasum (and related anorexia) represent a critical factor in the ruminant digestive homeostasis.

TRANSPYLORIC FLOW OF DIGESTA

The measurement of the passage of ingesta through the ruminant gastro-intestinal tract (GIT), when considered in relation with the motor patterns of activity, is hampered by the presence of the reticulo-rumen as a mixing pool system. The time of retention of stained particles in this reservoir depends on its volume and turnover rate which may vary with the level of feeding as well as physical form of forage (see Ch. 9). The volume of digesta flowing through the pylorus thus depends upon the transfer of contents from the rumen through the omasum and their further processing at the abomasal level.

Level of Feeding

The amount of time the average feed particle spends in the forestomach depends on the *level of feeding,* but is difficult to determine because of the uncertainty of how long it may stay in the omasum. In sheep which had their rumen surgically removed, the first and final appearances of marker (fuchsin) were 6 h and 6 d after feeding chopped oats, vs 22 h and 19 d with normal sheep. These data indicate that the rumen causes a delay of some 16 h in the initial appearance of the marker. However, the time of maximum excretion occurs on the 2nd and 3rd days in both cases (3), suggesting that the omasal influence seems rather that of sieving particles than retarding their passage onwards.

Nevertheless, the abomasum will be loaded rapidly with high levels of feeding. The mean retention time of hay stained with ^{198}Au in sheep on restricted vs ad libitum feeding decreased from $\sim$44 h to 30 h, indicating a shorter retention time for a higher level of DM intake in the whole gut as in the rumen (see also Table 9-9).

Frequency of Feeding

From a historical point of view, the use of re-entrant duodenal cannulas has been very popular, hence a large number of publications are available. They showed that low pressure beyond the pylorus due to sampling stimulates the abomasal outflow otherwise reduced by the cannulation system. Such problems can be avoided by the use of flowmeters and/or automated total collection from single T-shaped cannulas.

Frequency of feeding has a marked effect on amount of digesta flowing from the abomasum. In sheep fed once daily, the flow rate of ca. 270 ml/h increases to 785 ml/h when fed the same ration three times daily. A greater daily outflow from the abomasum is also found for different rations when fed hourly than when fed once daily, whatever the treatment or the ration. Finally, the same amount of food given in 3 daily meals vs 1 meal induced an increase by 30% in flow of digsta at the postpyloric level, due to the enhanced secretory and motor activity of the abomasum. Increased salivary secretion and rumen motility are also likely. Estimates of flow based either on the indicator method using Cr_2O_3 and lignin concentration or automated total collection in cattle on a diet of all forage vs a 80% sorghum grain diet (4 kg DM/d) were: 76 vs 46 ℓ/d, respectively (Table 4-6). Since DM intakes and DM outflwo were similar, a 55% greater volume of digesta at the postpyloric level of steers fed the forage diet than when fed the grain diet indicates a higher prepyloric dilution rate with the forage diet.

Table 4-6. Average daily flow rates and marker recoveries in 4 steers.[a]

Item	Grain diet	Forage diet
Marker recovery, %		
Cr_2O_3	92.6	91.6
Lignin	86.9	90.7
Digesta flow, ℓ/d		
Cr_2O_3	46.4	76.1
Lignin	49.8	72.3
Dry matter flow, g/d		
Cr_2O_3	2,299	2,583
Lignin	2,566	2,509

[a]From Wanderley (29)

Ultradian Variations

The abomasal outflow of digesta evaluated by a flow meter occurs in cattle as gushes varying between 50-160 ml every 1-3 min separated by periods of no flow corresponding to an ultradian rhythm of antral inactivity. In sheep the flow occurred as gushes of 6-20 ml every 0.5-1.2 min, which ceased regularly during the phases of antral quiescence (see Fig. 4-50). The increased flow of digesta corresponding to a same amount of food given 3 times daily resulted in gushes of greater volume rather than in higher frequency without changes in the ultradian variation of antroduodenal activity.

Diurnal Variations

In both cattle and sheep, superimposed diurnal variations in digesta flow were also recorded. The 24-h flow measured by total collection or Cr_2O_3 in steers on a grain diet (Fig. 4-51) increased to a peak before the afternoon feeding and a second peak was noted about midnight which was followed by very low flow between 2:00-4:00 (29). In sheep fed ad libitum, such circadian variations of flow across the pylorus were also noticed in relation with the rest-activity cycles including sheep (19). They probably represent an aspect of the stomach's link to the brain which is more apparent in animals fed on a liquid diet.

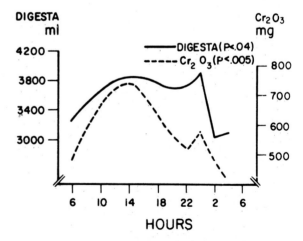

Figure 4-51. Flow patterns of duodenal digesta and Cr_2O_3 based on regression analysis of 2-h measurements of duodenal digesta from steers fed a grain diet. Feeding times were 07:30 and 15:30 h. From Wanderley (29).

When sheep were totally nourished by ruminal VFA and abomasal casein infusion (12), continuous measurement of the abomasal emptying of the casein solution infused at the constant rate of 200 ml/h showed one or two periods of low outflow at night lasting 1.5-3 h and a high flow rate, possibly a rebound phenomenon, at dawn. The low flow was characterized by gushes of 2-3 ml vs 6-7 ml for the high flow rate. These variations occurred without any major changes in the frequency of antral contractions or in the periodicity of the cyclical motor events at the gastroduodenal junction (unpublished observations).

SMALL INTESTINAL MOTILITY

To the diurnal variations of the abomasal outflow linked to the rest activity cycle of the animal (29) and sleep cycles (19) are superimposed along the small intestine ultradian changes of the flow at intervals of 90-120 min. The origin of this intermittent pattern of flow of digesta in ruminants is the periodic generation at the gastroduodenal junction of migrating motor complexes (MMCs) first identified by electromyography after an overnight fast in the dog. The part of the migrating complex during which regular and strong bursts of spike potentials are superimposed on consecutive slow waves (RSA phase) was initially termed segmental contractions because of its rhythmicity and its localization in successive segments of the small intestine. The segmental contractions which last from 3 to 9 min are preceded by a phase of irregular contractions (peristalsis) termed irregular spiking activity (ISA). The activity of maximal amplitude is the only one visible on replay from magnetic tape (Fig. 4-52) and no flow occurs during the subsequent period of quiescence. Direct measurements of the volume digesta passing a jejunal cannula in sheep confirm that almost all the contents flow during the ISA phase of the migrating myoelectric complex, i.e., in advance of the segmental contractions. A similar pattern of flow persists as far as the terminal ileum since digesta are expelled from an open ileal cannula as a rapid series of discrete boli at intervals of 1-2 h. In contrast, in the preruminant stage the cyclical motor activity is disrupted as in dogs or man by feeding (the activity becomes

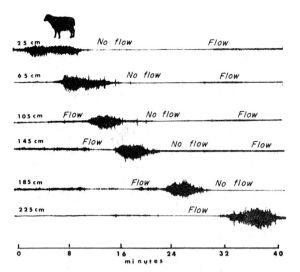

Figure 4-52. Replay from a magnetic tape record of the migration of the RSA phase of the MMC (segmental contractions) in a sheep along the jejunum for 6 electrode sites at intervals of 40 cm. This phase is followed by a period of quiescence (no spiking activity) during which there is no propulsion of the intestinal contents (20).

continuous by disappearance of the RSA phases and subsequent inactivity or no spiking or NSA), the MMCs recur without interruption in the adult ruminant with only slight variations in their frequency due to the amount of contents to be propelled. Furthermore, after combined vagotomy and splanchnicotomy, the MMCs not only persist but recur rather more frequently, which suggests that MMC generation may be an intrinsic property of the intestine controlled by an internal clock. Integrative networks within the intrinsic plexus control the pattern of reciprocal excitation and inhibition that regulates the initiation of migration of the MMC. These networks, although influenced by extrinsic nervous impulses, can function independently of external input.

The cyclical motor activity of the small intestine and the resulting effects on the flow of digesta are well understood in ruminant species, including its development during perinatal life and neurohormonal control. The peculiarities resulting from the cyclical activity of the duodenal bulb reservoir, the vertical configuration of the duodenum, the very distal flow of the pancreatico-biliary secretions into the duodenum at about 30 cm

102

beyond the pylorus, are consistent with a specific pattern in the ruminant. The mean pH value of digesta found in sheep fed 800 g hay and 200 g oats near the pylorus is 2.7 ± 0.02 and still 4.1 ± 0.06 at 10 cm caudal to the point of entry of the common bile duct. Indeed, the secretion of the Brunner's glands of the whole duodenal loop, even in the presence of the stimulatory effect of acid digesta, reaches only 15 ml/h at pH 7.5-9.0 and thus is unable to neutralize some 300 ml/h of acidic chyme.

Perinatal Development

The development of the ovine small intestine has received considerably more attention than that of other parts of the GIT. In the 60-d-old fetus, where the crown-rump length (CRL) is 16 cm, the small intestine is 1.76 m long. Over the last 3-4 weeks of gestation, the length of the small intestine is about 18 times that of the CRL, i.e., 7.9-8.8 m long and the first evidence of intestinal glands (crypts of Lieberkühn) is in the duodenum.

In the fetal lamb relatively mature at birth, the plasma gastrin levels are elevated prior to birth and the fetus secretes acid during gestation with a general trend for the gastric pH to decrease from 7.5 in the 105-d-old fetus to 4.3 in the 135-d-old fetus. During this period the irregular spiking activity is erratic and of low magnitude. As the gastric pH decreases, the unorganized spiking activity becomes organized in periods of quiescence (NSA) and regular spiking activity (RSA).

During the last week prior to lambing, the ISA increases from 30 to 50% of the recording time and is interspersed between the phases of RSA which, in turn, occur at a lower frequency. This ISA profile resembles the changes that can be induced during quiescence by artificially increasing the volume of intra-intestinal contents in adult sheep. The occurrence before birth of a pattern resembling the MMC is accompanied by a high slow-wave frequency on the antrum near the pylorus and on the duodenal bulb. The propagation of series of spike bursts on the antrum and through the gastroduodenal junction at intervals of 1 to 2.5 min can be seen 5 d before birth.

The 30-40 min interval between the RSA phases in the fetus increases progressively to values of 90-100 min after birth as a consequence of an increase in duration of the ISA phases and later in the adult by the development of inhibitory mechanisms. Two other factors are involved: an increased velocity of propagation of the MMCs and the presence of migrating action potential complexes (MAPCs) that we termed propulsive waves in the newborn calf (Fig. 4-53). The recovery in an adult of the rapid MMC rhythm seen in the fetus or newborn could be induced by the use of serotoninergic antagonists like methysergide, except for the velocity of propagation which remains as high as that seen during the postnatal evolution of the MMC pattern.

Finally, the adaptation of the GIT to propel digesta in response to its loading by milk involves the development of several motility changes: increased ISA/NSA ratio, higher velocity of propagation of the contractions, decreased orally propagated activity, and distinct bursts of intense spike activity, i.e., the propulsive waves or MAPCs.

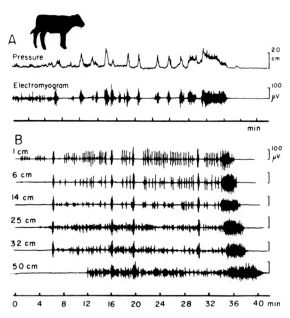

Figure 4-53. Mechanical (open tipped catheter infused at 0.2 ml/min) and electrical activity of the duodenum in a 6-d-old calf showing (A) the presence of isolated peaks of pressure lasting about 10 sec followed by a long-lasting increase in pressure corresponding to a period of segmental contractions. Below (B), electromyograms of the duodeno-jejunum showing during the phase of irregular activity the propagation of four propulsive waves along the upper part of the gut. From Dardillat and Ruckebusch (5).

Digesta Flow Characteristics

To study the factors involved in the rate of passage of digesta along the ruminant small intestine, the motor activity of the ovine duodenum has been examined by concomitant recording pressure and electromyographic (EMG) changes at the level of a T-cannula which can also receive a ring-like flowmeter probe. The motility over 24 h was represented by propagated contractions except for 15 to 18 periods of quiescence lasting 10-15 min and following periods of increased pressure of 4-5 min duration.

When a ring-like electromagnetic flowmeter probe is inserted into the lumen of the duodenum, the flow of contents consists of gushes during the propagated contractions (ISA phases of the MMC). This pattern of activity and thus the flow rate of digesta cease during the periods of quiescence (NSA phase of the MMC) (Fig. 4-54). Continuous recording over 24 periods in sheep fed hay ad libitum shows a mean flow of digesta of 1,200 ml during daytime vs 1,800 ml at night. The explanation for this diurnal variation is that the animal spends time during the day in eating and nibbling whereas nearly 70% of the time spent ruminating (during which the reticulo-rumen and thus the abomasal outflow increase) occurs at night. Conversely, on a grain or concentrate diet, the augmented flow rate of digesta occurs earlier after feeding and

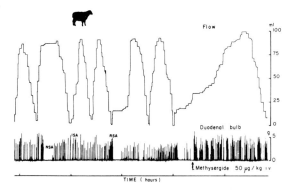

Figure 4-54. Relationship between the flow of digesta and the cyclical motor activity of the duodenal bulb in a sheep fed hay ad libitum. The periods of no flow corresponded to the RSA-NSA phases and occurred at intervals of 90-110 min. During the ISA phases the flow rate is ca. 400 ml/h. The enhancement of the cyclical motor activity as RSA-like phases by methysergide reduces the flow rate to ca. 100 ml/h.

decreases at night during the periods of deep sleep.

On the jejunum, the concept that propulsive activity of the small intestine is directly mediated by MMCs is defined by the observation that contents are propelled during the ISA phase and that maximal outflow occurs just before the occurrence of the RSA phase. The fact that radioopaque marker moves from the duodenum to the proximal ileum in 20-40 min, but requires a further 2 h to pass the distal ileum, is emphasized by the fading out of the RSA phase of an MMC after traversing 60% of the small intestine.

Neurohormonal Control

Several observations indicate that the extrinsic nerves have only a regulatory function because the MMC pattern persists after section of the splanchnic and vagus nerves. The presence of cyclic motor events and their responses to the intraluminal contents are under the control of the enteric nervous system (ENS) (see Fig. 4-26). The regulatory role of the vagus nerves is shown by the disappearance of the initiation of RSA phases by duodenal infusion of 0.5-3 meq HCl (0.05-0.1 M HCl). Vagotomy does not prevent the initiation or migration of the spontaneous MMC, but reduces its rate of propagation from 40.5 to 16.7 cm/min in the duodenum. The inhibitory responses of gastric emptying to the presence in the duodenum of the products of digestion and of the osmotic environment depend to varying degrees on a neural mechanism called the *enterogastric inhibitory reflex*. This protective reflex which avoids overload has also the vagus nerve as a component of the reflex arc. The enterogastric inhibitory reflex is mediated, from intestine to brain and back to the stomach, by both afferent and efferent fibers in the vagi. Vagal inhibition is mediated by vagal efferent noncholinergic nonadrenergic nerves. A variety of intestinal receptors (osmoreceptors, H^+ receptors, and mechanoreceptors), which respond to specific intraluminal stimuli (4), are able to initiate the reflex inhibition of abomasal motor activity.

The inhibition of gastric motility in response to acid solutions in the duodenum or fat beyond the entry of the bile duct is not completely removed following vagotomy. In the ruminant the inhibitory effect of acid and

104

fat affects also the reticulo-ruminal motility and, therefore, the abomasal outflow and the abomasal H$^+$ secretion.

Jaw movement recordings in the sheep show that the normal patterns of feeding and rumination are altered by duodenal infusion of 100 ml of peanut oil. The initial period of feeding is abbreviated, sometimes to half of that observed in control animals or in infused animals on "control", i.e., non-infusion days. This reduced period of feeding is usually succeeded by a period of rumination, but thereafter there is only aimless eating with short periods of rumination and long periods of inactivity. Intensive feeding is resumed 3-4 h after the infusion is ended. When emulsions of fatty acids (2-10 g) with gum acacia and water made up of fatty acid, water, gum (4:2:1, by wt.) and then diluted to the final volume of 120 ml are infused in sheep caudal to the bile duct aperture, a clear inhibitory effect was observed on the reticulum and to a lesser extent on the rumen.

Among the hormonal factors which might be involved, cholecystokinin (CCK), rather than secretin, GIP, SRIF or bovine pancreatic polypeptide seem to be implicated. The CCK released by fat from intestinal mucosa enters the mesenteric blood stream, passes via the portal system, liver, and hepatic vein to reach the general arterial circulation. Appreciable amounts of CCK are also synthesized in various regions of the brain; the role of brain CCK, beside activity as a CNS neurotransmitter, could be a regulator of food intake. However, the failure of systemic CCK to pass the blood-brain barrier suggests a separation of brain and gut CCK activities, so that when the nerve supply to (and from) the small intestine is sectioned, the meal-depressing action of CCK is greatly attenuated. The hypothesis that CCK exerts a "satiety" action peripherally, probably in the upper gastro-intestinal tract, by delaying gastric emptying has been examined and reinforced by the fact that anorexia in sheep infected by nematodes coincides with high plasma level of CCK.

LARGE INTESTINE

The homeostatic functions of the large intestine involve an electrolyte and fluid balance, a harbor for billions of microorganisms (hence the site for absorption of VFA) and a temporary store for excreta until convenient for controlled elimination. Great variation in the anatomy of the large bowel does not appear to be related to the formation of pelleted feces in sheep and goats. The indication of a role of the spiral colon in the formation of pellets is given by the mean retention time which averages 20 h in sheep instead of 8 h in cattle (20), due to the presence on sheep and goat's spiral colon of segmentation or the division of the lumen into fairly uniform segments by narrow ring contractions. These contractions propel feces over only short distances and in both directions, hence the formation of pellets. Accordingly, an increased motor activity of the spiral colon might be associated with constipation, while diarrhea could occur in a flaccid colon. The major pattern of activity of the proximal colon is retrograde flow of digesta into the cecum.

Motor Activity of the Cecum
The flow of digesta from the terminal ileum to the cecum and proximal colon is intermittent. From studies of flow at the level of the terminal ileum, it appears that a single peristaltic contraction can result in a flow of fluid of up to 70 ml. Such flows are followed by a lengthy period of quiescence varying from 30 min to 300 min. Estimated flows of ileal contents are in the range of 2 to 8.5 ℓ/d in cattle.

Regular coordinated contractions, peristaltic and antiperistaltic, are the predominant form of activity in the cecum and proximal colon at a frequency of 3-7/10 min. They last about 6 and 10 sec in cattle and sheep, respectively. Radiological observations have shown that the majority of these contractions originate either at the blind pole of the cecum or at the ileocecal junction (28). Contractions which originate at the ileocecal junction travel towards the pole and are followed by a wave of contraction which returns from the pole and may travel some distance along the proximal colon. When these contractions reach the pole, the gas cap is displaced, moving about half the distance to the junction and then reforming at the pole. On other occasions gas is displaced and occasionally it passes directly to the colon.

Single peristaltic contractions, originating as a continuation of cecal contraction, travel along the proximal colon often as far as the

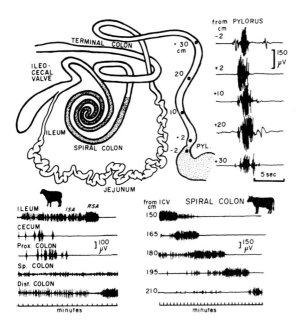

Figure 4-55. Schematic representation of the ruminant gastro-intestinal tract, showing contractions rapidly propagated along the duodenum (34 cm/min) in contrast to the slow migration (2 cm/min) of series of spike bursts in cattle and to the absence of propagation on the spiral colon where fecal pellets are formed in sheep.

spiral colon. Antiperistaltic contractions start in the proximal colon.

Trains of 4 to 12 intense contractions, lasting about 2 and 6 min in sheep and cattle, respectively, occur irregularly (intervals of 30-240 min) to evacuate contents from the cecum and are linked to the occurrence of a phase of RSA activity on the ileum.

The contractions of the cecum cause an almost complete evacuation of contents to the proximal colon. In cattle, they induce a phase of hyperactivity resembling the migrating spike burst (Fig. 4-55). Accordingly, analysis of digesta along the digestive tract has demonstrated that VFA concentration shows a small increase in the terminal ileum, a marked rise in the cecum and a steady decrease through the spiral colon.

Spiral Colon and Pelleted Feces

On the ovine spiral colon, spike burst potentials lasting only 4 sec occur at a rate of 15 per min during nearly 95% of the recording time so that the activity seems continuous. This basal activity is only disrupted on

the 1st coil by contractions (5-10/h) propagated from the proximal colon and which reach the last centripetal coil.

Plastic beads (5 mm in diameter), numbered and introduced sequentially through a cannula in the proximal end of the spiral colon, are recovered in essentially the same order in the fecal pellets. This indicates that segmentary contractions are the predominant form of activity in the ovine spiral colon. In cattle the electromyogram of the spiral colon consists of such an activity during only 25% of the recording time. A striking feature of the bovine spiral colon shown in Fig. 4-55 is the propagation of 8 to 10 phases of hyperactivity per day, corresponding to the propulsion of a large volume of digesta. They last about 5 min, are followed by a period of quiescence and propagated from the proximal colon to the distal colon at a velocity of 2 cm/min.

Neural Influences

Opinions are conflicting on the effect of feeding on cecal motility. In sheep the frequency and amplitude of regular pressure changes in the cecum are increased, reaching a peak of activity 15 to 20 min after the onset of feeding. The response is present, though diminished, in sham-fed animals. There is evidence for the presence of a *gastro-colic reflex* in sheep since colonic activity is almost doubled during the first ten minutes after feeding. Feeding grain diets was found to decrease cecal motor activity in sheep and cattle, presumably as a result of increased or abnormal cecal fermentation. Infusion of high levels of VFA, especially butyric acid, can inhibit motility and may be the causative factor in the pathological condition known as cecal dilatation. It is noteworthy that the duality of spiking activity of the colon seems to be a general phenomenon also described in other species. Spike burst potentials of long duration are characterized by their propagation and are predominant in cattle. Spike burst potentials lasting less than 5 sec (which remain located) are well-developed in the ovine spiral colon. Comparative studies of the motility patterns in the large intestine of rabbits, where soft and hard pellets are elaborated by changes in the duration of spiking activity, indicate that endogenous prostaglandins (EP) play a major role in the shift of

106

motor and secretory functions involved in soft feces formation. It is possible that EP levels of the spiral colon are at the origin of differences between the ovine and bovine species.

The motor role in defecation of the extrinsic nerve supply to the rectum in response to distension is demonstrated by the relaxation of the ampulla after epidural anesthesia, and in the case of tenesmus, by its disappearance after destruction of the sensor pathways in the pelvic nerves by alcohol.

SUMMARY

The condensed description of the motility patterns which are involved in the diversion of milk from the fermentation chamber, in the turnover of rumen digesta and in their propulsion from the abomasum along the intestine clearly implies different levels of nervous control of cyclic motor events coming from the brain and from intrinsic neurons which are stretched by digesta moving through the tract. All the mechanical motions of the digestive tract are influenced by the interplay of the two systems involved in the brain-gut axis: (a) the enteric nervous system which contains as many nerve cells as the brainstem and is at the origin of the migrating motor complexes of the small intestine and the mixing forms of motility of the large intestine, and (b) the

central nervous system which, through a high level of vago-vagal reflexes, controls the cyclical contractions of the reticulo-rumen.

The tactile stimulation generated by relative motion between the digesta and the gut wall, for example the cranial and caudal pillars, influences the onset of specific behaviors like rumination. Other sensory information derived from chemical receptors initiates the adaptive changes, for example those of the ruminal mucosa to the high-energy diets given at the time of calving, and required for the absorption of nutrients.

The passage of digesta from one region to another is only possible when no overloading is detected because this kind of feedback evokes inhibitory reflex responses via nervous and hormonal pathways. Distension or acidification of the duodenal bulb reduces abomasal emptying which in turn blocks the reticulo-rumen outflow, hence postponed food intake or even anorexia.

The fact that the complex machinery involved in digesta propulsion is, in addition, regulated for the post-gastric area by gastrointestinal hormones and neuropeptides, clearly implies that the assumption of food intake controlled in ruminants by signals coming from the reticulo-rumen has to be extended to signals issued from the transpyloric flow of digesta which govern the supply of nutrients other than VFA to the intestinal absorptive sites.

Literature Cited and Further Reading

1. Andersson, B., et al. 1959. Acta Physiol. Scand. 46:319.
2. Balch, C.C. and R.C. Campling. 1962. Nutr. Abstr. Rev. 32:669.
3. Church, D.C. 1976. Digestive Physiology and Nutrition of Ruminants. Vol. 1 – Digestive Physiology, 2nd Ed. O & B Books, Inc., Corvallis, Oregon.
4. Cottrell, D.F. and A. Iggo. 1984. J. Physiol. 354:457.
5. Dardillat, C. and Y. Ruckebusch. 1973. Ann. Rech. Vét. 4:31.
6. Dougherty, R.W., et al. 1962. Amer. J. Vet. Res. 23:205.
7. Dulphy, J.P., et al. 1980. In: Digestive Physiology and Metabolism of Ruminants, p. 103. Y. Ruckebusch and P. Thivend, eds. MTP Press Ltd, Lancaster, U.K.
8. Flatt, W.O., et al. 1959. In; Cornell U. Agr. Exp. Sta. Memoir 361.
9. Kay, R.N.B. and Y. Ruckebusch. 1971. Brit. J. Nutr. 26:301.
10. Leclerc, F. 1985. In: Ethology of Farm Animals. A.F. Fraser, ed. Elsevier, Amsterdam.
11. Ooms, L., et al. 1985. The Ruminant Stomach. Vol. I. Janssen Res. Foundation, Beerse, Belgium.
12. Ørskov, E.R., et al. 1984. Can. J. Animal Sci. 64:138.
13. Phillipson, A.T. 1970. In: Dukes' Physiology of Domestic Animals. 8th Ed., p. 424. Comstock Pub. Assoc., Ithaca, N.Y.
14. Reid, C.S.W. 1962. The Influence of the Afferent Innervation of the Ruminant Stomach on its Motility. Ph.D. Thesis, Cambridge Univ.

15. Reid, C.S.W. 1985. In: Ruminant Physiology. Concepts and Consequences, p. 79. S.K. Baker et al, eds. School of Agr., Univ. of W. Austr.

16. Reid, C.S.W. and J.B. Cornwall. 1959. Proc. N. Z. Soc. Animal Prod. 19:23.

17. Rousseau, J.P. 1970. Contribution à l'Etude de la Rumination et de l'Eructation chez le Mouton. Thèse Doct. Sci. Nat., Univ. Aix-Marseille.

18. Ruckebusch, Y. 1963. Recherches sur la Régulation Centrale du Comportement Alimentaire chez les Ruminants. Thèse Doct. Sci. Nat., Univ. Lyon.

19. Ruckebusch, Y. 1975. In: Digestion and Metabolism in the Ruminant, p. 77. I.W. McDonald and A.C.I. Warner, eds. The Univ. of New Engl. Publish. Unit, Armidale.

20. Ruckebusch, Y., et al. 1981. La Mécanique Digestive. INRA Masson, Paris.

21. Ruckebusch, Y. and M. Candau. 1968. C. R. Soc. Biol. 162:897.

22. Ruckebusch, Y. and R.N.B. Kay. 1971. Ann. Rech. Vét. 2:99.

23. Ruckebusch, Y and T. Tomov. 1973. J. Physiol. 235:447.

24. Ruckebusch, Y., et al. 1972. Life Sci. 11:55.

25. Sissons, J.W. 1983. J. Dairy Res. 50:387.

26. Stobo, I.J.F., et al. 1966. Brit. J. Nutr. 20:189.

27. Titchen, D.A. and J.C. Newhook. 1975. In: Digestion and Metabolism in the Ruminant, p. 15. I.W. McDonald and A.C.I. Warner, eds. The Univ. of New Engl. Publish. Unit, Armidale.

28. Ulyatt, M.J. 1982. In: Fibre in Human and Animal Nutrition, p. 103. G. Wallace and L. Bell, eds. The Royal Society of N. Z., Bulletin 20. Wellington.

29. Wanderley, R.C. 1985. J. Animal Sci. 61:1550.

30. Winship, D.H. 1964. Amer. J. Physiol. 207:1189.

31. Woodford, S.T., et al. 1984. J. Dairy Sci. 24:71.

32. Wyburn, R.S. 1980. In: Digestive Physiology and Metabolism of Ruminants, p. 35. Y. Ruckebusch and P. Thivend, eds. MTP Press Ltd., Lancaster, U.K.

5   INGESTION OF FEED AND WATER

by J. G. Welch and A. P. Hooper

EATING HABITS

Consuming a diet of forage is a full-time job for an adult ruminant. More than 12 h must be spent each day ingesting and ruminating food. An animal may chew 30,000-50,000 times in a 24-h period without an extended rest period (Table 5-1). Jaw motion recordings of high-producing dairy cows showed no more than 20 minutes of rest between periods of rumination and/or eating, night or day. Without the chewing which occurs during eating and rumination, it would be impossible for ruminants to sustain themselves on fibrous diets.

MECHANICS OF EATING

Ruminants lack upper incisors; instead they have a hard pad (see Ch. 2). When they eat a bite, they manipulate the feed into their mouths with their tongues and lips and cut or tear the feed off with their lower incisors and dental pads. They chew the feed briefly in the back of the mouth before swallowing. Because the dominant jaw movements are lateral, chewing in ruminants is a grinding rather than cutting operation. The limited chewing which occurs during eating breaks long forages into particles just small enough

to be formed into a food bolus and swallowed. Mixing feed with saliva which occurs during eating makes swallowing easier. Saliva also hydrates the feed causing an increase in the functional specific gravity of the feed, which affects passage from the rumen.

Particle breakdown occurs during eating as well as during rumination. During eating, from 10-50% of dry matter ingested is broken into particles of <1 mm depending on the composition and particle size of the forages consumed. Ryegrass, which has high tensile strength in its leaves, requires many chews per gram of dry matter, and is eaten slowly and not very efficiently. Therefore, many large particles remain after initial eating. The remaining large particles are broken down to

Table 5-1. Chewing behavior of cattle, sheep, goats and kid goats.[a]

Item	Cattle	Sheep	Goats	Kid goats
Eating, min/d	330	240	254	204
Rumination, min/d	465	491	446	381
Rumination, min/kg NDF	84	850	830	3,270
Chews/d	49,912	35,482	40,094	34,952
No. chews/bolus	52	71	78	112

[a]Author's unpublished data

Table 5-2. Body size and rumination capability of sheep, goats and cattle.[a]

Animal	No.	Body weight kg	Body weight kg$^{0.75}$	Rumination, min/g CWC	CWC load for 480 min, g	CWC load/d g/kg BW	CWC load/d g/kg BW$^{0.75}$
Lambs	4	40	16.0	2.05 ± .42	257	5.8	14.6
Goats	4	39	15.6	1.30 ± .29	370	9.4	23.7
Mature Sheep	3	82	27.3	1.18 ± .20	407	4.9	14.9
Calves	4	119	35.9	0.78 ± .15	618	5.2	17.2
Heifers I	4	213	55.7	0.42 ± .08	1,157	5.4	20.8
Heifers II	4	342	79.6	0.19 ± .07	2,528	7.4	31.8
Heifers III	4	456	98.6	0.16 ± .03	2,948	6.5	29.9
Cows	4	561	115.0	0.10 ± .05	4,610	8.2	40.1

[a]From Welch (1)

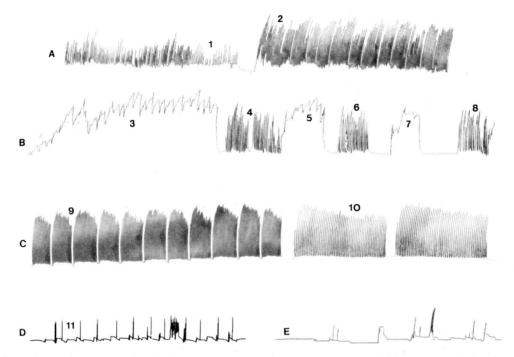

Figure 5-1. Jaw motion patterns. A, Steer eating. A1, Eating hay near the end of a meal followed by A2, enthusiastic grain eating. B3, B5, B7, Steer drinking out of a water bowl with a paddle in the bottom. B4, B6, B8, Drying nose by licking. C, Steer rumination. C9, Recorded at .025 cm/sec. and C10, Recorded at .10 cm/sec. D. Pseudorumination or intermittent regurgitation in a ram. D11, Pseudorumination timing is the same as in rumination. E, Idling.

<1 mm by rumination. Typical jaw motion recordings of eating, rumination and drinking appear in Fig. 5-1.

EFFICIENCY OF CHEWING

Eating and rumination efficiency (the number of chews required per unit of feed consumed) are related and depend both on the animal and on forage composition. Larger animals can break particles down more rapidly than can smaller ones (Table 5-2). Forages high in NDF require more chewing than do higher quality forages. Rumination time has been shown to be highly correlated with NDF intake in both sheep (r = .99) and cattle (r = .96) (Fig. 5-2). Level of intake also is a factor. Animals that eat more spend less time eating and ruminating each gram of feed than do animals that eat less total feed.

In addition to degradation of particles, chewing during eating affects bacterial fermentation and releases soluble material from the feed. Bacteria cannot easily penetrate the waxy cuticle which covers plant surfaces, so

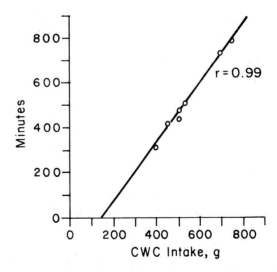

Figure 5-2. Relation of minutes of rumination time to cell wall constituent intake in sheep fed single meals of roughages of different quality. From Welch and Smith (2).

110

digestion lag time is longer in unchewed than in chewed material. Microbial fermentation and particle size are related; a gram of small particles has more surface area accessible to bacteria for digestion than does a gram of large particles. As a result the rate of fermentation is higher when feed particles have been reduced in size. The amount of soluble material released during chewing depends on plant maturity and species; more soluble nutrients escape from high-quality feeds than from fibrous feeds. Data indicate that 30-60% of the soluble N is released during eating with the remainder released during rumination.

FOOD SELECTION

From muskox in the arctic tundra to impala and wildebeests in the Kalahari desert, ruminants have demonstrated the ability to survive in many hostile environments. Species have developed different feeding strategies to feed themselves. Some maximize the quality of the feed they eat by careful selection (selectors), some consume large quantities of poor-quality feeds, and some adopt an intermediate approach to diet selection.

The selectors, such as giraffes, deer and duikers, are animals with a limited ability to digest fiber, yet they pass digesta rapidly through the gastro-intestinal tract. They consume a relatively low-fiber diet which is fermented rapidly. Their ability to select only the most digestible portions of plants is essential to their survival (3).

The feeding strategy of the second class of herbivores is "more is better" and "quantity not quality." These animals, such as buffalo, cattle and camels, have large gastro-intestinal tracts in which they retain feeds for relatively long periods (see Ch. 2). These animals derive significant energy from digesting the cell walls of plants.

Animals in the intermediate group, which includes grazers and browsers such as sheep and goats, are less discriminating in what they eat than are the selectors, but they are incapable of continuously consuming large quantities of highly fibrous feeds. The capacities of their digestive systems limit both the amount they can eat and the time feed is retained in the rumen.

Comparing the lips of different species reveals the anatomical adaptations that permit some animals to graze closely and others to browse selectively. Goats have well developed upper lips (philtrum) which enable them to pluck desirable leaves from among thorns. Cattle, which are quite unselective in their choice of feed, have relatively immobile lips and rely primarily on their tongues to bring feed into their mouths. Whether or not selectivity is a significant advantage depends on the composition of the available forage; the more uniform the forage, the less beneficial selective grazing is. On the other hand, when the quality of mature and immature parts of the plant differ greatly, as in tropical grasses, careful selection may enable an animal to survive in an environment in which less selective feeders cannot. Other factors, such as feed availability and taste preferences, also affect selection. Goats tolerate more bitter feeds than do sheep and cattle and often consume browse in preference to grasses. Season affects quality, quantity and palatability of forages so that diets consumed by animals vary throughout the year. Goats in parts of Texas prefer grass in the summer months before it matures, but select browse during the remainder of the year.

TIME SPENT EATING

Several factors influence the amount of time an animal spends eating: herbage density in a sward, photoperiod, temperature, weather, quality and form of feed, and physiological status of the animal. Feed supply, rather than feed quality, often is of major concern for both arctic and desert ruminants. In both of these environments the aerial parts of dormant plants contain acceptable amounts of digestible carbohydrate, but the total supply of vegetation is limited. Herbage intake is related both to the amount of time spent grazing and the rate of grazing. Rate of grazing is based on both number of bites per minute and bite size. In situations where bite size is limited, total intake is suppressed. Stobbs (4) estimated that with 400-kg cattle intake may be restricted unless bite size averaged at least 0.3 g of organic matter/bite for 36,000 bites/d. The muskox demonstrates this problem; between 61 and 78% of the range muskox graze is ground which is bare or covered with plants not consumed by muskox. They find it difficult to ingest enough feed per bite, particularly in the winter when they must graze through several inches of hard, granular snow that encrusts the plants. Similar intake limitations occur in animals which graze tropical grasses that contain a high proportion of stem and relatively little leaf material. Animals must spend more time grazing or searching for food when herbage is limited in order to compensate for decreased bite size.

Grazing animals usually eat during daylight, particularly in the early morning and at twilight (Fig. 5-3). In hot weather animals increase nocturnal grazing time to avoid eating during the heat. They spend less time grazing when weather is inclement than when it is fair. When days are short in the winter, the morning and afternoon eating periods are merged. Pastured animals spend between 5 and 12 h eating daily whereas confined, forage-fed ruminants spend 2 to 7 h. Steers on feedlot rations eat between 2.5 to 3 h/d. Dairy cows may eat up to 20 meals/d mostly during daylight hours, although half this number is more usual for beef cattle or sheep. Restricted-fed animals increase their rate of eating to maximize intake during periods when feed is available. Rapid ingestion of feeds can result in bursts of microbial activity that increase acid production. This effect is especially evident if animals are fed ground

rations or high-grain diets that lower rumen pH. Lower rumen pH and high solute concentration (osmotic pressure above 0.350 osm) stop rumination and inhibit normal intake (1).

The eating patterns of confined animals are influenced by the timing of feeding as well as by photoperiod. Animals prefer fresh feed and usually start eating their longest meals when new feed is placed in front of them. However, eating patterns cannot be manipulated by altering feeding times alone; to reverse eating and rumination patterns of confined animals, it is necessary to change both periods of light and darkness as well as mealtimes. The customary pattern of eating at the beginning and end of the day and ruminating at night is difficult to disrupt. For all eating and ruminating to occur during daylight would require almost constant chewing. Although ruminants do not sleep through the night as humans do, the periods of rumination are times of rest.

Eating patterns and intake differ among animals in different reproductive states. Animals in estrus decrease feed consumption as do animals before and after calving. Pregnant cows spend more time eating but eat more slowly than do those that are not pregnant.

RUMINATION

Rumination is defined as the regurgitation, reinsalivation, remastication and reswallowing of rumen ingesta (see Ch. 4). During a period of rumination which may last up to 2 h, this process is repeated approximately once per minute. The length of time a bolus is chewed is relatively independent of the actual amount of coarse material regurgitated. Chewing during eating breaks down hay into particles small enough to be regurgitated; particles 30 cm long cannot be regurgitated by cattle or sheep in significant amounts while 7-cm particles can be returned to the mouth (1).

Chewing during rumination is relatively deliberate and at a slower rate than during eating. The jaw motion recordings produced by eating are irregular in amplitude and frequency is high, often between 70 and 90 chews per minute in sheep, goats and cattle (Table 5-1). The rate can be influenced by the material ingested. Coarser roughages produce slower chewing rates than do those

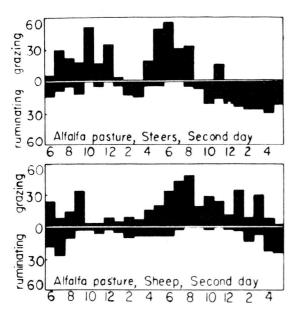

Figure 5-3. Grazing and ruminating patterns of steers and sheep on alfalfa pasture. From Lofgreen et al (5).

112

which are fine. The rate of chewing during rumination is much more uniform, 50-55 chews/minute in cattle, than is the eating rate. This is presumably because the material presented for remastication from the rumen has been chewed once and is more uniform (Fig. 5-1).

Level of intake can influence both number of chews per bolus and boluses per minute in animals fed hay (Fig. 5-4). Restricted intakes in sheep result in a lower number of chews per bolus and a higher number of boluses per minute.

Rumination is important in several ways: it contributes to particle size degradation, increases specific gravity of forages, breaks impervious plant tissue coatings and increases forage surface area available to the microbes for attachment and digestion. The average maximum dimension of particles that pass from the rumen is < 1 mm for almost all species. Although chewing during eating decreases particle size, most particle reduction of indigestible material occurs during rumination. Indigestible particles must be reduced to a size small enough to pass from the rumen to maintain normal intake levels (Fig. 5-5).

Rumination increases the specific gravity of forages by breaking down the plant structures that entrap gases. Light particles float so they are seldom found near the reticulo-omasal

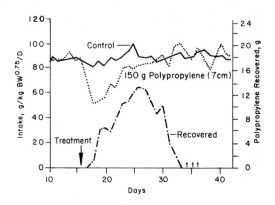

Figure 5-5. Hay consumption by wethers receiving 150 g of 7 cm length polypropylene fibers introduced into their rumens compared with that of controls receiving none, and recovery of finely ground polypropylene in the feces of the treated animals. From Welch (1).

orifice, and thus they are unlikely to pass from the rumen. As air and gas pockets are eliminated, the apparent or functional specific gravity of the forage moves closer to the true specific gravity of the plant material, which is usually between 1.4 and 1.6. Particles passed from the rumen usually have a specific gravity between 1.2 and 1.6.

Rumination is stimulated primarily by ingesta particles longer than 10 mm, such as long or chopped hay. Although particles between 1 and 10 mm in length do affect rumination, longer material is more important in stimulating rumination. Length of particles, therefore, is an important consideration in adjusting forage chopping machinery.

Fiber particles must be relatively light to be ruminated. Light plastic materials such as polypropylene ribbon float and are regurgitated and chewed thoroughly (Fig. 5-6). Heavier material that sinks in the rumen is not found in the vicinity of the cardia and thus is not regurgitated.

When ruminants are fasted for 36-48 h, rumination subsides gradually. The regurgitation pattern found in rumination continues, and is known as intermittent regurgitation or pseudorumination (Fig. 5-1). Because no chewable material comes up with the fluid for retention in the mouth, the fluid is reswallowed and the system waits for the next timed regurgitation. Two or three hours/d may be spent at this pseudorumination activity, most of it occurring in the latter part

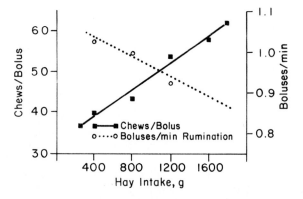

Figure 5-4. The relationship between number of chews per bolus (Y) and hay intake (X), Y = 32.79 + .0164X. The relationship between number of boluses per minute of rumination time (Y) and hay intake (X), r = -.98, Y = 1.08 - .000123X. From Welch and Smith (6).

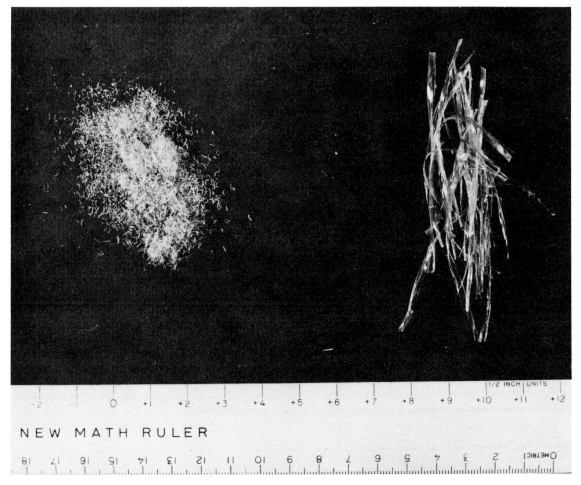

Figure 5-6. Right, polypropylene ribbon 7 cm long fed in the experiment from which results are shown in Fig. 5-5. Left, ruminated polypropylene particles recovered in feces from polypropylene fed sheep. The ribbon was chewed to the fineness shown here to permit passage from the rumen.

of the night. Similar activity is observed when diets of completely ground material are fed.

Total chewing time (rumination time and eating time) required for each unit of dry matter consumed is associated with forage quality, provided the forage is in the natural long form (Table 5-3). The forage component that is most strongly related to rumination time of long, dry hay is NDF (cell wall constituents) (Fig. 5-2). Although with some silages the same strong relationship between rumination time and the NDF content of the ration is observed, some high-moisture samples require much longer rumination.

Previous diet history may affect the amount an animal ruminates: lambs raised on a grain ration ruminate more per unit of NDF than do lambs reared on a high-roughage diet when both are challenged with an all-hay diet.

Table 5-3. Eating and ruminating time of cows given diets of single feedstuffs.[a]

Feedstuff	Time range observed*		
	Eating	Ruminating	Total
Oat straw	41-58	94-133	145-191
Medium quality hay	20-40	63-87	103-109
Good quality hay	27-31	55-74	87-104
Grass silage	31-58	60-83	99-120
Dried grass	8-18	33-39	44-53
Concentrates, pelleted	4-10	(0-25)**	(4-29)**
Finely ground oat straw	11-24	(0-20)**	(11-31)**
Finely ground hay	13	(0-6)**	(13-19)**
Finely ground dried grass	5-12	(0-11)**	(5-18)**

[a] Data from Balch (7).

*min/kg dry matter consumed.

**Higher values in the ranges shown in ( ) show the extent of irregular chewing with finely ground diets.

If material awaiting rumination accumulates in the rumen or if rumination is restricted, intake decreases in forage-fed animals (1). For example, polypropylene ribbon introduced into the rumen of sheep or cattle greatly depresses forage intake. The ribbon must be broken down to particles small enough to pass from the rumen before the animal can resume consumption of normal amounts of feed. When rumination was prevented by face masks which stopped the cattles' jaw motion for two 10-h periods/d, hay intake declined sharply. When this treatment was continued for several days, the cattle chose to ruminate during the two 2-h feeding periods rather than eat. When the mask treatment was discontinued, below normal intake levels persisted for several days, perhaps because the backlog of residual dry matter in the rumen had to be processed before additional material could be consumed (Fig. 5-7).

The drive to ruminate is very strong. It is a common observation that rumination can be disrupted just by mildly disturbing an animal. However, upon further investigation, the level of disturbance must be continually increased until severe measures are required to prevent rumination. Exact form-fitting face masks are necessary to stop rumination over a prolonged period (1). Surgical removal of the entire forestomach or rumen will not prevent regurgitation of ingesta (8).

Rumen environment can affect rumination. For example, rumination activity stops if rumen osmotic pressure rises above 0.350-0.380 osm, or if rumen pH falls below 5.6-5.4.

Both of these conditions can be caused by feeding ruminants excess fermentable carbohydrates (1). On the other hand, making the rumen basic will stop rumination also. While factors have been identified that disrupt rumination, no practical means to stimulate rumination have been found.

RUMINATION EFFICIENCY

Rumination efficiency, measured by units of NDF consumed/per unit of rumination time, is influenced by several factors. Level of intake is important; increasing the amount consumed decreases rumination time per unit of cell wall (NDF) ingested. This is evident when limited and ad libitum intakes are compared, and when cold stress stimulates higher than normal intakes. Because it has been shown that almost no particle degradation occurs post-ruminally, fecal particle size often is used to estimate the size of particles leaving the rumen. When the intake of mature cattle at maintenance was restricted, there was no change in fecal particle size. When animals were subjected to cold stress, fecal particle size was larger than in animals kept in a temperate environment.

Body size is a major determinant of rumination efficiency. Larger animals are more efficient, both within and between species, even when metabolic body size is the basis for comparison (Table 5-2). Smaller ruminants are unable to ruminate large amounts of plant cell wall and must select higher quality material to survive. Young growing ruminants cannot process as large a volume of cell wall material as can adults of the same species. Dry matter content of the rumen determines when rumination begins. Rumination efficiency at first is low; a relatively long time is required to ruminate a given amount of dry matter. In cattle, maximum NDF rumination efficiency (g NDF ruminated/d for each kg $BW^{0.75}$) was not reached until animals were over two years old (Table 5-2). The transition between the inefficient rumination during weaning and the more efficient adult rumination is a period of high risk for wild ruminants. This transition often occurs during winter in temperate climates or during the dry season in semi-arid tropical and subtropical areas when the small amounts of forage available are of poor quality. For domestic ruminants this

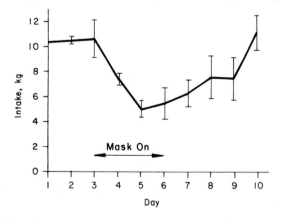

Figure 5-7. Voluntary intake of steers fitted with face masks to prevent rumination. Masks were on for 10 h and off for 2 h, on for 10, off for 2, for 4 d. From Welch (1).

hazardous period usually is bridged by feeding higher quality feed than is available in the unaltered natural environment. The greater processing ability found in adult ruminants may be due to differences in jaw strength, chewing efficiency and gut volume.

There are genetic differences both within and among breeds of domestic ruminants in rumination efficiency. The association between these differences and productivity remains to be determined.

BEHAVIOR INFLUENCES

The amount of feed ingested is influenced by many factors; it is not driven by appetite or limited by appetite control alone (see Ch. 10). For example, environmental and social effects must be considered. In pastures where there are manure pads, there is a zone of aversion around each manure deposit where animals will not graze unless no other feed is available. This must be due to smell or taste. Individual interaction within the social order of a herd of cattle affects feeding behavior as well. Cows on the lower end of the social order may be unable to meet their nutrient requirements even though ample feed is available. If feeding space at bunks or hay racks is limited, dominant animals may limit time of access. Cubed grass is consumed more readily when placed on the ground than when it is put in boxes. Contrary to what one might expect, there are data to indicate that cattle on a moving cattle car in a freight train will ingest adequate amounts of hay despite the apparent negative nature of the environment. The systematic study of behavior related to ingestion is in its infancy and more information will be available in the future.

DRINKING

Ruminants drink by immersing their lips in water, creating a negative pressure in the oral cavity, and delivering the fluid to the pharynx primarily by tongue action. Complex contractions in the pharynx and peristaltic contractions in the esophagus complete the movement of liquid to the cardia. Fluid may be delivered directly to the rumen as when adult ruminants drink water normally or it can bypass the rumen by flowing down the reticular groove to the omasum, as when

suckling animals nurse. Jaw motion during drinking is presented in Fig. 5-1.

Water consumption is affected both by the nature of the diet consumed and the requirement of the animal. Wet forages, such as succulent and dew-laden pastures or high moisture-silages, may provide most or all of the water needed by an animal. Frequency of drinking is highly variable among ruminants within species as well as among species. Lactating dairy cows may drink as often as eight times a day, while dry beef cows may drink only every other day. Some desert antelope rarely drink during the dry season. The efficiency of water recovery from the large intestine varies among species: sheep excrete dryer feces than do cattle, and thus reduce their water requirement and frequency of drinking. Kidney adaptation in some desert species allows for the production of very concentrated urine, which reduces the amount of water needed and drinking frequency.

Water consumption can be influenced by habit, which may cause water ingestion well beyond what is required to survive. Animal interaction can play a role as when a herd of grazing animals goes to drink; all probably will drink but not all actually need water.

SUMMARY

Forage-fed ruminants spend almost half of their lives chewing during eating and rumination. Without devoting such a large amount of time to chewing, they would be unable to break down fiber into particles small enough to maximize digestion by rumen microbes and to permit passage of indigestible residues. Their ability to use grasses and legumes which man cannot digest is dependent largely on maintenance of a healthy microbial population in the rumen and on their chewing ability. The typical ruminant day is structured; they eat in the early morning and in the evening and ruminate during the night. The amount of time spent chewing is dependent on the physiological state of the animal, the size of the animal and the composition of the available feed. Fibrous feeds require more chewing than do those which are more digestible. Chewing efficiency is important in determining how much an animal can consume; if particles are degraded rapidly, rumen capacity for additional feed will be available.

116

In animals genetically capable of sustaining moderate to high levels of production, maximizing feed intake is critical to increasing levels of production, especially in forage-fed animals.

Literature Cited

1. Welch, J.G. 1982. J. Animal Sci. 54:885.
2. Welch, J.G. and A.M. Smith. 1969. J. Animal Sci. 28:813.
3. Van Soest, P.J. 1982. Nutritional Ecology of the Ruminant. O & B Books, Inc., Corvallis, OR.
4. Stobbs, T.H. 1973. J. Agr. Res. 24:809.
5. Lofgreen, G.P., J.H. Meyer and J.L. Hull. 1957. J. Animal Sci. 16:773.
6. Welch, J.G. and A.M. Smith. 1979. J. Animal Sci. 49:1292.
7. Balch, C.C. 1971. Brit. J. Nutr. 26:383.
8. Church, D.C. 1976. Digestive Physiology and Nutrition of Ruminants. Vol. 1 — Digestive Physiology. 2nd Ed. O & B Books, Inc., Corvallis, OR.

Recent Reviews of Interest

Dulphy, J.P., B. Redmond and M. Theriez. 1980. In: Digestive Physiology and Metabolism in Ruminants. Y Ruckebusch and P. Thivend, eds. AVI Press, Westport, CT.

Ulyatt, M.J., et al. 1986. In: Control of Digestion and Metabolism in Ruminants. L.P. Milligan, W.L. Grovum and A. Dobson, eds. Prentice-Hall, Englewood Cliffs, NJ.

6 SALIVARY FUNCTION AND PRODUCTION

by D. C. Church

INTRODUCTION

Research studies in many different laboratories have documented that ruminants secrete large volumes of alkaline and well-buffered saliva. Information available has been obtained primarily on sheep, cattle, buffalo and goats; that on other ruminant species is generally restricted to gland weight and anatomy. Saliva, although only one of numerous secretions of the digestive tract, has been singled out for discussion in this chapter primarily because of its importance to the ruminant animal and because more information is available than on other secretions.

NASOLABIAL GLANDS

Nasolabial glands are small glands situated in the dermis of the muzzle skin of species such as cattle and buffalo. The watery secretion of the glands keeps the muzzle moist. Both buffalo and cattle are known to make deliberate efforts to mix this secretion with their food. They frequently thrust their muzzles into the feed and, during rumination, run their tongues into the nostril and over the muzzle, thus bringing the secretion into the mouth. The moisture on the muzzle may play a very small part in evaporative cooling; cessation of secretions occurs during many illnesses and a dry, hot muzzle is often used as evidence of disease. The rate of secretion in an adult cow is said to be about 80 mg/20 cm²/5 min, a rate which is increased threefold when food of high palatability is given (1). The chemical properties of nasolabial secretions are similar to saliva. Relatively high levels of amylase have been observed which may be the source of amylase sometimes reported to be present in ruminant saliva.

SALIVARY GLANDS

Most anatomical texts state that there are three pairs of well defined glands which produce most of the saliva. These include the parotid, which extends from the base of the ear to the posterior end of the mandible; the mandibular (or submaxillary), found at the base of the maxilla and mandible, and the sublingual, underneath the tongue. Other glands include the dorsal buccal (or palantine) in the hard and soft palate; the middle or medial buccal, in the cheek, and the ventral buccal (or inferior molar) in the cheek (see Fig. 6-1). Other salivary glands include the labial, in the corners of the mouth and the pharyngeal "gland", actually a group of glands in the oral and laryngeal parts of the pharynx and some additional glands in the lateral margins and root of the tongue (2).

Saliva from the various glands drains into the oral cavity via ducts from the glands. Data on weights, cell type, factors affecting rate of flow, estimated volume from sheep glands and saliva type are shown in Table 6-1. Note that the parotid and mandibular account for the majority of tissue weight. In adult cattle the parotid glands are said to weigh about 115 g and the mandibular about 140 g.

Saliva is produced by glands classified as serous—thin, watery saliva containing protein but no mucin; mucus—thick, slimy saliva which contains the glycoprotein, mucin; and mixed—combinations of both types. Note in Table 6-1 that the parotid and ventral buccal glands produce serous saliva; the dorsal and medial buccal and pharyngeal produce mucus type and the mandibular, sublingual and labial produce mixed secretions. Recent information is available on the histological structure of bovine and caprine parotid glands (3).

AMOUNT OF SECRETION

Salivary production by domestic ruminants has been studied in many different laboratories, although not many recent reports are available. Various methods have been used to measure saliva production. Mixed saliva can be collected by swabbing the mouth with sponges, but this is, obviously, not quantitative. Mixed saliva has been collected with the use of esophageal-fistulated animals or cardial collections have been made in rumen-fistulated

118

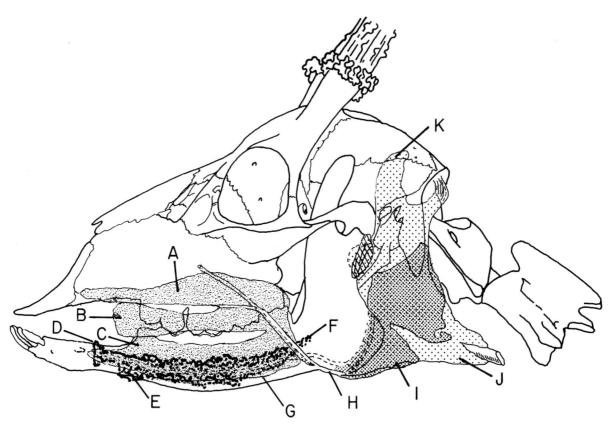

Figure 6-1. The salivary glands of the ruminant. A, dorsal buccal; B, medial buccal; C, G, ventral buccal; D, E, F, sublingual; H, parotid duct; I, mandibular; J, K, parotid. Labial and pharyngeal glands are not shown. Courtesy of R.R. Hofmann.

animals by collecting saliva with some type of container (at the terminal end of the esophagus in the rumen) or by feeding measured amounts of feed and weighing the boli after they were swallowed. In some instances mixed saliva has been collected by aspirating saliva from the mouth of normal or anesthetized animals. Carbachol or other drugs have been administered to stimulate saliva flow. However, most of the information available has been collected on production by parotid glands that have been cannulated (Fig. 6-2). In some instances parotid saliva has been collected from cannulated glands, measured in some manner and then placed in the rumen. This approach is less likely to have a marked effect on normal functioning of the animal, thus results should be more realistic than when other methods are used (4, 5).

One characteristic of salivary secretion is that it is quite variable in animals fed similar diets. For example, Tomas (4) found that parotid salivary flow of sheep ranged from 3

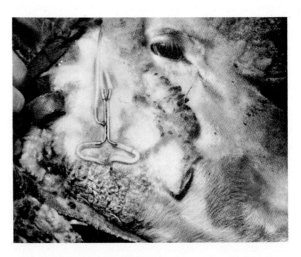

Figure 6-2. Photograph showing cannulas and collecting manifold in place during saliva flow measurement on a sheep. Courtesy of F.M. Tomas.

Table 6-1. Summary of characteristics of the salivary glands.[a]

Glands	Calves		Sheep		Cell type	Factors governing rate of flow	Estimated volume,* ℓ/24 h	Saliva type
	Weight, g	% of total	Weight, g	% of total				
Both parotid	63.5	32.2	23.5	29.3	Serous	Continuous flow when denervated. Respond to stimulation of mouth, esophagus and reticulo-rumen.	3-8	Fluid and isotonic. Strongly buffered with HCO_3 and HPO_4
Both mandibular	64.0	31.6	18.2	22.6	Mixed	No flow when denervated. Strongly stimulated by feeding. Little or no response to stimulation of esophagus or reticulo-rumen.	0.4-0.8	Variably mucus and hypotonic. Weakly buffered.
Both sublingual	11.3	5.6	1.3	1.6	Mixed	Continuous flow when not stimulated. Moderately stimulated from esophagus; other reflexes not studied.	0.1 (?)	Very mucus and hypotonic. Weakly buffered.
Labial	8.9	4.4	10.9	13.5	Mixed	Little or no flow when not stimulated. Little or no response to stimulation of esophagus and reticulo-rumen; other reflexes not studied.	?	Very mucus and hypotonic. Weakly buffered.
Both ventral buccal	13.5	6.7	5.9	7.3	Serous	Continuous flow when denervated. Responds to stimulation of mouth, esophagus and reticulo-rumen.	0.7-2.0	Fluid and isotonic or nearly so. Strongly buffered with HCO_3 HPO_4.
Both medial buccal	13.1	6.5	6.0	7.5	Mucus	Very slow continuous flow when not stimulated. Respond to stimulation of mouth, esophagus and reticulo-rumen.	2-6	Very mucus and isotonic or nearly so. Strongly buffered with HCO_3 and HPO_4.
Dorsal buccal	16.2	8.5	8.8	10.9				
Pharyngeal	9.1	4.5	5.9	7.3				

[a]From Kay (2); *Volume estimates done on sheep.

to 10 ℓ/d, but it was reproducible within sheep. Bartley et al (6) have also observed that salivary production of twin cattle was quite similar, but different among pairs of identical twins. These data are illustrated in Table 6-2. Based on the assumption that parotid secretion accounts for 40-50% of total saliva secretion, relatively recent studies (in which parotid saliva was returned to the animal) indicate that sheep will produce in excess of 15 ℓ/d when fed roughage diets ad libitum (6, 7). Cattle weighing about 434-450 kg will produce about 180 ℓ/d when fed on alfalfa forage (6).

It should be pointed out that there are marked differences in the relative sizes of salivary glands among ruminant species. Several species classed as concentrate selectors (see Ch. 2) have salivary glands that are 3-4 fold larger (as a % of body weight) than grass and roughage eaters (7). Whether they

Table 6-2. Saliva collected via cardial collections from identical twin cattle eating lush or mature alfalfa forage.[a]

Pasture	Water content of alfalfa, kg/kg DM	Twin pair	Saliva added/kg DM consumed, kg
Lush	6.32	A1	1.61±0.73
		A2	2.08±0.68
		B1	1.13±0.17
		B2	1.30±0.03
Mature	4.51	A1	3.66±0.64
		A2	3.53±0.60
		B1	2.49±0.05
		B2	3.50±0.30

[a]From Bartley et al (6)

produce relatively more saliva is not known at this time, but it is a logical assumption that they do produce larger amounts of saliva, although studies with young animals show that secretion rates are related to rumen size.

REFLEX CONTROL OF SALIVA SECRETION

Information from various sources shows that stretching of the terminal esophagus, cardia, reticulo-rumen fold or reticulo-omasal orifice causes large increases in parotid secretion. Light, tactile stimulation of these areas and the walls of the reticulum and cranial pillar has little effect, however. Inflation of the rumen of anesthetized sheep or calves to pressures below 20 mm Hg increases the flow of parotid and residual saliva up to 10 fold, but progressively inhibits secretion as pressure increases. Inflation of the esophagus alone stimulates parotid secretion; when only the rumen was inflated, secretion was inhibited. Inflation of the abomasum is slightly inhibitory. Inflation of the rumen (as in bloat) produces a marked increase in mucoprotein concentration of submaxillary saliva without materially altering the concentration of other components. Responses to ruminal infusions of volatile fatty acids, HCl and water have been variable, but do not appear to have much effect overall.

COMPOSITION OF SALIVA

The chemical composition of saliva from individual and mixed saliva from all glands has been studied by a number of laboratories. Data from four different species are shown in Table 6-3. Dry matter content is said to range from 1.0-1.4% and ash content from 0.7-1.5%. The major inorganic components in parotid saliva are Na, P and CO_2 with lesser amounts of Cl, K and small amounts of Ca, Mg and variable amounts of N and S (see later section).

Although the electrolyte concentration of parotid saliva is generally higher than that of plasma, the osmotic pressure of mixed saliva, as measured by freezing point depression, is isotonic to plasma. Consequently, the salivary glands, as a whole, are not required to work against an osmotic gradient. Kay (2) feels that this is a primary reason that the salivary glands are able to produce such copious quantities of saliva.

The N content of saliva is variable as are the other constituents, but is usually on the order of 0.1-0.2% of which 60-80% is urea N. Salivary protein comes primarily from the mucus-producing glands and is made up of glycoproteins. Sialic acid (N-acetylneuraminic acid) is found in large quantities. N-acetyl glactosamine and hexosamine are also found in appreciable amounts.

Table 6-3. Chemical composition of saliva from different ruminant species.[a]

Component	Sheep Parotid	Sheep Mixed	Cattle Parotid	Cattle Mixed	Buffalo parotid	Alpaca parotid
Dry matter, %	1.28	1.29			1.2	
Ash, %	0.97	0.84			0.85	
N, mg/dℓ	20	20				29 (urea)
Na, mEq/ℓ	177	193	127	126	146	165
K, mEq/ℓ	8	11	7	6	15	14
Ca, mEq/ℓ	0.4	1.2	3.3		5	
Mg, mEq/ℓ	0.6	0.6				
P_i, mEq/ℓ	52	40	23	26	49	33
Cl, mEq/ℓ	17	10	7	7		
CO_2, mEq/ℓ	104	69	127	126		121
pH	8.1	8.6			8.5	8.6

[a]Data from McDougall (8), Baily and Balch (9), Sinha et al (10) and Ortiz et al (11), respectively for sheep, cattle, buffalo and alpaca.

FUNCTIONS OF SALIVA

There are a number of salivary functions in ruminants that have been confirmed by experimental data and several that have been proposed by different writers. These are discussed in subsequent sections.

As an Aid in Mastication and Swallowing

Except in the case of lush vegetation, the feed consumed by ruminants is often dry, and that of farm species may frequently be of a powdery nature that would be extremely difficult to ingest if not for the moistening effect of saliva. A bolus collected in the cardial area may contain saliva equivalent to several times the weight of the dry feed ingested. In addition the location of mucus-secreting glands is such that a bolus may be easily coated with mucus, thus making it easier to swallow.

Enzymic Activity of Saliva

The saliva of many mammals contains salivary amylase, although this does not appear to be the case in ruminants (see previous section on nasolabial glands). Domestic ruminants are known to produce an enzyme (actually a group of enzymes) referred to as salivary lipase or pregastric esterase. Data from a number of different laboratories indicate that this enzyme(s) preferentially hydrolyzes short-chain fatty acids such as butyric or caproic from triglycerides. Hydrolysis of long-chain triglycerides is much slower and less complete. Activity is considerably less than that of pancreatic lipase and there is little activity remaining at a pH of 2.5 or in the small intestine. Thus, this enzyme is presumed to be of primary importance to suckling animals.

Buffering Activity

The buffering capacity of saliva is probably one of its more important functions, because some mechanism must be available to keep rumen pH within physiological ranges to which the tissues and microorganisms are adapted. In cattle, bicarbonate and phosphate buffers account for about 90% of the anion content and Na is at least 18 fold more concentrated than K. As noted in Table 6-1, saliva from some glands is strongly buffered. Various studies have shown that mixed saliva is a weak buffer above pH 7.5 and below 5.5;

thus, saliva is well buffered against acid but poorly buffered against alkali. Partially neutralized rumen acids also serve as buffers in the rumen. Some writers suggest that salivary buffers act as the first line of defense to buffer the rumen against acids (normal VFA), but that saliva, by itself, is not adequate to buffer the rumen against all of the acids produced. It is not very effective against a stronger acid such as lactic acid which is apt to be present when rumen pH drops below 5.5.

Other Properties

Saliva is, of course, an important factor in taste, particularly when an animal is consuming dry feed. In addition, mucin, urea, P, Mg and Cl are nutrients needed or used (mucin) by microbes. Other experiments (see Ch. 23) indicate that anti-frothing properties of saliva are an important factor in prevention or reduction in severity of rumen bloat.

The rumen has a high water content and it has been estimated that more than 70% of the water entering the rumen does so via saliva. Thus, saliva undoubtedly helps to maintain a desirable physio-chemical environment for microbial fermentation in addition to acting as a buffer. The various ions, both organic and inorganic, would help to maintain a relatively stable osmotic pressure in the rumen. In instances where rumen or blood osmotic pressure have been altered with various chemicals, studies show that an increased osmotic pressure of either blood or rumen fluid result in a reduction in salivary flow (12).

VARIABLES AFFECTING THE QUALITY OR QUANTITY OF SALIVA

The range in production of saliva can be partially accounted for by the fact that saliva secretion is greater when eating than when not eating (resting). In addition, the physical texture and moisture content of feed being consumed have a marked effect on salivary production. Presumably, palatability of a ration as affected by physical nature, taste and smell would be an important factor. One example of the effect of different feeds is shown in Table 6-4. In this instance production was measured by collecting swallowed boli and weighing them when animals were fed a known amount of feed. Note that

122

Table 6-4. Salivary production (cardial collections) by cattle consuming different types of feed.[a]

Feed	Salivary production		Eating rate, g food/min
	g/g food	ml/min	
Pelleted ration	0.68	243	357
Fresh grass	0.94	266	283
Silage	1.13	280	248
Dried grass	3.25	270	83
Hay	3.63	254	70

[a]From Bailey (13)

salivary production/min was not much different among feeds, but because some of the feeds were consumed at a faster rate, the amount of saliva produced (g/g of feed) ranged from a low of 0.68 for a pelleted ration to a high of 3.63 g when hay was consumed. Other studies of this type have shown that there may be more than a 10 fold range in saliva production as affected either by the physical nature of the feed or by different feeds, i.e., feeding dry, fibrous feeds as opposed to lush forage of low fiber content. Rate of swallowing is correlated with salivary production.

Numerous experiments have been done on animals with cannulated parotid glands. Although parotid secretion is continuous (Fig. 6-3), the rate of secretion increases during eating and rumination. In one study rates of secretion found at the end of each period of rest increased from about 5 ml/min immediately after eating to about 20 ml/min immediately before the next eating period. This pattern of gradual increase throughout the period between meals was also observed during rumination when mastication occurred on the operated side of the mouth. The rate of flow from one parotid gland (cattle) averaged 20, 25 and 10 ml/min during eating, rumination and rest, respectively, for a daily output of about 21 ℓ (9).

Chewing on the operated side of the mouth (cannula on only one side) is the most effective stimulus to saliva secretion by the parotid. When chewing occurs on the opposite side, the rate of secretion is raised little or not at all above that which occurs during periods of rest, indicating that mastication adjacent to the parotid gland is required for stimulation of secretions (ruminants can chew on only

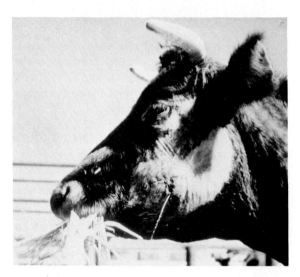

Figure 6-3. An illustration of the flow of parotid saliva during mastication in a cow with a parotid cannula. Courtesy of D.A. Denton, U. of Melbourne.

one side of the mouth at a given moment in time). With the mandibular gland, one study indicated that secretion during eating (30 min) was equal to that during a resting and ruminating period of 8-12 h (6).

Parotid secretion decreases during starvation or water depletion. After watering or administration of water via a rumen fistula, the flow of parotid saliva decreases.

Variation in Minerals or N Content

Denton (14) was the first to demonstrate that a Na-deficient diet has a marked effect on the Na and K content of parotid saliva, and he further demonstrated that a salivary fistula could be used to produce a Na deficiency quickly if the secreted saliva was not returned to the sheep either orally or intraruminally. In these studies it was observed that the Na-K concentration was about 180 and 10 mEq/ℓ with a normal diet and that adequate replacement of Na had little effect. If Na replacement was not allowed, the animal became grossly depleted, saliva volume decreased from about 3 to 1 ℓ/d; the Na concentration fell from about 180 to 60 mEq/ℓ and K concentration rose to approximately 120 mEq/ℓ. This type of response has been confirmed a number of times in other laboratories, and this information has been used in the field to evaluate the Na status of animals.

Several studies have shown that the N content of saliva may be variable, within a range of 8-40 mg/dl. Urea concentration is less than that of blood plasma; in one study urea N ranged from 37% of the N on a low-N diet to 85% on a high-N diet and the N in parotid saliva varied from 4 to 18 mg/dl. Both total and urea N may be increased by an increased intake of dietary N (15); these authors calculated that 4-8% of dietary N on good quality roughages and 4-22% on poorer diets might be recycled to the rumen via the saliva. Estimates from other laboratories are available on this topic (see ref. 15). High levels of ammonia in the rumen or jugular blood will inhibit salivary secretion by the parotid glands (16).

Total S in parotid saliva ranges from 1.4-12.5 mg/ℓ and reducible S from 0.3-10.0 mg/ℓ. It is not clear at this point if transfer from blood to saliva is primarily related to blood levels (15). Studies with sheep in which intravenous infusions of P were administered indicate that salivary glands probably have a major role in regulating P balance, at least during short periods of time (16). Various trace minerals have been found in saliva from time to time, but not enough information is available to know what typical levels might be.

DEVELOPMENT OF SALIVARY SECRETION IN YOUNG RUMINANTS

The parotid glands develop more slowly in lambs on milk diets than in grazing lambs. Glands of grazing, milk and hay, or milk-fed lambs are likely to be immature before 4 weeks of age. In one study grazing lambs reached adult flow rates at 7-10 weeks of age. Rate of flow was correlated to fresh weight of the rumen, but not to body weight. In adults, residual saliva (all except the parotid) comprised about 41% of the total saliva, but only 26% in lambs. Salivary composition varied with secretion rate and less with age. Cl concentration fell with age (2). In another study lambs were fed wood shavings and milk; milk; milk and hay; or a synthetic diet containing starch, fortified whole milk powder and $NaHCO_3$. Data showed that lambs receiving the milk and hay or the synthetic diet secreted less saliva than those receiving milk or milk plus shavings. In a different

experiment comparisons were made between lambs that were 63 d of age which had grazed with their mothers and lambs that were grazed until 63 d of age but were then confined to a milk diet for a further 70 d. Salivary production from the parotids of the grazing lambs was significantly greater than the secretion by lambs returned to the milk diet. It was concluded that the parotid glands developed in response to the mechanical stimulation of food and that there was a regression of gland development when this stimulation was removed.

In another study (17) it was demonstrated that a marked increase occurs in salivary production with age in calves; parotid secretion/g of tissue increased 7 fold between 1 and 13 weeks in calves fed milk, hay and grain, but very little increase occurred in calves fed milk only. Mixed saliva also increased in MHG animals. Salivary Na (mixed saliva) was slightly higher in calves fed MHG and K was slightly lower, but no effect of age was demonstrated. Bicarbonate increased with age and Cl fell to adult levels by 6 weeks in calves fed MHG and 9 weeks in milk-fed calves.

CONCLUSIONS

Saliva is produced in copious amounts by five sets of paired glands and three unpaired glands, with the parotid glands apparently accounting for 40-50% of total production. Evidence indicates that full grown sheep produce 15 ℓ or more/d when fed ad libitum and that cattle may produce 180 ℓ or more when on high quality pasture. The amount produced by large dairy animals would, undoubtedly, be appreciably higher. Saliva serves as an aid in forming and swallowing a bolus of food and as an important buffering agent in the rumen. A limited amount of lipase activity is present; some amylase activity may be derived from secretions of the nasolabial glands found in the dermis of the muzzle of some species. Saliva also provides some nourishment for rumen microbes.

Production of saliva—both in quantity and quality—varies with eating, rumination and resting times. Moisture content and physical nature of the food affect total production, and other dietary factors such as Na or urea may influence the composition of saliva. In the young animal, salivary glands develop in close coordination with rumen function.

Literature Cited

1. Toutain, P.L., L. Bueno and J.P. Mangol. 1973. Extrait des Cahiers de Med. Vet. 42:41.

2. Kay, R.N.B. 1960. J. Physiol. 150:515.

3. Suzuki, S., H. Nishinakagawa and J. Otsuka. 1981. Japanese J. Vet. Sci. 43:169;181.

4. Tomas, F.M. 1973. Quart. J. Exp. Physiol. 58:131.

5. Church, D.C. 1976. Digestive Physiology and Nutrition of Ruminants. Vol. 1—Digestive Physiology. 2nd Ed. O & B Books, Inc. Corvallis, Oregon.

6. Bartley, E.E. 1976. Bovine Saliva: Production and Function. In: Weinberg, M.S. and A.L. Sheffnor (eds.). Buffers in Ruminant Physiology and Metabolism. Church & Dewight Co., New York.

7. Hofmann, R.R. 1983. Digestive Physiology of the Deer. In: Proc. International Conf. Biology of Deer Production, Dunedin, New Zealand.

8. McDougall, E.I. 1948. Biochem. J. 43:99.

9. Bailey, C.B. and C.C. Balch. 1961. Brit. J. Nutr. 15:371.

10. Sinha, K.P., S.C. Sud and H.S. Bagha. 1972. Ceylon Vet. J. 20:109.

11. Ortiz, C., J. Cavero, H. Sillau and S. Cueva. 1974. Res. Vet. Sci. 16:54.

12. Warner, A.C.I. and B.D. Stacy. 1977. Quart. J. Exp. Physiol. 62:133; Carr, D.H. and D.A. Titchen. 1978. Quart. J. Exp. Physiol. and Cognate Med. Sci. 63:1.

13. Bailey, C.B. 1959. Proc. Nutr. Soc. 18:1.

14. Denton, D.A. 1956. J. Physiol. 131:516; 1957. Quart. J. Exp. Physiol. 43:72.

15. Doyle, P.T., J.K. Egan and A.J. Thalen. 1982. Austral. J. Agr. Res. 33:573.

16. Obara, Y. and K. Shimbayashi. 1979. Brit. J. Nutr. 42:497.

17. Sasaki, Y. 1969. Nutr. Abstr. Rev. 39:1140.

7 MICROBIOLOGY OF THE RUMEN AND INTESTINE

by M. T. Yokoyama and K. A. Johnson

THE RUMEN ECOSYSTEM

Although a myriad of microorganisms are found throughout the digestive tract of the ruminant, it is only with the microbiota in the rumen that a true symbiotic relationship with the host is apparent. These microorganisms, predominantly bacteria, protozoa, and anaerobic fungi, depend on the ruminant to provide the physiological conditions necessary for their existence. In turn, these microorganisms are essential for digestion and fermentation of the large amounts of fibrous feeds which the ruminant consumes, but otherwise cannot efficiently utilize. By providing a suitable habitat for these microorganisms, the ruminant is able to utilize the end products of microbial fermentation and biosynthetic activities to meet its own nutritional needs. According to Hungate (17), this is a classical example of the cooperative model in an animal-microbe relationship.

Rumen Characteristics

Because it is an open and continuous ecosystem, the rumen is an ideal environment for maintaining a stable microbial population which has evolved through millions of years of selection. A constant supply of substrates is provided by feed consumed by the animal and the large holding capacity of the rumen provides the necessary volume and retention time for complex dietary components (e.g., cellulose and other polysaccharides) to be degraded and fermented by the rumen microbes. The difference in the rate of passage of the liquid and particulate phases leaving the rumen also facilitates efficient fermentation. While soluble end-products of the fermentation are directly absorbed or rapidly removed with the liquid phase, larger particles are retained until degradation has occurred. Generally, digesta in the dorsal areas of the rumen has a dry matter content of 14-18%, while ventral areas are about 6-9%. These aqueous conditions provide for optimal microbial interactions and high activities of microbial enzymes. There is a further advantage in the longer retention time of feed particles. Those microbes with slower growth rates are able to attach to these particles and thus avoid being washed out of the rumen.

Microbial Characteristics

The types of microorganisms which develop and are sustained in the rumen are those which have adapted best to the specific conditions of the ecosystem. The microorganisms which predominate are mainly saccharolytic. Carbohydrates, such as cellulose and other polysaccharides, make up most of the ruminant diet and constitute the major substrate available for fermentation. The low oxygen concentration in the rumen, as indicated by a negative oxidation-reduction potential (E_h) of between –250 and –450 millivolts, encourages those microorganisms which can grow only in the absence of oxygen or when oxygen concentration is minimal (obligate anaerobes). A few bacteria also capable of growth under aerobic conditions are present (facultative anaerobes). The composition of the gas mixture in the rumen is about 65% CO_2, 27% CH_4, 7% N_2, 0.6% O_2, 0.2% H_2 and 0.01% H_2S. Rumen temperature is maintained at a relatively constant 38-42°C. Copious salivary secretions of bicarbonate and phosphate buffer the rumen fermentation usually to a pH of between 6-7. While extraneous microbes are constantly being introduced into the rumen with feed, water and soil, they never exert a significant influence on the fermentation because they cannot compete successfully with those microbes which have been selected under the conditions of the rumen environment.

THE RUMEN BACTERIA

The bacteria which are found in the rumen will number about 10^{10} to 10^{11} cells/g of rumen contents. The majority are obligate anaerobes, but facultative anaerobes may be present in numbers up to about 10^7 to 10^8 cells/g of rumen contents. Under certain conditions, Gram (+) cocci such as *Streptococcus bovis* can comprise a relatively large proportion of the rumen population. Facultative anaerobes representing a number of genera have also been found adhering to the rumen wall. Twenty-two genera and 63 species of bacteria have been described by M.P. Bryant in the rumen, of which only 16 genera and 28 species are believed to be functionally significant in terms of their numbers and metabolism. Scanning electron micrographs of some important rumen bacterial species are shown (Plate 7-1).

Methods of Classification

A system of differentiating these rumen bacteria according to morphological divisions is described by Ogimoto and Imai (37). The rumen bacteria are assigned to groups according to three main shapes (cocci, rods and spirilla), according to their size (which generally ranges from 0.3 to 50 μm) and according to their different structures (including the presence of a cell envelope, cytoplasmic structures and surface adherents or appendages). Preliminary classification of the rumen bacteria has largely followed a system based on the type of substrates the bacteria will attack and on the different end products of fermentation. The rationale for this approach is that the contribution of each bacterial species to the utilization of different dietary components must be assessed in order to determine their role in the overall fermentation process of the rumen. By this method of classification, eight distinct groups of rumen bacteria are recognized based on their utilization of cellulose, hemicellulose, starch, sugars, intermediate acids, protein, lipid or on methane production. An expanded classification might also include pectin utilizers, ammonia producers and other ecological niches occupied by the various rumen bacteria. There is a considerable amount of overlap in assigning rumen bacteria to these groups because most species are capable of fermenting more than a few substrates (Table 7-1).

Cellulolytic Bacteria

Based on their numbers in the rumen and ability to degrade cellulose, the important cellulolytic bacteria are: *Bacteroides succinogenes, Ruminococcus flavefaciens, R. albus* and *Butyrivibrio fibrisolvens.* Under certain conditions species such as *Eubacterium*

Table 7-1. Grouping of rumen bacterial species according to the type of substrates which are fermented.

Major Cellulolytic Species
Bacteroides succinogenes
Ruminococcus flavefaciens
Ruminococcus albus
Butyrivibrio fibrisolvens

Major Hemicellulolytic Species
Butyrivibrio fibrisolvens
Bacteroides ruminicola
Ruminococcus sp.

Major Pectinolytic Species
Butyrivibrio fibrisolvens
Bacteroides ruminicola
Lachnospira multiparus
Succinivibrio dextrinosolvens
Treponema bryantii
Streptococcus bovis

Major Amylolytic Species
Bacteroides amylophilus
Streptococcus bovis
Succinimonas amylolytica
Bacteroides ruminicola

Major Ureolytic Species
Succinivibrio dextrinosolvens
Selenomonas sp.
Bacteroides ruminicola
Ruminococcus bromii
Butyrivibrio sp.
Treponema sp.

Major Methane-Producing Species
Methanobrevibacter ruminantium
Methanobacterium formicicum
Methanomicrobium mobile

Major Sugar-Utilizing Species
Treponema bryantii
Lactobacillus vitulinus
Lactobacillus ruminus

Major Acid-Utilizing Species
Megasphaera elsdenii
Selenomonas ruminantium

Major Proteolytic Species
Bacteroides amylophilus
Bacteroides ruminicola
Butyrivibrio fibrisolvens
Streptococcus bovis

Major Ammonia-Producing Species
Bacteroides ruminicola
Megasphera elsdenii
Selenomonas ruminantium

Major Lipid-Utilizing Species
Anaerovibrio lipolytica
Butyrivibrio fibrisolvens
Treponema bryantii
Eubacterium sp.
Fusocillus sp.
Micrococcus sp.

127

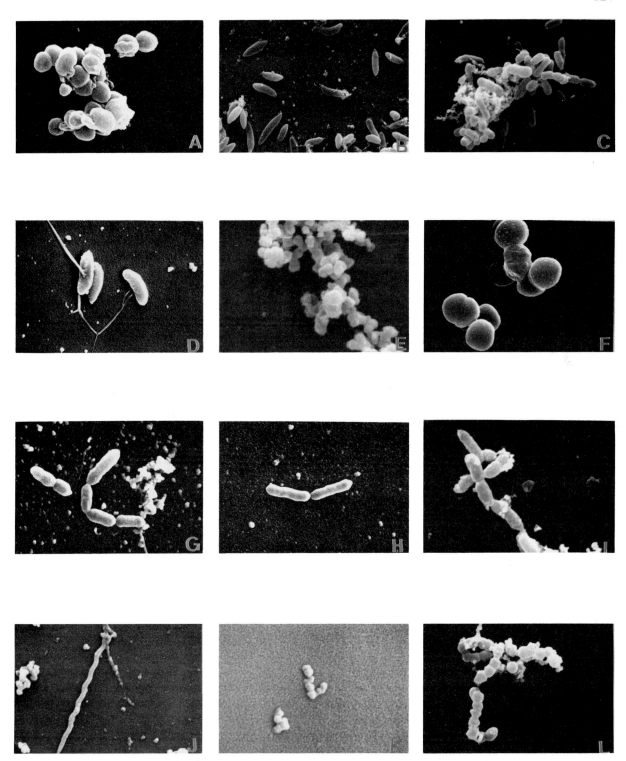

Plate 7-1. Scanning electron micrographs of some important rumen bacterial species. (A) *Bacteroides succinogenes* S85 (10,000X), (B) *Succinivibrio dextrinosolvens* 22B (6,600X), (C) *Bacteroides amylophilus* H18 (7,200X), (D) *Selenomonas ruminantium* HD4 (10,000X), (E) *Ruminococcus flavefaciens* C94 (20,000X), (F) *Megasphera elsdenii* B159 (15,000X), (G) *Butyrivibrio fibrisolvens* A38 (15,000X), (H) *Butyrivibrio fibrisolvens* D1 (15,000X), (I) *Bacteroides ruminicola* GA-33 (12,000X), (J) *Treponema bryantii* B₂5 (11,000X), (K) *Ruminococcus albus* 7 (20,000X), (L) *Streptococcus bovis* 24 (7,800X). From the collection of M.P. Bryant. Photographs taken by S.L. Flegler, Electron Optics Center, Michigan State University.

cellulosolvens can constitute the most abundant cellulolytic bacteria in the rumen. Other cellulolytic bacteria, such as *Clostridium lochheadii* and some minor cellulolytic isolates, are considered of lesser importance because of either their low numbers or inconsistent occurrence. Higher numbers of these cellulolytic bacteria are found when high roughage diets are fed, but very high numbers of cellulolytic bacteria are also found with some high-grain diets. *Bacteroides succinogenes* is known to possess an extracellular cellulase which is released from the cell and diffuses in the envi-environment. Studies with *Ruminococcus albus* have indicated that the cellulase is actually a complex of several enzymes with specific functions in the stepwise degradation of cellulose to glucose (61). The activity of the enzyme is regulated but the mechanism is still unclear.

Hemicellulolytic and Pectinolytic Bacteria

The major hemicellulolytic bacteria in the rumen are: *Butyrivibrio fibrisolvens, Bacteroides ruminicola* and *Ruminococcus* sp. Most of the predominant cellulolytic ruminococcus species will effectively degrade and utilize hemicellulose. The major pectin-degrading bacteria are also *Butyrivibrio fibrisolvens, Bacteroides ruminicola* and *Lachnospira multiparus*. Other pectinolytic bacteria include *Succinivibrio dextrinosolvens, Treponema* sp. and *Streptococcus bovis*. *Butyrivibrio fibrisolvens* possesses an extracellular pectinolytic enzyme which is an *exo*pectate lyase. This enzyme cleaves the pectin chain at the terminal end. Other pectinolytic rumen bacteria possess *endo*pectate lyase, which cleaves randomly along on the pectin chain (59).

Amylolytic Bacteria

The major starch-degrading (amylolytic) rumen bacteria are *Bacteroides amylophilus, Streptococcus bovis, Succinimonas amylolytica* and *Bacteroides ruminicola*. *Succinivibrio dextrinosolvens* will use dextrin but not all of the starch. Certain strains of the cellulolytic *Bacteroides succinogenes* will also degrade starch. Amylolytic bacteria usually tend to predominate in the rumen when high-starch diets are fed, but some amylolytic bacteria, such as *Bacteroides ruminicola,* appear to be more prevalent when low-starch diets

are fed. The degradation of starch by these bacteria involves an extracellular α-amylase which cleaves randomly along the starch chain. Production of this enzyme in *Bacteroides amylophilus* seems to vary with the growth of the bacteria and the pH of the medium (20).

Simple Sugar-Utilizing Bacteria

All of the rumen bacteria which degrade complex carbohydrates are also capable of fermenting some of the simple sugars. Some cellulolytic bacteria, such as *Ruminococcus flavefaciens,* cannot ferment glucose but will use cellobiose effectively. These bacteria possess an enzyme, cellobiose phosphorylase, which makes it energetically favorable for them to ferment cellobiose instead of glucose. Similar energy-conserving phosphorylating enzymes for sucrose and maltose have been identified in other rumen bacteria. *Treponema bryantii* is found in intimate association with rumen cellulolytic species. These spirochetes apparently use some of the sugars and cellulodextrins released during the degradation of the cellulose. *T. bryantii* has been shown to grow in coculture with *Bacteroides succinogenes* in a cellulose media. This would seem to be a means by which rumen bacteria, which can only use low molecular weight carbohydrates, are able to survive during periods of low sugar concentrations in the rumen. The lactobacilli, such as *Lactobacillus vitulinus* and *L. ruminus,* have been identified as sugar fermentors in the rumen. These sugar fermentors are usually found in high numbers in the rumen when high-grain diets or lush forages containing higher concentrations of soluble sugars are fed.

Intermediate Acid-Utilizing Bacteria

Intermediate acid-utilizing rumen bacteria carry out the secondary fermentation of the end-products of other rumen bacteria. These acids include lactate, succinate and formate. Lactate can be fermented to either acetate, propionate or larger chain fatty acids by bacteria such as *Megasphaera elsdenii* and *Selenomonas ruminantium*. Lactate turnover increases in the rumen with grain feeding and there is a corresponding increase in the numbers of lactate-utilizing bacteria. Succinate is the chief end-product of many important rumen bacteria including some cellulolytic species. Succinate is converted to propionate and CO_2 by *Selenomonas ruminantium, Veillonella alcalescens, Anaerovibrio lipolytica* and *Propionibacteria*. Formate is utilized as a precursor for methane production by *Methanobrevibacter ruminantium*.

Proteolytic Bacteria

Many predominant rumen bacteria are proteolytic, but highly specialized species which depend solely on protein as an energy source are not present. Proteolytic rumen bacteria include *Bacteroides amylophilus, B. ruminicola,* some strains of *Butyrivibrio fibrisolvens* and *Streptococcus bovis* (46). Proteolytic activity has been found in up to 38% of the isolates from the bovine rumen, indicating that a wide range of bacterial species has this capability. *Bacteroides ruminicola, Butyrivibrio* and *Bacteroides amylophilus* are particularly active species in proteolysis and the latter appears to possess a trypsin-like proteinase associated with its cell wall. Studies conducted with specific inhibitors indicate that at least three types of microbial proteinases are present in the rumen, specifically: cysteine-proteinase, serine-proteinase and metallo-proteinase. Many of these bacterial species also possess exopeptidases to further degrade oligopeptides to amino acids and shorter peptides. *Bacteroides ruminicola* requires either oligopeptides or ammonia for growth.

Ammonia-Producing Bacteria

Ammonia production from the deamination of amino acids is carried out by *Bacteroides ruminicola, Megasphaera elsdenii, Selenomonas ruminantium* and a few *Butyrivibrio* spp. Many rumen bacteria require ammonia as compared to amino acids or peptides as a N source. In general, ammonia is more important as a N source for those rumen bacteria which digest complex carbohydrates rather than simple sugars. The oxidative deamination of valine to isobutyrate, leucine to isovalerate, and isoleucine to 2-methylbutyrate with CO_2 production are of particular importance because these branched-chain fatty acids are essential growth factors for many rumen bacteria.

Ammonia is also derived from the hydrolysis of urea. Ureolytic bacteria have been found to account for 5% of all isolates from the rumen and include: *Succinivibrio dextrinosolvens,* certain strains of *Selenomonas, Bacteroides ruminicola, Ruminococcus bromii, Butyrivibrio, Treponema* and *Bifidobacterium*. Facultative anaerobes with high ureolytic activity, but which are low in numbers, are also found in the rumen.

Lipolytic Bacteria

Lipids are actively metabolized by rumen bacteria. *Anaerovibrio lipolytica* hydrolyzes triglycerides and phospholipids to release glycerol and free fatty acids. The lipase of this bacteria is extracellular and membrane-bound. Galactolipids, phospholipids and sulfolipids, which are found in forages, are hydrolyzed by a *Butyrivibrio* sp. Hydrogenation of long-chain unsaturated fatty acids by rumen bacteria is responsible for the relatively constant composition of the body fat of ruminants and the high concentrations of unusual fatty acids in their milk fat. Isomerization and partial hydrogenation of predominant unsaturated fatty acids found in feeds, such as linolenic acid and linoleic acid, can be carried out by *Butyrivibrio fibrisolvens, Treponema bryantii, Eubacterium* spp., *Fusocillus* spp., *Micrococcus* sp. and a strain of *Ruminococcus albus*.

Methane-Producing Bacteria

Methane-producing bacteria represent a special class of the rumen population because of their role in regulating the overall fermentation by the removal of H_2 gas. Reduction of CO_2 with H_2 gas is the primary way that CH_4 is produced in the rumen. However, *Methanosarcina barkerii,* a methanogen which uses methanol, methylamine and acetate to produce CH_4, is usually present. In keeping the H_2 concentration in the rumen low by producing CH_4, the methanogenic bacteria promote the growth of other rumen species and allow for a more efficient fermentation (see later section). The methanogenic bacteria include: *Methanobrevibacter ruminantium, Methanobacterium formicicum* and *Methanomicrobium mobile*. *Methanosarcina* will degrade acetate to CH_4 in the rumen of sheep fed a high molasses-based diet.

THE RUMEN PROTOZOA

The protozoa in the rumen number about 10^5 to 10^6 cells/ml of rumen contents. While flagellate species are present (10^3 to 10^4 per ml), the majority are ciliates. It has been estimated that the protozoa can comprise about 2% of the weight of rumen contents, 40% of total microbial N and 60% of microbial fermentation products in the rumen. The mass of the protozoa in the rumen may be equal to as much as that of the rumen bacteria. Because most rumen ciliates are about 20-200 μm in length, many can be seen with the naked eye, especially when they are allowed to sediment out of rumen fluid. All of the protozoa are strictly anaerobic. The ciliates are placed in the family *Isotrichidae* (of which the genus *Isotricha* and *Dasytricha* are prevalent in the rumen) and the family *Ophryoscolecidae* (of which the genus *Entodinium*, *Diplodinium*, *Epidinium* and *Ophryoscolex* are prevalent). An excellent outline of the classification and identification of rumen protozoa has been published by Ogimoto and Imai (37). Four genera are shown in Plate 7-2.

Ciliate Protozoa

The ciliates are very versatile in their ability to degrade and ferment a wide variety of substrates (Table 7-2). They ingest feed particles and attack all of the major plant constituents including cellulose, hemicellulose, pectin, starch, soluble sugars and lipids. However, there are differences between genera in their substrate specificity. *Isotricha* will utilize starch and many sugars, but not maltose, while *Dasytricha* can utilize many sugars including maltose but not starch. The oligotrichs use mainly particulate materials including starch. Higher numbers of protozoa are generally found in the rumen when diets of high digestibility are fed, but different types of diets seem to encourage different protozoal genera. *Isotricha* numbers are higher when

Table 7-2. Substrates fermented and end-products produced by rumen ciliate protozoa.

Genera	Substrates Fermented	End-products[a]
Isotricha		
intestinalis	starch, sucrose, glucose, pectin	A, p, B, L, H, Li
prostoma	starch, sucrose, glucose, pectin	A, p, B, L, H, Li, C
Dasytricha		
ruminantium	starch, maltose, cellobiose, glucose	A, B, L, H, C
Entodinium		
bursa	starch, hemicellulose	———
caudatum	starch, cellobiose, glucose, maltose, sucrose	A, P, B, L, H, Li, C
furca bilobum	———	Li
simplex	starch	Li
Diplodinium		
Polyplastron	cellulose, glucose, starch, sucrose	A, P, B, L, H, C
Diplodinium	cellulose, hemicellulose, starch	———
Diploplastron	cellulose, hemicellulose, starch	———
Eudiplodinium	cellulose, hemicellulose, starch	A, P, B, L, H, F, C
Ostracodinium	cellulose, hemicellulose, starch	———
Eremoplastron	cellulose, hemicellulose, starch -	———
Epidinium		
ecaudatum caudatum	cellulose, hemicellulose, starch, sucrose, maltose	A, p, B, l, H, f, Li
Ophryoscolex		
caudatus	cellulose, hemicellulose, starch	A, p, B, H

[a] Capital letter indicates major end-product, lower case indicates trace. Acetate (A), propionate (P or p), butyrate (B), lactate (L or l), hydrogen (H), formate (F or f), Lipids (Li), CO_2 (C).

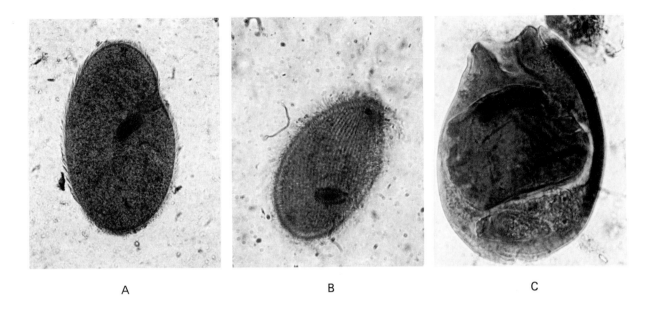

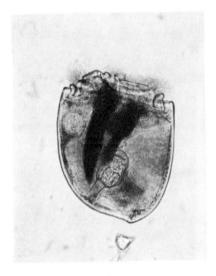

Plate 7-2. Different genera of rumen protozoa. (A) *Isotricha intestinalis* Stein 1859 (350X), (B) *Dasytricha ruminantium* Schuberg 1888 (800X), (C) *Entodinium vorax* Dogiel 1925. A small species of *Diplodinium* and one or two small *Entodinium* have been ingested and are visible inside the cell (800X), (D) *Diplodinium (Eudiplodinium) medium* Awerinzew and Mutafowa 1914 (350X). Courtesy of B.A. Dehority, Ohio State University.

diets containing large amounts of soluble sugars are fed and *Entodinium* usually predominates with high-starch diets. All of the protozoa store large quantities of reserve starch-like polysaccharide, which is used when exogenous energy supplies become exhausted. The rumen protozoa are proteolytic and appear to possess a cysteine proteinase along with high aminopeptidase and limited deaminase activity (16) Both amino acids and ammonia are excreted as end-products of their digestion of protein.

Predation by Protozoa

The protozoa actively ingest bacteria as a source of protein and effectively compete for substrates such that bacterial numbers in the rumen may be decreased by a half or more. Except for size, the protozoa show no preference for particular rumen bacterial species and will also ingest non-rumen species. There appears to be a difference in their mode of attacking bacteria. *Entodinium* will engulf bacteria and digest them internally while *Epidinium* apparently lyse the bacteria first and then ingest their cellular components (9). Ingested bacterial protein and other constituents are to a large extent used directly for cell synthesis by the protozoa. Rumen protozoa do not possess urease activity and ammonia is a poor N source for their growth. There is evidence that the protozoa contribute to the hydrogenation and desaturation of fatty acids in the rumen.

Role of Protozoa in Rumen

While the protozoa are an integral part of the microbial population and have a marked effect on the fermentation, their benefit to the ruminant is still controversial. Some studies have shown a higher digestibility and faster weight gain in animals when protozoa are present in their rumen. Higher rumen ammonia and total VFA concentrations are observed when protozoa are present, suggesting that there might be a higher digestibility. A recent study in which defaunated sheep were inoculated with individual genera of protozoa suggests that each genus has a specific effect on rumen fermentation. *Polyplastron multivesiculatum* significantly increased the dry matter and organic matter digestibility when inoculated into the rumen, while *Isotricha prostoma* significantly decreased these parameters (23).

Studies conducted with defaunated animals either by chemical agents or by dietary change, demonstrate that their absence often does not affect the animal adversely. This suggests that protozoa do not carry out specific functions which are essential to the ruminant. Paradoxically, it appears that by eliminating protozoa from the rumen the performance of animals can be improved under certain dietary conditions (e.g., high-energy, high-NPN diets). Significant predation of bacteria by the protozoa under these conditions might increase the turnover of bacterial cells and thereby decrease the rate of bacterial protein synthesis in the rumen. There might also be a decrease in the amount of microbial protein flowing out of the rumen because it appears that protozoa sometimes sequester in the reticulum or in the dorsal digesta and do not contribute substantially to this outflow (see later section).

If the protozoa do have a beneficial role in the rumen, it would appear to be as a stabilizing factor for the fermentation. By ingesting feed particles and storing reserve polysaccharides, they may control the level of available substrate thereby sustaining a more uniform fermentation over the intervals between feedings. The ingestion of bacteria by protozoa may also serve to hold the fermentation in check, especially when high-grain diets are fed. The protozoa could also be serving as a continuous source of protein in the rumen. By the conversion of bacterial protein into protozoal protein and with the apparent retention of protozoa in the rumen, adequate N could be continually available to the bacteria on the death and lysis of the protozoa. This microbial protein recycling would not be an advantage to the domesticated ruminant consuming a high-protein diet, but could be important when the ruminant is consuming either low-protein diets or during short periods of starvation. It is interesting that wild ruminants seem to maintain higher numbers of protozoa in their rumen than domestic ruminants.

OTHER MICROORGANISMS

Anaerobic Fungi

Anaerobic phycomycete fungal zoospores and vegetative cells have been observed in the rumen (Fig. 7-1). Several of these flagellated organisms, *Neocallimastix frontalis, Sphaeromonas communis* and *Piromonas communis,* have been identified and studied (38-40). Large numbers of these fungi have been observed in the rumen of sheep and cattle attached to and within plant fragments (5). When animals are fed high-roughage diets, the rumen fungi may contribute up to 8% of the microbial mass (41). Whether these fungi are functionally significant in the rumen is still unclear, but they have been shown to degrade

Figure 7-1. Sporangia of rumen anaerobic phycomycete fungi attached to alfalfa stem. These fungi may have a role in fiber digestion in the rumen. Courtesy of T. Bauchop.

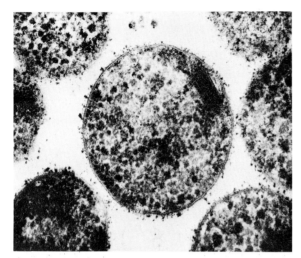

Figure 7-2. Rumen anaerobic mycoplasma, *Anaeroplasma bactoclasticum* (strain 7LA). The ecological significance of these organisms in the rumen is unknown (150,000X). Courtesy of I.M. Robinson (43).

cellulose and xylans, indicating at least some role in fiber digestion.

Mycoplasmas

Strictly anaerobic mycoplasmas have been isolated from the rumen (Fig. 7-2). The bacteriolytic species is usually present in numbers of 10^5 to 10^7 cells/g of rumen contents. Two species have been identified and named *Anaeroplasma bactoclasticum* and *A. abactoclasticum* (43).

Bacteriophages

Bacteriophages are found in the rumen of cattle and sheep. Minimal total count has been estimated as being about 5×10^7 phages per ml of rumen fluid. More than 125 different morphological types have been identified. Virtually nothing is known about either the specificity or significance of these bacteriophages in the rumen.

DEVELOPMENT OF THE RUMEN MICROBIAL POPULATION

Development of Bacteria Population

The newborn ruminant is exposed to many different microbial populations during parturition and thereafter that contribute to the establishment of a gastro-intestinal microbial population. These sources of bacteria and protozoa include: the dam's vagina, the dam's saliva, cud, manure, bedding and environmental flora, other animals, the udder and milk, and other food sources. Of these, the most important to the establishment of a rumen microbial population seems to be animal to animal contact, such as grooming and available food sources (14). The sequence of events leading to the establishment of a mature type rumen population has been described in a study involving four groups of calves fed either a milk diet for 9 weeks, normally-fed milk plus hay and concentrate, or limit-fed milk plus hay and concentrate, with and without antibiotics. Aerobic bacteria were initially high in numbers in the rumen (2.4×10^8/g of contents), but decreased considerably in all groups except the milk-fed group. The milk-fed group maintained high numbers of aerobic bacteria until solid food was provided at 9 weeks of age. Cellulolytic activity was found to increase in all groups up to 4 weeks after which the activity present in the rumen of the milk-fed calves leveled off. The other groups showed a gradual increase in cellulolytic activity and reached adult levels by 6 weeks of age. VFA concentrations in the rumen increased with time, with adult levels of butyrate present at 4 weeks, propionate at 3 weeks, and acetate at 6 to 7 weeks. The milk-fed calves had significantly lower VFA concentrations in their rumen until they were provided with solid food at 9 weeks of age.

The predominant rumen bacteria in these young calves were identified as the rumen population became established. High populations of other anaerobes were gradually replaced by the more typical rumen bacteria. Initial rumen strains isolated were *Butyrivibrio*-like (week 1), followed by *Ruminococcus* (week 3), *Bacteroides succinogenes* (week 6), *B. ruminicola* (week 6) and *Selenomonas*-like (week 6). The major bacteria present in the rumen of calves up to 3 weeks of age are different than those present in mature cattle. At 6 weeks predominant strains normally present in adults are found, as are some others that are not typical of adult animals. By 9 to 13 weeks the rumen bacterial population is fairly reflective of the adult animal.

Other studies in lambs (32, 33) concur with these changes observed in calves. *Streptococcus bovis* was the predominant bacteria present in the rumen of week-old lambs, with

134

Bacteroides fragilis and *Clostridium* making up about 15-20% of the isolates. By 2 weeks, *Streptococcus bovis* declined to 15% of the isolates, and *Bacteroides* sp. increased to 55% of the isolates. *Butyrivibrio fibrisolvens* also comprised 25% of the isolates from the rumen at 2 weeks of age. Both *Selenomonas ruminantium* and *Ruminococcus flavefaciens* were detected at 4 weeks of age, with *Bacteroides ruminicola* and *Succinivibrio dextrinosolvens* apparent at 6 weeks of age. As with calves, the change to the predominant species normally found in adult sheep occurred by 6 weeks of age in lambs.

Development of Protozoa Population

The establishment of the rumen ciliate protozoa population is especially dependent on the presence of other animals already containing protozoa in their rumen. Sheep have been maintained devoid of protozoa for 2½ years by preventing their contact with other ruminants. Normal transfer of protozoa to young animals occurs through salivary or cud transfer either during grooming and eating or by close airborne transfer. Protozoa have been detected in the rumen of young calves as early as one week of age, but permanent establishment takes longer to occur. The delay in establishing a protozoa population results from the highly acid characteristics of a lactic acid fermentation resulting when some milk escapes the esophageal groove. Protozoa are known to be particularly sensitive to low pH (see later section). With the addition of less fermentable feeds (such as roughages) and increases in salivary secretion, the rumen pH becomes more alkaline and the protozoa can then be established. Entodinia become established at pH 6.0, while the holotrichs and ophryoscolecids require at least a pH of 6.5. Until about 3 weeks of age, protozoal numbers are low in the rumen after which they begin to increase in numbers. Adult levels of protozoa in the rumen are reached between 5 and 9 weeks of age depending on the diet.

A great deal of research has been done in an attempt to establish a viable rumen population in young calves. These studies indicate that dry feed consumption is a prerequisite for the early development of a rumen microbial population; and that the amount of grain fed should be less than that of roughage to insure that the rumen pH is high enough to allow the establishment of cellulolytic bacteria and protozoa. Studies (15) indicate that other microorganisms must first be established in the rumen to provide the proper conditions (i.e., VFA, redox potential, pH and ammonia) necessary for the establishment of the cellulolytic bacteria and protozoa.

MICROBIAL INTERDEPENDENCE AND OTHER INTERACTIONS

The rumen fermentation is the net result of interactions between different microorganisms in the ecosystem. Many interactions are known to exist with some being essential to the survivability of the microorganisms involved and other being much more subtle in effect. Examples of *mutualism* (e.g., interaction is beneficial to both organisms), *commensalism* (e.g., interaction is beneficial to one organism without affecting the other organism) and *parasitism* (e.g., interaction in which one organism suffers) can all be found in the rumen. Because many of these interactions are impossible to study with the mixed population, much of our knowledge has been derived from studies with individual rumen species in pure culture. By examining the substrates utilized, the biochemical pathways involved and the end-products produced in pure cultures, much has been learned about the important metabolic interactions which occur between rumen bacteria.

Cross-Feeding of Intermediates

Early studies have established that cross-feeding of intermediate end-products is an important interaction between certain rumen bacterial species. End-products such as succinate, lactate, ethanol, formate and H_2, which are observed in pure cultures, do not usually accumulate in the rumen (due to their further conversion to the VFA) or are not produced due to interspecies H_2 transfer. *Selenomonas ruminantium,* although incapable of utilizing cellulose, will grow in co-culture with *Bacteroides succinogenes* in a cellulose medium by cross-feeding on the succinate produced by *B. succinogenes* from the cellulose. *Megasphaera elsdenii* utilizes lactate to produce propionate via the acrylate pathway and without succinate as an intermediate. Many ruminal species require CO_2 for succinate production as well as for incorporation into other biosynthetic pathways and will not grow well or at all when it is absent from the medium.

Synthesis of α-ketoglutarate by reductive carboxylation in *Selenomonas ruminantium, Bacteroides ruminicola* and *Veillonella alcalescens* requires both succinate and CO_2 (2). Ammonia is a preferred N source for many rumen bacteria. Some species which require ammonia, such as the cellulolytics, must depend on cross-feeding interactions with either proteolytic or ureolytic species which produce ammonia. Release of peptides and amino acids from proteins by protozoa and the more proteolytic bacterial species continually replenish these N sources required by other bacterial species.

VFA Requirement of Bacteria

Many rumen bacteria have a requirement for one or more of the VFA, specifically n-valeric, isobutyric, 2-methylbutyric or isovaleric acid. These acids are essential for the predominant cellulolytic species which must depend on the non-cellulolytic species to produce them either from deamination of the branched-chain amino acids (valine, isoleucine and leucine) or, in case of n-valeric, from amino acids such as proline, lysine, arginine or carbohydrate. The acids serve as the carbon skeletons for the resynthesis of the corresponding amino acids, but, more importantly, for the synthesis of long-chain fatty acids, such as n-pentadecanoic and isotetradecanoic acid, which are usually incorporated into the cell membrane of the bacteria. Studies have shown that this VFA interdependence can also occur by cryptic feeding (e.g., utilization of dead bacterial cells). When grown on starch and ammonia, *Bacteroides amylophilus* synthesizes branched-chain amino acids from starch, CO_2 and ammonia and incorporates them into its protein. On the death and lysis of this bacterium, released branched-chain amino acids can be deaminated to the branched-chain fatty acids by *Megasphaera elsdenii.* The branched-chain fatty acids produced will then support the growth of *Ruminococcus albus* and other rumen bacteria (31).

Aromatic Growth Factors

Other compounds from the degradation of amino acids, such as indoleacetic acid, phenyl-

acetic acid, and p-hydroxyphenylacetic acid, are also used as precursors for tryptophan, phenylalanine and tyrosine biosynthesis, respectively, by rumen bacteria. *Ruminococcus albus,* an important cellulolytic species, is stimulated in its growth by phenylacetic acid, which is used for phenylalanine biosynthesis (52). The use of these compounds for resynthesis back to their corresponding amino acids is expedient for rumen bacteria which otherwise must resort to de novo synthesis.

3-Phenylpropanoic acid is also stimulatory for growth and the digestion of cellulose by *Ruminococcus albus* (19). Studies suggest that 3-phenylpropanoic acid may be a component of the cell capsule and also be involved in the formation of the multi-enzyme complex required for cellulose degradation (51). The source of 3-phenylpropanoic acid in the rumen is still unclear, but some is derived from either phenylalanine or aromatic compounds, such as cinnamate and its derivatives.

Interspecies Hydrogen Transfer

A very important interaction between certain rumen bacteria is interspecies H_2 transfer. The interaction between H_2-producing species and H_2-utilizing species has a significant regulatory effect on the rumen fermentation. H_2 does not accumulate in the rumen because it is used by the methanogenic species to reduce CO_2 to CH_4. The effective removal of H_2 by these methanogenic species encourages important H_2-producing species such as *Ruminococcus albus, R. flavefaciens, Selenomonas ruminantium* and many others, to produce more H_2 and, thus, alter their metabolism towards higher energy-yielding pathways (60).

In the case of *Ruminococcus albus,* the end-products produced are acetate, ethanol, H_2 and CO_2 from sugar when the bacterium is grown in pure culture. However, when *R. albus* is grown in the presence of a methanogen in co-culture, the end-products are only acetate and CH_4 (Fig. 7-3). These results indicate that CH_4 production, rather than being a wasteful process to the ruminant, promotes a more efficient fermentation and higher yields of ATP synthesis by keeping the H_2 concentration low in the rumen (60). The higher yields of ATP result in the synthesis of more microbial cells which increases the available protein to the ruminant.

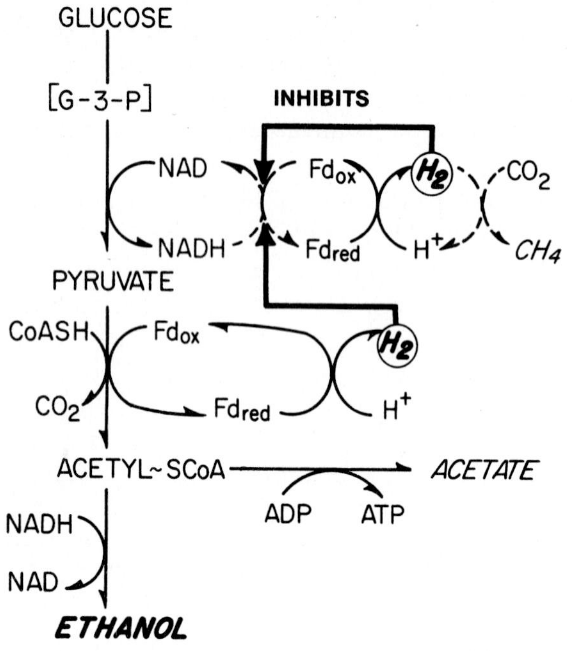

GLUCOSE

[G-3-P]

INHIBITS

Figure 7-3. Fermentation of *Ruminococcus albus* in pure culture and in co-culture with a methanogen. Acetate, ethanol, H_2 and CO_2 are end-products in pure culture, while only acetate and CH_4 are end-products in co-culture. Courtesy of Wolin and Miller (60).

Other Interactions of Bacteria

Numerous other interactions are found between rumen species in terms of growth factors required for biosynthesis (50). Hemin or other tetrapyrrole compounds are required by *Bacteroides ruminicola* and other species for cytochrome biosynthesis. One or more of the B-complex vitamins (biotin, p-aminobenzoic acid, folic acid, pyridoxine, thiamin, riboflavin, B_{12}) are required by most of the major rumen bacteria. Some strains of the CH_4-producing *Methanobrevibacter ruminantium* require for growth a compound, 2-mercaptoethanesulfonic acid (coenzyme M), which is produced by other methanogens in the rumen (27). *Succinivibrio* requires 1,4-naphthoquinone or closely related compounds for synthesis of menaquinone. These compounds are biosynthesized de novo by many other rumen bacteria.

VARIATIONS IN THE RUMEN MICROBIAL POPULATION

Specificity and Distribution

By and large the major species of bacteria and protozoa found in the rumen are quite ubiquitous in ruminants and there is no indication of a host specificity (i.e., a particular species being associated with only a certain host animal). While many species are certainly unique to the rumen, other species and strains closely resemble or are identical with species found in the digestive tracts of other mammals. At least for the major species there does not appear to be much limitation in their geographical distribution. For example, those cellulolytic species which tend to predominate in the rumen (e.g., *Ruminococcus flavefaciens, R. albus, Bacteroides succinogenes* and *Butyrivibrio fibrisolvens*) can generally be isolated from cattle, sheep, goats, water buffalo and other ruminants found in all parts of the world.

There are some data to suggest that geographical location may influence the relative proportions of rumen species which occupy the same ecological niche (i.e., compete for the same substrate). *Eubacterium cellulosolvens* and *Clostridium lochheadii,* which are regarded as of lesser importance in cellulolytic activity, may be the predominant cellulolytic species in the rumen of animals in a particular geographical location (18). Generally, a loss or decrease of a bacterial species from a particular niche is quickly compensated for by an increase in another bacterial species within the niche so that the niche is constantly occupied. However, much more research is needed to determine if differences between geographical locations can alter the balance of the bacterial species within a particular niche.

There are examples of geographically-limited species occupying specific niches in the rumen. The toxicity of the leguminous browse, *Leucaena leucocephala,* in Australia and the lack of toxicity of this plant in Hawaii, when consumed by ruminants, appears to be due to a geographically-limited rumen organism which effectively degrades the toxic compound responsible for the problem (22).

Variation in Bacteria

A comparison of either the rumen bacteria or protozoal population in a group of animals under the same dietary and environmental conditions will show a high level of variation (both quantitatively as well as qualitatively) from animal to animal, especially under dietary conditions where some stress may be present (e.g., high-grain diets).

Bacterial numbers may vary by as much as 2-5 times and protozoa numbers may vary by as much as 3-5 times. Presumably, these variations arise from specific animal factors including such variables as time spent ruminating, the quantity of saliva secreted and its buffering capacity, water consumption, and passage rate of digesta. Individual differences in these physiological parameters may be sufficiently great enough to result in significant effects on the rumen population. Rumen bacteria do show a wide range in sensitivity to pH, redox potential (28) and osmolality. These differences may also influence how rumen bacteria compete against each other by affecting substrate availability and concentration.

Variation in Protozoa

Marked differences in the numbers and type of ciliated protozoa in individual sheep have been observed when they were fed chopped alfalfa hay at different intake levels and feeding frequencies. In 32 sheep examined, four genera of protozoa were found—*Entodinium, Epidinium, Eudiplodinium* and *Dasytricha.* However, not all of the sheep contained all four genera. Entodinia and eudiplodinium were found in all of the sheep, but epidinia were absent in six sheep, and dasytricha was absent from one sheep. The entodinia were the most numerous protozoa in all of the sheep (10).

Like the rumen bacteria, the numbers of protozoa and their genera could be influenced by individual animal differences in the physiological parameters affecting the rumen environment. Differences, especially in pH and passage rate of digesta, can have a profound effect on the numbers and types of protozoa in the rumen (11, 12). Other factors which could be involved are the natural antagonism between protozoa species and the predation of protozoa by other protozoa.

Because protozoa effectively compete for substrates with the bacteria and can also affect bacteria markedly by predation, differences in their numbers in the rumen must also have an effect on bacterial numbers. The suggestion has been made that some of the animal to animal variation observed in dietary treatment responses is due to a tendency for individual animals to have different bacteria to protozoal ratios in the rumen (55).

INFLUENCE OF VARIOUS FACTORS ON RUMEN MICROORGANISMS

The large diversity in the types of microbes found in the rumen is a reflection to some extent of the complexity of the ruminant diet. Many different kinds of carbohydrates, proteins, fats and other dietary constituents are often available. Rumen microorganisms are either highly specialized, intermediate or very broad in the type of nutrients that they will use. This diversity is important in the rumen because the presence of diverse species provides a fuller gene pool and complement of enzymes and biochemical reactions necessary for the maximum conversion of various feedstuffs to microbial cells and fermentation products. Having species in the rumen which also overlap in their ability to use a particular substrate increases the efficiency with which that substrate is used. A diverse population will stabilize a fermentation by preventing large fluctuations in the amounts and proportions of the end-products formed.

Diurnal Variation of Population

The microbial population in the rumen is not static but in a state of flux. Diurnal variations in the total rumen population occur, especially as influenced by the feeding regime. These diurnal changes have been most obvious with rumen protozoa, but have also been observed with rumen bacteria. In general, these diurnal changes appear to vary with the individual characteristics of the organism, but factors such as the diet and its physical form, water intake, and frequency of feeding have modifying effects.

Protozoal numbers are generally higher on diets which contain more readily fermentable carbohydrates. Their concentrations are highest immediately after feeding, declining for a short time, due mainly to the dilution of the rumen contents by ingested water and saliva, and then increasing again until just before refeeding. Increasing the frequency of feeding appears to increase the protozoa concentrations, presumably by providing more substrate for their use. Culture counts made of the total bacteria population with time after feeding show diurnal variation patterns which differ significantly between diets (25). Increasing the frequency of feeding reduces the diurnal variation of both the bacteria and ciliate populations.

Nutrient Limitation

In the rumen periods of nutrient limitation or low availability may occur between feedings (short term) or as a result of starvation (long term). Under starvation conditions, rumen microorganisms show different survivabilities. Some microorganisms die very rapidly, especially the protozoa, and may be completely lost from the rumen population. When energy starved in continuous culture, *Selenomonas ruminantium* has been shown to have an ST_{50} of only 2.5 h (i.e., survival time for 50% of initial viable population to become non-viable) while *Megasphaera elsdenii* has an ST_{50} of only 3-5 h. While these values suggest that these species have a poor survivability, conditions in the rumen such as lysed cells and especially the presence of more slowly degraded materials such as cellulose and hemicellulose in plant cell walls could be sustaining many species.

When energy is limiting, *Selenomonas ruminantium* will shift its metabolism to higher energy-yielding pathways, resulting in less lactate and propionate and more acetate being produced. However, when N is limiting, it will expend more energy to incorporate N. Predominant species of rumen bacteria are efficient scavengers of ammonia and have very low ammonia saturation constants (49).

Effects of Diet

The diet is probably the most important factor which influences the numbers and relative proportions of the different species in the rumen. Changing the diet of the animal invokes a period of transition in the rumen microbial population. The proportions of the different species in the rumen will shift to a new balance, one which best accommodates the dietary change. This is referred to as an adaptation of the population.

Adaptation may take several days or weeks to take place, depending on how drastic a change is made in the diet. The metabolism of biuret, nitrite and oxalate in the rumen is enhanced by adapting the microbial population to these compounds over a period of time, thus avoiding a toxic effect. Probably the most dramatic changes which occur both in the rumen population and fermentation is with a change in diet to large amounts of readily fermentable carbohydrates (e.g., high-concentrate diets). Feeding diets of these types results in a succession of changes in the rumen microbial population during the adaptation period, specifically in those bacteria which produce and utilize lactate. Acid-sensitive, lactate utilizers, such as *Veillonella* and *Selenomonas,* are replaced by acid-tolerant, lactate utilizers such as *Anaerovibrio, Propionibacterium* and *Megasphaera.* Amylolytic bacteria, such as *Bacteroides,* are replaced by lactate producers such as *Lactobacillus, Eubacterium* and *Streptococcus.* Lactic acidosis (see Ch. 23) which arises from an abrupt shift to a high concentrate diet appears to result from the inability of the effective lactate utilizing species, such as *Megasphaera,* to increase in sufficient numbers to prevent the accumulation of lactate produced by *Streptococcus bovis* and *Lactobacillus* in the rumen and the resulting decrease in pH.

Feeding high levels of a liquid molasses diet ad libitum can result in a different manner of change in the microbial population and fermentation in the rumen. Under these conditions where the liquid turnover rate is slow and the fermentation of the soluble carbohydrates in molasses is rapid, the large quantities of VFA produced in the rumen of sheep can undergo a secondary fermentation. Bacteria not normally seen in such high numbers will increase greatly in the rumen. *Methanosarcina* sometimes proliferate and will cleave acetate to CO_2 and CH_4 (45). Beta oxidation of fatty acids to acetate and CH_4 might also occur.

Increasing the liquid turnover rate of the rumen by including mineral salts such as $NaHCO_3$ in the diet, or by providing salt in the drinking water will also alter the balance of bacterial species in the rumen. The increased turnover rate is believed to select for those bacterial species with faster growth rates. A decrease in the molar proportion of propionate and an increase in the molar proportions of acetate and butyrate usually occur in the VFA composition with an increased liquid turnover rate (44).

Effects of Rumen pH

Rumen pH is one of the more variable of the ecologic factors which can profoundly influence the microbial population. Studies have shown that the efficiency of growth of predominant rumen bacteria will vary considerably with pH (56). Cellulolytic bacteria and methanogenic bacteria are severely affected once the rumen pH falls below 6.0. The rumen protozoa are also affected by the low pH brought about by feeding excess concentrates in the diet. However, feeding smaller amounts of concentrate actually stimulates higher concentrations of protozoa in the rumen. With the pH maintained at about 5.5, large numbers of protozoa, primarily *Isotricha* and *Entodinia,* may be present in the rumen, but below 5.5 their numbers are greatly depressed. The holotrich protozoa appear to be more susceptible to a decrease in pH than the entodinia.

Effects of Antibiotics

Because antibiotics have been shown to affect the rumen microorganisms, there has been interest in attempting to control the rumen fermentation by feeding these compounds. Many antibiotics have a dramatic effect on the numbers and kinds of rumen bacteria, but usually for only a short time after the first supplementation to the diet. An examination of 15 of the most predominant rumen bacterial species showed that they are susceptible at low concentrations to many antibiotics. Feeding Tylosin to sheep has been shown to double the protozoa concentration in the rumen, concomitant with a drastic decrease in bacterial numbers and total VFA concentration.

The polyether ionophores, which include monensin and lasalocid, are used to alter rumen fermentation to improve efficiency of feed utilization. These ionophores affect the rumen fermentation by increasing the molar proportion of propionate, decreasing methanogenesis, and inhibiting proteolysis and deamination. Gram-positive bacteria (e.g., *Ruminococcus albus, R. flavefaciens* and

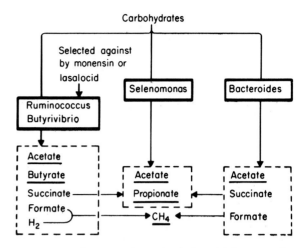

Figure 7-4. Proposed hypothesis by which monensin and lasalocid alter the rumen fermentation to increase propionate and decrease methane. Courtesy of Chen and Wolin (8).

Butyrivibrio fibrisolvens) are inhibited by low concentrations of monensin and lasalocid. Rapid selection of gram-negative bacteria (e.g., *Bacteroides succinogenes* and *B. ruminicola*) resistant to the ionophores will increase with a low level of exposure. These results have lead to the hypothesis (Fig. 7-4) that these ionophores select for succinate-producing *Bacteroides* and *Selenomonas ruminantium,* which produce propionate from succinate. They also select against the H_2 and formate producers, such as *Ruminococcus albus, R. flavefaciens* and *Butyrivibrio fibrisolvens,* which decreases the concentrations of precursors required for methanogenesis (8).

Because the ionophores also appear to be effective against *streptococci* and *lactobacilli* (13), they may be of value in controlling the problem of lactic acidosis when high-concentrate diets are fed (35). The mechanism by which these ionophores exert their effects appear to be by interfering with the normal transport of ions through the cell membrane (7). Avoparcin, a glycopeptide antibiotic, although differing in its mechanism of action, appears to exert a similar effect as the ionophores on the rumen bacterial population. *Ruminococcus flavefaciens, Butyrivibrio fibrisolvens* and *Bacteroides succinogenes* are particularly sensitive to avoparcin and *Selenomonas ruminantium, Bacteroides ruminicola* and *Megasphaera elsdenii* are more resistant to the antibiotic (53).

ATTACHMENT OF RUMEN MICROORGANISMS

The attachment of microorganisms to surfaces is an important factor which has numerous implications in an ecosystem where material is constantly being introduced and removed. In order for bacteria to maintain their numbers in the rumen, it is necessary that their generation time (e.g., time for doubling of a population) be shorter than the turnover rate of the rumen digesta. If this were not the case, the bacteria would eventually wash out of the rumen. Since the passage rate of the particulate phase is much slower than that of the liquid phase in the rumen, slower growing species are prevented from being washed out by attaching to various surfaces.

The majority of bacteria found in the rumen are attached to particulate matter. On high-roughage diets there is a stratification of the rumen contents (particularly in cattle) with higher numbers of bacteria found in the fibrous dorsal mat than the more liquid ventral contents. The same pattern probably applies to the protozoa. Earlier studies indicated that protozoa did not make a significant contribution to microbial N passing out of the rumen. Furthermore, the in vitro generation time of protozoa is inadequate to account for their maintenance in the rumen. It is now known that oligotrichs may be preferentially retained in the rumen by attachment to particulate matter while holotrichs sequester to the wall of the reticulum between feeding intervals. Large numbers of protozoa, such as the *Epidinium,* have been observed attached to plant fragments, thus avoiding being completely washed out with the liquid phase (6) (Fig. 7-5).

Attachment of Cellulolytic Bacteria

Cellulolytic rumen species, such as *Ruminococcus flavefaciens, R. albus* and *Bacteroides succinogenes,* adhere to plant cell walls by means of an extracellular glycoprotein coat surrounding the cell (24). Presumably, this attachment to the substrate facilitates more efficient degradation by enzymes located in the extracellular material or at the cell surface and also minimizes the loss of hydrolytic products of cellulose and hemicellulose to scavenging species.

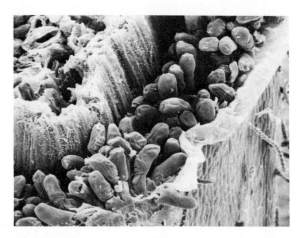

Figure 7-5. Dense attachment of the rumen protozoa *Epidinium* between the epidermis and vascular cylinder of alfalfa stem. Courtesy of T. Bauchop (4).

Examination of the attachment of different rumen species to plant cell walls suggest that an attachment by a morphologically distinct species initially occurs. This is followed by the adherence of another species to the glycoprotein coat of the first species so that both species are involved. As digestion proceeds, the adherent population will grow on the substrate until cells are released into the rumen fluid to either recolonize new substrate or pass out of the rumen (29).

Attachment of Amylolytic Bacteria

Bacteroides amylophilus, B. ruminicola and *Bifidobacterium* sp. will attach to starch granules. The attachment can be influenced by temperature and the end-products of the starch hydrolysis. These species have strong intracellular amylase activity. Species with strong extracellular amylase activity, such as *Butyrivibrio fibrisolvens* and *Streptococcus bovis,* are incapable of attaching to starch.

Attachment to Rumen Wall

A large population of bacteria are also found adhering to the rumen wall. Many of these bacteria are facultative anaerobes, and the suggestion is that the small population of these bacteria consistently found in the rumen contents may be due to continuous transfer from the rumen wall. Interestingly, a substantial number of these adherent bacteria are reported to be ureolytic. The distribution of bacteria on the rumen wall appears to be strongly influenced by the type of diet fed (29).

Bacterial Attachment to Protozoa

Attachment of bacterial species to protozoa has been observed, although the significance of this association is unclear (21) (Fig. 7-6). *Methanobrevibacter ruminantium* is found attached to the protozoal surface (58), and it is possible that such an association facilitates interspecies H_2 transfer. The frequency of attachment between the methanogenic bacterium and protozoa appears to increase during fasting and decrease with feeding of the animal (54).

While attachment does affect the numbers and types of microorganisms found in the rumen and is advantageous to the survivability and competitiveness of certain important rumen species, it does cause difficulty in experimental quantitation. Attachment of bacteria not only prevents an accurate count of microbial numbers in the rumen, but also creates a problem in the separation of microbial N from dietary N in digesta passing out of the rumen.

MICROORGANISMS OF THE INTESTINE

Microbial Characteristics

The bacterial population in the lower intestine of ruminants resembles that of the rumen in several ways. First, anaerobic species predominate at both sites. In the large intestine, obligate anaerobes outnumber aerobes at least 100 fold (57) with the greatest number of bacteria being associated with the cecum, colon and rectum. Secondly, the predominant bacteria isolated from the cecum include several genera found in the rumen. Gram-negative rods such as *Bacteroides, Butyrivibrio* and *Fusobacterium* have been shown to predominate. Also present are gram-positive cocci like *Streptococcus bovis* and *S. faecalis* and some *Selenomonas* species. Thirdly, the bacteria isolated from these regions of the lower intestine are found in several states of attachment much like those seen in the rumen.

Bacteria may be found associated with feed particles, free in the lumen, or attached to intestinal epithelium and mucous layer. Viable counts from the cecum of sheep ranging from 10^7 to 10^9 cells/g of cecal contents have been reported (57). Finally, methanogenesis has been shown to occur in the large intestine of the ruminant. Twelve percent of the total CH_4 production in a sheep was found to be from the large intestine (34).

Concentrations of Bacteria

Establishment of the bacterial population in the large intestine has been studied by measuring the VFA concentrations in various segments of the intestinal tract. The lower intestine was the major site of fermentation in lambs up to 28 d of age. After this age the reticulum-rumen became the major site of VFA production. As the lambs aged the proportion of VFA produced in the rumen increased while that of the large intestine remained constant. This indicates that fermentation of substrates in the lower intestine has an energetically important role in lambs and in adult animals as well.

Electron microscopy of various regions of the intestine of sheep show a gradual increase

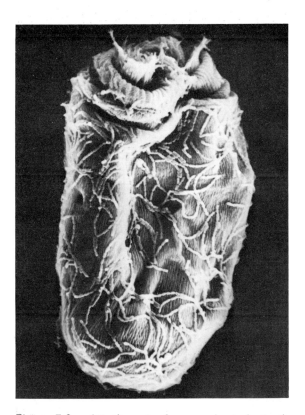

Figure 7-6. Attachment of rumen bacteria to the rumen protozoa, *Diplodinium.* Courtesy of C.L. Davis, Univ. of Illinois.

142

of bacterial numbers from the pylorus to the ileum. Viable counts from digesta collected along four different sites of the small intestine of a sheep ranged from 5×10^4 to 7×10^6 cells/g of digesta. Tissue counts ranged from 2×10^2 to 4×10^4 cells/g. The predominant bacteria isolated from the small intestine were gram-positive, facultative streptococci, and a rod-shaped isolate resembling *Propionibacterium.* Both of these isolates use starch as an energy source. Whether they compete with the host for starch digestion is not known (36).

Bacteria in the Cecum

The cecum provides an ideal environment for a large bacterial population as it has a relatively constant supply of substrate, constant temperature and pH. Substrate available includes previously undigested feed, residue from partially digested feed, sloughed cells and intestinal secretions such as bile, enzymes and mucins. Fluctuations in cecal pH have been shown to occur in lambs under different feeding conditions. Lambs fed alfalfa have cecal pH values ranging from 6.6-7.8, while lambs on grain diets have pH values ranging from 5.7-7.2 (57). Four types of organisms have been isolated from the sheep cecum: a coccus and coryneform rod, a spirochete, resembling *Treponema succinifaciens,* and a curved rod similar to *Butyrivibrio.*

Grain over-feeding may create a lactic acidosis condition in the large intestine much like that which occurs in the rumen (1). The presence of large amounts of starch induces a rapid fermentation which creates a drop in pH and increases amounts of lactic acid. This change in conditions in the cecum changes the bacterial population to increase numbers of *Streptococcus bovis*, coliforms and *Clostridium Perfringens*.

SUMMARY

The early nutrition and digestive physiology studies have revealed the importance of the rumen fermentation to the ruminant. In the last 30 years there has been considerable research on characterizing the diverse population of microbes found in the rumen. The development of anaerobic culturing techniques by Hungate in the 1940's greatly facilitated these research efforts by making it feasible to isolate and study rumen bacteria in pure culture. Based on their preference for various substrates and the end-products of their fermentation, the functional significance of most of the predominant bacterial species found in the rumen have now been identified. Pure culture and co-culture studies have described important interdependences and other interactions between rumen microorganisms which influence their growth rates, yield, and metabolism. This knowledge has been used to understand how to best manipulate the rumen fermentation to improve the efficiency and production of the ruminant.

The contribution of ciliate protozoa to the protein economy of the ruminant is still unclear. There is substantial evidence to indicate that protozoa exert a marked effect on the rumen fermentation and may be responsible for some of the animal to animal variation in dietary treatment responses. The attachment of protozoa to particulate matter and to the wall of the reticulum assists in their survivability in the rumen and also means that protozoa may make less than a significant contribution to the microbial protein available to the ruminant.

The functional significance of other microorganisms in the rumen, such as the anaerobic fungi, mycoplasma and bacteriophages, is very poorly understood. Some studies suggest that the anaerobic fungi have a role in facilitating fiber digestion in the rumen. More research is needed to determine the role of these microorganisms in the rumen fermentation.

Literature Cited

1. Allison, M.J., E.T. Littledike and L.F. James. 1977. J. Animal Sci. 45:1173.
2. Allison, M.J., I.M. Robinson and A.L. Baetz. 1979. J. Bacteriol. 140:980.
3. Bauchop, T. 1981. Agr. and Environ. 6:339.
4. Bauchop, T. 1979. Appl. Environ. Microbiol. 37:1217.

5. Bauchop, T. 1979. Appl. Environ. Microbiol. 38:148.

6. Bauchop, T. and R.T.J. Clarke. 1976. Appl. Environ. Microbiol. 32:417.

7. Bergen, W.G. and D.B. Bates. 1984. J. Animal Sci. 58:1465.

8. Chen, M. and M.J. Wolin. 1979. Appl. Environ. Microbiol. 38:72.

9. Clarke, R.T.J. 1977. In: Microbial Ecology of the Gut, p. 251. Academic Press, Inc., New York.

10. Clarke, R.T.J., M.J. Ulyatt and A. John. 1982. Appl. Environ. Microbiol. 43:1201.

11. Dehority, B.A. 1978. J. Protozool. 25:509.

12. Dehority, B.A., W.S. Damron and J.B. McLaren. 1983. Appl. Environ. Microbiol. 45:1394.

13. Dennis, S.M., T.G. Nagaraja and E.E. Bartley. 1981. J. Animal Sci. 52:418.

14. Ducluzeau, R. 1983. Ann. Rech. Vet. 14:354.

15. Fonty, G., Ph. Gouet, J.P. Jouany and J. Senaud. 1983. J. Gen. Microbiol. 129:213.

16. Forsberg, C.W., L.K.A. Lovelock, L. Krumholz and J.G. Buchanan-Smith. 1984. Appl. Environ. Microbiol. 47:101.

17. Hungate, R.E. 1984. Proc. Nutr. Soc. 43:1.

18. Hungate, R.E. 1975. Ann. Rev. Ecol. System. 6:39.

19. Hungate, R.E. and R.J. Stack. 1982. Appl. Environ. Microbiol. 44:79.

20. Hobson, P.N. and R.J. Wallace. 1982. Microbial Ecology and Activities in the Rumen: Part I and II. CRC Critical Rev. in Microbiology.

21. Imai, S. and K. Ogimoto. 1978. Japan J. Vet. Sci. 40:9.

22. Jones, R.J. and R.G. Megarrity. 1983. Australian J. Agr. Res. 34:781.

23. Jouany, J.P., et al. 1981. Reprod. Nutr. Develop. 21:871.

24. Latham, M.J., B.E. Brooker, G.L. Pettipher and P.J. Harris. 1978. Appl. Environ. Microbiol. 35:156.

25. Leedle, J.A., M.P. Bryant and R.B. Hespell. 1982. Appl. Environ. Microbiol. 4:402.

26. Leng, R.A. 1982. Brit. J. Nutr. 48:399.

27. Lovley, D.R., R.C. Greening and J.G. Ferry. 1984. Appl. Environ. Microbiol. 48:81.

28. Marounek, M. and R.J. Wallace. 1984. J. Gen. Microbiol. 130:223.

29. McCowan, R.P., K.J. Cheng, C.B.M. Bailey and J.W. Costerton. 1978. Appl. Environ. Microbiol. 35:149.

30. McDonald, I.W. and A.C.I. Warner (eds). 1975. Digestion and Metabolism in the Ruminant. Univ. New England Publishing Unit, Armidale, N.S.W., Australia.

31. Miura, H., M. Horiguchi and T. Matsumoto. 1980. Appl. Environ. Microbiol. 40:294.

32. Mueller, R.E., J.M. Asplund and E.L. Iannotti. 1984. Appl. Environ. Microbiol. 47:715.

33. Mueller, R.E., E.L. Iannotti and J.M. Asplund. 1984. Appl. Environ. Microbiol. 47:724.

34. Murray, R.M., A.M. Bryant and R.A. Leng. 1976. Brit. J. Nutr. 36:1.

35. Nagaraja, T.G., et al. 1981. J. Animal Sci. 53:206.

36. Nicoletti, J.M., C.L. Davis, R.B. Hespell and J.A.Z. Leddle. 1984. J. Dairy Sci. 67:1227.

37. Ogimoto, K. and S. Imai. 1981. Atlas of Rumen Microbiology. Japan Scientific Soc. Press, Tokyo, Japan.

38. Orpin, C.G. 1977. J. Gen. Microbiol. 99:107.

39. Orpin, C.G. 1976. J. Gen. Microbiol. 94:270.

40. Orpin, C.G. 1975. J. Gen. Microbiol. 91:249.

41. Orpin, C.G. 1981. In: Agricultural Science Seminar: Degradation of Plant Cell-Wall Material, p. 36. Agr. Res. Council, London.

42. Orpin, C.G. and A.J. Letcher. 1979. Current Microbiol. 3:121.

43. Robinson, I.M. 1979. The Mycoplasmas. Vol. I. Academic Press, Inc., New York.

44. Rogers, J.A., C.L. Davis and J.H. Clark. 1982. J. Dairy Sci. 65:577.

45. Rowe, J.B., M.L. Loughnan, J.V. Nolan and R.A. Leng. 1979. Brit. J. Nutr. 41:393.

46. Russell, J.B., W.G. Bottje and M.A. Cotta. 1981. J. Animal Sci. 53:242.

47. Savage, D.C. 1977. Microbial Ecology of the Gastrointestinal Tract. Ann. Rev. Microbiol. 31:107.

48. Savage, D.C. 1981. The Microbial Flora in the Gastrointestinal Tract. In: Nutrition in Health and Disease and International Development: Symposia from the XII International Congress of Nutrition, p. 893. Alan R. Liss, Inc., New York.

49. Schaefer, D.M., C.L. Davis and M.P. Bryant. 1980. J. Dairy Sci. 63:1248.

50. Slyter, L.L. and J.M. Weaver. 1977. Appl. and Environ. Microbiol. 33:363.

51. Stack, R.J. and R.E. Hungate. 1984. Appl. Environ. Microbiol. 48:218.

52. Stack, R.J., R.E. Hungate and W.P. Opsahl. 1983. Appl. Environ. Microbiol. 46:539.

144

53. Stewart, C.S., M.V. Crossley and S.H. Garrow. 1983. Eur. J. Appl. Microbiol. Biotechnol. 17:292.
54. Stumm, C.K., H.J. Gijzen and G.D. Vogels. 1982. Brit. J. Nutr. 47:95.
55. Teather, R.M., S. Mahadevan, J.D. Erfle and F.D. Sauer. 1984. Appl. Environ. Microbiol. 47:566.
56. Therion, J.A., A. Kistner and J.H. Kornelius. 1982. Appl. Environ. Microbiol. 44:428.
57. Ulyatt, M.J., D.W. Dellow, C.S.W. Reid and T. Bauchop. 1975. In: Digestion and Metabolism in the Ruminant. I.W. McDonald and A.C.I. Warner, eds. Univ. of New England Publ. Unit, Armidale, Australia.
58. Vogels, G.D., W.F. Hoppe and C.K. Stumm. 1980. Appl. Environ. Microbiol. 40:608.
59. Wojciechowicz, M., K. Heinrichova and A. Ziolecki. 1982. J. Gen. Microbiol. 128:2661.
60. Wolin, M.J. and T.L. Miller. 1983. Fed. Proc. 42:109.
61. Yu, I. and R.E. Hungate. 1979. Ann. Rech. Vet. 10:251.

8 RUMINAL FERMENTATION

by F. N. Owens and A. L. Goetsch

INTRODUCTION

Fermentation in the rumen is the result of physical and microbiological activities which convert components of the diet to products which are useful (VFA, microbial protein, B-vitamins), useless (CH_4, CO_2) or even harmful (ammonia, nitrate) to the host animal. Ruminant animals culture the microbial population in the rumen by supplying and masticating feed regularly, by adding buffers and removing acids produced, by flushing out microbial products and indigestible feed residues, and by maintaining conditions (pH, temperature and moisture) appropriate for microbial growth. This chapter will address physiological and biochemical aspects of ruminal digestion of various feed nutrients, fermentation of these nutrients and growth of ruminal microbes.

HOST-MICROBE SYNERGISM

In the synergistic relationship between the functional ruminant and its ruminal microbes, the animal regularly provides chewed or re-chewed substrate in a fluid environment (Ch. 5) which is mixed or churned (Ch. 4). Carbohydrates, proteins and lipids in feeds are usually polymers which must be cleaved to monomeric forms for fermentation or absorption as outlined in Table 8-1. With intermittent feed intake, the rumen is similar to repeated fermentations in batch or non-continuous cultures. End products of fermentation, which are continually removed, include VFA, CH_4, CO_2, ammonia-N and microbial organisms as presented in Table 8-1.

Microbes exist in three distinct locations in the rumen as illustrated in Fig. 8-1. Though some microbes adhere tightly to the wall of the rumen, most microbes are associated with particles in the rumen or float freely in ruminal liquid. The wall-adhering bacteria hydrolyze urea diffusing into the rumen and may use a limited amount of oxygen. Most other bacteria in the rumen are anaerobic and find O_2 toxic. O_2, present in feed particles or diffusing through the rumen wall, is consumed rapidly by the adherent microbes along the rumen wall and the few facultative anaerobes in the rumen itself. Because most ruminal microbes have no O_2 available, their metabolic options are limited. Anaerobic microbes work with a surplus of reducing equivalents (NADH) and utilize a variety of reactions to dispose of surplus reducing power. Hence, they reduce all available compounds. CO_2 is reduced to CH_4, sulfates and nitrates are reduced to sulfides and ammonia and

Table 8-1. Overview of ruminal digestion.

Feedstuff proximate component	Chemical constituent (polymer)	Chemical components (monomers)	Ruminal fermentation products
Nitrogen-free extract	Carbohydrates (hexosan)	Glucose and other hexoses	Acetate, propionate & butyrate
Crude fiber	(pentosan)	Pentoses	As above
Crude protein	True protein Non-protein N	Amino acids	Above & isobutyrate Isovalerate & ammonia
Crude fat	Triglycerides Galactosides	Glycerol Fatty acids	Propionate & saturated fatty acids
Crude ash	Minerals	Elements	Reduced elements + microbial cells + CO_2 and CH_4

146

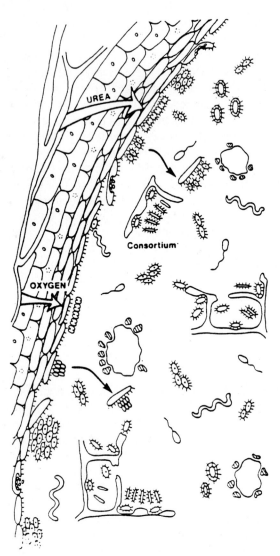

Figure 8-1. Locations of microbes in the rumen with facultative anaerobes found near the epithelial cells of the rumen wall and anaerobes partially associated with plant cell walls, starch particles or floating free. From Cheng and Costerton (7).

unsaturated fatty acids are saturated. Despite the surplus of reducing power, growth of microbes remains limited by the amount of ATP available. If O_2 were present, yield of ATP and microbial growth could be increased. But if O_2 were used, the products of digestion would be CO_2 and H_2O, not volatile fatty acids which serve as the primary source of energy available for the host animal.

CHARACTERISTICS OF THE RUMEN ENVIRONMENT

Osmolarity, pH and Redox Potential

Ruminal conditions vary tremendously due to environmental and dietary conditions. Normal fermentation proceeds at osmolarities between 260 and 340 mOsm. Osmolarity is usually reasonably constant near 280 mOsm but can increase to 350 or 400 mOsm after a meal of concentrate or pelleted alfalfa. An osmotic pressure near 260 mOsm is most favorable for ciliate protozoa. Above 350 mOsm, digestion of starch and fiber is inhibited through a direct effect upon microbial metabolism. Rumination is impaired, also. Net flux of water through the ruminal wall is small at normal osmaloarities, but water influx through the rumen wall is detected at higher osmolarities while efflux of water to blood is noted at lower osmolarities. Ruminal pH can range from 5.5 to 7.2, with lower pH values being detected shortly after a high concentrate meal. Cellulolytic bacteria are inhibited whenever pH falls below 6.0. The redox potential in the rumen is usually between –250 and –450 mV, reflecting the absence of oxygen and excess of reducing power (30).

Ruminal Volume

Compared to non-ruminant animals, ruminants have a very large gut capacity. This large capacity is necessary to retain fibrous particles in the gut long enough for microbial fermentation. The liquid volume of the rumen of mature sheep is about 5.3 ℓ (SE = 1.0) or 13% of body weight. In cattle, rumen liquid volume averages 48 ℓ (SE = 3.7) or 15 to 21% of body weight. Generally, as body weight increases, ruminal volume increases, but at a decreasing rate (rumen volume = kg weight$^{0.57}$). Total gut capacity appears to increase proportionally to body weight. As level of feed intake increases, ruminal volume increases as well (Fig. 8-2). From this figure, cattle at 500 kg consuming 10 kg of dry matter (2% of body weight) should have a rumen volume equal to 16% of body weight or 80 ℓ. Individual animals which consume larger amounts of feed in a meal generally have a larger rumen volume. Ruminal volume also is greater when the diet contains more roughage (Fig. 8-3). If the animal above were fed diets consisting of 100% concentrate, 50% concentrate or 0% concentrate (all roughage), rumen volumes (*'s on graph) would be 13.5, 15.5 or 17.2% of body weight or 68, 78 and 86 ℓ, respectively.

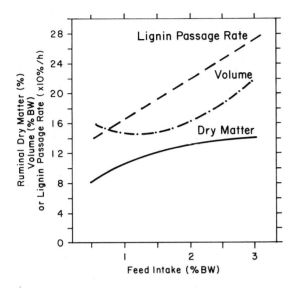

Figure 8-2. Influence of level of feed intake (FI) as a percent of body weight on ruminal dry matter, ruminal volume and lignin passage rate for cattle. [(DM = 5.37 + 5.81 FI - 1.04 FI * FI; r^2 = .48, N = 49, P < .01) (Volume = 18.4 - 6.21 FI + 2.45 FI * FI; r^2 = .25, N = 49, P < .01) (Lignin passage rate = 1.06 + .547 FI; r^2 = .48, N = 42, P < .01)].

Ruminal Dry Matter

The dry matter percentage of rumen contents can range from below 7% to over 14% of rumen wet weight in cattle (Fig. 8-2) with the 500 kg animal above having about 12.5% dry matter in the rumen. Again, dietary roughage level alters dry matter (Fig. 8-4) with means of 11.8, 12.3 and 12.8% for 100, 50 and 0% concentrate diets above, respectively. Ruminal volume also will change with forage source or processing, animal age and pregnancy. Crowding of the abdominal cavity by the products of conception will reduce feed intake by ewes and may cause pregnancy disease, a disorder similar to ketosis of lactating cows (see Ch. 24).

Ruminal volume limits feed intake of high roughage diets (5). However, ruminal volume by itself is an incomplete description of ruminal action because solids and liquids are flushed through the rumen continuously at various rates. Both volume and rate of passage, often called fractional outflow, must be combined to determine the amount of material which can be handled each day (13).

Ruminal Passage Rate

Ruminal output or flow to the omasum divided by ruminal volume gives the fractional passage rate (k_p). For liquids, this is often called "dilution rate". With an output of 4 ℓ/h

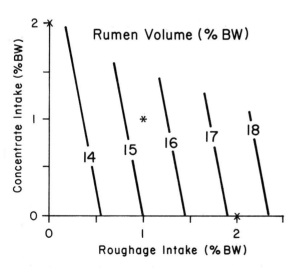

Figure 8-3. Rumen volume with various intakes of concentrate (CI) and roughage (RI) all expressed as a percentage of body weight for cattle. (Volume = 12.8 + .49CI + 2.25RI; r^2 = .184, N = 49). With CI = RI = 1.0, volume = 15.4% (*) of body weight.

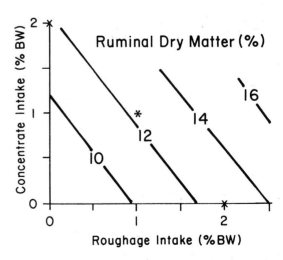

Figure 8-4. Ruminal dry matter with various intakes of concentrate (CI) and roughage (RI) as a percentage of body weight for cattle. (DM = 7.65 + 2.08CI + 2.55RI; r^2 = .46, N = 48). With CI = RI = 1.0, DM = 12.3% (*).

148

and a ruminal volume of 50 ℓ, k_p calculates to be 0.08/h or, as often cited, 8%/h. Ruminal contents do not all flow together. Certain portions not dense enough or not small enough in particle size are preferentially retained in the rumen. For such portions, time for ruminal digestion is lengthened. Liquid k_p always exceeds k_p for concentrate or roughage particles. If the dry matter of the rumen contents were 12% and output was 4% dry matter for the animal above, k_p for dry matter was 2.7%/h (4 ℓ/h @ 4% dry matter/50ℓ @ 12% dry matter).

Disappearance Rate

Another common measurement is total disappearance rate (k_t) of a substance from the rumen. Disappearance rate differs from k_p and is calculated from daily intake and amount of material in the rumen rather than from output and amount of material in the rumen. If the animal above was fed 8 kg of dry matter/d and the rumen had 12% dry matter, then the amount of dry matter in the rumen was 6.0 kg (50 kg x 0.12). The k_t is calculated as daily intake (8 kg/24 h) divided by ruminal contents (6.0 kg) which equals 1.33/24 h, 0.055/h or 5.5%/h. Note that k_t exceeds k_p from above (2.7%/h) because k_t includes loss both by passage (k_p) and by digestion, commonly called k_d, while k_p considers passage alone. For indigestible compounds or markers which disappear from the rumen only by passage to the omasum, k_t equals k_p. For digested components, k_t equals k_p plus digestion rate (k_d). In addition, a lag time before digestion begins can be considered. Ignoring lag time, k_d above determined by subtraction (5.5%/h minus 2.7%/h) is 2.8%/h.

All organic matter must leave the rumen by flow to the omasum or fermentation within the rumen, thus the proportion of material digested in the rumen can be calculated easily. It is the ratio of k_d to k_t (k_d plus k_p) or 51% (2.8/5.5). The residual proportion of material escaping ruminal digestion equals $k_p/(k_p+k_d)$ or 49% (2.7/5.5). Escape of various feed components like protein usually is not equal to escape of dry matter or organic matter because rates of digestion (k_d) for specific feed components differ.

Differential Passage

Though liquids and particles share the rumen, particles leave the rumen less rapidly than liquid. This is due to location of particles in the rumen or to filtration by the omasum. To leave the rumen, particles must be near the reticulo-omasal orifice. Larger particles become trapped in the raft floating in the dorsal portion of the rumen and do not pass close to the exit orifice. Also, large particles passing through the orifice are screened by omasal lamina and returned to the rumen. Hence, larger particles are retained for a longer time in the rumen. The k_p for fluid, concentrate and roughage particles changes with level of feed intake and level of roughage in the diet. These factors are combined in Fig. 8-5, 8-6 and 8-7 to illustrate their impact on fluid, concentrate and roughage passage as summarized from the literature available for cattle (22).

The k_p for fluids usually ranges from 4-10%/h (Fig. 8-5), while the k_p for concentrate particles ranges from 2-7%/h (Fig. 8-6) and for roughage particles from 1-6%/h (Fig. 8-7). With a 50% roughage diet consumed at 2% of body weight, hourly k_p for liquids, concentrates and roughage (*'s on figures) would be 7.2, 5.5 and 3.5%, respectively. Though k_p

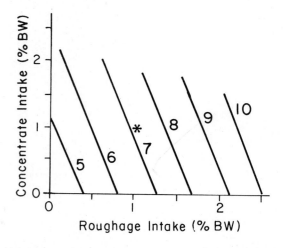

Figure 8-5. Fluid passage rate (%/h) with various intakes of concentrate (CI) and roughage (RI) for cattle as a percentage of body weight. (FPR = 4.21 + .77CI + 2.32RI; r² = .29, N = 119). With CI = RI = 1.0, FPR = 7.2% (*).

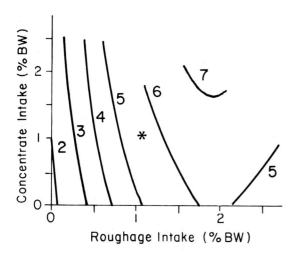

Figure 8-6. Concentrate passage rate (%/h) with various intakes of concentrate (CI) and roughage (RI) for cattle as a percentage of body weight. (CPR = 1.30 + .61CI + 4.88RI − 1.25RI*RI; r^2 = .61, N = 70). With CI = RI = 1.0, CPR = 5.5% (*).

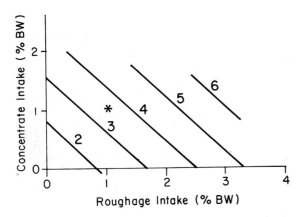

Figure 8-7. Roughage passage rate (%/h) with various intakes of concentrate (CI) and roughage (RI) for cattle as a percentage of body weight. (RPR = .94 + 1.34CI + 1.24RI; r^2 = .38, N = 130). With CI = RI = 1.0, RPR = 3.5% (*).

for both concentrate and roughage particles tends to increase with feed intake, changes differ in degree (Fig. 8-8; 22) and k_p for concentrates generally exceeds k_p for roughage particles by about 10%. Rates of passage are measured with various markers which are water soluble and mark the fluid or adhere to particles. Most markers are not indelible but can migrate and can alter density and digestion; thus estimates of passage are imperfect.

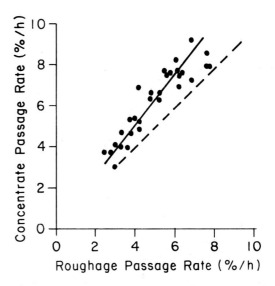

Figure 8-8. Concentrate passage rate versus roughage passage rate (%/h) for cattle.

Ruminal Digesta Positioning

Particles with densities of between 1.0 and 1.2 leave the rumen most rapidly. As consumed, most feed particles are buoyant due to entrapped air and become part of the floating raft atop the rumen contents. With particle disintegration through mechanical mastication and microbial digestion, entrapped gasses are released and fluid fills the vacated space so that specific gravity is altered. Rate of specific gravity change is affected by chemical and physical properties of the particle. Particle size also affects rate of change in specific gravity. The longer the particle, the greater the extent of rumination. The higher the cell wall content and the greater the resistance to microbial degradation, the slower the increase in density of the particle. Hence, long ruminal retention times for undigested mature forage particles are dependent not only on their large particle size, but also on low specific gravity of the particle.

Optimal characteristics of particles for ruminal exit have not been precisely defined and can differ from particle densities measured in a sterile media. The CO_2 produced by microbes can adhere to the particle making it buoyant. Gas production is generally proportional to rate of fermentation of the particle. Degree of bubble adherence and floatation will vary with physical properties of the particle. Fate of the floated particle also depends on adherence to other particles

150

floating in the rumen. Dense materials such as whole grains usually fall into the ventral sac and, unless masticated, do not float but move gradually toward the reticulum with ruminal contractions. Presence of whole corn in the rumen is a stimulus for rumination.

Ruminal Digesta Sub-Fractions

Ruminal liquids and solids do not exist independently in the rumen. From 20 to 80% of the liquid (and of fluid markers) is absorbed or entrained within particles. Greater amounts of fluid may be associated with particles with coarse roughage diets than diets of concentrate or processed roughage. This relationship forces ruminal k_p values for liquid and solid particles to increase and decrease together within a diet and intake level. Beside the fact that solids pull fluids along as they leave the rumen, very small particles, under 100 microns in size, are dispersed and readily swept from the rumen with fluid.

The k_p for ruminal liquid generally increases when either roughage percentage in the diet or feed intake increases (Fig. 8-5). In addition, source of roughage can influence ruminal stratification. Raft formation not only traps particles to delay their passage but also stimulates rumination to increase fluid input and fluid passage rate. Small particle diets, including those high in concentrate, do not facilitate raft formation. Cottonseed hulls, though roughage, are dense, have a small particle size and are digested slowly which reduces gas buoyancy so they do not form a raft in the rumen. In contrast, long grass hays and straws are conducive to very extensive ruminal stratification. On the same

diet, sheep have less digesta stratification than do cattle, probably due to more extensive chewing during eating by sheep than by cattle.

Probability of removal from the rumen increases with proximity to the reticulo-omasal orifice. Long particles and low density particles which become entangled with the ruminal raft are retained in the rumen for a longer time than smaller, denser particles. Raft entrapment and extent of particle floatation can explain some effects of feed processing on ruminal digestion. For example, grinding of long forage reduces ruminal stratification, rumination and ruminal retention time. This is why grinding of forage depresses digestibility and increases feed intake. Ruminal stratification stimulates rumination and re-insalivation. The prime aim of rumination appears to be destruction of the ruminal raft.

RUMINAL FERMENTATION AND HOST METABOLISM

With forage diets, VFA provide 50-85% of the metabolizable energy used by ruminant animals. Capacity for absorption of VFA is about six to eight times the maintenance energy requirement of growing sheep and about nine times the maintenance requirement of lactating cows. Thus, absorption is not a limiting step in metabolism. Estimated capacities for fermentation, digestion and absorption are presented in Table 8-2. Note that 66-80% of the total energy is derived from fermentation in the rumen. These values suggest that the total capacity for digestion and absorption is proportional to gut volume.

Table 8-2. Fermentation and digestive capacities (excluding protein).[a]

Species	Live weight, kg	Rumen volume, ℓ	Energy absorption, Mcal/d			
			Rumen	Small	Large	Total
Lamb	20	4.4	4.2	1.9	0.26	6.3
Lamb	40	7.5	7.2	3.1	0.45	10.8
Steer	200	29	27.7	10.5	1.5	39.7
Steer	400	49	46.8	17.6	2.6	67.0
Cow, fresh	600	78	74.5	23.9	3.5	101.9
Cow, high lactation	600	114	109.0	23.9	3.5	135.3

[a]Adapted from Ørskov (23)

Ruminal volume expands with higher production while the intestines generally do not, so capacity for ruminal digestion may place a ceiling on production. Genetic selection for increased gut capacity may increase this ceiling. Also, increasing k_p will increase capacity for digestion, though extent of ruminal digestion, especially of cell wall components, usually decreases as level of feed intake (and k_p) increases due either to a shorter retention time for digestion or a reduced rate of fermentation due to altered pH in the rumen.

Capacity for tissue metabolism of VFA is generally believed to considerably exceed the amounts of nutrients provided. Yet, studies from Scotland suggest that propionate production may exceed the capacity for its metabolism by lambs fed barley diets. Fat deposited by such lambs contains elevated levels of odd-chain length fatty acids and branched fatty acids which have an objectionable flavor. Such limits have not been detected with other diets or with cattle to date. Degradation of protein to amino acids and ammonia in the rumen parallels digestion of organic matter and will be discussed in Ch. 12. Though convenient to consider rates of digestion for various feed components separately, association of various components, such as starch or protein with cell walls or large particles, can limit rate of digestion by physically limiting exposure of the component to attack by microbes.

FACTORS AFFECTING RUMEN DIGESTION

Means of Expression

Digestion can be expressed in several ways. For the total digestive tract, digestibility is usually expressed as total extent of digestion independent of time. Within any segment of the digestive tract, digestion is usually calculated as the percentage of the digestible residue of the nutrient which is digested per unit of time or fractional rate of digestion k_d. This can be combined with time for digestion (retention time) to determine the actual extent of digestion at any point in time. Calculations are based on only the digestible fraction as some portion of most nutrients resists digestion and must be deducted from the total to determine fractional rate of digestion. To determine the quantity of a nutrient which is indigestible, feeds can be fermented for various times with one time period being very extended to estimate total extent of digestion. Digestion rate is then calculated from the slope of the logarithm of residual, potentially digestible polymer plotted against time. Similar to k_p, k_d is a "first order reaction" or logarithmic decay. Such a model of digestion implies that the absolute amount of a polymer which is digested decreases at a rate proportional to the amount remaining over time until all the digestible material is gone. This model is based on the assumption that the amount of a nutrient available for digestion limits digestion. As the nutrient is used, less remains to be digested, so that the amount digested per unit time decreases. Rate of digestion studies with fiber components generally fit this kinetic model quite well if an initial lag time is included. Whether the amount of other components of particulate feedstuffs available for digestion decrease in a similar fashion remains to be proven. Considering the potential physical limitations to digestion and changes in particle size during digestion, the amount of nutrient available for digestion from particles may not decrease proportionally with time. Alternate models of digestion which consider particle size and rate of reduction in particle size become quite complex mathematically.

The amount of a digestible nutrient which is digested in the rumen per unit of time depends on two factors—k_d and potential digestibility of the material. Either of these can change. Alkali or chemical treatment often increases the potential extent of digestion of polymers. Altered ruminal conditions, bacterial types and mechanical treatment can alter k_d. Processing to increase the surface area usually increases rate but not potential extent of digestion. Particles normally leave the rumen before digestion is complete, thus extent of digestion usually increases if either k_d or potential extent of digestion increases.

Particle Size

If access to feed components limits k_d, reducing particle size is useful. For example, corn in the ground or flaked form is fermented rapidly while most whole grains resist bacterial attack until they are masticated. Reducing the diameter of a spherical particle by half doubles relative surface area and

152

potentially doubles access for microbial digestion. For example, a 1 cm diameter sphere has a surface area of 1.05 cm² and a volume of 1.57 cm³ for a surface to volume (weight) ratio of about 0.67. A 0.5 cm diameter sphere has a surface area of 0.261 cm² and a volume of 0.196 cm³ for a surface to volume ratio of about 1.33.

Generally, particle size is determined by weighing the amount of wet or dry particles caught by sieves of various sizes. Most particles in the rumen, especially with forage diets, are long strands, not cubes or spheres, so surface area is not necessarily proportional to sieve size. With sieving of a dry material, particle size is reasonably similar to the width of a rectangular particle, while with wet samples, particle size more closely approximates particle length.

Particle size can be reduced at several points. Many feeds are processed prior to feeding to reduce particle size. Mastication further reduces particle size both during eating and rumination. In addition, microbial attack in the rumen weakens larger particles. During the churning and tumbling action of the rumen, weakened particles are broken. Chewing during the meal is more thorough for sheep and goats than for cattle. Generally, younger animals chew their feed more extensively than older ones. Hence, the need for and benefit of feed grinding is greater for older than younger cattle, and for cattle more than for most other species of ruminants that chew their feed more thoroughly.

Extent of mastication during eating and rumination also differs with feed type and moisture level. Rate of salivation usually limits the rate at which harvested feeds are consumed. Feed must be held in the mouth until it is moistened sufficiently to swallow. During this time period the feed is being chewed. Since dry roughage is retained in the mouth longer than silage or wet roughage, it is chewed more thoroughly before swallowing. Grains can be swallowed easily so they are not retained in the mouth as long as forages for ensalivation. Feeding of grains in the whole rather than the ground form may increase chewing time during eating or rumination. Because grains are chewed less thoroughly than roughages, processing will increase the extent of ruminal digestion much more with grains than forages.

Mastication pulverizes particles with a shear force. Shear is much more effective than simple slicing or grinding to increase surface area. Moisture content aids grinding, as well. Rumination is more effective than mastication during eating because the particles being chewed are wet rather than dry. Further, only coarse, undigested particles are selectively regurgitated for remastication which improves the efficiency of this process (30). For ruminants fed forage diets, the amount of dry matter ruminated each day is usually double or triple the amount of feed eaten per day. Hence, particles retained in the rumen can be ruminated several times. The relative importance of remastication and rumen microbial action to particle disintegration with different diet types has not been established clearly. However, the sharp reduction in feed intake which occurs when sheep are equipped with muzzles to prevent rumination indicates that rumination is the primary mode of particle disintegration with dry roughage diets.

Post-Feeding Changes
Rate of release of energy from fermentation varies with time after a meal. When animals are fed one or two meals per day, availability of digestible feed and activity of most microbial groups is greatest shortly after the meal. More rapidly solubilized nutrients and cell contents are released and fermented first followed sequentially by more resistant components. Though most species of microbes are present in the rumen at all times, growth rate and digestive action of each species can vary as ruminal conditions and microbial growth change. Post-prandial changes in microbial types and enzyme concentrations are more extreme when mixtures of concentrate and forage are fed due to the wider variety of substrates and particle sizes provided and also due to shifts in ruminal pH. Measurements of these shifts with limit-fed animals detected only minimal post-prandial changes in the numbers of microbes digesting cellulose, hemicellulose and amylose in the rumen of dairy cows. Such constant values could reflect ability of organisms to digest a wide variety of substrates or reasonably stable conditions for fermentation under the experimental conditions tested. With high feed intakes and mixed diets, post-prandial shifts might be greater because pH, substrate and k_p

may change more drastically. Alteration in rumen function with time after feeding would be expected to be greatest when feed intake per unit of ruminal volume is highest and when meals are consumed infrequently. With ad lib access to feed, most animals develop a nibbling pattern of feed intake which would reduce post-prandial fluctuations in ruminal fermentation.

Microbial Type-Substrate Interactions

Soluble carbohydrates are partially liberated as cell walls are fractured during eating. Remaining cell contents are rapidly released and hydrolyzed to monomers which are fermented to VFA in the rumen. These acid products reduce ruminal pH. With concentrate diets, the pH of ruminal fluid is usually between 5.5 and 6.5 while with roughage diets, values from 6.2 to 7 are expected. The time after feeding when pH is lowest, usually between 1/2 to 4 h after a meal, reflects the balance between rates of (a) acid production, (b) input of buffers from saliva and (c) presence or release of buffers or bases from the feed. Cellulose digestion is inhibited at a pH below 6. The low pH may retard attachment of microbes to cellulose due to lack of compounds which enhance attachment like bicarbonate or presence of attachment inhibitors like soluble starch. Lack of specific nutrient or growth factors at a low pH also can reduce rate of cell division and growth efficiency of cellulolytic bacteria. If cellulose-digesting bacteria do not divide at a rate equal to the rate at which they are swept out of the rumen, their prevalence decreases. Fortunately, many cellulose digesters can digest carbohydrates besides cellulose and grow. Hence, lack of cellulose need not decrease their survival. Even though the cellulolytic microbes remain in the rumen, their prevalence may decline as the population of other microbes increases with low-cellulose diets. Types of ruminal microbes appear to be less altered by diet composition than factors which decrease ruminal pH such as extensive feed processing, meal feeding of large meals and high levels of feed intake.

Grains are processed to increase starch digestibility. This can be achieved through increasing surface area, gelatinizing starch granules or solubilizing the protein matrix surrounding granules of starch. However, as k_d

and acid production increase, ruminal pH is depressed which halts cellulose digestion. Extensive processing makes the pH depression more extreme, but pH depression after a concentrate meal is more transient with processed grain than with whole grain. Therefore, despite the immediate depression in fiber digestion associated with extensive grain processing, such processing may reduce the time during which fiber digestion is depressed. This permits resumption in the digestion of fiber either late in the feeding cycle or later in the digestive tract to compensate. Conversely, the degree of inhibition of fiber digestion immediately after the meal is less with whole grains, but pH depression lasts longer as grain is masticated and made available for fermentation later in the feeding cycle. With processed grains, fiber digestion in the cecum plus large intestine can compensate for the depressed fiber digestion in the rumen, while for less well processed diets, compensatory fiber digestion in the lower gut is inhibited. This is probably because more fermentable starch passes to the large intestine with unprocessed than processed diets and this starch inhibits compensatory fiber digestion.

Post-prandial pH changes are most obvious with meal-fed animals. With continuous feeding of high concentrate diets, animals nibble many meals per day and ruminal pH never rises sufficiently to initiate substantial cellulose digestion. Feeding concentrate and roughage in alternate meals for lactating cows may increase the time for and extent of cellulose digestion, but alternate feeding also can increase the diurnal fluctuations in levels of metabolites and hormones which can alter production.

Microbe-Substrate Adherence

Digestion of native plant structures depends largely on microbial action and most microbes must adhere to particles prior to digesting them. Some 40 to 75% of the ruminal bacteria tightly adhere to particles. All fiber-digesting ruminal bacteria possess structures which facilitate adherence, though the method of association varies with bacterial species. Glycolcalyxes or cell capsules are formed which adhere to certain plant cell wall structures. Besides permitting rapid digestion, adherence influences the flow of microbes from the rumen. Particle-bound bacteria pass from the rumen attached to the particles whereas unassociated bacteria are flushed from the rumen with liquids. Hence, the k_p of adherent bacteria is lower than the k_p of free-living bacteria. Both change with level of feed intake and dietary roughage as discussed earlier.

The polysaccharide glycocalyx binds bacteria to surfaces and protects bacteria from phages. Formation of microcolonies may serve a similar function. Rosettes of bacteria growing from a central starch granule are often observed in rumen fluid of animals fed grain diets. Tight binding to forages or existence in microcolonies facilitates trapping of the nutrients released from particles during digestion. Hence, nutrient availability for microcolonies or bacteria with glycocalyxes differs from that of free-living microbes. The concentration of the nutrients which are released from particles should be greater for the attached than for free-living bacteria, but concentrations of soluble nutrients such as ammonia which must diffuse from ruminal liquid would be higher for free-living than for bacteria associated with particles or in microcolonies. If nutrient availabilities differ, microbial growth rates and efficiency should differ as well. Further, nutrient concentrations in strained ruminal fluid, though reflecting availability for free microbes, may not necessarily match concentrations available for attached or encapsulated microbes.

Sequential Microbial Digestion

Bacterial adherence and movement among particles varies with time after a meal. Immediately after feeding, inoculating bacteria rapidly colonize the new feed particles. Speed of microbial colonization depends on particle composition and size (surface area) and familiarity of ruminal microbes with the feed. Presence of competing substrates or inhibitory factors can reduce or delay adherence. Cell contents are rapidly solubilized and attacked. Rupture of cell walls not only releases cell contents to provide nutrients but also permits access for internal colonization for further disintegration of plant cell walls. Feed intake by animals usually is greater for forages which are higher in soluble dry matter, possibly due to an increased speed of colonization of fiber and to the reduced amount of ruminal space occupied by undigested fiber.

Many bacteria adhere only to specific plant structures. Rapidly and easily digested mesophyll and phloem tissues are digested first, leaving the more resistant sclerenchyma and xylem tissues. Colonization of these more resistant plant structures awaits removal of more digestible particles. Availability of cell components is rather continuous with grazing animals, but with meal feeding, microbes adept in colonizing a variety of different particle types are more competitive.

Digestion of plant tissues by adherent bacteria appears to be progressive and sequential, even with easily digestible forages. Specific bacterial types attack first and other types follow. This may result in layering of bacteria by type. Bacteria initially penetrate cell walls through stomata and fractures created by processing or mastication. Most of the colonization of the cell wall is on the inside, not on the exposed surface. Working inside, bacterial colonies are protected from protozoal predation and competition from other bacterial species for nutrients.

The rate of nutrient solubilization and release varies with chemical composition and physical structure of the plant. When freshly consumed and chewed forage enters the rumen, a portion of dry matter has already been released from disrupted plant cells and bacterial growth on exposed surface is rapid. A second surge of bacterial growth occurs when cell walls are ruptured. Later, as plant tissues are fragmented and subdivided, microbes remain attached to the particles which become progressively smaller. Although refractory plant portions are not colonized extensively in early hours after consumption, colonization occurs as the more readily accessible plant parts are depleted. If plants in the diet are more mature, internal cell walls are more lignified and cell walls are more resistant to bacterial digestion. Extensively lignified tissues may not be colonized at all.

Protozoa, though not attached to fiber components, actively swim among the fiber particles and may aid in physical disruption of softened fiber particles. This may speed rate of particle size reduction in the rumen. Anaerobic fungi are also active in the rumen and appear to be directly involved in fiber digestion. Fungi attack resistant fiber, especially lignified, chlorine sulfite-positive tissue.

Fungal activity differs with forage type and cultivar and may be influenced by nutrient content of the forage. In one Australian study, S fertilization increased the numbers of fungal sporangia on forage leaves, k_d and feed intake by sheep.

Diet type and the depletion rate of specific nutrients varies with time after feeding in meal-fed animals (16). Fig. 8-9 illustrates the sequential fermentation of alfalfa components. Both the number of microbes and their activity shift within a feeding cycle though the importance of these alterations has not been determined. Coordinating fermentation pattern with ruminal outflow through timed feeding of specific dietary ingredients could be used to elevate ruminal escape of some dietary components and to maximize ruminal digestion of other materials.

More extensive feed processing or cell damage during mastication increases the amount of feed available for microbial association. With whole grain, the hard seed coat limits access to internal starch. Amylolytic bacteria are able to attach immediately to processed grain particles. Colonization of starch is very rapid, especially with gelatinized starch. Yet, the proportion of total microbes attached to particles is surprisingly constant—between 50 and 70% with diets ranging from 25 to 75% concentrate.

PATTERN OF RUMINAL DIGESTION AND REGULATION

Diet Composition

Fermentation products differ with diet composition because different microbes have higher affinities for and prefer to digest specific carbohydrates. Roughage diets are high in cellulose, intermediate in soluble sugars and low in starch. Hence, cellulolytic and saccharolytic bacteria are most active. With extensive cellulose digestion by cellulolytic microbes and soluble carbohydrate fermentation by saccharolytic microbes, acetate production is high. With high starch diets, in contrast, the bacterial population is largely amylolytic. Amylolytics compete for soluble carbohydrates and products of starch and hemicellulose hydrolysis (Fig. 8-10), especially at a lower pH, and produce larger amounts of propionate.

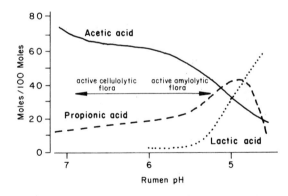

Figure 8-10. Relationship of ruminal pH to ruminal proportions of acetic, propionic and lactic acids. From Kaufmann et al (15).

Passage Rate

Passage rate influences fermentation pattern, as well. Fast passage rate of ruminal liquid generally is associated with higher acetate concentrations. Duration and intensity of rumination is determined largely by the level and form of fiber ingested. As rumination increases, saliva production increases both adding buffer and diluting ruminal contents (Fig. 8-11). Dilution causes total

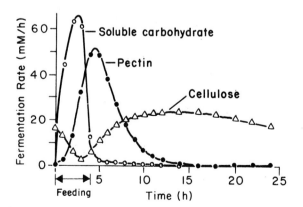

Figure 8-9. Fermentation of alfalfa components in the rumen. From Baldwin as cited by Smith and Oldham (28).

156

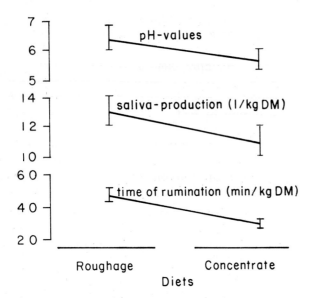

Figure 8-11. Relationship of ruminal pH, saliva production and rumination time to diet composition. From Kaufman et al (15).

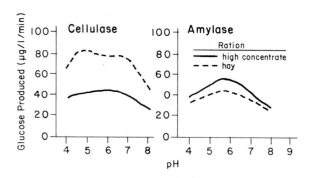

Figure 8-12. Cellulase and amylase activities at various pH values for two diets. From Kaufman et al (15).

ruminal acid concentrations to be generally lower with roughage than with concentrate diets (50-100 vs 80-150 mm/ℓ). As a percentage of ruminal liquid, the VFA total is between 0.5 and 1.5%. This is lower than the total acid concentration in certain feeds like corn silage (about 2% of liquid).

During adaptation to a high-concentrate diet, pH exerts selective pressure against microbes intolerant of a low pH (15). As pH drops, amylolytic and acid-tolerant bacteria increase while cellulolytic microbes decrease, so relative activity of amylase in relation to cellulase increases (Fig. 8-10). The optimal pH for ruminal amylase has been suggested to be about 5.6 (Fig. 8-12). Inhibition of fiber digestion can be a problem with adaptation to a concentrate diet as fiber can accumulate in the rumen. Less fiber is present in high concentrate diets and the roughage is often processed, so k_p would be increased unless selective ruminal retention time of fiber lengthens the time for ruminal digestion. Depending on this balance, even though k_d of fiber may be depressed, extent of ruminal digestion of fiber may not be depressed markedly until ruminal pH falls and remains below pH 6.0.

With high concentrate diets, protozoa are usually absent from the rumen whereas with roughage diets, protozoa thrive. Adding small amounts of concentrate to a forage diet elevates protozoal numbers. Initially, the absence of protozoa from the rumen with concentrate diets was attributed to the low ruminal pH. But protozoa thrive at a pH of 5.5 in the rumen of limit-fed cattle consuming high-starch purified diets. A more logical explanation is that protozoa require a suitable physical habitat for retention and survival in the rumen. Unless selectively retained in the rumen, protozoa are washed out of since they cannot replicate rapidly. Structural roughage permits sequestration of protozoa in an area with a low density and low passage rate.

Type and size of protozoa may change with concentrate level. As grain percentage increases, the proportion of Entodinium increases. These protozoa are adept at accumulating polysaccharide from engulfed starch and soluble carbohydrates and thereby reduce the concentration of readily fermented starch in the rumen and the rate of acid production in the rumen. Protozoa flushed from the rumen carry this carbohydrate to the small intestine for digestion. Engulfed starch particles are usually released gradually within the rumen during a feeding interval as protozoa die and lyse. Not all protozoa stabilize fermentation, however, as some species catabolize stored carbohydrate to lactic acid.

Absorption of VFA stabilizes ruminal pH. VFA are absorbed most rapidly in the nondissociated form. The pKs for most VFA are about 4.1; thus as pH drops toward 4.1 the amount of each VFA in the non-dissociated form increases and rate of absorption increases. Only 2-5% of VFA are non-dissociated at pH 6 while at a pH of 5, about

25% are non-dissociated. Ruminal papillae enlarge at a lower pH, so the absorption surface of the rumen also is increased. Papillae size is maximal at pH near 5.5. Butyrate availability delays this modification of epithelial cells while acetic and lactic acids stimulate the change. When ruminal pH is below 5.5, rumen and animal function are usually abnormal due to acidosis. At this pH and high lactic acid concentrations, rumen papillae are sloughed from the rumen surface, decreasing absorptive capacity. Breaks formed in the ruminal surface permit bacteria to enter the blood stream (sepsis) and, depending on prevalence of pathogenic bacteria in the blood, can cause ruminal and liver abscesses (Ch. 23).

Microbes and Acidity

Acid concentrations in the rumen are higher with concentrate diets (Fig. 8-13) for several reasons. First, with more dense feed ingredients, eating and rumination times are reduced which decreases the amount of saliva which enters the rumen. Reduced salivary input reduces buffering, dilution of acids and k_p from the rumen. Secondly, rate and extent of acid production are greater with diets of high energy density and availability. Third, forages exert some buffering capacity directly. Feed ingredients or additives which neutralize ruminal acids or stimulate salivation, either during eating or later during rumination, modulate any swings in ruminal pH. Unfortunately, not all buffers act in the rumen, and of those which do, most have their greatest activity immediately as they enter the rumen. With acute acidosis, pH depression is greatest

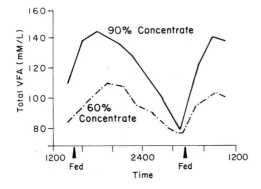

Figure 8-13. Ruminal VFA concentrations with two levels of dietary concentrate. From Oldham (21).

6 to 10 h after grain has been engorged. Buffer feeding often increases k_p, however, which will reduce the amount of fermentable organic matter available for acid production in the rumen.

When pH falls from 7 to between 5.0 and 5.5, many ruminal microbes cease growing despite an ability to survive even higher concentrations of H^+. Cell membranes of rumen microbes do not permit H^+ or OH^- to enter, but other nutrients such as lactic acid enter and alter the proton motive force. The proton motive force is responsible for some ATP generation by microbes and relies on an ion gradient across the cell membrane to generate ATP. As pH is altered, ion concentrations and cell permeability can both change, reducing the potential for ATP generation. Certain lipophilic acids, such as lactic, act as proton conductors to equilibrate the internal and external concentrations of H^+ and reduce the proton motive force. Ionophores also may cause ion leakage, reduce the proton motive force and reduce ATP production (2). High K concentrations or presence of ionophores selects microbes which are less dependent on the proton motive force for ATP synthesis or for microbes either with walls resistant to ion movement or high intracellular H^+ concentrations. Microbial growth per unit of fermented energy is lower with diets causing low pH or with addition of ionophores to the diet, possibly due to a reduction in ATP generation through the proton motive force.

Most acids like lactic, which inhibit microbes at high concentrations, are more effective when pH is low, presumably due to greater penetration of cell membranes by acid in the non-ionized than in the ionized form. During silage fermentation lactic acid accumulates and hinders further fermentation. Concentration of non-ionized rather than total lactic acid appears to halt further fermentation. With addition of buffers to silage, both pH and concentration of total lactate are increased and fermentation is extended.

A third factor altered by acidity is availability of nutrients for microbes. Cellulolytic bacteria require the bicarbonate ion for growth. Bicarbonate or CO_2 in solution is depleted at a low pH. A decreased pH also can alter the ionic state of other nutrients and change their availability to microbes Rates of VFA production are controlled primarily by availability of substrate for amylolytic and saccharolytic bacteria. Production of VFA is rapid when large amounts of feed are available to be digested. When free glucose is present in rumen fluid, *Streptococcus bovis,* a microbe which grows inefficiently, thrives and produces lactic acid which lowers the pH and can cause acidosis. With roughage diets, carbohydrate availability is limited by fiber barriers so that rate of VFA production is slower which, combined with a constant rate of absorption, reduces absolute VFA concentrations.

Regulation of Fermentation

Accumulation of acetate depresses microbial growth at physiological ruminal pH values (6-7) much more than accumulations of propionate and butyrate. Propionate and butyrate only depress microbial growth when concentrations considerably exceed physiological levels. Effects of VFA on growth are greater when pH is low. Selective effects of VFA or chemicals on enzymes can alter metabolism of the microbial flora without shifting the species of microbes, so changes in end-products do not necessarily reflect changed populations in the rumen.

With roughage diets, slow and gradual enzymatic hydrolysis of fiber sets the pace for fermentation and controls release of easily degraded cell contents (26). Under these conditions ruminal pH effectively controls composition of the ruminal microflora. Most ruminal microbes thrive when pH exceeds 6.5. In contrast, with high intakes of low-fiber diets, pH is typically below 6 intermittently or continuously. A low or unstable ruminal pH limits diversity of the microbial population and, due to pH or substrate supply, selects for amylolytic species. Cellulolytic microbes which can shift from fiber digestion to fermentation of sugars will survive. Relative to cellulolytic microbes, an amylolytic population is less adaptable to changes in substrate source or supply.

With medium- to high-roughage diets, rates of fermentation and liquid outflow help prevent accumulation of fermentation end-products to inhibitory levels. Conversely, with high-concentrate diets, a rapid rate of acid production and slow outflow of fluid permits VFAs to accumulate which can inhibit certain fermentation reactions. Very

high VFA concentrations exist in animals grazing lush wheat pasture due, presumably, to the high availability of soluble carbohydrates and to rapid intake with little salivation. To prevent VFA accumulation an increase in particulate k_p is more effective than an increase in fluid k_p.

VFA Ratios and Uses

Despite wide swings in the microbial population and differences in feed intake, ruminal VFA proportions are remarkably stable with molar ratios (moles of acetate:propionate:butyrate) usually being near 65:25:10 with roughage diets and 50:40:10 for concentrate diets, but dependent on pH (Fig. 8-10). With roughage diets, this ratio is quite stable due to slow digestion of fiber. Changes from these ratios with roughage diets are abrupt and unpredictable. Changes in fermentation pattern with concentrate diets are more predictable because the microflora are less diverse than with roughage diets.

VFA Concentrations vs Production Rates

VFA are produced by specific microbial pathways (Fig. 8-14) and absorbed continually from the rumen. Ruminal concentrations represent the balance between rates of production and of removal for each VFA as well as their interconversions. Often, VFA values are expressed relative to all other VFA by listing their molar percentages (moles of each VFA/100 moles of total ruminal VFA). Relative *concentrations* (either as moles/100 moles or as mM) must not be confused with relative *production* rates (moles/h) of VFA in the rumen. As absorption rates for the various VFA change with pH and some VFA are absorbed more completely than others, relative concentrations need not parallel relative rates at which VFA are produced de novo in the rumen (Fig. 8-15). With a pH near 7, absorption rates for all VFA are similar so relative concentrations reflect relative production rates (19).

Another means of expressing and comparing ruminal VFA is by absolute concentration (mM/ℓ or ruminal fluid). Absolute concentrations can be calculated from molar percentages by multiplying the molar percent by the total VFA concentration. Absolute concentrations vary with sampling site. Near the cardia, water and saliva entering the rumen dilute the acids, decreasing their total

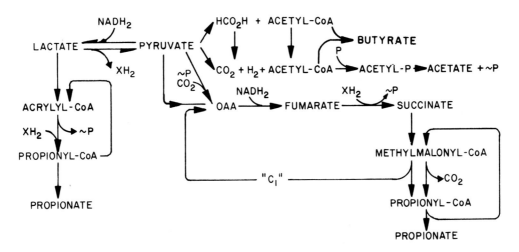

Figure 8-14. Pathways for VFA production from pyruvate. Modified from Baldwin and Allison (1).

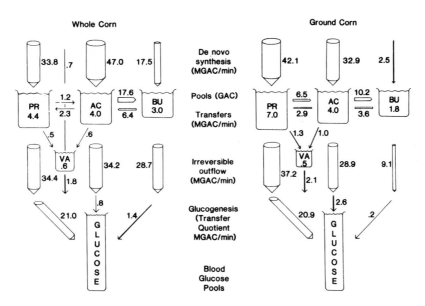

Figure 8-15. Synthesis and interconversions of VFA in the rumen of steers fed a concentrate diet. MGAC is milligram atoms of carbon and GAC is gram atoms of carbon. PR is propionate ACs' acetate, BU butyrate and VA valerate. From Sharp et al. (27).

concentration without altering their relative proportions. Concentrations of lactate and acetate are generally higher in liquid associated with the ruminal raft than with free fluid from the ventral sac of the rumen.

Energy availability can influence fermentation by altering fermentation reactions, also. When grain is fed, high availability of energy and rapid fermentation results in production of more metabolic H_2 than can be shunted through normal channels. Numbers of

methanogenic bacteria could increase to use this surplus, but they are quite sensitive to low pH (<6.0) and inept at adapting to sudden diet changes. Hence, excess reducing equivalents combined with a low pH cause pyruvate to be reduced to lactate and propionate. Lactic acid presence exacerbates the problem by depressing pH and CH_4 production; it further increases the concentrations of lactate and propionate. Hence, inactivity of methanogenic bacteria at low pH is partially responsible for the shift in VFA patterns with concentrate level of the diet.

Fermentation Balance

During fermentation, input and output of carbon and energy and reducing equivalents must be equal. If the quantities of products of fermentation are known, one can calculate how much carbohydrate was fermented and how much CO_2, CH_4 and ATP were produced. In Table 8-3 the relationships between fermentation products, substrate and other end-products are presented. Even if the total extent of fermentation in the rumen is not known, relative energetic efficiency and yield ATP and CH_4 can be estimated based on ratios of VFA produced. Relative concentrations of VFA rather than production rates are commonly used in such calculations because

Table 8-3. Fermentation balance relationships.

Product		Amount, moles	Glucose = G used, moles	NADH formed, moles	ATP yield, moles	$CH_4 + CO_2$ yield, moles	CH_4 yield, moles	Energy = E content, Mcal
Measurements								
Acetate	= A	0.5A	2A	2A	A	0.5A	0.2094A
Propionate	= P	0.5P	-1P	3A	O	-0.25P	0.3672P
Butyrate	= B	B	2B	3B	2B	0.5B	0.5243B
Calculated yields								
Methane	= M	0.5A + 0.5B - 0.25P moles						
or	M		-4M	1M	-1M	-1M	0.2108M
CO_2	= C	0.5A + 1.5B + 0.25P moles						
or	C		0C		-1C	0C	0C
Column sums above			O	E	O	O	T
Glucose used	0.5A + 0.5P + B moles						
or	G						0.673G
Total ATP	2.5A + 2.75P + 3.5B moles						
or	E						0.007E

Energy recovered as VFA

        Mcal   0.2094A + 0.3672P + 0.5243B

  or   % of initial   100 × (0.2094A + 0.3672P + 0.5243B)/0.673G

Energy lost as methane

        Mcal   0.2108M

  or   % of initial   100 × 0.2108M/0.673G

Energy not recovered in VFA and methane (total heat + ATP)

        Mcal   (0.673G - T) or (0.0217A + 0.022P + 0.0433B)

  or   % of initial   100 × (0.673G - T)/0.673 G

Heat loss, considering ATP contains 0.007 Mcal/mole

        Mcal   (0.673G - T - 0.007E) or (0.0042A + 0.0028P + 0.0188B)

  or   % of initial   100 × (0.673G - T - 0.007E)/0.673G

ATP per mole glucose   E/G

Potential microbial yield, at Y_{ATP} = 10 g dry cells/mole ATP

        Total g = (10E) or (25A + 27.5P + 35B)

  or   g per kg glucose fermented = 10,000E/180G

  or   g crude protein synthesized (@ 60% of dry matter)/kg starch (111% glucose) fermented

        = 6000E/162G

Acetate:Propionate ratio   A/P

Non-glucogenic ratio   (A + 2B)/P

true production rates are difficult to measure. Although concentrations may not be proportional to true production rates, the errors that this causes should be relatively small.

By inserting values for ruminal production of acetate, propionate and butyrate for A, P and B into Table 8-3, the amounts of glucose used and CH_4, CO_2 and ATP produced are calculated. From ATP yield and an estimated Y_{ATP} (grams of dry microbial cells per mole of available ATP), microbial yield is estimated. Based on protein content of ruminal bacteria the total amounts of protein produced and N needed can be calculated from microbial yield. In addition, energy release (ATP + heat) during fermentation can be estimated based on the heats of combustion of glucose and VFA plus CH_4.

These equations have some limitations so that calculations cannot be directly applied in vivo. First, incorporation of carbon and reducing equivalents into microbial cells is not considered. The only end products considered are acetate, propionate, butyrate, CO_2 and CH_4. Second, the percentage of consumed dry matter which is fermented in the rumen can vary with dietary and animal conditions. Third, relative VFA production rates may differ from their concentrations in the rumen. Nevertheless, these relationships generally match in vitro results very closely (6). An example of calculations based on these fermentation balance equations is presented in Table 8-4 for various levels of the ionophore monensin.

Table 8-4. Fermentation balance with various monensin levels.[a]

Monensin level, mg/steer/d	0	100	500
Molar VFA proportions			
Acetate, moles/100 moles	56.00	49.30	47.80
Propionate, moles/100 mol	31.90	41.00	43.50
Butyrate, moles/100 moles	7.10	5.30	4.80
Calculated values			
Glucose used, moles	51.05	50.45	50.45
Gas ($CO_2 + CH_4$) production	70.20	59.90	57.40
CH_4, moles	23.58	17.05	15.43
CO_2, moles	46.63	42.85	41.98
ATP yield, moles	252.58	254.55	255.93
Energy			
Input, glucose, Mcal	34.36	33.95	33.95
Output			
VFA, Mcal	27.16	28.16	28.50
Methane, Mcal	4.97	3.59	3.25
ATP, Mcal @ 7 Kcal/mole	1.77	1.78	1.79
Heat, Mcal	0.46	0.42	0.41
Potential microbial yield			
g dry cells @ $Y_{ATP} = 10$	2525.75	2545.50	2559.25
g protein @ 60% of DM	1515.45	1527.30	1535.55
g prot/100 g starch fermented	18.32	18.69	18.79
ATP/mole glucose	4.95	5.05	5.07
Energy lost with fermentation			
Methane, % of initial energy	14.46	10.59	9.58
ATP, % of initial energy	5.15	5.25	5.28
Heat, % of initial energy	1.33	1.24	1.21
Heat + ATP, % of initial energy	6.47	6.48	6.49
CH_4 + Heat + ATP, % of initial energy	20.94	17.07	16.06
Non-glucogenic ratio	2.20	1.46	1.32

[a]Calculated from fermentation balance equations (Table 8-3).

MICROBIAL EFFICIENCY

To maximize efficiency of animal production and reduce the need for intact protein in the diet, increased output of microbial protein from the rumen is desired. The relationship of a number of factors to microbial output is outlined in Fig. 8-16. These factors will be discussed individually below.

Output of microbial organic matter from the rumen is the multiple of the (a) amount of organic matter digested (or ATP yield) in the rumen and (b) the efficiency with which microbes in the rumen use organic matter (or ATP) for growth. Efficiency of microbial growth (MOEFF) can be expressed in terms of yield of dry cells (or of microbial protein) per mole of ATP (Y_{ATP}) or per 100 g (or kg) of organic matter either apparently or truly fermented in the rumen. Total microbial yield from the rumen generally increases as the amount of organic matter fermented in the rumen increases. In contrast, microbial efficiency (MOEFF) is independent of yield, often being greater with less extensive digestion in the rumen and with a lower total microbial yield. For example, MOEFF is usually greater with whole than processed corn diets despite lower total microbial yield.

Microbial yield must not be confused with microbial efficiency. If total yield or output of microbial protein from the rumen were the goal, increasing the amount of organic matter fermented in the rumen currently appears to be more fruitful than trying to increase MOEFF. At present, it is difficult to predict and control MOEFF. The relationship between the amount of organic matter incorporated into cells versus other products at various efficiencies of microbial growth can be calculated (18) as presented in Table 8-5.

Expression and Measurement

Microbiologists usually express MOEFF as the number of grams of dry microbial cells formed per mole of substrate fermented (Y_{SUB}) or per mole of ATP (Y_{ATP}) available. Yields are determined with batch cultures or continuous flow systems. In continuous cultures (chemostats) under steady state conditions, efficiency of substrate (ATP) use can be determined directly from bacterial yield and substrate (ATP) disappearance at specified dilution rates. At steady state conditions bacteria must have a specific growth rate (replication rate minus lysis rate) equal to the passage rate (k_p). Extent of microbial lysis in the rumen has been estimated to be as

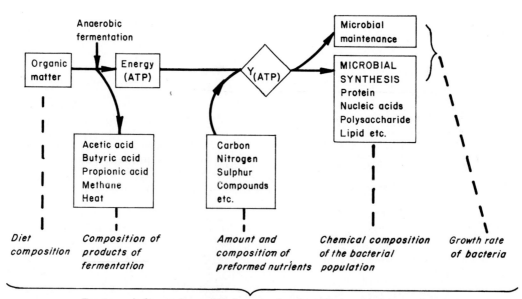

Factors influencing efficiency of microbial protein synthesis

Figure 8-16. Factors influencing the efficiency of microbial growth. From Smith and Oldham (28).

Table 8-5. Dry matter and nitrogen balance at various efficiencies of microbial growth.

True efficiency, Y_{ATP} g cells per mole of ATP	Dry matter destination		Efficiency		Protein needed[b] g protein per 100 g OMF
			True	Apparent	
			g cells per		
	Microbes[a] %	VFA, CH_4, CO_2 %	100 g OMF[c]	100 g OMF	
8	24.2	75.8	24.2	31.9	14.5
10	30.2	69.8	30.2	43.3	18.1
12	36.3	63.6	36.3	57.0	21.8
14	42.3	57.7	42.3	73.3	25.4
16	48.3	51.7	48.3	93.4	29.0

[a]Calculated from Y_{ATP} assuming 4.9 moles of ATP generated per mole (162 g) of carbohydrate fermented which applies over a wide range in VFA ratios.

[b]Calculated from microbial yield and OM truly fermented considering that 60% of microbial dry matter is crude protein.

[c]Organic matter fermented in the rumen based on amounts truly or apparently (input minus output of OM) fermented.

high as 30% though non-growing pure cultures generally exhibit limited lysis in vitro. In chemostats, similar to the rumen in most conditions, bacteria grow to the limit of available nutrients or energy. Energy (ATP) usually is the limiting factor. $Y_{glucose}$, similar to Y_{sub}, is usually between 40 and 90 (g dry cells/mole glucose) which equals 22 to 50% of substrate weight as shown in Table 8-5. Y_{ATP} averages about 10 (g dry cells/mole ATP). ATP yield can be estimated from VFA production as discussed previously. ATP yield and thereby Y_{sub} can change with species and pathways involved or with phosphoroclastic cleavage of carbohydrates.

The theoretical maximum for Y_{ATP}, calculated from the amounts of ATP required for biosynthesis of various cell components, is 25-34 for ruminal bacteria. Batch cultures of isolated bacteria usually have a much lower Y_{ATP}, between 10 and 12, though a wide range (4.6-20.9) has been observed in vitro. Extreme values have been attributed to experimental problems such as failure to exclude all oxygen or to account for all electron acceptors. Electron acceptors permit oxidative metabolism and increase ATP yield. Many of the low MOEFF estimates came from batch culture systems in which growth was not continuous. Continuous culture techniques circumvent some of these problems and have demonstrated that Y_{ATP} is not constant. Instead, MOEFF varies with ionic

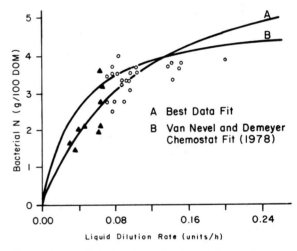

Figure 8-17. Relationship of microbial protein synthesis to liquid dilution rate in chemostat systems. Modified from Van Soest et al. (31).

composition of the medium, cell composition and, especially, bacterial growth rate.

Similar to animals, bacteria require energy for maintenance and are more efficient when growing or multiplying more rapidly as illustrated in Fig. 8-17. Maintenance costs reduce Y_{ATP} below the theoretical maximum. These microbial maintenance costs are the total of energy and nutrients used for all non-growth purposes including motility, turnover of cell constituents, production of extracellular proteins and carbohydrate polymers, active transport, inefficiency of phosphorylation, energetic uncoupling, synthesis to replace

164

non-viable or lysed cells and unknown functions. Species of bacteria differ in their maintenance costs and also in their speed and capacity to adapt from growth to maintenance conditions.

Composition of microbial cells also can influence MOEFF. Composition can vary dramatically (25). Direct storage of lipid and carbohydrate is much more efficient energetically than biosynthesis and storage of protein. Storage rather than synthesis will increase MOEFF when MOEFF is expressed as grams of *dry cells* per ATP. But expressed as grams of *protein* synthesized per unit of organic matter truly fermented, MOEFF decreases with storage of carbohydrate because ATP is used to polymerize the carbohydrate. Rate of turnover probably is greater for active protoplasm (protein) than stored energy reserves, so maintenance cost would be expected to be greater for microbes having a higher protein content.

Apparent vs True Organic Matter Digestion

Two different bases have been used to calculate MOEFF—APPARENT and TRUE OM digestion in the rumen. Most nutritionists calculate MOEFF from ruminal outflow and express MOEFF as grams of microbial cells (or protein) per unit weight of OM APPARENTLY disappearing from (or digested in) the rumen. However, disappearance of feed in the rumen differs from the amount of feed truly digested in the rumen because 24-50% of the digested weight is incorporated into bacterial cells (Table 8-5). This OM has been metabolized by ruminal microbes so it must be added to the mass of unfermented OM flowing from the rumen to determine TRUE OM digestion from APPARENT OM disappearance in the rumen. APPARENT OM digestion always underestimates TRUE digestion of OM. (Note that in the rumen, the relationship is similar to apparent versus true digestibility of nutrients in the total tract. In the total tract, true digestibility always exceeds apparent digestibility due to metabolic losses of nutrients.) MOEFF calculated from either the appearance of VFA or the net disappearance of OM are estimates of APPARENT digestion. In contrast, if microbial cells in a chemostat are provided with all components and use glucose only as a source of

energy, yield per unit of glucose disappearing is an estimate of MOEFF on a TRUE basis.

The TRUE fermentation exceeds APPARENT fermentation by the amount of OM incorporated into microbial cells. TRUE OM fermentation is calculated by adding the amount of microbial OM to the amount of OM disappearing from the rumen by digestion which increases OM fermentation and decreases MOEFF. MOEFF differs whether it is based on TRUE or APPARENT OM digestion, but the literature on MOEFF is confusing and the concept of OM digestion and ATP yield needs reconsideration.

The OM incorporated into microbial cells is largely converted to other products, so to calculate the full extent of digestion in the rumen, correction for the amount of OM incorporated into microbial cells is proper. Yet, ATP is not generated from much of the OM which is incorporated, so ATP yield from incorporated carbon is not equal to that from OM catabolized to VFA. The amount of energy incorporated into microbial cells can be estimated from the redox potential of microbial cells. If the redox potential were the same as for other end-products of fermentation such as VFA, CO_2 and CH_4, then ATP could be generated from incorporated OM. This would make TRUE digestibility the most realistic estimate of energy availability for growth of microbes. But if the redox potential of cells is the same as that of the nutrients before fermentation, APPARENT OM fermentation is the more appropriate term to calculate ATP yield.

It is important to differentiate between MOEFF calculated on an "apparent" basis from that calculated on a "true" basis because the former exceeds the latter by 30 to 90% (Table 8-5). If Y_{ATP} is 10, about 30 g of dietary OM are incorporated into microbial OM. This is based on the assumption that ATP yield is 4.9 moles/mole of carbohydrate which, with a Y_{ATP} of 10, equals 49 g dry cells/mole of carbohydrate (162 g fermented) of which 49 g equals 30.2%. Unfortunately, published results often fail to mention whether MOEFF is based on apparent or true OM disappearance from the rumen. Though calculation to a "true" basis adjusts for incorporated organic matter, the redox state of microbial OM is not considered. Though most of the more recent publications express

MOEFF on a TRUE digestion basis and values on a TRUE basis may be more uniform, superiority of one means of expression over the other is difficult to justify.

For application to production of microbial protein in the rumen, nutritionists often express MOEFF as grams of microbial N (or protein) output from the rumen per unit of OM apparently or truly fermented in the rumen. Measurements in vivo indicate that MOEFF usually ranges from 7.6-20.3 g microbial crude protein (or 1.2-3.2 g microbial N) per 100 g of OM truly fermented in the rumen with a mean value of about 16 g crude protein synthesized per 100 g of OM fermented. The amount of degraded protein or NPN which must be provided for microbes to use for growth can be calculated as ammonia and amino acids are used for synthesis of microbial protein. For every 100 g of OM *truly* fermented, some 14-20 g of ruminally available crude protein are needed as shown in Table 8-5.

MOEFF Measurement In Vivo

Measurement of microbial yield in vivo to calculate MOEFF is not an easy task. In vitro, when all substrates provided are soluble, the effluent from the fermenter can be filtered to recover microbial matter. Measurement becomes more difficult with insoluble substrates because complete separation of microbes from substrate is difficult if not impossible. Hence, microbial mass is usually estimated by determining the amount of one of several compounds incorporated by or inherent within microbes. Isotopes which are continuously infused that become incorporated by growing microbes can be used as a marker. Isotopes commonly used include ^{35}S, ^{15}N and ^{32}P. The amount of microbes in digesta can then be calculated based on the concentration of the compound or the isotope within microbes isolated from rumen fluid and the amount of the compound or the isotope passing with digesta. The concentration or activity of the marker in postruminal (usually omasal, abomasal or duodenal) digesta can be compared directly with the concentration of the marker in isolated microbial dry matter, so no external standard is needed. For example, if isolated ruminal microbes contain 0.16 g purine per g of total N and duodenal dry matter contains 0.09 g

purine per g of total N, 56% of the duodenal N is microbial. If 160 g N passes to the duodenum/d, duodenal N is composed of 90 g of microbial N and 70 g non-microbial N.

Several problems complicate this approach. If samples of ruminal microbes or digesta or uptake of an isotope by microbes are non-representative, errors in calculated MOEFF can be large. For example, microbes may incorporate substantial quantities of N and S directly from amino acids. As microbes deep in the fiber raft or inside plant cells should have more continual access to released amino acids than do free-floating microbes, isotope enrichment would be lower for attached microbes. Non-representative sampling of ruminal microbes is a problem with any marker or isotope method as microbes attached to larger particles are difficult to remove and measure. Because microbes leaving the rumen most rapidly are those associated with small particles and fluid, concentrations of markers in such microbes are usually used as a sample of all bacteria, but not necessarily protozoa, in the rumen. Composition of microbes leaving the rumen certainly differs from that of all microbes in the rumen when one considers the long retention time of the protozoal fraction of the ruminal population. Though sampling and marker procedures are imperfect, differences between animals and in measurement of the indigestible marker often are even larger sources of variation.

Pulse dosing of isotopes is often used to monitor microbial growth and passage. Isotopes are incorporated into microbial cells even with no net growth due to turnover of cell components. Hence, incorporation of a pulse dose represents gross production, not net growth. Mistaking gross for net growth is no problem with studies if the isotope is administered continuously, but with short-term studies and ruminal sampling, results can be erroneous.

In addition to the isotope markers, inherent components of microbial cells have found widespread use as microbial markers. Those widely used in vivo include nucleic acids (RNA, DNA or purines), diaminopimelic acid (DAP), amino ethyl phosphonic acid (AEP), D-alanine and the general amino acid profile of digesta. Some of these chemical components are found throughout bacterial cells while others (AEP, DAP and D-alanine) are associated with cell walls. With turnover of microbial cells, the cell wall components resist digestion more than cell contents. Hence, digesta may become unduly enriched with microbial cell wall components which results in an overestimate of outflow of microbes. Certain components such as DAP and D-alanine are found only in bacteria while AEP is thought to be specific for protozoa. Nucleic acids are found in both protozoa and bacteria at much higher concentrations than in plant materials. Combining AEP with DAP or D-alanine permits one to estimate both protozoal and bacterial flow.

Chemical composition of bacteria in synchronous growth varies with stage of growth. As a percentage, cells growing slowly have less RNA (primarily ribosomal) than rapidly growing cells. The ratio of RNA to N in bacteria is of considerable interest because RNA is commonly used as a microbial marker. Whether the RNA to N ratio of microbes in the rumen varies sufficiently with time after feeding to bias experimental results remains to be demonstrated. Ratios of other markers also change with cell size, growth rate and microbial type and species.

Age of bacteria in the rumen under different conditions has been a topic of speculation. Typical rumen bacteria are at a stage of transition between exponential growth and the stationary phase (3), but microbes of all ages must be present because the population is replicating. Bacteria in fluid may be more subject to feast and famine than attached bacteria which have substrate available continuously until digestion is complete.

For discussion of MOEFF, the microbial mass in the rumen must be considered to be a population and not an individual organism. If considered individually, their metabolic mass cannot change abruptly to consume a surplus of feed. If mass is fixed and more feed is provided, production increases while maintenance remains constant as would be the case with animals. This increases efficiency because the amount of energy used for maintenance is constant. This increase in efficiency is due to "dilution of maintenance".

In contrast with the fixed mass condition above, the microbial population or metabolic mass within the rumen readily increases if the amount of energy provided increases. If the biomass increases as more energy is provided,

dilution of maintenance is no longer possible and efficiency will not increase simply because nutrient supply increases. Instead, in a chemostat or in the rumen under steady state conditions, the population reaches a level dictated by the amount of energy available. In this case, growth rate of microbes is dictated not by energy supply but by k_p. This is because the population, to maintain itself under steady state conditions, is forced to replicate at a rate equal to its removal. Consequently, increasing k_p usually increases MOEFF though it decreases the population of microbes in the rumen. Under steady state ruminal conditions it is difficult to believe that the average age of bacteria in the rumen varies markedly with dietary conditions. Even with a shift in k_p from 6%/h to 10%/h, mean retention time (the inverse of k_p) changes only from 16.7 to 10 h.

Measurement of Ruminal Output

Total flow of postruminal digesta must be determined to calculate microbial yield, the amount of OM fermented and MOEFF. Usually, only small samples of daily digesta flow are obtained and from concentration of an indigestible diet component or passage marker and knowledge of daily intake of this component, total daily flow is extrapolated. As an example, if 7 g Cr_2O_3 is fed daily and duodenal digesta contains 4.0 mg Cr_2O_3/g of dry matter, duodenal dry matter flow extrapolates to be 1,750 g dry matter/d (7,000/4). Errors associated with sampling and measuring the indigestible marker often have a greater impact on calculated MOEFF than choice of the microbial marker.

Ruminal output usually is calculated by sampling digesta from the omasum, abomasum or proximal duodenum. If a representative sample of digesta leaving the rumen could be obtained by sampling the rumen directly, surgical modifications in the intestines could be avoided. Unfortunately, ruminal stratification and the potential for omasal filtration of particles cause ruminal sampling errors to be large. Cannulation of the omasum is more complex surgically than cannulation of the abomasum or duodenum and has been rarely used. Cannulas in the omasum probably would alter flow or filtration of digesta. Extent of microbial activity in the omasum is not certain, though some carbohydrate digestion and absorption of simple sugars can occur there. Though the omasum absorbs ammonia-N and VFA, it is doubtful that substantial amounts of other compounds disappear from the omasum. In some studies, flow of ammonia-N through the abomasum has been greater than flow from the rumen, possibly due to N recycling or proteolysis and deamination in the omasum or abomasum. Because the extent of fermentation in the omasum is currently unclear, it seems advisable to consider omasal fermentation as part of fermentation in the reticulo-rumen and to sample from some later point in the digestive tract to calculate the total postruminal supply of nutrients.

Abomasal cannulas work well in lambs but are difficult to maintain in cattle. Digesta can stratify in the abomasum which again causes samples to be non-representative, especially with concentrate diets. Also, the omasum and abomasum serve as a mixing pool with meal-fed animals and outflow may be irregular. Hence, care to set sampling schedules to obtain numerous samples at various times or to feed continuously is helpful.

Sampling from the duodenum circumvents most problems of digesta stratification. Maintenance of cannulas, especially of re-entrants, requires considerable time and expertise. To measure output from the forestomachs, cannulas must be placed in the proximal duodenum at a point before the pancreatic and bile ducts enter. Through these ducts, enzymes, bicarbonate, lipids and bile salts are being added to digesta. Although surgery is more difficult in the proximal area due to tension on the duodenum, cannulas placed in the ascending portion of the proximal duodenum give reliable and reasonably continuous samples of material leaving the abomasum. One check on cannula placement is pH. In the proximal duodenum, digesta has a pH below 2.5 whereas digesta pH with added bile is usually over 6.0.

Flow from the rumen can exhibit cyclic variation. Though this complicates calculation of daily flow from re-entrant cannulas, irregular flow does not invalidate marker data providing digesta composition and marker concentrations vary together.

Digesta k_p and Microbial Efficiency

At a k_p of 2%/h, about 65% of the ATP is used for maintenance compared with only 32% at a k_p of 6%/h (Fig. 8-17). This is due to a reduction in the amount of time bacteria in the rumen need to be maintained before they are flushed out and reduced time for both lysis and protozoal predation of bacteria. Though protozoal predation increases the growth rate of bacteria, most engulfed bacteria are digested, so predation causes a net decrease in MOEFF.

Initial studies with MOEFF used chemostats and liquid media. When increased liquid dilution rate increased MOEFF in chemostat systems, researchers initially concluded that liquid k_p would be very important in vivo. But MOEFF has not always been directly related to fluid passage and occasionally the relationship has been inverse of that expected. Instead, particulate k_p is often found to be more closely related to MOEFF than liquid k_p. The relationship of MOEFF to k_p of various fractions logically depends on the relative proportions of bacteria and potentially digestible OM in different digesta phases. In addition, changes in microbial species, such as prevalence of protozoa, and in ruminal conditions, such as pH and osmotic pressure which influence maintenance cost of microbes, will alter MOEFF.

MOEFF in vivo represents an amalgam of efficiencies from many ruminal microenvironments. Hence, the mean k_p of bacteria from the rumen is intermediate between the k_p's of fluid and particles. The mean k_p is considerably lower than the k_p for fluid because about half of the bacteria in the rumen are attached to larger particles. Most of the remaining bacteria are associated with small, free flowing particles which flow with fluids from the rumen. Microbes in the fluid pool would be forced to replicate at a faster rate to avoid washout while microbes attached to large slowly degraded particles will grow more slowly, more similar to batch cultures. In contrast, the attached microbes would not have the "feast and famine" fluctuations in nutrient supply which free-living organisms experience. Because faster growing organisms grow more efficiently, increasing k_p only for fluid, which is already 6 to 20%/h, will have less impact on total MOEFF than increasing the k_p of particles, which is usually between 2 and 6%/h.

As MOEFF varies with k_p and degree of microbial association with different fractions may change with diet, MOEFF changes with diet composition and level of feed intake. With a low k_p and long ruminal retention time, the extent of ruminal digestion is highest and the bacteria in the free, unassociated fluid pool would be the prime contributors to MOEFF. As feed intake and k_p increase, k_p of microbes associated with particles increases and adherent microbes contribute to MOEFF, as well. With roughage diets a higher proportion of the microbial protein reaching the lower tract would be of adherent microbe origin, because roughage necessitates more intimate association with microbes for digestion.

Almost invariably, MOEFF is greater with forage than concentrate diets. With processed concentrate diets, the small particles need not be retained in the rumen for reduction and can leave the rumen rapidly, so the k_p for adherent bacteria should be high. Relative to roughage diets the liquid k_p with concentrate diets is low (Fig. 8-5). With grazed forage, the array of particle sizes is large with some particles being retained and others being readily passed from the rumen as consumed.

Total microbial yield must not be confused with MOEFF. As feed intake increases, both the rate of passage and the size of particles leaving the rumen will increase; both should increase MOEFF. But as k_p increases, extent of digestion of slowly digested OM decreases and more OM will pass from the rumen undigested. Because bacterial yield is the multiple of MOEFF and amount of organic matter truly fermented in the rumen, when rate of k_d is low and k_p is high, total microbial yield can decrease as k_p increases despite an increase in MOEFF. This relationship for several rates of passage and digestion is illustrated in Table 8-6.

Passage rate has limited application to ruminal protozoa or to other microbes which adhere to the rumen wall. In addition, microbes which attach to particles have a sufficient energy supply so that population size changes over time are minimal. If population size changes in microenvironments, growth rate is no longer tied to passage rate and MOEFF will vary with particle output instead of k_p of liquid or particles. In this case MOEFF would be directly related to the amount of particles passing from the system, with particles being the vehicle for transport of microbes.

Initially, the size of the ruminal population or biomass was suggested to be an index of efficiency of fermentation with higher

Table 8-6. Changes in microbial efficiency and yield with various rates of digestion and passage.

Microbial		Ruminal OM digestion		Microbial yield,[c]
Passage rate, %/h	MOEFF,[a] g protein per 100 g OMF	Rate %/h	Extent,[b] g per 100 g OM fed	g protein per 100 OM fed
5	14.2	5	50	7.1
10	21.5	5	33	7.1
15	26.0	5	25	6.5
5	14.2	10	67	9.5
10	21.5	10	50	10.8
15	26.0	10	40	10.4

[a]Based on the equation: $1/Y_{OM} = 0.015/k_p + 0.1406$ (31) where Y_{OM} is g of N incorporated per 100 g OM truly fermented (converted from N to a crude protein basis) and k_p is passage rate as a decimal fraction.
[b]Calculated as $k_d/(k_d + k_p)$.
[c]Calculated as MOEFF times extent of organic matter fermented in the rumen.

numbers being desired. But in chemostats, it became apparent that this was not true. Though population was greater when k_p was 2%/h than when it was 6 or 10%/h, MOEFF was lower. Hence, the rumen microbial biomass may decline with faster passage rate, despite providing the same or an increasing amount of microbial protein to the small intestine. A large microbial biomass is undesirable for maximizing MOEFF.

The composite growth rate for bacteria in the rumen would be about 6 to 7%/h. This means that microbes must replicate at least 1.5 times each day. At this growth rate a large proportion of energy is used for maintenance. With shortages of nutrients such as N or S, energy no longer will limit growth. Under such conditions, OM fermentation will continue despite little or no increase in microbial yield. This has been attributed partly to uncoupling of ATP yield from microbial metabolism. This condition also could be ascribed to increased activity of futile cycles with generation of heat or to increased storage of polysaccharide.

Protozoa flow from the rumen at a considerably slower rate than bacteria. The time for most types of protozoa to double usually is about twice as long as ruminal retention time based on in vitro studies. This means that ruminal protozoa have a very low k_p which produces a very low MOEFF. Only some 20-30% of ruminal protozoal biomass produced ever flows to the small intestine according to some studies. Slow passage is probably due to their low density and association with particles or the reticulum wall. Studies of protozoa have been hampered by limited marker procedures specific to protozoa. Protozoa normally sequester with particles and may settle in the ventral rumen following carbohydrate engorgement. Hence outflow may resemble kinetics of particles. Increasing the k_p or decreasing the population of protozoa greatly increases MOEFF because protozoa often comprise over half of the microbial biomass in the rumen. Defaunation in recent studies increased MOEFF considerably and also increased growth rate of lambs fed low-protein diets (8, 9). This could have several causes in addition to inefficient growth of protozoa. Methanogenic and proteolytic bacteria may be associated with protozoa in the rumen. Defaunation reduces CH_4 loss and proteolysis, both of which may alter efficiency of growth of both microbes and animals. With defaunation, digestibility and feed intake may be reduced as protozoa can aid in physical disruption of feed particles in the rumen. MOEFF of individual microbial species also varies, so the prevalence of bacterial types within the rumen may alter MOEFF.

Competitiveness of a given microbial species in the ruminal ecosystem varies with a number of factors. These include maximal growth rates, substrate affinity and preference, maintenance requirements, growth efficiency, tolerance of adverse conditions (pH, energy supply, osmotic shock), ability to store nutrients for later use and efficiency of metabolic pathways to generate and use ATP. The relative importance of these factors changes with feeding conditions. Though it is usually advantageous to have low maintenance requirements and a high MOEFF, other factors such as high maximal growth rates, wide tolerance of pH conditions and ability to catabolize a broad spectrum of substrates often may be more important to a microbial species than MOEFF.

IN VITRO SYSTEMS

Rate and extent of digestion in the rumen can be studied using a variety of laboratory procedures (12, 14, 30). In vitro (in glass) fermentation studies are usually lower in cost and more rapid and repeatable than trials with animals. Laboratory fermentation studies fall into two general classes. The first is commonly termed an "in vitro" system in which ruminal microbes in a batch, a continuous or a discontinuous culture are incubated with a feedstuff, drug or test component. The most common in vitro procedure is the batch incubation as described by Tilley and Terry (29). The test feedstuff is fermented first with buffered rumen fluid for 24 or 48 h and secondly with a pepsin-HCl mixture to solubilize protein. Total disappearance of the feed is measured. This procedure is commonly used in forage evaluation systems to appraise digestibility. In vitro dry matter disappearance (IVDMD) measured by this procedure is highly correlated with in vivo digestibility. With in vitro experiments, only small amounts of test compounds are needed and many feedstuffs or test compounds can be evaluated rapidly.

170

Extrapolating results of in vitro studies to the in vivo (in the animal) system can be erroneous, however. In vivo, microbes can adapt to new compounds or conditions and ruminal volume and passage rate may change. Hence, in vitro findings must always be checked in vivo. Most compounds which are ineffective in vitro are ineffective in vivo, but compounds effective in vitro are often ineffective in vivo due to microbial or animal adaptation. In modified in vitro procedures, isolated microbes are used and production of a variety of end products such as VFA, gas, or microbial mass can be measured. Various enzymes including cellulase, amylase and proteases can be substituted for microbes in the incubation to develop predictive models for digestion by animals. Although such modifications permit forage evaluation without access to an animal which donates rumen fluid, their reliability has been questioned.

A second fermentation approach is the "in situ" or "in sacco" procedure. The test material is placed in a polyester bag with small pores. This bag is then suspended in the rumen for specific time periods. Microbes, fluids and end-products of digestion are flushed in and out through the pores. Material disappearing from the bag is considered to be digested. Results are subject to both influx and efflux errors because soluble components and small particles can leave the bag without being digested and microbes can enter the bag during fermentation. Nevertheless, digestibility of forages and protein sources can be screened rapidly in situ. Microbial action in situ closely mimics ruminal fermentation and wide swings in microbial types, which can occur in batch culture systems, are avoided in situ. Though bag procedures can be standardized, using a single diet appears undesirable because diet type and adaptation can alter digestive capacity of the ruminal population (4).

SUMMARY

Microbial fermentation in the rumen must be considered to function independently of needs of the host ruminant or desires for maximal efficiency of energy or protein utilization. Even though the animal exerts control over certain ruminal factors such as feed intake, saliva input and possibly k_p, the animal has limited control over the wild, often rampant fermentation in the rumen. Inadequate control is reflected by the incidence of bloat, ammonia toxicity, nitrate toxicity and acidosis encountered with ruminant animals. In the ecosystem of the rumen, fierce competition helps prevent invasions by pathogens and usually selects for a high MOEFF. Thanks to ruminal fermentation the ruminant animal can thrive on diets insufficient in energy or protein for survival of other animals. Manipulation of rates of passage and digestion as well as microbial species promises to improve efficiency of production by ruminants. Though buffering the ruminant from fluctuations in nutrient supply, the rumen also complicates bypass of desired nutrients. Strong microbial competition, useful to increase microbial growth and efficiency within the rumen, would be expected to complicate survival of genetically engineered rumen microbes. Means to provide new substrates to aid survival of selected organisms and to remove deleterious types could improve energetic efficiency of animal production.

Literature Cited and Additional Readings

1. Baldwin, R.L. and M.J. Allison. 1983. J. Animal Sci. 57(Suppl. 2):461.
2. Bergen, W.G. and D.B. Bates. 1984. J. Animal Sci. 58:1461.
3. Bergen, W.G. and M.T. Yokoyama. 1977. J. Animal Sci. 45:573.
4. Broderick, G.A. 1982. Estimation of protein degradation using in situ and in vitro methods. In: Protein Requirements for Cattle: Symposium, Okla. State University MP-109:265.
5. Campling, R.C. 1970. In: Physiology of Digestion and Metabolism in Ruminants, p. 226. A.T. Phillipson, ed. Oriel Press, Newcastle, England.
6. Chalupa, W. 1980. Chemical control of rumen microbial metabolism. In: Digestive Physiology and Metabolism in Ruminants, p. 325. Y. Ruckebusch and P. Thivend, eds. AVI Publishing Co., Westport, CT.
7. Cheng, K.J. and J.W. Costerton. 1980. Adherent rumen bacteria—their role in the digestion of plant material, urea and epithelial cells. In: Digestive Physiology and Metabolism in Ruminants, p. 227. Y. Ruckebusch and P. Thivend, eds. AVI Publishing Co., Westport, CT.

8. Demeyer, D.I. and C.J. Van Nevel. 1975. Methanogenesis, an integrated part of carbohydrate fermentation, and its control. In: Digestion and Metabolism in the Ruminant, p. 366. I.W. McDonald and A.C.E. Warner, eds. Univ. New England Publ. Unit, Armidale, NSW, Australia.

9. Demeyer, D.I., C.J. Van Nevel and G. Van de Voorde. 1982. Archiv fur Tierer. 32:595.

10. Dulphy, J.P., B. Remond and M. Theriez. 1980. Ingestive behaviour and related activities in ruminants. In: Digestive Physiology and Metabolism in Ruminants, p. 103. Y. Ruckebusch and P. Thivend, eds. AVI Publishing Co., Westport, CT.

11. Eadie, J.M. and S.O. Mann. 1970. Development of the rumen microbial population: High starch diets and instability. In: Physiology of Digestion and Metabolism in the Ruminant, p. 335. A.T. Phillipson, ed. Oriel Press, Newcastle upon Tyne, England.

12. Goering, H.K. and P.J. Van Soest. 1970. Forage Fiber Analyses. USDA Agr. Handbook No. 379.

13. Grovum, W.L. 1982. Integration of digestion and digesta kinetics with control of feed intake—A physiological framework for a model of rumen function. In: Herbivore Nutrition in the Subtropics and Tropics, F.M.C. Gilchrist and R.I. Mackie, eds. Science Press, Craighill, South Africa.

14. Johnson, R.R. 1966. Techniques and procedures for in vitro and in vivo rumen studies. J. Animal Sci. 25:855.

15. Kaufmann, W., H. Hagemeister and G. Dirksen. 1980. Adaptation to changes in dietary composition, level and frequency of feeding. In: Digestive Physiology and Metabolism in Ruminants, p. 587. Y. Ruckebusch and P. Thivend, eds. AVI Publishing Co., Westport, CT.

16. Leedle, J.A.Z., M.P. Bryant and R.B. Hespell. 1982. Appl. Environ. Microbiol. 44:402.

17. Leng, R.A. 1970. Formation and production of volatile fatty acids in the rumen. In: Physiology of Digestion and Metabolism in the Ruminant, p. 406. A.T. Phillipson, ed. Oriel Press, Newcastle upon Tyne, England.

18. Leng, R.A. and J.V. Nolan. 1984. J. Dairy Sci. 67:1072.

19. MacLeod, N.A. and E.R. Ørskov. 1984. Can. J. Animal Sci. 64(Supp. 1):354.

20. Montgomery, M.J. and B.R. Baumgardt. 1965. J. Dairy Sci. 48:569.

21. Oldham, J.D. 1981. Patterns of nutrient utilization—Implication for nitrogen metabolism. In: Isotope-aided Studies on Non-protein Nitrogen and Agro-industrial By-products Utilization by Ruminants with Particular Reference to Developing Countries and Nuclear Techniques for Assessing and Improving Ruminant Feeds. FAO/IEAA. Vienna, Austria.

22. Owens, F.N. and A.L. Goetsch. 1986. Digesta passage rates and microbial protein synthesis. In: Control of Digestion and Metabolism in Ruminants, pp. 196-223. L.P. Milligan, W.L. Grovum and A. Dobson, eds. Reston Pub. Co., Reston, VA.

23. Ørskov, E.R. 1980. Possible nutritional constraints in meeting energy and amino acid requirements of the highly productive ruminant. In: Digestive Physiology and Metabolism in Ruminants, p. 309. Y. Ruckebusch and P. Thivend, eds. AVI Publishing Co., Westport, CT.

24. Prins, R.A. and R.T.J. Clarke. 1980. Microbial ecology of the rumen. In: Digestive Physiology and Metabolism in Ruminants, p. 179. Y. Ruckebusch and P. Thivend, eds. AVI Publishing Co., Westport, CT.

25. Russell, J.B. and R.B. Hespell. 1981. J. Dairy Sci. 64:1153.

26. Schwartz, H.M. and F.M.C. Gilchrist. 1975. Microbial interactions with the diet and the host animal. In: Digestion and Metabolism in the Ruminant, p. 165. I.W. McDonald and A.C.I. Warner, eds. Univ. of New England Publishing Unit, Armidale, NSW, Australia.

27. Sharp, W.M., R.R. Johnson and F.N. Owens. 1982. J. Animal Sci. 55:1505.

28. Smith, R.H. and J.D. Oldham. 1981. Rumen metabolism and recent developments. In: Isotope-aided Studies on Non-protein Nitrogen and Agro-industrial By-products Utilization by Ruminants with Particular Reference to Developing Countries and Nuclear Techniques for Assessing and Improving Ruminant Feeds. FAO/IEAA. Vienna, Austria.

29. Tilley, J.M.A. and R.A. Terry. 1963. J. Brit. Grassland Soc. 18:104.

30. Van Soest, P.J. 1982. Nutritional Ecology of the Ruminant. O & B Books, Inc., Corvallis, OR.

31. Van Soest, P.J., et al. 1982. A net protein system for cattle: The rumen submodel for nitrogen. In: Protein Requirements for Cattle: Symposium, Okla. State Univ. MP-109:265.

32. Wolin, M.J. 1975. Interactions between the bacterial species of the rumen. In: Digestion and Metabolism in the Ruminant, p. 134. I.W. McDonald and A.C.I. Warner, eds. Univ. of New England Publishing Unit, Armidale, NSW, Australia.

by N. R. Merchen

INTRODUCTION

Digestion can be broadly defined as the summation of processes by which macromolecules in food are degraded to simpler compounds which are absorbed from the gastrointestinal tract. In virtually all mammalian species, digestion is accomplished both by fermentative metabolism of dietary constituents by microbes occupying certain parts of the gut and by hydrolytic/enzymatic breakdown of complex nutrients mediated by secretions into the gastric stomach and small intestine. Ruminants are animals that have achieved maximum specialization in fermentative digestion. Although the ruminant is characterized by microbial fermentation occurring in the forestomach, postruminal digestion is vital to the animal. Digestion and absorption in the abomasum and small intestine are essential because lipids, proteins, vitamins, many minerals and any non-structural carbohydrates escaping ruminal fermentation are all made available to the host animal by this route. This chapter will examine some of the fundamental processes involved in digestion and absorption of dietary nutrients. Methodology for determining extent of digestion and factors influencing this will also be discussed.

SECRETIONS INTO THE DIGESTIVE TRACT

Secretions of the Abomasal Mucosa

The abomasum is the only compartment of the ruminant stomach that contains secretory tissue. It is analogous to the gastric stomach of non-ruminants and contains fundic and pyloric regions which are histologically similar to those in simple-stomached animals (see Ch. 2). The fundic mucosa contains parietal cells, which secrete HCl and chief cells, which are responsible for pepsin secretion as well as mucous-secreting cells. The pylorus is characterized by secretions which are largely mucous in nature and alkaline in reactivity but which exhibit low peptic activities when

adjusted to pH 2 (1). Table 9-1 contains compositional data of abomasal secretions in sheep.

Estimates of the quantity of gastric juice secreted have largely been obtained by measuring amount secreted by innervated abomasal pouches and correcting this figure by adjusting for the proportion of total abomasal mucosa in the pouch. Some error may be associated with this approach because it assumes that the secretory activity of the pouch mucosa is representative of that of the remainder of the organ. Using this methodology with sheep, Harrop (2) reported that the fundic region was responsible for secretion of 1,100-4,500 ml/d of gastric juice. An additional 200-400 ml were secreted by the pyloric region in the abomasum. Fundic juice contained variable concentrations of H ions (43-77 mEq/ℓ), but virtually no H ions were secreted by the pylorus. Total N content of these secretions was also variable (36-55 mg N/100 ml from fundic mucosa and 38-70 mg N/100 ml of pyloric juice). Most N was secreted as a component of protein (65-90%, as determined by tungstic acid precipitation), but an additional 3-13% was secreted as urea- or ammonia-N. Sedimentary N, consisting of cellular debris and visible strands of mucus, accounted for an additional 0.51-2.77 g N/d in the abomasum. Other reports (3) suggest that total secretion of gastric juice in sheep is in

Table 9-1. Composition of gastric juice in sheep.[a]

Constituent	Concentration, mEq/ℓ
H^+	Up to maximum of 124
K^+	2-19
Na^+	21-167
Ca^{++}	1.0-2.2
Mg^{++}	0.5-0.9
Cl^-	138-172
HCO_3^- (when abomasum is empty and juice is neutral)	6-9
Total N, mg/100 ml	15-33

[a]From Phillipson (1)

the range of 4-6 ℓ daily and that a cow produces 30-35 ℓ/d of abomasal secretions, but it is unclear how this figure was derived.

A salient feature of the digestive process in ruminants is its more or less continuous nature. Free-ranging animals and those fed ad libitum invest a large proportion of their time in eating or ruminating. These activities, coupled with the large pool of digesta in the reticulo-rumen, result in movement of digesta into the postruminal tract on a fairly continuous basis. This, in turn, stimulates a continuous release of digestive secretions into the abomasum and small intestine. In fact, it has been observed (3) that abomasal secretions in sheep fed ad libitum occur in a continuous fashion with only minor fluctuations in amount and acidity during a 24-h period.

A number of factors interact to regulate secretion, particularly of HCl, by the abomasal mucosa. The factor of greatest importance generally is amount and chemical nature of digesta entering and flowing through the abomasum. In contrast to the secretion patterns noted in sheep fed ad libitum, Hill (3) reported a drastic decrease occurs in volume and acidity of abomasal secretions in fasted sheep. Subsequent meals and the act of feeding in sheep fed twice daily results in increased secretion (volume, acidity and sometimes pepsin) within 10 minutes of the beginning of a meal. Maximum rates of secretion in meal-fed sheep occur within 1-3 h after initiation of eating (3). There is a close relationship observed between flow of digesta to the abomasum and volume and acidity of the gastric juice secreted. Emptying the rumen results in reduced total secretion by the abomasum and virtually no acid secretion. Feeding animals subsequent to emptying the rumen produces only slight increases in secretion rates. Such secretory responses in meal-fed animals are probably associated with increased flow of digesta postruminally.

Artificial distension of the abomasum to volumes approximating those reported for normal animals stimulates increased volume and acidity of secretions (3), thus increasing volume associated with accelerated inflow of digesta may be partially responsible for regulation of secretion by the abomasal mucosa. Increased food intake, which presumably increased amount of digesta leaving the rumen, stimulates production of gastric juice (3).

Acidity of abomasal contents seems to be important in initiation or cessation of HCl secretion by parietal cells. Imposing a number of possible stimuli on the abomasum results in extreme variation in total output of acid by the mucosa (3), but concentration of acid in abomasal contents is maintained within a relatively narrow range (pH 1.6-2.5). Infusion of HCl causes a drastic reduction in secretory activity, but infusion of an isotonic solution of NaCl has no such inhibitory effects. Infusion of phosphate buffers at pH 6 results in a pronounced increase in secretory activity, but virtually no response occurs when buffer pH is adjusted to 2.1 prior to infusion (3). Entry of VFA into the abomasum has a direct stimulatory effect on secretory activity. In all cases, secretory activity declined when abomasal pH dropped to 1.9-2.8 (3).

Secretory activity may be initiated in response to certain psychic stimuli. Teasing sheep with food resulted in an onset of increased secretion within 15-30 minutes, although this act also produced an increase in frequency of ruminal contractions which could have induced a secretory response by increasing digesta flow to the abomasum (4). Hill (3) reported that a conditioned response in secretion may occur since meal-fed animals displayed an increase in secretory activity at their normal feeding times even when food was not offered.

At birth numbers of parietal cells in abomasal mucosa are sparse and abomasal pH is concomitantly high. However, numbers and activity of parietal cells increase by a factor of at least 10 within 72 h after birth and a consequent decrease occurs in pH of the abomasal contents. The relatively high pH in the abomasum of neonatal ruminants coupled with a corresponding lack of pepsin (pH optima 2.1) activity may provide a mechanism for conservation from digestion of intact proteins in the early neonate. Because newborn ruminants rely upon absorption of colostral immunoglobulins for provision of passive immunity, it would seem advantageous that these proteins be spared from hydrolysis prior to their absorption from the small intestine.

In young milk-fed ruminants, ingested milk passes rapidly to the abomasum via closure of the esophageal groove. The peptic cells of the gastric glands in these animals secrete, in

174

addition to pepsinogen, the proteolytic enzyme rennin (actually secreted as the zymogen prorennin). Rennin differs from pepsin largely in its potent milk-clotting ability, although pepsin also causes some formation of milk clots. The presence of rennin, as well as the acidic abomasal environment, results in coagulation of casein and fat in the milk to form a clot consisting of a casein matrix interspersed with milk fat globules (5). Soluble whey proteins and lactose pass through the abomasum rapidly, but the casein-fat clot is retained and digested over a period of 12-18 h postfeeding.

Hill et al (5) have reported that secretory activity in abomasal pouches in one-week-old calves responded to feeding in a manner similar to that seen in older animals, with increases in volume and acidity of secretions for 30-120 minutes after eating. Rennin has a higher pH optima (ca. 4.0) than does pepsin, and milk-fed animals tend to maintain higher abomasal pH than do adults. The relative proportions of pepsin and rennin secreted in the abomasum of milk-fed calves vary markedly among individuals and do not seem to be dependent either on age or on consumption of solid food. However, after weaning, little or no rennin is secreted (5). It has been observed that the presence of casein in digesta entering the abomasum stimulates secretion of rennin but that other proteins (soy, fish, whey) do not elicit a response in secretion (6).

Secretions Into the Small Intestine

Digestion in the small intestine (SI) is mediated by secretions of the liver, pancreas and small intestinal mucosa. Bile and pancreatic secretions enter the intestine through the common bile duct in the anterior duodenum and most of the enzymes secreted by the intestinal mucosa are produced by cells lining Brunner's glands of the duodenum. Digesta leaving the gastric stomach of the ruminant is more acidic than that of most non-ruminants and pH increases at a relatively slower rate as digesta passes through the SI. Duodenal pH in sheep is typically 2.6-3.0 (7, 8) and intestinal pH does not reach neutrality for a distance of 7 m or more past the pyloric sphincter (8). The increased pH has important implications with regard to enzymatic activity in the intestine because amylolytic and proteolytic enzymes secreted by the pancreas and intestinal mucosa generally have pH optima which are neutral to slightly alkaline.

Bile is synthesized in the liver and stored and secreted by the gall bladder in most species. Ruminant bile consists of a solution containing mucus, electrolytes and the bile salts (especially Na taurocholate) and pigments. Some of the components of bile taken from the gall bladder of sheep and collected by cannulation of the common bile duct are presented in Table 9-2. Bile salts are synthesized in the liver from cholesterol and have an important role in digestion by emulsifying and solubilizing lipids entering the SI and enhancing the activity of lipase secreted by the pancreas. Most bile salts are recycled efficiently because more than 95% of those secreted into the duodenum are reabsorbed in the ileum and returned to the liver by the enterohepatic circulation (9). Bile pigments have no digestive function and consist largely of bilirubin which is produced as a breakdown product of hemoglobin by hepatic cells. In cattle, bilirubin is oxidized to the greenish biliverdin (9).

The rate of secretion of bile varies depending upon whether or not bile which is removed is returned to the intestine. Harrison (10) reported secretion rates of approximately 17 ml/h in sheep when bile was not returned to the intestine. However, bile flow was increased to 20-40 ml/h when the material was re-infused into the duodenum at rates approximating the rate at which it was secreted. The increase in secretion may be attributed to a stimulatory effect of the re-absorbed bile salts which are returned to the liver. Infusion of solutions of bile salts into the duodenum (10) or portal vein (11) likewise produce an increase in secretion rate.

Table 9-2. Composition of bile in sheep.[a]

Constituent	Gall bladder	4-24 h collection[b]
Total solids, g/100 ml	8.66	2.86
Cl^-, mEq/ℓ	73.6	122.2
Na^+, mEq/ℓ	196.6	153.6
K^+, mEq/ℓ	8.03	6.68
Total N, mg/100 ml	247.7	76.5

[a] From Harrison (10)
[b] Collected from cannulae in the common bile duct without return of collected bile to the duodenum.

Enterohepatic circulation of bile salts apparently exerts a more or less continuous stimulatory effect on bile secretion. Entry of digesta into the duodenum also influences secretion rate of bile (10). Continuous passage of digesta through the abomasum and duodenum and the return to the liver of recycled bile salts probably are the most important factors regulating bile secretion by sheep.

Bile composition may also be influenced by amount and/or composition of digesta reaching the intestine. Injection of modest amounts of HCl into the duodenum of sheep caused an increase in output of bicarbonate in bile (11). Administration of exogenous secretin likewise stimulated increased secretion of electrolytes (particularly bicarbonate) and water into both bile and pancreatic juice (11). Because secretin is released by the duodenum in response to the entry of digesta of low pH into that organ, this mechanism probably provides a means of partially neutralizing the acidic chyme leaving the abomasum.

Pancreatic juice secreted by ruminants contains amylolytic, lipolytic and proteolytic enzymes in a solution of electrolytes and water. Activities of these enzymes are approximately the same as those found in the pancreatic secretions of the dog. The dog secretes much more pancreatic juice in proportion to its body weight than do ruminants, thus the total activity of pancreatic enzymes in the ruminant intestine is much lower (1). Composition of pancreatic juice collected from sheep is in Table 9-3.

Total volume of pancreatic juice secreted is 2.2-4.8 ℓ/d in cattle (1) and 350-450 ml/d in sheep (7, 12). Unlike bile, non-return of collected pancreatic secretions to the intestine does not cause decreases in secretion. In sheep fed normally, pancreatic juice is secreted continuously with only slight fluctuations in secretion rate over a 24-h period (12). There is no consistent pattern of secretion in response to eating nor does the act of eating seem to produce any direct stimulation of pancreatic secretion, suggesting lack of any cephalic phase of secretion (12). Entry of digesta into the duodenum is probably the most important factor regulating volume of pancreatic juice secreted since the continuous pattern of secretion observed in ruminants corresponds to the continuous flow of digesta

Table 9-3. Composition of pancreatic juice in sheep.[a]

Constituent	Concentration, mEq/ℓ
Na$^+$	135-165
K$^+$	3.9-5.4
Cl$^-$	110-126
HCO$^-_3$	15-30
Ca^{++}	4.0-5.7
Mg^{++}	0.66-1.52
Total N, mg/100 ml	480-720
pH	7.2-7.8

[a]From Taylor (12)

previously described in these animals. Furthermore, Taylor (12) reported that preventing digesta from flowing into the duodenum resulted in decreases in secretory rates by 70%.

Vagal stimulation results in an increase in secretion and this response is blocked by administration of atropine sulfate. Several hormones have also been shown experimentally to influence secretion of pancreatic juice. Intravenous infusion of insulin results in increased rates of secretion, both of total volume and of pancreatic amylase. This response may be mediated by an increase in gut motility and possible increases in digesta flow noted when insulin is administered (12). Secretin also enhances flow of pancreatic juice (12) and, as with bile, increases bicarbonate content of secretions (11). Cholecystokinin administration to sheep does not influence total volume of pancreatic secretions but increases enzyme output of pancreatic juice (11).

Extent of postruminal digestion of starch escaping ruminal fermentation is partially dependent upon secretion of adequate amounts of pancreatic amylase. Evidence suggests that amount of starch arriving at the intestine affects amount of amylase secreted. Van Hellen et al (13) reported that total volume and total amylase secreted by the pancreas were increased by 150-250% when steers were fed an 80% concentrate diet compared to those fed 20% concentrate. Likewise, steers fed a concentrate diet at 3X maintenance intake had secretion rates of pancreatic amylase 129% greater than if fed alfalfa hay at maintenance (14). Mechanisms by which such responses are elicited are unknown and

176

likely to be quite complex, but volume and composition of digesta arriving at the duodenum are probably the major determinants of volume and composition of pancreatic secretions. It would be logical to suggest that the relationships between these factors are, in part, integrated by the release of duodenal and pancreatic hormones.

Mucosa of the SI secretes mucus and is also the site of origin of certain enteric enzymes which are especially important in postruminal digestion of carbohydrates. Brunner's glands lining the proximal duodenum secrete a neutral to slightly alkaline juice which contains amylase and ribonuclease (1). Harrison and Hill (7) reported a secretion rate of duodenal juice of 13 ml/h in sheep fed once daily. Increasing feeding frequency from one to three times/d and increasing rate of flow of digesta into the duodenum produced an increase in secretory rate to 26 ml/h.

In addition to enzymes found in duodenal secretions, various disaccharidases (especially lactase, maltase and isomaltase) are present throughout the SI. These enzymes are not secreted into the intestinal lumen but are, instead, believed to act upon their various disaccharides at the brush border of intact mucosal cells. Age of the animal and, possibly, diet influence relative activities of different disaccharidases along the SI. Huber and coworkers (15) reported activities of these enzymes measured in dairy calves ranging from 1-44 d of age. Lactase activity was highest at one day and declined steadily thereafter. Maltase activity was not affected by age. In contrast to non-ruminants, sucrase activity was entirely absent from the intestinal mucosa of calves in this experiment and there is no evidence to indicate that sucrase activity is ever found in ruminant intestine. Type of carbohydrate entering the intestine (lactose vs sucrose-starch) had no influence on relative activities of different disaccharidases (15). However, in subsequent work (16) calves fed diets containing increased levels of lactose had substantially higher levels of lactase activity in the intestine at 11 weeks of age than did controls.

Activity of both intestinal disaccharidases and pancreatic proteases seems to be distributed in a similar fashion along the length of the SI. Activities of lactase, maltase and isomaltase appear to be highest in jejunum with lower levels in both duodenum and ileum (15). Ben-Ghedalia et al (8) observed that activities of trypsin, chymotrypsin and carboxypeptidase A secreted by the pancreas increased gradually between the duodenum and a point 7 m caudal to the pylorus and then declined gradually throughout the remainder of the intestine. This pattern may be a function of the characteristic pattern of pH values reported in ruminant intestine. The pH of the mid-jejunum is 6-7 which approximates the pH optima of most of these enzymes. The duodenum and proximal jejunum (pH 2.6-5.1) are probably too acidic and the ileum too alkaline (pH 7.8-8.2) for optimal activity of many digestive enzymes (8).

ABSORPTION FROM THE GASTRO-INTESTINAL TRACT

Absorption of VFA from the Reticulo-Rumen

Although some VFA leave the rumen with digesta flowing to the lower gastro-intestinal tract and are absorbed from the omasum and abomasum, the vast majority of the acids produced by ruminal fermentation are absorbed directly from that compartment of the stomach. In fact, continuous removal of VFA by absorption from the reticulo-rumen is important in maintenance of a stable ruminal pH. There is no evidence of any active transport of VFA across the rumen epithelia and the concentration gradient between the ruminal contents, rumen epithelial cells and blood seems to be important in dictating rate of VFA absorption. Considerable epithelial metabolism of some VFA occurs (see Ch. 14) which aids in maintenance of the concentration gradient between the lumen and blood and increases rate of absorption from the rumen (17).

Rate of absorption of VFA is influenced by ruminal pH and by the chain length of the individual acids. As pH on the luminal side of the epithelia decreases, rate of VFA absorption is increased, suggesting that increasing the proportion of the acid present in the undissociated (free) form favors more rapid absorption (17). Increasing chain length also results in increased absorption rates with relative rates of absorption of undissociated acids as follows: butyric>propionic>acetic (1). Because the rumen wall preferentially metabolizes individual VFA in the same order, it is likely that differential concentration gradients created by selective metabolism of different acids are responsible for enhanced rates of absorption of the larger acids.

Reduced pH and resultant increases in the proportion of the free acids in the rumen favor more rapid absorption. However, at normal rumen pH (6-7), relatively low concentrations of free acids (pK_a of VFA is ca. 4.8) are present and yet efficient removal of these fermentation end-products still occurs. Removal by absorption of undissociated acids results in formation of undissociated acid because of the equilibrium maintained between the two species. However, it is apparent that some absorption of the dissociated (anionic) form of the acids does occur (17).

Early work on the mechanisms of VFA absorption indicated a close relationship between VFA disappearance across the epithelia and the subsequent accumulation of bicarbonate on the luminal side of the epithelia. The molar quantity of bicarbonate ion which accumulated was equal to approximately half the amount of acid absorbed. When no VFA were present, concentration of CO_2 in rumen contents was greater than in plasma, while bicarbonate was found in lower concentration in rumen fluid than in plasma. When VFA (acetate) was present, the relationships between rumen and plasma concentrations of CO_2 and bicarbonate were reversed, indicating that the process of VFA uptake was accompanied by consumption of CO_2 and production of bicarbonate in the rumen fluid. These exchanges apparently occur within the rumen epithelia and require that one membrane of the epithelial cells be more permeable to the undissociated acid than to the dissociated form. It is believed that half the VFA absorbed is in the free form and that this is neutralized in plasma. Thus, 50% of the VFA produced in the rumen is neutralized by this route with the remaining 50% neutralized by salivary buffers (17). A summarization of these events is depicted in Fig. 9-1.

Absorption of Ammonia from the Reticulo-Rumen

Significant quantities of NH_3 are produced in the rumen via microbial degradation of dietary protein, hydrolysis of dietary and

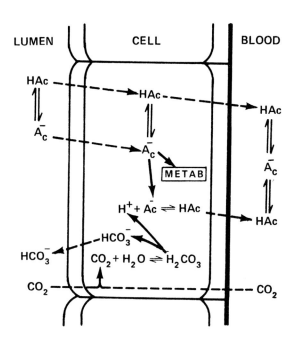

Figure 9-1. Hypothetical model of VFA transport across the rumen epithelia. The membrane on the luminal side is permeable to both free and anion forms of the acid while the membrane facing the blood is permeable only to the free acid. Metabolism of fatty acids by epithelial cells influences the concentration gradient on both sides of the membrane. Carbonic acid formed from CO_2 produced by cellular metabolism or absorbed from rumen or blood acts as a H donor for VFA transport. From Stevens (17).

endogenous NPN-containing compounds and turnover and degradation of microbial cells. The NH_3 produced enters a dynamic pool which may be utilized as a source of N for amino acid biosynthesis by rumen microbes (see Ch. 8, 12). A large proportion of the ammonia not taken up by the microbes is absorbed directly through the rumen wall. Concentrations of NH_3 are ordinarily very low in peripheral arterial and venous blood, but concentrations in portal blood are often several times higher than at these sites (18). Under some circumstances, a substantial proportion of the total N disappearing in the GI tract may be absorbed as NH_3.

NH_3 is absorbed through the rumen wall strictly by passive diffusion and the quantity absorbed is positively related to ruminal NH_3 concentrations and to rumen pH (18). The dependency of rate of absorption of NH_3 on pH is dictated by the behavior of NH_3 as a

178

weak base. In solution, NH_3 exists in a state of equilibrium,

$$NH_3 + H^+ \rightleftharpoons NH_4^+$$

and the extent of ionization is highly pH dependent. The pK_a for this equilibrium is approximately 9 and, thus, the proportion of free NH_3 vs NH_4^+ increases at higher pH. Free NH_3 diffuses across cell membranes much more rapidly than does NH_4^+ (18). Consequently, increased rates of absorption occur at high pH due to the increase in concentration of free NH_3. Rate of transport of NH_3 across the rumen wall, for example, is three times greater at pH 6.5 than at pH 4.5 (18).

NH_3 toxicity may occur in ruminants due to excessive consumption of rapidly hydrolyzed NPN and subsequent accumulation of NH_3 in the peripheral circulation (see Ch. 23). However, rumen pH plays an important role in determining the concentration of ruminal NH_3 at which intoxication occurs.

Absorption of Monosaccharides from the Small Intestine

Digestion and absorption of starches and simple sugars in the SI of ruminants is generally less important quantitatively than in simple-stomached animals. In adult ruminants virtually all of the soluble sugars (lactose, sucrose, etc.) incorporated into the diet, as well as a large proportion of the dietary starch, are fermented by the rumen microbial population. However, in animals fed high concentrate diets at high levels of intake, as much as 50% of the dietary starch may escape ruminal fermentation and be presented to the lower gut for digestion (19). In such cases, substantial amounts of glucose may be absorbed from the SI.

Starch entering the duodenum is attacked by pancreatic and intestinal amylases and broken down to maltose and isomaltose which are cleaved by action of the appropriate disaccharidases to produce glucose. Glucose or other monosaccharides derived from intestinal digestion is subsequently absorbed by an active process which appears to be coupled to Na transport. While the actual mechanism of glucose absorption is still largely undefined, substantial evidence supports the model of glucose transport described below.

Glucose and other monosaccharides enter the mucosal cell membrane by binding to a specific carrier molecule which also binds Na. The co-transport of Na by the carrier molecule facilitates absorption of glucose against a concentration gradient since the inward transport of carrier-bound Na down a gradient results in transport of the glucose bound to the same carrier. Because respiring cells maintain a low intracellular concentration of Na by constantly pumping Na out of the cell, glucose will be accumulated in the cell so long as the combined intracellular concentration of Na and glucose is lower than that in the intestinal lumen. As glucose accumulates within the cell, it diffuses to the serosal side and into the bloodstream. Sugars can thus be absorbed even when intra-intestinal concentrations are low as long as Na is present and the energy required for glucose absorption is furnished by maintenance of low intracellular Na concentrations as a result of the Na-K-ATPase system on the cell membrane (20).

Absorption of Lipids from the Small Intestine

In non-ruminants little digestion of dietary lipid occurs prior to the duodenum and only after mixing with bile and pancreatic juice at this site does digestion commence. By contrast, considerable qualitative changes occur in composition of lipids during microbial digestion in the reticulo-rumen prior to arrival at the SI. These changes include (a) hydrolysis of triglycerides, galactoglycerides (principal form of lipid in fresh forage) and other esterified lipids; (b) hydrogenation of unsaturated fatty acids and (c) microbial biosynthesis of lipids. These events are discussed in Ch. 15. No appreciable degradation of long-chain fatty acids occurs in the rumen, and although some evidence indicates that very small amounts of long-chain fatty acids may be absorbed across the rumen wall, the actual digestion and absorption of lipids other than the VFA occurs almost exclusively in the SI (21). As in non-ruminants, intestinal digestion of lipid is dependent upon the presence of biliary and pancreatic secretions and exteriorization of flow of these materials results in only 15-20% of dietary lipid being absorbed (11).

The largest proportion (70-80%) of the lipids arriving at the abomasum is in the form of free fatty acids produced by microbial lipolysis of dietary triglycerides in the rumen (21, 22). Most of the remainder is in the form of phospholipids, which are largely microbial in origin. Due to ruminal hydrolysis of triglycerides and subsequent fermentation of glycerol, very little glycerol of dietary origin escapes the rumen. Duodenal digesta typically contains a larger fraction of esterified fatty acids and phospholipids than does abomasal digesta due to the presence of biliary secretions which contain these lipids. Bile also contributes lecithin (phosphatidylcholine) to the duodenum. Following hydrolysis to lysolecithin via the action of pancreatic lipase, this compound, along with the bile salts, acts as a potent emulsifying agent.

Triglycerides which escape ruminal breakdown and esterified fatty acids of microbial origin are readily hydrolyzed by pancreatic lipase to release free fatty acids. Free fatty acids are subsequently taken into micellar solution by bile salts and lysolecithin. The micelles are disrupted on the surface of the microvilli on the intestinal mucosa and free fatty acids are taken up by the mucosal cells. Most absorption of lipids occurs in the proximal half of the SI with the bile salts reabsorbed in the distal jejunum and in the ileum. Note that, in comparison to non-ruminants, virtually no monoglycerides are absorbed from the intestine (22).

Absorbed lipids are transported from the intestine by the lymphatic circulation. Lipids derived from intestinal absorption appear in the lymph in chylomicron form and composition of the lipid in these chylomicrons is approximately 70-80% triglyceride and 15-20% phospholipid with smaller proportions of free fatty acids, cholesterol and cholesterol esters (22). Because lipids are taken up by the mucosa as free fatty acids, it is apparent that the absorbed fatty acids are re-assembled into triglycerides within the mucosal cells. Little glycerol is available for absorption from the intestine, thus most of that required for the resynthesis of triglycerides at this site is of endogenous origin. The intestinal mucosal cells rely largely upon α-glycerol phosphate obtained from glycolytic intermediates as a source of glycerol.

Triglycerides and phospholipids synthesized in the mucosa are incorporated into chylomicrons and lipoproteins which are delivered to lymph and later enter the venous circulation via the thoracic duct. The continuous nature of digestion in ruminants results in continuous absorption of lipid from the gut, leading to a constant milky appearance of the lymph (22).

Absorption of Amino Acids from the Small Intestine

Protein reaching the SI of the ruminant is derived from three sources: (a) dietary protein which has escaped breakdown by rumen microbes; (b) protein contained in bacterial and protozoal cells which flow out of the rumen and (c) endogenous proteins contained in sloughed cells and secretions into the abomasum and intestine. Postruminal protein digestion and amino acid absorption are expected to occur in fashions similar to those observed in non-ruminants. Ruminants rely upon the same complement of pancreatic and intestinal proteases to effect breakdown of protein as do non-ruminants and absorb amino acids and small peptides by similar mechanisms (23). In contrast, ruminants differ from their simple-stomached counterparts in the large fraction of protein of microbial origin reaching the lower gut, the relatively continuous flow of digesta previously discussed and the more acidic nature of the chyme arriving at the duodenum. The pH of digesta entering the duodenum increases slowly during passage through the intestine and protease activity (pH optima >7.5) is not maximized until 7-15 m past the pylorus in sheep (8). Consequently, active absorption of amino acids is carried on largely in the jejunum and ileum.

The mechanism by which amino acids are absorbed is a Na-dependent, carrier-mediated transport which is similar to the process for glucose absorption discussed previously. As in glucose absorption, the consumption of energy is actually associated with the continuous outward flux of Na from the mucosal cells due to the activity of a NaK "pump". Na then re-enters the cell, down a concentration gradient, while coupled to a carrier molecule which simultaneously transports an amino acid molecule across the cell membrane. Amino acid transport (and glucose transport

180

as well) can thus be described as a type of secondary active transport (23). At least four (and possibly as many as six) carrier mechanisms have been identified, each with specificity for a different group of amino acids. These mechanisms include those for: (a) neutral amino acids with long side chains; (b) neutral amino acids with short side chains; (c) dibasic amino acids; and (d) acidic amino acids (23). It also appears likely that proline is absorbed by a carrier mechanism specific for itself.

The digestive and absorptive capacity of the SI for amino acids is very high and summaries (23) of studies in which apparent intestinal amino acid digestion were measured indicate that 65-80% of the total amino acid supply reaching the duodenum is absorbed. However, significant differences in the absorption coefficients for individual amino acids occur. Lindsay and coworkers (24) employed regression analysis to determine true digestibilities of amino acids in the SI of sheep fed forage diets. Their work suggested a true digestibility for total amino acids of 70%, but the true digestibility of individual amino acids ranged from 52% (cystine) to 86% (arginine). Williams (25) previously demonstrated that substantial differences in relative rates of absorption from isolated sheep intestinal loops existed for individual amino acids. It was noted that the following groups of amino acids were absorbed at descending rates: (a) isoleucine, arginine, methionine, valine; (b) leucine, lysine, phenylalanine; (c) aspartic acid, serine, tyrosine, alanine; (d) alanine, proline, threonine; (e) proline, threonine, glutamic acid, histidine, and (f) glycine (least rapidly absorbed).

In addition to free amino acids, considerable quantities of di- and tripeptides are taken up by the intestinal mucosa and, in fact, such small peptides may be absorbed more rapidly than amino acids (23). These peptides are subsequently cleaved by dipeptidases in the cytosol of the epithelial cells and are transferred into the blood as free amino acids.

EXCRETION AND COMPOSITION OF FECES AND URINE

Fecal Excretion and Composition

Feces consist of materials of both dietary and endogenous origin. The largest single factor affecting quantity of fecal dry matter excreted is amount of indigestible dry matter consumed by an animal. In practical situations, ruminants are fed diets which vary in digestibility much more than do diets of other domestic animals and level of intake may vary from maintenance to as much as 4-5X maintenance. Digestion in the ruminant has been described as continuous in nature; consequently, it is also characteristic of these species to exhibit a higher frequency of defecation than most simple-stomached animals.

Minson and Cowper (26) fed sheep diets of alfalfa hay once daily or at hourly intervals in order to study effects of feeding frequency on diurnal variation in excretion of feces and urine. In animals fed once daily, some excretion (4-21 g of fecal dry matter) occurred at every 2-h interval throughout the day, with the maximum quantity excreted at 2-6 h postfeeding. When the animals were fed every hour, the total quantity of feces collected daily was unaffected, but there was a slightly more uniform pattern of excretion. In both situations animals defecated at least twelve times daily. Frequency of defecation in cattle has been less systematically studied, but a survey of literature (27) indicates that cattle maintained in grazing and drylot conditions have been observed to defecate 7-15 times per day.

Dry matter content of feces is typically 30-50% in sheep and other species which excrete pellets, and much lower (15-30%) in cattle. Fecal dry matter contains undigested dietary material, undigested cell walls of rumen bacteria, microbial cells from the cecum and large intestine, and residues of many endogenous substances including digestive enzymes, mucous and other secretions and epithelial cells sloughed from the walls of the alimentary tract into the lumen. The proportion of materials of dietary origin relative to those of metabolic and endogenous origin would be greatest when diets containing substantial amounts of poorly digested feedstuffs (i.e., low quality roughages) are fed. Conversely, animals consuming diets that are highly digestible (i.e., high grain) excrete feces containing very little material of dietary origin.

Analyses of ruminant feces indicate that microbial cells and their residues constitute a large proportion of total fecal dry matter. Mason and Frederiksen (28) fractionated the

N in feces of sheep by neutral and acid detergent extraction and reported that an average of 86% (range of 71-94%) of the total N was of bacterial and endogenous origin. Samples analyzed included feces from animals fed diets ranging from all forage to 92% concentrate. Subsequent work (29) indicated that an average of 74% of fecal N of non-dietary origin was bacterial N. In addition, the amino acid profile of feces as a whole was very similar to that of isolated gastro-intestinal bacteria. Mason (29) also related the quantity of bacterial and endogenous N excreted to various dietary characteristics and found that it was most closely related to the quantity of truly digestible dry matter consumed. With most ruminant diets the major losses of N in feces were from bacterial N. This is determined, in large part, by amount of energy available at fermentation sites in the gut. Modifying the supply of fermentable substrate presented to either the rumen or the hindgut influences amount of N excreted in feces. Infusion of starch into the cecum does, in fact, increase excretion of microbial N in feces (29) due to enhanced fermentation at this site. Cattle consuming high levels of grain probably increase fecal output of microbial N due to increased quantities of starch arriving at the hindgut.

Feces also serve as a route for excretion of some endogenous waste products. In particular, bilirubin and biliverdin are eliminated by this route. Urobilinogen, produced by the microbial conversion of these compounds in the large intestine, is the compound which gives feces a characteristic brown coloration. Biliary secretion is also the typical excretory route for many mineral elements. The odor of feces is due to the presence of certain aromatic compounds, mainly indole and skatole, produced by microbial degradation of tryptophan.

Urinary Excretion and Composition

Urine is a solution consisting of the products of N and S metabolism, inorganic salts (particularly Na, K and Cl) and some pigments. Urine is usually yellowish in color, but normal variation in color may extend to dark brown. Ruminant urine is normally clarified at the time of excretion, but becomes turbid after standing due to precipitation of crystals of $CaCO_3$ (30).

The amount of urine excreted varies and is dependent upon intake of water and salts, diet composition, exercise, ambient temperature and other factors. Normal volumes of urine produced are 17-45 ml/kg body weight/d for cattle and 10-40 ml/kg body weight/d for sheep and goats. Specific gravity of ruminant urine averages about 1.030 with ranges of 1.030-1.045 reported for cattle and 1.015-1.045 for sheep and goats (30). Generally, increasing volume of urine output results in decreased specific gravity.

Ruminants typically excrete substantial amounts of K in the urine and, in grazing animals where Na intake may be limited, this excretion is associated with conservation of Na. However, if Na intake is adequate or high, increased amounts of this electrolyte are excreted. Na and K are the principal cations in urine and, in combination, are found in concentrations of approximately 700 mEq/ℓ in sheep urine. When animals have free access to salt, Na concentrations range from 300-500 mEq/ℓ and those of K from 200-400 mEq/ℓ. However, when Na-free diets are fed, the concentration of K alone rises to 700 mEq/ℓ (30). Bicarbonate and Cl are the major anions found in urine and bicarbonate concentrations may be as high as 300 mEq/ℓ (30).

Ruminant urine is normally alkaline (pH 7.5-8.5) and alkalinity and high K excretion are reflective of the herbivorous nature of the diet of these animals. However, there are many situations in which ruminants excrete significant quantities of H ions, resulting in acidic urine. In particular, animals grazing pastures high in residues of sulfate and/or phosphate and animals fed high concentrate diets and producing large quantities of acid in the rumen excrete urine with a decreased bicarbonate content and acidic pH. The increase in excretion of protons occurs primarily via an increase in excretion of NH_4^+ (30).

Urine is the primary excretory route for most waste products produced by metabolism of N-containing compounds in the body and many different nitrogenous compounds are found in urine. N-containing compounds in urine arise from both dietary and endogenous sources and amounts and proportions of these various compounds are indicative of the dietary N status of the animal. Urea is the major end-product of N metabolism in nearly

182

all mammals and amount of urea excreted by ruminants, as well as the proportion of total urinary N excreted as urea, have been shown to be positively correlated with digestible N intake (31). Allantoin is produced and excreted by most mammals as a consequence of the metabolism of purines. Ruminants excrete relatively larger amounts of allantoin in the urine than do non-ruminants due to intestinal digestion of large quantities of microbial cells and resultant absorption of purines. As with urea, amount of allantoin excreted is positively correlated to digestible N intake (31), but this relationship probably exists only as long as intestinal supply of microbial protein is limited by N intake.

Data shown in Table 9-4 illustrate the nature of the nitrogenous components of ruminant urine and the relationship between N intake and the proportions of these compounds excreted. For example, as crude protein content of the diet increases from 4 to 10%, proportion of urea N increases from 27 to 68% of the total urinary N. In addition to urea and allantoin, small amounts of NH_3 and varying proportions of creatinine, creatine, uric acid and hippuric acid are excreted by ruminants.

Components of the endogenous fraction of urinary N have been characterized by Swanson (32). When diets devoid of digestible protein are fed, 25-30% of the N in urine is excreted as creatinine. The quantity of creatinine excreted daily is constant for a given animal, irrespective of diet, and creatinine excretion is almost strictly a function of

body muscle mass. Urea and NH_3 constitute about 5-10% of the endogenous urinary N and increases in the proportions of these constituents indicate that catabolism of exogenous protein is occurring. Other components of endogenous N excretion include bilirubin, allantoin, hippuric acid, uric acid and some amino acids, especially 3-methylhistidine, the presence of which is an indicator of muscle turnover.

Ruminants also excrete significant quantities of aromatic acids in the urine. The most important of these is hippuric acid, the glycine conjugate of benzoic acid. Urinary benzoic acid is the ultimate end-product of the rumen microbial metabolism of a number of aromatic compounds and may be excreted in substantial amounts under certain circumstances. Benzoic acid may be derived from alicyclic acids such as 3-phenylpropionic acid and cinnamic acid (33), although these compounds are not found in significant quantities in most diets. However, phenolic derivatives of cinnamic acid yield 3-phenylpropionic acid due to rumen microbial metabolism and absorption and metabolism of this compound may account for a large part of benzoic acid in urine (33). Other phenolic compounds in urine are apparently microbially-derived metabolites of phenolic precursors that are widely distributed in plants and include hydroxybenzoic, protocatechuic and vanillic acids (33). Intake and, consequently, urinary excretion of such compounds are appreciable in animals consuming certain forages.

APPARENT DIGESTIBILITY

Digestibility coefficients determined in many nutritional studies refer to the fraction of a given feedstuff or diet which disappears during passage through the gut, thus implying that the absorption process is also involved in this assessment of nutritive value. The ability of different feeds to support maintenance and productive functions of animals is highly variable and depends upon their capacity to supply energy and essential nutrients to animals consuming them. Digestibility coefficients by themselves are limited expressions of nutritive value, but are a common means of evaluating feedstuffs.

While digestibility alone is an oversimplified expression of nutritive value, such data

Table 9-4. Distribution of nitrogenous components in the urine of sheep fed different levels of crude protein.[a]

Item	Crude protein in diet, %			
	4	6	8	10
	. . . . g/d			
Digestible N intake	0.14	2.90	5.69	9.08
Urinary N loss	1.35	2.17	4.08	6.98
	. . . . % of total urinary N			
Ammonia	21.8	7.5	6.3	4.4
Urea	27.2	41.8	58.6	68.0
Creatinine	17.0	11.3	6.2	4.1
Creatine	0.9	1.3	1.2	0.8
Uric acid	2.9	2.4	1.4	0.9
Hippuric acid	15.9	14.6	8.9	6.2
Allantoin	14.1	15.3	9.4	6.4

[a]From Topps and Elliott (31)

are useful. Fecal energy losses represent the single largest loss encountered in utilization of most feedstuffs and knowledge of their magnitude is required in assigning meaningful energy values to different feeds. Digestibility is influenced in large part by nutrient composition of the feedstuff/diet studied but is also affected by factors unrelated to composition. Some appreciation of these factors, both intuitive and quantitative, is required to understand the limitations and value of simple digestibility coefficients as predictors of nutritive value.

Digestibility is conventionally determined by calculation of the difference in amount of a given nutrient consumed and amount excreted in feces. Because feces contain substantial quantities of material of non-dietary origin, coefficients of digestibility determined in this fashion are *apparent* digestibilities which typically underestimate the actual or *true* digestibility of many dietary components. In addition, total tract digestibility does not consider site of digestion of various nutrients and, hence, does not reflect the nature of the digestive end-products absorbed from the gut. Consideration of these shortcomings will be explored in subsequent sections of this chapter. At this point, it is appropriate to discuss methodology employed in determination of apparent digestibility.

METHODS OF MEASUREMENT OF APPARENT DIGESTIBILITY

Conventional Digestion Trial

The goal of a digestion trial is to accurately measure amount of feed consumed and of feces excreted over a given period of time. Accomplishment of this goal is dependent upon the conscientious control of feeding and collection of excreta by the researcher. Basic procedural considerations will be outlined here and have been described comprehensively by Schneider and Flatt (34).

In conventional digestion trials, experimental animals are fed the test diets for a preliminary period of at least two weeks to ensure that residues of feedstuffs consumed prior to the trial have been eliminated from the digestive tract. Consistent levels of intake are established during the preliminary period, to aid in avoiding drastic fluctuations in excretion. The preliminary period is followed by a

collection period of 7 to 10 d in length. Feces (and urine, if nutrient balance data are desired) are collected daily and composite samples representative of the collection period are prepared for further laboratory analyses. Collection of feces may be accomplished by housing the animals in crates which have been designed to allow for the separation and quantitative collection of feces and urine (Fig. 9-2). Alternatively, animals may be fitted with specialized harnesses and bags which facilitate collection of feces (Fig. 9-3).

After collection of feeds and feces have been completed, data obtained from collection and subsequent laboratory analyses may be used to compute digestibility by using the

Figure 9-2. Metabolism crate used for collection of both feces and urine. Courtesy of J.P. Fontenot, Virginia Polytech.

Figure 9-3. Steer fitted with collection bag for complete collection of feces. Courtesy of D.C. Clanton, Nebraska Agr. Expt. Station.

following equations:

I) Apparent dry matter (DM) digestibility (%)

$$= \frac{\text{DM consumed (g/d)} - \text{Fecal DM (g/d)}}{\text{DM consumed (g/d)}} \times 100$$

II) Apparent nutrient digestibility (%)

$$= \frac{\begin{array}{c}\text{(DM consumed)(Propor. of nutrient in feed DM)}\\ - \text{(Fecal DM)(Propor. of nutrient in feces DM)}\end{array}}{\text{(DM consumed)(Propor. of nutrient in feed DM)}} \times 100$$

EXAMPLE

A sheep consumes 1,050 g of chopped alfalfa hay (89% dry matter) per day for three weeks. During the last 7 d feces were collected and, over the collection period, the animal excreted 6,779 g of feces containing 41% dry matter. Calculate the apparent dry matter digestibility of the alfalfa hay.

Daily DM consumption = 1,050(0.89) = 935 g

$$\text{Daily fecal DM excretion} = \frac{6,779(0.41)}{7} = 397 \text{ g}$$

$$\text{Apparent DM digestibility} = \frac{935 - 397}{935} \times 100 = 57.5\%$$

Analysis for acid detergent fiber (ADF) in the hay and feces revealed that the hay contained 37% ADF and the feces 45% ADF (both on a dry matter basis). Calculate the apparent digestibility of ADF in the alfalfa hay.

Apparent ADF digestibility

$$= \frac{935(0.37) - (397)(0.45)}{935(0.37)} \times 100 = 48.4\%$$

Thus, apparent digestibilities of dry matter and ADF in alfalfa hay are 57.5 and 48.4%, respectively. Because metabolic fecal matter contains virtually no fibrous constituents, apparent and true digestibilities of most dietary fiber components (such as ADF) are generally considered to be equal.

Calculation of Digestibility of a Feedstuff by Difference

In many situations it may be necessary to determine digestibility of a feedstuff when it is fed in combination with one or more other feedstuffs. This occurs most often when evaluating feeds such as grains or protein supplements which are seldom fed as the sole ingredient in a diet. Digestibilities of such feedstuffs may be calculated by determining digestibility of a mixed diet containing the feedstuff of interest if digestibilities of other dietary ingredients have been determined previously. Calculation of digestibility of a feedstuff by difference requires the assumption that digestibility of a mixed diet is equal to the summation of the proportions of the diet supplied by each ingredient multiplied by the digestibility of that ingredient if it were fed alone, or:

Digestibility of a mixture of feeds

= Fraction of total nutrient supplied by feed A

  x Digestibility of nutrient in feed A

+ Fraction of total nutrient supplied by feed B

  x Digestibility of nutrient in feed B

+ . . .

Digestibility of the test feedstuff may be calculated by employing the following equation:

III) Digestibility of nutrient in test feedstuff (%)

$$= \frac{(A) - (B)(C)}{(D)} \times 100$$

where: A = digestibility of nutrient in total diet; B = digestibility of nutrient in basal feed; C = proportion of total nutrient in diet supplied by basal feed; and D = proportion of total nutrient in diet supplied by test feed.

EXAMPLE

A lamb is fed a diet consisting of 60% alfalfa pellets and 40% ground corn (dry matter basis) and apparent dry matter digestibility of the diet is determined to be 68%. In a preliminary experiment the apparent dry matter digestibility of the alfalfa pellets was found to be 55%. Calculate the apparent dry matter digestibility of the ground corn.

Apparent DM digestibility of ground corn

$$= \frac{(68) - (55)(0.60)}{(0.40)} \times 100 = 87.5\%$$

In the preliminary experiment apparent digestibility of crude protein in the alfalfa pellets (18% crude protein, dry matter basis) was 76%. If the apparent crude protein digestibility of the alfalfa pellet:ground corn mixture is 74.6%, calculate the apparent digestibility of crude protein in the corn (9% crude protein).

Crude protein in mixed diet

$$= (0.60)(18) + (0.40)(9) = 14.4\%$$

Proportion of total crude protein supplied by corn

$$= \frac{(0.40)(9)}{14.4} \times 100 = 25\%$$

Proportion of total crude protein supplied by alfalfa

$$= \frac{(0.60)(18)}{14.4} \times 100 = 75\%$$

Digestibility of crude protein in corn

$$= \frac{(74.6) - (76)(0.75)}{0.25} \times 100 = 70.4\%$$

Thus, apparent digestibilities of dry matter and crude protein in the corn are calculated, by difference, to be 87.5 and 70.4%, respectively. The appropriateness of calculation of digestibility by difference is limited due to the required assumption that one feedstuff does not influence the digestibility of another when fed in combination or that no *associative effects* occur. The phenomena of associative effects will be explored later in this chapter.

Use of Markers to Measure Digestibility in Ruminants

It may sometimes be difficult or impractical to utilize total collection methods for determination of digestibility. In such instances use of inert reference substances known as indicators or markers may be employed. Types of markers that have been used in nutritional studies include *internal markers,* which are indigestible materials occurring naturally in feeds and *external markers,* which are materials that are either added to the diet or administered orally or intraruminally to the animal. Markers have been utilized as experimental tools for many years and a large number of materials have been evaluated as markers for studying digestive function in both ruminants and non-ruminants. Kotb and Luckey (35) outlined criteria that a substance must meet in order to be regarded as an "ideal" marker: (a) it must be inert with no toxic effects; (b) it must be neither absorbed nor metabolized in the gastro-intestinal tract; (c) it must have no appreciable bulk; (d) it must mix intimately with and remain uniformly distributed in the digesta; (e) it must have no influence on gastro-intestinal secretions, digestion, absorption or normal motility; (f) it must have no influence on the microflora of the gastro-intestinal tract; and (g) it must have physicochemical properties, readily discernible throughout the gastro-intestinal tract, which allow ready, precise quantitative measurement. Virtually none of the materials utilized as markers absolutely fulfill all these criteria, but a number of them are sufficiently adequate to provide meaningful data. Markers are employed not only for measurement of digestibility coefficients but for partitioning digestion in various segments of the alimentary tract and for measurement of digesta retention time as well. It should be recognized that different markers have different properties and that appropriate markers, methods of administration and sampling schemes are dictated by the type of data an individual experiment is intended to provide. Methodology for the use of markers for quantifying rate of passage and extent of digestion in different segments of the gut will be discussed in subsequent sections of this chapter. Following is a brief discussion of the qualities of different substances which have been used as markers. More extensive discussion of markers and methods for their use are provided by several excellent reviews (35, 36, 37).

Internal Markers

Lignin. Lignin has often been regarded as indigestible and, consequently, has been used extensively as a marker in digestion studies. However, a survey of the literature indicates that significant problems exist in measuring lignin and in obtaining complete fecal recoveries of this substance. Fahey and Jung (38) recently reviewed use of lignin as a marker and indicate that it is degraded or modified in structure during passage through the gastro-intestinal tract with the result that fecal recoveries are low. There are numerous reports in the literature of lignin disappearance during digestion, with apparent digestibility coefficients ranging from –8 to 53%. Several studies demonstrated that most disappearance occurs in the rumen (38). The loss of material during passage through the

186

gut is a violation of one of the most stringent criteria of marker behavior and, for this reason, use of lignin as a marker should be viewed with caution. Incomplete recoveries of lignin (or any other marker) result in underestimation of digestibility, the magnitude of the error increasing as extent of loss increases and as dietary lignin content decreases.

The ambiguous nature and lack of precise chemical definition of lignin also contribute to a lack of reliability in its use as a marker. Analytical techniques for lignin are largely empirical and differ significantly in their estimation of lignin content. Muntifering (39) demonstrated that choice of technique for determination of lignin may drastically affect lignin recovery and, consequently, measurement of fecal excretion or digesta flow. In this work, digestibilities as determined by reference to lignin analyzed as acid detergent lignin (ADL), permanganate lignin ($KMnO_4$ lignin) or acetyl bromide-soluble lignin (ABSL), were compared to those obtained by total fecal collection. Fecal recoveries of lignin determined by different techniques and for different diets ranged from 53% to 107%. Recoveries, across diets, were approximately 78% for ADL and $KMnO_4$ lignin and 65% for ABSL. Perhaps ever more worrisome than low recovery was the fact that a significant diet x marker interaction occurred, indicating that highest recoveries varied among method of lignin determination for different diets. This observation raised a serious question about the value of lignin for determination not only of absolute values for digestibility, but of relative values as well.

Several reasons may account for low recoveries of lignin in feces. These have been summarized by Fahey and Jung (38) as follows: true digestion; apparent digestion resulting from formation of soluble lignin-carbohydrate complexes which are not recovered (as lignin) in the feces; partial destruction of fecal lignin during analysis and physical and/or chemical differences between feed and feces in the nature of materials empirically defined as lignin. In light of data suggesting that substantial losses of lignin occur during digestion, use of lignin as a marker should probably be limited to situations in which total fecal recovery may be confirmed.

Silica. Silica was first assessed to be indigestible and recommended as a marker over 100 years ago and its use and viability as such have been investigated periodically. Subsequent work indicated that consistent over-recovery of silica in feces occurs, particularly in grazing animals or animals held in barn or drylot conditions. This observation is probably due to underestimation of silica intake because of contamination of feed with dust or soil ingestion during grazing. Some silica is also apparently absorbed and excreted in urine (35).

Acid-Insoluble Ash. Studies with swine and poultry suggested that use of an ash fraction in feed which was insoluble in boiling HCl as a digestibility marker gave results of similar accuracy to those obtained by total fecal collection. Van Keulen and Young (40) investigated the use of this material in digestibility trials with sheep and reported nearly complete fecal recoveries and estimates of digestibility which were not significantly different from those obtained by conventional methods. Acid-insoluble ash (AIA) can act as a reliable marker because little diurnal variation in AIA content of feces is noted and because analytical techniques are quite precise (40). As with all markers the accurate determination of digestibility by reference to AIA is dependent on the accurate determination of intake of this material. This presents no problem in confined animals, but problems similar to those occurring with the use of silica (i.e., soil contamination of feedstuffs or ingestion of soil or bedding) arise when applied to free-ranging animals. The precision of AIA as a marker is poorest when feedstuffs with a low AIA concentration (such as grains and alfalfa) are fed due to the magnitude of analytical error relative to the absolute AIA content of the feed (40).

External Markers
Stained Feeds. Treatment of feeds with a variety of dyes including acid fucsin or magenta, brilliant green or blue, crystal violet and carmine red results in the irreversible staining of the feed particles (35). Stains were the first particulate-bound markers used and their use is responsible for much of the early data obtained on digesta retention times

(41). Stained feed particles have certain virtues as markers because they allow for identification of specific particles during passage through the gut and because different stains may be used to indelibly mark different feedstuffs within a mixed diet. However, satisfactory methods of quantitating bound stains are not available (37). Analysis of stained particles must be done by visual inspection and counting of stained particles in a given sample. This is laborious and subject to human error. Stained feeds are not used in studies designed to measure digestibility. In addition, digesta retention times measured through the use of stained feeds should probably be considered as relative, not absolute, due to the semiquantitative nature of analysis (42).

Chromic Oxide. Several insoluble metal oxides have been employed as markers in nutritional studies. The most common of these is chromic oxide (Cr_2O_3) which, as a single marker, has probably been more widely used for measurement of both digestibility and digesta flow than any other substance. Chromic oxide offers certain advantages as a marker in that many studies indicate complete recovery in feces (35) and that several reliable analytical methods are available. Chromic oxide is a dense powder which tends to travel as a suspension in digesta at a rate independent of that of either the particulate or liquid phases. For this reason, chromic oxide is not suitable as a marker in studies designed to determine digesta retention times (36, 37). Chromic oxide may also form a sediment in the reticulo-rumen and be transferred sporadically to the lower gastrointestinal tract. Consequently, excretion of chromic oxide in feces is subject to both diurnal and daily variation (36, 37). It is useful as a marker for measuring digestibility and, possibly, postruminal digesta flow as long as experiments are designed (i.e., by frequent marker administration and/or fecal or digesta sampling) to account for these variations in excretion. Chromic oxide has been used frequently to correct digesta flows obtained in animals with re-entrant cannulae to a 24-h basis. Its use, however, as a marker for measuring flow rates in animals spot-sampled from a simple T-cannula has been questioned. Some reports (36, 43) contend that the use of

chromic oxide, or of any single marker, is inappropriate for the accurate measurement of digesta flow in animals fitted with simple cannulae in the postruminal tract. However, this conclusion is debatable because other studies (44, 45) indicate that calculated digesta flows obtained using chromic oxide as a marker in spot samples taken from simple or re-entrant cannulae were in close agreement with those obtained by total collection from re-entrant cannulae.

Rare-Earth Elements. Several of the rare earth elements, including lanthanum (La), samarium (Sm), cerium (Ce), ytterbium (Yb) and dysprosium (Dy), have been investigated and employed as markers in both digestibility and rate of passage studies. Rare earths are excreted quantitatively and sensitive methods for their detection are available. At very low concentrations rare earths exhibit strong adsorptive properties (36). Application of rare earths to feedstuffs resulted in tenacious binding of the elements by feed particles with little migration from labelled to unlabelled feeds during digestion (46). Thus, it was felt that the rare earths could serve not only as reliable markers of the particulate phase of digesta but of particles of specific feedstuffs within a diet as well. However, later work established that extent of migration among digesta particles may be considerable and is influenced by factors such as the method of application of the elements to feeds, binding capacities and affinity constants of individual feedstuffs and extent of digestion of labelled particles (37). Changes in physicochemical conditions during passage through the gastrointestinal tract, particularly at acidic pH such as in the abomasum, also enhance migration as well as solubilization of rare earths (47, 48). Combs et al (48) also noted that a major proportion of Yb and Ce which has been applied to hay particles was found in a bacterial pellet following in vitro rumen incubations, indicating retention of these elements by rumen bacteria. Such findings led to suggestions that the rare earths may be inappropriate particulate markers. The degree of association of rare earths with particulate digesta is probably variable and use of these elements to obtain meaningful data on digesta flow and digesta retention time is dependent upon use of appropriate methodology for

188

application to diets being studied. In addition, caution should be exercised in assuming that these elements remain associated with particulate digesta in acidic samples such as those obtained from the abomasum or proximal duodenum.

The ruthenium (II) chelate of tris- (1,10 phenanthroline) (Ru-phen) has, like the rare earths, been reported to have a high binding capacity for particulate matter (36, 37). The advantages of Ru-phen as a marker are very similar to those of the rare earths, i.e., quantitative excretion in feces and availability of reliable analytical techniques. Also like the rare earths, some migration and dissociation of Ru-phen occurs during digestion and movement through the tract. Ruminal bacteria may act as a vector for transfer of Ru-phen between particles (37).

Chromium Mordanted Fiber. A procedure referred to as "mordanting" results in formation of strong complexes between chromium and plant cell walls (37, 49). This complex is stable in rumen fluid and acidic media and is essentially indigestible when Cr content of the mordanted material is greater than 8% (37). This complex is the most specific marker of a given particle now available and, thus, has considerable value as a marker for both digestibility and digesta passage. The most serious drawback to the use of the Cr mordant is that due to the severe chemical treatment received during preparation and the resultant indigestibility of the mordanted particle, it may behave in a fashion different from other feed particles in a given diet. Use of Cr mordants to measure particle retention times probably reflects relative differences in retention times, but not absolute values, because of the differential movement of the marked material through the alimentary tract. Ehle and co-workers, for example, demonstrated clearly that concentration of Cr in the mordant influences the density of the material (50). As Cr content was increased, density likewise increased and measured values for ruminal turnover rates increased in animals fed identical diets. Despite such problems, Cr-mordanted fiber should be regarded as a marker with considerable potential due to its irreversible labelling of specific particles and the fact that it can be quantified easily.

Water-Soluble Markers. In contrast to problems which compromise in one way or another virtually all of the particulate markers, several materials are available which exhibit nearly ideal behavior as markers of the liquid phase of digesta. Polyethylene glycol (PEG) is very soluble in water, nearly completely recovered in feces and has been used as a marker in ruminant studies for many years. However, techniques for analysis of PEG are imprecise, although some workers have overcome this restriction through the use of radiolabelled (^{14}C or ^{3}H) PEG (36, 37). Other research indicates that PEG may adsorb to certain types of dietary ingredients or that it may be precipitated by the presence of tannins (36, 37). The ethylenediaminetetraacetic acid chelates of Cr (CrEDTA) and Co (CoEDTA) have largely replaced PEG as liquid phase markers of choice in ruminant studies. Both CrEDTA (36, 37) and CoEDTA (49), like PEG, are readily solubilized and have been utilized extensively for estimation of rumen liquid volumes and dilution rates. In contrast to PEG, analyses for these compounds are simple and very precise. Small amounts of CrEDTA may bind to particulate matter in the rumen (37, 40) and some (<5%) of both complexes are absorbed and excreted in urine (36, 49). It is likely that these deviations from ideal behavior result in only minor errors in most cases.

Situations in Which Markers are Useful

A. Feed intake is known but total fecal collections cannot be made. In this case either internal or external markers may be used. Animals are fed diets containing the marker or are dosed orally with the marker at regular intervals. Samples of feces are then taken as they are excreted or directly from the rectum. Fecal samples must be taken at intervals which are defined relative to time of feeding or marker dosage to help avoid bias caused by diurnal variations in marker excretion. Fecal samples are then analyzed for the marker substance. Digestibilities can then be determined in the following manners:

IV) Fecal DM output (g/d)

$$= \frac{\text{marker consumed (g/d)}}{\text{marker concentration in feces (g/g DM)}}$$

Fecal output of a given nutrient can be calculated as the product of fecal DM output and the concentration of the desired nutrient in fecal dry matter. Alternatively, nutrient digestibility may be directly calculated using the formula below:

V) Digestibility of nutrient (%)

$$= 100 - (100 \times \frac{\% \text{ marker in feed}}{\% \text{ marker in feces}} \times \frac{\% \text{ nutrient in feces}}{\% \text{ nutrient in feed}})$$

EXAMPLE

A sheep being fed fescue hay consumes 1,200 g of DM daily. The AIA content of the hay is 1.6% of DM and the fecal DM contains 3.3% AIA. Assuming that the dietary AIA is excreted quantitatively in feces, calculate the DM digestibility of the fescue hay.

$$\text{Fecal DM} = \frac{1,200 \times 0.016}{0.033} = 582 \text{ g/d}$$

$$\text{DM digestibility (\%)} = \frac{1,200 - 582}{1,200} \times 100 = 51.5\%$$

or

$$\text{DM digestibility (\%)} = 100 - (100 \times \frac{\% \text{ marker in feed}}{\% \text{ marker in feces}})$$

$$= 100 - (100 \times \frac{1.6}{3.3}) = 51.5\%$$

If the crude protein content of the hay is 9.5% of DM and that of feces is 7.7% of DM, calculate the apparent digestibility of crude protein in the hay.

Apparent crude protein digestibility

$$= 100 - (100 \times \frac{1.6}{3.3} \times \frac{7.7}{9.5}) = 60.7\%$$

B. Neither feed intake nor fecal output is known, but an estimate of digestibility is desired. In this instance an internal marker must be used. Calculations of DM and nutrient digestibility are identical to those illustrated by equation V above. Use of this method is especially applicable to grazing studies. One difficulty in such a case is obtaining a representative sample of the material that the grazing animal is actually consuming. Grazing animals are selective and, as such, do not consume different forages in the same proportions as they are found in the area being grazed. A means of improving quality of the sample is through the use of animals with esophageal fistulas.

C. Neither feed intake nor fecal output is known and estimates of both digestibility and intake are desired. In such a situation, digestibility can be determined through use of an internal marker. Fecal output is measured concurrently by using an external marker and intake may be calculated as follows:

VI) $\text{DM intake} = \text{fecal output} \times \dfrac{100}{\% \text{ indigestibility of DM}}$

EXAMPLE

A steer is grazing on bromegrass pasture. It is determined that the AIA content of the material consumed by the steer is 1.8% of DM and that the fecal DM contains 4.2% AIA. The steer is dosed twice daily with a bolus containing 8 g of chromic oxide (16 g chromic oxide/d). Analysis of feces reveals a chromic oxide content of 0.51%. Calculate the apparent DM digestibility and DM intake.

$$\text{Fecal output} = \frac{16 \text{ g chromic oxide/d}}{0.0051 \text{ g chromic oxide/g feces}}$$

$$= 3.14 \text{ kg/d}$$

$$\text{DM digestibility (\%) (using AIA)} = 100 - (100 \times \frac{1.8}{4.2})$$

$$= 57.1\%$$

$$\text{DM intake} = 3.14 \times \frac{100}{42.9}$$

$$= 7.32 \text{ kg/d}$$

True vs Apparent Digestibility

As discussed previously, feces include components not only of dietary origin but of endogenous and microbial origin as well. The presence of non-dietary substances in feces means that apparent digestibility values for dietary components except fiber are always lower than values for true digestibility, with the magnitude of the difference between apparent and true digestibility being dependent upon quantity of non-dietary material excreted. The discrepancy between apparent and true digestibilities of fiber components is very small because the only material of this nature which is apparently excreted from endogenous sources is a result of analytical artifacts. Apparent digestibilities of many minerals, ether extract and, most profoundly, N are often greatly different from their true digestibilities.

Excretion of microbial and endogenous N (metabolic fecal N, MFN), in fact, is the

190

major determinant of values for apparent N digestibility of many diets. The quantity of MFN excreted is related to total DM intake with 0.45-0.55 g MFN excreted/100 g of food DM (34). Thus, apparent N digestibility may be considered to become a function of N intake in animals fed similar levels of DM. Because of the relationship between MFN and DM intake, differences between apparent and true digestibility of N increase as the N content of the diet decreases. The relationship between N intake and apparent N digestibility is illustrated in Fig. 9-4. The depressing effect of MFN on apparent N digestibility significantly masks the fact that, for diets other than those in which Maillard products may accumulate due to heating, true digestibility of N is usually estimated to be greater than 90% (28). In certain cases, excretion of MFN may be enhanced by factors which increase availability of energy at sites of fermentation in the gastro-intestinal tract. This presumably results in increased microbial growth at these sites and more N of microbial origin excreted in feces. As noted previously, increasing the supply of carbohydrates to the hindgut will increase MFN excretion (29).

Factors Influencing Apparent Digestibility
  Level of Intake. Tabulated values for TDN or DE content of most feedstuffs are based largely on digestibility data obtained with

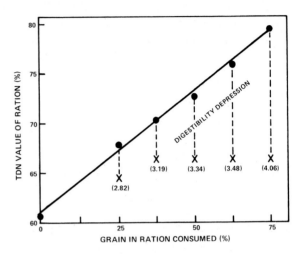

Figure 9-5. Data illustrating the relationship between proportion of grain in the diet and digestibility (as reflected by TDN value). Diets containing hay as forage source were fed to dry cows at maintenance (o) and to lactating cows to meet production requirements (x). Numbers in parentheses are average intakes in multiples of maintenance. This illustration is taken from Tyrrell and Moe (53).

animals fed at maintenance levels of intake. Such data generally overestimate the value of the same feeds when fed to animals at high levels of production (rapid growth or lactation) because digestibility is often depressed at higher levels of DM consumption. Intake effects on diet digestibility are much more pronounced with mixed diets than with diets consisting of single feedstuffs (51, 52). Digestibilities of mixed forage-grain diets fed to lactating dairy cows decrease by approximately 4% for each increase in intake equivalent to maintenance intake (53). Rate of depression increases with increasing proportions of grain in the diet and is greater at lower percentages of grain when corn silage serves as the primary source of forage (51). The influence of intake on digestibility in diets containing increasing levels of grain is illustrated in Fig. 9-5, which summarizes data based on diets containing varying proportions of hay and grain. Depressions in digestibility due to increasing dry matter intake are due to increased rate of passage through the digestive tract and include depressions in digestibility of both starch and fiber components of the diet.

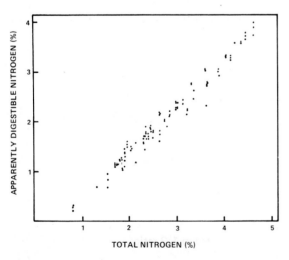

Figure 9-4. Relationship between concentrations of total N and apparently digestible N in dietary dry matter. Data are summarized for 47 diets fed to sheep (28).

Associative Effects. Associative effects refer to non-additive differences in digestibilities of feedstuffs fed as components of mixed diets fed at high intakes compared to digestibilities determined for the same feedstuffs when fed alone. Intake effects and negative associative effects are basically the same phenomena—a reduction in digestibility of mixed diets occurring at high levels of intake. Digestibilities of feedstuffs in mixed diets may be additive at maintenance intakes (51, 52), but at high feed intakes, negative associative effects of forage-concentrate diets often occur. For example, Joanning et al (52) noted no negative associative effects on digestibility of mixed corn silage-corn diets when fed at levels less than 2X maintenance, but reported an average decrease of 11% in DM digestibility of the same diets fed at 2.4-3.1X maintenance. As summarized in Table 9-5, depressions in digestibility of starch, NDF and protein accounted for 57, 32 and 12% of the total depression in digestibility at high intakes of mixed diets. DM and nutrient digestibilities of the corn silage and corn were largely unaffected at high intakes when fed alone. Incomplete digestion of starch apparently accounts for the major proportion of the decrease in digestibility noted for mixed diets at high intakes (Table 9-5; Fig. 9-6).

In comparison to negative associative effects observed for forage-concentrate diets, some evidence exists of the occurrence of positive associative effects in certain diets. Soofi et al (54) reported that positive associative effects on both feed intake and digestibility occurred in blends of poor quality (soybean stover) and higher quality (alfalfa)

forages fed to sheep (Table 9-6). Such work illustrates clearly that these effects occur with regard to intake, but true associative effects on digestibility are more difficult to interpret due to confounding effects of intake on digestibility.

Feed Processing. Grinding and pelleting of forages results in decreases in digestibility (55). Reduction in forage particle size decreases amount of time particles must reside in the rumen before being reduced to a size small enough to exit through the reticulo-omasal orifice. Grinding and pelleting thus result in increased rate of passage from the rumen and decreased extent of ruminal

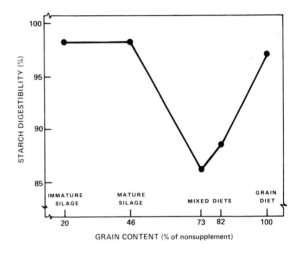

Figure 9-6. Starch digestibility of corn silage and corn diets and mixed corn silage-corn diets. From Joanning et al (52).

Table 9-5. Expected and observed nutrient digestibilities of mixed corn silage-corn grain diets and individual nutrient components of depression in dry matter digestibility.[a]

Nutrient	Expected[b]	Observed	Depression, % of expected	Nutrient in mix, %	Digestibility decrease	Fraction of total[c]
Dry matter	78.6	69.8	11.2	100	8.9	--
Starch	97.1	87.4	10.0	52.0	9.7	57
NDF	55.8	45.1	19.2	26.1	10.8	32
Protein	69.7	61.4	11.9	12.7	8.5	12

[a]Data summarized from Joanning et al (52). Corn silage and corn were fed in 1:2 ratio (dry matter basis) at intakes of 2.4-3.1X maintenance.

[b]Calculated as the algebraic mean of nutrient digestibilities when feeds were fed separately and weighted to amounts of nutrients from each feed.

[c]Percentage of total depression of dry matter digestibility accounted for by the depression in digestibility of nutrient.

Table 9-6. Dry matter intakes and digestibility of dry matter and neutral detergent fiber in soybean stover (SBS) and alfalfa (ALF) and SBS:ALF blends by sheep fed ad libitum.[a]

	SBS	2 SBS:1 ALF	1 SBS:2 ALF	ALF
Dry matter intake, g/kg$^{0.75}$/d				
Observed	39.7	72.7	90.3	107.5
Expected[b]		62.3	84.9	
Dry matter digestibility, %				
Observed	37.4	47.8	53.6	57.1
Expected		44.0	50.5	
NDF digestibility, %				
Observed	34.5	44.8	42.0	40.7
Expected		36.6	38.6	

[a] Taken from Soofi et al (54)
[b] Calculated from weighted means from observations on forages fed separately.

Table 9-7. Relationship between forage maturity, composition, voluntary intake and digestibility.[a]

	Stage of maturity (*Phalaris tuberosa*)		
Item	I	II	III
	.. % of dry matter ..		
Structural carbohydrate	40.6	58.7	67.5
Soluble carbohydrate	20.9	15.1	11.3
Crude protein	26.1	19.9	11.3
Lignin	3.0	4.1	7.4
Voluntary intake, g OM/kg$^{0.75}$/d	61.4	53.7	46.3
Organic matter digestibility, %	80.4	73.7	53.6

[a] Data of Hogan et al summarized by Ulyatt (56).

digestion (55). However, animals fed forages processed in this manner also increase their level of voluntary intake (55) such that consumption of digestible energy is equal to or greater than that for animals fed more coarsely chopped forages or long hay.

Cracking or grinding of some cereal grains often increases digestibility, especially in cattle fed ad libitum (53). Such processing does not enhance digestibility of grains such as barley and wheat but appears to have positive effects when applied to corn or sorghum which contain starch that is more resistant to ruminal degradation.

Forage Maturity. As forages approach physiological maturity, characteristic compositional changes occur. Most notably, fiber components increase in concentration in the plant while concentrations of soluble components decrease (Table 9-7). Animal responses to such changes are manifested by decreases in both voluntary intake and dry matter digestibility (56). These responses are illustrated by data in Table 9-7. Reductions in digestibility of more mature or poorer quality forages are likely a result of these compositional changes as fibrous components of the diet are digested to both a lesser and more variable extent than are soluble components.

Environmental Temperature. Lowering the environmental temperature below the thermal neutral zone results in a decrease in digestibility in comparison to measurements made at temperatures at or near thermal neutrality (57, 58). This effect is probably a result of decreased retention times in the rumen of animals maintained at cold temperatures (57, 58).

PARTITION OF DIGESTION IN THE GASTRO-INTESTINAL TRACT

One of the limitations of interpretation of apparent digestibility data is that apparent total tract digestibility provides no information regarding sites in the tract (stomach, SI or hindgut) in which digestion and absorption occur. For most nutrients site of digestion is an important factor with regard to the nature of absorbed end-products and the extent of nutrient losses encountered due to digestion (Fig. 9-7). Ruminants rely heavily on fermentation in the forestomach as a mechanism for digestion. Fermentation is an expensive strategy for digestion because microbial metabolism of carbohydrates to produce VFA is accompanied by substantial losses of energy as methane and heat. Ruminal microbes may also degrade high quality dietary proteins to such an extent that net losses of N occur due to NH_3 absorption from the rumen. The profile of amino acids presented to the small intestine is also often altered radically from that of the diet due to microbial degradation of feed protein and synthesis of microbial protein in the rumen. These qualitative and quantitative differences in end-product absorption as a result of digestion of certain nutrients (especially non-structural carbohydrates and protein) at different sites are likely to be important in predicting animal responses to some diets and feeding practices. For this reason, and because of increasingly

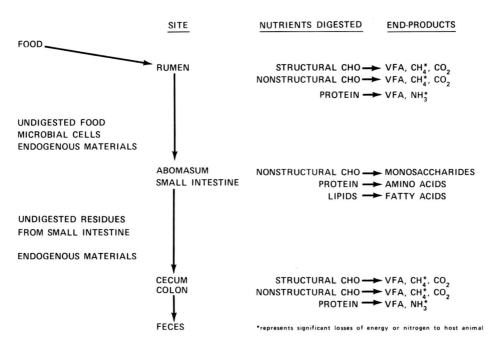

Figure 9-7. Sites and end-products of digestion of energy-yielding nutrients in the ruminant.

Methods for Partitioning Digestion in Ruminants

Partitioning of digestion in ruminants requires methods for accurately measuring nutrient flow at various points in the gastrointestinal tract. Measurement of digesta flow requires (a) animals fitted with cannulae at specific sites in the tract (usually the abomasum, proximal duodenum and/or terminal ileum) and (b) suitable methods for calculation of flow rates at these sites. The two types of cannulae most commonly used are the re-entrant cannula (Fig. 9-8) and the simple T-type cannula. Use of such cannulae has been reviewed (59, 60) and each has specific advantages and disadvantages. Re-entrant cannulae are placed in the intestine by completely bisecting the gut and placing one end of the cannula in each stump (Fig. 9-9). The cannulae are then brought through the body wall and connected. This technique exteriorizes digesta flowing past that point in the tract. The greatest advantage offered by this type of cannula is that it allows for direct measurement of total digesta flow. However, animals with re-entrant cannulae are more difficult to maintain than those with simple cannulae (60) and some interference with normal motility may occur as a result of bisection of the intestine. Animals with simple cannulae are easier to maintain, but flow measurements in such animals are totally reliant on the use of indigestible markers and the collection of spot samples of digesta.

Experiments designed to measure digesta flow in the postruminal tract must be planned carefully. Most experiments involve limited numbers of animals and between-animal variation is usually the greatest source of variation in these measurements (59). Therefore, experimental designs should allow for separation of effects due to animal. Other considerations must be made for factors such as feeding frequency, sampling technique, type of marker used and method of marker administration. More detailed discussion of the importance of these factors is available elsewhere (36, 59, 60).

Factors Affecting Site of Digestion

Many factors which affect total digestibility of diets fed to ruminants also influence site at which digestion occurs. It is likely that much of the change in digestibility observed

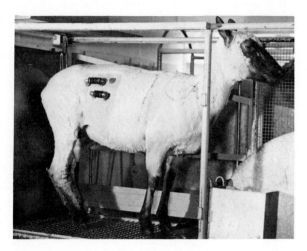

Figure 9-8. A sheep with multiple cannulae. The lower re-entrant cannula in the flank is an abomasal-duodenal cannula, in which the flow from the abomasum enters caudally and passes into the duodenum from the cranial entry. The upper cannula is a duodenal re-entrant cannula which is placed caudal to the common bile duct with flow in a caudal direction. Note the round "Thomas-type" cannula placed in front of the upper cannula; this is opposite the common bile duct and is used for collection of bile and pancreatic juices. Note the catheter on the shoulder. It goes from the thoracic lymph duct to the jugular vein and is used for studying flow of lymph, fat absorption, etc. Courtesy of F.A. Harrison, ARC, Institute of Animal Physiology, Babraham, Cambridge.

Figure 9-9. Diagrammatic representation of digesta flow through a re-entrant cannula. From MacRae (59).

as a result of factors such as level of feed intake and feed processing are the result of changes in extent of ruminal digestion, although available data to confirm this

conclusion are limited. In some circumstances the proportion of digestion occurring in the rumen is reduced considerably. In animals fed mixed forage:grain diets at high levels of intake, as much as 50% of the starch and 30% of the fiber may be digested postruminally (61). Changes in site of digestion are, in large part, dictated by changes in rate of passage and possibly rate of digestion. Firm conclusions about dietary effects on site of digestion are difficult to draw in many cases because of limited data and large errors associated with techniques for measuring digesta flow. An especially serious drawback to much of the work conducted to date arises from the fact that most trials involve animals consuming feed at maintenance levels of intake and extrapolation to animals at high levels of production may be meaningless. However, studies summarized in recent reviews (19, 62) indicate that level of intake, type of grain, feed processing methods and several other factors have some effect on site of digestion.

Level of Intake. In general, increasing levels of dry matter intake produce a shift in site of digestion from the reticulo-rumen to the SI and hindgut (19, 62). However, this generalization must be qualified because differences in intake in these experiments have not always been great. Also, this response seems to be dependent on the nature of the diet. For example, in sheep fed pelleted forage diets the proportion of organic matter digested in the rumen decreased by 6% as intake increased from 1.6 to 2.7X maintenance. This reduction was not apparent when the forages were coarsely chopped (19). Data of Sutton (62) illustrate the relationship between level of intake, source of grain and site of nutrient digestion (Table 9-8). In this work overall digestibility of energy decreased slightly with increased intake when barley served as the primary concentrate source, but extent of ruminal digestion was unaffected. Total tract digestibility and ruminal digestibility of total energy were decreased by 11 and 13% at high intakes, respectively, when ground corn replaced barley. Starch digestion was likewise depressed. Other experiments (19, 62) reflect mixed effects of intake on site of digestion, and it is clear that more research is needed to define these effects with different types of diets.

Table 9-8. Apparent digestibility of energy and starch in the rumen and total tract of dairy cows at different levels of intake.[a]

Intake	Energy		Starch	
	Rumen	Total	Rumen	Total
	. . . . . % of intake			
Barley				
Maintenance (5 kg/d)	51	72	91	100
Maintenance x 3 (15 kg/d)	53	69	91	99
Corn				
Maintenance (5 kg/d)	52	75	81	99
Maintenance x 3 (15 kg/d)	45	67	69	90

[a]Data of Sutton (62). Diets were 40:60 mixtures of hay:concentrate. Concentrate sources were either rolled barley or ground corn.

Type of Grain and Grain Processing. As much as 40% of the organic matter in diets based on dry rolled or ground corn is digested postruminally (19, 61). This observation is due to less extensive digestion of cornstarch in the rumen in comparison to barley starch (62, 62; Table 9-8). Waldo (63) indicates that starch derived from corn or sorghum is more resistant to ruminal breakdown than that from barley or wheat. Processing of grains such as barley has little influence on extent of ruminal digestion, but reducing the particle size of whole corn by grinding results in a substantial increase in the proportion of starch digested in the rumen (64). Such a response is probably due to an increased surface area available for microbial attack. Gelatinization of starch, particularly in corn, resulting from processes such as steam flaking also increases the proportion of starch and organic matter digested in the stomach (19).

Forage Processing. Grinding and pelleting of forages have pronounced effects on site of digestion. As discussed previously, reducing forage particle size by fine grinding results in decreased retention time of particulate matter in the rumen (55). This reduces amount of time that the forage is exposed to rumen microbes and reduces extent of digestion of structural carbohydrates. While this results in an overall decrease in forage digestibility, an increase in the proportion of total fiber and organic matter digestion occurring postruminally also occurs due to grinding and pelleting (19).

RETENTION TIME OF FEED RESIDUES IN THE GASTRO-INTESTINAL TRACT

Extent of digestion of any feedstuff or component of a feedstuff is a function of the rate of digestion and the length of time that the material is exposed to digestive action. Amount of time that a feed particle spends at the various sites of digestion in the gastro-intestinal tract is inversely related to the rate at which it moves through those compartments of the gut. In ruminants passage of digesta from the reticulo-rumen is of special importance. Passage of forage particles from the rumen is associated with extent of digestion of fibrous components of forage and to some extent passage rate is responsible for regulation of voluntary intake in animals fed forages of varying quality (56). Retention time of protein supplements in the rumen is likewise positively related to extent of degradation of protein by rumen microbes (65). Increasing dilution rate of fluid digesta from the rumen may also increase efficiency of microbial protein synthesis (66, 67) and could enhance escape of soluble nutrients from the rumen. Many dietary factors influence retention time of digesta in different compartments of the gut, and it is probable that effects of level of intake and feed processing on total tract digestibility occur largely as a result of altered passage rates. Understanding more about factors affecting retention time of digestion is likely to lead to greater appreciation of animal responses to different feeding strategies.

Methods of Measuring Retention Time

The gastro-intestinal tract of ruminants contains at least two voluminous compartments (reticulo-rumen, cecum-proximal colon) in which mixing and passage rate interact and affect residence time of feed residues. In addition, digesta is composed of at least two phases of material, particulate digesta, consisting of undigested particles which are insoluble, and liquid digesta, consisting of soluble materials in aqueous solution. These fractions travel at different rates and, in some cases, at rates independent of one another. Attempts at quantitating rates of passage and retention times have relied on the use of indigestible markers and the ability to measure

196

the passage of a specific phase depends, in large part, on use of a marker specifically associated with that phase. In order to monitor passage of undigested particles from a specific meal, it is necessary that markers remain attached to particles derived from that meal. Ideally, such attachment would be maintained through the entire gastrointestinal tract, but, at a minimum, should occur within that portion of the tract of interest in a given experiment (37). Digesta turnover or passage rate may be estimated by continuous administration of marker, followed by slaughter and measurement of gut volume and marker concentrations (68). Application of appropriate mathematical treatment may then be used to calculate turnover and retention times (68). While this approach is not inaccurate, it has largely been discarded in favor of techniques in which markers are pulse-dosed and kinetics of digesta passage are determined by mathematical interpretation of data on marker concentration relative to time at different sites in the tract.

One method commonly employed for measurement of rumen volume and dilution rate is the dilution technique whereby a single dose of marker is administered, either by inclusion in a single marked meal or by dosing through the rumen fistula. The marker dose must be allowed to mix adequately with the rumen contents after which sequential samples of the contents are collected. Typically, the concentration of the marker declines in an asymptotic fashion. Regression of the natural logarithm of marker concentration on time results in a straight line, the negative slope of which represents the fractional dilution rate of the marker from the rumen. Extrapolation of the line to the y-intercept produces a value for marker concentration at time zero. Division of the quantity of marker dosed by this value provides a reasonable estimate of rumen volume (68). Use of this technique requires the assumption that the rumen operates in a fashion similar to that of a continuous flow fermentor. While this is broadly true, noncontinuous flow into and out of the rumen and imperfect mixing and marker behavior certainly introduce some variation into measurements taken in this manner.

Rates of passage of particulate digesta may be determined by a similar technique in which a single dose of marker is incorporated into a

meal. To identify feed residues derived from the specific meal, it is important that the marker remain intimately associated with those particles. Stained feeds, rare earth elements and Cr mordants, previously discussed in this chapter, have generally been the markers of choice in such studies. Fecal excretion of markers is then monitored from a point in time before which any marker has been excreted until all of the marker dose has been eliminated. Many approaches have been taken to utilize data obtained on marker concentration relative to time post-dosing for calculating retention times or rates of passage.

In early studies animals were fed meals containing stained hay particles and excretion of stained particles were monitored for up to 140 h post-dosing. Numbers of stained particles were determined per unit dry matter in feces and accumulated with time. These data were then graphically depicted as a cumulative excretion curve (Fig. 9-10). It has been proposed (41) that the time required for 80% of the marker dose to be excreted minus that for excretion of 5% of the marker would reflect the ruminal retention time of the marked particles. Alternatively, Castle (69) proposed that the "R value", calculated by adding the times of excretion from 5 to 95% at 10% intervals and dividing the sum by 10, represented the mean retention time of the stained particles in the entire digestive tract.

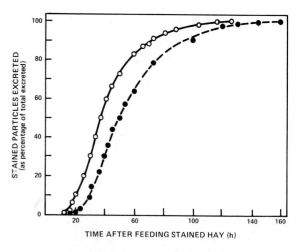

Figure 9-10. Typical cumulative excretion curve for recovery of a single marker dose in feces. This graph compares the cumulative excretion of stained hay particles fed to goats (○) or cattle (●). From Castle (69).

Both of these approaches are empirical and arbitrary in nature and bear no theoretical relationship to gastro-intestinal phenomena which may be involved in regulation of passage.

A more favorable approach is mathematical analysis of curves relating fecal marker concentrations to time post-dosing. Such curves (Fig. 9-11) typically include a time delay before first appearance of marker in feces. This is interpreted as transit time for feed particles whose passage is not delayed by mixing in the rumen or hindgut. Curve peeling techniques may be employed to determine

separate rates for the ascending (K_2) and descending (K_1) portions of the curve. It is assumed that K_1 and K_2 represent separate turnover rates for two digestive tract compartments of unequal size (68). Different models, including those of Grovum and Williams (70, 71) and Ellis et al (72) have been used to separate K_1 and K_2, although interpretation of the compartments identified by K_1 and K_2 differs between these groups. Grovum and Williams (71) interpret K_1 to represent rate of passage from the rumen and K_2, that of the cecum and proximal colon. Ellis and coworkers suggest that K_1 represents the rate of transformation (via rumination and microbial degradation) of large particles of feed to particles small enough to exit from the rumen and that K_2 corresponds to a mixing phenomenon within the rumen (72). It is also possible that K_2 represents a composite rate of turnover for several small and rapidly moving pools in the digestive tract (68). Grovum and Williams (70) propose that total mean retention time may be calculated as the sum of the reciprocals of K_1 and K_2 plus the transit time.

Factors Affecting Residence Time of Feed Residues

Level of Intake. Increasing level of intake of ruminants fed forage-based diets increases turnover rate of both fluid and particulate digesta from the rumen. Data of Grovum and Williams (71), presented in Table 9-9, illustrate this relationship. As intake of chopped alfalfa by sheep increased from 400

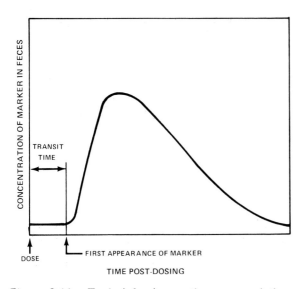

Figure 9-11. Typical fecal excretion curve relating concentration of a pulse-dosed marker in feces to time post-dosing.

Table 9-9. Effect of level of intake on rumen volume and kinetics of digesta passage from the rumen.[a]

Item	Feed intake, g/d				
	400	625	850	1075	1300
Rumen fluid volume, g	5041	5690	6660	7478	7214
Rumen particulate volume, g	387	484	613	623	702
Water intake, g/d	842	1215	1702	2095	2596
Particulate kinetics					
Turnover rate (K_1), %/h	3.56	4.47	5.26	6.33	6.90
Turnover time, h	28.1	22.4	19.0	15.8	14.5
Fluid kinetics					
Turnover rate (K_1), %/h	3.77	4.74	5.95	6.90	8.01
Turnover time, h	26.5	21.1	16.8	14.5	12.5

[a]Taken from Grovum and Williams (71). Data obtained in mature sheep (41 kg) fed chopped alfalfa.

198

to 1,300 g/d, rumen particulate contents increased by 81% and dilution rate of particulate-bound markers increased from 3.56 to 6.90%/h with a resultant decrease of 48% in ruminal turnover time. The increase in feed consumption was accompanied by an increase in water intake and in fluid dilution rate from the rumen. Similarly, a number of other reports indicate that rate of passage through the rumen and the rest of the gastro-intestinal tract can be anticipated to increase as intake of forage increases (73, 74). Residence time of feed is a major factor determining extent of digestion of fibrous components of forage, and total tract digestibility would be expected to decrease with increasing intake. This seems to be the case when forages are fed in ground and/or pelleted form (74), but increasing intake of long hay or coarsely chopped forages results in little or no depression in digestibility (73). The minimal ruminal retention time required for reduction in particle size of forages fed in these forms to sizes small enough to pass from the rumen is probably long enough to ensure extensive breakdown of the digestible portion of the feedstuff. Very little information is available regarding the effect of intake on passage rates of diets containing substantial proportions of grain. Such data would be useful in interpreting reasons for the negative associative effects discussed previously in this chapter.

Physical Form of Forages. Reducing particle size of forages by fine grinding results in increased rate of passage of particulate matter from the rumen and resultant decreases in digestibility of organic matter and fiber (55, 73). The depression in digestibility of finely ground material compared to more coarsely chopped forage is small at maintenance intakes (Table 9-10). However, mean retention time of finely ground and pelleted grass decreased from 70 to 44 h as intake increased from maintenance to 3.1X maintenance and organic matter and fiber digestibilities decreased by 12 and 35%, respectively. In contrast, feeding coarsely chopped forages also resulted in decreased retention times, but digestibilities were only slightly depressed. Decreasing retention time by feeding ground and pelleted forages results in increases in voluntary intake in compensation for the reduced digestibility (55).

Mineral Salts. Introduction of readily soluble mineral salts (NaCl, NaHCO$_3$ or mixtures approximating the composition of salivary salts) by inclusion in the diet (75) or by intra-ruminal infusion (76) results in increased fluid dilution rates from the rumen. Administration of such salts results in increased water consumption and the more rapid turnover is probably attributable to increased flux of water through the rumen as a result of the increase in drinking. Concomitant alterations in ruminal fermentation patterns occur as molar proportions of acetate are increased and those of propionate decreased. These changes in dilution rate and fermentation

Table 9-10. Effect of grinding of forage and level of intake on apparent digestibility of organic matter and crude fiber and on mean retention times of food residues in the gastro-intestinal tract.[a]

Diet	Level of intake, x maintenance	Organic matter digestibility, %	Crude fiber digestibility, %	Mean retention time,[b] h
Chopped grass	1.0	82.7	84.8	110
	2.0	82.4	85.5	87
	2.6	81.4	83.8	73
	3.1	80.9	82.4	61
Ground[c] and pelleted grass	1.0	80.5	78.7	70
	2.0	75.9	66.7	58
	2.6	73.6	59.0	50
	3.1	70.7	50.9	44

[a]From Alwash and Thomas (73)
[b]R value (Castle [69])
[c]0.32 cm screen

Table 9-11. Effect of cold exposure on digestibility and ruminal turnover times.[a]

Item	Warm (22-25 C) Low intake	Cold (2-5 C) Low intake	Cold (2-5 C) High intake
Dry matter intake, g/d	1410	1410	2350
Dry matter digestibility, %	57.4	51.8	48.4
Dry matter digested in the stomach, g/d	514	335	535
Ruminal turnover times			
Particulate, h	18.6	12.1	10.4
Fluid, h	14.6	8.7	7.4

[a]From Kennedy and Milligan (58). Sheep, closely shorn and fed pelleted bromegrass.

patterns occur in animals fed diets containing significant levels of concentrates, but are not observed in those fed all forage diets (76). Such alterations may influence site of digestion of some nutrients. Increased postruminal flows of amino acids have been reported (67) in conjunction with mineral salt infusions and other soluble nutrients may be washed out of the rumen as a result of increasing fluid turnover.

Environmental Temperature. In sheep exposed to temperatures below the zone of thermal neutrality for extended periods, turnover rates of both fluid and particulate digesta from the rumen have been increased dramatically (57, 58; Table 9-11). Increased passage from the rumen under these conditions is reflected by decreased extent of digestion of the diet in both the stomach and the total digestive tract. In cold-stressed animals, these observations may result from increases in motility of the reticulo-rumen and/or the lower gastro-intestinal tract (see Ch. 22). Increasing passage in these circumstances could serve as a strategy for increasing dry matter consumption (and caloric intake) to meet high demands for energy imposed by such conditions.

SUMMARY

Digestion in ruminants is accomplished via microbial breakdown of dietary nutrients in the reticulo-rumen, hydrolytic and enzymatic activity in the abomasum and small intestine and a secondary microbial fermentation in the cecum and large intestine. The end-products of digestion of complex carbohydrates, lipids and proteins are absorbed as simple compounds, chiefly from the forestomach and small intestine. The proportion of a diet or feedstuff which disappears during passage through the alimentary tract, or apparent digestibility, is often measured and used as an indicator of nutritive value. Apparent digestibility values, while meaningful, are oversimplified expressions of nutritive value because other factors, both related to and independent of apparent digestibility, also contribute to the overall nutritive value of a diet. Apparent digestibility values likewise do not reflect the nature of the absorbed end-products of digestion or the amount of energy lost as a result of digestive processes, both of which are influenced by sites in the gastro-intestinal tract in which digestion occurs. Retention time of feed residues in the digestive tract has profound effects on both total tract digestibility and site of digestion. Factors such as level of feed intake, ingredient and nutrient composition of the diet and methods of feed processing affect rate of passage, apparent digestibility and site of digestion. As future research delineates the relationship of dietary factors to rate of passage and site of digestion, in particular, our ability to develop more sophisticated approaches to defining nutrient requirements and to predicting animal responses to different feeding practices will be enhanced.

Literature Cited

1. Phillipson, A.T. 1977. In: Dukes' Physiology of Domestic Animals, 9th Ed. pp. 250-286. M.J. Swenson, ed. Cornell University Press, Ithaca, NY.
2. Harrop, C.J.F. 1974. J. Agr. Sci. 83:249.
3. Hill, K.J. 1965. In: Physiology of Digestion in the Ruminant, pp. 221-230. R.W. Dougherty, ed. Butterworth Inc., Washington, DC.
4. McLeay, L.M. and D.A. Titchen. 1970. J. Physiol. 206:605.
5. Hill, K.J., D.E. Noakes and R.A. Lowe. 1970. In: Physiology of Digestion and Metabolism in the Ruminant, pp. 166-179. A.T. Phillipson, ed. Oriel Press Ltd., Newcastle upon Tyne, UK.
6. Otterby, D.E. and J.G. Linn. 1981. J. Dairy Sci. 64:1365.
7. Harrison, F.A. and K.J. Hill. 1962. J. Physiol. 162:225.
8. Ben-Ghedalia, D., H. Tagari, A. Bondi and A. Tadmor. 1974. Brit. J. Nutr. 31:125.
9. Sellers, A.F. 1977. In: Dukes' Physiology of Domestic Animals, 9th Ed. pp. 240-246. M.J. Swenson, ed. Cornell University Press, Ithaca, NY.
10. Harrison, F.A. 1962. J. Physiol. 162:212.
11. Caple, I.W. and T.J. Heath. 1975. In: Digestion and Metabolism in the Ruminant, pp. 91-100. I.W. McDonald and A.C.I. Warner, eds. University of New England Publishing Unit, Armidale, Australia.
12. Taylor, R.B. 1962. Res. Vet. Sci. 3:63.
13. Van Hellen, R.W., et al. 1978. J. Animal Sci. 47 (Suppl. 1):445 (Abstr.).
14. Russell, J.R., A.W. Young and N.A. Jorgensen. 1981. J. Animal Sci. 52:1177.
15. Huber, J.T., N.L. Jacobson, R.S. Allen and P.A. Hartman. 1961. J. Dairy Sci. 44:1494.
16. Huber, J.T., R.J. Rifkin and J.M. Keith. 1964. J. Dairy Sci. 47:789.
17. Stevens, C.E. 1970. In: Physiology of Digestion and Metabolism in the Ruminant, pp. 101-112. A.T. Phillipson, ed. Oriel Press Ltd., Newcastle upon Tyne, UK.
18. Visek, W.J. 1968. J. Dairy Sci. 51:286.
19. Johnson, D.E. and W.G. Bergen. 1982. In: Protein Requirements for Cattle: Symposium, pp. 113-127. F.N. Owens, ed. Oklahoma State University Press, Stillwater, OK.
20. Levine, R. 1973. In: Modern Nutrition in Health and Disease, pp. 99-116. R.S. Goodhart and M.E. Shils, eds. Lea & Febiger, Philadelphia.
21. Garton, G.A. 1965. In: Physiology of Digestion in the Ruminant, pp. 390-398. R.W. Dougherty, ed. Butterworths, Inc., Washington, DC.
22. Leat, W.M.F. and F.A. Harrison. 1975. In: Digestion and Metabolism in the Ruminant, pp. 481-495. I.W. McDonald and A.C.I. Warner, eds. University of New England Publishing Unit, Armidale, Australia.
23. Armstrong, D.G. and K. Hutton. 1975. In: Digestion and Metabolism in the Ruminant, pp. 432-447. I.W. McDonald and A.C.I. Warner, eds. University of New England Publishing Unit, Armidale, Australia.
24. Lindsay, J.R., J.P. Hogan and J.B. Donnelly. 1980. Aust. J. Agr. Res. 31:589.
25. Williams, V.J. 1969. Comp. Biochem. Physiol. 29:865.
26. Minson, D.J. and J.L. Cowper. 1966. Brit. J. Nutr. 20:757.
27. Church, D.C. 1976. Digestive Physiology and Nutrition of Ruminants. Vol. I—Digestive Physiology. 2nd Ed. O & B Books, Inc., Corvallis, OR.
28. Mason, V.C. and J.H. Frederiksen. 1979. Tierphysiol., Tierarnahrg. u. Futtermittelkde. 41:121.
29. Mason, V.C. 1979. Tierphysiol., Tierarnahrg. u. Futtermittelkde. 41:131;140.
30. Gans, J.H. and P.E. Mercer. 1977. In: Dukes' Physiology of the Domestic Animals, 9th Ed. M.J. Swenson, ed. Cornell University Press, Ithaca, NY.
31. Topps, J.H. and R.C. Elliott. 1966. Proc. Nutr. Soc. 25:xix (Abstr.).
32. Swanson, E.W. 1982. In: Protein Requirements of Cattle: Symposium, pp. 183-197. F.N. Owens, ed. Oklahoma State University Press, Stillwater, OK.
33. Martin, A.K. 1982. Brit. J. Nutr. 47:139;155; Brit. J. Nutr. 48:497.
34. Schneider, B.H. and W.P. Flatt. 1975. The Evaluation of Feeds through Digestibility Experiments. University of Georgia Press, Athens, GA.
35. Kotb, A.R. and T.D. Luckey. 1972. Nutr. Abstr. Rev. 42:28.
36. MacRae, J.C. 1974. Proc. Nutr. Soc. 33:147.

37. Ellis, W.C., C. Lascano, R. Teeter and F.N. Owens. 1982. In: Protein Requirements of Cattle: Symposium, pp. 37-56. F.N. Owens, ed. Oklahoma State University Press, Stillwater, OK.

38. Fahey, Jr., G.C. and H.G. Jung. 1983. J. Animal Sci. 57:220.

39. Muntifering, R.B. 1982. J. Animal Sci. 55:432.

40. Van Keulen, J. and B.A. Young. 1977. J. Animal Sci. 44:282.

41. Balch, C.C. and R.C. Campling. 1965. In: Physiology of Digestion in the Ruminant, pp. 108-123. R.W. Dougherty, ed. Butterworth Inc., Washington, DC.

42. Van Soest, P.J. 1982. Nutritional Ecology of the Ruminant. O & B Books, Inc., Corvallis, OR.

43. Faichney, G.J. 1980. J. Agr. Sci. 94:313.

44. Corse, D.A. and J.D. Sutton. 1971. Proc. Nutr. Soc. 30:18A (Abstr.).

45. Rohr, K., M. Brandt, P. Lebzien and H. Schafft. 1984. Can. J. Animal Sci. 64 (Suppl.):116 (Abstr.).

46. Hartnell, G.F. and L.D. Satter. 1979. J. Animal Sci. 48:375.

47. Crooker, B.A., J.H. Clark and R.D. Shanks. 1982. J. Nutr. 112:1353.

48. Combs, D.K., R.D. Shaver, N. Singh and L.D. Satter. 1984. Can. J. Animal Sci. 64 (Suppl.):66 (Abstr.).

49. Uden, P., P.E. Colucci and P.J. Van Soest. 1980. J. Sci. Food Agr. 31:625.

50. Ehle, F.R., et al. 1983. J. Dairy Sci. 66 (Suppl. 1):188 (Abstr.).

51. Moe, P.W. 1981. J. Dairy Sci. 64:1120.

52. Joanning, S.W., D.E. Johnson and B.P. Barry. 1981. J. Animal Sci. 53:1095.

53. Tyrrell, H.F. and P.W. Moe. 1975. J. Dairy Sci. 58:1151.

54. Soofi, R., G.C. Fahey, Jr. and L.L. Berger. 1982. J. Animal Sci. 55:1206.

55. Thomson, D.J. and D.E. Beever. 1980. In: Digestive Physiology and Metabolism in Ruminants, pp. 291-308. Y. Ruckebusch and P. Thivend, eds. AVI Publishing Co., Westport, CT.

56. Ulyatt, M.J. 1973. In: Chemistry and Biochemistry of Herbage, Vol. 3, pp. 131-178. G.W. Butler and R.W. Bailey, eds. Academic Press, New York.

57. Kennedy, P.M., R.J. Christopherson and L.P. Milligan. 1976. Brit. J. Nutr. 36:231.

58. Kennedy, P.M. and L.P. Milligan. 1978. Brit. J. Nutr. 39:105.

59. MacRae, J.C. 1975. In: Digestion and Metabolism in the Ruminant, pp. 261-276. I.W. McDonald and A.C.I. Warner, eds. University of New England Publishing Unit, Armidale, Australia.

60. Thomas, P.C. 1978. In: Ruminant Digestion and Feed Evaluation, pp. 3.1-3.12. D.F. Osbourn, D.E. Beever and D.J. Thomson, eds. ARC, London.

61. Garrett, W.N. and D.E. Johnson. 1983. J. Animal Sci. 57 (Suppl. 2):478.

62. Sutton, J.D. 1980. In: Digestive Physiology and Metabolism in Ruminants, pp. 271-290. Y. Ruckebusch and P. Thivend, eds. AVI Publishing Co., Westport, CT.

63. Waldo, D.R. 1973. J. Animal Sci. 37:1062.

64. Galyean, M.L., D.G. Wagner and F.N. Owens. 1979. J. Animal Sci. 49:204.

65. Stern, M.D. and L.D. Satter. In: Protein Requirements for Cattle: Symposium, pp. 57-71. F.N. Owens, ed. Oklahoma State University Press, Stillwater, OK.

66. Isaacson, H.R., F.C. Hinds, M.P. Bryant and F.N. Owens. 1975. J. Dairy Sci. 58:1645.

67. Harrison, D.G., D.E. Beever, D.J. Thomson and D.F. Osbourn. 1976. J. Sci. Food Agr. 27:617.

68. Van Soest, P.J., P. Uden and K.F. Wrick. 1983. Nutr. Rep. Int. 27:17.

69. Castle, E.J. 1956. Brit. J. Nutr. 10:15.

70. Grovum, W.L. and V.J. Williams. 1973. Brit. J. Nutr. 30:313.

71. Grovum, W.L. and V.J. Williams. 1977. Brit. J. Nutr. 38:425.

72. Ellis, W.C., J.H. Matis and C. Lascano. 1979. Fed. Proc. 38:2702.

73. Alwash, A.H. and P.C. Thomas. 1971. J. Sci. Food Agr. 22:611.

74. Alwash, A.H. and P.C. Thomas. 1974. J. Sci. Food Agr. 25:139.

75. Thomson, D.J., D.E. Beever, M.J. Latham, M.E. Sharpe and R.A. Terry. 1978. J. Agr. Sci. 91:1.

76. Rogers, J.A. and C.L. Davis. 1982. J. Dairy Sci. 65:953.

10 APPETITE, PALATABILITY AND CONTROL OF FEED INTAKE

by W. L. Grovum

THE STATE OF THE ART

Animal production can be increased by increasing intake or by making digestion and metabolism more efficient. Unfortunately, our understanding of what controls food intake in ruminants is still poor. This is partly because the mechanism is extremely complex but intake is also highly variable within and among animals. As well, the usual method of studying intake, although in accordance with standard scientific practice of changing only one factor at a time in a controlled manner, may be limiting progress in understanding the subject. For example, satiety probably results from multiple inputs into the satiety center(s) in the brain. Some inputs may occur simultaneously toward the end of a meal but others may be delayed somewhat to prolong satiety. Nevertheless, when the anorexic properties of one factor are examined in isolation from the others, it is likely that the treatments imposed will have to be more severe than normal to depress intake even to a moderate extent. This factor may then fail to achieve the status of being significant physiologically even if the intake result is significant statistically. The solution is obviously to do experiments where two or more different treatments are imposed simultaneously in a controlled manner so that it is possible to examine their individual and additive effects on food intake. This is more difficult than single factor experimentation due to the need for multiple vascular and gastro-intestinal cannulation and a larger number of animals, but it has been done successfully in at least two laboratories.

Although the concept of multiple controls over intake is fairly well established in the literature, there has been an attempt to segregate the likely signals of satiety into those which limit the intakes of roughage (physical factors) and others which limit the intakes of high-concentrate diets (physiological or chemical factors) (25, 60). The scientific basis for this is not clear because there are no experiments indicating that distension of the

reticulo-rumen is more effective in limiting the intakes of roughage than of concentrated diets or that VFA in the rumen contents is more effective in limiting intakes of concentrates as opposed to roughages. An alternative but equally theoretical concept is to consider all signals of satiety as being effective for all diets, but not equally so. However, no one knows what the relative weights should be for the various signals of satiety when ruminants are fed long roughage, concentrates, mixtures of roughages and concentrates, silages or ground and pelleted roughages.

Finally, there appears to be a number of deeply ingrained concepts in the literature that are questionable because they are not supportable by critical experiments. Examples of this are, first, that a certain level of "factor x" will signal satiety at all times; secondly, that energy intakes will essentially be constant for all diets exceeding certain energy densities or DE values; and, thirdly, that fat in ruminants is capable of generating a long-term signal limiting intake. These issues will be discussed at length in the body of this chapter.

Numerous other reviews on food intake in ruminants are presently available. Some are general (3, 6, 8, 14, 15, 22, 24, 35, 37, 50), whereas others are oriented to palatability (24), the dairy cow (51, 59, 61, 76), the grazing situation (1, 31, 54, 75), forages (74), the brain (7, 11), short-term controls (7), long-term controls (11), physical regulation (21), peptides and hormones (4, 5, 27, 42), the role of the fat depots and intake stimulants in establishing intake (2) and an integration of food intake with rumen function and rate of passage (45). Recent symposia on the control of intake of farm animals (Proc. Nutr. Soc., 1985, 44:303-362), and on neuropeptidergic regulation of food intake in ruminants and other mammals (Fed. Proc., 1984, 43:2888-2907) are indicative of current interest in this subject.

The purpose of this chapter is to critically assess current thinking of what controls the intake of food by ruminants. The intent of questioning some of the well-established concepts in the literature is to stimulate students at the undergraduate and graduate levels of education as well as established researchers to think carefully about these issues and to initiate new research which will improve the knowledge base in this important aspect of animal production.

CONTROLS OVER ROUGHAGE INTAKE

Intake of food is often postponed in spite of hunger by competing drives which enhance survival during extreme thermoregulatory stresses and other life threatening situations. Food intake is also often suppressed by disease or injury but, assuming that none of these conditions apply, palatability is the first determinant of what a moderately hungry animal will eat when food supplies are abundant (Fig. 10-1). Palatability includes olfaction and all of the oral pharyngeal sensations arising from the food but does not include any of its post ingestive effects. Campling (21) has referred to instances when cattle fed straw ad libitum were found to have less contents by weight in the reticulo-rumen than when they were fed a diet of hay. One must therefore wonder if the intake of straw was limited by its palatability before a distension level capable of signalling satiety was achieved. Palatability is, no doubt, of lesser importance as a determinant of intake when life is threatened

by starvation, but ruminants in productive circumstances are not in that plight.

Beyond palatability effects, daily intake of food can be increased or decreased by long-term controls which are also detailed in Fig. 10-1. In spite of their obvious importance to production, very little is known about how they function, except that the effects of season (low intakes in winter, high intakes in summer) may reflect photoperiod (18, 19) and, hence, be mediated at least in part by the pineal gland (70).

Daily food intake, regardless of whether it is set at a high or low level by the long-term controls, is normally consumed as a number of spontaneous discrete meals. Factors which begin and end each meal are referred to as short-term controls over intake (Fig. 10-1). They must operate by altering the activity of the hunger and satiety centers in the brain. This is accomplished as far as we know either by nervous receptors and afferent neurons which relay impulses from the gut, liver and perhaps other organs into these centers or by humoral or blood-born factors whose mechanisms of action are presently not understood. Intakes are not limited by energy per se in food. The energy-containing components of food or some metabolite(s) might constitute a satiety signal(s), but energy would not. The signal of satiety for roughage diets was thought to be distension of the reticulo-rumen

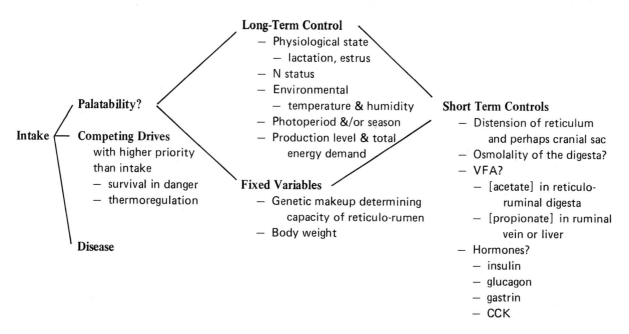

Figure 10-1. Determinants of roughage intake in ruminants.

(8) but the intake of ground and pelleted alfalfa during one meal could be limited by reticular but not by ruminal distension (ventral sac) with relatively small amounts of warm water in balloons (41). Perhaps this was to be expected because electrophysiology studies had demonstrated the density of slowly adapting tension receptors, which could sense distension over the duration of a meal, to be highest in the reticulum. Density was less in the cranial sac, whereas few of the receptors were found in the dorsal and ventral sacs of the rumen. Thus, it is possible that distension of the reticulum and the cranial sac limits roughage intake and that the reductions in intake seen in other studies after distending the rumen (ventral and/or dorsal sacs) resulted from a redistribution of digesta into either the reticulum or the cranial sac. In addition to distension, intakes of roughages may also be limited by the osmolality, H^+ and VFA (acetic acid) in digesta in the reticulo-rumen, by VFA (propionic acid) in the ruminal veins or the liver or by hormones such as insulin, glucagon, gastrin or cholecystokinin. One might venture to conclude, albeit tentatively, that the intakes of hay of moderate quality may be limited mainly by distension but that when better quality roughage is fed, additional factors may become important as signals of satiety.

CONTROL OF ENERGY INTAKES WITH MIXED AND HIGH CONCENTRATE DIETS

The arguments presented above about competing drives, palatability and long- and short-term controls over roughage intake probably apply with these diets as well. Although not proven, it is possible that distension of the reticulum and cranial sac may, at least in part, act to limit intakes of concentrate diets. There are no data available presently to evaluate this concept except for the observation that dense foods drop into the reticulum of cattle after being swallowed (66) and reports that feeding of concentrate diets is associated with lower fill levels in the reticulo-rumen than when roughages are fed (8). However, this latter finding may not be relevant because distension in the reticulum and cranial sac rather than in the entire reticulo-rumen may

be the critical factor determining whether or not intakes of high concentrate diets are limited by physical factors. Furthermore, one could argue that fill per se was irrelevant because a partially filled stomach with a high degree of tone may generate just as much afferent activity from tension receptors as a completely filled stomach with normal tone.

There is presently a debate occurring as to whether the intakes of diets containing large proportions of concentrates are being limited by VFA in rumen fluid (acetic acid) and liver (propionic acid) (6, 34) or by endocrine factors such as insulin and glucagon (27, 28). DeJong (27) considered it unlikely that VFA would play anything more than a minor role in limiting the size or frequency of spontaneous meals taken by ruminants. However, he conceded that VFA may depress intake when ruminants are meal fed. The administration of growth hormone has been demonstrated to increase milk production and intake (9, 10), but its normal role in hunger and satiety is unclear at present.

The gastro-intestinal hormones (gastrin, cholecystokinin and secretin) will depress intake in a dose-related manner when administered intravenously (42). Evidence is also available for cholecystokinin activity, produced and released within the brain, acting as a signal of satiety, but the normal mechanism triggering its release and satiety has not been established (4, 5). The writer (43) demonstrated that peripherally administered cholecystokinin does not suppress intake by acting centrally. There was some evidence that the lungs may produce a metabolite of cholecystokinin which might subsequently act as a signal of satiety at an undefined location in the body. Pentagastrin, a synthetic peptide with the activity of gastrin, appeared to act on the brain to depress intake by sheep (44).

Opioid peptides administered centrally stimulate feeding in sheep (5), but the stimuli releasing endogenous opiates centrally to induce hunger or feeding are not known. As yet, we do not know if these putative central mechanisms of hunger and satiety involving the opioid peptides and peptides with cholecystokinin activity respectively are operating in a general sense for all diets or if there are diet-specific mechanisms.

SATIETY SIGNALS—ONE CRITICAL LEVEL OR MANY?

An increase in the level of production is usually associated with an increase in the ad libitum intake of food mediated by long-term controls over intake. The extra consumption takes the form of bigger meals, more frequent meals or some combination of the two. Presumably, the short-term controls over intake, that operate within each meal, remain the same in qualitative terms, but it is not clear what happens in the animal to permit intake to increase. For example, the volume of contents in the reticulo-rumen of dairy cattle during the peak of lactation is markedly greater than that occurring in the dry or dry and pregnant state. Why should this occur if distension of the reticulo-rumen was limiting intake in the dry state? Similarly, why should ruminants accommodate more digesta in the reticulo-rumen with increases in N status or with increases in day length (18, 19, 45)? The answers to these questions are not known, but at least three possibilities exist: (A) the sensitivities of the peripheral receptor mechanisms may be decreased with no change in the central mechanisms controlling intake; (B) the same but vice versa; or (C) there is a combination of these effects. Nevertheless, it is clear that there is not just one critical level of fill which will signal satiety but several levels depending upon the physiological state and various other long-term controls over food intake. The same is probably true for all of the short-term signals of satiety. Thus, the concept of one level of 'factor x' being critical in the initiation of satiety in all circumstances is probably false and should be abandoned.

The concept of homeorhesis defined by Bauman (9) as the "orchestrated changes for the priorities of a physiological state" is similar in some respects to the existence of long-term controls which serve to match intake with energy expenditures in the production situation. The homeorhetic controls involve the coordination of metabolism and result in the directed partitioning of nutrients to support requirements specific for each physiological state. Food intake does follow the increase in milk production resulting from administering growth hormone to cows (10), but the mechanism is still not known. The extra intake could result from the extra demand for nutrients induced by the growth hormone (mechanism unclear), or the hormone could conceivably be acting both to control metabolism and to direct intake upwards to support the extra demand for nutrients. The latter may involve altering activities of neurons in the hypothalamus or altering the activities of neuronal receptors which sense nutrient availability. However, given the response to growth hormone in cattle, an opportunity now exists to investigate at least one of the long-term mechanisms controlling intake. Another possibility exists with regard to photoperiod since Blaxter and Boyne (18) reported that the seasonal effect on intake in sheep housed indoors was associated with a seasonal variation in basal metabolic rate such that low intakes were paired with low rates (winter) and high intakes with high rates (summer). The effect of photoperiod on intake and body weight changes in Soay rams was also shown to be reduced by 50% following bilateral superior cervical ganglionectomy which is thought to be equivalent to pinealectomy (70). However, investigations are still needed to help us understand how increasing N balance or protein status in ruminants given poor quality roughages increases their intakes (30).

It is hoped that investigations into the long-term controls over intake and how they interact with the short-term controls will be done with ruminants fed roughages as well as production rations common in feedlot situations. This is desirable because most of the world's population cannot afford to purchase concentrates to support production by ruminants. Such work hopefully will lead to new ways of substantially increasing food intake and production by ruminants.

INFLUENCES OVER ROUGHAGE INTAKE

Numerous influences over roughage intake related to rumen function and agronomic and management practices have been identified in Fig. 10-2 in order to differentiate them from the controls over intake. For simplicity here, roughage intake is shown to be controlled by distension of the reticulum and the cranial sac. However, anything that increases the rate of breakdown of the plant material in the reticulo-rumen (increase in microbial activity,

206

CONTROL INFLUENCES OVER DIGESTA THROUGHPUT AND HENCE INTAKE

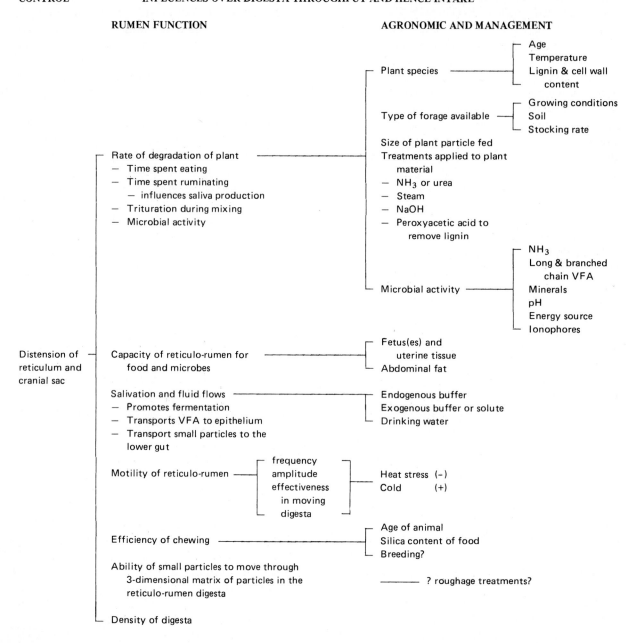

Figure 10-2. Influences over throughput and hence intake of roughage that can be achieved assuming intake is initially controlled only by distension of the reticulum and the cranial sac. It is postulated as throughput increases that factors other than distension will assume increasingly greater importance as signals of satiety.

an increase in rumination time or treatment of the roughage with NH_3) would be expected to increase the rate of small particle production and hence the throughput or intake that could be attained for the given distension level which would signal satiety (45). Conversely, influences which inhibit the rate of

degradation (antibiotics, a low pH due to readily available carbohydrates in the diet or high-lignin hay) would be expected to slow the rate of degradation of plant material and decrease throughput and intake for a given level of distension. Thus, one can clearly differentiate those influences over intake which cannot be sensed by the animal from the controls over intake which, by definition, must be sensed.

Abdominal fat, fetal tissue or the addition of inert ballast to contents in the reticulo-rumen could also influence roughage intake in a negative manner by decreasing the amount of digesta and, hence, the total amount of microbial activity in the reticulo-rumen. The microbes normally weaken particles by digesting away structural materials. These particles can then be broken by trituration during mixing cycles of motility and escape to the lower gut. This method of producing small digesta particles may account for the fact that animals that are muzzled to prevent rumination will still consume substantial amounts of roughage (63; Milligan, personal communication). This process may also contribute to the fact that some of the domesticated sheep and goats in Africa, whose reticulo-ruminal contents can make up a quarter of their body weights, will do well on extremely poor food. An additional consideration in this instance is the longer than normal retention times of digesta in the reticulo-rumen which are likely to have a positive effect on digestibility.

Saliva has a positive influence on intake in spite of its contribution to fill. This is partly because the buffer and urea content stimulate fermentation, partly because it dilutes VFA and transports them to the wall of the reticulo-rumen for absorption and partly because it helps to minimize the osmotic pressures which develop in reticulo-ruminal contents during and after a meal. Salivary fluid also contributes substantially to rumen fluid which in turn transports small particles of digesta out of the reticulo-rumen. This would help to stimulate intake by relieving distension. Frequent and strong contractions of the reticulo-rumen would be expected to have a positive influence on intake for the same reason. Heat stress decreases motility of the reticulo-rumen, intake and the rate of passage of digesta (see Ch. 22), whereas cold stress increases motility of the reticulo-rumen as well as intake and the rate of passage of digesta. However, the effect of an increase in motility per se on intake is not known. One should wonder why, under normal conditions, such a large proportion of digesta particles in the reticulo-rumen are of a size which could pass to the lower gut but do not. The reason

for this apparent inefficiency in clearing small particles from the forestomachs is not known but may be related to fluid flows, motility or to some characteristics of the particles which prevent their movement through the digesta.

A highly efficient set of teeth for grinding the food would have a positive influence on roughage intake by increasing small particle production during eating or ruminating. It is not known if this trait can be improved by breeding, but there is evidence indicating that poor teeth, resulting from age or undue wear, will not support high intakes.

The density of foodstuffs will probably influence intake by an extent related to the importance of distension as a signal of satiety. Inverse associations exist between the dry bulk densities as well as the intakes of forages (grasses and legumes) and their neutral detergent fiber (NDF) or cell wall contents (49, 55, 56, 58, 67, 68, 73). NDF levels are, in turn, negatively associated with digestibility and positively associated with the time spent ruminating (see Mertens, 56). The total NDF intakes over a wide range of forages (NDF contents ranging from 30-80%), although quadratically related to forage cell wall content (55, 74), were relatively constant. This was taken to indicate that the cell walls were influencing intake through an effect in the reticulo-rumen (74). The capacity of the intestines to transport digesta was not seen as a limitation to intake because daily fecal output increases with increasing voluntary roughage intakes (55, 74) and the voluntary intake of alfalfa hay by sheep was unaffected when wet fecal output was more than doubled by infusing methyl cellulose into the abomasum (40). Both high and low density categories of NDF were reported by Mertens (56), but within each category, intake was negatively associated with the NDF content of the foodstuff as was mentioned above. Thus, it is possible for two foodstuffs having the same NDF contents to have different bulk densities and therefore potentially different intakes. According to Mertens (56), by-product feeds of high density such as soybean mill feeds and cottonseed hulls are consumed in quantities that are greater than expected. The work of Wheeler et al (78) is an example of this. Intakes of a diet consisting mainly of cottonseed hulls exceeded that of finely chopped diets of orchard grass, barley straw and corn

208

stover in spite of the lower digestibility of the hulls. One might conclude that this resulted from the higher density of digesta in the reticulo-rumen of the cattle fed the cottonseed hulls and therefore from a greater amount of dry digesta in the organ/100 kg empty body weight. However, there may also be something special about the particles in this diet which allows them to escape relatively easily from the reticulo-rumen. It is interesting to note that the turnover rate of reticulo-ruminal digesta was calculated to be slower for the cottonseed hulls than for the orchardgrass hay in spite of the higher intakes of the cottonseed. This was mainly due to the fact that the higher density of digesta from cottonseed hulls markedly increased the amount of dry matter in the reticulo-rumen relative to that observed with the orchardgrass hay.

The rate of passage of digesta through the reticulo-ruman does not have any causitive effect on intake except, perhaps, for its influence on digestibility and protein supply to the small intestine. The rate constant, k, used frequently now to report rate of passage information, is the result of an interaction between the outflow rate and the volume of contents in the pool [k = (Flow rate/Volume) = F/V]. Numerous interactions between F and V are possible to cause rate of passage or k to increase. This would occur if (A) F increased (V constant), (B) V decreased (F constant), (C) F increased and V decreased, (D) both F and V decreased but V decreased more than F and (E) both F and V increased but F increased more than V. It is clear then that either increases or decreases in F (throughput) or volume (fill or distension) could theoretically be associated with a faster rate of passage. In some instances rate of passage measurements have been useful in making inferences about fill in the gastro-intestinal tract. For example, it has been demonstrated that average retention times (ART = V/F) are not altered even though intakes (F) increased markedly. This could only be explained by increases in V which matched increases in F in various locations throughout the gut. Of course, the possibility exists that an increase in ART in one part of the gut could be balanced by a decrease in another part. Thus, a degree of caution is required when relating rate of passage measurements to intake

In conclusion, it is clear that intakes of roughages of moderate quality can be influenced in numerous ways, but, in spite of this, distension of the reticulum and the cranial sac appears to be the main control that is operative to limit intake. The influences mentioned above can alter throughput for a given level of distension and, hence, alter intake but under no circumstances should they be thought of as factors that control intake. Such a distinction between influences over intake and controls is necessary in order that new treatments may be devised to increase the productivity of ruminants consuming roughage diets. Conversely, an understanding of how our present practices increase productivity should allow us to check whether we are correct in our thinking of what controls intake.

PALATABILITY

Palatability has received scanty attention considering its importance in animal production. Palatability has been defined as the hedonic response of an animal to its food depending on taste, smell, flavor and texture (21) and as the relish which an animal shows when consuming any given feedstuff or ration (24). Clearly, productivity and profits will suffer if feedstuffs are being rejected in whole or in part because of dust, rancidity, taste, smell or texture. Molasses often makes a food mixture more acceptable to livestock because of its effect in controlling dust. However, in this instance, the sweet taste itself may be partially responsible for any increases in intake, especially in deer, cattle or goats. This conclusion is based on the comparative responses of these species and sheep to sweet, sour, salty and bitter substances in drinking water (24). These data indicate that there are species differences in both their sensitivity to and tolerance of these tastes. Church (24) has also reviewed the effects of vision, smell and texture or the sense of touch on intake.

Palatability and novelty effects must be differentiated, especially when a new food such as silages are first fed or when a new form of food is given. If cattle are used to whole grain, it may take them some time to get accustomed to ground grain. Similarly, sheep fed mixed hay containing alfalfa were shown in sham feeding studies to require 6 d to adapt to alfalfa pellets. One could not say in these instances that the silage, the ground corn or the alfalfa pellets were unpalatable because the diets were eaten with relish after a short adaptation period. The search for intake stimulants should continue because they could be useful in some instances to shorten these adaptation periods to new foods or to the same food presented in a different form. They may also be useful in masking objectionable tastes or smells arising from feed additives or from concentrates such as malt sprouts or distillers dried grains.

Palatability is clearly a major factor in the selection of food by ruminants when they are grazing, browsing or when they are fed hay composed of high quality leaves and poor quality stems (74). For example, sheep in Scotland will graze grass before heather. The amount of selection occurring is dependent on the variety of plants in the sword, browse or hay as well as on the grazing pressure or the amount of hay fed relative to ad libitum intakes. When there is abundant choice at pasture, Arnold (1) reports that as much as 80% of the diet grazed is taken from species contributing as little as 1% of the available food. Selection is also greater in mature than in young forages and in tropical as opposed to temperate forages. Finally, it is clear that palatability rankings of foods will differ depending on species or type of animals within the species (74). This probably relates back partly to differences in taste.

The effect of palatability may have been seen in a number of studies on the effects of dietary dilution which were reviewed by Baumgardt (11) and Baile and Forbes (6). Intake was often reduced when high dilutions of the starting diet were made with sawdust, vermiculite, perlite, polyethylene and similar diluents. The reductions in intake which occurred at the highest dilutions were at least partly due to palatability (77), but the true extent of this effect cannot be judged until sham feeding studies have been done with esophageal-fistulated sheep. Palatability also seems to have limited the intakes of straw by cattle on some occasions (21) because digesta loads in the reticulo-rumen were found to be less when straw as opposed to hay was fed ad libitum. The experiments of Greenhalgh and Reid (39) involving oral and intra-ruminal feeding of dried grass and straw also support the concept of palatability as a determinant

of roughage intake. Arnold (1) found that decreases in intake at pasture of up to 61% and increases of up to 35% were due to sensory stimuli. For these and other reasons one should not be surprised that the intake of a roughage cannot always be predicted from its digestibility.

The two-choice preference test has been widely used on ruminants and other species to assess the palatability of various chemicals (13, 38). This test does, however, have grave weaknesses. The worst flaw is that the animal consumes the chemical. The amount consumed in solution relative to water could reflect either palatability or the post-ingestive effects of the chemical. The second point, which may or may not be a flaw depending on objectives, is that the chemical is usually carried in water rather than the food which is the usual vehicle for many of the chemicals given to ruminants today. These two disadvantages with the two-choice preference test in testing the palatability of chemicals for inclusion in food were circumvented by using sheep prepared with esophageal fistula (23) as monitors of palatability (47). In these experiments the sheep were maintained on a basal diet of mixed hay but were trained following a deprivation period of 5.5 h daily to eat ground and pelleted alfalfa during a 30 minute period of sham feeding (esophageal plug removed and most of the ingesta recovered in a bag). Sham intakes of the alfalfa pellets in the 30 minute periods increased to plateau values after 6 d. Sheep required a further 8 d to adapt to pellets containing 10% NaCl on the basis of air-dry weight but then, surprisingly, their sham intakes were unaffected by adding up to 20% NaCl to the diet. In fact, their intakes were a little higher on this diet than on the control, the intakes being 1,136, 1,433, 1,309, 1,496 and 1,485 g/30 min for NaCl levels of 0, 5, 10, 15 and 20%, respectively. These results make one conclude that NaCl in food is not unpalatable to sheep and therefore its effect in supplements, etc., to limit intake must arise from its post ingestive effects on the animal. However, the use of the two-choice preference test by Goatcher and Church (38) led them to believe that NaCl was unpalatable because sheep strongly rejected solutions containing more than 2.2% of the chemical. This conclusion would be correct for NaCl in water if there were no postingestive effects of NaCl on intake of the solution. Similarly, sheep were shown to reject solutions of hydrochloric (0.018%), acetic (0.158%), propionic (0.029%) and butyric acids (0.052%) at these relatively low concentrations using the two-choice preference test, whereas sheep with esophageal fistulae did not reduce food intakes until levels of 5, 5, 5 and >3% w/w were offered in the food, respectively (unpublished observations). These and other difficulties with the two-choice preference test indicates that new data are needed to assess basic aspects of palatability when chemicals are given to ruminants in dry food. Much of this work has been done in the author's laboratory but only for sheep and as yet it is essentially unpublished.

Large quantities of poor quality roughage materials exist in most parts of the world. Progress has been made in improving the degradability and the intakes of these materials (cereal straw, corn stover, various industry by-products) by treating them with NH_3, urea, steam or various chemicals to remove lignin, but there appears to be an opportunity of further increasing intakes of these improved roughages by enhancing their palatability. For example, sheep in sham feeding studies consumed more straw which was ground and pelleted and then sprayed with monosodiumglutamate (MSG) and NaCl than they did ground and pelleted alfalfa (46). The straw used was not improved in any way but if it was and if the MSG additions increased consumption in the normal feeding situation, then one might expect ruminants not only to maintain themselves but also to sustain a moderate level of production while feeding on straw plus the N from ammoniation or urea treatment. The sham intake of coarse chopped straw was only 27.4 g/30 min, but this was increased to 155 g/30 min simply by spraying the straw immediately before feeding to add MSG to 4% of the air-dry weight of the untreated straw. Grinding and pelleting the untreated straw increased its intake from 440 g/30 min on the first day of sham feeding to values fluctuating around 1,087 g/30 min from the fourth to the seventh day of sham feeding. This improvement in intake may have been due to an improvement of texture and/or to compacting the straw. Still further improvements in sham

intakes of the ground and pelleted straw were made by spraying the pellets with MSG and NaCl immediately before feeding, the intakes being 1,068 g/30 min for the control pellets sprayed with water and 1,532 g/30 min for the treated pellets. This response must have been due to an improvement in the taste and/or the smell of the straw. Experiments have not been done to ascertain if MSG will increase roughage intakes in practical feeding situations. However, the maximal effect on production with poor quality roughages is likely to be achieved only if (A) the roughage is improved by some technique to increase its degradability, (B) it is mixed with a palatability enhancer and, (C) the diet is compressed in some way before feeding. Conventional grinding and pelleting procedures are not recommended because of handling difficulties and high processing costs.

Recent work on palatability of roughages indicates that the preference for a forage by sheep is strongly related to the rate at which it can be eaten (17, 52). This applies to straw as well as hay.

ENERGY INTAKES IN RELATION TO DIGESTIBILITY

Relationships between voluntary intake and either digestible (DE) or metabolizable energy (ME) contents of the diet or roughage: concentrate ratios are cited frequently in the literature. Intakes are often reported as dry matter (g/d) and as DE or ME (Kcal/d), whereas net energy (NE) is reported only rarely. Publishing intakes in terms of metabolic body size should only be done if body weights are also reported so that intakes can be viewed by themselves uncomplicated by ratios and logarithmic transformations. One might reasonably ask if any of these terms are satisfactory from a mechanistic point of view because an animal does not sense dry matter or cell walls per se nor can it sense calories or differentiate between DE, ME or NE! It can sense distension, osmolality, concentrations of VFA and hormones, as well as temperatures and various other parameters, but these factors are rarely reported in this context. We seem to have lapsed rather uncritically into simply repeating the theories that, within a wide range of diets, intake is controlled either by physical or chemical and physiological factors as will be recounted below. The point in this argument is that we must look more often beyond the nutritional niceties such as the various expressions of energy intakes over a spectrum of diets and focus on what is being sensed to limit intake. Ideally, we need data on (A) what we suspect is being sensed, (B) intakes of dry matter, (C) intakes of indigestible dry matter and/or cell walls and (D) intakes of DE, ME and NE all related to digestibility or some other measure of energy available in the diet determined in the species concerned at ad libitum intakes. If digestibility in this situation is determined at maintenance levels of feeding, the data are confounded because the effect of intake on digestion is not accounted for. The use of DE intakes might be most relevant if a component in the food or its metabolite(s) was being sensed by receptors in the gut wall to generate satiety signals. On the other hand, ME or NE intakes may be most relevant depending on whether the satiety signal is closely related to the total energy available to the cells for metabolism or to the energy available for maintenance and production after losses are incurred for heat increment. One of the ramifications from assuming that DE intakes are constant for high energy diets is that NE intakes will be increasing with increasing proportions of concentrates in the diet. This occurs because the fraction of DE or ME that is NE is larger as the DE concentration of the feed increases. The references cited below for dairy cattle, beef cattle and sheep indicate clearly that we should start again with open minds to re-define the relationships between these aspects of energy metabolism and intake and that we should relate the various categories of energy to factors which can be sensed by ruminants and therefore constitute signals of satiety.

A review of the literature indicates that energy intakes by cattle (lactating cows and steers) are lower for high concentrate or all grain diets than they are for diets containing in some instances substantial amount of roughage. This is contrary to what is commonly believed, namely that energy intakes increase up to a certain energy density of diet and thereafter remain constant. This apparently erroneous concensus appears to have been originated by Montgomery and Baumgardt (60). They proposed that

distension of the rumen limited intakes of roughages before ruminants could maximize their energy intakes and that chemostatic and thermostatic factors were operative to limit energy intakes at a constant maximal value when high-concentrate diets or other diets with a high nutritive value were fed. A similar scheme for the control of intake was published by Conrad et al (25), but they wrote of physical and physiological factors limiting dry matter intakes below and above 67% dry matter digestibility respectively.

Dairy Cows

The early review of Kesler and Spahr (53) and the data of Conrad et al (26) indicated that diets containing between 40-50% roughage maximized nutrient intake in high-producing dairy cows. Similarly, the papers of Bines and Davey (16) and Wangsness and Muller (76) demonstrated that energy intakes (DE or TDN) by dairy cows are maximized with diets containing betwen 20 and 50% roughage. Flatt et al (32, 33) have also reported 7-9% higher intakes of DE for diets containing 60:40 ratios of roughage to concentrates than for ratios of 20:80. Other researchers have found maximal energy intakes (TDN) with diets containing about 15.7% crude fiber (69). Freer and Campling (36) reported that dry cows consumed much more digestible organic matter as dried grass than as concentrates or hay. The recent paper of Mertens (57) demonstrates that outputs of 4% fat-corrected milk and, perhaps, energy intakes are related in a quadratic manner to the NDF content of the diet. The optimal level of NDF supporting maximal output depended on the level of production of the cow (45% for <14 kg/d; 27% for >29 kg/d). Although he did not measure digestibility in the experiments, he was confident that cows given diets containing <25% NDF had lower than optimal energy intakes because of problems with acidosis, diarrhea and intermittent eating patterns (personal communication). Adverse effects of high-grain feeding on health of the cows was also mentioned by Kesler and Spahr (53). Thus, regardless of the way of expressing the results, it appears that lactating cows will consume less energy from an extremely high energy diet containing mainly grain than they will when the mixture of grain and roughage is such that rumen function is within physiological limits. Whether the intake reductions with high concentrate diets are due to the so called physiological factors, pathophysiological factors or health problems appears to be an open question. However, when a number of experiments apparently contradict the general hypothesis, it seems prudent to ask why and, if necessary, to question the validity of the original hypothesis.

Beef Cattle

The situation with finishing most classes of feedlot cattle in the USA is to reserve the feeding of the "hottest" ration (highest proportion of concentrates) for periods of about 60 d at the end of the finishing periods (64). However, some roughage is usually still fed to maintain rumen function and to prevent the development of feedlot diseases (acidosis, rumenitis and associated disorders). Nevertheless, the important piece of data from the point of view of the control of food intake is the roughage-concentrate ratio or energy concentration in the diet which allows feedlot cattle to maximize consumption of DE. According to Plegge et al (65), maximal ME intakes in feedlot cattle were achieved by having dietary energy concentrations of 3.1-3.2 Mcal ME/kg, which is just short of the value of 3.35 for corn grain. Dry matter intakes started to decline with energy concentrations between 2.5-2.8 Mcal ME/kg. Similarly, ME intakes of Hereford steer calves given only whole or crimped corn were 86% of intakes of diets containing these types of corn plus 4.5 or 6.8 kg corn silage/head/d (71). Calculations from the data of Woody et al (79) also show that intakes of DE and ME by Hereford cattle fed diets of 96% corn were only 78% of corresponding intakes of silage diets containing 67% corn (gave maximum DE and ME intakes). With Charolais crossbred steers the DE and ME intakes of the 96% corn diet were 83% of those for silage diets containing 91% corn (also gave maximal DE and ME intakes in these animals). NE intakes for maintenance and for gain were both maximized with the 91% corn diet given to the Charolais steers. However, with the Hereford steers, the NEm was maximized with 67% corn in the diet, whereas the NEg was the greatest with 96% corn. DE intakes of beef steers in the studies of Joanning et al (48) were also about

9% lower for an all-grain diet than they were for a diet containing a 30:60 mix of immature corn silage and cracked corn grain. Thus, in beef cattle given fattening rations, energy intakes appear to be maximized with diets containing a mixture of roughage and concentrations, although the amount of roughage required to maximize intake seems to be less than that required in the dairy cow. From a practical point of view, the relatively high costs of handling roughages and the lower cost of NE from concentrates would tend to reduce the amounts of roughage fed in feedlots.

Sheep

Lambs given a basic concentrate mixture diluted from 5 to 50% with various inert substances were shown to maximize their intakes of DE with rations containing 2.5 Mcal DE/kg ration (11). The reduction in energy intakes for the diets having lower energy contents could be due to the diets becoming progressively less palatable, although the extent of this effect could only be proven with sham feeding studies. Above this energy value the intakes of DE decreased progressively with increases in concentration of dietary energy, but in the text it is stated that DE intake remained constant. This probably reflects a lack of significance in negative value for slope. However, one could possibly question whether the line through the data to the right of 2.5 Mcal DE/kg actually fits the data as the real slope is probably more negative than that shown. It may also be improper to arbitrarily divide that data into two linear components because a curvilinear relationship may be more appropriate. The difference between the maximal energy intake displayed in Fig. 3 of Baumgardt (11) (225 Kcal/kg $BW^{0.75}$) and the intake at the highest energy level is substantial, being about 32 Kcal/kg $BW^{0.75}$) or 14% of the maximal value. Owen et al (62) also reported that lambs given mixtures of ground oat husks (0-40%) and barley (32-85%) controlled their consumption to achieve the same energy intakes of the various diets, but again, their data for Experiments I and II do not appear to support this statement. If anything, their data indicate that maximal digestible dry matter intakes were achieved with between 20-24% oat husks and 60-64% barley in the pelleted ration. Donefer et al (29) likewise stated that the DE intakes of lambs fed pelleted mixtures of alfalfa and barley (85:15 to 40:60) "remained essentially constant with increasing increments of barley", but, the fact that intakes of pure alfalfa exceeded those of the mixtures of alfalfa and barley by about 14% has been overlooked. Just prior to this, Brent et al (20) reported that lambs consumed about 10% less DE when the pelleted ration contained 60% as opposed to 10% sorghum. The statistical significance of this difference is not known. Ewes also consumed 15% less DE when given a diet having a forage:concentrate ratio of 21:79 compared with one having a ratio of 58:42 (12). These five studies all indicate that sheep consume less DE when high-concentrate as opposed to low- to moderate-concentrate diets are fed.

In conclusion, dairy cows and beef cattle appear to maximize their energy intakes when the diet consists of a mixture of roughage and concentrates. The energy intakes attained when all concentrate diets are fed can be expected to be less than when the diet contains roughage, the amount of roughage needed to maximize intake appearing to depend on species, age of animal and, in cows, on the level of milk production. Sheep appear able to consume the most energy with diets containing relatively large amounts of alfalfa compared with concentrates. The work of Baumgardt (11) should not be allowed to cloud this issue because the high concentrate diet used in that experimentation was diluted with inert substances and the low intakes that were obtained at high dilutions were shown in part to be a reflection of the unpalatable nature of these diets (77).

The concepts outlined above are not commonly recognized in the food intake literature, but should be given more consideration as it will help us to understand what controls food intake by ruminants. The conclusions formed seem to be such a radical departure from what is in the literature that one is almost reluctant to state them, but, as mentioned previously, the purpose is to stimulate critical thinking and research. Specifically, we need to understand better why roughage helps ruminants to maximize energy intakes and we also must decide if the intake of energy from high-concentrate diets is being limited by physiological or pathophysiological factors.

BODY FAT AND FOOD INTAKE

It is difficult to explain why we hang on so tenaciously to the concept that body fat produces a signal(s) which limits intake when it appears that most if not all domesticated animals in North America will become extremely fat if a management scheme is not in place either to curtail the development of fat or to slaughter the animals before excessive fat is deposited. It is well recognized that feedlot operators have to be extremely careful not to feed their animals too long and thus allow the fat buildup on the carcasses to become excessive. We also have fat cows, fat bulls, fat broiler chickens, fat pigs and fat sheep. The question about body fat and energy intake was addressed specifically in the experiment of Blaxter et al (19) with sheep grown to maturity on pelleted diets fed ad libitum for 4.5 years. They demonstrated conclusively that the concept of fat being able to generate signals which subsequently limit intake is clearly untenable. If domesticated animals ever had such a mechanism in place, it appears now to have been bred out of them. The role of fat in intake control is supportable in rats (35), but does not appear to apply to ruminants or other classes of domesticated animals. Blaxter et al (19) mentioned that there were several episodes in which individual animals (very large and fat) refused to eat for days at a time without apparent reason after two years of feeding. However, this cannot be construed in the light of their entire data to mean that some signal originated from the fat depots to limit intake. One way that fat appears to limit intake in ruminants is by decreasing the amount of contents held in the reticulo-rumen as was illustrated in Fig. 10-2 and explained in the text in the section entitled "Factors influencing roughage intake". A decrease in daily food intake by sheep in response to prolonged intravenous infusions of oleic and palmitic acids indicated to Vandermeerschen-Doize and Paquay (72) that these acids might be intermediaries in the long-term control of voluntary food intake in ruminants. However, it is difficult to understand how this would work because plasma levels of free fatty acids increase during fasting or fat mobilization, exercise and other forms of stress, whereas they can either increase or decrease with feeding (Baile and

214

Forbes, 6; pp. 182, 187). Others have suggested that the increases in plasma free fatty acids that occur with starvation might act as a signal to induce feeding (6). DeJong (27) is skeptical about free fatty acids in plasma having a role in the short-term control of intake whereas Journet and Remond (51) obviously think that free fatty acids control intake. It is clear that the whole area of fat, free fatty acids and the control of food intake is loaded with controversy at the present time.

CONCLUSIONS

(A) There appears to be a lack of critical thinking about what limits the intake of food by ruminants. Questionable concepts include the commonly held beliefs (a) that a constant level of factor "x" should act as a signal of satiety at all times, (b) that stores of body fat produce a signal which acts as a long-term control over intake and depresses consumption of food, and (c) that energy intakes with diets exceeding a certain proportion of concentrates or energy density are constant. There are good reasons to look beyond intakes of dry matter, DE, ME, and NE to identify more precisely the factors limiting intake. A preoccupation with energy intakes appears to have stifled research into the control of intake and has hindered progress toward the goal of manipulating intake to increase production.

(B) Palatability is an important determinant of food intake. However, if one assumes that palatability is not limiting consumption, then, the intake of most diets is probably limited by a mixture of physical, hormonal and chemical factors. The relative importance of the different signals of satiety in limiting intakes of roughage, mixed diets, high concentrate diets, silage and diets which are ground

and pelleted needs to be quantified. There is also a need to assess the role of pathophysiological factors in limiting the intakes of high concentrate diets by ruminants.

(C) There appears to be less emphasis being given to VFA as signals of satiety, but more attention to endocrine factors such as insulin, glucagon, growth hormone and gastrointestinal hormones.

(D) There is a need to quantify more accurately the energy concentration of the diet or the roughage concentrate ratios which will maximize energy intakes by different species of ruminants and by classes within species. The data reviewed indicate that there may be differences in this regard between cows in lactation, beef cattle and lambs, but species comparisons cannot presently be made with confidence because no one has compared these species on a standard set of diets ranging from all roughage to all concentrate.

(E) Little is understood about how long-term controls change food intake by ruminants. Research into these areas is needed because, if the mechanisms are understood, there appears to be a potential here for manipulating the animal in various ways to substantially increase intake and production.

(F) A distinction should be made between the factors which control intake (sensed by definition) and those which influence intake (not sensed by the animal). The present feeding practices which increase the intakes of roughages by ruminants appear to be acting mainly by influencing the rate of degradation and the clearance (throughput) of plant material in the reticulo-rumen. Changes in N status may also be involved. Ad libitum intakes are however ultimately controlled largely but perhaps not exclusively by distension of the reticulo-rumen (reticulum and cranial sac).

Literature Cited

1. Arnold, G.W. 1970. In: Physiology of Digestion and Metabolism in the Ruminant, pp. 264-276. Phillipson, A.T., ed. Oriel Press, Newcastle upon Tyne, UK.
2. Baile, C.A. 1977. In: Feed Composition, Animal Nutrient Requirements and Computerization of Diets, pp. 472-483. Fonnesbeck, P.V., L.E. Harris and L.C. Kearl, eds. International Feedstuffs Institute, Logan, Utah.
3. Baile, C.A. and M.A. Della-Fera. 1981. J. Dairy Sci. 64:1140.
4. Baile, C.A. and M.A. Della-Fera. 1984. Fed. Proc. 43:2898.
5. Baile, C.A. and M.A. Della-Fera. 1984. J. Animal Sci. 59:1362.
6. Baile, C.A. and J.M. Forbes. 1974. Physiol. Revs. 54:160.

215

7. Baile, C.A. and J. Mayer. 1970. In: Physiology of Digestion and Metabolism in the Ruminant, pp. 254-263. Phillipson, A.T., ed. Oriel Press, Newcastle upon Tyne, UK.
8. Balch, C.C. and R.C. Campling. 1962. Nutr. Abstr. Revs. 32:669.
9. Bauman, D.E. 1984. In: Herbivore Nutrition in the Subtropics and Tropics, pp. 505-524. Gilchrist, F.M.C. and R.I. Mackie, eds. The Science Press (Pty) Ltd of Donker Holdings (Pty) Ltd., Craighall, South Africa.
10. Bauman, D.E. and S.N. McCutcheon. 1985. In: Control of Digestion and Metabolism in Ruminants, pp. 436-455. L.P. Milligan, W.L. Grovum and A. Dobson, eds. Prentice-Hall, Inc., Englewood Cliffs, NJ.
11. Baumgardt, B.R. 1970. In: Physiology of Digestion and Metabolism in the Ruminant, pp. 235-253. Phillipson, A.T., ed. Oriel Press, Newcastle upon Tyne, UK.
12. Baumgardt, B.R., L.F. Krabill, J.L. Gobble and P.J. Wangsness. 1977. In: Feed Composition, Animal Nutrient Requirements and Computerization of Diets, pp. 464-469. Fonnesbeck, P.V., L.E. Harris and L.C. Kearl, eds. International Feedstuffs Institute, Logan, Utah.
13. Bell, F.R. 1959. Vet. Rec. 71:1071.
14. Bell, F.R. 1984. J. Animal Sci. 59:1369.
15. Bines, J.A. 1971. Proc. Nutr. Soc. 30:116.
16. Bines, J.A. and A.W.F. Davey. 1970. Brit. J. Nutr. 24:1013.
17. Black, J.L. and P.A. Kennedy. 1984. Australian J. Agr. Res. 35:565.
18. Blaxter, K.L. and A.W. Boyne. 1982. J. Agr. Sci. 99:611.
19. Blaxter, K.L., V.R. Fowler and J.C. Gill. 1982. J. Agr. Sci. 98:405.
20. Brent, B.E., D. Richardson, W.S. Tsien and C.S. Menzies. 1961. J. Animal Sci. 20:526.
21. Campling, R.C. 1970. In: Physiology of Digestion and Metabolism in the Ruminant, pp. 226-234. Phillipson, A.T., ed. Oriel Press, Newcastle upon Tyne, UK.
22. Campling, R.C. and I.J. Lean. 1983. In: Nutritional Physiology of Farm Animals, pp. 457-475. Rook, J.A.F. and P.C. Thomas, eds. Longman, London.
23. Chapman, H.W. and W.L. Grovum. 1984. Can. J. Animal Sci. 64 (Suppl):106.
24. Church, D.C. 1971. In: Digestive Physiology and Nutrition of Ruminants. Vol. 2. Nutrition, pp. 737-762. Church, D.C., ed. and publisher, Corvallis, Oregon.
25. Conrad, H.R., A.D. Pratt and J.W. Hibbs. 1964. J. Dairy Sci. 47:54.
26. Conrad, H.R., J.W. Hibbs and A.D. Pratt. 1966. J. Dairy Sci. 49:1038.
27. DeJong, A. 1985. In: Control of Digestion and Metabolism in Ruminants, pp. 459-478. L.P. Milligan, W.L. Grovum and A. Dobson, eds. Prentice-Hall, Inc., Englewood Cliffs, NJ.
28. Deetz, L.E. and P.J. Wangsness. 1981. J. Animal Sci. 53:427.
29. Donefer, E., L.E. Lloyd and E.W. Crampton. 1963. J. Animal Sci. 22:425.
30. Egan, A.R. 1965. Australian J. Agr. Res. 16:463.
31. Ellis, W.C. 1978. J. Dairy Sci. 61:1828.
32. Flatt, W.P. et al. 1969. In: Energy Metabolism of Farm Animals, pp. 221-234. Blaxter, K.L., J. Kielanowski and G. Thorbek, eds. Oriel Press Ltd.
33. Flatt, W.P., P.W. Moe, A.W. Munson and T. Cooper. 1969. In: Energy Metabolism of Farm Animals, pp. 235-251. Blaxter, K.L., J. Kielanowski and G. Thorbek, eds. Oriel Press Ltd.
34. Forbes, J.M. 1980. Ann. Zootech. 29:189.
35. Forbes, J.M. 1983. In: Nutritional Physiology of Farm Animals, pp. 177-202. Rook, J.A.F. and P.C. Thomas, eds. Longman, London.
36. Freer, M. and R.C. Campling. 1963. Brit. J. Nutr. 17:79.
37. Gallouin, F. and M. Focant. 1980. Reprod. Nutr. Develop. 20:1563.
38. Goatcher, W.C. and D.C. Church. 1970. J. Animal Sci. 30:377.
39. Greenhalgh, J.F.D. and G.W. Reid. 1971. Brit. J. Nutr. 26:107.
40. Grovum, W.L. and G.D. Phillips. 1978. Brit. J. Nutr. 40:323.
41. Grovum, W.L. 1979. Brit. J. Nutr. 42:425.
42. Grovum, W.L. 1981. Brit. J. Nutr. 45:183.
43. Grovum, W.L. 1982. J. Physiol. 326:55P.
44. Grovum, W.L. 1983. Appetite: Journal for Intake Research 4:202.
45. Grovum, W.L. 1984. In: Herbivore Nutrition in the Subtropics and Tropics, pp. 244-268. Gilchrist, F.M.C. and R.I. Mackie, eds. The Science Press (Pty) Ltd of Donker Holdings (Pty) Ltd. Craighall, South Africa.
46. Grovum, W.L. 1984. Can. J. Animal Sci. 64 (Suppl):150.

216

47. Grovum, W.L. and H.W. Chapman. 1982. Proc. Nutr. Soc. 41:73A.
48. Joanning, S.W., D.E. Johnson and B.P. Barry. 1981. J. Animal Sci. 53:1095.
49. Jones, D.I.H. and R.W. Bailey. 1974. J. Agr. Sci. 83:105.
50. Jones, G.M. 1972. Can. J. Animal Sci. 52:207.
51. Journet, M. and B. Remond. 1976. Livestock Prod. Sci. 3:129.
52. Kennedy, P.A. and J.L. Black. 1984. Australian J. Agr. Res. 35:551.
53. Kesler, E.M. and S.L. Spahr. 1964. J. Dairy Sci. 47:1122.
54. McClymont, G.L. 1967. In: Handbook of Physiology, Section 6: Alimentary Canal. Vol. 1. Food and Water Intake, pp. 129-137. Code, C.F., ed. American Physiological Society, Washington.
55. Mertens, D.R. 1973. Ph.D. Thesis, Cornell University.
56. Mertens, D.R. 1980. Distillers Feed Conference 35:35.
57. Mertens, D.R. 1983. Cornell Nutr. Conf. for Feed Mfg., pp. 60-68.
58. Moir, K.W., L. Laws and G. Blight. 1975. J. Agr. Sci. 85:39.
59. Monteiro, L.S. 1972. Animal Prod. 14:263.
60. Montgomery, M.J. and B.R. Baumgardt. 1965. J. Dairy Sci. 48:569.
61. Neal, H.D. St.C., C. Thomas and J.M. Cobby. 1984. J. Agr. Sci. 103:1.
62. Owen, J.B., D.A.R. Davies, E.L. Miller and W.J. Ridgman. 1967. Animal Prod. 9:509.
63. Pearce, G.R. and R.J. Moir. 1964. Australian J. Agr. Res. 15:635.
64. Perry, T.W. 1980. Beef Cattle Feeding and Nutrition. Academic Press, New York.
65. Plegge, S.D., R.D. Goodrich, S.A. Hanson and M.A. Kirick. 1984. 45th Minnesota Nutr. Conf.
66. Schalk, A.F. and R.S. Amadon. 1928. N. Dakota Agr. Exp. Stn. Bull. No. 216.
67. Seoane, J.R., M. Côté, P. Gervais and J.P. Laforest. 1981. Can. J. Animal Sci. 61:403.
68. Seoane, J.R., M. Côté, and S.A. Visser. 1982. Can. J. Animal Sci. 62:473.
69. Spahr, S.L., A.E. Branding, E.M. Kesler and W.H. Cloninger. 1966. J. Dairy Sci. 49:1046.
70. Suttie, J.M., R.N.B. Kay and E.D. Goodall. 1984. Livestock Prod. Sci. 11:529.
71. Vance, R.D., R.L. Preston, V.R. Cahill and E.W. Klosterman. 1972. J. Animal Sci. 34:851.
72. Vandermeerschen-Doize, F. and R. Paquay. 1984. Appetite 5:137.
73. Van Soest, P.J. 1965. J. Animal Sci. 24:834.
74. Van Soest, P.J. 1982. Nutritional Ecology of the Ruminant, pp. 276-293. O & B Books, Inc., Corvallis, Oregon.
75. Vera, R.R., J.G. Morris and L.J. Koong. 1977. Animal Prod. 25:133.
76. Wangsness, P.J. and L.D. Muller. 1981. J. Dairy Sci. 64:1.
77. Welton, R.F. and B.R. Baumgardt. 1970. J. Dairy Sci. 53:1771.
78. Wheeler, W.E., D.A. Dinius and J.B. Coombe. 1979. J. Animal Sci. 49:1357.
79. Woody, H.D., D.G. Fox and J.R. Black. 1983. J. Animal Sci. 57:710.

Grovum, W. L., A New Look at What Is Controlling Food Intake. International Symposium on Feed Intake by Beef Cattle. Oklahoma City, November 20-22, 1986. Organizer, Dr. F. N. Owens et al.

11 WATER AND ITS FUNCTIONS, REGULATION AND COMPARATIVE USE BY RUMINANT LIVESTOCK

by Victor R. Squires

INTRODUCTION

Water is a nutrient in the real sense of the word and, as with any other nutrient, there is a continual excretion and loss which has to be supplemented. The concentration of water in the animal body must be kept as constant as possible for normal tissue function to be maintained.

Water molecules are by far the most numerous of any in a mammal and represent about 99% of all molecules. Five to ten times more moles of water move through cells than moles of oxygen, and the water flux is about 100 X as great as the molecular turnover of all other substances. The rate of energy use in the cell is linked with and probably determines the flux of water in which the other cell processes take place. According to Macfarlane and Howard (8) about 45% of bodyweight is intracellular water and 25% is extracellular, divided between plasma (5%) and interstitial fluids (20%).

BODY WATER POOL

For many of the world's ruminant livestock it would be reasonable to assume that they would use or turnover, between 5 and 30% of their body water pool daily. The body water pool is taken as 70% of liveweight (Table 11-1). There is a strong correlation between metabolic rate and bodywater turnover; a lower metabolism uses less water for the transfer of nutrients and for evaporative cooling because less heat is generated. Thus, metabolic rate and water turnover are higher in young and highly productive animals, and lower in older or less productive animals (8).

The rate at which mammals use water is slightly faster than the rate at which they use energy because water is used in cooling as well as metabolism. Water turnover is best expressed in relation to the size of the body pool rather than to bodyweight, because the ruminant body contains varying amounts of fat and bone. Table 11-2 shows the water content of a lean young steer which was fed a dry ration at or about maintenance level. It

Table 11-1. Body water pools in different species of livestock in relation to body size.[a]

Species	Mean weight, kg	Metabolic weight, $kg^{0.75}$	Body water* pool, $l^{0.82}$
Camels	350	80.92	91.02
Cattle	300	72.08	82.21
Sheep	30	12.82	12.14
Goats	25	11.18	10.45

[a] Adapted from King (4)
*Body water pool (I) is taken as 70% of bodyweight.

Table 11-2. Water content of carcass components of a 2-year-old *Bos indicus* steer.[a]

Carcass component	Weight, kg	Water content %	Water content I*
Slaughter loss	7.0	80[†]	5.6
Blood	7.2	81	5.8
Hide	18.0	67	12.0
Horns	---	--	6.9
Head	13.0	54	---
Feet	6.0	49	2.9
Heart, diaphragm, respiratory, urinary and genital tracts	5.6	72	3.8
Urine and bile	0.1	90[†]	0.1
Liver	2.4	72	1.7
Contents of forestomachs	18.8	86	16.1
Contents of small intestine	4.3	90	3.9
Contents of large intestine	4.9	82	4.1
Gut wall	10.9	80	8.8
Dissectable fat: internal	3.4	40	1.4
Dissectable fat: subcutaneous, intermuscular, hump	11.2	47	5.3
Butcher's bone: legs	14.6	20	2.9
Butcher's bone: loin	2.8	42	1.2
Butcher's bone: neck and thorax	7.7	34	2.6
Carcass lean	74.3	75	56.0
Kidney	0.3	75	0.3
Dissection loss	3.6	80[†]	2.9
Total or average	216.1	67	144.3

[a] From King (4)
*Body water pool (I) is taken as 70% of fresh weight of body component.
[†] Estimate

217

218

can be seen that the components with the lowest water content are bone and fat, although the values are higher than the 20% and 6-20%, respectively, reported in the older literature, presumably because of a high proportion of connective tissue. Bone is relatively inert, but fat represents the main energy pool of the animal, with a value of 39.3 KJ/g compared with protein at 18.0 KJ/g and carbohydrate at 17.6 KJ/g. Because of its low water content, an increase in the proportion of fat is often associated with decrease in percentage body water pool. At birth the fat content of the body is negligible and the body water pool is about 77% of bodyweight. As the animal matures, fat is deposited until it accounts for up to 35% of bodyweight in ruminants in temperate regions, while total body water can drop to 50%. It is difficult to measure the fat content of a live animal directly, but it has often been estimated indirectly from the tritium-predicted body water pool. King and Finch (5) have established the following regression

$$y = 60.46 - 0.802 \; x \; (r^2 = 0.798, P < 0.001),$$

where y equals dissectable body fat and x equals tritium-predicted body water pool, all expressed as a percentage of bodyweight of *Bos indicus* steers, with dissectable body fat of <10%. For those who wish to pursue this aspect further, the main considerations are described elsewhere (6).

FUNCTIONS AND REGULATION

Water serves two similar functions in all mammals; intermediary metabolism and cooling. These are discussed in the following section.

Water and Intermediary Metabolism

All of the biochemical reactions and interconversions that take place in an animal require water. The mammalian cell is a complex structure of macromolecules organized to oxidize carbon in order to release energy. Oxygen and carbon, components from which energy are released, are carried through the tissues in a stream of water which transports them from lung or gut through cells and out to the renal filter or evaporative cooler. Within the cells and throughout the extra

cellular spaces of ruminants, water acts as the solvent of absorbed substances, conveying them to and from their sites of metabolism. Waste products, like CO_2, are derived from the catabolic activity of mammalian cells. Water has a role in the transport of such wastes. Water is also required to facilitate removal of undigested particles and waste materials, such as urea, from the body. Urea is the end product of N metabolism and requires water for its elimination. In addition the resulting solutions osmotically control the distribution of fluids within various compartments. Within the body, water movement is reversible between the pools.

Water as a Coolant

Water possesses certain characteristics which are essential to the maintenance of body temperature. The specific heat of water is considerably higher than that of any other liquid (or solid). Many animals rely on the cooling capacity of water as it gives up its latent heat during evaporation, by panting or sweating. As 1 g of water changes from liquid to vapor, whether by panting or sweating, it binds about 2,425 J of heat. In terms of heat exchange this is a very efficient use of water when it it realized that to heat 1 g of water from freezing to boiling point requires only 490 J. Because of this great capacity to store heat, any sudden change in body temperature is avoided. Water has greater thermal conductivity than any other liquid and this is important for the dissipation of heat from deeply situated regions in the body. Many ruminants (such as sheep, goats and cattle) dissipate internal and absorbed heat by evaporation of body water. For example, in one study sweating accounted for 21%, conduction and convection from the skin 16% and respiratory evaporation 5% of the net loss of heat in a *Bos indicus* steer.

These physical properties of water which make it ideal as a heat-regulating medium are enhanced by other purely physiological factors. The mobility of the blood and the rapidity with which it may be redistributed quickly in the body together with the special physical properties makes it a highly efficient body temperature regulator.

The functions of water within the ruminant are basically for intermediary metabolism (as outlined above) or for cooling and have been

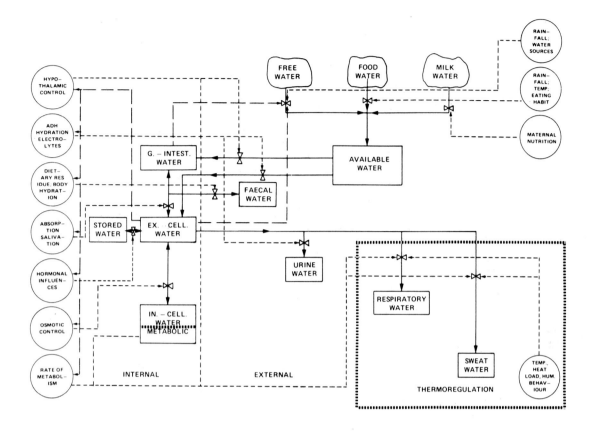

———— Water flow   ----- Information flow   —— —— Feed back information

Figure 11-1. A flow diagram of water-flow in vertebrates. Water is seen to flow into and out of the ruminant's body. Both internal and external factors influence the rates of movement between pools (12).

summarized in a flow diagram (Fig. 11-1). Water is considered to flow from a number of sources outside the body to compartments within it. Most of the flows in this simplified model can be quantified and an energy and moisture budget derived (4). For those who wish to pursue these aspects further, the main components of the intermediary metabolic system are described by Siebert (12) while King (4) elaborates on the energy and water model.

Gains and Losses of Water

Water is gained by drinking free water or milk, by absorbing water through the skin, by eating moist food and by using that gained in the oxidation of food (although food itself may be limiting at times). In specific circumstances certain glands of the animal's body (e.g., salivary, mammary, lachrymal) secrete water.

Water is lost with feces, as urine, in respiration from the lungs and as sweat. In all cases such losses can be associated with energy, either that of food or that of heat derived from food or from radiant sources. The nutritional level affects water requirements (see later section), through the amount of heat produced in metabolism and the amount of feces to be excreted.

Under temperate conditions the loss of water from the intra- and extra-cellular spaces (excluding the gastro-intestinal tract) is small. Less than 5% of body water is lost as urine, in excreting waste metabolites, and insensibly through the skin and respiratory tract. Special adaptations have evolved in ruminants which inhabit the more arid regions. These help to conserve water (see later section).

Regulation of urine flow is a key factor in all animals. The kidney is one of the major organs monitoring electrolyte homeostasis.

Urine flow may be reduced by decreasing renal infiltration as well as by concentrating the tubular infiltrate. Daily volume of urine and its composition are affected by the kind and amount of food ingested and absorbed, water intake, environmental temperature, physical activity being performed, and other factors.

COMPARATIVE USE

The rate at which an animal uses water in a given environment depends on the genetically-determined drives from the limbic cortex and hypothalamus. These determine water intake, while the gut-kidney machinery regulates output. The varying patterns of solar radiation and air temperature interacting with rainfall during seasonal changes of environment alter the flow of water and energy through ruminants. In most animals exposed to heat there is an increase in body fluids, particularly in the extracellular volume. Because there is often a deficiency in food supply during some seasons, this may exacerbate the problem of maintaining the water and energy balance.

Cattle have a high rate of water use (Table 11-3). The camel has only half the water turnover of cattle during the hot season. By comparison with cattle, sheep and goats are economical with water, turning it over at a rate of only 50-60% that of cattle in the same environment. Differences have also been found in water economy between breeds of livestock (8). The economy of water use is a desirable feature for livestock in arid or semi-arid regions, but other factors such as food intake or growth rate may also be important. For example, some livestock overdrink under conditions of unrestricted access. Restricting

Table 11-3. Comparative water metabolism of camel, sheep, goats, and cattle at pasture on the equator.[a]

Species	Body weight, kg	Body solids, %	Water turnover/d	
			ml/kg	ml/kg$^{0.82}$
Cattle (Boran)	197	23	135	*347 ± 12
Sheep (Ogaden)	31	32	107	197 ± 29
Goats (Somali)	40	31	96	185 ± 32
Camel (Somali)	520	30	61	188 ± 37

[a] From Macfarlane and Howard (8)
*Mean ± standard deviation

access to water may be beneficial under some circumstances (see later section).

Adaptation

Because of the large external component in the regulation of water intake and loss, behavioral avoidance of extreme climatic conditions plays a large part in water conservation. Internal or physiological processes support behavioral adaptations. The ability to endure harsh environments is made possible by selection of milder conditions (microhabitats) which lessens the stress on animals and sometimes removes the need for physiological adaptations. This is particularly critical in arid regions. Adaptation of domestic ruminants (camel, sheep, goats and *Bos indicus*) to arid conditions involves, of necessity, the regulation of rate of water loss from the body.

An additional characteristic is that of being able to rehydrate rapidly. For example, cattle can replace 72-79% of the weight lost after a period without water in the first rapid fill. Sheep can replace 65-70% and camels 60-62% (12). Cattle pass into diuresis within 4 to 6 h, but camels reduce excretion of water and Na for a day or more while the ingested water is made isotonic with the plasma (12).

Animals with low water turnover rates, like the camel or goat, have a better chance of survival during water deprivation or drought than animals with high water turnover such as cattle. Some desert-adapted animals such as camels, sheep, gazelle and eland, use about the same quantity of water per unit BW$^{0.82}$ when water is not restricted. Under similar conditions bovids use two to three times the water used by desert-adapted wild ungulates (4). There are some bovids such as boran (*Bos indicus*) and banteng (*Bibos banteng*) types that use a little less than common *Bos taurus* types. The greatest metabolic and physiological strain is placed on mammals during lactation. Efforts of synthesis increase both energy and water consumption rates by 40-60%. For example, lactating camels in some arid environments use 44% more water than non-lactating female camels grazing with them (4).

Water Conservation

One of the ways in which ruminants can conserve water is to reduce fecal water excretion. Fecal water is a potentially larger source of water loss than urine. About one-third to one-fifth of the total daily water loss is in the feces. For instance a bovid of 350 kg body weight, will excrete about 10 ℓ of fecal water/d. A camel of similar weight fed the same diet will excrete only 5 ℓ. Part of this difference is due to fecal output per se and the remainder is due to the lower concentrations of water in the feces egested (12). *Bos taurus* cattle can only reduce fecal moisture content to 60%, and sheep to 50%. In desert animals such as camels, even when ample water is available, fecal water concentration can be kept down to about 50%. Genetically-adapted animals can reduce this value still further with water restrictions.

WATER REQUIREMENTS OF RUMINANT LIVESTOCK

There is a well recognized hierarchy of water need among wild and domesticated ruminants. Camels, sheep and goats are more efficient than cattle in terms of water needs, but all livestock require considerable amounts of water to produce at a high level. The water requirements of ruminant livestock are provided by three sources: drinking water, water in and on forage and metabolic water which is formed by the oxidation of nutrients and body tissues.

Watering Behavior

Drinking is a vital part of the daily activities of livestock in summer. Most ruminant livestock are generally inefficient users of water and have a high rate of water turnover if allowed unrestricted access to water. It is usual under free range conditions for at least one drink to be taken each day in summer; in winter individual animals have been observed to go for 3 d without water. For a watering regime to be adequate for ruminants eating dry forage, the following criteria must be met: the degree of dehydration must not exceed the temporary water holding capacity of the alimentary tract; the animal must have time to drink its fill; and the frequency of watering must be such as to prevent body water loss from reaching the stage of clinical dehydration. Dehydration does not reach a critical level in desert-adapted animals until they have lost 30% of the bodyweight (4).

In general, ruminants can replace 15-20% of their bodyweight at the first drink and 20-25% within 1-2.5 h. The capacity and speed of fluid replacement appears to be higher in more desert-adapted animals. Under herded conditions in Africa or India, a three-day drinking cycle is common for cattle, sheep and goats. Camels can go for longer periods without drinking.

When water availability is restricted, there is a reduction in food intake. The affects of water restriction are felt mainly in the areas of energy production and thermoregulation, but several authors (4) have reported an increase in the efficiency of digestion of fiber when water is restricted.

When the quality of forage is low, free-ranging cattle and sheep voluntarily restrict their intake and turnover of water, thereby controlling their N balance and achieving protein maintenance on diets which would normally be below maintenance requirements. On a low N diet a high water intake and a high urine volume flush urea out of the plasma so that it is not available for recycling to the rumen to stimulate microbial digestion (14).

Water in Forage

It is important to realize the role played by the water content of forage consumed by animals. Significant amounts of water per day may be provided via consumption of fresh, green forage (see Table 11-4). For example, this can amount to 4 ℓ/d for sheep. Sufficient moisture can be obtained from ingested

Table 11-4. Relationship between water drunk and moisture content of forage.[a]

Water intake, ℓ/kg of dry matter	Moisture content of forage, %
3.7	10
3.6	20
3.3	30
3.1	40
2.9	50
2.3	60
2.0	65
1.5	70
0.9	75

[a]From Hyder et al (3)

221

forage to satisfy water requirements of a grazing sheep when the moisture content of the forage is in the range of 65-70%. High levels of water intake from forage are usually associated with high levels of body water turnover. Nonetheless there are occasions when, and ways in which, the body water turnover can be kept below the water intake from forage, so that the animal does not need to drink.

It has been shown experimentally that the productivity of breeding sheep grazing on sown pasture without access to drinking water was not significantly different from that of sheep allowed water although mortality was higher among lactating ewes (7). When forage is dry, it may provide as little as 0.1 ℓ. Sheep and cattle grazing mineralized forage, e.g., *Atriplex*-dominated desert ranges, require considerably more water than is normal (15), and a lack of adequate drinking water would prove fatal in summer. This is despite the relatively high moisture content of the *Atriplex* leaves.

Role of Metabolic Water

The oxidation of nutrients and tissues leads to the formation of water from the H present. Water thus formed may also aid in supplementing water supply. The overall impact is small though, because 1 kg of fat has to be oxidized to produce 1.2 ℓ of water, and 1 kg of protein and carbohydrate only produces 0.5 ℓ (see earlier section). In addition, there is the problem of respiratory loss of water incurred when oxygen is inspired. It has been calculated that in a hot, dry environment (ambient temperature 26°C, relative humidity 10%) an animal loses 23.5 g of respiratory water in the process of producing 12.3 g of metabolic water. As well as water, metabolic heat is generated (418 KJ). Part of this heat (13.6%) is offset by the heat of vaporization of the expired water. If the remainder (361 KJ) had to be dissipated by sweating, it would cost 149 ml of water. The relationship between metabolic water yield and the water that could be required to dissipate the heat of combustion varies with the organic matter being oxidized. Thus, 1 g of fat yields 1 ml of water, but could require 14 ml for vaporization; 1 g of protein or carbohydrate yields about 0.5 ml of water and could require 6.5 ml of sweat.

Schmidt-Nielsen (11) has argued that the role of oxidation is only of value where the vapor pressure gradient between the expired air and the environment is shallow, and when the endogenous heat production is low enough to allow heat storage or dissipation by non-evaporative means, for instance as metabolic rate decreases. Low metabolic rates may be expected to be associated with low rates of water turnover. Then the relative contribution of metabolic water to total input is much higher (15-35%) when the rate of turnover (k) of the body water pool is low (k < 0.05) than when it is high (k > 0.15, metabolic water 5%).

Quantitative Requirements

As there are many factors that affect water consumption, it is difficult to determine the quantitative requirements of livestock. One method is to correlate the intake of water with the quantity of fodder on a dry-weight basis (Table 11-4). Various loadings are used in this approach to account for changes in physiological status such as age, pregnancy and lactation (4). The values derived from this approach are generally satisfactory only in temperate regions, where complications such as extremely high ambient temperatures and saline food and water do not apply but showed better than expected utility when applied to indigenous breeds of livestock in Africa (4). An alternative is to measure the actual consumption by different types of livestock under various combinations of pasture type, season, and geographic location. Not too surprisingly, this amount of documentation has only been collected for a few localities.

There is a dearth of published information on the water consumption by livestock under normal *commercial* management. Some published data, although not all of them, cover extended periods or encompass normal grazing practices. For example, the total amount of water consumed by flocks of sheep over a 12-month period has been measured in Australia (15). Water intake varied drastically with the vegetation on which the livestock grazed. For example, the total water needed by sheep on salt-desert range in Australia was five times greater than for comparable sheep on grassland (2,000 vs 400 ℓ). Water intakes are generally also dependent on season. In summer, if water is available, all species consume a much greater amount than in winter. There is an interaction between diet selected (and its quality) and season of use. For example, livestock on high N diets require more water as do livestock on saline diets.

Environmental temperatures play a significant role in determining water requirements. At an environmental temperature which causes no heat stress, water intake tends to be about 3-5 units per unit of dry matter in adults. As temperatures increase the water requirements rise dramatically (Table 11-5). The impact of cold temperatures on water consumption is well documented from North American studies. Water intake is correlated with the air temperature over a wide range of values (1).

Water turnover increases dramatically during periods when animals rely on evaporative cooling. For example, the amount of water vaporized by a wooly sheep in hot (35°C) weather is in the range of 2-3 ℓ/d. This value will be higher when the animals are involved in physical activity such as walking long distances to water, although the data of King (4) on this subject suggest that for *Bos indicus* cattle in East Africa the extra water cost of walking per se may be negligible if the solar heat load is moderate. For example, when the total solar radiation was 2,140 ± 138 J/cm^2/d, the cost of walking 16 km instead of 8 km/d was an extra 4.4 ml/kg/d for non-lactating animals on a half maintenance ration. When the total solar radiation rose to 2,385 ± 59 J/cm^2/d, the water cost of traveling the extra 8 km was higher by an extra 11 ml/kg/d. The reason appeared to be behavioral. The impact and avoidance of high solar heat loads is discussed in the previous section.

Breeds of livestock, or indeed strains within a given breed, vary in their water requirements. The most important implication of the difference in water requirements relates to the provision of water supplies for livestock. Annual requirements of some breeds and/or classes of livestock can be up to three times as high as for others. Any plan to change the mix of livestock should taken this factor into account. It may require greater water storage capacity and bigger pumps. No less important is the indirect effect of water need on drinking frequency and, concomitantly, the distance trailed to water.

Water Needs of Types of Livestock

The water requirements of cattle are high, especially in summer. Allowing that the quality of water will vary from region to region and that a variable portion of the daily requirement is met from forage-moisture (Table 11-5), a guide to the daily needs of *Bos taurus* cattle might be as in Table 11-6. *Bos indicus* cattle are more efficient water-users, turning over body water at a slower rate. The difference in water use may be as great as 40%.

Young animals require more water than mature stock. The needs of pregnant or lactating animals are even greater.

Influence of Salinity on Water Requirements

Where saline waters are the only source of drinking water, there are additional requirements because extra water is required to flush the salt through the animal's system. Sheep grazing predominantly on salt desert range can ingest up to 200 g of salt/d. They can cope with this load only when adequate water is available to allow the excretory system to do its work. In summer they must drink up to three times as much water as sheep on

Table 11-5. Effect of increasing ambient temperature on water requirements of mature cattle.[a]

Environmental temperature, °C	Water intake, ℓ/kg DM intake
10-15	3.6
15-21	4.1
21-27	4.7
Over 27	5.5-6.4

[a]Cattle over 100 kg live weight, non-pregnant, non-lactating on fresh (non-saline) water.

Table 11-6. Daily drinking water requirement of a *Bos taurus* and a *Bos indicus* bovine.[a]

| Species | Weight, kg | Daily water requirement, kg | | |
		Mean	Theoretical maximum	Practical guideline
*Bos indicus**	350	16.4	56.1	25.0
Bos taurus	400	31.3	65.0	30.0

[a]From King (4) and Church (1)
*Non-lactating

224

grasslands and they may have to trail to water points at least twice a day. In large pastures this salt-induced thirst limits the area grazed and thus increases the risk of over-grazing around water points (13).

Artesian and sub-artesian bores and wells are the most common source of permanent water in many of the world's rangeland grazing areas. As natural water sources (lakes, springs, and soaks) dry up salt concentrations normally increase. These water sources provide water which varies in chemical composition. The dominant ions or anions are chlorides, bicarbonates and sulfates. Bicarbonate waters are highly acceptable to livestock and generally have less than 5,000 ppm of total soluble salts. Some sources are high in nitrates, which may be toxic, or in sulfates which are not tolerated in high concentrations (10). In general, the total salinity is more important than the specific dissolved salts. There are a few exceptions and some chemicals are not tolerated as well as the more common salts found in drinking water (1).

Tolerance of Livestock to Salt

The tolerance of livestock to dissolved chemicals is a matter of considerable interest and has been studied in some detail. Recommended limits for the major elements likely to be found in drinking water are listed in Table 11-7. Camels, sheep and goats have a greater tolerance to dissolved salts than cattle, so these livestock species are commonly grazed in areas where almost sole reliance is placed on saline ground waters. For example, camels can tolerate up to 5.5% of total soluble salts, goats 1.5% and sheep 1.3-2.5%.

There is some interrelationship between genetically-determined low water turnover and tolerance of salt. Tolerance to high salt is related in part to cellular resistance to NaCl. The camel can drink saline water of 850 mM (5%) NaCl concentrations without losing weight. Goats will tolerate 250 mM (1.5%) NaCl and sheep 225 mM (1.3%) with somewhat greater turnover then camels. Cattle live satisfactorily only when salt concentration is below 170 mM. Dehydrated camels may have their plasma Na concentrations raised to 200 meq./ℓ without ill effect. By comparison at 170 meq./ℓ both man and cattle have circulatory difficulty and may die (8).

Sheep and goats can tolerate about 4 mole of Na and K salts daily, but need 10-18 ℓ to

Table 11-7. Safe levels of toxic elements and ions in livestock drinking water.[a]

Element	Level, mg/ℓ[†]	Remarks
Arsenic	1.0	Inorganic oxide, especially from dips.
Boron		Present at <4 mg/ℓ, whereas 450 mg/ℓ inhibits growth.
Cadmium	0.01	Accumulates in liver and kidneys.
Calcium	1,000	<700 mg/ℓ desirable for beef, especially if Mg present.
Chromium	1-5.0	Industrial effluent, but not readily absorbed.
Copper	0.5-2.0	Essential trace element, but could reach toxic level from wide agricultural use.
Fluoride	2.0	Fluorosis can be a problem.
Iron	10.0	Scouring caused by grazing pasture irrigated with high-Fe water.
Lead	0.5	Cumulative poison.
Magnesium	250-500	Predisposes to rickets if Ca content low, sulfate causes scouring.
Mercury	0.002	Health hazard to human beings consuming meat.
Molybdenum	0.01	Only dangerous if accumulated in (irrigated) pasture.
Nitrate (as NO_3^-)	90-200	Sources are deep wells filled by seepage from highly fertile soil, or dams containing much decaying organic matter, e.g., manure.
Selenium	0.02	To compensate for plant ability to concentrate Se.
Sulfate (as $SO_4^=$)	1,000	High Mg sulfate causes severe problems.
Zinc	20	Natural and industrial contamination, but relatively non-toxic.

[a]From Hart (2)

[†]Expressed as elemental concentration except for nitrate and sulfate

wash it through. This does not require an osmolality of urine above 2,500 mole-osmole/ℓ for removal of salts. Tolerance to salinity and voluntary intakes of saline water are apparently related. Variations in intake are most pronounced when livestock are first given saline water, but these can be apparent up to 15 months after initial exposure.

Attempts to separate the effects of taste (palatability) from physiological tolerance by either infusing saline solutions directly into the rumen or offering it as drinking water, suggest that low food intake by sheep is attributed to a low intake of saline water, rather than to a low tolerance to NaCl (15). The combined effects of varying the volume of water ingested and the concentration of salts in the water have also been assessed. The food intakes of the sheep increased as the volumes of either fresh or saline waters were increased from 0.5 to 6 ℓ/d. The addition of NaCl to the water decreased the food intake, but the decrease was restored by an increase in the volume of water given. The increase was approximately 50% for the 1.5% NaCl, and 100% for the 2% solution. The results show that the volume of water consumed is as important as the degree of salinity. Clearly, much of the variation between sheep in tolerance to NaCl observed in other experiments can be accounted for by variations in the volume of water consumed (16).

Experiments with Merino sheep in Australia (10) revealed that ewes and lambs had a lower tolerance to saline water then wether sheep. A concentration of 2% was detrimental to only a few sheep and 1.0% was not harmful to any. Affected animals went off their food, scoured, lost weight and became weak and listless. A post mortem examination of one such sheep showed changes in the lungs, gall bladder and adrenals. Omental and kidney fats were almost completely absent. These experiments showed that sheep differed in their ability to adapt to saline waters. Adaptation is likely to be physiological and not due to adaptation of rumen microflora (15).

One way in which saline drinking water can be a liability is its effect on wool production. There is not much measurable reduction in wool-growth rate until salinity is well above 1% or 1,000 ppm (Fig. 11-2).

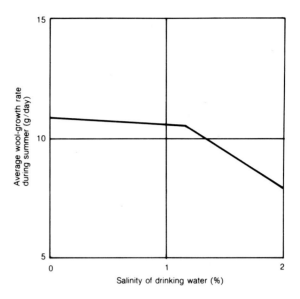

Figure 11-2. One way in which saline drinking water can be a liability is its effect on wool production. There is not much measurable reduction in wool-growth rate until salinity is well above 1% (data of A.D. Wilson).

CONCLUSIONS

Most livestock have to drink at least every other day to be productive, and every few days to survive. The provision of water is therefore of prime importance in all animal production systems. The overall water cost of animal production is rarely calculated, but a rough estimate can be made using a number of assumptions about body weight, body water pool and rates of water turnover. A 4-year-old steer weighing 400 kg would have used about 28 tons of water. McMillan (9) estimated that the total amount of water (including that required to grow the forage) to produce 1 kg of steak was 110 metric tons. Such information serves to point up the significance of water to livestock production systems.

The problems of providing water for livestock vary with different species and breeds of livestock and the ecological zone in which livestock are raised. It raises questions about species mixes, e.g., sheep and goats or goats and cattle and about breed selection.

Modern strategies for livestock production require exogenous inputs of skills, equipment and money. A fundamental element of these strategies is the ability to provide quality drinking water at sites where water is required

226

and in sufficient quantity to obtain optimum production from the class of livestock being raised.

Under rangeland conditions successful livestock management is the art of balancing production objectives against highly unpredictable and variable forage and water resources (13). In more intensive management systems the problems are mainly related to cost. Clearly, there is an optimum level of water provision but as the costs of supplying and maintaining livestock water increases judgments must be made. This is the act of management. It is hoped though that the consideration raised in this chapter will assist the decision-maker.

Literature Cited

1. Church, D.C. 1979. Digestive Physiology and Nutrition of Ruminants. Vol. 2 – Nutrition, 2nd Ed. O and B Books, Inc., Corvallis, Oregon.
2. Hart, B.T. 1974. A Compilation of Australian Water Quality. Australian Water Res. Council Tech. Paper No. 7, Canberra.
3. Hyder, D.N., R.E. Bement and J.J. Norris. 1968. J. Range Mgmt. 21:392.
4. King, J.M. 1983. Livestock Water Needs in Pastoral Africa in Relation to Climate and Forage. ILCA Res. Report No. 7, Addis Ababa.
5. King, J.M. and V.A. Finch. 1982. In: Use of Tritiated Water in Studies of Production and Adaptation in Ruminants, pp. 57-67. IAEA, Vienna.
6. Little, D.A. and R.W. McLean. 1981. J. Agr. Sci. 96:213.
7. Lynch, J.J., G.D. Brown, P.F. May and J.B. Donnelly. 1972. Australian J. Agr. Res. 23:659.
8. Macfarlane, W.V. and B. Howard. 1972. Symp. Zool. Soc. Lond. 31:261.
9. McMillan, J.R.A. 1965. Australian J. Sci. 28:135.
10. Peirce, W.A. 1961. Wool Tech. Sheep Breed. 3(1):123.
11. Schmidt-Nielsen, K. 1965. Desert Animals: Physiological Problems of Heat and Water. Clarendon Press, Oxford.
12. Siebert, B.D. 1978. Function, Regulation and Comparative Use of Water in Vertebrates. In: Water in Rangelands, pp. 153-164. K.M.W. Howes, ed. CSIRO, Melbourne.
13. Squires, V.R. 1985. Livestock Management in the Arid Zone. INKATA Press, Melbourne.
14. Vercoe, J.E. 1971. J. Agr. Sci. 76:487.
15. Wilson, A.D. 1978. Water Requirements of Sheep. In: Water in Rangelands, pp. 178-189. K.M.W. Howes, ed. CSIRO, Melbourne.
16. Wilson, A.D. and M.L. Dudzinski. 1973. Australian J. Agr. Res. 24:245.

12 PROTEIN METABOLISM OF RUMINANT ANIMALS

by Fred N. Owens and Richard Zinn

INTRODUCTION

The ruminant animal has the unique ability to subsist and produce without a source of dietary protein due to the synthesis of microbial protein within the rumen. Ruminal microbes are harvested by the animal and, together with dietary protein which escapes (bypasses) degradation in the rumen, supply the small intestine with protein for digestion and absorption. Digestion of protein and metabolism following absorption appear to be similar for ruminant and non-ruminant animals, so this chapter will concentrate on degradation and synthesis of protein in the rumen. The amount of information about the supply of protein far exceeds the amount of information about the quantities of each amino acid needed by animals under various conditions. Several models of N metabolism have been proposed which amalgamate current concepts and should prove useful in the future for diet formulation to more fully utilize ruminal fermentation and increase productive efficiency of ruminant animals.

IMPORTANCE OF RUMINAL MICROBES AS A PROTEIN SOURCE

Ruminal microbes generally contain between 20 and 60% of their dry matter as crude protein. Rumen bacteria as a whole tend to vary only slightly in crude protein content, averaging 50% (±5%). Protozoa on the other hand, are much more variable, averaging 40% crude protein with a range of 20 to 60%.

The source of N which microbes use for protein synthesis consists of both dietary protein and non-protein N (NPN) as well as N recycled to the rumen for re-utilization (Fig. 12-1). Cattle can grow, reproduce and lactate when the diet contains only NPN as a source of N. This illustrates the synthetic capacity of ruminal microbes. Microbial crude protein (MCP) is flushed to the omasum, abomasum and then on to the small intestine for digestion in concert with other residual materials from the rumen.

Microbial N comprises about 40% of the non-ammonia-N entering the small intestine

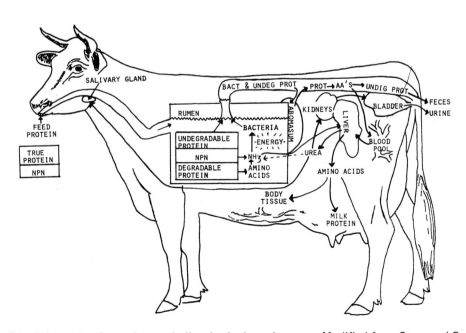

Figure 12-1. Schematic of protein metabolism in the lactating cow. Modified from Stern and Satter (19).

228

with high dietary protein levels, some 60% with low protein diets and 100% with purified NPN-supplemented diets. With lower protein diets or with more extensively degraded dietary sources, the percentage of protein coming from MCP increases though the absolute amount of MCP usually is limited by the amount of some nutrient or energy (ATP) available for microbial growth.

Though protozoa and fungi are active in the rumen, both MCP synthesis and outflow depend primarily upon bacteria. Indeed, half of the MCP in the rumen can be protozoal protein; yet as a proportion of the MCP leaving the rumen, protozoal protein is usually under 10%. Lack of satisfactory isolation and culture procedures for protozoa and for fungi has complicated microbiological study of these organisms. By feeding selective antibiotics and detergents, the types and activities of certain ruminal microbes can be controlled. Reducing the number of protozoa and of specific bacteria in the rumen can decrease proteolysis within the rumen and increase the passage to the small intestine of dietary protein or MCP for the animal.

Ruminal microbes generally adapt within a few days to use new energy or protein sources though longer adaptation times are required for certain compounds like the NPN source, biuret. Inoculation or feeding of adapted organisms has been used to speed development of rumen function in newborn animals or diet adaptation in older animals. These procedures usually show little benefit as microbial species appear ubiquitous. Nevertheless, ruminal manipulation can be used to inhibit specific microbial strains or inefficient metabolic pathways. Such manipulation can increase the efficiency of energy and protein metabolism in the rumen. Overall, efficiency of animal production usually is limited by energy intake and efficiency of energy utilization, not protein supply. However, protein supply can alter feed intake and in this manner alter efficiency of production. Protein consumed in excess of need is used as a source of energy by ruminal microbes or by the animal and is not a complete waste. NPN, in contrast, is useless in excess and can be deleterious if it reduces feed intake or increases energy loss by the animal. Catabolism of either energy or protein in the rumen is not without cost. Loss of energy as heat and as

methane and for synthesis of poorly utilized nucleic acids can reduce efficiency of energy use. If dietary nutrients could be digested in and absorbed from the small intestine instead of being fermented in the rumen, energy would be conserved. Yet, when protein quality is poor or quantity is low or if fermentation is needed to release energy trapped in plant cell walls, the rumen is essential for production. These dietary limitations make energy and protein inefficiencies tolerable.

Although they require the same essential amino acids as non-ruminants, ruminants differ from non-ruminants in quantitative essential amino acid requirements, interorgan essential amino acid transfer and metabolism, as well as in N salvage pathways for both ammonia and nucleic acids.

NUTRITIVE QUALITY OF MICROBIAL PROTEIN

The amino acid composition of duodenal digesta is more constant than amino acid composition of feedstuffs due to dilution with MCP. The nutritive value of microbial protein and complementarity with dietary escape protein has not been fully assessed. Early studies indicated that MCP has a high but not ideal protein quality as measured by biological value (BV). The BV of MCP was found to be from 66 to 87 compared with an ideal value of 100. The BV, true digestibility and net protein utilization (NPU) of protein (6.25 N) have been reported to be 66-87, 74-79, and 63 for ruminal bacteria and 82, 87-91, and 71 for ruminal protozoa. Both digestibility and net protein utilization (BV times digestibility) are higher for ruminal protozoa than for ruminal bacteria. Because numbers of protozoa found in the rumen are variable and outflow may be limited, the true protozoal contribution to the postruminal protein supply is not known at present.

Considering that amino acids make up approximately 80% of the MCP, estimates of BV of MCP suggest that BV of the true proteins present in MCP is near 100. Resembling casein (the principal milk protein), microbial protein tends to be high in lysine and threonine and marginal in methionine relative to requirements by animals for maintenance and growth. Diet appears to have no major influence on the BV of protein of microbial origin, but dietary protein which escapes ruminal digestion will dilute MCP and thereby alter the composition of protein reaching the small intestine. While individual pure strains of ruminal bacteria have been found to have different digestibilities, amino acid profiles are similar.

The quantity and quality of protein reaching the small intestine is modulated by the combined effects of degradation and synthesis in the rumen. When dietary protein has a low BV, the protein reaching the small intestine is complemented by microbial action, but when the dietary protein has a high BV, microbial degradation of dietary protein in the rumen may decrease the BV. Microbial action also alters the quantity of protein which reaches the small intestine. Microbial action reduces the protein supply with natural diets containing a high level of protein but increases the supply with diets low in protein. When the protein level is below 13-15%, crude protein output from the rumen generally exceeds input from the diet, while above this point, diet N input exceeds protein-N outflow. The difference between input and output represents the net balance between absorption of ammonia from the rumen and recycling of N to the rumen. Recycled N enters the rumen either with saliva or by diffusion from the blood stream directly through the rumen wall. Thus, ruminant animals can survive without having essential amino acids in the diet because microbes synthesize essential amino acids in the rumen. However, amino acid synthesis by rumen microbes is not sufficient to meet the essential amino acid needs for rapid growth and high production of domestic ruminants. Level of performance may be increased when additional post-ruminal essential amino acids are provided.

RUMINAL AMMONIA AND NITROGEN RECYCLING

Most ruminal bacteria can use NH_3-N as a source of N though some species require additional N compounds (intact protein or carbon chains of certain amino acids) for most efficient or rapid growth. Bacteria actively absorb NH_3-N while protozoa do not. Although the majority of bacterial strains in the rumen can survive with ammonia as the sole source of N,

measurements with labelled ammonia indicate that in the rumen less than 40% of the bacterial protein passes through the ammonia pool. This suggests that with diets containing intact protein, much of the N used by ruminal bacteria is derived from amino acids or peptides and not from ammonia.

Ammonia in the rumen is a pool with several inputs and exits. Ammonia is derived from degradation of dietary protein and dietary NPN, from hydrolysis of urea recycled to the rumen and from degradation of MCP. Ammonia disappears from the rumen pool due to uptake by microbes, absorption through the rumen wall and flushing to the omasum. Changes in any of these six factors will alter ammonia concentration in the rumen. Ammonia concentration also differs with location in the rumen, often being lower in the floating mat in the rumen than in free liquid. With meal-fed animals, ruminal ammonia concentrations change with time after feeding (Fig. 12-2). With dietary urea, ammonia concentrations usually peak about 1-2 h

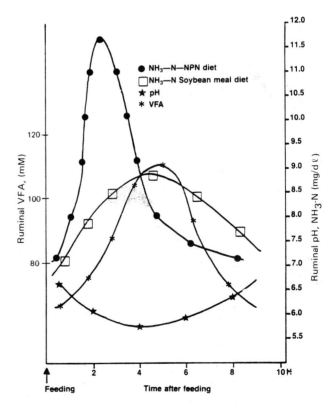

Figure 12-2. Changes in ruminal pH, ammonia and VFA concentrations with time after a meal. Modified from (4).

230

after a meal whereas with diets with plant proteins at high levels, peaks are usually 3-5 h post-feeding. Ammonia absorption increases as ruminal concentration increases; ammonia toxicity often occurs when ruminal ammonia concentration exceeds 100 mg/dl. No peaks in ammonia concentration will be detected with low protein diets. Rate of digestion and feed intake are reduced with low ruminal ammonia concentrations due to starvation of ruminal bacteria for ammonia.

Ammonia Fixation

Ammonia-N is fixed to carbon by ruminal bacteria by two enzymes—glutamine synthetase (GS) and glutamate dehydrogenase (GDH). The concentration of GS is highest when extracellular ammonia-N is low, while GDH is a constitutive enzyme (not subject to metabolic control) which does not vary in concentration. Hence, at higher ammonia concentrations uptake is primarily via the GDH system, but at low ammonia concentrations the GS pathway is more extensively used because GS has a higher affinity for ammonia-N. GS requires one mole of ATP for each mole of ammonium ion fixed, while no ATP is used with GDH action. Hence, if ammonia-N concentration is low, efficiency of microbial growth is reduced because ATP is diverted from growth to the process of ammonia uptake. Ammonia-N flux is generally from extra- to intracellular pools, but concentrations in the two pools appear to be related. For N fixation, extracellular N concentrations must be high enough to maintain minimal intracellular concentrations. An extracellular concentration of ammonia-N slightly above the intracellular concentration (2-3 mmol/l) is required to maximize synthesis of glutamine.

NITROGEN RECYCLING TO THE RUMEN

N is continually recycled to the rumen from the blood stream for re-utilization (Fig 12-1). This conservation mechanism permits ruminant animals to survive on diets very low in N. From 23 to 92% of plasma urea is recycled to the digestive tract, with higher values associated with lower N intake. The quantity of N recycled to the rumen is reduced when ruminal ammonia concentration is high or when plasma urea concentration is low. Plasma urea enters the rumen by two routes—with saliva and by diffusion through the ruminal wall. With forage diets, from 15 to over 50% of the total urea recycled can follow the salivary route. How diet influences route and amount of recycling of N remains to be determined.

Transfer across the rumen wall occurs by attenuated diffusion. When urea diffusing from the blood stream into the ruminal tissues meets urease from adherent ruminal bacteria in the ruminal epithelium, it is hydrolyzed to ammonia and CO_2. Liberated ammonia is attracted by the acid pH of the rumen and trapped by conversion to the ammonium ion, so the process of urea hydrolysis during transfer to the rumen facilitates further transfer. The more acid the rumen, the greater the capture of ammonia as the ammonium ion (NH_4^+). Ammonia has a pK of 9.3, so at a pH of 9.3, half of the ammonia is ionized whereas at a pH of 7.3, 99% of the ammonia is ionized. The ammonium ion (NH_4^+) is less readily absorbed through the rumen wall than the un-ionized (NH_3) form. High ruminal ammonia concentrations reduce recycling either by inhibiting urease in the ruminal wall or by decreasing the diffusion gradient for ammonia.

No urease is produced by animal tissue, but 10-15% of the bacteria which adhere to the ruminal wall produce urease. Urease in the ruminal contents is presumably due to sloughing of epithelial cells which carry adherent bacteria. With adaptation to urea, rate of hydrolysis is reduced due either to substrate or product (NH_4^+) inhibition or to shifts in microbial species. Rapid production of ammonia from urea can precipitate urea or ammonia intoxication as described in Ch. 23.

The amounts of N recycled to the rumen can be as high as 15 g for sheep and 60 g/d for cattle. N recycling to the rumen equals 10-15% of dietary N intake with typical diets. The total amount of N recycled through saliva depends on blood urea concentration and the amount of saliva produced. Because saliva production increases with roughage level in the diet, salivary recycling increases with dietary roughage level. Carbohydrate supply, ammonia-N concentration and pH determine the rate of ammonia recycling through the ruminal wall.

Recycled N becomes useful to the ruminant animal only when it is incorporated into MCP. Incorporation of recycled N causes daily duodenal N flow to exceed N intake when the level of protein in the diet is low. But with higher protein diets, net loss rather than net gain of N in the rumen is more commonly observed. When diets contain below 13-15% protein, recycled N causes duodenal N to exceed dietary N, while above this level of protein, duodenal N is usually less than dietary N, reflecting ruminal absorption of ammonia. Besides N, other nutrients, notably P and S, also are recycled to the rumen. Proportional recycling of S is lower than for N, presumably because it is recycled only via the salivary route.

Absorption of ammonia from the rumen is dependent on ammonia-N concentration and pH. Because the non-ionized ammonia is absorbed while the ammonium ion is not, a lower ruminal pH automatically decreases ruminal absorption of NH_3-N. Inhibiting ammonia absorption (by lowering rumen pH as with, for example, a vinegar drench) is one method to treat ammonia toxicity, but such action is useful only prior to the onset of tetany. Feeding urea generally increases ruminal pH which in turn increases ammonia absorption.

Though urea in the blood stream is harmless, hydrolysis yields ammonia which at high levels is toxic to all mammals. Clinical symptoms of toxicity are well illustrated in a videotape by Osweiler (18) and are described in Ch. 23. Clinical indicators of ammonia toxicity include ruminal NH_3-N concentrations above 100 mg/dl, ruminal pH above 8 and blood plasma ammonia concentrations above 2 mg/dl. Toxicity may be reduced by increasing capacity of the liver to synthesize urea, possibly by supplying higher levels of certain amino acids.

NON-PROTEIN NITROGEN UTILIZATION, SOURCES AND BLOOD LEVELS

Substitution of dietary NPN such as urea for protein from plant and animal sources always lowers the cost of N and often lowers the cost of protein supplementation. Whether total cost of production is decreased depends on changes in production. Production seldom increases with added NPN. If production is maintained, NPN will usually reduce cost, but if production decreases when NPN is substituted for intact protein, cost of production is not likely to be reduced with NPN. Plant and animal sources of protein provide energy and minerals in addition to protein. If the other nutrients contribute to animal performance, they must be considered in least cost formulation of mixed diets which lowers the relative value of NPN. NPN use reduces competition of ruminants with humans and other non-ruminant animals for plant and animal proteins which may be scarce or costly at certain periods of time or in various regions of the world.

Dietary NPN generally is useful only if it provides needed ammonia for ruminal bacteria. Ammonia can have additional effects in the rumen or in tissues. First, ammonia as a base in the rumen maintains pH nearer neutrality which is a desirable range for cellulose digestion. Second, animals fed NPN often develop a meal-feeding pattern for supplement. Frequent feeding should improve efficiency of growth of ruminal microbes. Third, ammonia can be used by the liver to synthesize non-essential amino acids. Supply of non-essential amino acids could limit production under certain conditions. If total N, not just amino acids, are limiting, added ammonia could increase N retention. Finally, added ammonia can be used in the large intestine to meet a N deficiency there.

Supplementation of NPN diets with amino acids and B-vitamins generally has not improved performance though milk production can be stimulated by small additions of dietary protein. Nutrient deficiencies of ruminal bacteria are usually avoided by cross-feeding, as organisms which produce more of a nutrient than they require often secrete surpluses into ruminal fluid. This helps prevent bacterial deficiencies of nutrients such as B-vitamins. Supplemental dietary branched-chain VFA neutralized with ammonia or with Ca, and certain B-complex vitamins, especially choline which is destroyed within the rumen, have proven useful with silage diets for dairy cows.

Feed grade urea, at 287% crude protein, is the most commonly used commercial source of NPN. Enzymes from bacteria in the rumen, in ensiled feeds and in legume seeds hydrolyze urea to CO_2 and ammonia. Ruminal bacteria

232

have the capacity to hydrolyze up to 1 g/ℓ/h which greatly exceeds the amount available, even with diets high in urea. When ruminant animals are fed urea, the rate of ruminal ureolysis decreases slightly. When animals are initially fed a urea diet, feed intake and performance are generally reduced slightly for about a month, possibly due to a reduced supply of essential amino acids from dietary protein which escapes ruminal digestion. Later, performance usually improves as animals adapt to urea. Though much has been discussed about adaptation to urea, reasons for this adaptation period remain undefined. Ruminal microbes need not adapt to urea because urea is normally recycled continuously.

Sources of NPN in addition to urea are sometimes used. Ammonia, in anhydrous or solution form, is typically the least expensive source of NPN to produce. Application of liquid or gaseous ammonia to ensiled crops and low-quality forages helps to distribute the NPN throughout the diet and helps to avoid any reduction in feed intake. Various ammonium salts including the chloride, phosphate and lactate are all useful sources of NPN but are usually more costly per unit of N than urea. By reducing ruminal pH and thereby slowing ammonia absorption, such compounds are safer to feed than urea which will often increase ruminal pH. Other forms of NPN such as biuret, triuret, cyanuric acid and complexes of urea with formaldehyde or molasses have been tested. With these forms of NPN, rate of ammonia release is usually retarded. With certain NPN compounds, binding of ammonia may be so tight that ammonia is never released in the rumen. Others require adapted microbes for hydrolysis.

Feeding behavior of animals often changes when urea is fed. Cattle often eat shorter but more frequent meals with urea-based diets. Toxicity occurs most frequently when hungry cattle unaccustomed to a urea supplement are provided with a supplement containing urea. Ammonia odors initially were thought to be responsible for the reduced feed intake and aversion to urea diets. Ammonia odors can develop from urea supplements during warm, damp weather. However, ammonia odors

strong enough to cause dairy cattle to form tears did not reduce feed intake in one recent study.

Rate of ammonia release has been of interest for many years. Because ruminal ammonia is used for microbial growth and microbial growth is dependent on energy availability, the concept has developed that the rate of ammonia-N liberation should coincide with rate of digestion. Certainly, if ammonia-N production and utilization are not coordinated in time, ammonia concentrations in the rumen fluctuate (Fig. 12-2) and dependency on N recycling mechanisms increases, especially in latter periods of the feeding interval. Many "slow release" compounds were developed based on this concept. Attenuated ammonia release certainly helps avoid ammonia toxicity. NPN toxicity has been reduced through the use of Starea, biuret, certain coating materials and most complexes of urea with formaldehyde or molasses. But slowing the ammonia release rate to more closely parallel the rate at which energy becomes available for bacterial growth has failed to improve utilization of N or performance of cattle in either laboratory or field trials. Feed intake, digestibility, N retention or performance by animals is not improved by slowed release of ammonia. Apparently, the system for recycling of N to the rumen readily compensates for rapid ammonia release, providing concentrations are not toxic. Restated, "slow release" compounds help avoid ammonia intoxication, but do not otherwise appear to improve usefulness of NPN.

In contrast, treatment of low quality forages with ammonia usually increases the rate of fiber digestion and intake of feed. The greatest benefit from ammoniation is noted with straws at specific levels of ammonia (usually about 4% of dry matter) and moisture. Urea treatment of low-quality forages prior to ensiling has had similar effects, providing the urea was hydrolyzed to ammonia. Due to the low cost of ammonia, commercial ammoniation of forage is becoming a popular practice for adding N to a diet and upgrading the quality of the forage. Ammoniation or addition of urea to whole grains also may be useful to control ruminal pH as well as to substitute for grain processing.

ESSENTIAL AMINO ACID REQUIREMENTS

Tissues of cattle and sheep, like those of other animals, cannot synthesize the carbon chain of the essential amino acids, so the ruminant animal relies upon MCP synthesized in the rumen plus dietary protein which escapes digestion in the rumen for its supply of essential amino acids. Little quantitative data on essential amino acid needs for ruminants are available, though several estimates have been made based on net protein deposition coupled with an assumed ideal essential amino acid pattern. These estimates of requirements are useful as approximate values but are no substitute for experimentally determined values.

Requirements for essential amino acids have proven difficult to assess on a quantitative basis due to (a) intervention of ruminal fermentation between the diet and the duodenum and (b) variation in requirements due amino acid utilization for various functions. Wool growth in lambs, for example, responds to an increase in amino acids containing S while responses in cattle to the S-amino acids have been inconsistent or absent. The amino acid composition of protein deposited in tissue and secreted in milk plus the need for maintenance should total the need for amino acids by the animal. If true, both the amounts as well as the ratios of amino acids required will change with the level of production.

The approach generally used to assess quantitative essential amino acid requirements has been to supplement postruminally with the most limiting amino acid and determine the optimum level for supplementation based on the response in N balance, plasma amino acids, albumin and urea concentrations, urea excretion, amino acid oxidation or in feed intake and milk production. By adding the quantity of supplemented amino acid to the amount flowing to the small intestine, one obtains an estimate of the total amount required. Using another approach, all nutrients for animal survival and growth can be supplied parenterally by infusion directly into the gut or into the blood stream. Essential amino acid requirements may be altered because this method alters digestive function. Essential amino acid requirements for lactation are now being assessed by the parenteral feeding method.

Essential amino acid requirements are influenced by the growth rates of the animals. Animals in metabolism stalls often have reduced feed intake and growth rates. Hence, essential amino acid requirements will be underestimated. Procedures to determine essential amino acid requirements under commercial production conditions have not been developed. To prevent amino acid degradation in the rumen, supplemental amino acids can be "bypassed" using the reticular groove reflex or by coating the test amino acid with chemicals to prevent ruminal destruction. Use of such enteric coatings and ruminally stable amino acid complexes simplifies assessment of specific amino acid deficiencies under production conditions but provides no information on the total requirement for essential amino acids. Chemicals which specifically decrease degradation of amino acids within the rumen also may prove useful in the future.

Supplementation with specific ruminal escape amino acids may prove economically feasible under certain feeding conditions, especially when amino acid demand is high or when protein intake is very low. However, under many diet and animal conditions, response to an increased amino acid supply with commerical diets should not be expected. Diets reformulated to combine amino acid supplementation with greater use of NPN may become economically feasible in the future.

LIMITS OF MICROBIAL PROTEIN SYNTHESIS

The quantity of MCP which can be synthesized within the rumen is limited by the amount of energy (quantity of ATP or digestible organic matter) available for the microbes and the efficiency with which microbes use available energy. The various requirements and inputs for microbial growth are shown schematically in Fig. 12-3. Both of these factors appear quite variable in vivo. Measurement of MCP production in the rumen is limited by accuracy of the analytical methods available, so extrapolation from in vitro methods has been necessary.

The benefit of added amino acids on MCP synthesis remains controversial. Most bacterial

234

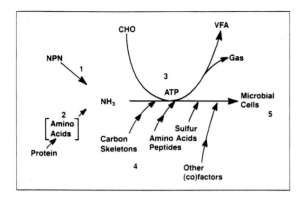

Figure 12-3. Flow diagram of the major reactions of carbohydrate fermentation, nitrogen catabolism and cell biosynthesis by ruminal bacteria.

species can survive and grow with ammonia as the only source of N, yet in the rumen, 20 to 50% of the microbial amino acid N is derived from preformed amino acids or peptides. Additions of small amounts of amino acids to purified diets containing urea have increased MCP yield in vitro. In vivo, efficiency of microbial N synthesis does not appear to be altered by the presence of amino acids. Cross-feeding by and lysis of bacteria in the rumen could account for the difference between in vitro and in vivo results. Certain peptides and amino acids serve as sources of branched-chain fatty acids (BCFA) which are growth factors for cellulolytic bacteria. Fiber digestion is dependent on a supply of BCFA from the diet or from other microbes in the rumen. Though only a small amount of the total energy used by bacteria is apparently used for amino acid biosynthesis, a deficiency of BCFA, ammonia and other nutrients can cause energy (ATP) uncoupling. With energy uncoupling, fermentation continues but ATP which is produced is not used by microbes for growth. Uncoupling in metabolic systems of bacteria and animals is wasteful. In animals uncoupling is used to generate heat for survival though added heat should not be useful for ruminal microbes. In bacteria uncoupling could aid in survival of bacteria by depleting energy which will reduce competition from other organisms. With an ammonia deficiency some of the ATP which would otherwise be used for growth by ruminal microbes is diverted to polysaccharide storage. Such diversion could explain why efficiency of

ATP use is low if nutrient deficiencies limit microbial growth.

Few bacteria can grow without a source of carbohydrate for energy. Certain strains of bacteria require the carbon structures of essential amino acids and amino acids can be incorporated into microbial protein. Certain microbes prefer peptides as a N source. Ability to use amino acids or peptides from the media can reduce energy requirements slightly, but dependence on the media as a source of nutrients limits the adaptability of an organism. With mixed rumen populations in vivo, substrate supply in microenvironments will dictate the need and time for shifts in enzymatic machinery to synthesize carbon skeletons of amino acids. Bacteria using amino acids often exhibit a two-phase growth pattern (diauxie) in batch culture if provided with only low levels of free amino acids plus ammonia. Growth is rapid as long as amino acids remain in the media, but when the amino acid supply is exhausted, growth slows as the metabolic machinery to use ammonia-N is engaged and amino acid biosynthetic enzymes are synthesized. Growth then begins anew but at a slower rate than earlier with amino acids because the microbes must now synthesize their own ketoacids and transaminate them to form amino acids. With slower bacterial growth rates, time for amino acid biosynthesis may not limit growth. But at higher growth rates, amino acids may increase efficiency of microbial growth (MOEFF) due to the greater demand for ATP and shorter ruminal residence times. The need to shift to ammonia as a source of N will be reduced if amino acids are supplied by frequent feeding of a gradually but continuously degraded source of protein. Most high-escape protein sources have a large portion of protein which resists ruminal attack but provide a small amount of rapidly degraded protein. In contrast, certain protein sources like soybean and alfalfa meals are continuously degraded within the rumen. If a continuous supply of amino acids improves microbial growth, the continuously digested proteins may be beneficial.

Bacteria in pure culture excrete certain amino acids, especially alanine, glutamic acid, valine, aspartic acid and glycine. Excretion in a mixed culture permits crossfeeding of nearby bacteria. Free amino acids in ruminal fluid are catabolized very rapidly by bacteria. Hence, within the rumen crossfeeding must be very localized or in a microenvironment, or may involve peptides instead of amino acids.

Amino acids in the media can enhance bacterial growth rate in vitro. However, addition of amino acids to typical ruminant diets does not increase efficiency of microbial growth in the rumen. Apparently, enough amino acids or their degradation products are available from normal ruminal proteolysis of either feed or microbial matter to provide adequate amounts for microbial growth. With very high feed intakes, however, growth of protozoa may be retarded by inadequate crossfeeding. Methionine supplementation often increases the population of protozoa in the rumen. In vitro studies also suggest that phenylalanine, methionine and histidine may limit growth of rumen bacteria under very low protein, high NPN conditions.

Ammonia-N concentrations required for ruminal bacteria have been estimated to be between 0.35 to 29 mg/dl in various studies. Pure cultures generally have very low ammonia needs, while digestion rate in situ plateaus only at much higher concentrations of ammonia. Beneficial effects of higher levels of ammonia might be due to indirect effects on ruminal pH and microbial metabolism. High concentrations may be needed to penetrate microenvironments to reach microbes within isolated niches within the rumen. Protozoa do not appear to use ammonia-N directly as a N source but derive over 70% of their N from bacteria. Bacteria on and in protozoa use ammonia-N, however.

When N availability in the rumen is low, bacteria shift from synthesis of MCP to synthesis of intracellular polysaccharide. Storage of polysaccharide can be reduced with diets lower in starch and soluble sugars or with faster growth rates. Though polysaccharide storage will increase carbohydrate flow to the small intestine and aid in microbial survival during times of starvation, this process wastes ATP. Over one-third of the potential anaerobic ATP yield from glucose would be used simply to store that glucose as polysaccharide by standard metabolic pathways.

Few rumen bacteria require purines or pyrimidines for growth yet nucleic acids disappear rapidly from the rumen. Nucleic acids can be assimilated intact by microbes.

Ruminal S deficiencies can reduce N utilization by microbes. If the N:S ratio exceeds 10.9, MCP production in sheep decreases. Wool is a sink for S amino acids in sheep which reduces the amount of S available for recycling to the rumen. Ruminal fermentation in cattle should continue with lower levels of dietary S. Deficiencies of other essential nutrients have similar effects on energetic efficiency and protein production by ruminal microbes.

GROWTH EFFICIENCY OF RUMINAL MICROBES

MOEFF in vitro usually is expressed in terms of Y_{ATP} as discussed in Ch. 8. Y_{ATP} represents the grams of bacterial dry matter synthesized per mole of ATP available. Efficiency of protein synthesis in the rumen, in constrast, is expressed as grams of MCP or of N fixed per unit (100 g or 1 kg) of organic matter apparently or truly disappearing from the rumen. Because incorporated organic matter has been partially metabolized, it usually is added to the amount apparently digested in the rumen to calculate the true amount of organic matter fermented. With high roughage diets, MOEFF on an apparent OM digestion basis is often extremely high.

MCP synthesis in the rumen averages about 20 g/100 g of total organic matter apparently digested in the rumen (range = 9.6 to 33.2) or 14.5 g/100 g organic matter truly fermented in the rumen (range = 7.6 to 20.3). Though partly due to analytical errors, the three fold range suggests that efficiency of MCP synthesis is not a constant but a variable number. Such variability also indicates that alteration and manipulation of MOEFF is possible. Efficiency values generally are higher for sheep than cattle and with forage than concentrate diets.

Variation in MOEFF also is partly due to several technical problems. Methods to estimate both MCP and organic matter flow from the rumen are imprecise. Any compound proportional to MCP and located only within microbes could be employed to calculate microbial protein flow. Compounds commonly used include ribonucleic acid (RNA), diaminopimelic acid (DAP), deoxyribonucleic acid (DNA), D-alanine and total purines. Ratios of these compounds to MCP

236

change with dietary conditions so the proper ratio must be determined within each experiment if one is to calculate MOEFF accurately. All component microbial markers present some problems. Protozoal mass often is ignored in efficiency calculations though its contribution may be considerable with certain types of diets. Calculations of organic matter flow from the rumen rely on measurement of flow of some indigestible dietary marker.

Table 12-1. Calculation of efficiency of microbial growth and protein escape based on experimental data.[a]

Factor	Method	Animal A	B	C	D
Feed intake, g/d	Measure	5827	5812	5799	5779
Feed dry matter, %	Measure	91.3	91.3	91.3	91.3
Feed N, %	Measure	3.26	3.68	3.52	2.96
Feed ash, %	Measure	4.97	4.72	4.48	4.50
Organic matter					
Intake, g/d	Calc	5056	5068	5056	_____
Chromium, ppm in:					
Feed	Measure	1860	1860	1860	1860
Duodenal DM	Measure	4076	3734	3371	3041
Duodenal DM, g/d	Calc	2659	2895	3200	_____
Duodenal ash, %	Measure	11.4	16.9	12.5	16.8
Duodenal OM, %	Calc	88.6	83.1	87.5	_____
Duodenal OM, g/d	Calc	2356	2406	2800	_____
Duodenal N, %	Measure	5.61	4.93	4.38	4.18
Duodenal N, g/d	Calc	149	143	140	_____
Duodenal ammonia, %	Measure	0.48	0.37	0.43	0.27
Purine, % in					
Bacterial cells	Measure	1.50	1.38	1.47	1.51
Duodenal DM	Measure	0.39	0.29	0.36	0.27
Bacterial N, %	Measure	8.1	8.4	7.3	7.9
Bacterial ash, %	Measure	20	20	20	20
Duodenal flow					
Bacteria, g/d	Calc	689	608	784	_____
Bacterial N, g/d	Calc	55.8	51.1	57.2	_____
Bacterial OM, g/d	Calc	551	487	627	_____
Apparent OM digested					
In rumen, g/d	Calc	2700	2662	2256	_____
% of intake	Calc	53	53	45	_____
True OM digested					
In rumen, g/d	Calc	3251	3149	2883	_____
% of intake	Calc	64	62	57	_____
MOEFF, g N/kg OM					
Apparently dig.	Calc	21	19	25	[24]
Truly digested	Calc	17	16	20	[19]
Duodenal nitrogen					
Total, g/d	Calc	149	143	140	_____
Microbial, g/d	Calc	55.8	51.1	57.2	_____
Ammonia, g/d	Calc	12.8	10.8	13.8	_____
Feed, g/d	Calc	81	81	69	_____
Escape of feed N, %	Calc	42	38	34	[51]

[a]From laboratory data (Unpublished, F.N. Owens)

Variation in flow of the digesta marker in research trials may be more critical than the choice of component microbial marker. Calculations of MOEFF are illustrated in Table 12-1.

Growth rate of ruminal microbes influences the efficiency of MCP production because it alters the relative proportions of energy used for maintenance versus growth. Energy for growth equals total ATP minus that needed for maintenance (moles of ATP required/g of cells/h). The amount of energy expended for maintenance is dependent on time. Hence, the shorter the time which microbes spend in the rumen or the faster the passage or dilution rate, the less energy microbes expend for maintenance. Efficiency of growth, Y_{ATP}, will approach a maximum, Y_{ATP}^{MAX}, as time for maintenance approaches zero and rate of growth approaches infinity. For mixed ruminal bacteria, estimates of Y_{ATP}^{MAX} range from 21 to 33. The mean value, 26, matches with the Y_{ATP}^{MAX} of 25 extrapolated from continuous culture data. To achieve such a high efficiency all nutrients required for growth must be present simultaneously and at adequate concentrations. Nutrient deficiencies contribute to the variability observed in efficiency of microbial growth. If microbial processes in the rumen were aerobic rather than anaerobic, bacterial growth and ATP yield could be enhanced almost 10 fold at the expense of VFA production.

Efficiency of microbial growth is influenced by rate of passage of bacteria in various fractions within the rumen. Faster passage decreases the amount of energy used for maintenance, decreases time for lysis of bacteria and engulfment of bacteria by protozoa, and reduces concentration of inhibitory products and of competing microbes. This has been described in Ch. 8.

Through effects on the microbial population, efficiency of microbial growth can be altered by feed additives, feed processing or environmental conditions. Fractional passage rate can be increased either by reducing ruminal volume or increasing intake of feed or ions. Efficiency of microbial growth also can be increased by reducing lysis associated with ruminal shocks in temperature, osmolarity or pH. In addition, inhibiting carbohydrate storage or futile cycles could prove beneficial.

Limitations in certain nutrients such as ammonia, BCFA, vitamins or minerals may also reduce efficiency of microbial growth.

PROTEIN DEGRADATION IN THE RUMEN

The quantity of protein presented to the small intestine for absorption is the sum of the MCP and the feed protein which escapes or bypasses ruminal digestion unscathed. For high rates of production, MCP alone may be insufficient to meet the demands for production of animal protein. Providing additional high quality protein to the small intestines will increase production in such cases. Added dietary protein is subject to degradation in the rumen and only a variable proportion will escape to the small intestine.

The extent of ruminal degradation of dietary protein for various protein sources estimated for cattle has been tabulated in Table 12-2. Note that escape values are variable even within a protein source. Of the total protein fed, from 20-100% will be degraded to ammonia in the rumen while the residual fraction (0-80%) will escape or bypass ruminal

Table 12-2. Estimates of ruminal escape of protein from common feedstuffs from animals trials.[a]

Feedstuff	In vivo N escape, %	Escape, % Mean	SD
Protein Supplements			
Blood meal	54, 71, 82	69	14.0
Corn gluten meal	55, 46-61, 62, 57	55	6.3
Cottonseed meal	24-61, 27-33, 35-57	40	15.7
Feather meal	71	71	---
Fish meal	71, 69-100, 78	68	13.0
Linseed meal	44	44	---
Meat meal	49, 70, 76, 77	65	14.0
Rapeseed meal	23	23	---
Soybean meal	10, 27, 29, 61, 35, 18, 17, 15, 18, 20, 24, 25, 26, 22, 21, 24, 46, 23, 43, 14	26	12.0
Sunflower meal	19-28	24	6.4
Energy Feeds			
Corn, flaked	50	50	
Corn, ground	73, 58, 47	59	13.0
Corn, high moisture	54-72	63	12.7
Corn, whole	52	52	
Sorghum grain	49, 20, 38, 64, 58, 52, 69, 65	52	16.3
Roughages			
Alfalfa hay	30, 41, 21, 28, 20-24	27	7.7
Corn silage	27	27	

[a]Compiled and updated from NRC (11)

238

digestion and reach the small intestine for digestion there. Calculation of protein escape is illustrated in Table 12-1. Escape values vary with feeding conditions used in an experiment and a number of microbial factors. Considering the variation in escape values for any given feed as well as these other factors which alter escape, it is useless to seek a single precise value for ruminal degradation of a particular protein source. Even determined values will apply only under specific in vivo conditions. Nevertheless, one can generally classify protein sources into groups with high, medium and low escape. Methods for determining protein degradation in the rumen were discussed and compiled in recent publications (11, 19).

Due to the complexity of measuring protein escape in animals, many in vitro systems have been devised in an attempt to predict the extent of ruminal proteolysis. These include measurements of solubility in various solvents, loss of protein or accumulation of ammonia or amino acids in vitro, and loss of protein upon incubation with various proteolytic enzymes. In vivo measurements and animal responses must be regarded as the standards to which such methods are compared, not vice versa. Combinations of procedures such as solubility plus in situ disappearance appear to have some promise to predict in vivo escape values.

Protein hydrolysis in the rumen is a multistep process. First, insoluble protein is solubilized. Next, the peptide bond of solubilized protein is cleaved enzymatically by a variety of endo- and exo-proteases to peptides and amino acids are released. Free peptides and amino acids are absorbed rapidly by bacteria and used as such or deaminated. Concentrations of soluble protein and amino acids in the rumen are always very low and often undetectable except immediately after a meal. This indicates that soluble protein is degraded rapidly.

Although ruminal proteases and peptidases are primarily bound to microbial cell walls, protein in solution appears to be absorbed rapidly onto the bacterial cell walls for enzymatic attack. Hydrolysis at the surface of cells permits microbes direct access to the products of protein degradation. However, some proteolytic bacteria cannot use amino acids but, instead, use only ammonia as a

source of N. For such microbes, protein serves only as a source of carbon and energy. Peptides are found in ruminal fluid in detectable quantities only when protein is being degraded rapidly.

PROTEIN SOLUBILITY

Solubility has received the most commercial attention in the search for a simple predictor of extent of proteolysis. Actually, solubility is more useful as an index of rate of proteolysis than of extent of proteolysis. Soluble compounds in the rumen are attacked more rapidly and digested more completely than are insoluble compounds due in part to differences in microbial access. Yet soluble compounds are digested at different rates. For example, soluble proteins from soybean meal, rapeseed meal and casein are hydrolyzed at different rates. Regression of ruminal protein degradation on solubility in various buffers accounted for less than half of the variability in escape values reported in the literature. With most feedstuffs, soluble protein is only a small fraction of the total protein degraded in the rumen, so when comparing escape with different feedstuffs, differences in degradation of the insoluble fraction accounts for more of the variation than solubility alone. Estimates of ruminal degradation of protein insoluble in ruminal buffers generally range from 35 to 50%. This supports the concept that solubility alone is a poor predictor for extent of ruminal degradation across a variety of diets and feeding conditions. Yet, if limited to high feed intakes of a high concentrate diet, solubility alone may prove useful as an index of escape. Escape for some of the amino acids may be greater than for others because the amino acid composition of the more soluble fraction can differ from that of the insoluble fraction. Gross changes in amino acid composition with ruminal degradation remain to be quantitated.

The amount of protein which is pulled into a solution varies not only with characteristics of the protein, but also with characteristics of the solvent including pH and ionic and osmotic strength. Differences in structural as well as chemical characteristics of the protein are probably involved in both solubility and rate of protein degradation in the rumen. Presence of disulfide bonds in protein conveys resistance to microbial degradation, though other factors, such as numbers of accessible hydrolyzable sites in the protein molecule, enzyme concentration and media pH probably are involved.

Autoclaved ruminal fluid presumably most closely represents the solvent within the rumen for obtaining solubility estimates. However, saline and borate solvents are more convenient to prepare and use in the laboratory and should be less variable. Not all soluble proteins are degraded. Certain proteins such as ovalbumin and specific proteins from soybean meal and rapeseed meal, though soluble in rumen fluid, resist proteolysis. Disulfide crosslinking and blocking of terminal amino acid decreases susceptibility to enzymatic attack. Most other soluble proteins are hydrolyzed rapidly. Degradation products including peptides, amides and branch-chained VFA can be detected in ruminal fluid after a meal.

METHODS TO PREDICT ESCAPE

Ruminal digestion of protein has been studied using "in situ" or "in sacco" procedures as described in Ch. 8. Disappearance is very rapid initially. This represents loss of soluble protein plus washout of fine particles through the pores in the bag. Disappearance of the residue continues at rates characteristic for the source of protein and ruminal conditions until only indigestible material remains.

In situ disappearance with some sources of protein is a continual process whereas, for other protein sources, rate of disappearance decreases with time of incubation as would be expected if supply of substrate limits rate of digestion. Differences among proteins in slopes and shapes of in situ loss also reflects the presence of several types of protein within a feedstuff as well as degree of association of protein with plant cell walls. Presence of multiple types of protein within a single feedstuffs simplifies understanding of the process but complicates the kinetics of digestion and interpretation of in situ data because specific rates of digestion must be determined for the various classes of protein present. Association of protein with the cell structure also complicates ruminal proteolysis. If protein is released only as the cell wall structure is digested, loss of protein parallels loss of dry matter. Parallel loss of dry matter and protein is observed with most feedstuffs, but with certain feeds such as fish meal, sunflower meal and alfalfa meal, protein loss appears to proceed independent of dry matter loss. Heat treatment presumably causes cell content protein to adhere to the cell wall which can limit access for digestion. Considering the multiple types of protein present and association of protein with cell wall components, disappearance of potentially digestible protein from a feedstuff cannot be considered to be a simple first order reaction (logarithmic disappearance over time). Instead it is the sum of a series of proteolytic rates with various protein types with additional dependence on cell wall digestion. Because rate of cell wall digestion varies with ruminal conditions, proteolytic rate for cell wall proteins will vary with diet. Escape values or rankings determined with sheep may not apply directly to cattle because extent of ruminal cell wall digestion differs with species. Most models of protein digestion assume that passage rate and digestion rate are first order reactions. This assumption needs to be modified to consider interactions among feed components.

Though generally considered less important quantitatively than the *rate* of digestion, the *time* for ruminal digestion of protein will alter escape. This effect is more pronounced with certain protein sources such as soybean, sunflower and alfalfa meals which are degraded at a constant and continuing rate within the rumen. Many high escape protein sources, such as distiller's products, fish meal and meat meal, release a burst of protein initially but protein disappearance almost ceases after four to six hours of in situ incubation. Time for digestion will have less impact on escape with such proteins.

Increased feed intake can increase protein escape markedly in both dairy cattle and steers. In one study each 10% increase in feed intake of a high-concentrate diet increased ruminal escape of plant protein by 6.5%. Increased escape is probably due both to a decrease in the amount of time the protein spends in the rumen and to changes in ruminal conditions including pH and the microbial population within the rumen.

In addition to level of feed intake, diet type also influences protein escape. Extent of ruminal protein degradation is usually much

240

greater with forage diets than with concentrate diets. Ruminal pH may be involved because the optimum pH for most proteolytic and deaminase enzymes in the rumen is thought to be between 6 and 7. Also the percentage of a feed protein which is soluble often is greater at a neutral than an acid pH. Another possibility is that the ruminal population changes. At a neutral pH proteolytic bacteria may be more prevalent or greater degradation of cellulose and cell walls expose more protein to microbial attack.

BYPASS TREATMENTS

A variety of chemical and physical treatments has been used to increase ruminal escape of dietary protein sources. These include treatment with formaldehyde, tannins and heat to reduce ruminal solubility. Some but not all of the crosslinks formed by these treatments are cleaved under the acid conditions of the abomasum. Most trials reporting beneficial effects have been with casein as a protein source for which ruminal degradation without treatment approaches 100%. Overtreatment can render protein totally indigestible. But to maximize the supply of digestible protein to the small intestine, some depression in total tract digestibility is inevitable. N retention, rather than fecal loss, should be used as an index of the value of treatment. Grain processing methods also alter ruminal digestion of both protein and starch in opposite (steam flaking) or parallel (ensiling) directions through heat or solubilization effects.

Currently, the choice between protein and NPN in feed supplements depends primarily upon the relative costs of protein versus NPN plus added energy. Animal responses deserve greater attention. Protein or NPN should always be added at sufficient levels so that an ammonia deficiency does not limit MCP production in the rumen. Beyond this, the goal is to match amino acid needs with amino acid supply to the small intestine. If MCP is adequate to meet animal needs, added escape protein is useless if not deleterious due to reduced ruminal and total tract digestion. In contrast, if MCP is inadequate to meet animal needs, amino acid composition and escape need consideration. Ideally, dietary protein sources need to complement the amino acid

composition of MCP with escape, digestible protein. Many high escape proteins are grain by-products and thereby contain very limited amounts of lysine and tryptophan. In addition to deficiencies of limiting amino acids, excesses of other amino acids may be deleterious. Energetic efficiency of lactation is reduced by elevated levels of dietary protein though no explanation for this effect is apparent. Excesses of certain amino acids will reduce feed intake of non-ruminant animals. Similarly, amino acid imbalances can be induced in ruminants with amino acid infusions. But because it takes a gross imbalance to reduce intake and dietary proteins are diluted with MCP, the probability of amino acid imbalances with ruminants fed common diets appears remote.

In selection of an escape protein, two factors in addition to amino acid composition become important—intestinal digestibility and ruminal ammonia supply. Proteins which resist degradation in the rumen usually have a depressed total tract digestibility. Many of the protein sources naturally resistant to ruminal proteolysis, such as distiller's by-products, chemically treated proteins and heat-damaged materials, contain high amounts of indigestible N. If the protein escapes ruminal digestion, less ammonia becomes available in the rumen which can result in ammonia deficiency for ruminal microbes. Hence, with slowly degraded dietary proteins, additional NPN may need to be added to the diet to meet the ammonia needs of ruminal microbes. Excess NPN can precipitate ammonia toxicity problems but high ammonia levels generally do not reduce efficiency of microbial growth.

Though many gram-positive bacteria produce extracellular proteases, gram-negative bacteria appear to be more actively proteolytic. No specific ruminal microbe strains have proteolysis as a primary function, though many ruminal microbes possess proteolytic activity. *Bacteroides ruminicola* is often implicated in protein hydrolysis. Most amino acids are absorbed by this organism as peptides, not as free amino acids, and are hydrolyzed intracellularly to amino acids. Proteases are constitutive enzymes and not subject to metabolic control, but exoprotease production decreases as bacteria enter the stationary phase of growth. Glucose limitation increases activity or production of exoproteases, whereas peptide limitation decreases exoprotease production. Proteases are released into the ruminal medium when microbial cells lyse.

DIET MODIFICATION

Modifiers of ruminal fermentation, such as ionophores, may affect proteolytic activity through selective inhibition of certain species of microbes. Ruminal degradation of a protein can be depressed by restricting microbial access to protein or amino acids through coating or encapsulating such material with lipids or other insoluble substances. Rate of ruminal disruption of the coating will control the extent of ruminal digestion. Protozoa also possess intracellular proteolytic enzymes which hydrolyze engulfed protein from both bacteria and feed. Excess amino acids are deaminated and ammonia-N is released. In defaunated (protozoa-free) animals the concentration of ammonia-N in ruminal fluid is lower than in faunated animals, probably due either to reduced excretion of ammonia by protozoa or to greater ammonia use by the bacteria. The bacterial density in the rumen increases markedly when protozoa are removed.

Proteolytic activity is not affected greatly by diet though the pH optimum for most ruminal proteolytic enzymes is about 6.5. Yet, the extent of ruminal degradation of protein drops as pH decreases. This may be due to changes in the protein itself, access of microbes to protein or in the microbial population. The isoelectric point, the pH of greatest protein solubility, for many sources of supplemental protein is near or above 7. If solubility influences rate of degradation, pH can thereby influence rate of proteolysis. As diet influences ruminal pH, it also alters susceptibility to digestion. The pH influences solubility of plant source proteins much more than of animal source proteins, but response can vary with protein source. Corn grain protein, for example, is most soluble near a pH of 5 and decreases above this point.

A higher pH also may increase exposure of feed protein to digestive enzymes through increased degradation of fiber. If fiber is a barrier to proteolytic attack or solubilization, a higher pH can increase exposure and extent of proteolysis. Finally, protozoa numbers usually decline as pH falls. Absence of protozoa as well as changes in the bacterial population appear to be partially involved in the reduction in the extent of ruminal proteolysis at a low pH.

Microbes adapt over time to deaminate specific amino acids, but microbial adaptation to degrade particular protein sources, though possible, has not been demonstrated with any consistency. Because no specific strains are particularly proteolytic, adaptation of the microbial population to attack specific protein sources would not be expected unless the protein supplement is fed as a major portion of the diet. Ruminal microbes interact in protein catabolism and utilization of degradation products. Proteases from one microbe may hydrolyze protein to peptides and free amino acids which subsequently are used by other microbes or catabolized to NH_3-N and α-keto acids which, in turn, are catabolized to VFA.

Ruminal microbes convert amino acids primarily by non-oxidative deamination to α-keto acids and ammonia. Free amino acids disappear rapidly with half lives from 0.8 to 2 h. At a low pH, amino acids can be decarboxylated to amines and CO_2 (the Stickland reaction). This reaction is prevalent both during ensiling and during ruminal fermentation. The keto acids are further catabolized to VFA with branched-chain VFA being derived from certain amino acids.

Dietary nucleic acids also are hydrolyzed rapidly in the rumen if accessible for microbial attack. Bacteria can use nucleic acids from the feed or synthesize their own. Nucleic acids from bacteria which are used by protozoa generally are degraded to the nucleotide level before being incorporated into protozoal nucleotides.

POSTRUMINAL DIGESTION AND ABSORPTION OF N COMPOUNDS

Postruminal protein digestion and absorption largely parallel these processes in nonruminant animals. Feed processing and N sources do not alter intestinal proteolytic activity and absorption in ruminants greatly, though pancreatic protease secretions can increase as flow of protein increases. Because outflow from the rumen is reasonably constant, the flow of protein is also constant, reducing the need for regulation.

As productive capacity of ruminants has increased and protein requirements increase, limits to digestion of protein in and absorption of amino acids from the small intestine have been of interest. Digestion and absorption capacity for protein has not been exceeded in either non-ruminant animals or duodenally infused sheep at very high levels of protein. This suggests that the digestive and absorptive capacity of the small intestine is very high. Compared to non-ruminant animals, ruminants have a lower gastric and duodenal pH which could alter protein digestion. Virtually all protein which is solubilized by gastric juice (pepsin plus HCl) is digested in the small intestine. If dietary buffers or gastric parassites reduce protein solubilization within the abomasum, protein digestion in the small intestine could be compromised.

Postruminal apparent digestibility of N compounds has been estimated by several workers. Most values fall between 65 and 75% of duodenal N. Though the digestibility of bacterial cell walls has been suggested to be low, MCP appears to have a digestibility similar to that of escape feed protein with typical diets.

Availability of nutrients post-ruminally is generally ignored when one considers efficiency of escaping and absorbing protein and starch in the small intestine. Supply to the small intestine and digestibility in the small intestine must be considered separately. The more extensively a compound is fermented in the rumen, the lower the supply to the intestines. Extensive processing shifts site of digestion toward the rumen and away from the intestines. Treatment to increase extent of digestion in the rumen also increases the potential extent of digestion of escape material in the small intestine. Except for cell walls, compounds which are more readily accessible and extensively digested by bacteria in the rumen are also more readily and completely digested in the small intestine. Hence, treatment to increase intestinal digestion alone is futile because such treatment will increase ruminal attack, as well. Feed components which resist digestion within the rumen and pass to the intestines automatically have lower digestibility than ruminally digested components. Processes which reduce accessibility to microbial attack in the rumen generally reduce digestion in the small intestine.

This is of special concern for heat or chemical treatment of protein to escape the rumen. Heat treatment to increase binding with the cell wall usually makes the protein less soluble and reduces the extent of protein digestion in the rumen. But extensive heat damage, through binding of protein with cell wall components, may drastically reduce total tract digestibility of proteins. A small degree of heat damage increases the flow of protein to the small intestine at some sacrifice in total tract protein digestion. Some index of total tract digestibility of the protein, such as acid-detergent fiber bound N (ADF-N) or acid-pepsin insolubility can be employed to monitor total tract true digestibility. Solubility by an acid-pepsin solution has been used successfully as an index of total tract digestibility of protein in diets for non-ruminants and should be useful for ruminant diets, as well. With either chemicals or heat treatment, availability of certain amino acids may be depressed more than others. Binding and crosslinking usually involve amino acids with reactive end groups such as cystine and lysine. Selective binding may or may not reduce BV of escape protein, depending on which specific amino acids are limiting. Effect of treatments on both postruminal digestibility and amino acid availability can be most easily measured in bioassays with non-ruminant animals.

Another characteristic unique to ruminants is an abundant secretion of pancreatic ribonuclease. Postruminal digestion of microbial nucleic acids has been estimated to be about 80%. RNA cleavage is high even in the proximal duodenum of sheep. A small proportion of the pyrimidines absorbed is used by animal tissues though the purines are largely excreted in urine. RNA digestion helps conserve N and can increase N recycling as pyrimidines are catabolized in the liver. However, the major benefit of ribonuclease action is not for conservation of N but for conservation and recycling of P. Amino acids in the L form are actively absorbed from the jejunum and ileum and, similar to non-ruminants, certain groups of amino acids compete with others for absorption. The relevance of such competition is questionable because all free amino acids are absorbed before digesta leaves the small intestine.

MEASUREMENT OF PROTEIN STATUS AND QUALITY

Protein sources for animals are usually compared by measuring N digestibility (disappearance of N from the gut) or N balance or retention (N intake minus output in feces plus urine). Inevitable losses of excreta result in overestimation of N retention. N retention serves as an estimate of productive (milk, tissue, wool) plus non-productive (skin, hair) protein deposition. N balance trials continue to be useful in study of N metabolism of ruminant animals.

Generally, digestibility of N is not adjusted for secretion or excretion of N into the gut. Over half of the N secreted into the gut is reabsorbed. Regression of N digestibility against N intake yields a straight line across a wide variety of diets so that apparent N digestibility varies with N level. The formula, Digestible Protein (%) = 0.898 Crude Protein (%) − 3.18, has been interpreted to mean that true digestibility of protein is near 90% (89.8%) and that 3.18 g of protein is lost in feces for every 100 g of dry matter consumed by the ruminant. If this metabolic loss represents loss of tissue protein which must be replenished with amino acids subject to digestibility and BV losses at an efficiency of only 50%, the diet must contain over 6% protein simply to replace this fecal loss. Some of the fecal N loss can be due to association of N with fibrous residues and a portion consists of microbial residues. These latter fractions may be derived partially from non-specific N (NPN) and not be subject to the efficiency loss of 50% discussed above for tissue protein synthesis. To determine how much of the fecal N comes from microbial protein, DAP and purine concentrations in fecal material have been measured. DAP concentrations suggest that much of the fecal N is microbial but nucleic acids concentrations are quite low. Possibly the microbial N in feces contains more bacterial cell walls than cell contents.

Recent infusion studies cast doubt on metabolic fecal N estimates; if only digestible protein is infused, no feces and hence no MFN are produced. With non-ruminant animals and young calves, MFN estimates are much lower than with adult ruminants, being near 2 g of fecal protein/100 g dry matter consumed. MFN of ruminants is probably overestimated upward due to the increase in protein flow to the duodenum with low protein diets. If MFN were reduced, true digestibility also must be reduced, becoming more similar to apparent N digestibility in the small intestine. Because MFN replacement calculates to be such a large expense for ruminants, it needs to be studied more extensively.

Route of N loss changes with energy status of microbes in the large intestine. The greater the amount of fermentable carbohydrate in the large intestine or cecum, the greater the fecal N output and the lower the urinary N loss. Hence, as more energy is supplied to the large intestine, apparent digestibility decreases. This in turn causes retention of apparently absorbed N to increase. This means that site of energy digestion alters N digestibility. BV will also change because apparent absorption of N is altered. The magnitude of this effect with various diets remains to be determined.

Digestibility of N, dry matter and cellulose can be depressed drastically with heat damage during processing or storage of feeds, especially forages. The depression in N digestibility parallels the amount of N bound to certain fiber fractions. The amount of heat damage and indigestible dietary N can be estimated chemically as the amount of N present in acid-detergent fiber or the amount of protein insoluble in a pepsin-HCl solution. Total tract digestibility of these components needs re-examination because certain treatments such as ammoniation may release some of the bound N.

Assays for heat damage need to be applied to improve methods of harvest and storage and to find feed additives to reduce heat damage. Methods to assess site and extent of digestion based on the distribution of N in various fecal and urinary fractions (urea, purines) are being developed. Such procedures will help assess N status of animals under production conditions.

UTILIZATION OF ABSORBED AMINO ACIDS

Amino acids are not stored as such in the body. Unless used for synthesis of protein or other essential compounds, amino acids are catabolized with the amino-N being removed and converted to urea and the carbon skeleton being oxidized to CO_2. Recycling of urea to and absorption of NH_3-N from the rumen and large intestine precludes study of amino acid metabolism by simply measuring urinary urea and NH_3-N excretion.

Absorbed amino acid-N from MCP is utilized very efficiently. Because the amino acid profile of protein in digesta flowing to the small intestine is relatively constant and well balanced, extensive degradation of excess amino acids would not be expected.

In addition to supplying building blocks for protein, amino acids also supply a major proportion of the glucose needed by ruminant animals. Alanine, aspartate, glutamate and glutamine are the primary amino acids used as a source of carbon for glucose. Because of the constant turnover of tissues, the total flux of amino acids in the body exceeds the amount of amino acid carbon converted to glucose. The good balance of essential amino acids absorbed from the small intestine may be responsible in part for the low contribution of essential amino acid carbon to glucose synthesis in ruminants. Several workers have considered amino acid use for gluconeogenesis as part of the total protein requirement, though this could also simply reflect utilization of excess amino acids and not a requirement. Protein synthesis, not glucose synthesis, should have first priority when energy is available. Indeed, the lower K_m for transfer RNA-amino acid ligase than for the first enzymes in amino acid catabolism assures this priority.

MEASURING AMINO ACID STATUS

N balance or retention, the difference between N intake and N output in urine and feces, is the most common index of protein status of ruminant animals. With non-ruminant animals, N balance studies can be conducted with animals fed a purified or natural diet with various levels of a test amino acid to estimate the animal's requirement for that amino acid. With ruminant animals, diet manipulation has little impact on protein status because amino acids are both catabolized and synthesized in the rumen. Hence, it is impossible to study amino acid requirements of ruminant animals by simply manipu-

lating the diet. Instead, more complex methods to administer amino acids by some parenteral or post-ruminal route (infusions via cannula or coated "bypass" amino acids) are needed to alter amino acid flow in order to estimate requirements. Using marker procedures one can measure digesta flow in order to separate total tract digestion into proportions occurring in the reticulo-rumen, in the abomasum plus small intestine, and the large intestine plus cecum.

Blood plasma amino acid concentrations have been used as an index of amino acid status. Plasma amino acid concentrations respond rapidly to altered nutritional status though the free amino acid pool is only a small proportion of the total body protein-amino acid pool. When an amino acid is limiting, its concentration in blood plasma is very low. Blood plasma amino acid profiles also vary with dietary energy level and endocrine factors.

Abomasal or duodenal infusions of amino acids have suggested that the first limiting amino acids in bacterial protein for maintenance of sheep and cattle are methionine, lysine and threonine. With commercial diets for sheep and cattle, results have been less consistent, probably due to variability in amino acid composition of ruminal escape protein. With growing lambs and cattle, responses to methionine are reported most frequently though other resports have suggested that lysine, threonine, histidine or phenylalanine may be limiting. With higher levels of feed intake and performance, the supply of all amino acids may already be adequate for rapid gain. Only when amino acid needs for protein synthesis are high, as with high levels of milk production or very rapid rates of muscle growth, and supply of amino acids is limited, as with limited energy intake, would post-ruminal supplementation of amino acids be expected to be beneficial. However, if supplemental amino acids have additional effects on hormone levels or feed intake, they could be useful commercially. In over 85% of the feeding trials in which added protein has increased rate of gain, feed intake has been increased, as well. Why post-ruminal protein supply increases feed intake of ruminants remains to be determined.

EFFECTS OF HORMONES AND ADDITIVES ON PROTEIN METABOLISM

Protein synthesis and degradation rates in tissues tend to parallel each other, both being higher in young, growing animals than adult animals. Protein accretion equals protein synthesis minus protein degradation. Protein synthesis and degradation rates can be modulated by hormones and exogenous anabolic agents which alter either synthesis or degradation or both. Accretion rate of carcass protein in growing steers seldom exceeds a mean of 120 g protein/d though administration of anabolic hormones may increase this ceiling.

Heavy emphasis recently has been placed on hormones or additives to increase protein flow to the intestine of ruminants by altering ruminal function to enhance MCP synthesis or to depress microbial proteolysis and deamination of preformed dietary protein. Benefits from an increased supply of absorbable amino acids need to be defined more clearly.

MATHEMATICAL MODELS OF PROTEIN METABOLISM

Several mathematical models have been developed to describe N metabolism and can be used to (a) balance diets and (b) guide future research. These models have helped to expose many problems in formulation of practical diets when using the crude protein or digestible protein standards. The initial models helped to balance diets and to estimate the usefulness of NPN. More complex whole animal N metabolism models have been presented more recently. Unfortunately, results from many of the current models are not sufficiently integrated to be useful in diet formulation.

A number of practical models have been advanced to use current knowledge of N metabolism in ruminants to formulate diets. As reviewed by Waldo and Glenn (26) and by the NRC (11), these models include the ARC system, the metabolizable protein system from Iowa State, the German, French and Danish systems, the Net Protein System of Cornell and of Michigan and a protein system keyed to ruminal NH_3-N concentrations.

All these models are based on similar concepts but differ in the equations used to relate the components of the model. All systems attempt to quantitate the usefulness of NPN, to estimate N requirements of the animal and predict the amount of MCP synthesized in the rumen. Most systems also consider (a) animal N requirements for maintenance, production and excretion of metabolic fecal N and endogenous urinary N, (b) ruminal escape and degradation of dietary protein, (c) upper limits of NPN utilization and NH_3-N recycling, (d) digestibility of MCP and escape protein, (e) amounts of nucleic acid N from MCP, (f) nutritional quality of MCP and escape protein, and (g) efficiency of utilization of absorbed amino acids by the ruminant for maintenance and production. Unfortunately, many of the proposed systems do not match experimentally measured values of N excretion and flow (26) and produce spurious values when extrapolated to production conditions. Though "fudge factors" can be added to make the models behave properly, such factors should not be needed if the biology were adequately understood. Future testing and application of models will increase and extend our understanding of N metabolism in the ruminant. Movement from the current static systems into more dynamic models of N metabolism will be possible as more information accumulates.

NITROGEN REQUIREMENTS, SAFETY MARGINS AND ECONOMICS

Due to degradation of dietary protein in the rumen, a high dietary protein intake does not guarantee that animals have an adequate supply of amino acids at the small intestine. In one study with grazed forages containing over 17% protein, more than 40% of N consumed disappeared from the rumen and the ratio of N to OM entering the duodenum was suboptimal for animal growth. Under these conditions, feeding protein with a high potential for ruminal escape or adding energy to the diet will increase the supply of amino acids to the duodenum and increase N retention. Energy supplementation increased the capture of released N and increased microbial N flow from the rumen. But response to added energy usually is less than response to supplementation with a high escape protein supplement. Response to an increased amino acid supply depends both on the extent of ruminal digestion of the fed protein and the

246

need for amino acids for growth or lactation. Mixed supplements containing both energy from grain and a high escape protein feed may prove useful.

Fermented feeds present another feeding condition with which added protein may be useful. Compared with a fresh forage, a fermented or wilted wet forage usually reduces microbial yield and amino acid flow to the duodenum. This may be due to reduced ruminal digestion of carbohydrate in fermented forage or to loss of soluble carbohydrate or escape protein during the ensiling or fermentation process. Supplementation with certain amino acids or derivatives such as the branch-chained fatty acids often will increase growth efficiency and yield of ruminal bacteria and may increase rate of fiber digestion and intake of fermented feeds. Production responses also are dependent on the endocrine balance of the animal which can alter energy demand and feed intake. In most cases where addition of protein to a diet has increased production, feed intake has increased. If intake of digestible energy is increased, animal performance is usually increased.

The total requirement for N in the diet can be estimated by two different methods. The empirical method measures response to added dietary N either in the rumen or in animal performance as illustrated in Fig. 12-4. Requirements for specific diets, ages and levels of production can be estimated from results of feeding or lactation trials. Empirical methods have the advantages of simplicity and direct application, but results have limited use due to lack of flexibility and applicability to other diets, to new feed additives and to untested animal conditions. Though results of empirical studies are immediately applicable, they usually ignore the complex biology of response to supplementation.

By the factorial method, in contrast, estimates of the N requirement for specific functions and levels of production are calculated by summing the requirements for each function. This approach has been used by committees to estimate protein requirements for dairy cattle (9) and for beef cattle (10). Uses or losses of N typically considered in factorial equations are (a) metabolic fecal, (b) endogenous urinary, (c) scurf-skin, hair, hoof and (d) deposition in milk, in the products of conception or in lean tissues as shown in Tables

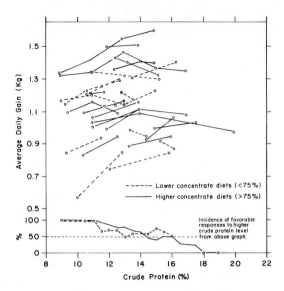

Figure 12-4. Rates of gain by feedlot cattle fed various protein levels for empirical estimation of protein requirements (5).

12-3 and 12-4. General equations have been developed to calculate the N needed for each of these purposes. Changes in body composition, as occurs during early lactation when cows mobilize large amounts of protein from body reserves, complicate the factorial approach. Also, rate of protein deposition in tissue varies with stage of growth, rate of weight gain, and breed type or mature size in ways which are incompletely understood.

Limitations of the factorial approach to N requirements are (a) rate of loss of N may vary from standard equations due to diet, animal or environmental conditions, (b) results are not readily tested, (c) problem points in the system are not easily identified, (d) the system is not readily updated with results from feeding studies and (e) mathematics can hide logical biological relationships. Compared with empirical results, factorial results allow evaluation of new diets, animal types and feeding conditions. The factorial approach also helps to point out knowledge gaps. More quantitative information about metabolic fecal N and BV is needed to refine factorial estimates.

Requirements calculated by either method are a compromise between providing enough N to maximize performance but not so much that it will be wasted. Some studies show no

Table 12-3. Influence of weight gain on protein need of a 500 lb large framed steer.[a]

	Daily gain, lb						
	0.5	1.0	1.5	2.0	2.5	3.0	3.5
Feed intake, lb DM	12.0	12.8	13.4	13.8	14.0	14.0	13.6
Diet TDN, %	52.5	56.0	59.5	63.5	67.5	72.0	78.5
Protein uses, g/d							
Metabolic fecal	181	194	204	208	212	213	206
End. urinary	41	41	41	41	41	41	41
Scurf	5	5	5	5	5	5	5
Tissue	46	86	127	167	207	247	285
CE*D*BV,[b] value	. . . . 0.59						
Dietary protein need,							
Pounds/d	1.01	1.21	1.40	1.56	1.73	1.88	2.00
Percent of DM	8.5	9.5	10.4	11.4	12.4	13.4	14.7

[a]Calculated as described in (10)   [b]Ruminal output/input x digestibility x BV.

Table 12-4. Protein expenditures and estimated requirements of large framed steers of various weights gaining 2 lb/d.[a]

	Steer weight, lb						
	400	500	600	700	800	900	1,000
Feed intake, lb DM	11.7	13.8	15.8	17.8	19.6	21.4	23.2
Protein uses, g							
Fecal	176	208	239	268	297	324	351
End. urinary	37	41	45	49	52	56	59
Scurf	5	5	6	6	7	7	8
Tissue	179	167	156	144	135	125	116
CE*D*BV,[b] value	. . . . 0.59						
Dietary protein need							
Pounds/d	1.47	1.57	1.66	1.74	1.82	1.90	1.98
Percent of DM	12.7	11.4	10.5	9.8	9.3	8.9	8.6

[a]Calculated as described in (10)   [b]As from Table 12-3.

response to low, definitely sub-optimal protein levels, while others show performance responses to additional protein with diets which already contain very high amounts. Even within a feeding period, responses to added protein may be transitory, being detected during the early weeks but disappearing later as unsupplemented animals recover and compensate for reduced performance. Meeting the requirement for all animals of a type at a given age, stage and level of performance without providing an excess for other animals in the same pen is impossible. Hence, most requirements are calculated to meet needs of an average animal.

At this point half of the animals will be underfed while half are overfed. Mathematically, the estimated requirement based on performance is actually biased upward if animals are fed in a pen because reduced performance of a single animal in the pen decreases the mean performance of the pen of animals which causes the calculated requirement to be overestimated.

Nutrient allowances or recommendations differ from nutrient requirements by addition of an excess to provide a safety margin. Safety margins usually are based on the expected variation not only among animals within a type but also within feed ingredients.

248

Determining the amount of variation within these two factors is very difficult. With greater diversity in animal type, a greater safety margin needs to be added to the mean. Economics and the law of diminishing returns also play roles in calculating safety margins. Currently, nutrient requirements are based on the maximum level of performance ignoring the cost of the nutrient. With low cost nutrients, excesses have little economic impact, but with expensive nutrients, excesses are costly. If the marginal cost of a nutrient is very high, deficiencies can become tolerable. Few farmers seek maximum corn yields because, at very high levels of fertilization, the cost of additional N exceeds the value of the added yield. Similarly, yield of milk by high producing cows continues to increase with dietary protein level to at least 20% dietary protein. As the cost of additional protein exceeds the value of the added milk, higher levels become uneconomical.

More information about the relative sacrifice in animal performance at various levels of nutrient deficiency is needed to determine the most economic nutrient level to feed. Excluding NPN, protein supplied in slight excess is used for energy, so at lower protein levels the marginal cost of protein is small. Most commercial feedlot diets contain more protein than is required simply to avoid the possibility of a deficiency. In contrast, with lactating cows energetic efficiency can be reduced by gross excesses in protein and the marginal cost of protein at higher protein levels increases, so excesses are avoided. Recent economic analysis (6) has shown that the penalty of protein deficiency is greater during the latter part of the feedlot finishing period. This may be due to the potential for compensatory gain during the latter portion of a finishing period if protein is marginal during the early periods. In contrast, with lactating cows, performance for the total lactation period is sacrificed if nutrient deficiencies occur early in lactation and reduce the amount of milk produced at peak lactation.

SUMMARY

Protein requirements for ruminant animals can be divided into two components—ammonia needs for growth of bacteria within the rumen and amino acids for absorption from the small intestine of the ruminant animal. A deficiency of ammonia within the rumen limits microbial activity, microbial protein synthesis and rate of digestion which in turn reduces feed and energy intake. A deficiency of amino acids for the animal reduces production of meat, milk or wool. The requirements for amino acids by the animal depend on rate and type of production. For maintenance and slow growth, the supply of amino acids from the high quality protein of ruminal microbes alone is adequate, but at high rates of milk production or of growth, microbial protein alone is inadequate. A fraction of the dietary protein escapes degradation by microbes within the rumen and supplements the microbial protein for the animal. Ruminal escape of dietary protein, though difficult to measure and predict, varies with protein source as well as ruminal and feeding conditions. Increased escape is useful only when the animal has an amino acid deficiency and the escape protein is digestible and satisfactorily complements the amino acid supply from microbial protein. Ruminal ammonia deficiencies can be met most economically by adding non-protein nitrogen to the diet, but, again, addition of non-protein nitrogen to the diet is useless if the supply of ammonia is already adequate. Several innovative systems to estimate requirements for ruminally degraded and escape protein have been proposed. But balancing a diet to most economically meet the amino acid requirements of ruminant animals awaits more precise determination of amino acid requirements for maintenance and production. Meanwhile, methods to increase ruminal escape of dietary protein, to enhance microbial protein yield and to supplement specific diets with amino acids or protein which has been coated to escape ruminal attack may be used to increase level of production.

References and Additional Readings

1. Allison, M.J. 1970. In: Physiology of Digestion and Metabolism in the Ruminant, pp. 226-234. A.T. Phillipson, ed. Oriel Press, Newcastle upon Tyne, England.

2. Beever, D.E. 1983. In: Proc. National Wheat Pasture Symposium. Okla. Agr. Exp. Sta. MP-115:65-98.

3. Bergen, W.G., D.E. Johnson, J.C. Waller and J.R. Black. 1982. In: Protein Requirements for Cattle: Symposium. Okla. Agr. Exp. Sta. MP-109:99-112.

4. Bergen, W.G. and F.N. Owens. 1985. Animal Health Nutr. 40(10):32.

5. Braman, W.L. 1972. Protein sources and concentrations for finishing ruminants fed high concentrate diets. Ph. D. Thesis, University of IL., Urbana, IL.

6. Black, J.R. 1985. Mich. Agr. Exp. Sta. Res. Rep. 353:114.

7. Hogan, J.P. and R.H. Weston. 1970. In: Physiology of Digestion and Metabolism in the Ruminant, pp. 474-485. A.T. Phillipson, ed. Oriel Press, Newcastle upon Tyne, England.

8. Leng, R.A. and J.V. Nolan. 1984. J. Dairy Sci. 67:1072.

9. NRC. 1978. Nutrient Requirements of Dairy Cattle, Fifth Revised Ed., Nat. Academy Sci., Washington, DC.

10. NRC. 1984. Nutrient Requirements of Beef Cattle, Sixth Revised Ed., Nat. Academy Sci., Washington, DC.

11. NRC. 1985. Ruminant Nitrogen Usage. Nat. Academy Sci., Washington, DC.

12. Nikolic, J.A., A. Pavlicevic, D. Zeremski and D. Negavanovic. 1980. In: Digestive Physiology and Metabolism in Ruminants, pp. 603-620. Y. Ruckebusch and P. Thivend, eds. AVI Publishing Co., Westport, CT.

13. Nolan, J.V. 1981. In: Isotope-aided Studies on Non-protein Nitrogen and Agro-industrial By-product Utilization by Ruminants with Particular Reference to Developing Countries and Nuclear Techniques for Assessing and Improving Ruminant Feeds. FAO/IAEA. Vienna, Austria.

14. Oldham, J.D. 1984. J. Dairy Sci. 67:1090.

15. Oldham, J.D. 1981. In: Isotope-aided Studies on Non-protein Nitrogen and Agro-industrial By-product Utilization by Ruminants with Particular Reference to Developing Countries and Nuclear Techniques for Assessing and Improving Ruminant Feeds. FAO/IAEA. Vienna, Austria.

16. Ørskov, E.R. 1980. In: Digestive Physiology and Metabolism in Ruminants, pp. 309-324. Y. Ruckebusch and P. Thivend, eds. AVI Publishing Co., Westport, CT.

17. Ørskov, E.R. 1982. Protein Nutrition in Ruminants. Academic Press, London, England.

18. Osweiler, G. 1975. Urea and NPN Toxicosis in Ruminants. Biomedical Communications, Col. Veter. Med., Iowa State Univ., Ames, IA.

19. Owens, F.N. 1982. Protein Requirements of Cattle: Symposium. Okla. Agr. Exp. Sta. MP-109.

20. Owens, F.N. and W.G. Bergen. 1984. J. Animal Sci. 57(Suppl. 2):498.

21. Owens, F.N. and W.G. Bergen. 1985. Animal Health Nutr. 40(10):4

22. Owens, F.N. and A.L. Goetsch. 1986. Digesta passage rates and microbial protein synthesis. In: Digestive Physiology and Metabolism in Ruminants. L.P. Milligan, W.L. Grovum and A. Dobson, eds. Prentice Hall, Englewood Cliffs, NJ.

23. Smith, R.H. and J.D. Oldham. 1981. In: Isotope-aided Studies on Non-protein Nitrogen and Agro-industrial By-product Utilization by Ruminants with Particular Reference to Developing Countries and Nuclear Techniques for Assessing and Improving Ruminant Feeds. FAO/IAEA. Vienna, Austria.

24. Steinhour, W.D. and J.H. Clark. 1982. In: Protein Requirements for Cattle: Symposium. Okla. Agr. Exp. Sta. MP-109:166-182.

25. Van Soest, P.J. 1982. Nutritional Ecology of the Ruminant. O & B Books, Inc., Corvallis, OR.

26. Waldo, D.R. and B.P. Glenn. 1982. In: Protein Requirements of Cattle: Symposium, pp. 296-309. Okla. Agr. Exp. Sta. MP-109:296.

13 ENERGY METABOLISM

by C. L. Ferrell

INTRODUCTION

In the living animal energy is required to perform the "work" of living. A mature fasting sheep weighing 70 kg loses about 1,600 Kcal of heat daily. Body tissues must be metabolized to produce this heat. About 1.2 kg of a moderate quality feed is required daily to maintain body weight and composition of this animal, that is, to offset the body tissue loss. This amount of feed contains about 5,300 Kcal of gross energy (heat of combustion). Of the gross energy consumed, about 2,400 Kcal are lost as feces, 600 Kcal are lost as urine and combustible gases and 2,300 Kcal are lost as heat. Of course, in domestic species it is hoped that animals do more than simply maintain themselves. Thus, animals require feed not only for maintenance but also to support the work of production, e.g., growth fattening, gestation, and lactation. For example, in a beef production cycle feed is required for maintenance of the cow, gestation, lactation and maintenance, growth and fattening of the calf. Of the total gross energy required in this system, about 45% is lost as heat, 40% is lost as feces, 10% is lost as urine and combustible gases and only 5% is retained in the calf to be slaughtered. Of the 5% retained, less than half is edible.

These examples have been presented to emphasize three important points. First, to supply energy to an animal is more costly both biologically and economically than supplying any other nutrient. Second, the primary factors that determine the efficiency of utilization of feed energy are the amounts lost as feces and as heat. Finally, the efficiency of converting feed energy to products for human consumption by ruminants is very low.

Three classic books are available that relate specifically to energy metabolism of animals (1, 2, 3). These books provide a historical perspective as well as an excellent foundation to the field of energy metabolism. Proceedings of the triennial symposium on energy metabolism (beginning in 1958) sponsored by the European Association of Animal Production are available and chronicle the research that has occurred over the last several years. In addition a recent publication of the Agricultural Research Council (4) provides an excellent technical review of many facets of energy utilization and requirements of ruminant livestock.

DEFINITIONS AND ABBREVIATIONS

Energy is defined as the potential to perform work. Energy is an abstraction that can be measured only in reference to defined, standard conditions. Thus, all defined units to measure energy are equally absolute. The joule is the preferred unit for expressing electrical, mechanical and chemical energy. The joule can be converted to ergs, watt-seconds and calories; the converse is also true. The calorie is related to the joule by the expression: 1 calorie = 4.184 joules, and is defined as the heat required to raise the temperature of one gram of water from 16.5° to 17.5°C.

Many of the energy requirements of animals are expressed in terms of energy requirements per unit time. The energy requirements for maintenance of a steer might be expressed as 12 Mcal/d, 50 MJ/d or 580 watts. The joule is used as the standard unit of energy for nutritional work in many countries, however, the calorie is presently used as the standard unit in the USA, thus, will be used throughout this chapter. In practice the calorie is so small that nutritionists work with multiple units. For this reason the kilocalorie (1 Kcal = 1,000 calories) and megacalorie (1 Mcal = 1,000 Kcal) will be used.

A number of abbreviations have been used to describe energy fractions in the animal system. The abbreviations used throughout this chapter are those recommended by the NRC (5). The first measurement in a nutritional evaluation of energy exchange is gross energy. Gross energy (E) or heat of combustion is the energy released as heat when an organic substance is completely oxidized to carbon dioxide and water.

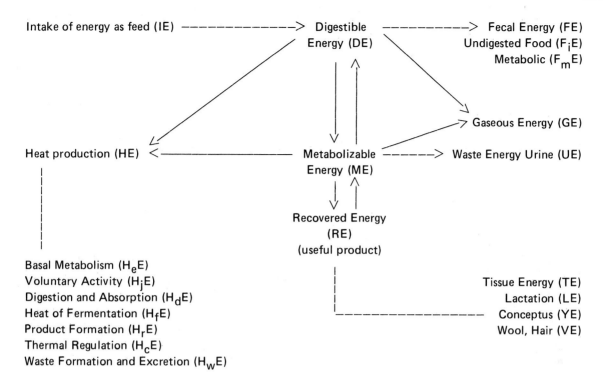

Figure 13-1. Flow of energy through the animal. From NRC (5).

The flow of energy, as outlined by NRC (5), is shown in Fig. 13-1. Definitions and abbreviations of terms used have been described in detail in that publication. Briefly, intake of food energy (IE) is the gross energy of the food consumed. A substantial portion of IE is lost from the animal as fecal energy (FE) and the difference (IE–FE) is termed apparently digested energy (DE). Portions of IE are also lost as urinary energy (UE) and gaseous energy (GE). The remainder (IE–FE–UE–GE) is termed metabolizable energy (ME). ME may be recovered as a useful product (RE) such as tissue energy (TE), milk energy (LE), conceptus energy (YE) or wool or hair (VE) or may be lost as heat. Energy lost as heat (HE) may be the results of a variety of functions including basal metabolism (H_eE), activity (H_jE), digestion and absorption (H_dE), fermentation (H_fE), product formation (H_rE), thermal regulation (H_cE) and waste formation and excretion (H_wE). An increase in heat production following consumption of food is termed heat increment (H_iE) and includes H_dE, H_fE, H_rE and H_wE.

PARTITION OF ENERGY

The laws of thermodynamics and the law of Hess state the fundamental principles on which bioenergetics (the study of energy transformations in biological systems) is based. Simply stated, these laws assert that (a) energy can be neither created nor destroyed but may be converted from one form to another, (b) all forms of energy can be quantitatively converted to heat, and (c) heat generated in a net transformation is independent of the path of conversion.

The basis of bioenergetics as defined by these laws and application to animal nutritional energetics may be stated by use of terminology defined earlier: IE = FE + GE + UE + HE + RE. This identity partitions the food energy consumed by an animal into the major components associated with animal energetics. It can be expanded to include a few or many of the intermediate steps involved and each component can be divided into component parts. For example, in a young, lactating, pregnant heifer, RE may be replaced by

252

TE + LE + YE. The expression will remain compatible with the laws described above, that is, the inclusion or exclusion of more detailed information on intermediate transformations does not prejudice the balance of the equation. All energy balance techniques and all systems used to describe the relationship between the animal's requirement for energy and the usefulness of a food to supply those needs are related to this classical energy balance identity.

Gross energy intake (IE) or the total energy contained in a feedstuff provides little useful information in assessing the value of a particular diet or dietary component as a source of energy for an animal. Gross energy expressed per unit weight may give some index of the potential of a substance to furnish energy. For example, carbohydrates have an E of about 4.2 Kcal/g, thus a feedstuff consisting primarily of carbohydrates might have a similar E, whereas one containing a large amount of protein or fat might have a higher E and one containing a large amount of inorganic substances might have a lower E. Regardless of this, a gross energy value does not provide any information as to how available the energy is to the animal.

DE has some value for the assessment of an animal's requirements and for feed evaluation because the energy lost as feces (FE) is associated with the ability of a diet to meet an animal's need for energy. The major weakness of DE as a basis for a feeding system of ruminants is that it overestimates the value of high-fiber diets in relation to low-fiber diets. This weakness is of less importance in non-ruminant diets because the range in DE or fiber contents of the diets is much less.

ME is of greater value than DE for the assessment of energy values and requirements because it considers gaseous and urinary energy losses. Thus, ME is an estimate of dietary energy available to the animal. However, ME has many of the same weaknesses as DE. Energy lost as UE and GE are highly predictable from DE, thus DE and ME are highly correlated. For most forages and mixtures of forages and cereal grains, the ratio of ME to DE is about 0.82. The definition of ME and the energy balance identity indicate ME can appear only as HE or RE. Thus, ME = HE + RE. As indicated by this relationship, a major value of ME is as a reference unit and as a

starting point for most systems based on the net energy (NE) concept.

The NE of a feed or diet has classically been illustrated by the equality: $NE = \Delta RE \div \Delta IE$. The value of food energy for the promotion of energy retention is measured by determining the RE at two amounts of IE. Determination of NE by this method assumes the relationship between retained energy and food intake is linear. Actually the relationship is curvilinear. This curvilinear relationship is conventionally approximated by two straight lines (Fig. 13-2). The intersection of the two lines is the point at which RE = 0 and is defined as maintenance (M). The relationship between food intake and body tissue loss (negative RE) comprises one portion of the curve and the relationship between food intake and body tissue gain (positive RE) comprises a second portion of the curve. The heat production at zero food intake (H_eE) is equivalent to the animal's NE requirement for maintenance. The ability of the food consumed to meet the NE requirement for maintenance is expressed as NE_m and is represented by the following expression: $NE_m = H_eE/I_m$, where I_m is the amount of food consumed at RE = 0. Similarly, the ability of food consumed to promote energy retention is represented by the expression NE_r and is determined as: $NE_r = RE/I - I_m$, where $I - I_m$ represents the amount of food consumed above maintenance.

The relationship ME = RE + HE can be rewritten in terms of NE. Thus,

$$ME = RE + H_eE + H_jE + H_iE$$

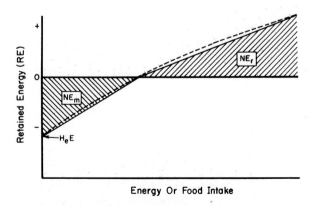

Figure 13-2. The relationship of retained energy to food intake. Adapted from NRC (5).

or, because in practical situations, the heat of activity associated with obtaining food (H_jE) is often included with H_eE, the expression becomes $ME = NE_r + NE_m + H_jE$. The NE_r used in this expression does not distinguish among the different forms in which energy may be retained, e.g., body tissue, milk or tissues of the conceptus. It is not possible to assign a single NE_r value to a food for all productive functions because ME may be used with different efficiencies. Thus, the former expression might be expanded such that in a pregnant, lactating heifer it becomes the following:

$$RE = LE + YE + TE$$
or
$$NE_r = NE_l + NE_y + NE_g,$$
thus,
$$ME = NE_g + NE_l + NE_y + NE_m + H_iE.$$

A portion of the heat increment (H_iE) is associated with the food consumed for maintenance and each of the productive functions. For a NE system to have practical application, multiple NE values must be assigned to each feed. Alternatively, ME values may be adjusted for maintenance and the various productive functions or the animal's energy requirements may be expressed in terms of a single NE value.

It is possible to convert ME values to NE values if the efficiency of ME use (k) for a particular function is known. The efficiency of use of ME for maintenance can be expressed as:

$$k_m = H_eE/ME_m \quad \text{or} \quad k_m = NE_m/ME_m.$$

Likewise, the efficiency of ME use for tissue energy retention may be expressed as:

$$k_g = TE/ME - ME_m$$
or
$$k_g = NE_g/ME - ME_m.$$

Efficiencies of ME use for other productive functions may be expressed similarly. It is important to note that efficiencies of use of ME vary depending on the source of ME and on function for which it is to be used.

TECHNIQUES FOR THE STUDY OF ENERGY METABOLISM

Balance Studies

Many of the techniques currently used to study energy metabolism have been reviewed recently (6). As indicated previously, a major proportion of IE of an animal is lost as feces. The amount of FE is primarily a function of the physical and chemical characteristics of the food consumed and to a lesser extent the level of intake. As a result the digestion trial has often been used on the basis of many studies (see Ch. 9). From the data obtained the DE content of the diet can be determined. These are very laborious procedures to follow, thus many alternative procedures have been evaluated. These include the use of markers such as chromic oxide, polyethylene glycol or the rare earths, in vitro fermentation, or laboratory analysis of the chemical characteristics of the feedstuff. To date, none of the indirect methods approach the accuracy of the direct approach, but in many situations are useful because the direct approach is impossible or impractical.

In many circumstances energy lost as urine (UE) is determined in conjunction with the determination of FE. This measurement involves the quantitative collection of urine during the collection period and the subsequent determination of its gross energy content by bomb calorimetry. An assessment of the gaseous energy loss (GE) in conjunction with these measurements allows the assessment of the ME content of the diet. The measurement of GE is usually determined by respiratory exchange in a respiration calorimeter.

In addition to the above measurements, some researchers have, by determining the C and N contents of the feed, feces, urine and respired gases, obtained estimates of C and N balance of the animal. From those estimates RE may be calculated. Alternatively, calorimetry may be used to estimate heat loss as described below.

Calorimetry

Techniques of calorimetry have been discussed in detail by Blaxter (3), and in the proceedings of the 4th symposium on energy

254

metabolism (7), thus only a brief description of the procedures involved will be included in this chapter. An animal loses heat to the environment as sensible heat or as evaporative heat. Sensible heat is lost through convection, conduction and radiation, and evaporative heat is lost through the excreta, or via the skin and respiratory tract. Heat loss can be measured directly (direct calorimetry) using either heat sink or gradient layer calorimeters. In the heat sink calorimeter, sensible heat loss is measured as a rise in temperature of an absorbing medium such as the air stream ventilating the chamber or water circulating outside its walls. Evaporative heat loss can be determined from the increase in humidity of the ventilating air. The gradient layer calorimeter measures sensible heat loss from the temperature differences across a conducting layer between the animal and a constant temperature source. Evaporative heat loss can be measured with precision as the heat balance across the air conditioning system for the chamber. Because of the extremely high costs of these types of systems, few are presently in operation.

Indirect calorimetry is based on the principle that metabolic heat production is the result of oxidation of organic compounds. Thus, if all compounds were completely oxidized, heat production could be readily calculated from the amounts of O_2 consumed and the amount of CO_2 produced. However, in the animal, incomplete oxidation of protein results in combustible nitrogenous compounds, primarily urea, that are excreted in the urine. In addition, anaerobic fermentation yields combustible gases, primarily CH_4. For ruminants, the equation to estimate heat production is:

$$HE = 3.886\ O_2 + 1.200\ CO_2 - 0.518\ CH_4 - 1.431\ N,$$

where HE is in Kcal, O_2, CO_2 and CH_4 refer to gaseous exchange in liters and N refers to urinary N in grams (8). The contribution of CH_4 and N to the above equation is small. It is often sufficient to estimate HE from O_2 and CO_2 or even from O_2 alone.

Indirect or respiration calorimeters may be of the closed circuit or open circuit type. In the closed circuit type the animal is enclosed in a temperature controlled chamber. The air

in the chamber is continuously circulated through an absorbant such as silica gel or KOH which removes water and CO_2. Constant pressure is maintained within the system by a supply of pure O_2. CH_4 is allowed to accumulate within the chamber. CH_4 production is calculated as the concentration difference between the beginning and end of the test period times the volume of the system.

The most common type of calorimeter is the open circuit indirect calorimeter. In this type of system, a mask, hood or animal chamber may be used. Air is drawn past the animal at a precisely determined rate. O_2, CO_2 and CH_4 concentrations must be accurately determined in both the incoming and outgoing air. Rates of consumption or production of these gases are calculated as the difference in concentration between incoming and outgoing air times the flow rate. This type of system is relatively inexpensive and easy to construct but is susceptible to error because of the high degree of accuracy required in the measurement of air flow and gas concentrations.

The CO_2 entry rate technique is based on principles similar to those of indirect calorimetry. This technique involves the infusion of $NaH^{14}CO_3$ at a constant rate into the animal and observation of the specific activity of CO_2 in the body. After the $NaH^{14}CO_3$ has reached equilibrium with the body pool of CO_2, the CO_2 entry rate is calculated from the ratio of the infused radioactivity to the specific activity of CO_2 in the body. Energy expenditures are then estimated using a previously determined relationship between energy expenditures and CO_2 entry rate. This procedure generally is less accurate than other procedures based on gaseous exchange, but has an advantage in that it can be applied to unrestrained animals, e.g., animals on pasture.

Various physiological variables have been proposed for use as indices of energy expenditures in unrestrained animals. Perhaps one of the more viable of these is heart rate. However, it appears that the individual animal's relationship between heart rate and energy expenditure must be calibrated for each situation.

Comparative Slaughter
In contrast to calorimetry, in which ME intake and HE are determined and RE estimated by difference, comparative slaughter

procedures measure RE directly. Briefly, a uniform group of animals are fed a common ration for a minimum of two weeks. At the end of the adaptation period, a sample of the animals is slaughtered and the body energy content is determined. The remaining animals undergo predetermined treatments for a period of time, and are then slaughtered and energy contents of the bodies are determined. The RE is then calculated as the difference in body energy contents between the initial and final slaughter groups. These techniques have advantages over the calorimetric techniques because they usually allow experiments to be conducted under situations more similar to those found in the livestock industries. They must be conducted over an extended time period, however, to allow accurate assessment of body energy changes.

Body energy content has often been determined by the accurate but expensive technique of whole body grindings and chemical analysis. This technique is expensive, laborious and destructive (i.e., an animal can be used only once). Thus, this technique is often used to calibrate other less expensive techniques such as carcass density or specific gravity. The search for non-destructive, inexpensive methods of estimation of body composition (hence, energy retention) has led to the evaluation of numerous methods including various water dilution procedures, ultrasonic scanning, ^{40}K counting, three dimensional photography, nuclear magnetic resonance and computer assisted tomography. Although several of these methods show promise, each has limitations that have restricted their application.

Other Techniques

The techniques briefly described above have been used to study energy metabolism in th whole animal. However, it should be noted that studies of energy metabolism at lower levels may facilitate greater understanding of the origins and source of heat production or energy expenditures in the animal. To present a detailed description of the numerous techniques that have been employed to study energy metabolism at the organ or tissue, cellular or subcellular level is beyond the scope of this chapter. However, a few of the procedures will be presented briefly to indicate

that several techniques are available and are useful for the study of energy metabolism.

Blood flow has been used as an index of energy expenditures by various body organs or tissues. Thus, blood flow to a specific tissue as a proportion of cardiac output has been used as a relative index of the energy expenditure of that tissue. Measurement of O_2 arterial-venous concentration difference or blood temperature difference across a specific tissue in conjunction with blood flow, allows a direct quantitation of the energy use or the heat output of that tissue. These approaches have facilitated assessment of the relative importance of different body tissues as they contribute to heat production or energy expenditures of the whole animal. These approaches have been used, for example, to measure and separate heat generated from the digestive tract into anaerobic and aerobic origins and have been used successfully to measure energy expenditures or substrate flux across the digestive tract, liver, gravid uterus, fetus, and hind limb. In vitro tissue preparations or isolated cell preparations have proven useful to evaluate treatment effects on tissue energy expenditures and to assess the relative energy costs of various metabolic processes. For example, these techniques have been useful for the assessment of energy costs associated with protein synthesis and with ion pumping.

As much as these types of approaches have contributed to the understanding of energy metabolism within the animal, their contribution is relatively small compared to that potentially available from studies of physiological and biochemical mechanisms associated with energy expenditure at the cellular or subcellular level. For example, numerous catabolic (e.g., glucose-glucose-6-phosphate; pyruvate - phosphoenolypyruvate), anabolic (e.g., triglyceride-fatty acid+glycerol; protein-amino acid) and translocation (Na pump; Ca pump) cycles are known to exist in the animal body. The energy costs of these types of cycles and how they impinge on energy transactions of the animal are only beginning to be understood. Their importance is suggested, for example, by observations that the Na-K pump may account for 20-30% of basal energy expenditures. Other observations suggest that increased rate of cycling of the

256

triglyceride-fatty acid cycle in response to feeding may be equivalent to 10% of the H_eE.

Obviously, intuitive integration of knowledge of energy expending processes at the subcellular level for application to the animal level is difficult, if not impossible. Mathematical modeling is proving to be a useful, objective and quantitative tool to bridge that gap. This approach is proving useful not only to integrate knowledge, but to identify critical areas in which information or concepts are deficient or inaccurate. The usefulness and some of the limitations of this tool are indicated in a recent publication edited by Baldwin and Bywater (9).

DIGESTIBILITY AND METABOLIZABILITY

In the ruminant retained energy increases as the amount of feed given increases; however, this relationship is not linear and, as shown in Fig. 13-3, the relationship varies with type of diet. The reasons for these types of response are not completely understood, but involve, in part, differences in rate and extent of digestion, amounts and proportions of energy-yielding products of digestion, efficiency of energy utilization when body tissues are being oxidized versus use of food energy for energy retention, rate of body metabolism associated with level of feeding and efficiency of synthesis of different products (eg., protein vs fat).

The rate and extent of digestion as well as ciency of synthesis of different products are primarily influenced by the chemical and physical nature of the diet. For example, fecal losses contain about 13% metabolic fecal components plus 2% from the non-structural components plus 10-90% of the structural components (depending on lignification and physical structure) of the feedstuff. Thus, in general, feedstuffs such as grains that contain a low proportion of structural components are highly digestible whereas those such as straws that contain a high proportion of structural components are of lower digestibility. Digestibilities may be depressed under conditions in which rate of passage is increased or when fiber digestion is depressed as in high starch diets. The fecal loss form non-structural components may be much greater than expected for unprocessed

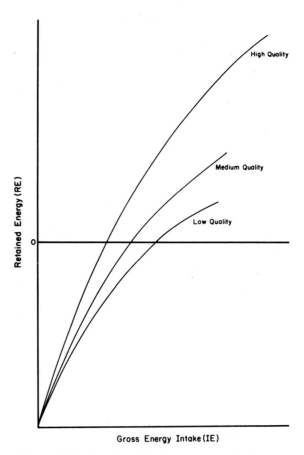

Figure 13-3. Relationship between retained energy and gross energy intake for foods of differing qualities. From ARC (4).

or minimally processed grains in grain-forage mixed diets, especially at high intakes. The numerous factors influencing the digestibility of feedstuffs have been discussed in greater detail in Chapter 9 and in the proceedings of the symposium on physiology of digestion and metabolism in the ruminant, held every five years beginning in 1959.

Differences in digestibility within species and between breeds are negligible. For example, in studies cited by Wainman (10), no differences in digestibility were found when six breeds of sheep were compared, when *Bos indicus* and *Bos taurus* breeds of cattle were compared or when different breeds of *Bos taurus* cattle were compared. Only small differences have been observed when different species of ruminants have been compared. Goats appear to digest low-protein diets with slightly greater efficiency than sheep or cattle. Food appears to be retained in the digestive tract of red deer for a shorter time than in the digestive tract of sheep. This is associated with lower digestibility of the fibrous components of the diet. Although the data are limited, bison appear to digest low quality forage diets slightly better than cattle; however, this difference has not been observed with higher quality forages. Again, it should be noted that differences in these comparisons have been small. Thus, tables of DE or ME for ruminants can be applied to all ruminant species of economic importance with reasonable confidence.

Intake Level

In ruminants, when the amount of food ingested is increased, the proportion of IE lost as feces increases and the apparent digestibility decreases. The depression in apparent digestibility is greater for finely ground forages and for mixed diets containing grain than for long forages and may be greater for less digestible grains (or less processed grains). The ARC (4) concluded the decrease in apparent digestibility depended on the digestibility of the diet determined at the maintenance level. Thus, the change in digestibility (Δd_e) associated with a change in feeding level, expressed as a multiple of maintenance, was expressed relative to the digestibility (d_e) of the diet by the equation: $\Delta d_e = 0.107 - 0.113 d_e$. This equation implies, for example, that a diet having a digestibility of 0.70 at maintenance would have a digestibility of $0.70 - (0.107 - 0.113*0.70)$ or 0.672 at twice maintenance and 0.561 at five times maintenance. The depression in digestibility may not be of major importance in a growing-finishing animal in which intake rarely exceeds three times maintenance, but can become quite meaningful in lactating dairy cows where intake may exceed five times maintenance.

The proportional losses of energy as CH_4 and in urine decrease as level of intake or digestibility decreases. Thus, an increase in the proportion of energy lost as feces tends to be compensated for by decreased losses as CH_4 and in the urine. The net effect is that metabolizability or ME is less affected by intake than is digestibility or DE. For example, the metabolizability of a diet having a digestibility of 0.70 is expected to be about 0.57 at maintenance. At two and five times maintenance the metabolizability is expected

to be about 0.56 and 0.53, respectively. Thus, an increase in feed consumption of a diet of this type from maintenance to five times maintenance is expected to result in a decrease in metabolizability of less than 7% whereas a decrease in digestibility of about 20% is expected. In most practical situations, diets used for growing or finishing ruminants are of sufficient quality and food consumption sufficiently low (3X maintenance) that correction of ME for feeding level is not necessary. Correction for feeding level may be recommended if poor quality diets are used or if food consumption is extremely high.

Associative Effects

In most feeding systems the ME content of different feedstuffs are considered to be additive. Thus, if foods A and B have ME contents of 3.00 and 1.50 Mcal/kg, then a diet containing equal amounts of A and B is expected to contain 2.25 [(3.00 x 1.50)/2] Mcal/kg. The term "associative effect" is used in reference to the influence one food has on the utilization of another when the two are fed in combination. Thus, any deviation from additivity is considered an associative effect; however, the term is most commonly used when one food has a negative effect on the utilization of another, i.e., a negative associative effect. A schematic representation of additivity and negative associative effects is shown in Fig. 13-4.

An associative effect can be considered only in conjunction with the term balanced diet. A balanced diet may be defined as one in which all nutrients are present in amounts which do not limit the utilization of other nutrients. However, in ruminants this concept is complicated by the presence of ruminal digestion. For example, a given diet may contain adequate amounts of protein; however, if inadequate amounts of protein are available to the rumen microbes at the proper time, growth of the microbes and, as a result, microbial digestion of fibrous components of the diet may be depressed. As a result of this type of phenomenon, many of the observed negative associative effects may be in fact attributable to dietary imbalance. Negative associative effects between grains and forages are most likely to occur with high intakes and may occur, in part, due to low ruminal pH

258

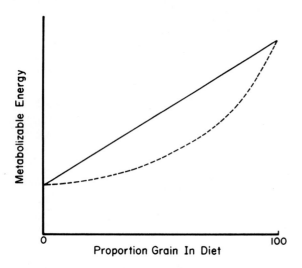

Figure 13-4. Schematic representation of additivity (—) and negative associative effects (— —).

and increased rate of passage. A depressing effect of certain types of fiber on starch digestion overall or an amylase function is a possibility that has received some support.

Feed Additives

Ruminants lose, as combustible gases (primarily CH_4) from 5-12% of the dietary energy ingested, depending on the nature of the diet and the level of intake (11). Many compounds such as chloroform, fatty acids or their analogs or halogenated methane analogs are known to suppress methanogenesis. The same compounds influence the fermentation pattern by increasing the proportion of propionate and reducing the proportion acetate. Thus, potential benefits could result from a reduction of the energy loss as CH_4 and, with some diets, increased gluconeogenic precursors. However, to date, addition of CH_4 inhibitors has resulted in little practical benefit. In some studies additions of CH_4 inhibitors have resulted in decreased food consumption. In others the microbiol population has apparently adapted to the inhibitor over time such that the CH_4 production and other fermentation products have returned to normal patterns within a few weeks.

Monensin and lasalocid are antibiotic feed additives that have been used effectively with ruminants. In general, feed consumption is reduced when these compounds are added to the diet whereas rate of gain is usually not affected, resulting in increased feed

efficiency. The mechanisms of action of these compounds have not been fully elucidated, however, part of the benefit of these compounds may result from a reduction in methanogenesis and an increase in the propionate to acetate ratio. These effects are similar to those of other methane-inhibiting compounds. In addition, some evidence is available indicating ruminal lactic acid production is decreased and ruminal pH is increased when these compounds are added to high-grain diets. This effect may be of substantial benefit in situations conducive to chronic or subacute acidosis (see Ch. 23). These compounds appear to have no major effect on digestibility. However, additional benefits of these compounds may result from a reduction in maintenance requirements by altering the flux of Na and K in tissues, thus decreasing the energy expenditures for Na transport.

UTILIZATION OF ME

The animal uses ME for maintenance, tissue gain, gestation, lactation and muscular activity. Energy expenditures and efficiency of energy utilization vary within and among each of these functions. Some of the factors contributing to energy expenditures and efficiencies of ME utilization will be addressed in the following paragraphs.

Maintenance

The ME requirement for maintenance (ME_m) is defined as the ME intake at which RE = 0, thus ME_m is equivalent to fasting heat production (H_eE) plus the heat increment of the food consumed (H_iE). The importance of maintenance energy requirements to the overall animal economy is demonstrated by the observation that 65-70% of the ME needed for beef production is utilized to meet the needs of maintenance functions (12). Thus, an understanding of the factors contributing to maintenance energy expenditures and to efficiencies (or conversely inefficiencies) of energy use for maintenance is a necessary part of developing an understanding of the animal's energy economy.

As the above definition of maintenance indicates, ME_m is a function of H_eE and H_iE or, expressed in a different manner, ME_m is a function of the energy required for essential life processes and the efficiency with which the ME from food is used to meet those requirements. Thus, both the animal and food source contribute to the amount of ME required for maintenance.

To be precise, the term maintenance should be used to refer to the amount of energy required to keep a non-pregnant, non-lactating adult (i.e., non-productive) in energy balance. Brody (1) and Kleiber (2) have shown that H_eE in different species of adult, non-productive mammals is about 70 Kcal/kg$^{-0.75}$/d. In practice, the term maintenance has been used frequently to apply to productive animals, that is growing, pregnant and/or lactating animals, as well as non-productive adults. When so used the meaning and measurement of maintenance become less clear. For example, a growing animal may gain structural components and body weight but lose tissue energy; a lactating cow generally produces milk at the expense of tissue energy. Body weight in kilograms raised to the 0.75 power, often referred to as metabolic body size, was originally used to confer proportionality on measurements of H_eE made in species differing considerably in mature weight (i.e., mice to elephants), but has been adopted with varying degrees of success for use in expressing H_eE and food energy requirements of animals within a species. In fact H_eE even in adult ruminants may differ substantially from 70 Kcal/kg$^{0.75}$/d. This value varies among species and has a mean value of about 60 for sheep and about 80 for cattle.

Elements of the animal's maintenance requirements (H_eE) may be viewed as being of two types: service functions and functions associated with cell maintenance. Service functions include functions that are performed by tissues or organs for the benefit of the entire, integrated organism. Included in these functions are the work of circulation and respiration, liver and kidney work (eg., detoxification, maintenance of body osmolarity and pH) and nervous functions. In total these functions account for about 35-50% of H_eE (13).

Major components of cell maintenance are ion transport (especially Na and Ca transport), protein turnover and lipid turnover (Table 13-1). These metabolic functions are examples of what is often referred to as substrate or futile cycles. These three cycles alone may account for as much as 30-50% of H_eE. Other

Table 13-1. Contributions of substrate cycles to maintenance energy expenditures.[a]

Cycle	Percentage contribution
Ion transport	20-30
Protein turnover	10-20
Triacyglycerol turnover	2-3
Glucose, glucose-6-phosphate	2
Pyruvate, Phophoenolypyruvate	1
Fructose-6-phosphate, Fructose-1,6-bisphosphate	2

[a]Adapted from Baldwin and Bauman (13)

substrate cycles such as those indicated in Table 13-1 contribute further to H_eE, but appear to be of lower energetic cost. Although these types of processes contribute significantly to H_eE and, in the case of protein, to the apparent costs of protein accretion, their role in the animal's rapid adaptation to constantly changing internal and external environments is essential to life. Other metabolic processes such as glycogen turnover, gluconeogenesis, ketogenesis, urea synthesis, RNA and DNA synthesis, among many others, require the expenditure of energy, thus contribute to the animal's maintenance energy expenditures.

Maintenance energy expenditures vary with age, body weight, breed or species, sex, physiological state, season, temperature and previous nutrition (12). The reasons are complex and have not been explained fully. However, part of this variation may be explained by differences in rates of substrate cycles. For example, energy expenditure for ion transport varies among tissues and is apparently greater in lactating than in non-lactating animals, is higher in young than in mature animals and is greater in cold-adapted animals than in those not cold-adapted (14). Similarly, protein turnover rates vary tremendously among tissues, are higher in young than in mature animals and decrease in response to lower planes of nutrition. Triacylglyceride turnover, likewise increases in response to increased plane of nutrition.

Variation in H_eE may also be explained, in part, by variation in proportions of various body tissues or organs. Table 13-2 shows typical masses, as proportions of body weight, of the various body organs or tissues, the relative proportion of cardiac output they receive and an estimate of their relative energy expenditures. These estimates illustrate that although the combined masses of nervous tissue, heart, kidney, digestive tract and liver account for less than 10% of body mass, they receive about 55% of cardiac output and account for about 50-60% of H_eE. The high energy expenditures of these tissues may be partially explained by high rates of protein turnover and ion transport activities as well as the numerous other metabolic and service functions they perform. It is obvious that energy expenditures of these tissues per unit mass are considerably above the average of all body tissues. A change in the proportion of these tissues may have a large impact on overall animal H_eE. Proportions of liver and digestive tract tissues and, to a lesser extent, kidney and heart differ in response to nutritional level, physiological state and breed. As shown in Table 13-3, changes in masses of these tissues appear to account for a large proportion of the change in H_eE associated with nutritional manipulations. In other studies, changes in the proportion of liver, heart and digestive tract of lactating as compared to non-lactating animals, were sufficiently large to account for a 24% increase in maintenance. Proportions of certain metabolically active internal organs have also been shown to vary among cattle breeds (12).

The proportions of protein and fat in the body may also contribute to variations in H_eE. Several reports have shown that H_eE or ME_m is highly correlated with body lean or protein mass and less highly correlated with body fat mass. Further, genetically lean animals generally have higher maintenance requirements than genetically obese animals. These observations may reflect, in part, strong

Table 13-2. Estimated mass, blood flow and energy expenditures of tissue and organ systems of a ruminant 24 h post-feeding.[a]

Tissue	Mass, % of empty body weight	Cardiac output, %	Total energy expenditures, %
Nervous tissue	2.0	10.0	12.0
Skin	6.3	8.0	2.7
Heart	0.4	4.1	10.0
Kidney	0.3	13.4	5.0
Digestive tract	4.0	23.0	15.0
Liver	1.5	27.0	20.5
Muscle	41.0	18.0	23.0
Adipose tissue	15.0	9.6	7.0
Other (skeleton, etc.)	29.5	9.9	4.8

[a] Adapted with modifications from Smith (15). Liver percentage of cardiac output includes venous blood flow from the digestive tract as well as arterial flow.

Table 13-3. Effect of nutritional treatment on organ weight and fasting heat production.[a]

Nutritional treatment	Body weight, kg	Digestive tract, g	Liver, g	Kidney, g	Heart, g	Fasting heat production, Kcal/d
High	44.0	1.889	668	121	155	1,674
Medium	47.2	1.653	625	114	143	1,549
Low	39.9	1,304	428	93	126	1,143
Very low	34.4	1,162	350	83	130	966

[a] Adopted from Ferrell and Jenkins (12)

relationships between body lean and energetically expensive metabolic processes such as certain substrate cycles and between body lean mass and energy required for service functions as well as higher energy expenses of maintenance of lean tissues as compared to adipose tissues.

Numerous other factors may effect H_eE. To discuss all or even a major part of the potential sources of variation in H_eE is beyond the scope of this chapter. In any case, many of the contributors to variation in H_eE are only beginning to be understood and the magnitude of their contribution is yet to be appreciated.

The ME requirement for maintenance varies as a function of H_iE or k_m as well as H_eE. Over the range of ME concentrations fed to beef cattle, for example, of 2.0 to 3.0 Mcal/kg, the k_m increases about 10 percentage units, i.e., from about 65-75% (17). Thus, a 450-kg steer having a daily maintenance requirement of 13 Mcal ME when fed a diet containing 2.0 Mcal ME/kg would require about 11 Mcal ME when fed a diet containing 3.0 Mcal ME/kg. The change in H_iE due to diet is, in part, related to the nutrients available to the animal. This is because nutrients do not replace one another in proportion to their heats of combustion, but rather to the extent that they provide free energy to the cells of the body. The efficiency with which energy is trapped and becomes available to the cell as high-energy phosphate bonds varies among different metabolic pathways and can be calculated for different nutrients from the stoichiometry of the pathways involved. For example, if the relative value of glucose is set at 100%, acetate, proprionate, butyrate, stearate and proteins have values of 85, 87, 91, 95 and 76-79%, respectively (13). These estimates imply that ME_m can vary by as much as 20-25% depending on the nutrients available to the animal.

In actuality, this range in efficiencies due to nutrient source is rarely observable in the ruminant animal; mixtures of these and other nutrients are presented to the animal. In the ruminant animal particular attention must be given to the efficiency of utilization VFA because their heats of combustion account for about 65% of the energy absorbed from the digestive tract. In general the molar proportions of acetate and butyrate are higher on high-forage diets and lower on high-concentrate diets. Conversely, the molar proportion of proprionate is lower on forage diets and higher on concentrate diets. The range in k_m that can be attributed to varying proportions of VFA observed with diets typically consumed by ruminants is about 5%. Additional energy is supplied from the diet primarily as longer chain fatty acids, lactate and proteins. The proportions of these nutrients available also contribute to differences in k_m.

In addition to the varying efficiencies of utilization of nutrients to supply free energy to cells, the k_m of diets differ as a result of differing heats of fermentation and differing amounts of work required for prehension, mastication and rumination and to propel the food through the digestive tract (4). Evidence to date indicates that inefficiencies of nutrient metabolism account for about 65-70%, the energy costs of eating and rumination account for about 20-25% and the work of digestion accounts for about 10% of H_iE.

Tissue Gain

It should be recognized at the outset of this discussion that separation of energy retention (whether energy retention is in the form of tissue gain, conceptive tissue development or milk production) from maintenance is strictly artificial. In the animal these are highly integrated, interrelated processes; the separation is for simplicity and for "accounting" purposes. With this thought in mind, it is of considerable advantage to view the process of growth as the net result of synthesis and degradation rather than as simple accretion of body water, protein, fat and minerals. Taken in this context many of the concepts relating to energy retention represent extensions of concepts discussed previously in regards to maintenance.

In considering factors that influence the efficiency of utilization of ME for tissue energy gain, it is instructive to first consider the normal pattern of growth as determined by the net result of protein and fat synthesis and degradation. A schematic of the typical relationship between body protein and fat as growth proceeds with reasonably good nutrition is shown in Fig. 13-5. There have been numerous experiments with cattle and sheep on how nutrition can shift the normal pattern of growth. In general, protein levels below

262

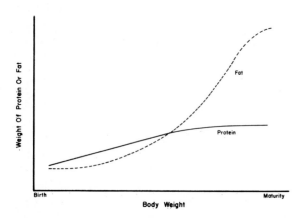

Figure 13-5. Schematic representation of the protein and fat contents of the body. Adopted from Garrett (17).

that which permits expression of the genetic potential for growth may result in a measurable difference in the composition of the animal. These differences, when observed, have been relatively small. Protein intakes above that necessary to permit protein deposition to the animal's genetic potential does not stimulate protein deposition. Several studies have shown that feeding of high-concentrate diets to appetite from weaning may result in animals being fatter at a given weight than those fed diets having lower energy densities. However, in some studies no effect of energy density of the diet on body composition has been observed. Overall, assuming reasonably good nutrition, nutritional manipulations have a relatively small influence on the body composition of the animal at a given weight as compared to differences that may be achieved through selection of genotype. That is, with reasonably good nutrition, the genotype of the animal is the primary determinant of body composition and composition of body tissue gain. This is not to say that body composition cannot be altered substantially by severe nutritional treatment, however, nutritional manipulations beyond the range normally feasible due to economic restraints are required.

The efficiency of utilization of ME above maintenance for tissue energy gain (k_g) is a function of an array of metabolic functions within the animal and the ability of absorbed nutrients to meet those metabolic demands. It is possible to calculate, with a knowledge of the metabolic pathways involved, estimates of

the theoretical maximum efficiencies by which animals can perform productive functions. Using this approach Baldwin and co-workers (13) have estimated the theoretical maximum efficiency of growth of ruminants to be 70-80%. Estimates of k_g in growing ruminants has been in the range of 30-60%, however. These observations are used to indicate that few animals achieve theoretically maximum efficiencies and there is wide variation in efficiencies among animals.

In the previous section, turnover and repair were discussed as elements of maintenance. The energy costs of turnover also contribute substantially to the apparent inefficiencies of tissue accretion. The data presented in Table 13-4 emphasize that turnover rates of protein vary considerably among body tissues. For example, in the growing animal as much as 70% of the protein of the jejunum must be replaced each day. In addition to varying among tissues, protein turnover rates have been shown to vary with age, body size, physiological state and level of nutrition. High protein turnover rates certainly lower

Table 13-4. Fractional rate of protein synthesis and proportion of total protein synthesis of different tissues of the pig.[a]

Tissue	Fractional rate, %/d	Percentage of total synthesis
Stomach	22.9	
Duodenum	45.2	
Jejunum	70.0	19.4-22.6
Ileum	42.5	
Caecum	57.2	
Colon	44.0	
Liver	28.0	
Pancreas	88.0	16.5-17.0
Kidney cortex	15.1	
Kidney medulla	15.7	
Gastrocnemius muscle	3.6	
Soleus muscle	4.7	24.1-27.6
Heart	5.9	
Skin	8.6	6.0-6.9
Other		30

[a]From Simon et al (16)

the net efficiency with which protein accretion can occur. For example, if protein accretion only required the digestion, absorption, transport and uptake of amino acids and the synthesis of the peptide bond, net efficiency of protein accretion would be in the 75-85% range (13). Turnover of protein alone can reduce this efficiency by 15-40%. Factors in addition to turnover that might reduce the net efficiency of protein accretion include the use of amino acids as energy sources and rearrangements among non-essential amino acids that might be required to match the balance of amino acids in the protein being synthesized. As a result of these and other factors as well as turnover, the net efficiency of protein accretion in ruminants has been observed to be 12-40%.

Estimates of the net efficiency of fat accretion have been relatively similar to theoretical estimates of efficiencies of fat synthesis in ruminants. Estimates of the efficiency of fat accretion have been in the 60-80% range and average about 70%. The apparently high efficiency of fat accretion may be the result of relatively low rates of turnover and relatively high efficiency of synthesis from the nutrients available.

Also associated with the apparent inefficiencies are the increases in other substrate cycles such as ion transport with increases in feed intake. Work associated with service functions such as liver, kidney, and digestive tract work and possibly the work associated with respiration must increase in response to increased nutrition. Some of the differences among animals may be attributed to differences in rates of the substrate cycles and other metabolic functions as well as differing amounts of energy required for service functions.

The source of ME certainly has a marked influence on k_g. In general, k_g decreases as ME concentration in the diet decreases. As can be seen in Fig. 13-6, not only is k_g lower than k_m, the change in k_g varies more with ME than does k_m. Over the range of ME concentrations of diets commonly fed to growing cattle (2.0 to 3.0 Mcal/kg), this decrease in k_g associated with diets lower in ME indicates that a 300-kg steer depositing 5.0 Mcal of energy per day would have to consume 15.6 Mcal ME above maintenance of a diet containing 2.0 Mcal/kg versus 10.2 Mcal ME of a diet

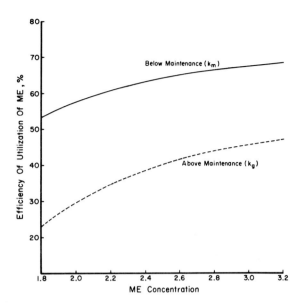

Figure 13-6. The effect of ME concentration in the diet on the efficiency of utilization of ME for maintenance and tissue energy gain in cattle. After NCR (25).

containing 3.0 Mcal/kg (17). Available evidence suggests only a small proportion of the differences in k_g can be attributed to the work of ingestion and digestion. The primary reasons for these differences appear to relate to the nature of the substrates made available to the animal and the metabolic decisions made within the animal for use of the substrates that are available. For example, efficiencies of 30-60% have been observed when acetate is used for fatty acid synthesis. In comparison, efficiencies of 60-80% have been reported when glucose was used and 90% or greater have been reported when dietary fat was used for fatty acid synthesis. Similarly, gluconeogenesis is much more efficient when propionate or lactate is available as glucose precursors than when amino acids must be used. The pattern of nutrient use within the animal can have an impact on apparent k_g. If, for example, VFA are used for fat synthesis and fatty acids are used for maintenance functions versus the reverse, heat increment can vary about two fold (13).

Gestation

The growth of the tissues of the gravid uterus (uterus, fetus, placenta and fetal fluids) together with the mammary gland represents a high priority requirement for energy in

264

animals. Growth of these tissues can be modified only to a limited extent by diet, sheep being more susceptible to modification than cattle. Energy accretion in the tissues of the gravid uterus has been determined in several serial slaughter experiments and estimated from respiration calorimetry trials with sheep and cattle. A typical energy accretion curve for cattle is shown in Fig. 13-7.

The efficiency of energy utilization for growth of gravid uterine tissues (k_y) is usually defined as energy recovered in these tissues divided by the ME used for growth of those tissues. When this definition is used, k_y has been relatively uniform and low (i.e., 10-20%) and average about 13%. Some of this variation is possibly of dietary origin. A review of data in sheep (18) suggests the evidence would tentatively justify the hypothesis that k_y is related to the ME concntration in the diet in a similar way as k_m or k_g. Robinson et al (18) also suggested ME from diets containing less than 2.4 Mcal/kg were used with less efficiency than were body tissues.

Recent evidence indicates that about half of the increase in heat production during gestation is the result of increased maternal energy expenditures. Presumably, a large part of this is attributable to increased work of service functions, e.g., increased cardiac output and increased liver and kidney work. In addition, a large proportion of the energy actually used by the tissues of the gravid uterus is used by the uterus and placenta. These tissues account for 50-80% of the energy expenditures of the gravid uterus. Although the

reasons for the high energy expenditures of these tissues have not been fully elucidated, they, in general, may be viewed as service functions necessary to maintain an optimum intra-uterine environment for fetal growth. Of the energy actually made available to the fetus for growth and maintenance, about 35-40% is retained in fetal tissues. The reasons for the loss of 60-65% of the energy available to the fetus are similar to those discussed previously in relation to efficiencies of maintenance and tissue energy gain.

Lactation

The efficiency of utilization of ME was defined previously as the increase in energy retention as a result of a unit increase in the ME supplied. Assuming change in body composition can be measured, this can be determined in the growing animal in which energy is retained as tissues. However, in the lactating animal milk is produced although the animal may be losing, maintaining or gaining tissue energy. Thus, in the lactating animal three efficiency terms may be defined as (a) efficiency of utilization of body constituents for milk production when ME intake is less than needed to achieve maintenance of body tissues, (b) efficiency of utilization of ME for milk production in the absence of body tissue energy change and (c) utilization of ME for tissue energy gain and milk production simultaneously.

Estimates of the efficiency of utilization of body tissues for milk production have been consistently high and average about 84% (4). Efficiency of utilization of ME for milk production in the absence of tissue energy change varies around 62%. This efficiency varies linearly with the metabolizability (q) of the diet ($k_1 = 0.35 q + 0.42$) (ARC, 4), e.g., k_1 increases from 56-67% when q increases from 0.40 to 0.70. The concomitant deposition of energy in body tissues is more efficient than that which occurs in the non-lactating animal and appears to be about 95% of k_1, that is about 53-64%. The apparent costs of milk synthesis when ME intake is below that necessary to maintain body energy equilibrium have been partitioned among biosynthetic costs (50%), changes in physiological work such as work of circulation and respiration (17%), change in the costs of ion transport (17%) and decreases in the energy costs of

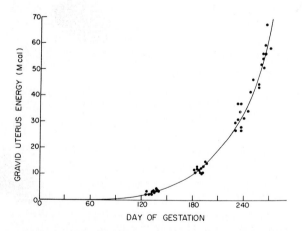

Figure 13-7. Relationship between energy content of the gravid uterus and day of gestation in cattle.

body component (primarily protein) resynthesis (16%) which accompany increasing rates of body energy loss (19). Partition of apparent costs for milk production when ME intake is sufficient or in excess of that required for tissue energy equilibrium may be similar.

It should be noted that the above discussion of the efficiency of utilization of energy for milk production was based primarily on data obtained by the use of dairy cows. Only limited information is available with other species or with non-dairy breeds of cattle. Insufficient information is available on how these efficiencies vary among species or among breeds within species. Data are available to suggest that k_1 may vary by as much as 35% (i.e., from 40-75%) within a breed of dairy cows, thus considerable variation among individuals, breeds or species is expected.

Muscular Activity

Determination of the efficiency of utilization of ME for muscular activity is difficult because it involves measurement of the amount of work done by an animal in moving its body. However, the amount of work done in ascent can be estimated from the mass of the body, the vertical distance and the acceleration due to gravity. The energy expended can be calculated as the difference between walking on the level and walking on a grade and the efficiency of muscular work can be calculated as the ratio of work done to the energy expended (4). Values obtained in this manner with several species indicate the efficiency of muscular activity to be about 0.30.

The other types of work done such as standing or walking can best be expressed in terms of an energy expenditure. The ARC (4) has concluded the energy costs of standing over lying to be about 2.4 Kcal/kg/d for cattle and sheep. For sheep, horizontal movement and vertical movements were estimated to require 0.6 and 6.7 cal/kg/m, respectively. Horizontal and vertical movements of cattle were estimated to require 0.5 and 6.7 cal per kg/m. Energy expenditures for eating appear to depend primarily on the time spent for that activity. It should be noted that these estimates are based on a very limited amount of data. Energy costs of muscular activity may be quite important to the energy economy of ruminant animals, especially in a range environment. For example, if a 500-kg cow travels 5 km (about 3.1 mile) horizontally and ascends 500 m during a day, her ME requirements would be about 2.9 Mcal or 23% greater than those of a similar, confined animal.

FEEDING SYSTEMS

All feeding systems seek to match the supply of feed energy to the energy requirements of the animal. As have been shown previously, the capacity of a feed to meet the requirements of the animal depends on the chemical and physical nature of the feed, the requirements of the animal and how the feed is used to meet those requirements. Most nutritionists would agree that the dynamics and complexity of the relationships involved in animal metabolism make the term "constant" a misnomer when applied to feeds or to animal requirements. Energy values of feeds or energy requirements can only be constants in a relative way. The chief limitation to all systems is in the application of general concepts and relationships to specific, practical situations (6).

Essentially all currently recommended feeding systems are based on NE concepts, but the procedures by which these concepts are applied to practical conditions vary. Descriptions of the systems currently recommended in France, Germany, Great Britain, the Netherlands, Switzerland and the United States can be found in the publications of INRA (20), Nehring and Haenlein (21), ARC (4), Van Es (22), Bickel and Landis (23), and NRC (24, 25). In the following paragraphs the ARC (4) and the NRC (25) systems will be discussed briefly to show two different approaches to the application of NE concepts to practical situations.

The equations used by the ARC (4) and NRC (25) to obtain estimates of the energy requirements of beef cattle are shown in Table 13-5. The ARC has retained ME as the unit of measure; the ME content of the diet and the metabolizability (q) of the diet are determined at maintenance intake, thus are standardized. As can be seen, the ARC system includes explicit corrections for activity on ME requirements for maintenance, tissue gain and lactation. These estimates are also explicitly adjusted for efficiency of utilization

Table 13-5. Calculations to estimate energy requirements of beef cattle.

ARC^a	$NRC^{b,c}$

Maintenance

1) $H_eE = 0.53 (W/1.08)^{0.67}$
2) $H_iE = 0.0043 W$
3) $Z = H_eE + H_iE$
4) $k_m = 0.35 q + 0.503$
5) Maintenance $= Z/k_m$

$ME = 0.82 DE$
$NE_m = 1.37 ME - 0.138 ME^2 + 0.0105 ME^3 - 1.12$
$NE_g = 1.42 ME - 0.174 ME^2 + 0.0122 ME^3 - 1.65$

Retained Energy (RE)
steers: $RE = 0.0635 W^{0.75} EBG^{1.097}$
heifers: $RE = 0.0783 W^{0.75} EBG^{1.119}$

Tissue Gain

1) Heat of combustion of live weight gain (Hc)
   $= (4.1+0.0322 W-0.000009 W^2)/(1-0.1475 W)$
2) $R = H_c \times W/Z$
3) $k_f = 0.78 q + 0.006$ (at L = 2)
4) $B = k_m/(k_m-k_f)$
5) $p = k_m \log_e(k_m/k_f)$
6) Requirement $= Z/p \log_e[B/(B-R-1)]$

Maintenance:
   NE_m requirement $= 77 Kcal/W^{0.75}$

Tissue Gain:
   $NE_g = RE$

Pregnancy

1) For a 40-kg calf, daily energy retention
   (RE/day) $= E(t) \times 0.0201 \exp(-0.0000576 t)$
   where $\log_{10} E(t) = 151.665 - 151.64$
   $\times \exp(-0.0000576 t)$ and t is the number of days
   from conception.
2) $k_y = 0.133$
3) Requirement $= (RE/d)/k_y$

Pregnancy:
   NE_m = birth weight $(0.0149-0.0000407 t)$
        $\times \exp(0.05883 t-0.0000804 t^2)$

Lactation

1) R = milk yield $\times [(1.509+0.0406 \times (g \ fat/kg)]$
2) $k_1 = 0.35 q + 0.420$
3) Approximate feeding level $L = 1 + (R/k_1)/Z/k_m)$
4) Correction for feeding level $= 1 + 0.018(L-1)$
5) Requirement $= [1+0.018(L-1)] (R/k_1+Z/k_m)$

Lactation:
   NE_m = milk yield $\times [0.1(\text{percent fat})+0.35]$

[a] All requirements are in MJ/d; W and ΔW are live weight (kg) and change in live weight (kg/d).

[b] All requirements are expressed in Kcal or Mcal units; W is digesta free body weight (empty body weight in kg) and EBG is empty body weight gain (kg/d).

[c] Requirements for tissue gain are adjusted to a live weight gain (LWG) basis by use of the following equations: EBG = LWG × 0.956 and MEBW = MLW × 0.891 where MEBW and MLW are mean empty body and live weights, respectively.

of ME for those functions and the influence of q on those efficiencies. Explicit corrections for feeding level are also included in estimates of requirements for tissue gain and lactation.

Conversely, although based on similar concepts, the NRC (25) expresses the energy content of feeds in NE_m or NE_g units. These have been defined earlier in the chapter. In contrast to the ARC in which estimates of

parameters used in the equations are based on calorimetric studies and on ME determined at maintenance, estimates of feed energy values and requirements have been determined by the use of comparative slaughter studies in which animals were housed outdoors and fed at least two levels of feed above maintenance. As a result, influences of activity, feeding level and diet quality are implicitly and explicitly accounted for in the estimates of the energy value of the feed and in the estimates of animal requirements. Some differences between the two systems are inherent because of the different data bases that were used to develop the systems. Adjustments to the estimates for differences in mature size of the animal and sex condition are suggested by both the ARC (4) and NRC (25). The NRC (25) further suggests corrections for previous nutrition. The NRC (25) has expressed requirements for pregnancy and lactation in NE_m units for the sake of simplicity and because of the similarity between k_m and k_1. Tables of requirements, feed energy contents and examples of how to use the systems in practice are provided in the above publications.

In many cases, the series of equations used by the ARC (4) and NRC (25) result in similar estimates of energy requirements. For example, a typical "British" breed of steer weighing 400 kg (live weight) and consuming a diet having a q of 0.65 (ME = 2.8 Mcal/kg) and gaining 1.0 kg/d would require 40.5 MJ/d or 3.46 kg/d for maintenance and 37.9 MJ/d or 3.23 kg/d for gain based on the ARC equations (Table 13-5). NE_m and NE_g values of this diet are 1.86 and 1.23 Mcal/kg, respectively, and the requirement for maintenance would be 6.32 Mcal NE_m or 3.39 kg and for gain would be 4.96 Mcal NE_g or 4.03 kg. Thus, total requirements estimated by the ARC (6.69 kg/d) are about 10% lower than those estimated by the NRC (7.42 kg/d). This difference results primarily from the difference in the estimates of the energy content of live weight gain. Part of the difference may be attributed to differences in k_f estimated by the two systems, i.e., from the ARC equation, $k_f = 0.51$ whereas k_f in the NRC system $(NE_g/ME) = 0.44$. These types of differences

relate, primarily, to the different data bases used in the development of the two systems.

Estimates of the extra feed requirement for pregnancy in cattle differ substantially between the two systems. For example, at 280 d postmating, assuming a 40-kg calf weight at birth, the requirements for pregnancy estimated by the ARC are 3.59 kg of the diet described above. This is about 80% greater than the requirements estimated by NRC (1.96 kg of the above diet). Both assume ME is utilized with an efficiency of 13%, however the ARC based their estimates on rates of energy accretion in tissues of the gravid uterus (uterus, placenta, fetal fluids and fetus), whereas the NRC based their estimates on rates of energy retention in the concepts (placenta, fetal fluids and fetus). In essence the ARC estimate is based on the rate of energy accretion in tissues directly due to pregnancy, whereas the NRC estimate is based on the rate or energy accretion in tissues (directly due to pregnancy) that are lost from the maternal system at parturition.

SUMMARY

Many of the systems currently in use for the expression of the energy requirements of ruminants and the energy contents of feedstuffs are based on similar principles. They differ to varying degrees on how those principles are applied to the production situation. Although all of the systems have limitations, reasonably good estimates of the animal's requirements and energy values of feedstuffs are obtained from most systems currently in use if proper consideration is given to the adaptation of those recommendations to the situations in which they are to be applied.

Literature Cited

1. Brody, S. 1945. Bioenergetics and Growth. Reinhold Pub. Co., New York.
2. Kleiber, M. The Fire of Life. John Wiley and Sons, New York.
3. Blaxter, K.L. 1962. The Energy Metabolism of Ruminants. Charles C. Thomas, Springfield, IL.
4. ARC. 1980. The Nutrient Requirements of Ruminant Livestock. Agr. Res. Council, Commonwealth Agricultural Bureax, London.
5. NRC. 1981. Nutritional Energetics of Domestic Animals and Glossary of Energy Terms. Nat. Acad. Sci., Washington, DC.
6. Garrett, W.N. and D.E. Johnson. 1983. J. Animal Sci. 52(Supplement 2):478.

7. Blaxter, K.L., Greta Thorbek and J. Kielanowski. 1967. Energy Metabolism of Farm Animals. Proc. 4th Symposium. EAAP Pub. No. 12. Oriel Press, Newcastle upon Tyne, England.

8. Brouwer, E. 1965. In: Energy Metabolism. K.L. Blaxter, ed. Proc. 3rd Symposium. EAAP Pub. No. 11. Academic Press, London.

9. Baldwin, R.L. and A.C. Bywater. 1984. Modeling Ruminant Digestion and Metabolism. Proc. Second International Workshop. University of California, Davis.

10. Wainman, F.W. 1977. Proc. Nutr. Soc. 36:195.

11. Reid, J.T., et al. 1980. J. Animal Sci. 51:1393.

12. Ferrell, C.L. and T.G. Jenkins. 1985. J. Animal Sci. 61:725.

13. Baldwin, R.L., et al. 1980. J. Animal Sci. 51:1416.

14. Milligan, L.P. and B.W. McBride. 1985. J. Nutr. 115:1374.

15. Smith, N.E. 1970. Quantitative simulation analyses of ruminant metabolic functions: Basal; Lactation; Milk Fat depression. PhD. Dissertation. University of California, Davis.

16. Simon, O., H. Bergner and R. Muchmeyer. 1982. Brit. J. Nutr. 48:571.

17. Garrett, W.N. 1980. J. Animal Sci. 51:1434.

18. Robinson, J.J., et al. 1980. J. Agr. Sci. 94:331.

19. Baldwin, R.L. and D.E. Bauman. 1984. In: Modeling Ruminant Digestion and Metabolism. Proc. Second International Workshop. R.L. Baldwin and A.C. Bywater, eds., University of California, Davis.

20. INRA. 1978. Alimentation des Ruminants. Ed. INRA. Publications, 78000 Versailles, France.

21. Nehring, K. and G.F.W. Haenlein. 1973. J. Animal Sci. 36:949.

22. Van Es, A.J.H. 1978. Livestock Prod. Sci. 5:331.

23. Bickel, H. and J. Landis. 1978. Livestock Prod. Sci. 5:367.

24. NRC. 1978. Nutrient Requirements of Dairy Cattle. Nat. Acad. Sci., Washington, DC.

25. NRC. 1984. Nutrient Requirements of Beef Cattle. Nat. Acad. Sci., Washington, DC.

14 CARBOHYDRATE NUTRITION OF RUMINANTS

by G. C. Fahey, Jr. and L. L. Berger

INTRODUCTION

The important role of dietary carbohydrates in the nutrition of the ruminant animal cannot be disputed. Metabolism of carbohydrates by ruminal microorganisms results in the production of VFA which, in turn, supply 70-80% of the host animal's total caloric requirement. Due to efficient degradation of dietary carbohydrates by rumen microorganisms, insufficient glucose may be absorbed from the small intestine to meet the demands of the host animal. Therefore, the process of gluconeogenesis is extremely important to ruminant species, and the supply of glucose precursors and the rate of glucose synthesis by certain organs may be limiting factors in the animal's overall productivity and even in its survival (1). Prevention of bovine ketosis, ovine pregnancy toxemia and low milk fat syndrome, maintenance of milk production in dairy cattle and optimal utilization of rumen additives which enhance performance responses are all dependent upon level and type of dietary carbohydrate fed (2). This chapter will cover a number of aspects relating to the carbohydrate nutrition of ruminants. The topic has been developed by first identifying and defining the properties of nutritionally important carbohydrates and then discussing their metabolism by ruminal microorganisms, the factors affecting site, rate and extent of carbohydrate digestion, the contribution of the small and large intestines to carbohydrate digestion, the gluconeogenic process in the host animal, unique features of carbohydrate nutrition of the young ruminant, procedures for evaluating the nutritive value of dietary carbohydrates and, lastly, feedstuff processing and conservation factors affecting carbohydrate utilization. Both structural and non-structural carbohydrates will be considered.

CLASSIFICATION OF NUTRITIONALLY IMPORTANT CARBOHYDRATES

Carbohydrates include a large group of compounds which chemically are hydroxy-aldehydes or hydroxyketones and their derivatives. For classification purposes, they are divided into monosaccharides and their derivatives, oligosaccharides (two to ten saccharide units) and polysaccharides (starch, cellulose, hemicellulose and pectin).

Monosaccharides (Fig. 14-1)

Aldopentoses. Two nutritionally important aldopentoses exist. These are DL-arabinose and D-xylose (α-D-xylopyranose). DL-arabinose does not occur in the free form but rather as a unit of gums (viscous polysaccharides) and hemicelluloses (major cell wall polysaccharides). Arabinose occurs as a furanoside in glycosidic linkage.

D-xylose, a pyranosidic aldopentose also known as wood sugar, is a major constituent of the hemicelluloses. Cottonseed hulls, corncobs and various cereal straws are good sources of this sugar.

Aldohexoses. D-glucose (dextrose) is found in biological systems in the free form, as a component of the disaccharides sucrose and lactose, in polysaccharides and as glycosides (e.g., cyanogenic glycosides). It is obtained commercially from the hydrolysis of starch at 40 psi and at pH 1.5.

D-mannose does not occur in the free form but rather as a component of polysaccharides. It may be recovered after acid hydrolysis.

D-galactose is a constituent of the oligosaccharides lactose, melibiose and raffinose, and of such polysaccharides as gum arabic, agar and other gums and mucilages. It is generally prepared from lactose by hydrolysis followed by direct crystallization of the D-galactose. It occurs in combination with glucose as the disaccharide, lactose, which is an important constituent of the milk of mammals.

Ketohexoses. D-fructose (levulose) is a levorotatory sugar obtained commercially from the enzymatic conversion of cornstarch. It is fermentable by yeast and is the sweetest

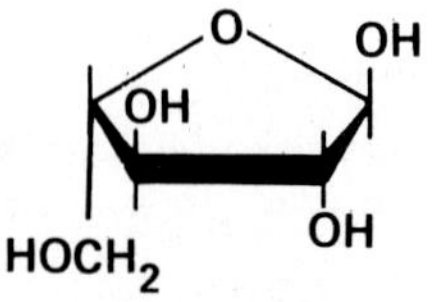

ARABINOSE

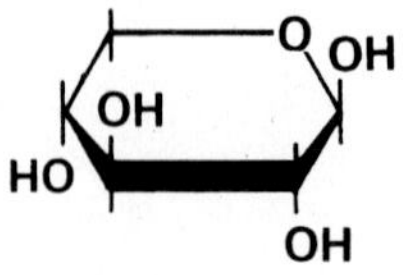

XYLOSE

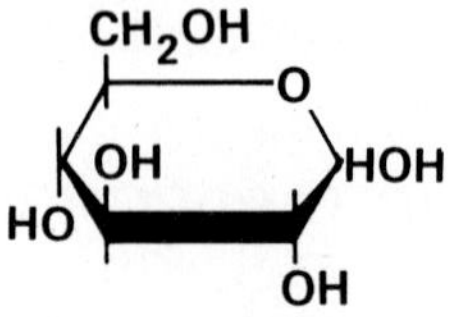

GLUCOSE

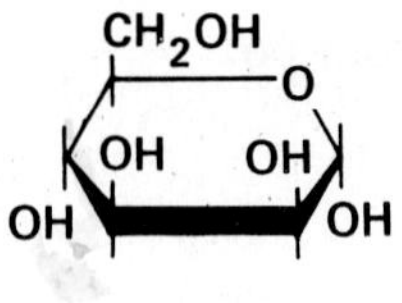

MANNOSE

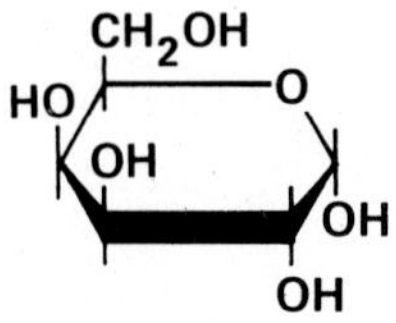

GALACTOSE

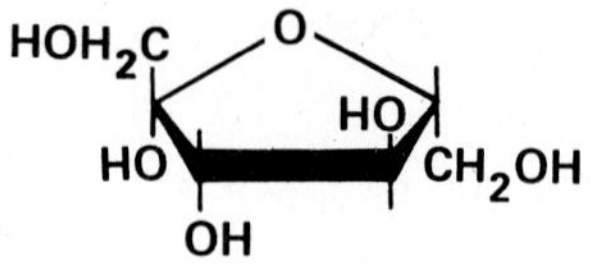

FRUCTOSE

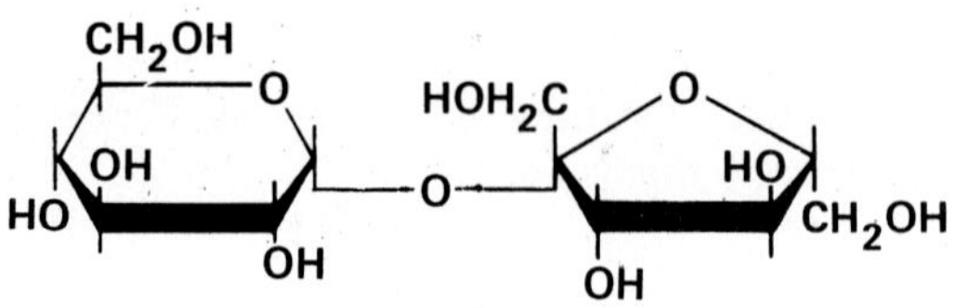

SUCROSE

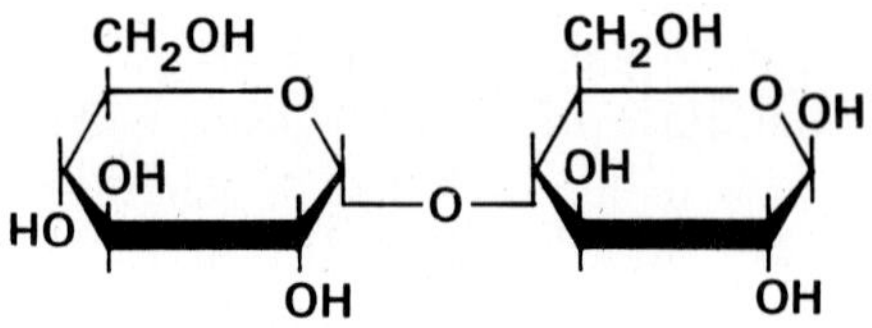

MALTOSE

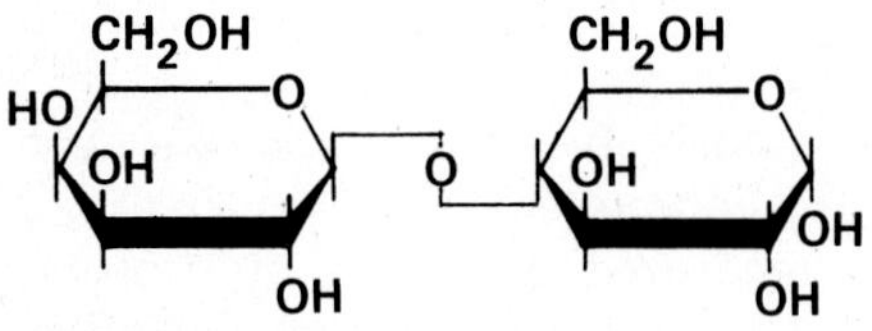

LACTOSE

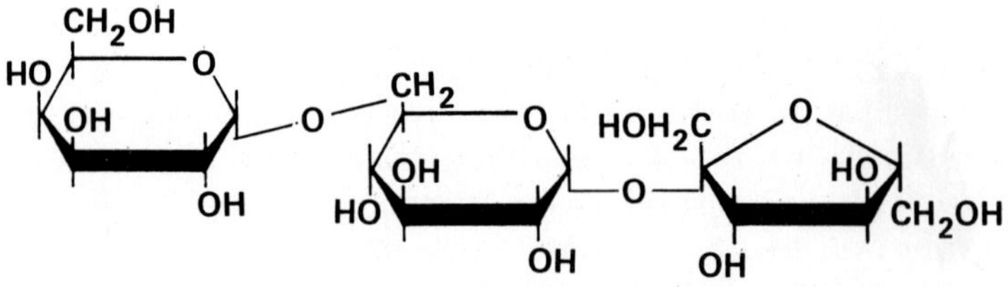

RAFFINOSE

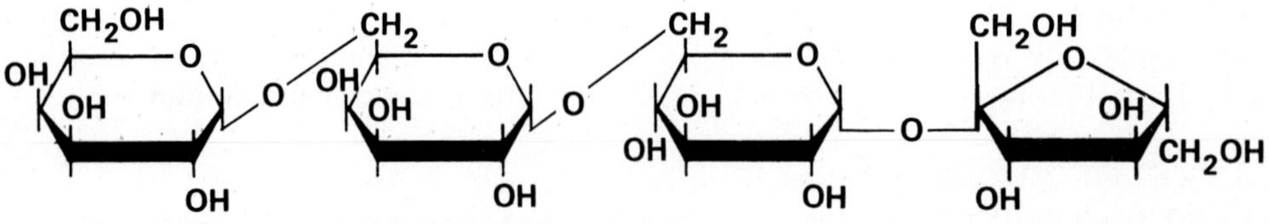

STACHYOSE

Figure 14-1. Structural formulae of nutritionally important monosaccharides and oligosaccharides.

sugar known. This is of major industrial importance as invert sugar (glucose + fructose) has greater solubility than does sucrose, yields 5% more sugar and is sweeter than sucrose.

Oligosaccharides (Fig. 14-1)

These carbohydrates are found free or combined in natural products. They are of lower molecular weight than the polysaccharides and yield only sugar or sugar derivatives upon acid hydrolysis. They are composed of monosaccharide residues connected through glycosidic linkages.

Sucrose is a disaccharide which does not exhibit reducing action on metallic ions. It occurs almost universally throughout the plant kingdom. It is found in commercially important concentrations in sugar cane, sugar beet and sorghum. Sucrose is hydrolyzed by acid treatment or enzyme action to a mixture of equal amounts of glucose and fructose. Since there is a change in optical rotation from the dextrorotatory sucrose to the levorotatory mixture of glucose and fructose, the hydrolysis of sucrose is called inversion and the resultant sugar mixture is called invert sugar.

Maltose is a reducing disaccharide obtained from the enzymatic degradation of starch and glycogen. It is comprised of two glucopyranose units linked through an α-1,4 glucosidic linkage.

Lactose, also called milk sugar, is not fermentable by ordinary yeasts. It is comprised of a galactopyranose and glucopyranose linked β-1,4. Lactose is a product of mammary gland metabolism and is secreted in milk. Lactose occurs in milk either free or as a lactose-containing oligosaccharide. In unheated milk, the ratio of free to bound lactose is 8:1. Lactose is about one-sixth as sweet as sucrose and is relatively insoluble.

Raffinose is the best known trisaccharide. It is 6-(α-D-galactopyranosyl)-α-D-glucopyranosyl-β-D-fructofuranoside. It occurs in small quantities in sugar beets and in appreciable quantities in soybean and cottonseed meals. It is a non-reducing sugar and is not digested other than by microbial action.

Stachyose is the best known tetrasaccharide. It is a non-reducing sugar found primarily in soybeans and is comprised of galactose-1,6-galactose[1,6]glucose[1,2]-β-D-fructose. This oligosaccharide, as well as raffinose and the five sugar oligosaccharide, verbascose, is not degraded by mammalian digestive enzymes but is fermented by intestinal microbes.

Non-Structural Polysaccharides (Fig. 14-2)

Starch is the natural glucose storage polysaccharide of plants. It occurs as microscopic birefringent granules which stain blue or red with iodine. The size and appearance of the starch granule is characteristic for each plant species. Starch is found in seeds, tubers, roots, pith and leaves of plants. The most common industrial starch is obtained from corn although that from potatoes and tapioca is of importance. Starch granules are completely insoluble in cold water but, when heated in aqueous suspension, swell and lose their birefringence at a temperature characteristic of the starch. This occurs over a temperature range of about 10°C and is called the gelatinization range. The two types of starch are an unbranched structure consisting of long chains of α-D-glucose units linked through carbons 1,4. The other is branched and consists of short chains of α-1,4-linked glucose units joined with other chains to form a large molecule. The linear component is amylose and the branched one is amylopectin. Most starches contain between 15 and 30% amylose, with cornstarch containing 22 to 28%. Waxy corn contains none. Methylation of amylose has shown it to consist of some 300 glucose units joined in α-1,4 glucosidic linkages. The enzyme, β-amylase, of malted barley completely degrades amylose to maltose. There are a few α-1,3 linkages in amylose. These are hydrolyzed by a specific enzyme in plants called the Z enzyme. β-amylase does not completely degrade amylopectin; rather, it stops acting after approximately 50% of the amylopectin is converted to maltose. Amylopectin consists of chain lengths of 25 to 30 glucose units with some 50 to 70 branches connected through α-1,6 glucosidic linkages.

Only the amylose fraction of starch reacts with iodine to yield a blue color. As starch undergoes acid hydrolysis or enzyme action, there is a change in the color produced by iodine. The color changes from blue-black-purple to red to colorless.

Starches from different plants differ substantially in both histological features and

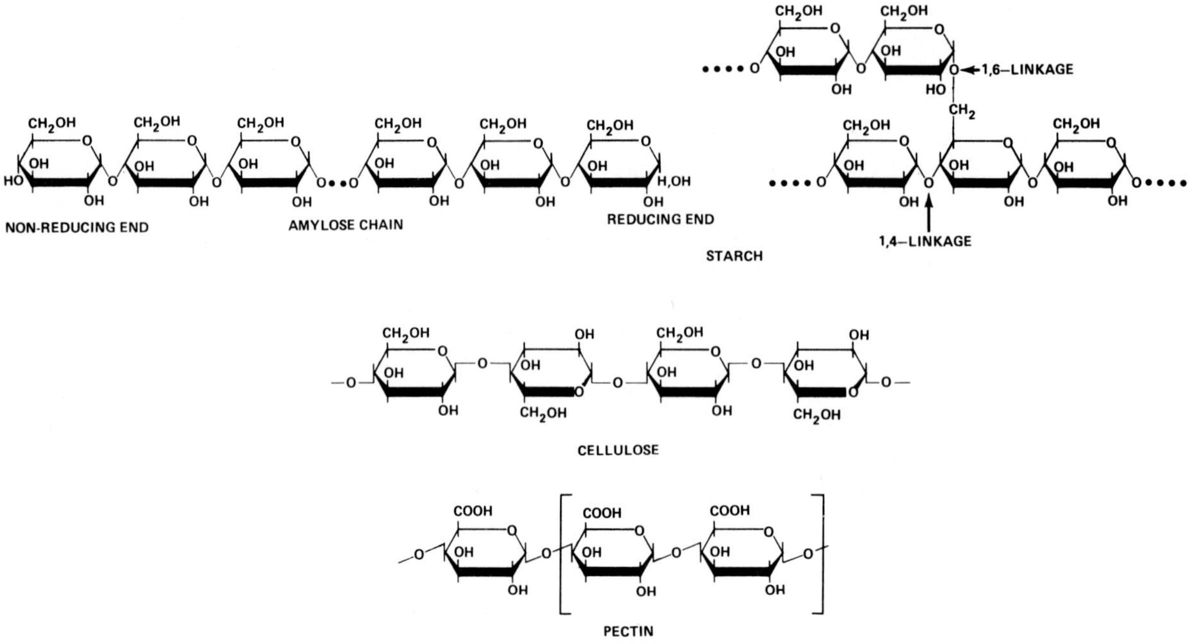

Figure 14-2. Structural formulae for starch, cellulose and pectin.

chemical heterogeneity of the granule components. Starches from various sources have been shown to differ in their digestibility. Uncooked starches from cereal grains, cassava roots, rice and sweet potatoes have been shown to be approximately 90% digestible. In contrast, uncooked starches from white potato, arrowroot and sago palm are much less digestible. It has been suggested that the relatively low utilization of these starches is due to the degree of crystallization or character of the outermost layers of the starch granule. To increase digestibility of these starches, the granular structure must be disrupted. This may be accomplished by gelatinization through cooking, by dextrinization (degradation to lower molecular weight units) through enzymatic or acid hydrolysis or by ball-milling for two or more hours. Although starch-containing cereals are generally not heated before feeding to swine or poultry, it has been found that this might be economically advantageous in certain instances.

Starches, even from the same grain, vary considerably in their concentration of amylose and amylopectin. Amylose, the linear polymer of starch, may be separated from amylopectin, the highly branched component, by precipitation of amylose from a hot starch dispersion through the use of butanol, nitrobenzene or thymol. The amylose complex is collected by centrifugation and the amylose is regenerated by washing with ethanol. The quantitative determination of amylose content of starches may be accomplished by making use of the fact that only amylose combines with iodine and the colored complex can be measured colorimetrically. Amylose in solution has a tendency to undergo retrogradation. In retrogradation, the linear amylose chains can coalesce, causing the solution to become increasingly cloudy and resistant to enzyme action.

Glycogen is the reserve polysaccharide of animal metabolism found in muscle and liver and is closely related in structure to amylopectin. It gives a brown color with iodine. It consists of 8 to 12 α-D-glucopyranosyl units which are united in α-1,4 linkages, but a considerable degree of cross linking through α-1,6 glycosidic bonds occurs.

Since glycogen is very resistant to the action of alkali, it is usually obtained from tissue by boiling in 30% KOH. This degrades the other organic constituents, making it possible to recover the glycogen by precipitating it in alcohol. Glycogen does not reduce Fehling's solution but is strongly dextrorotatory and is degraded to α-D-glucose by acids.

Structural Polysaccharides (Fig. 14-2)

Structural polysaccharides represent the majority of the cell wall material in plant cells. The structural carbohydrate present in greatest quantity in nature is cellulose. The hair of cottonseed consists of nearly pure cellulose. Raw cotton, which is the material used for most structural studies, contains 91% cellulose, 9% water and 1% impurities. In contrast to this high purity, cellulose that serves as a major component of plant cell walls contains other closely associated compounds. These substances are less resistant than cellulose to the action of acids and are generally considered to be the hemicelluloses.

The cell wall of plants has been shown to have its inception as a pectinous membrane, which is gradually replaced by deposition of cellulose, hemicelluloses and lignin. The pectin content decreases markedly as the plant ages and a simultaneous increase in lignin and cellulose occurs. In most grasses, cellulose increases from about 20% at the stage of first growth of leaves to about 28% at full bloom and between 35 and 45% when the seeds have fallen and the plant has died.

Hydrolysis of cellulose by treating with 72% sulfuric acid yields over 98% glucose, and acetolysis gives over 50% cellobiose (4-O-β-glucopyranosyl-β-D-glucopyranose) as the octoacetate, indicating that cellulose is built up of glucose residues in 1,4 glycosidic linkages. Hydrolysis of fully methylated cellulose gives quantitative yields of 2,3,6-tri-O-methyl glucose, indicating a lack of branching.

Cellulose is degraded by the enzyme complex, cellulase. Cellulase is composed of at least two major subunits: C-1, which breaks hydrogen bonds, making glucose chains susceptible to further hydrolysis, and C-x, which hydrolyzes these chains to cellobiose and glucose. A great deal of work conducted on cellulase activity is based on studies with *Trichoderma* since these organisms secrete extracellular enzymes which can be isolated with activity retained. However, rumen microbial cellulolytic activity may differ greatly from that of aerobic fungi. Leatherwood (3) proposed a mechanism in which an affinity factor and a hydrolytic factor were necessary for the formation of a complete cellulase complex which could act as a single entity and hydrolyze native cellulose to cellobiose. Studying the cellulase complex of *Ruminococcus albus* and its adsorption to cellulose, he suggested that the hydrolytic factor should be held in position on the insoluble cellulose by the affinity factor in order to hydrolyze insoluble cellulose effectively. Celluloses apparently differ in their ability to adsorb the hydrolytic factor, with acid-swollen and ball-milled celluloses having higher binding capacities. Cellulose with the higher level of binding was also digested more readily. On the basis of this mechanism of cellulose digestion, resistance to hydrolysis would be expected if inert substances were adsorbed to the binding sites on cellulose, thus blocking the binding of the complete cellulase complex.

The hemicelluloses are a heterogeneous group of polysaccharides associated with the cellulose and lignin of the cell wall of plants. They are defined in a general way as polysaccharides which are insoluble in water but extractable with dilute alkali and which, upon acid hydrolysis, yield sugars and sometimes sugars and sugar acids. Hemicelluloses contain two different types of polysaccharides: (a) short-chain polysaccharides (or cellulosans) that form part of the cellulose fabric itself and are oriented in the micellar structure and (b) amorphous encrusting polysaccharides which are closely associated with the lignin of the cell wall.

Cellulosans may consist of pentosans and hexosans. The hemicelluloses which are apparently linked to lignin to form a structural component of the cell wall contain both sugars and uronic acids. The most common cellulosan is xylan, a polysaccharide occurring in nearly all plants. It is composed primarily of a chain of D-xylose units which may be attached to a single L-arabinose unit or, in some cases, to a D-glucuronic acid unit. Available evidence indicates the existence of two types of xylan occurring in plants, one with glucuronic acid and the other without it. β-1,4 linkages predominate. Xylan is insoluble in water, soluble in alkaline solution, is readily hydrolyzed, levorotatory and is nonreducing to Fehling's solution. Xylan occurs in practically all land plants. In both botanical distribution and abundance, it ranks next to cellulose and starch. It is abundant in annual crops, particularly in agricultural residues such as corncobs, cornstalks and grain hulls and straw. In such instances, it

274

comprises 15 to 30% of the residue. The manner in which it is associated with cellulose might be explained on the basis of its capacity to be compressed into highly associated groups which might fit into spaces in the place of cellulose. Apparently, xylan is entangled in the cellulose fiber but is not a constituent of the crystalline micellar region, as it does not influence the X-ray diffraction pattern of cellulose. Xylan obtained from corncobs contains approximately 95% D-xylose and 5% glucuronic acid. The linkages are always of the β-1,4 type. Cottonseed hull hemicelluloses have been shown to contain xylose and D-glucuronic acid as the predominant sugars, but the percentage of glucuronic acid is higher than in corncob xylans.

With regard to the amorphous encrusting polysaccharides, it is known that hemicelluloses and lignin together form the encrusting material of secondary plant cell wall thickening (4). Ester linkages to xylose and possible glycosidic linkages provide evidence for the direct bonding of hemicellulosic sugars to lignin.

Hemicellulases studied to date appear to be of the endo type which randomly attack the glycosidic chain (4). Enzymes that attack side chains include α-D-glucosiduronidase which attacks the α-D-(1,2) linkage in glucuronoxylans and α-L-arabinofuranosidases which hydrolyze the 1,3 linkage branch points in arabinoxylan. Xylanases include β-D-xylanase endoenzyme as well as a dextrinase that attacks oligomers but not xylan or xylobiose. These enzymes degrade linear xylan while branched molecules are more slowly or incompletely degraded. Also, the progress of xylan hydrolysis is at least partially dependent on action of arabinosidase to remove branching groups (4).

The pectic substances are high molecular weight colloidal carbohydrates of the cell wall. However, upon extraction of plant material with neutral detergent solution, pectins are solubilized and become part of the cell soluble fraction. They are often referred to as "intercellular cement". Although arabans and galactans are associated with the pectic substances, they can be removed by repeated precipitation of the sample in 60% ethanol or by washing the sample with this solvent until it is free of these polysaccharides.

The pectic substances are regarded as chains of galacturonic acid with the arabans and galactans merely being associated with them.

The term protopectin is applied to the water-insoluble parent pectic substances that occur in plants and which, upon restricted hydrolysis, yield pectin or pectinic acids. The term "pectinic acid" is used for colloidal polygalacturonic acids containing more than a negligible proportion of methyl ester groups. Pectinic acids, under suitable conditions, are capable of forming gels with sugars and acid, or, if suitably low in methoxyl content, with certain metallic ions. Salts of pectinic acid are either normal or acid pectinates. The general term "pectin" designates those water-soluble pectinic acids of varying methyl ester content and degree of neutralization which are capable of forming gels with sugars and acid under suitable conditions. The term "pectic acid" is applied to pectic substances comprised primarily of colloidal polygalacturonic acids and essentially free from methyl ester groups. The salts of pectic acids are either normal or acid pectates.

Enzyme hydrolysis of pectin yields about 85% D-galacturonic acid, but acid hydrolysis causes the yield to drop considerably, perhaps as the result of decarboxylation of uronic acids. The galacturonic acid molecules are probably united through α-1,4 linkages. The evidence for this consists in finding 2,3 dimethyl galacturonic acid after hydrolysis of methylated pectins. Although the ring structure could be a furanose or pyranose type, it is thought that the high dextrorotation of pectins and their resistance to acid hydrolysis is such that a pyranose structure exists.

Pectic enzyme is the term applied to the enzyme which hydrolyzes or dissolves protopectin with the resultant separation of plant cell walls from each other. It is found in fungi, plants and bacteria. Pectase, or pectin esterase, is the name applied to the enzyme which converts pectin into pectic acid, the latter becoming a gel, especially in the presence of Ca ions. Many workers identify this enzyme as pectin esterase because its action is to remove methoxyl groups joined to the carboxyl groups through ester linkages. Pectinase is the term applied to the enzyme which hydrolyzes pectin and pectic acid into galacturonic acid. This enzyme is also called polygalacturonase. Pectinase or polygalacturonase acts upon soluble pectin, calcium pectate and pectic acid. Pectinase breaks down pectin to galacturonic acid. It is secreted, usually along with pectin esterase, by numerous fungi.

Table 14-1 presents compositional data describing changes in carbohydrate and lignin content with advancing maturity of four grass species (5). Structural carbohydrate and lignin content increase with maturation of first growth herbage until approximately the middle of June. Concentrations of these moieties then gradually decline with time in the pasture regrowth. Concentration of cell solubles follows an opposite trend.

Table 14-2 presents the monosaccharide composition of certain ruminant feedstuffs and their distribution in cell walls and cell solubles (6, 7). Major differences among feedstuffs occur in monosaccharide content and distribution. For example, in the case of alfalfa, glucose, uronic acids and xylose comprise 85% of the total monosaccharides. Glucose, and particularly xylose, are virtually confined to the cell wall, whereas the uronic acids and the minor sugars (excluding arabinose) are present mostly in a soluble form, presumably as components of pectic substances (6).

Table 14-1. Changes in carbohydrate and lignin content with advancing maturity of four grass species.[a]

Species and chemical fraction	Harvest date				
	4/19	5/3	7/23	9/26	10/24
Tall fescue					
NDF[b]	46.5	56.4	65.7	56.4	54.6
ADF[c]	24.6	30.2	36.5	28.7	30.8
Hemicellulose	21.9	26.2	29.2	27.7	23.8
Lignin[d]	2.8	3.8	5.5	4.2	4.3
Cell solubles	53.5	43.7	34.4	43.7	45.5
Perennial ryegrass					
NDF	42.2	51.0	55.8	53.0	38.3
ADF	22.3	28.3	32.9	24.6	20.4
Hemicellulose	19.9	22.8	22.9	28.4	18.0
Lignin	3.0	3.6	6.4	4.2	3.3
Cell solubles	57.8	49.0	44.2	47.1	61.7
Smooth bromegrass					
NDF	43.9	52.8	63.1	55.4	40.3
ADF	22.8	29.5	37.7	27.1	20.7
Hemicellulose	21.1	23.4	25.4	28.3	19.6
Lignin	3.0	3.5	6.9	4.9	2.8
Cell solubles	56.1	47.2	37.0	44.7	59.7
Orchardgrass					
NDF	46.6	56.3	64.3	54.4	47.9
ADF	23.3	30.0	39.8	28.0	24.8
Hemicellulose	23.3	26.4	25.0	26.4	23.1
Lignin	3.4	4.0	6.6	4.3	3.9
Cell solubles	53.4	43.7	35.3	45.7	52.2

[a] From (5)
[b] NDF = neutral detergent fiber (cellulose + hemicellulose + lignin)
[c] ADF = acid detergent fiber (cellulose + lignin)
[d] Permanganate lignin

Table 14-2. Monosaccharide composition of certain ruminant feedstuffs and their distribution in cell walls and cell solubles.

Feedstuff and distribution	Carbohydrate composition						
	Glucose	Xylose	Arabinose	Galactose	Mannose	Rhamnose	Uronic acids
Alfalfa, g/100 g DM[a]	23.9	7.60	2.57	1.79	2.03	0.62	7.78
% in cell wall	95.3	100	77.8	40.2	35.4	14.0	19.9
% in cell solubles	4.7	0	22.2	59.8	64.6	86.0	80.1
Corn silage, g/100 g DM[b]	42.8	8.69	2.19	0.69	0.86	0.12	4.19
% in cell wall	53.8	90.0	68.1	52.4	12.6	42.5	35.8
% in cell solubles	46.2	10.0	31.9	47.6	87.4	57.5	64.2
Oat hay, g/100 g DM[b]	38.6	15.5	2.40	1.54	1.20	0.28	4.82
% in cell wall	88.0	98.5	94.1	49.2	24.0	35.9	66.9
% in cell solubles	12.0	1.5	5.9	50.8	76.0	64.1	33.1
Vetch hay, g/100 g DM[b]	31.5	8.88	1.68	2.30	1.78	0.74	14.4
% in cell wall	92.4	87.6	65.8	38.7	63.7	56.2	29.3
% in cell solubles	7.6	12.4	34.2	61.3	36.3	43.8	70.7
Wheat straw, g/100 g DM[c]	37.2	18.7	5.6	tr	tr	--	3.8

[a] From (6)
[b] Ben-Ghedalia (personal communication)
[c] From (7)

276

MICROBIAL FERMENTATION OF CARBOHYDRATES

Most carbohydrates consumed by ruminants are polymers of glucose present in the form of cellulose or starch. However, large amounts of hemicellulose and pectin may be present in some diets. Feeds like molasses and food processing by-products are high in mono- and disaccharides, but usually do not constitute a large portion of the diet. Consequently, for fermentation to occur, most carbohydrates must undergo hydrolysis in the rumen.

Four bacterial species, *Bacteroides amylophilus, Streptococcus bovis, Succinimonas amylolytica* and *Succinivibrio dextrinosolvens,* are the most common amylolytic and dextrinolytic bacteria in the rumen (8). The rapidity with which starch is hydrolyzed by these bacteria to maltose and some glucose is greatly affected by source of starch and type of feed processing method used. Once starch is degraded to maltose, it is fermented rapidly by saccharolytic microbes. The role of ruminal protozoa in starch degradation is unclear because it is difficult to differentiate between starch digested by protozoa per se and that degraded by engulfed bacteria.

Bacteroides ruminicola, Butyrivibrio fibrisolvens and *Selenomonas ruminantium* are the most common saccharolytic bacteria in the rumen. Fermentation of glucose and other monosaccharides occurs mainly by the Embden-Meyerhof pathway (Fig. 14-3). Conversion of hexose to two moles of pyruvate yields two adenosine triphosphates (ATP) and two reduced nicotinamide adenine dinucleotides ($NADH_2$). The ATP generated is the primary energy source for growth and maintenance of bacteria.

Conversion of cellulose to glucose and then to pyruvate is a more complex process and one that is less well understood. Cellulose exists in amorphous and crystalline forms with the crystalline forms being the most difficult to degrade in the rumen (9). The most common cellulolytic bacteria in the rumen are *Bacteroides succinogenes, Ruminococcus albus* and *Ruminococcus flavefaciens.* The cellulase(s) produced by *Ruminococcus*

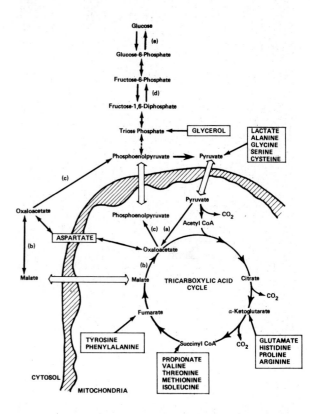

Figure 14-3. The relationship between pathways of gluconeogenesis and glucose precursors. Key for enzyme identification is as follows: (a) pyruvate carboxylase, (b) NAD-malate dehydrogenase, (c) phosphoenol-pyruvate carboxykinase, (d) fructose-1,6-diphosphatase and (e) glucose-6-phosphatase.

species are believed to be extracellular because of the clear zones produced around distinct colonies when incubated in cellulose agar media.

The cellulase(s) produced by *R. albus* degrades only amorphous cellulose while those produced by *R. flavefaciens* can hydrolyze crystalline cellulose (10). These bacteria also produce a non-hydrolytic protein which enhances the action of cellulase. The mechanism by which this occurs is not completely understood but it has been suggested that this protein is necessary to bind cellulase to cellulose (3).

B. succinogenes is the most common cellulolytic bacterium in the rumen when diets are high in crystalline cellulose. This is due to the greater activity of cellulase(s) from *B. succinogenes* as compared to that from *Ruminococci.* The cellulase of *B. succinogenes* is apparently bound to the outer membrane and the bacterium must come in physical contact with cellulose to hydrolyze it.

The quantitative importance of protozoa in ruminal cellulose degradation is unclear. It has often been difficult to determine if cellulase(s) present inside protozoa is protozoal or bacterial in origin. Coleman (11) reported that 70% of the cellulase inside *Eudipdodinium maggi* was of protozoal origin. However, the actual amount of cellulose degraded by protozoa in the presence of cellulolytic bacteria remains unknown.

The same bacterial species which hydrolyze cellulose are common hemicellulose degraders; however, some cellulolytic bacteria like *B. succinogenes* do not themselves ferment the released pentoses (12). Hemicellulose appears to be degraded by cellulase through a non-specific hydrolysis of β-1,4 xylosidic linkages. Rate of hemicellulose degradation is usually very similar to that of cellulose in most feedstuffs. Because hemicellulose is much easier to solubilize than is cellulose, a faster rate of degradation might be expected. However, there usually is little difference, suggesting that the physical relationship of cellulose and hemicellulose in the plant cell wall may dictate similar rates of degradation.

Pectins are degraded in the rumen by *B. succinogenes, B. ruminicola* and *B. fibrisolvens* as well as by several genera of protozoa. At least two enzymes are required for pectin hydrolysis, a methylesterase and polygalacturonidase. These enzymes degrade pectin to galacturonic acid, methyl esters of galacturonic acid and other sugars. The pentoses produced from hemicellulose and pectin degradation are transformed before being converted to VFA. In essence, three pentose phosphates are converted to two hexose phosphates and a triose phosphate via the reactions of transketolase and transaldolase (8) prior to entering the Embden-Meyerhof pathway.

Pyruvate is the intermediate through which all carbohydrates must pass before being converted to VFA, CO_2 and CH_4. The proportion of the end product depends on type of carbohydrate fermented, bacterial species involved and rumen environment during fermentation. For example, two mechanisms for conversion of pyruvate to acetate have been elucidated in rumen bacteria. The most common pathway for acetate production is via the pyruvate-formate lyase system which produces formate and acetyl-Coenzyme A (CoA) as intermediates. Formate is then converted to CO_2 and H_2 by other bacteria in the rumen. The second pathway involves pyruvate-ferredoxin oxidoreductase yielding reduced ferredoxin, CO_2 and acetyl-CoA. This pathway has been observed in *Clostridia, Megasphaera elsdenii* and *Veillonella alcalesens.* Acetyl-CoA is converted to acetate plus ATP by phosphotransacetylase and acetokinase.

Propionate is produced from pyruvate primarily by the dicarboxylic acid pathway. Baldwin and Allison (8) described three enzymes that catalyze the conversion of pyruvate to propionate: phosphoenolpyruvate (PEP) carboxykinase, which converts PEP plus adenosine diphosphate (ADP) or guanidine diphosphate (GDP) plus CO_2 to oxaloacetate (OAA) + ATP or guanidine triphosphate (GTP); pyruvate carboxylase, which converts pyruvate plus CO_2 plus ATP to OAA plus ADP; and methylmalonyl-CoA carboxyltransferase, which is required for conversion of succinate to propionate via the intermediate, methylmalonyl-CoA. In the rumen, the amount of propionate produced via the dicarboxylic acid pathway is determined by the species of bacteria present, which is controlled largely by amount and form of dietary carbohydrate.

A second pathway for propionate production, the acrylate pathway, has been identified in *M. elsdenii* and *B. ruminicola*. In this pathway, pyruvate is converted to lactate which is converted to acrylyl-CoA and then reduced to propionyl-CoA. The portion of the total propionate produced via the acrylate pathway may approach one-third of the total production.

Two pathways for synthesis of butyrate and higher fatty acids have been described. The most common route for butyrate synthesis is a reversal of the β-oxidation pathway. In the other pathway, malonyl-CoA is combined with acetyl-CoA yielding acetoacetyl CoA which is then reduced via crotonyl-CoA to butyrate. In general, butyrate is synthesized primarily by reversed β-oxidation and higher fatty acids are synthesized via the malonyl-CoA pathway. Benefits to bacteria from the conversion of acetate to butyrate are unclear. The main purpose of this conversion

278

may be to oxidize reduced cofactors in bacteria, allowing further fermentation.

The molar proportion of VFA produced in the rumen is often of interest to ruminant researchers. In general, as the forage:concentrate ratio decreases, the acetate:propionate ratio also decreases (13; Table 14-3). The acetate:propionate ratio has been used to compare diets and to predict relative nutritive value. Generally, as cellulose and hemicellulose levels in a diet increase relative to soluble carbohydrate and starch levels, the acetate:propionate ratio also increases. However, data of Murphy et al (14; Table 14-4), relating feed analysis data to VFA formation, showed that VFA production from a given substrate (starch, cellulose, etc.) varied with diet composition. For example, the acetate:propionate ratio resulting from fermentation of hemicellulose in a high roughage diet was 3.2, but only 2.2 when fermented in a high grain diet. The acetate:propionate ratio

resulting from cellulose fermentation also varied with diet, 13.1 for a roughage diet and 7.3 for a grain diet, both being much higher than that produced by hemicellulose. Although cellulose and hemicellulose are usually digested simultaneously in forages, the end-products produced may vary greatly depending on diet.

METHANE PRODUCTION

Rumen microbes metabolize carbohydrates primarily by converting them to glucose or glucose-1-phosphate which is then oxidized to pyruvate by the Embden-Meyerhof pathway and subsequently converted to acetate by pyruvate lyase reactions. Metabolic energy for the bacteria is released by substrate phosphorylation in two reactions. The first step is nicotinamide adenine dinucleotide (NAD)-linked dehydrogenation of glyceraldehyde-3-phosphate. Secondly, the pyruvate lyase reactions produce acetyl-CoA which is converted to acetate and ATP. In the first reaction, electrons and protons are transferred to NAD and in the second, electrons are transferred to ferredoxin, flavodoxin or related compounds and, further, to protons (H) or H and CO_2, yielding formate (HCOOH) (15). Formate is actively converted to CH_4 by rumen contents: $4\ HCOOH \rightarrow 3\ CO_2 + CH_4$. In order to obtain maximum energy yield from anaerobic carbohydrate fermentation, an electron sink for regeneration of NAD^+ not involving pyruvate or acetyl-CoA is required. Methane generation should be

Table 14-3. Effect of forage to concentrate ratio on the volatile fatty acid ratios in the lactating dairy cow.[a]

Forage:concentrate ratio	Molar ratios		
	Acetate	Propionate	Butyrate
100:0	71.4	16.0	7.9
75:25	68.2	18.1	8.0
50:50	65.3	18.4	10.4
40:60	59.8	25.9	10.2
20:80	53.6	30.6	10.7

[a]From (13)

Table 14-4. Estimated rumen fermentation characteristics.[a]

Substrate	Diet[c]	Proportion of carbohydrate converted to			
		Acetate	Propionate	Butyrate	Valerate
Soluble carbohydrate[b]	R	0.69	0.20	0.10	0
	C	0.45	0.21	0.30	0.04
Starch	R	0.59	0.14	0.20	0.06
	C	0.40	0.30	0.20	0.10
Hemicellulose	R	0.57	0.18	0.21	0.05
	C	0.56	0.26	0.11	0.07
Cellulose	R	0.66	0.09	0.23	0.03
	C	0.79	0.06	0.06	0.09

[a] From (14)
[b] Soluble carbohydrate fraction includes organic acids and pectin in this analysis.
[c] R codes roughage diets; C codes diets containing more than 50% of a cereal-based concentrate diet.

viewed as an energy sink where H from all rumen microorganisms drains, allowing a greater total yield of ATP. Other H sinks exist in the rumen. For example, conversion of NO_3 to NH_3, SO_4 to H_2S and the saturation of unsaturated fatty acids all are H sinks. However, these H acceptors are usually at relatively low levels in the diet and thus are not quantitatively important.

The quantity of methane generated (H sink needed) is related to the end-products produced from carbohydrate fermentation. For example, if a high grain diet is fed, resulting in an acetate:propionate molar ratio of 1, the following fermentation equation might exist: 3 glucose $\rightarrow$ 2 acetate + 2 propionate + butyrate + 3 CO_2 + CH_4 + $2H_2O$. In contrast, if a high forage diet is fed resulting in an acetate:propionate molar ratio of 3, the following fermentation equation might exist: 5 glucose $\rightarrow$ 6 acetate + 2 propionate + butyrate + 5 CO_2 + 3 CH_4 + 6 H_2O. When the fermentation equations are compared, it is obvious that an inverse relationship between propionate and CH_4 production exists. The reason for this relationship is that CO_2 and H are by-products of the conversion of glucose to acetate and butyrate. In contrast, when both the succinate and acrylate pathways are being used for propionate synthesis, all C and H atoms present in glucose are accounted for in the two propionate molecules produced (4).

Methanogenic bacteria are very sensitive to changes in dietary conditions. For example, increased rate of passage, increased rate of fermentation, decreased rumination or a decrease in pH all reduce amount of H available to the methanogens. The reason that animal performance is often improved with these changes in rumen environment is that the C and H normally lost as CH_4 are retained in propionate, thereby increasing the ME level of the diet. Ionophores, such as monensin, lasalocid, salinomycin and others, shift the rumen population such that propionate production is increased and CH_4 decreased. Although this is not the only mode of action of ionophores, it is a major contributor to the improved animal performance often observed.

VFA ABSORPTION AND METABOLISM

The importance of VFA as a source of ME for ruminants is well recognized. Nearly all VFA produced are absorbed in the rumen, reticulum and omasum, with very little reaching the abomasum.

Although a small amount of acetate absorbed through the rumen wall is converted to ketone bodies, most is carried by portal circulation to the liver unchanged. The initial reaction in acetate metabolism is conversion to acetyl-CoA in the cytoplasm via acetyl-CoA synthetase, an enzyme widely distributed in animal tissues. Approximately 80% of the acetate reaching the liver escapes oxidation and passes into the peripheral circulation (16; Table 14-5). Once absorbed from the blood, most of the acetate is oxidized via the tricarboxylic acid (TCA) cycle or used for fatty acid synthesis. Acetate is the main precursor for lipogenesis in ruminants because, in the absence of adequate levels of ATP-citrate lyase, glucose can supply only limited quantities of acetyl-CoA for fatty acid synthesis (see Ch. 15). Activity of acetyl-CoA synthetase is 2-3 times higher in ruminant adipose tissue than in rat adipose tissue, reflecting the relatively high rate of acetate conversion to fatty acids in ruminant adipose tissue. Production of adequate levels of acetate in the rumen is essential to maintain adequate quantities of milk fat. Acetate is a precursor of milk fatty acids up to and including palmitic acid.

During absorption through the rumen epithelium, 2-5% of propionate is converted to lactic acid with the remainder entering the portal blood as propionate (17). Most of the propionic acid reaching the liver is either oxidized or converted to glucose as shown by the difference between portal and hepatic vein blood propionate concentrations (Table 14-6). To enter the TCA cycle, propionyl-CoA must undergo CO_2 fixation by the biotin-containing enzyme, propionyl-CoA carboxylase, to form methylmalonyl-CoA and, subsequently, be converted to succinyl-CoA.

Table 14-5. Site of acetate utilization in fed and fasted sheep.[a,b]

| Item | Site of acetate utilization as a percentage of total acetate turnover | | |
	Portal viscera	Liver	Peripheral tissues
Fed	18 ± 5	4 ± 7	78 ± 11
Fasted	15 ± 3	8 ± 6	77 ± 4

[a] n = 4/treatment
[b] From (16)

280

Table 14-6. Absorption of propionate and butyrate by the sheep liver.[a,b]

	Blood concentration, μM		
VFA	Arterial	Portal vein	Hepatic vein
Propionate	12 ± 2	187 ± 20	20 ± 4
Butyrate	4 ± 2	25 ± 5	5 ± 3

[a] n = 6
[b] From (16)

Butyric acid is largely converted to ketones during absorption through the rumen epithelium, resulting in very low butyrate levels in portal blood. β-hydroxybutyric acid (βHBA) accounts for more than 80% of the ketones formed, with the remainder comprised of acetoacetate and acetone. βHBA is oxidized in cardiac and skeletal muscle, and is used for fatty acid synthesis in adipose and mammary gland tissue. Butyrate reaching the liver is rapidly metabolized by hepatic tissue as shown by the difference in concentration between portal and hepatic vein (16; Table 14-6).

SITE, RATE AND EXTENT OF CARBOHYDRATE DIGESTION

Non-Structural Carbohydrates

Waldo (18) summarized results of 51 experiments dealing with starch digestion and utilization by ruminants. Total tract digestion of starch, across various grain sources, was 99±1.2%. This high mean and low standard deviation suggested that very little starch escaped digestion in these experiments which involved barley, corn or sorghum fed to sheep or cattle.

Waldo (18) noted that 94±2.4% of barley starch was digested prior to the abomasum or duodenum. Little variation occurred in these data obtained using different lots of barley, feeding either cattle or sheep, using different processing methods or feeding different amounts of starch either by changing the percentage in the diet or by changing dry matter intake. Much more corn than barley starch escaped ruminal digestion. Cornstarch digestion was 78±12.5% prior to the abomasum or duodenum. Because the variation was greater relative to the average percentage starch passing to the intestine, this suggests that cornstarch digestion is sensitive to experimental

methods used. The particular lot of corn used, its genetic type, the ruminant species studied, the processing technique used, the particle size and the percentage corn in the diet all influence the results obtained. Sorghum starch is probably the most resistant to ruminal digestion of any common feed starch. Ruminal digestion is 76±22.4%. Sorghum varietal and type differences appear even greater than for corn. Oat and wheat starches probably have relatively high ruminal digestibilities.

Fewer data are available on starch digestion in the small intestine. Data on barley starch digestion at this site are quite variable, with values ranging from 44 to 99%.

The capacity for and consequences of starch digestion in the large intestine are not clearly defined (18). Sheep digested 138 g cornstarch, provided via cecal infusion, to the extent of 94%, but with larger amounts, digestion dropped to 40% (19). Other values from the literature range from 83 to 88%. Sorghum starch also appears to be highly digestible in the large intestine.

Site of starch digestion is relatively important as a factor affecting efficiency of digested energy to meet the ruminant's metabolic needs. Concentrate-containing diets that result in the introduction of starch into the small intestine for enzymatic digestion should be more efficient than those extensively fermented in the rumen, provided that the majority of starch entering the small intestine is digested prior to arrival in the large intestine.

Structural Carbohydrates

In the presence of a microbial population which elaborates enzymes active against structural carbohydrates, the rate of breakdown of plant cell walls and the extent to which they are degraded may be determined by the holistic nature of the walls themselves rather than to the physico-chemical properties of their component polymers (20). For example, isolated wheat straw cellulose is rapidly and fully degraded in the rumen at a rate which is dependent solely on its physico-chemical nature, notably its degree of molecular order, or crystallinity (21). This represents the maximum rate at which cellulose can be lost from intact wheat straw cell wall under the same conditions. In practice, the upper rate is

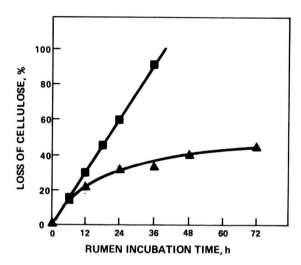

Figure 14-4. Rate and extent of degradation of wheat straw cellulose in the rumen. Isolated cellulose (■); cellulose lost from wheat straw (▲). From (20)

Table 14-7. Composition of barley straw and its undigested residue recovered after 72 h of rumen incubation.[a]

	Percentage dry weight[b]		
Straw components	Original straw (1.00)	Undigested fraction (0.51)	Digested fraction (0.49)
Monosaccharide residues			
Rhamnose	0.20	0.16	0.24
Fucose	0.05	0.04	0.06
Arabinose	2.40	1.77	3.04
Xylose	15.83	16.04	15.62
Mannose	0.67	0.35	0.97
Galactose	1.19	0.67	1.72
Glucose	28.02	28.00	28.04
Uronic acid	2.88	2.63	3.14
Total carbohydrate	51.24	49.66	52.56
Non-carbohydrate components			
Acetyl groups	1.69	1.75	1.63
Phenolic acids	0.71	0.62	0.82
Total phenolics	17.36	21.02	13.55

[a]From (22)
[b]Values for the digested fraction were calculated from these figures.

achieved only during the initial stages of cell wall breakdown (Fig. 14-4). Thereafter, the rate of loss, and more important from a practical viewpoint, the ultimate extent of loss, is determined not by the chemical nature of cellulose itself but by its specific environment within the cell wall and by its association with other wall components. Fibrous carbohydrates, as they exist in plants, vary in their susceptibility to enzymes produced by ruminal microorganisms. The material remaining after adequate ruminal incubation is generally very resistant to further microbial attack. Analysis of the undigested fraction, as well as of the original plant material, enables the composition of material released into the rumen as a result of microbial action (the digested fraction) to be calculated. Results from such an experiment indicate that constraints to the degradation of structural carbohydrates are not simply a product of the accumulation of any specific cell wall component. As noted in Table 14-7, monosaccharide composition of digested and undigested fractions of barley straw is essentially the same. Of the non-carbohydrate components, only total phenolics showed any tendency to accumulate. However, phenolic material, including lignin, is lost from straw at much the same rate as the major cell wall components during cell wall degradation. Thus, the proportions of cellulose, xylose (representing

hemicellulose) and total phenolics remain virtually constant throughout the course of degradation (20). The absence of evidence to suggest that major differences in gross composition of cell walls are responsible for the resistance to degradation shown by a fraction of the structural polysaccharides raises the possibility that differences in the manner in which cell wall components are organized may be important. However, methylation analysis of entire cell walls, before and after incubation in the rumen, showed that any difference in molecular architecture contributing to increased resistance could not involve the manner in which sugar residues are glycosidically linked (20). Linkage patterns for barley straw and the recovered undigested fraction, and the pattern calculated for the digested fraction, are all very similar. Any difference in organization of cell walls would thus have to reside entirely within the non-carbohydrate components of the wall or involve differences in the manner of association of polysaccharides with non-carbohydrate components.

Common feedstuffs vary in their amount and type of structural carbohydrate. Greater than 50% of the variation in digestibility observed among forages can be attributed to different kinetic characteristics of digestion (22). Mechanics of digestion of structural carbohydrates can be divided into three components: (A) an initial lag time during which little or no microbial digestion takes place, (B) rate of digestion of the potentially digestible fiber portion, described as a first order reaction and (C) maximum extent of digestion (23). Although forages differ in their rate of fiber digestion (24, 25), attempts to relate chemical composition of a forage to its digestion rate have been unsuccessful (25).

Digestion kinetics of structural carbohydrates in feedstuffs can be altered by addition of nutrients (e.g., soluble carbohydrates, nonprotein N, VFA, branched chain fatty acids) and (or) by treatment with chemicals (e.g., alkalis). When large amounts of starch, sugar or grain are added to diets, fiber digestion is generally depressed. Mertens and Loften (26) found that purified corn and wheat starch increased lag time and reduced in vitro dry matter digestibility when added to alfalfa, orchardgrass or coastal bermudagrass at 50-80% of as-is substrate. Digestion rate remained unaffected. Little depression of fiber digestibility occurs when a neutral pH is maintained, indicating the importance of this criterion to ruminal fiber digestion.

Chemical treatment of structural carbohydrate-containing feedstuffs also affects rate and extent of digestion. For example, NaOH has been found to increase digestibility of a number of feedstuffs. Many studies indicate that this chemical increases digestion rate; however, alkali treatment effectiveness as related to digestion rate is known to be plant species specific (27).

Level of feed intake is another factor affecting structural carbohydrate digestion kinetics. An inverse relationship between apparent digestibility of a roughage:concentrate diet and level of feed intake by the animal has been documented (28). Correlations between these measurements are not as high when ruminants consume long or chopped all-roughage diets. Changes in environment of the digestive tract and changes in kinetics of the digestion process are brought about by feeding concentrates with roughages. Factors within the rumen such as dry matter digestion rate, particulate passage rate, digesta pH and the nature of the microbial population all influence digestion of a diet. Staples et al (29) found that apparent digestibility of dry matter, NDF, cellulose and hemicellulose decreased linearly as level of feed intake by steers increased from 55 to 100% of ad libitum consumption. The diet fed consisted of 45% alfalfa haylage, 20% corn silage and 35% concentrates. As feed intake increased, NDF digestion decreased more than did cell solubles (20.4 vs 7.5%, respectively). In digestion studies with cattle fed various amounts of roughage:concentrate diets in which whole grain comprises the majority of the concentrate portion, the depression in apparent dry matter digestibility is most closely linked to the cell soluble fraction. However, when grain is cracked or ground, the fiber portion of the diet is primarily responsible for digestibility changes. Hemicelluloses are apparently more sensitive to feed intake changes as compared to other fiber fractions (30).

Digestibility depression is a function of the competition between digestion and passage rates. The more slowly digested fractions present in the plant cell wall are influenced to the greatest extent. The more digestible the cell wall, the greater the potential for digestibility depression through the effect of intake level, physical form, passage or concentrate addition. Digestibility depression is directly proportional to digestible cell wall content and rate of passage whereas it is inversely related to rate of digestion.

Rate of fiber digestion is also affected by feed intake level. Staples et al (29) found that rate of cellulose digestion decreased linearly with increased feed intake. Both animal and microbial factors may be responsible for this change in digestion rate. Time spent ruminating per unit dry matter or cell wall constituents decreased with increasing dry matter intake when sheep consumed a mixed diet of cracked corn and grass hay (31). Increased mastication at lower feed intakes would reduce particle size and increase surface area for enzymatic attack. Robles et al (32) found that in vitro dry matter digestion rates of alfalfa increased with decreasing particle size. Another factor capable of potentially depressing cellulose digestion rate is low ruminal pH. In the study of Staples et al (29), ruminal pH of steers eating at 55% of ad libitum consumption tended to remain > 6.3. However, steers eating at 100% ad libitum often experienced a ruminal pH < 6.3. Stewart (33) reported that optimum pH for fiber digestion was between 6.7 and 7.1.

Cellulose digestion is depressed by 20 to 55% when pH falls to 6.3. Whether the mode of action of pH on fiber digestion is related to cellulolytic numbers, activity of microbial enzymes or both is unclear (34).

Site of digestion may also be influenced by certain of the above-mentioned criteria. In certain instances, large amounts of cellulose and hemicellulose escape rumen digestion and thus become available for fermentation by cecal and large intestinal bacteria. With a range of diets including fresh grass, dried grass, silage, hay and cereals, between 5-30% of digestible cellulose was found to be digested in the large intestine (35). The amount of hemicellulose digested in the large intestine is higher than that of cellulose. Partial resistance of hemicellulose to rumen fermentation could be an important factor limiting rate of degradation of cell wall carbohydrates in the rumen. A major influence on extent of cell wall carbohydrate digestion in the large intestine is nutritive value of the diet. As apparent digestibility of a diet decreases, there is an increase in the proportion of fiber digested in the large intestine. Referring again to the study of Staples et al (29), it was noted that retention time in the digestive tract decreased from 55.6 h to 39.0 h as feed intake increased from 55 to 100% of ad libitum consumption. Digesta spent approximately 14.1, 14.6, 10.9 and 12.1% of total retention time in the lower tract of steers eating at 100, 85, 70 or 55% of ad libitum, respectively. This may imply that digestion in the lower tract is somewhat more important at high feed intakes. Also, the lower tract may play a more important role in dry matter digestion at higher intakes of low roughage diets. When roughages are pelleted or as concentrates become a larger portion of the diet, a greater percentage of digestible cellulose disappears in the cecum. Rate of passage of the average forage diet indicates a ruminal retention time of plant cell wall of approximately 40-50 h (4). A doubling of the intake will decrease this time to approximately 30-35 h in sheep. Cumulative integrated digestion curves indicate that cell walls susceptible to the greatest digestibility depressions are those exhibiting substantial digestibility increases between 30-48 h of fermentation (7). This accounts for the generally

greater depression observed in grasses as compared to legumes.

Associative effects (see Ch. 9) are important considerations in a discussion of extent of digestion of structural carbohydrates by ruminants. Both positive and negative associative effects can occur. It is known that grain supplements reduce digestibility of fiber in forage-containing diets. This may be due to either preferential digestion of the soluble carbohydrate by ruminal bacteria or to a decrease in both the extent and rate of fiber digestion in forages at the lower pH in the rumen of grain-fed animals. Soluble carbohydrates such as starch or sugar may impede cellulose digestion due to factors such as lowered pH, competition between cellulolytic and non-cellulolytic bacteria for essential nutrients other than energy or use of alternative energy sources by certain of the cellulolytic bacteria per se (36). Thus, the effect of feed combinations on apparent digestibility can possess true nutritive significance. The greatest associative effects usually occur when feeds that are widely different in rate of digestion or that result in different rates of passage are fed at the same time. True associative effects under practical feeding conditions remain unpredictable and require more research into their nature.

SECONDARY FACTORS AFFECTING DIGESTION AND UTILIZATION

A number of secondary plant compounds affect the site, rate and extent of carbohydrate digestion as well as carbohydrate utilization by the animal. These include lignins and simple phenolics, alkaloids, tannins, cutin, silica, estrogenic compounds and cyanides.

Lignins and Phenolics

Lignins appear to inhibit degradation of plant structural carbohydrates by rumen microorganisms. They are polymeric products arising from an enzyme-initiated dehydrogenative polymerization of three primary precursors. The phenylpropanoid precursors, phenylalanine and tyrosine, give rise to three monomers that account for most of the lignin molecule: p-coumaryl, coniferyl and sinapyl alcohols (37). These monomeric alcohols form free radicals under the influence of

284

phenol oxidase and these radicals then undergo non-enzymatic reactions to form polyphenols. Strong C-C and ether linkages of lignin are not susceptible to simple hydrolysis, making the structural analysis of lignin difficult. Plant lignins differ mainly in the proportions of the three alcohols from which they are formed. Gymnosperm lignins are approximately 80% coniferyl, 14% p-coumaryl and 6% sinapyl alcohols. In contrast, angiosperm lignins are composed of 56% coniferyl, 4% p-coumaryl and 40% sinapyl alcohols (37). Grass and herbage lignins are often high in p-coumaric, ferulic, diferulic and p-hydroxybenzoic acids and vanillin (38). Nitrobenzene oxidation of grass lignins yields vanillin, syringaldehyde and p-hydroxybenzaldehyde (39, 40). Gordon and Neudoerffer (41) refer to the highly condensed phenylpropanoid matrix of lignin as "core" lignin. The lignin core appears to be linked to the structural carbohydrates of the plant cell wall via carbohydrate esters of ferulic acid (42). p-Coumaric and ferulic acids, which represent a fraction termed "non-core" lignin (43), may act as cross linkages between lignin and structural carbohydrates because they possess two important functional groups, hydroxyl and carboxyl. Linkages are of at least three types: those cleaved by reduction, those cleaved by alkali and those resistant to alkali (44). Ester linkages between "non-core" lignin and branched hemicelluloses are most prominent in forages (45).

Alkali and dimethyl sulfoxide extraction of grass cell walls yields lignin-carbohydrate complexes (LCC) ranging from 10,000 to 100,000 molecular weight (45). The carbohydrate portion of alkali extracts contain mainly xylose (70%) and arabinose (20%) with smaller quantities of galactose (5%) and glucose (5%), while the sulfoxide extracts contain primarily glucose (50%) and xylose (30%) with lesser amounts of arabinose (12%) and galactose (5%). Alkali extracts a greater proportion of lignin and the associated sugars resemble grass hemicelluloses in composition, whereas the sulfoxide sugars are similar in content to the overall cell wall carbohydrates (45). The glucose of sulfoxide-extracted LCC is linked β-1,4 and the xylose is linked β-1,4 with arabinose and galactose attached to the C-3 position of xylose (44).

Lignin content of forages is quite variable, but a few patterns emerge. As physiological maturity of a plant advances, lignin content increases (46) both in grasses and legumes. Content of phenolic acids also increases with advancing maturity of grasses but not of legumes (47, 48). Legumes are generally higher in lignin content than are grasses (46), but solubility in alkali is lower for legumes (38). Legume lignins appear to be more condensed and potentially less reactive than are grass lignins (43). Within the grasses, tropical species exhibit higher lignin values than do temperate species (49).

Lignin is the chemical component of fiber that is most frequently associated with nutrient indigestibility and that has been shown to be useful for predicting extent of fiber digestion. Lignification of plant material has also been associated with poor animal performance. Low apparent digestibility of lignin and increased lignin content associated with advancing maturity serve as a basis for the assumption that lignification is one of the major factors responsible for the low feeding value of mature forage plants (50). Also, lignin apparently affects animal utilization of cell wall polysaccharides. However, quantity of lignin present in forage, as measured by current techniques, may be of little importance. For example, legumes generally have higher lignin contents than do grasses of similar digestibility.

Various mechanisms have been suggested as to the manner in which lignin affects cell wall digestibility. These include encrustation, effects on digestive tract microbes and the formation of lignin-polysaccharide complexes. Each has been discussed in depth by Jung and Fahey (50).

Phenolics also interfere with carbohydrate digestion by means other than binding. p-Coumaric acid, when added to in vitro incubation systems, inhibits degradation of cellulose and intact plant cell walls by rumen microorganisms and interferes with growth of bacteria and protozoa (51). Pure cultures of fiber-digesting bacteria are also inhibited by phenolic acids. Chesson et al (52) found that p-coumaric and ferulic acids limited microbial growth but that microbial transformation of these compounds occurred within the rumen with less toxic compounds being formed.

Differences also exist in the complexing of phenolic acids with structural carbohydrates of forages. Hartley (53) found higher levels of p-coumaric acid in fecal residues than in forages. Harris et al (54) found that the more digestible plant cells contained only 13% as much p-coumaric acid as did less digestible cells whereas levels of ferulic acid were similar in these fractions. Phenolic acids could influence cell wall degradation in vivo by virtue of their binding capabilities or by their toxic nature, thus reducing the nutritive value of the feed.

Alkaloids

Festuca arundinacea (tall fescue) contains the alkaloid, perloline, which causes problems for ruminants grazing this forage. Perloline is a normal constituent of *Lolium* species and has been shown to inhibit ruminal cellulose digestion as well as VFA production and growth of cellulolytic bacteria, ultimately decreasing the availability of energy and other nutrients to the animal (55).

Tannins

Tannins are naturally occurring compounds of high enough molecular weight (500 to 3,000) and containing a large number of phenolic hydroxyl groups (1-2/100 molecular weight) to enable them to form effective cross-links with proteins and other molecules. While not specifically affecting the carbohydrate fraction of the plant, tannins depress the nutritive value of plant dry matter by reducing both voluntary feed intake and nutrient digestibility. Two types of tannins exist, namely, the hydrolyzable and the condensed varieties, which may be differentiated by their structures and reactivity towards hydrolytic agents. The principal forage tannins are usually of the condensed type and have been found in legumes, sorghum grains, tree leaves and in certain agricultural waste products (56). The most serious concern regarding the presence of tannins in plants is their ability to react with protein in the digestive system of the ruminant. Negative response in feed intake by ruminant animals is influenced primarily by the astringent nature of the tannins; the tannin level required for rejection of the plant by grazing animals was approximately 20 mg/g dry matter in one study. Besides rendering plant tissue unpalatable by precipitating salivary proteins (57), tannins also diminish the permeability of the gut wall by reacting with the outer cellular layer of the gut such that passage of nutrients through the gut wall is reduced (58). Both factors may affect voluntary feed intake by ruminants.

Dry matter (59) and N (60) digestibility are also decreased by the presence of tannins. A potential cause of this decrease is the inhibition of digestive enzymes (61). Tannins are potent inhibitors of digestive enzymes due to their capacity to bind with enzymic proteins as well as with substrate. Ruminal digestion may also be impaired by the presence of tannins. Other negative consequences of tannin ingestion by ruminants include: low milk yield, reduction in S availability, toxic degenerative changes in intestine, liver, spleen and kidney, mucus appearance in urine and constipation (56).

Other Compounds

Other secondary compounds which may affect carbohydrate digestion include the encrusting agents cutin and silica as well as agents which affect animal metabolism such as isoflavones and cyanides. The problem with these secondary substances is that they are peculiar to certain types of feeds and forages (4). Examples include silica in rice, reed canary grass and horsetails, and isoflavonoid estrogens in subterranean clovers and some other legumes. Certain of these substances such as estrogens and cyanides have more effect upon the animal and its metabolism than upon the digestion process. Compounds that especially limit digestibility such as cutin and silica tend to work additively with lignin.

CARBOHYDRATE DIGESTION IN THE SMALL AND LARGE INTESTINE

The majority of the non-structural carbohydrates present in feeds is fermented in the rumen. However, with high levels of feed intake, significant amounts of starch may reach the small intestine undegraded. Bacterial polysaccharides can also be a significant source of non-structural carbohydrate entering the small intestine. The α-glucan content of rumen bacteria on a dry matter basis increased from 2.5% on an all-roughage diet to 7.0% on a 50% roughage diet to 15.0% on a

30% roughage diet (62). The carbohydrate content of rumen protozoa can be as high as 38% when a high starch diet is fed. However, the actual amount of carbohydrate reaching the small intestine from protozoa is probably fairly low, due to their slow exit rate from the rumen.

Enzymes involved in hydrolysis of α-linked glucose polymers are the amylases and maltases secreted by the pancreas and intestinal mucosa, and oligo-1,6 glucosidase of intestinal mucosa. The low activities of pancreatic maltase and intestinal amylase relative to pancreatic amylase and intestinal maltase, respectively, suggest a greater importance of pancreatic amylase and intestinal maltase in starch hydrolysis (63). Studies of pancreatic and intestinal carbohydrases in sheep suggest that maltase may be the enzyme limiting the capacity for post-ruminal starch digestion. Most of the starch entering the small intestine is broken down before reaching the terminal ileum. For example, in sheep, 85, 77 and 95% of the α-linked glucose polymer entering the small intestine from corn, barley and oat-based diets, respectively, disappeared prior to the cecum (64).

The efficiency figure for glucose absorption directly from the small intestine is unknown. An increase in portal blood glucose levels in lambs and an increase in the concentration of reducing sugars in the mesenteric vein draining the ileum of dairy cows when ground corn was added to diets in both experiments suggest that there is direct glucose absorption from the small intestine. If a lactating dairy cow was fed high levels of corn and all of the cornstarch available in the small intestine was absorbed as glucose, this could supply 60-75% of the animal's glucose requirement.

The proportion of α-linked glucose polymer which remains to be fermented in the hindgut is normally very small. In sheep fed diets containing approximately 70% concentrates, less than 2% of the digestible α-linked glucose disappears in the cecum and colon. However, when cattle are fed diets containing 80% ground corn, 11.3% of the digestible α-glucan disappears in the cecum and colon.

Structural carbohydrates are degraded primarily in the rumen. With forages fed in the long or chopped form, approximately 85% or more of cellulose digestion occurs in the rumen. However, when forages are ground and pelleted, a greater proportion of cellulose digestion occurs in the cecum and large intestine. The proportion of the digestible hemicellulose disappearing in the cecum and large intestine tends to be greater than for cellulose and is often between 15 and 30% (63). Part of this difference in site of digestion between cellulose and hemicellulose may be due to the greater susceptibility of hemicellulose to partial acid hydrolysis in the abomasum and duodenum.

The pathways of fiber degradation in the cecum and large intestine are very similar to those occurring in the rumen, yielding VFA, CH_4, CO_2 and microbial biomass. The proportion of acetate in cecal VFA tends to be higher than in the rumen, reflecting the greater proportion of structural polysaccharides arriving at this site. In addition, relatively large proportions of iso-acids reflect rapid protein degradation. In sheep fed dried grass cubes, 5.3% of total VFA production occurred in the cecum. Similarly, in sheep fed ground alfalfa, cecal CH_4 production accounted for 10% of total CH_4 production.

Unlike microbial protein synthesized in the rumen, there is no evidence that cecal microbial protein is digested and absorbed in the large intestine. Consequently, fermentation of carbohydrate in the cecum and large intestine tends to decrease apparent N digestion by increasing metabolic fecal N.

GLUCONEOGENESIS

In general, microbial fermentation of carbohydrates in the rumen results in little glucose being absorbed directly from the gastrointestinal tract. An exception to this rule may occur when large amounts of slowly degraded starch are fed. Consequently, glucose required at the tissue level is provided primarily via gluconeogenic pathways from propionate, amino acids, glycerol and lactate. In spite of the extra metabolic steps required to provide glucose to the tissues, ruminants have about the same glucose requirement for basal metabolism as do other species, even though their blood glucose level (40 to 60 mg/dl) is about half that of non-ruminants.

There are at least five tissues which require glucose: nervous tissue, muscle, adipose, mammary gland and fetus. The ruminant central nervous system is different from that of non-ruminants in that it can tolerate long periods of hypoglycemia, as low as 18 mg glucose/dl blood for 6 h, without deleterious effects. The brain and spinal cord tend to be lower as a percentage of body weight in ruminants as compared to other animals. For example, mean weight of brain and spinal cord of sheep is approximately 130 g while the mean value for man is approximately 1,400 g. Thus, in terms of whole animal glucose requirements, the nervous system of sheep requires about 15-20% of the total glucose supply, while in the human, this figure would be 70-80% (65).

Muscle requires glucose primarily to produce glycogen, although a small amount of glucose is oxidized directly. Ruminant muscle contains much less glycogen than do those of other species, reflecting the lower amount of glucose available at the tissue level.

Glucose is also required for fat metabolism in that it furnishes NADPH which is formed by glucose oxidation via the hexose monophosphate pathway. NADPH is required as a reducing agent at recurring steps in the synthesis of long-chain fatty acids.

The largest quantities of glucose are used for fetal growth and milk production in ruminants. The fetus receives a continuous supply of glucose from the mother and is the principal carbohydrate source. Fetal glucose metabolism can account for 40-70% of the total glucose metabolized by the whole body of sheep during late pregnancy. Glucose requirements for lactation are even greater than those required by the fetus. Lactose production alone can require 2,000 g of glucose/d for a high producing dairy cow and about 200 g/d for a ewe nursing twins. In high producing ruminants, lactose production can account for 60-85% of total body glucose metabolism.

The major metabolic difference between ruminants and non-ruminants is the extent to which ruminants utilize acetate instead of glucose as the major substrate for energy storage and oxidation, and their reliance on gluconeogenesis for glucose during both fed and fasted states. Consequently, rate of gluconeogenesis in ruminants is greatest shortly after a meal when gluconeogenic substrates are most plentiful. This is different from non-ruminants consuming high carbohydrate diets where large amounts of hexose are often absorbed shortly after a meal.

Propionate is the only VFA which makes a net contribution to glucose synthesis (Fig. 14-3) and is quantitatively the most important precursor. Isotope dilution techniques have been used to measure ruminal propionate production, total glucose entry rates and the contribution of propionate to glucose entry in sheep. These studies suggest that 27-54% of the glucose was synthesized from propionate (66). In these studies, a portion of the propionate was converted to lactate which is also available for glucose synthesis. Consequently, more than 27-54% of the glucose may have had propionate as the original precursor. The amount of propionate absorbed from the rumen varies with amount and type of diet consumed. For example, in sheep fed alfalfa hay, approximately 30% of the glucose is derived from propionate whereas approximately 66% of glucose is formed from propionate when ruminants consume high grain diets (65).

Amino acids can be used for gluconeogenesis except for lysine, leucine and taurine. The liver utilizes some excess amino acids derived from the diet and (or) available from normal turnover of body and plasma proteins for the formation of glucose and urea. The kidney also uses amino acids not only for gluconeogenesis but also for ammonia production and regulation of acid-base balance.

The actual amount of glucose synthesized from amino acids is difficult to determine. If one assumes that 55 g of glucose can be synthesized from 100 g protein, then about 70% of glucose production for a well-fed non-pregnant sheep could arise from amino acids (65). Of course, not all amino acids arriving at the small intestine are available for gluconeogenesis. Some are metabolized by gut tissue and used for chylomicron formation, growth of new mucosal cells or are deaminated and used for energy.

Not all amino acids absorbed from the gut have the same glucogenicity in the liver. On a molar basis, alanine, glutamine, glycine and serine account for about 70% of the total amino acids removed by liver. Alanine and glutamine are the most glucogenic and account for 40-60% of the glucose formed from amino acids in sheep. Glutamate and

288

aspartate are not removed by liver but are taken up by kidney and used for renal gluco-genesis. When glucose synthesized in both liver and kidney is considered, ruminants fed at maintenance derive at least 15% of their glucose from amino acids. The maximum contribution of amino acids to the glucose requirement is about 36%, with 32 percent-age units coming from liver and 4 percentage units coming from kidney (65).

The fact that alanine and glutamine are the major amino acids used for gluconeogenesis raises the question as to the non-dietary sources of these amino acids available to the liver. Data from both ruminants and non-ruminants show that these amino acids are released from skeletal muscle. This suggests that other amino acids are deaminated to organic acids, and that the N is then transami-nated with pyruvate, α-ketoglutarate or gluta-mate to form alanine and glutamine. This system has several advantages. First, since urea cannot be synthesized in muscle, amino acids can still be oxidized without release of toxic quantities of ammonia. Secondly, it provides liver with glucogenic precursors and kidney with glutamine for neutralizing acids, especially during acidosis.

Fig. 14-5 summarizes interorgan transport of amino acids used for gluconeogenesis in liver and kidney. Amino acids absorbed into portal blood are removed either by liver or are transported through systemic circulation for use in the turnover of body protein or other productive processes. Alanine and glutamine are released by muscle and converted to glu-cose and urea in liver. For animals at mainte-nance, most of the amino acids absorbed from the gut are eventually converted to glucose and urea. In well-fed herbivores, the kidney is a major source of glutamine and provides approximately half the glutamine removed by liver. During fasting, release of alanine and glutamine from muscle is increased to meet the needs of the kidney and liver (67).

Glycerol is a third compound used for gluconeogenesis. Most of the glycerol in the body is bound with fatty acids in triglycerides and is released only during lipolysis. Glycerol is taken up by liver and kidneys and is used for glucose synthesis, triglyceride formation or oxidation to CO_2. Based on ^{14}C studies in sheep, it has been estimated that one-third of the glycerol removed from the blood is used

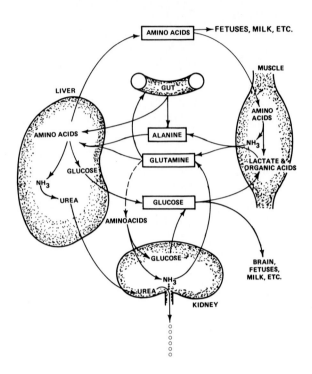

Figure 14-5. Diagram illustrating alanine and gluta-mine as major forms of interorgan N transport for gluconeogenesis and ureogenesis. Dashed line indi-cates acidosis or starvation. From (65)

for gluconeogenesis and 10% is oxidized directly to CO_2. The remaining glycerol is used primarily for synthesis of triglycerides. In sheep, glycerol accounts for about 5% of the C of total glucose synthesis. However, in fasted or starved ruminants, propionate absorption drops sharply and glycerol contrib-utes a much larger portion of glucose synthe-sized.

Lactate is formed during anaerobic metabo-lism of glucose in nearly all tissues and large quantities can be produced in the rumen when high grain diets are fed. Rate of absorp-tion of lactate from the rumen is slower than for the other VFA because of the lower pk_a of lactate (3.7) and the fact that undissoci-ated, less polar forms are absorbed the fastest. Of the lactate that is absorbed, about 20% is converted to glucose and 30-50% is oxidized to CO_2 (68). In ruminants, only about 5% of the glucose formed comes from lactate via the Cori cycle (65). In fed sheep, about 15% of the glucose can originate from blood lactate when both endogenous lactate produced from the Cori cycle and exogenous lactate absorbed from the digestive tract are considered. Only lactate absorbed from the gut can form new glucose for the body.

Dietary and Hormonal Control of Gluconeogenesis

The quantity of glucogenic precursor available to liver is the major factor determining amount of glucose formed. In ruminants, gluconeogenesis increases after feeding and decreases during fasting, due mainly to amount of precursor available. This is in contrast to non-ruminants where maximum gluconeogenesis occurs only if a meal has not been consumed recently.

Amounts of propionate and lactate available for gluconeogenesis are directly related to amount of non-structural carbohydrate in the diet and amount of diet consumed. In contrast, amounts of glycerol and amino acids available are under complex hormonal control. If blood glucose concentration decreases, glycogenolysis and release of glucose from liver begins. Simultaneously, secretion of insulin by the pancreas decreases and that of glucagon increases. The molar ratio of insulin and glucagon may be more important in controlling rate of gluconeogenesis than the actual amount of each hormone. Because liver is more sensitive to glucagon than to insulin, an insulin:glucagon ratio of 6 or less reflects an effect on liver due to glucagon rather than to insulin (69).

If the glucose deficiency continues, glucose receptors in the hypothalamus will be stimulated and send impulses to the adrenal medulla which increases secretion of epinephrine. Reduced insulin and increased glucagon and epinephrine increase glycogenolysis and cause lipolysis in adipose tissue, resulting in mobilization of glycerol and free fatty acids. The increased glucagon:insulin ratio quickly stimulates amino acid release from muscle, resulting in more glucose precursors, especially alanine and glutamine.

Amino acid uptake by liver is increased by glucagon, cortisol and growth hormone. Glucagon, especially, rapidly increases uptake of alanine, glutamine and other glucogenic amino acids. While uptake of lactate by liver is increased by glucagon, there is no evidence that propionate or glycerol uptake is under hormonal control. Flux of these metabolites in or out of the liver can be changed merely by changes in blood concentration which may or may not be in response to a change in hormonal status.

The overall metabolic pathways leading to glucose synthesis are controlled by five rate-limiting reactions (Fig. 14-3). The key enzymes which control these reactions in ruminants are: (A) pyruvate carboxylase, for formation of OAA from pyruvate; (B) NAD-malate dehydrogenase, for conversion of malate to OAA; (C) PEP carboxykinase, for conversion of OAA to PEP; (D) fructose-1,6-diphosphatase, for conversion of fructose-1,6-diphosphate to fructose-6-phosphate; and (E) glucose-6-phosphatase, found only in liver and kidney, for release of free glucose into the blood. All of these reactions are influenced by factors which alter enzyme activation or synthesis and are altered by factors such as diet, fasting, lactation, pregnancy and hormone status. As a rule, glucagon and glucocorticoids increase reaction rates while insulin depresses reaction rates of all five enzymes (65).

METABOLISM OF CARBOHYDRATES BY THE YOUNG RUMINANT

Blood glucose levels in young ruminants are higher than those of mature ruminants and fall to adult values usually within three months of birth. The decrease in blood glucose level with age may be related to development of the rumen, although it may be independent of rumen development, dietary changes or increased levels of VFA in the rumen or blood. The fall in blood glucose is probably the result of decreasing alimentary hyperglycemia associated with diminishing intake of milk as well as loss of glucose from red blood cells. The latter event could occur as a result of dilution of fetal erythrocytes high in glucose with new cells of lower glucose content. It appears that in the period from 3-8 weeks of age, the importance of glucose in the metabolism of the young ruminant decreases but, from plasma VFA data, rumen development is not sufficiently advanced to provide enough VFA to satisfy energy requirements of the animal. Thus, a mild stress, such as an overnight fast, is sufficient to deplete liver glycogen and stimulate fat mobilization, with a resultant rise in plasma free fatty acids (70).

290

Other changes in glucose metabolism of young ruminants occur with age. Tolerance of injected glucose is high in young lambs but decreases with age to become very low in adult sheep. Glucose tolerance in young lambs resembles that of normal humans whereas glucose tolerance in adult sheep resembles that of diabetic humans. There is a decrease in size of the glucose pool and the rate of glucose utilization with increasing age of lamb. The ability of extrahepatic tissues to utilize glucose is lower in ruminants than in non-ruminants. Insulin secretion in response to injected glucose is marked in two-week old lambs, decreases by six weeks of age and is very low in adult sheep. The rate of glucose absorption from the intestine of the adult sheep is very much less than that found in the non-ruminant; however, it is rapid in the neonatal lamb. This may be related to the hexokinase activity of the intestinal mucosa which, in lambs, reaches a maximum at about five days postpartum and then declines (70).

Associated with development of a functional rumen, there is a reduced capacity for glucose oxidation in liver by glycolytic and hexose monophosphate pathways (70). These changes are reflected in the enzyme activities of some key processes in carbohydrate metabolism. Activities of hepatic glucose-6-phosphate dehydrogenase and 6-phosphogluconate dehydrogenase, key enzymes in the hexose monophosphate shunt, and of fructose-1,6-diphosphate aldolase and glyceraldehyde-3-phosphate dehydrogenase, important glycolytic enzymes, are higher in neonatal ruminants than in adults.

Changes also occur in hepatic enzymes concerned with gluconeogenesis and with glucose release from liver. In lambs, activities of enzymes catalyzing formation of glycogen from glucose are high in the fetus and young lamb but decrease to adult values 2-3 months postpartum, presumably as a result of decreasing availability of glucose. Glucose-6-phosphatase, hexose diphosphatase and incorporation of pyruvate and propionate into glycogen increase to adult values a few weeks after birth. Hepatic glucose-6-phosphatase activity is also higher in the mature bovine than in calves where values increase to those of adults at 8-12 weeks postpartum. Hexokinase activity of sheep liver is very low. In newborn lambs, the activity is slightly higher but decreases to adult values within six weeks.

Enzyme changes correlate well with changes in carbohydrate metabolism as affected by age (70). The young lamb absorbs glucose, and enzymes are present in liver capable of converting glucose to glycogen. As the lamb matures, the importance of dietary carbohydrates decreases because less milk is ingested with time and, in later stages of development, rumen microorganisms ferment most of the dietary carbohydrates, resulting in little glucose available for absorption from the intestinal tract. Therefore, the lamb relies increasingly on gluconeogenesis for its supply of glucose. In the adult sheep, little net uptake of glucose by liver occurs and the activity of hepatic glucokinase is negligible. However, liver is well equipped enzymatically for release of glucose into blood and for synthesis of glucose from pyruvate and from propionate produced by rumen fermentation. The decrease in activity of enzymes associated with glucose breakdown and the increase in those associated with gluconeogenesis are probably induced by increasing amounts of VFA. The CoA derivatives of these acids tend to stimulate gluconeogenesis by activating pyruvate carboxylase and the increased ratio of acetyl-CoA:CoA would tend to inhibit some of the enzymes associated with glycolysis.

Hormonal control of carbohydrate metabolism of the young ruminant is also of importance. The rates at which pancreatic, pituitary and adrenal cortical hormones are released appear to be reduced in the newborn animal (71). Also, the exaggerated response to insulin and to hypophysectomy or adrenalectomy (death from hypoglycemia) indicate that maintenance of a normal blood glucose concentration is directly dependent on the functional integrity of these endocrine systems during this period, possibly due to enhanced sensitivity of the peripheral tissues. Activity of the sympathetic nervous system is intimately connected with control of the blood glucose concentration at this stage. The sympathetic nervous system is also implicated in the mobilization of liver glycogen and, in the event that this mechanism fails to maintain blood glucose concentration, the central nervous system is protected from the effects of hypoglycemia by release of adrenalin from the adrenal medulla (71).

PROCEDURES FOR EVALUATING THE NUTRITIVE VALUE OF DIETARY CARBOHYDRATES

Determination of the nutritive value of non-structural carbohydrates in ruminant feeds using laboratory techniques is a matter receiving little attention. This may be due to the fact that most non-structural carbohydrates are nearly 100% available to the animal because they are easily digested by gut microbes and(or) enzymes secreted by the host animal. Procedures exist for the quantitative analysis of individual sugars as well as for the analysis of larger molecular weight non-structural carbohydrates of feedstuffs. Starch and total non-structural carbohydrates can be measured in feed and feces with subsequent calculation of their digestion coefficients—such results provide insight into utilization of these moieties in feeds. Two categories of methods for starch determination exist. In the direct method, starch is first separated from other materials by solubilization, with minimum degradation, and then estimated by methods utilizing physical or physico-chemical properties of the polymer. In those methods classified as indirect, starch is degraded to products which can be determined simply and accurately and which bear a constant proportionality to the weight of starch.

Determining the total non-structural carbohydrate (sugars, starches, fructosans) content of feeds and(or) biological samples collected from animals is an alternative to measuring separate chemical moieties. However, values generated from this analysis are more appropriate in an evaluation of plant material since animals have no digestive enzymes to degrade galactans and certain oligosaccharides (4).

Determining the nutritive value of feedstuffs having significant amounts of structural carbohydrates is a matter of great importance and one which has received much attention in recent years. The presence of structural carbohydrates in a diet affects both digestibility and amount of feed consumed by the animal. Classical methods of structural carbohydrate (crude fiber, CF) analysis attempted to simulate the digestive process occurring in the animal by a hydrolysis with dilute acid and alkali. However, it is apparent that the CF and NFE fractions of the proximate analysis system do not represent a nutritionally realistic separation of structural carbohydrates. The NFE fraction contains a significant part of the hemicellulose and lignin fractions, as well as some cellulose, in addition to starch, pectin, sugars and other soluble matter. CF contains residual cellulose and lignin. Cellulose and hemicelluloses are partially digestible by the animal while starch, pectin and sugars are highly (if not completely) digestible. In addition to in vivo digestion and metabolism experiments, chemical, in vitro, in situ, electron microscopic and infrared reflectance methods are in use today for determining the nutritive value of feedstuffs containing structural carbohydrates.

The systems of fibrous feed analyses devised by Van Soest and associates have become the primary standards for chemical evaluation of forages in the USA (72). Details of the original forage fiber analyses are presented in the USDA Handbook by Goering and Van Soest (73). Methods are described for the determination of NDF (cellulose, hemicellulose, lignin, insoluble ash), acid detergent fiber (ADF-cellulose, lignin, silica), acid detergent lignin, acid detergent cutin, acid detergent insoluble N (artifact lignin produced by non-enzymatic browning reactions), permanganate lignin, cellulose, insoluble ash, silica and pepsin-insoluble N. ADF and lignin contents of feedstuffs are considered to be indicators of relative digestibility, whereas NDF content is more often considered as an indicator of intake potential among or within forage species. The NDF procedure separates the completely digestible (>98%), soluble forage constituents (cell contents) from those that are not completely available but that depend on microbial fermentation in the rumen to become partially available to the animal. However, the gravimetric NDF procedure does not adequately remove starch, and occasionally N, from some feedstuffs unless the NDF residue is incubated with appropriate enzymes for their removal. Also, because the NDF method fails to recover the water-soluble, viscous polysaccharide fraction of fiber (pectin, mucilages, gums), it is sometimes criticized as a reproducible but misleading method. Therefore, it is important to be aware that the NDF method does not measure *total* cell wall.

Other chemical methods used to measure structural carbohydrate content of plant material include colorimetric techniques, gas-liquid chromatographic (GLC) analysis and high-pressure liquid chromatographic (HPLC) analysis. Colorimetric techniques suffer from interference by other compounds. Sample preparation for GLC analysis is more time-consuming than that for HPLC; however, GLC is more sensitive than is HPLC.

The two stage (rumen liquor/pepsin-HCl) in vitro technique of Tilley and Terry (74) is widely recognized as the preferred method for assessment of relative differences in fiber digestion in the laboratory. Factors that must be considered when using this technique are donor animal diet standardization, time of feeding the donor animal, time of rumen fluid removal, rumen inoculum preparation and use of standard samples of known digestibility in each batch run. The original in vitro procedure, as well as the various modifications that have been proposed (72), have been used primarily to study extent of structural carbohydrate digestion rather than rate phenomena. Fungal enzyme methods have also been developed to evaluate fiber digestion (75). Fungal cellulases often predict relative fiber digestion nearly as well as in vitro rumen fermentation methods. However, fungal enzymes currently marketed vary greatly in their capacity to digest fiber; therefore, standardization of enzyme activity is of paramount importance for correct interpretation of results from these types of experiments.

In situ, or nylon bag, methods involve placement of fiber-containing materials in bags made of indigestible fabrics such as nylon, dacron or silk directly into the rumen (72). Both rate and extent of digestion may be measured by loss of dry matter or specific nutrients after incubation for various periods of time. Among the factors that affect in situ digestion values are sample size, time in the rumen, incubator animal diet, fineness of grind of the sample and bag characteristics such as pore size and surface area.

Electron microscopy has been used to establish a structural basis for forage and fiber digestibility (76). Transmission electron microscopy is useful in elucidating the specific interrelationships of plant cell walls and microorganisms and the manner of forage degradation. Scanning electron microscopy is used to establish relative rates and extents of digestion of specific tissue types. The scanning electron microscope confers high depth of focus and relatively high magnification (up to 80,000x) (77). In contrast to light or transmission electron microscopy, effort in specimen preparation is minimal. Most examinations require an evacuation of the sample under study, but newer developments allow use of backscattered electrons in a high vapor pressure environment. Transmission electron microscopy allows higher magnifications (500,000x), but preparations such as gold coating, shadowing, freeze-etching, embedding and thin-sectioning are required (78).

The Near Infrared Reflectance (NIR) analysis is a rapid means of obtaining compositional, bioassay or quality estimates of forages. The method was initially used for the rapid determination of moisture, oil and protein in grains and oilseeds and more recently has been used to predict nutritive value of feedstuffs (79) and composition of forages (80, 81). The method involves use of a near-infrared spectrometer equipped for diffuse reflectance, a mini-computer for data handling and calibration and suitable samples and calibration data to generate prediction equations. After a set of samples is selected for calibration, the spectra are taken and approximately 700 data points for each sample are stored in a computer file. Data for several compositional factors are added to the spectral file and multiple linear regression techniques are used to generate prediction equations. Spectra of an unknown sample are taken and the results predicted. Calibration is an important aspect of this technique and accuracy of the method depends on the appropriateness of the calibration set, the quality of the calibration data and the mathematical treatment of the spectral data.

FEEDSTUFF PROCESSING AND CONSERVATION

Feed processing has been used to improve utilization of both structural and non-structural carbohydrates by ruminants. In most cases, digestion of non-structural carbohydrates is complete. However, with cattle fed whole grains, appreciable amounts of grain may pass through the digestive tract undegraded. Table 14-8 shows the effect of different grain processing treatments on utilization of barley, maize and sorghum grain starch by sheep and cattle. Although data are taken from several different experiments and one cannot directly compare starch source, processing technique or animal species, several observations can be made. First, over 90% of barley starch is digested in the rumen except when fed whole to cattle. When whole barley was fed to sheep, 95% of the starch was digested in the rumen. This suggests that sheep are much more efficient in cracking the whole barley during chewing than are cattle. Wheat, like barley starch, is rapidly fermented in the rumen except when fed whole to cattle. By comparison, larger proportions of corn and sorghum grain starch tend to escape rumen fermentation unless it is steam-flaked.

Sorghum grain is very poorly utilized when fed to cattle in the whole form and is very responsive to processing. For example, amount of sorghum grain starch fermented in the rumen of cattle doubled when the grain was steam-flaked as compared to when fed ground. Grinding or rolling is considered the mildest form of grain processing where the only effect is to crack the seed coat and reduce particle size. In contrast, steam flaking usually increases moisture content, reduces particle size and gelatinizes many of the starch granules, making them much more susceptible to enzymatic attack. This type of grain processing not only increases extent of ruminal digestion but often shifts rumen fermentation towards increased propionate and decreased acetate production. For example, the molar ratio of acetate:propionate was 1.8 and 1.0 in rumen fluid from steers fed rolled and popped milo, respectively. Other processing techniques which have similar effects on the starch granule include pelleting, extruding, roasting, popping, exploding and micronizing, all of which use heat, steam and(or) pressure to make the starch more readily available.

Ensiling high moisture grains (22-35% moisture) has become a common method of preservation. During the ensiling process, water-soluble carbohydrates are fermented to lactic

Table 14-8. Starch intake and digestion in the reticulo-rumen and total gastrointestinal tract of diets fed to both sheep and cattle.[a]

| | Grain | | | Starch intake, g/24 h | Digestibility, % | |
Type	Form in which fed	Percentage in ration	Animal		In reticulo-rumen	In total tract
Barley:						
	Rolled	100	Sheep	479	92	100
	Whole	100	Sheep	573	95	--
	Steam-flaked	68	Sheep	369	95	100
	Ground	58	Cattle	2560	93	--
	Ground	78	Cattle	3150	98	--
	Whole	90	Cattle	1850	64	--
Maize:						
	Ground	80	Sheep	613	78	100
	Steam-flaked	80	Sheep	626	96	100
	Ground	20	Cattle	645	59	100
	Ground	60	Cattle	1610	50	99
	Ground	80	Cattle	2158	70	99
Sorghum:						
	Rolled	68	Sheep	398	89	100
	Steam-flaked	69	Sheep	373	89	100
	Ground	83	Cattle	2070	42	97
	Steam-flaked	83	Cattle	2290	83	100

[a]From (63)

294

and acetic acids which lower pH and preserve the grain. When the grain is ground or rolled, increases in ruminal rate of starch degradation occur, resulting in less starch being degraded in the small intestine. Reconstitution of grains involves addition of water to dry grain to raise moisture content to 25-30% and then ensiling the wetted grain for 2-3 weeks. Grain processed in this manner is fermented in the rumen similar to that of ensiled high moisture grains.

Processing of feedstuffs can also affect utilization of structural carbohydrates by ruminants. Reducing forage particle size by grinding generally improves animal performance by allowing greater voluntary intake. Increased voluntary intake and smaller particle size both contribute to an increased rate of passage through the rumen, resulting in decreased structural carbohydrate digestion. Reducing particle size increases surface area for attachment of cellulolytic bacteria and increases both rate and extent of cellulose digestion in vitro. This suggests that the shorter mean retention time in the rumen is the cause of the reduced cell wall digestibility observed when finely ground forage is fed.

Grinding forages to a small particle size and then pelleting them has the same effect as grinding alone, but to a greater extent. With many grasses, pelleting reduces total tract cellulose and hemicellulose digestibility by as much as 10 percentage units as compared to the same forage fed in the chopped form. In addition, due to increased rate of passage, a greater proportion of the digestion occurs in the cecum and large intestine and less in the rumen. Because of the faster rate of cell wall digestion for legumes as compared to grasses, grinding and pelleting legumes has less depressing effect on total tract digestion and less effect on site of digestion as compared to grasses (63).

Although processing generally improves performance when animals are fed high roughage diets, the opposite effect may occur on a low roughage-high concentrate diet. When the diet is low in roughage or the roughage is finely ground, metabolic disorders often occur, even though the diet is adequate in all known nutrients. Metabolic disorders resulting from low roughage intake include the fat cow syndrome, rumen parakeratosis, displaced abomasum, laminitis, acidosis and, in dairy cows, reduced milk fat percentage. These disorders are due to both amount and texture of the roughage and to the end-products produced from non-structural carbohydrate fermentation. For example, absence of coarse roughage reduces chewing activity resulting in less saliva flow to the rumen, thus decreasing the buffering capacity of the rumen liquor. Rumen motility is also reduced on low roughage diets. This diminishes muscle tone, contributing to displaced abomasum. Also, diets high in soluble carbohydrate may result in a more acidic rumen, causing cyclic feed intakes and the metabolic disorders listed previously. In order to evaluate the ability of a roughage to prevent these problems, a roughage value index (RVI) has been proposed (82). The three factors used to calculate the RVI are particle size, dry matter intake and percentage NDF. This system allows the minimum amount of roughage required in a diet to be determined and is more accurate than expressing the roughage requirement only as a percentage of the diet.

Ensiling fresh forage generally has little effect on site or extent of structural carbohydrate digestion in ruminants. However, some fermentation of hemicelluloses and pectins occurs during ensiling.

Chemical treatment of forages can markedly improve structural carbohydrate digestion by ruminants. As early as 1900, "fodder cellulose" was prepared by boiling rye straw in a solution containing NaOH and other alkali salts. Organic matter digestibility was increased to 88% and crude fiber digestibility to 96% while both components of the control straw were less than 50% digestible. Many variations of this technique have been researched but most have involved NaOH as an alkali source. NaOH has several effects on structural carbohydrates of the plant cell wall. First, there is solubilization of hemicellulose. NaOH saponifies ester linkages of uronic acids and acetyl groups associated with xylan in the lignin-hemicellulose complex. Secondly, NaOH disrupts H bonds in crystalline cellulose, causing cellulose to swell and to be more accessible to cellulase enzymes. The net effect of NaOH treatment is to increase both rate and extent of digestion of cellulose and hemicellulose in the rumen. In reality, the full potential of NaOH has often not been realized because consumption of large amounts of

NaOH-treated forage increases rate of passage through the rumen and decreases rate of cellulose digestion by negatively affecting the cellulolytic population. The net result is that less of the potentially digestible cellulose is digested as compared to that of the untreated forage (83).

Recently, anhydrous ammonia treatment has received widespread acceptance as a means of improving acceptability and digestibility of cereal grain straws. Ammonia appears to have a mode of action similar to that of NaOH, with the exception that the reaction time is much longer (up to 20 d) than for NaOH. In addition, roughages must be treated in an air-tight structure to prevent ammonia loss. Ammonia has no detrimental effects on rumen environment and can serve as a non-protein N source, allowing potential improvements in cellulose and hemicellulose digestion to be expressed in the animal. Ammoniation of high quality forages should be avoided as the ammonia may react with soluble sugars, forming a product, which can cause the "crazy cow syndrome". Calves nursing cows fed ammoniated high quality forage are the most susceptible to this condition (84).

Other chemicals such as $Ca(OH)_2$, KOH, calcium hypochlorite, sodium peroxide and ozone have been used to treat forages to improve structural carbohydrate digestibility. In general, these chemicals have been less effective than those described above. However, ozone treatment of cotton straw has resulted in delignification and a marked increase in cellulose and hemicellulose digestibility by ruminants (85).

SUMMARY

Type of dietary carbohydrate and level of carbohydrate intake are factors which most often determine level of performance of ruminants under practical production systems. Rumen fermentation is currently the only practical means to convert structural carbohydrates to metabolic intermediates which can be used for synthesis of meat, milk and wool. Many factors such as site of digestion, secondary plant compounds and feed processing and conservation methods can greatly affect end product yields from carbohydrate digestion in the ruminant. Carbohydrate metabolism in the ruminant is unique compared to the non-ruminant in that acetate is the main energy source and gluconeogenesis is the primary source of glucose at the cellular level. Because of the complex nature of carbohydrate digestion and metabolism in the ruminant, much remains to be learned concerning the carbohydrate nutrition of ruminants.

References Cited

1. Bergman, E.N. 1973. Cornell Vet. 63:341.
2. Bergman, E.N. 1983. In: Dynamic Biochemistry of Animal Production, p. 173. P.M. Riis, ed. World Animal Science, A3.
3. Leatherwood, J.M. 1973. Fed. Proc. 32:1814.
4. Van Soest, P.J. 1982. In: Nutritional Ecology of the Ruminant. O & B Books, Inc., Corvallis, OR.
5. Powell, K., R.L. Reid and J.A. Balasko. 1978. J. Animal Sci. 46:1503.
6. Ben-Ghedalia, D. and J. Miron. 1984. J. Nutr. 114:880.
7. Reddy, N.R., J.K. Palmer, M.D. Pierson and R.J. Bothast. 1983. J. Agr. Food Chem. 31:1308.
8. Baldwin, R.L. and M.J. Allison. 1983. J. Animal Sci. 57(Suppl. 2):461.
9. Prins, R.A. 1977. In: Microbial Ecology of the Gut. R.T.J. Clarke and T. Bauchop, eds. Academic Press, London.
10. Pettipher, G.L. and M.J. Latham. 1979. J. Gen. Microbiol. 110:21.
11. Coleman, G.S. 1978. J. Gen. Microbiol. 107:359.
12. Dehority, B.A. 1973. Fed. Proc. 32:1819.
13. Annison, E.F. and D.G. Armstrong. 1970. In: Physiology of Digestion and Metabolism in the Ruminant, p. 422. A.T. Phillipson, ed. Oriel Press, Ltd., Newcastle-upon-Tyne, England.
14. Murphy, M.R., R.L. Baldwin and L.J. Koong. 1982. J. Animal Sci. 55:411.
15. Demeyer, D.I. and C.J. Van Nevel. 1975. In: Digestion and Metabolism in the Ruminant, p. 386. I.W. McDonald and A.C.I. Warner, eds. Univ. of New England Publishing Unit, Armidale, Australia.

16. Bergman, E.N. 1975. In: Digestion and Metabolism in the Ruminant, p. 292. I.W. McDonald and A.C.I. Warner, eds. Univ. of New England Publishing Unit, Armidale, Australia.

17. Elliot, J.M. 1980. In: Digestive Physiology and Metabolism in Ruminants, p. 485. Y. Ruckebush and P. Thivend, eds. AVI Publishing, Westport, CT.

18. Waldo, D.R. 1973. J. Animal Sci. 37:1062.

19. Ørskov, E.R., C. Fraser, V.C. Mason and S.O. Maun. 1970. Brit. J. Nutr. 24:671.

20. Chesson, A., A.H. Gordon and J.A. Lomax. 1983. In: Biodeterioration 5, p. 652. T.A. Oxley and S. Barry, eds. John Wiley and Sons, Ltd., London.

21. Chesson, A. 1981. J. Sci. Food Agr. 32:745.

22. Mertens, D.R. and L.O. Ely. 1982. J. Animal Sci. 54:895.

23. Mertens, D.R. 1977. Fed. Proc. 36:187.

24. Smith, L.W., H.K. Goering, D.R. Waldo and C.H. Gordon. 1971. J. Dairy Sci. 54:71.

25. Smith, L.W., H.K. Goering and C.H. Gordon. 1972. J. Dairy Sci. 55:1140.

26. Mertens, D.R. and J.R. Loften. 1980. J. Dairy Sci. 63:1437.

27. Rexen, F. and K.V. Thomsen. 1976. Animal Feed. Sci. Tech. 1:73.

28. Reid, J.T., D. White, R. Anrique and A. Fortin. 1980. J. Animal Sci. 51:1393.

29. Staples, C.R. et al. 1983. J. Dairy Sci. 67:995.

30. Robertson, J.B. and P.J. Van Soest. 1975. Animal Prod. 21:89.

31. Welch, J.G. and A.M. Smith. 1969. J. Animal Sci. 28:827.

32. Robles, A.Y., R.L. Belyea, F.A. Martz and M.F. Weiss. 1980. J. Animal Sci. 51:783.

33. Stewart, C.S. 1977. Appl. Environ. Microbiol. 33:497.

34. Mertens, D.R. 1979. In: Regulation of Acid-Base Balance, p. 65. W.H. Hale and P. Meinhardt, eds. Church and Dwight Co., Inc., Piscataway, NJ.

35. Ulyatt, M.J., D.W. Dellow, C.S.W. Reid and T. Bauchop. 1975. In: Digestion and Metabolism in the Ruminant, p. 119. I.W. McDonald and A.C.I. Warner, eds. The Univ. of New England Publishing Unit, Armidale, Australia.

36. Bryant, M.P. 1973. Fed. Proc. 32:1809.

37. Harkin, J.M. 1973. In: Chemistry and Biochemistry of Herbage, Vol. 1, p. 323. G.W. Butler and R.W. Bailey, eds. Academic Press, New York, NY.

38. Hartley, R.D. and E.C. Jones. 1977. Phytochemistry 16:1531.

39. Higuchi, T., Y. Ito and I. Kawamura. 1967. Phytochemistry 6:875.

40. Higuchi, T., Y. Ito, M. Shimada and I. Kawamura. 1967. Phytochemistry 6:1551.

41. Gordon, A.J. and T.S. Neudoerffer. 1973. J. Sci. Food Agr. 24:565.

42. Hartley, R.D. 1973. Phytochemistry 12:661.

43. Gordon, A.J. 1975. J. Sci. Food Agr. 26:1551.

44. Morrison, I.M. 1974. Biochem. J. 139:197.

45. Morrison, I.M. 1973. Phytochemistry 12:2979.

46. Allinson, D.W. and D.F. Osbourn. 1970. J. Agr. Sci. 74:293.

47. Jung, H.G., G.C. Fahey, Jr. and N.R. Merchen. 1983. Brit. J. Nutr. 50:637.

48. Theander, O., P. Uden and P. Aman. 1981. Agr. Environ. 6:127.

49. Van Soest, P.J. 1975. In: Digestion and Metabolism in the Ruminant, p. 351. I.W. McDonald and A.C.I. Warner, eds. Univ. of New England Publishing Unit, Armidale, Australia.

50. Jung, H.G. and G.C. Fahey, Jr. 1983. J. Animal Sci. 57:206.

51. Akin, D.E. 1982. Agron. J. 74:424.

52. Chesson, A., C.S. Stewart and R.J. Wallace. 1982. Appl. Environ. Microbiol. 44:597.

53. Hartley, R.D. 1972. J. Sci. Food Agr. 23:1347.

54. Harris, P.J., R.D. Hartley and K.H. Lowry. 1980. J. Sci. Food Agr. 31:959.

55. Bush, L. and R.C. Buckner. 1973. In: Antiquality Components of Forages, p. 99. A.G. Matches, ed. Crop Sci. Soc. of America Spec. Pub. No. 14, Madison, WI.

56. Kumar, R. and M. Singh. 1984. J. Agr. Food Chem. 32:447.

57. Harborne, J.B. 1976. In: Chemistry and Biochemistry of Plant Pigments, Vol. 1, p. 734. T.W. Goldwin, ed. Academic Press, New York, NY.

58. Mitjavila, S., C. Lacomber, G. Carrera and R. Derache. 1977. J. Nutr. 47:498.

59. Burns, J.C. and W.A. Cope. 1974. Agron. J. 66:195.

60. Van Soest, P.J. 1981. Agr. Environ. 6:135.

61. Bressani, R. and L.G. Elias. 1979. In: Proc. Symp. Polyphenols in Cereals and Legumes, p. 61. St. Louis, MO.
62. McAllan, A.B. and R.H. Smith. 1974. Brit. J. Nutr. 31:77.
63. Armstrong, D.G. and R.R. Smithard. 1979. Proc. Nutr. Soc. 38:283.
64. Armstrong, D.G. 1974. In: Cereal Supply and Utilization, p. 21. Technical Publication, U.S. Feed Grains Council, London.
65. Bergman, E.N. 1983. In: Dynamic Biochemistry of Animal Production, p. 137. P.M. Riis, ed. World Animal Science, A3.
66. Lindsay, D.B. 1970. In: Physiology of Digestion and Metabolism in the Ruminant, p. 439. A.T. Phillipson, ed. Oriel Press, Ltd., Newcastle-upon-Tyne, England.
67. Heitman, R.N. and E.N. Bergman. 1978. Amer. J. Physiol. 234:E197.
68. Glesecke, D. and M. Stangassinger. 1980. In: Digestive Physiology and Metabolism in Ruminants, p. 523. Y. Ruckebush and P. Thivend, eds. AVI Publishing, Westport, CT.
69. Basset, J.M. 1975. In: Digestion and Metabolism in the Ruminant, p. 383. I.W. McDonald and A.C.I. Warner, eds. Univ. of New England Publishing Unit, Armidale, Australia.
70. Leat, W.M.F. 1970. In: Physiology of Digestion and Metabolism in the Ruminant, p. 211. A.T. Phillipson, ed. Oriel Press, Ltd., Newcastle-upon-Tyne, England.
71. Edwards, A.V. 1970. In: Physiology of Digestion and Metabolism in the Ruminant, p. 180. A.T. Phillipson, ed. Oriel Press, Ltd., Newcastle-upon-Tyne, England.
72. Marten, G.C. 1981. In: Forage Evaluation: Concepts and Techniques, p. 39. J.L. Wheeler and R.D. Mochrie, eds. CSIRO, East Melbourne, Victoria, Australia and The American Forage and Grassland Council, Lexington, KY.
73. Goering, H.K. and P.J. Van Soest. 1970. USDA Handbook 379, Washington, DC.
74. Tilley, J.M.A. and R.A. Terry. 1963. J. Brit. Grassland Soc. 18:104.
75. Marten, G.C. and R.F. Barnes. 1979. In: Standardization of Analytical Methodology for Feeds, p. 61. W.J. Pigden, C.C. Balch and M. Graham, eds. Inter. Dev. Res. Ctr., Ottawa, Canada.
76. Akin, D.E. 1983. In: Proc. XIV Int'l Grassland Congress, p. 511. J.A. Smith and V.W. Hays, eds. Westview Press, Boulder, CO.
77. McManus, W.R. 1981. In: Forage Evaluation: Concepts and Techniques, p. 103. J.L. Wheeler and R.D. Mochrie, eds. CSIRO, East Melbourne, Victoria, Australia and The American Forage and Grassland Council, Lexington, KY.
78. Akin, D.E., D. Burdick and G. Michaels. 1974. App. Microbiol. 27:1149.
79. Norris, K.H. and R.F. Barnes. 1976. In: 1st Int'l Symp. Feed Comp., Anim. Nutr. Req. and Computerization of Diets, p. 237. P.V. Fonnesbeck, L.E. Harris and L.C. Kearl, eds. Utah Agr. Exp. Sta., Utah State Univ., Logan.
80. Barton, F.E., II and D. Burdick. 1979. J. Agr. Food Chem. 17:1248.
81. Barton, F.E., II and D. Burdick. 1980. In: Proc. 10th Res. Ind. Conf. Coastal Bermudagrass Processors Assoc., p. 103. Athens, GA.
82. Sudweeks, E.M., L.E. Ely, D.R. Mertens and L.R. Sisk. 1981. J. Animal Sci. 53:1406.
83. Berger, L.L., T.J. Klopfenstein and R.A. Britton. 1980. J. Animal Sci. 50:745.
84. Faulkner, D.B. 1984. In: Illinois Beef Cattle Handbook, University of Illinois, Urbana, IL.
85. Ben-Ghedalia, D., G. Shefet, J. Miron and Yosef Dror. 1982. J. Sci. Food Agr. 33:1213.

15 LIPIDS IN RUMINANT NUTRITION

by F. M. Byers and G. T. Schelling

INTRODUCTION

Probably the most fundamental concern in understanding the contribution and role of lipids in ruminants is that much of the material that is typically analyzed as fat in ruminant feedstuffs is, in fact, something other than fat, as indicated in Table 15-1. What this really means is that ether extract (EE) contains things other than true fats. Forage EE is typically less than 50% fatty acid, while the EE of grains is somewhat higher in fatty acid content (65-80%). In oilseeds such as cottonseed and soybeans, the EE fraction is nearly all fatty acid (90%). Much of the mystique surrounding the merit and role of feedstuff fat vs added fat in ruminant diets disappears when the types and forms of EE material present in basal feedstuffs and supplements are considered.

The interaction of added fat and rumen function, intestinal absorption, systemic transport, systemic metabolism and secretion and/or deposition are principal concerns in ruminant lipid metabolism. Aspects of lipid metabolism germane to ruminants are addressed in this chapter. Excellent reviews of lipid metabolism across animal species are provided in "Fats in Animal Nutrition", a 1984 publication edited by J. Wiseman (1).

Table 15-1. Composition of ether extract from forage leaves.[a]

	% of the dry matter	% of the ether extract
Ether extract	5.3	100
Fatty acids	2.3	43
Non-fatty acid		
Wax	0.9	17
Chlorophyll	0.23	4
Galactose	0.41	8
Other unsaponifiable	1.0	19

[a]From Palmquist and Jenkins (2)

CLASSIFICATION OF FATS

Fat in the diet is found in many forms and the form is often very important in both utilization of the fat and its impact on other ration components. **Chain length:** The first obvious classification of fatty acids is chain length which may range from C1 to C30. Fatty acids of C1-C6 are commonly referred to as volatile fatty acids and if present (fermented feeds) are usually found in the free form. **Hydrogenation:** Fatty acids may be saturated, mono-unsaturated or poly-unsaturated. Both the number and location of the double bonds (C=C) in each fatty acid are important. **Optical isomers:** If double bonds are present, the fatty acid may be present in either a *cis* or *trans* configuration. The *cis* optical isomer is prevalent in plant lipid sources. **Linkages:** The fatty acids may be present as free fatty acids or esterified as glycerides. This can change with handling, storage and processing of the fat-containing product or ration. **Availability:** Fat may be encapsulated in an intact plant structure such as in an oil body membrane in a whole seed or it may be free flowing either due to processing or through addition as free fat to the ration. It may also be intentionally protected physically from rumen microbial degradation by processing techniques. Another type of ruminal protection is provided when fatty acids are provided as soaps (4) or when free fatty acids and divalent cations combine in the rumen to form soaps.

DIETARY LIPID SOURCES—PLANT LIPIDS

Structural Lipids
Leaves of forage plants (Table 15-1) contain from 3-10% of their dry matter as lipids, some present as surface lipids and others as components of leaf cells, and especially chloroplast membranes (2). While surface lipids are commonly referred to as waxes,

298

compounds other than just esters of long-chain alcohols are also present (3). Some of these include long-chain (C29) hydrocarbons, free fatty acids, alcohols and ketones. The cuticle contains an additional compound—cutin, comprised of cross-linked polymers of normal and hydroxy fatty acids. Most leaf lipids are found as components of cellular membranes. Phospholipids, similar to those found in animal membranes, are the predominant lipids occurring in plant tissues. The glycolipids (mono and digalactosyl diacylglycerols) and chlorophylls make up 40-50 and 20% of membrane lipids. Sulphoquinovosyl diacylglycerol, a compound with an unusual carbon-sulfur bond, is a characteristic leaf lipid not found in animal membranes, and accounts for 5% of chloroplast membrane lipids. Other lipids include carotenoids, sterols and acylated sterol glycosides. Predominant fatty acids in plant membrane lipids include alpha linolenic (major), palmitic, linoleic, oleic, and *trans* hexadecanoic acids. Surface lipids include fatty acids of C10-C30 and the cutins contain a large fraction of C18 hydroxy acids.

Storage Lipids

The form of storage energy affects the type of lipids in seeds. In plants that store energy primarily as carbohydrate in the seed, such as corn, the lipids present will be predominantly structural in nature (phospholipids and glycolipids). However, in plants storing energy reserves in the form of lipids, such as soybeans, lipids are found primarily as triglycerides with typical patterns of fatty acids (Table 15-2) unique to specific seeds (2). Generally, oilseeds contain high levels of unsaturated fatty acids, with linoleic predominating and with some seeds having high levels of linolenic, i.e., linseed oil. Specific fatty acids also show preference for specific positions on the triglyceride. In common vegetable oils, saturated fatty acids are mostly at position 1 with unsaturated fatty acids usually occurring at position 2 and long-chain fatty acids at positions 1 and 3. While the fatty acids in oilseeds are stored primarily in the glyceride form, hydrolysis during storage following harvesting and in processing can be extensive, and a significant fraction of the fat as fed may in fact be in the free fatty acid form. The form of fat in conjunction with the level of fat is important in nutrition of ruminants.

RUMEN MICROBIAL METABOLISM

Hydrolysis

Rumen microbes rapidly and extensively modify dietary lipids on their sojourn through the rumen, and under typical circumstances very little fat escapes the rumen unscathed. Rumen microbes modify lipids in several ways. Fatty acids are typically found in the esterified form, at least in conventional diets, and the rumen microbes hydrolyze them rapidly and extensively to free fatty acids and glycerol or other compounds, depending on the nature of the lipid fed. Following lipolysis, biohydrogenation occurs. Because

Table 15-2. Fatty acid composition of commonly used feedstuffs.[a]

Fatty acid	Alfalfa hay	Grass pasture	Soybean seed	Corn seed
	. . . . total fatty acids, %			
Myristic (14:0)	0.9	1.1	---	---
Palmitic (16:0)	33.9	15.9	12.4	14.3
Palmitoleic (16:1)	1.2	2.5	---	0.1
Stearic (18:0)	3.8	2.0	3.7	1.9
Oleic (18:1)	3.0	3.4	25.4	39.0
Linoleic (18:2)	24.0	13.2	50.6	43.5
Linolenic (18:3)	31.0	61.3	7.9	1.1
Total fatty acid content, % of ether extract	40	57	90	65

[a]From Palmquist and Jenkins (2)

biohydrogenation depends on the presence of a free carboxyl, lipolysis is an obligatory first step in modification of esterified lipids provided in the diet.

Not all bacteria are capable of lipolysis, and protozoa may not have lipolytic activity. The fraction of lipolytic and biohydrogenating organisms is lower on high grain diets, allowing greater escape. Although lipolysis is rapid, it is still likely rate limiting and possibly serves to prevent the buildup of excessive quantities of free poly-unsaturated fatty acids which may interfere with fiber digestion and may inhibit biohydrogenation. The extent of hydrolysis is dependent on the nature of the lipid fed; plant oils such as linseed oil are hydrolyzed more completely (typically over 90%) than fish oils which tend to have less than 50% hydrolysis. Because the fatty acids must be present in the free form to allow further microbial metabolism, limits to hydrolysis become limits to rumen modification of lipids.

A wide variety of plant lipids are metabolized in the rumen. Phospholipids are a significant fraction of plant lipids and a number of these are hydrolyzed rapidly and extensively. For example, galactolipids are readily degraded and galactose is released, indicating that galactosyl glyceryl esters are metabolized extensively.

Biohydrogenation and Production of Fatty Acid Isomers

The great disparity between dietary and secretory or depot fat in ruminants is a ready clue that extensive modification of dietary fatty acids must occur. Biohydrogenation occurs in the rumen and the microbes are responsible. This process results in the addition of H to fatty acids with double bonds. Biohydrogenation of unsaturated fatty acids provides an important mechanism through which microbes can dispose of H from the reducing environment of the rumen. If carried to completion, all double bonds are converted to single bonds and the fatty acid is saturated. While most unsaturated fatty acids are modified through rumen metabolism, saturation is normally not complete and a variety of fatty acids result from this incomplete hydrogenation.

Nearly all plant unsaturated fatty acids are present in the *cis* configuration between unsaturated C atoms and, as a consequence, depot fat in non-ruminants reflects the diet and most fatty acids present will be in the *cis* form. However, rumen microbes normally produce a variety of *trans* isomers of the fatty acids provided as well as alterations of chain length, changing the position of double bonds, and production of odd-chain and branched-chain fatty acids, all of which serve to make the depot and secreted fat of ruminants differ markedly from the dietary fat. Biohydrogenation is the obvious fate of most fatty acids, irrespective of other modifications.

Free fatty acids are non-ionically bound to particulate matter. When high-grain diets are fed, biohydrogenation is less complete than with less grain (6). Rumen fluid from cattle fed high-grain diets contain less particulate surface and fewer numbers of biohydrogenating organisms. Whether the reduction in hydrogenation with a decrease in particulate matter is a direct or an indirect effect is unclear; however, both fatty acids and microbes are associated with the particulate matter. Biohydrogenation is a multistep process, and the evidence indicates that it is unlikely that any one species of bacteria is capable of completely saturating a poly-unsaturated fatty acid.

Protozoa are very active in hydrogenation, and the degree of hydrogenation occurring is usually much less extensive when protozoal populations are suppressed or eliminated. Thus, higher levels of unsaturated fatty acids are found in the blood, milk and in adipose tissue when protozoa are either not present or present in limited numbers. This, however, reflects not only the elimination of protozoa, but reflects all other changes in rumen metabolism and fermentation also occurring in animals fed diets not favoring protozoal function. It is likely that changes in pH, turnover, particulate matter present, bacterial populations present and their relative predominance also serve to impact the degree of saturation occurring. Studies with pure cultures indicate that individual bacterial species usually do not totally saturate a fatty acid with multiple double bonds, and will biohydrogenate one double bond, such as 18:3 to 18:2, 18:2 to 18:1 or 18:1 to 18:0, while studies with mixed cultures commonly result in complete saturation. As a consequence, changing the proportion of bacterial and protozoal species may significantly alter the degree of hydrogenation.

In the process of hydrogenation of a common fatty acid such as linolenic (C18 with double bonds at 9, 12, 15), a conjugated *cis-trans* double bond mediated by a Δ12-*cis*, Δ11-*trans* isomerase is formed and subsequent hydrogenation occurs at the 9 position. In this case hydrogenation of the Δ11-*trans* double bond appears to be rate limiting. End products of biohydrogenation are rather diverse with stearic and Δ11-*trans* octadecenoic acids predominating. While total saturation of linoleic to stearic acid occurs when added in the esterified form, hydrogenation when added as free linoleic is usually incomplete with formation of *trans*-11 octadecenoic acid as a primary end product, suggesting inhibition at the second step of biohydrogenation (2). Excessive quantities of free linoleic acid appear to be responsible for this inhibition. This documents one mechanism through which polyunsaturated fatty acids, especially in the free form, inhibit microbial function.

Hydrogenation is also inhibited through more deliberate mechanisms. Feeding lipids protected by a formaldehyde-treated casein coating or other processes, partially prevents hydrogenation. Feeding diets that limit protozoal function, provide limited particulate matter, and allow microbial inhibition by dietary fat will result in less than complete saturation of dietary fatty acids. Also, feeding fats such as fish oils which are not completely hydrolyzed will similarly prevent hydrogenation because hydrogenation is possible only with unesterified fatty acids.

RUMEN SYNTHESIS OF LIPIDS

In addition to modification of dietary fatty acids, rumen microbes synthesize a wide variety of odd-carbon chain and branched-chain fatty acids, many with a *trans* configuration. Protozoa as well as bacteria carry out de novo synthesis of long-chain fatty acids. The precursors used for fatty acid synthesis include odd- and even-chain and branched-chain substrates, with the products reflecting the initiating substrate with respect to odd vs even chain and branching. Odd-carbon substrates, including propionic and valeric acid, result in

odd-chain fatty acids. Butyric and caproic acids end up in even-carbon fatty acids, and iso-acids, isobutyric and isovaleric, result in odd-, even- and branched-chain fatty acids. Rumen microbes also modify fatty acid chain length through both α- as well as β-oxidation.

Microbial synthesis is generally moderate, but is greater when the diet contains little lipid, and may increase with concentrate feeding. Rumen bacteria and protozoa readily incorporate dietary fatty acids into cellular lipids, and this inhibits de novo synthesis. Thus, feeding dietary fat, and especially oils such as fish oils, reduces microbial fatty acid synthesis. Rumen microbes do not store triglyceride, and the fatty acids present are primarily in membrane phospholipid or as free fatty acids.

INTESTINAL DIGESTION AND ABSORPTION

Digestion in the Intestine

In contrast to the situation with most non-ruminants, where fat enters the intestinal region essentially unaltered from the form fed, fat presented to the small intestine in ruminants may bear little resemblance to the fat in the diet. In ruminants, most of the fat enters the small intestine as unesterified fatty acids, highly saturated and non-ionically bound in an insoluble complex to particulate matter. The pH of the ingesta flowing from the abomasum is very low and it remains somewhat low through the proximal half of the small intestine due to the limited buffering of pancreatic secretions which have low levels of bicarbonate. As a consequence, fatty acids are protonated at this pH and fatty acid soaps insoluble in the rumen are solubilized, increasing absorption of both fatty acids as well as minerals.

Generally, digestibility of EE is lower in ruminants than in non-ruminants, primarily due to the large fraction of non-lipid material in the ether extractable fraction of diets commonly fed. Ruminants usually digest unsaturated fatty acids to a lower degree than non-ruminants. However, the situation is different for saturated fatty acids, which are digested more completely in the intestinal tract of ruminants than non-ruminants (8). Essentially no long-chain fatty acids leave the digestive tract prior to the small intestine (9) and, as a

302

consequence, with the contribution of rumen microbial synthesis, the quantities of lipid arriving at the duodenum commonly exceed the amount fed. The small intestine is therefore responsible for absorption of all long-chain lipids. While this places ruminants in the same position as non-ruminants, constraints in digestion differ.

Probably the greatest difference concerns the differences in digestive tract secretions which impact pH, buffering, enzyme levels and enzyme activity. The low pH in the upper half of the small intestine decreases solubility of fatty acids and bile acids. Bile acids are essential for fatty acid absorption in ruminants, due to a dispersion of fatty acids as a result of detergent action. For digestion to occur the fatty acids must be transferred from the insoluble particulate phase and emulsified into the micellar phase. This transfer is essentially eliminated if bile is not present, even if pancreatic juice is present. For normal digestion to proceed, both pancreatic juice and bile are required. In ruminants the pancreatic duct and bile duct converge to a common duct at the entry to the duodenum. Flow rate of bile is greater (i.e., 5X) than that of pancreatic juice (10), which, coupled with the low bicarbonate content of pancreatic secretions, limits the contribution of pancreatic secretions relative to bile in lipid digestion in ruminants.

Biliary Secretions

Bile in ruminants contains (11, 12) about 1,400 mg lipid/dl, with phosphatidylcholine accounting for 80% of this fraction. Lysophosphatidylcholine, phosphatidylethanolamine, cholesterol and cholesterol esters account for the remainder of the lipid. The principal fatty acids in phosphatidylcholine in bile of ruminants fed normal diets include palmitic ($>1/3$), stearic (10%), oleic (30%), and linoleic and linolenic (ca. 5% each), along with small percentages of intermediates of rumen biohydrogenation of polyunsaturated fatty acids. In contrast to non-ruminants, ruminant phosphatidylcholine contains very little linoleic or arachadonic and contains appreciably more oleic; this is in large measure a reflection of systemic supply because when fed protected lipids, linoleic content of phosphatidylcholine is similar to that of non-ruminants.

The concentration of bile acids ranges from 5,000 to 8,000 mg/dl, with a uniquely and importantly high ratio of taurine to glycine conjugated bile acids. The ratio of taurine to glycine in bile acid conjugates is about 2.5:1, while in non-ruminants it is approximately 1:3. Taurine conjugated bile acids are soluble and ionized at pH's as low as 2.5, whereas glycine conjugated bile acids are insoluble at pH 4.5 and below.

Pancreatic Secretions

Pancreatic secretions, although of much lesser magnitude than bile, are nonetheless important in lipid digestion. In contrast to earlier reports, pancreatic juice in ruminants does have lipase activity. Although lipase activity is much lower in ruminant pancreatic juice, the properties of the enzyme are similar to the lipase from non-ruminants. Optimal activity of the enzyme requires a pH of 7.5 to 7.8, with little activity below pH 5.0. With the low bicarbonate content of ruminant pancreatic secretions and the low rate of secretion, the small intestine remains acid until the lower portion of the jejunum. It is unlikely that the limited lipase activity makes a substantial impact in lipolysis of any esterified lipid reaching the small intestine under these circumstances. Two pancreatic phospholipases (A1 and A2) are present (9); A1 is very acid labile, being irreversibly inactivated at pH 2.5 in the duodenum while A2 appears to survive and is effective in the distal jejunum. It is stimulated by secretions from Brunners glands. A third enzyme, lysophospholipase, also is present. Inactivation by the low intestinal pH of both triglyceride and phospholipid lipases may be limited or moderated by pancreatic and bile secretions, which also stabilize these enzymes. In spite of these constraints, lipolysis of triglyceride escaping rumen degradation is accomplished, primarily in the lower jejunum.

Sites of Action in Digestion and Absorption

The influx of dietary lipid to the small intestine is accompanied by the entry of perhaps half as much additional lipid in the form of intestinal secretions (13), primarily of biliary origin. This greatly increases the fraction of phosphatidylcholine which remains through the remainder of the duodenum and the upper jejunum. Hydrolysis of phospho-lipids becomes substantial in the mid-jejunum. Over the majority of the small intestine, the lipid in the digesta remains predominantly associated with the particulate fraction. The adsorbed lipid, both of exogenous as well as endogenous origin, must be transferred to the micellar fraction before any absorption can occur, a function primarily accomplished by bile constituents. While quantitatively in less abundance, phosphatidyl ethanolamine, of both microbial and bile origin, is more effective than the phosphatidyl choline present in larger quantities. This is because it is effective at the lower pH's normally encountered. Phosphatidyl ethanolamine, together with taurocholic acid, allow solubilization of fatty acids and conversion to micelles in the upper portion of the small intestine in the presence of an acid pH.

About 20% of the fatty acids absorbed in the small intestine are absorbed in the upper jejunum, where the pH is usually 4.0 or below. The other 60% are absorbed from the remainder of the jejunum, with nearly complete absorption prior to the ileum. Therefore, most of the fatty acids are absorbed from the small intestine in the area where the environment is very acid as contrasted to non-ruminants where absorption occurs in a more neutral medium. When ruminants are fed diets including protected lipids, digestion of lipid resembles that of non-ruminants where 2-monoglycerides are important in micellar solubilization of fatty acids (14).

Absorption of Lipids

Several steps are involved in absorption. Absorbed lipid diffuses into the villous cell, re-esterification occurs in the smooth endo-plasmic reticulum membranes, apoprotein biosynthesis occurs in the rough endoplasmic reticulum, final chylomicron synthesis occurs in the Golgi apparatus, and the chylomicrons are released into the intercellular space by exocytosis. They then enter the lamina propria through gaps in the basement membrane and proceed to the lymph lacteals. In summary, fatty acids are absorbed into intestinal cells, re-esterified, and packaged with tri-, mono- and di-glycerides, phospholipid, cholesterol and apoproteins and exit through the cells to the lymph system. Fatty acids of less than C14 enter the blood directly, and are

shuttled to the liver which oxidizes them rapidly. Rate of absorption decreases with increasing chain length and decreases with increasing degree of saturation.

The primary lipids entering the ruminant intestinal cell (enterocyte) are unesterified fatty acids—predominantly saturated and lysophospholipids; only on occasions of rumen escape do 2-monoglycerides appear. A fatty acid desaturase may convert as much as 10% of the stearic to oleic acid in the entero-cyte.

RESYNTHESIS AND TRANSPORT OF LIPIDS

Triglycerides

Synthesis of triglycerides can occur by either the 2-monoglyceride pathway as in non-ruminants or by the α-glycerophosphate pathway. Because little or no monoglyceride is normally present in the mixture of fatty acids absorbed due to rumen lipolysis, the 2-monoglyceride pathway is normally of only minor importance in ruminants. However, the 2-monoglyceride pathway is fully functional and assumes primary importance when escape lipids are fed providing substantial amounts of glyceride fat to the small intestine. Glucose serves as the glycerol source, with small amounts of glycerophosphate available from utilization of glycerophosphoryl-choline following lysophospholipase action.

Essential fatty acids are conserved in ruminants through preferential absorption and esterification as phospholipids. While phospholipid is only 20% of the total esterified fatty acid, it carries over 50% of the linoleic acid, assuring conservation. Resynthesis of 1-acyl lysolecithin is the predominant pathway. Absorption is rapid, and esterification is preferential for linoleic acid (16).

Lipoprotein Synthesis

The absorbed lipid fractions are assembled into lipoprotein particles in the enterocyte and the two primary lipoproteins are chylo-microns of 75-1,000 nm diameter and very low density lipoproteins (VLDL) of 25-75 nm diameter. Triglyceride transport is accomplished through these lipoprotein fractions. While it is convenient to differentiate these classes, the animal in fact makes little attempt to do so and there is really a continuous spectrum of particle sizes present in ruminants. Ruminants differ from non-ruminants in several important ways relative to lipoprotein synthesis. In ruminants, fatty acids absorbed are predominantly incorporated into VLDL rather than chylomicrons, whereas the opposite is true for non-ruminants. The reason for this apparent dichotomy is mechanistic. Lipid absorption in ruminants is a more or less continuous process that operates at a slow rate, while in non-ruminants, absorption is meal oriented. As a result, surface film synthesis (phospholipids, cholesterol and apoproteins) in ruminant enterocytes is synchronized with synthesis of core material-triglycerides and small VLDL particles result. However, in non-ruminants synthesis of triglycerides following a meal is very rapid and occurs more rapidly than synthesis of surface film material, resulting in large particles—chylomicrons. Also, fatty acids absorbed in ruminants are more saturated, and saturated fatty acids favor synthesis of VLDL, while unsaturated fatty acids result in synthesis of chylomicrons.

When fed normal diets, ruminants synthesize predominantly VLDL, but chylomicrons predominate when unsaturated fatty acids are provided to the small intestine for absorption (17). In any case, chylomicrons, in addition to being less prevalent, are smaller in ruminants than in non-ruminants. They range in size from 1,000 to 5,000 nm in non-ruminants. As a consequence the ratio of surface material to triglyceride core is greater in ruminant chylomicrons, making triglyceride content lower and phospholipid content higher. The phospholipid content of ruminant chylomicrons is more than double that of human chylomicrons. The ratio of free to esterified cholesterol also reflects this difference, and is 4 for ruminants vs 1 for humans, primarily as a result of the greater surface area because all of the free cholesterol is located on the surface as a film component.

TRANSPORT OF LIPOPROTEINS

In general, the transport and metabolism of lipoproteins in ruminants parallels mechanisms observed in non-ruminants with differences reflecting the types and forms in which they are delivered to the circulatory system (for reviews see 18, 19). Lipids are transported as chylomicrons and as VLDL, both of which are transported by the lymph. Lipids are also present as low (LDL) or high (HDL) density lipoproteins or as non-esterified fatty acid complexes which are associated with albumin in the blood.

Upon entry to plasma the chylomicrons and VLDL acquire apoproteins—apo-C and apo-E from liver-synthesized plasma HDL (20, 21). Apo-C inhibits liver removal of chylomicrons and VLDL and allows diversion of these entities to other tissues. One of the apo-C components activates lipoprotein lipase in capillaries in skeletal muscle, adipose and mammary tissue sites. Fatty acids and glycerides are taken up by cells and used for energy or for synthesis of triglycerides in adipose and mammary sites. Remnants of chylomicrons and VLDL in the form of LDL or IDL are taken up and metabolized by the liver.

Chylomicrons and VLDL are short-lived in ruminants, and have half lives of only 2 to 11 min (22) which results in low to undetectable levels after only a short period following absorption and entry into the blood. In contrast, the half life of LDL is in the range of 1 to 3 h (23). As a consequence the blood lipids reflect these differences in metabolism and are predominantly HDL (70%) and LDL (20%) with the remainder in VLDL and other fractions. Actual proportions of blood lipids vary with types and levels of lipid absorbed and with production status of the animal. For example, feeding large amounts of fat as protected lipids increases total plasma lipid concentration and reduces density of the LDL fraction and increases the chylomicron fraction to the extent that it becomes visible in plasma. The VLDL fraction is also greater in suckling animals. Fractions present reflect stage of growth, lactation and gestation.

Because of the smaller chylomicron size in ruminants, the concentration of phospholipids is greater in the core and the free cholesterol is found on the surface of the particle. Both the core and surface fractions are a greater proportion of the total in smaller particles. As a result the lipoproteins in ruminants have over double the phospholipid content of chylomicrons as compared to humans, and the ratio of free to esterified cholesterol is 4 times greater (4:1 vs 1:1 ratio).

Most lipoproteins in ruminants originate from intestinal absorption because liver synthesis is not extensive. Because synthesis of fatty acids by the liver in ruminants is limited (24), its role in providing endogenous VLDL depends on circulating non-esterified fatty acids (NEFA) and available glycerol either from glucose or from lipolysis at other tissue sites. This will obviously depend on metabolic state of the animal, and may be extensive in early lactation when large quantities of adipose tissue fatty acids are being mobilized.

Serum NEFA provide a fatty acid shuttle system without the requirement for esterification and are important in several ways. Because liver synthesis of fatty acids is small, and essentially insignificant, NEFA turn over more rapidly than any other plasma lipid and provide an important mechanism whereby VLDL can be generated in the liver. This serves to deliver lipoprotein triglycerides to the mammary gland for the support of lactation when exogenous supply from the diet is inadequate, as in early lactation. NEFA can be taken up and metabolized by all tissues except the brain and testes and, although it has been calculated that up to one-third of milk long-chain fatty acids could originate from NEFA, no net uptake is observed (25). In fed states, where glycerol and/or glucose precursors are available, the liver uses the NEFA to make VLDL which are then taken up by the mammary gland. However, when glycerol cannot be obtained, as in the fasted state or when metabolic glucose demands are very high, the liver oxidizes the NEFA to ketones. Elevated blood levels of ketones result in the metabolic disorder ketosis which is discussed in Ch. 24.

TISSUE METABOLISM

Synthesis and metabolism of lipids in ruminants parallels that of non-ruminants in a general sense (26, 27), but there are several important differences. Ruminants, like other species, are capable of synthesizing large quantities of long- and short-chain fatty acids. However, unlike non-ruminants, fatty acid synthesis is minimal in the liver of ruminants, but very extensive in adipose tissue (26). Long-chain (C18) fatty acids are synthesized readily in adipose tissue and fatty acid synthesis of C4-C16 occurs in the mammary gland.

Synthesis of fatty acids and composition of stored and of secreted fat is not a random process. In fact, fatty acids in lipid components of tissues rather directly reflect tissue function (28). The composition of lipids in structural components, membranes and in milk change to maintain fluidity and physiological function. This is of no small consequence; were these changes not to occur, fluidity of milk at body temperature would not be maintained, vital organs of hibernators would cease to function at low temperatures, and extremities (i.e., lower legs) of caribou and cattle would become solid in cold climates if fatty acids of greater unsaturation and of lower melting points were not preferentially synthesized and/or deposited. Lipid is unique in that it is the only structural component in which composition is regulated to maintain fluidity and physiological function as temperature changes (28). This is obviously very important for ruminants expected to adapt and survive in the wild and for domesticated ruminants required to survive without environment modification in cold climates.

Precursors for fatty acid synthesis in ruminants differ from those for non-ruminants. In non-ruminants the primary precursor to supply acetyl-CoA is glucose. However, in ruminants little glucose is normally available for lipogenesis and acetate and β-hydroxy butyrate are important substrates. Butyrate is the preferred substrate for fatty acid synthesis in the mammary gland, and is synthesized through reversal of β-oxidation via crotonyl CoA if sufficient supplies are not available. Acetate and lactate are the principal precursors for adipose tissue, although glucose may be a significant contributor to lipogenesis in fetal growth and when available from the digestive tract.

Sources of reducing equivalents also differ between runimants and non-ruminants. In non-ruminants $NADPH^+$ is generated through the pentose cycle as well as the malate transhydrogenation cycle. However, in ruminants the transhydrogenation cycle is insignificant and one-fourth of the $NDAPH^+$ is generated by cystolic NADP-isocitrate dehydrogenase, which allows generation of $NADPH^+$ from oxidation of acetate. Thus, ruminants have systems of providing both substrates and $NADPH^+$ for lipogenesis that allow conservation of glucose for other functions.

306

Partitioning of substrates between adipose and mammary sites is of primary importance in ruminants, especially if high milk-fat production is desired. This becomes especially critical when cattle are fed high-grain diets to increase energy intake, because the increased propionate enhances adipose fat deposition at the expense of mammary fat production. Partitioning of nutrients between muscle and adipose tissue is of critical importance in cattle grown for production of meat (29). When fed to grow rapidly on high grain diets, nutrient partitioning increasingly favors fat deposition as rates of gain increase beyond physiological limits for protein growth. In both instances repartitioning agents that, through homeorhetic mechanisms, establish new priorities and limits for milk or for muscle growth are required to divert nutrients from adipose to mammary or to muscle tissues (29). Estradiol 17β and zeranol effectively serve this function in beef cattle. In dairy cattle, growth hormone administration increases milk production through repartitioning.

ESSENTIAL FATTY ACIDS

The area of essential fatty acids has received attention in ruminants, primarily because offspring are born with low reserves of linoleic (18:2) and linolenic (18:3) acids (30). Linoleic is important because arachidonic which is needed for prostaglandin synthesis is synthesized from linoleic by chain elongation and desaturation. Probably the only real essential fatty acid is arachidonic, and linoleic is simply a precursor for it. The relative constancy of arachidonic in tissues across animals of all ages provides further evidence for this concept. Any deficit at birth can easily be corrected with omega-6 fatty acids in the milk within a few days, and thus essential fatty acid deficiencies should not normally occur. An example of a calf with a deficiency produced on an experimental diet is shown in Fig. 15-1.

ADIPOSE TISSUE—COMPOSITION AND FUNCTION

Adipose is a very simple term for a very complex array of tissues. While lipids are found in most tissues, adipose is a tissue

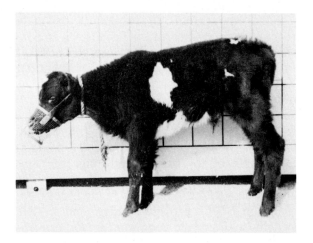

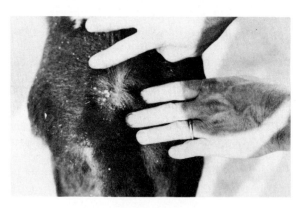

Figure 15-1. Male calf exhibiting fat deficiency symptoms at 56 days of age. Note the scaly dandruff. Other symptoms included loss of part of the hair over the back, shoulders and tail. Courtesy of N.L. Jacobson, Iowa State University, Ames, Iowa.

composed primarily of lipids and is found concentrated in depots. These include subcutaneous (external) sites, inter- and intramuscular sites, in bone marrow, lining of the abdominal and thoracic cavities, as visceral and omental fat, and as fat associated with vital organs. Fat in all sites is broadly categorized as white adipose tissue or as brown adipose tissue, although this distinction is not entirely real or appropriate. Composition of fat, size of adipocytes, distribution of sizes and priorities for deposition of fat differ among sites, over stages of growth, among species of ruminants, among sex classes, and with season and temperature. Composition also varies to some extent with diet, especially when fatty acids escape rumen saturation. In general, depot fat in ruminants varies less with diet then depot fat of non-ruminants, but it is a gross oversimplification to conclude that diet does not impact composition of adipose fat of ruminants.

Fats Present

Fats located within adipose depots in ruminants occur nearly entirely as triglycerides, with a predominance of C16 and C18 fatty acids. Normally, over 80% of fatty acids are 14:0, 16:0, 18:0 and 18:1, and in contrast to non-ruminants, ruminants have little 18:2 or 18:3 present (33). Also in contrast to non-ruminants, both *trans* as well as *cis* isomers of unsaturated fatty acids are present along with odd-length (C15, C17, etc.) and branched-chain fatty acids, all of which reflect rumen microbial synthesis and modification. The fatty acids in adipose are derived from three routes: dietary supply with microbial modification, microbial synthesis and denovo synthesis in the cytosol of the adipocyte. Endogenous synthesis in the adipocyte from acetate derived during rumen fermentation results in palmitic (C16:0) as a major end product which can subsequently be elongated to stearic and desaturated to oleic (C18:1). In general, 40-50% of the fatty acids in adipose tissue are saturated, with oleic being the principal unsaturated fatty acid.

Effect of Diet

Diet normally has only a marginal impact on composition of depot fat because of the extensive hydrogenation that occurs in the rumen. This would, of course, not be true for milk- or milk replacer-fed animals, because stimulation of the esophageal groove would allow the diet to bypass the rumen. Feeding poly-unsaturated oils at levels in excess of rumen limits for hydrolysis and hydrogenation, in complexes with formaldehyde and protein, or as fatty acid soaps with Ca, allows escape of some or much of the lipid from the rumen and passage to the lower tract for absorption. In these instances depot fat will change to reflect the composition of fatty acids absorbed, as in non-ruminant species. The level of grain vs forage in the diet, through its impact on rumen fermentation, results in changes in depot fat. Feeding high-grain diets results in a shift toward greater ruminal propionate production which causes an increase in branched-chain fatty acids in depot fat of sheep and goats vs an increase in deposition of mono-unsaturated fatty acids in

cattle. High forage diets increase the deposition of saturated fatty acids, primarily palmitic. Feeding of some antibiotics also may result in an increase in deposition of unsaturated fat if rumen microbial activity is significantly depressed.

While composition of depot fat varies with age in ruminants, this is primarily a reflection of supply (i.e., fetal, followed by milk, forage and then grain in typical management programs for domesticated ruminants). The greatest changes occur between composition at birth, which reflects de novo synthesis, and following development of a functional rumen when ruminal biohydrogenation increases stearate levels provided. These changes normally peak near a year of age in common feeding systems and then decline as de novo synthesis of unsaturated fatty acids in adipocytes becomes prominent.

Location in Body

When deciding on a site from which to obtain fat samples to characterize an animal, it readily becomes clear that fat composition at various sites is not consistent. In ruminants as in other species, the degree of unsaturation depends on the anatomical location (33) and, in general, subcutaneous sites are most unsaturated followed by inter- and intramuscular fat and internal organ fat being most saturated (Table 15-3). In addition, within subcutaneous locations, the most external layers of fat are most unsaturated with saturation increasing with depth or distance from the exterior. Patterns of unsaturation are inversely related to temperature of the depot location, a well known concept that applies across many species. For example, extensor muscles in the fore and hind limbs are maintained at cooler temperatures and have greater percentages of C16:1 (elk) and both C16:1 and C18:1 (moose) than fat in muscles maintained at warmer temperatures such as the *Longissimus dorsi* (34).

Species, Breed and Age Differences

Differences in composition of fat exist (35) between species of ruminants (Table 15-4), and this has been used in identification of meat products (34). Meat from elk can be distinguished from cattle, deer and moose because it has a much lower ratio of C18 relative to C14+C16 fatty acids in all sites.

308

Table 15-3. Fatty acid composition (mg/g) of lipid from four body sites in cattle 16-22 months of age fed a hay diet.

Fatty acid	Body site			
	Subcutaneous[a]	Intramuscular[b]	Intermuscular[c]	Perirenal
14:0	33	30	35	45
16:0	260	316	312	336
9-16:1	94	43	41	20
18:0	82	189	224	252
9-18:1	447	366	322	282
9,12-18:2	21	12	11	10

[a]Brisket
[b]*M. longissimus,* 10th rib
[c]Adjacent to intramuscular sample. From Leat (33).

Table 15-4. Fatty acid composition of fats from different species, molar %.

Fatty acid	Butter[a] (cattle)	Beef[b]	Sheep[b]	Deer[a]	Camel[a]	Pig[a]
Myristic (14:0)	11	4	4	3	5	1
Palmitic (16:0)	29	30	24	24	31	28
Palmitoleic (16:1)	5	5	3	3	4	3
Stearic (18:0)	9	13	21	31	31	15
Oleic (18:1)	27	14	43	36	28	42
Linoleic (18:2)	4	3	3	2	1	9
Linolenic (18:3)	tr	--	2	1	tr	2

[a]Mattson et al (35).
[b]USDA, Handbook 8-13, 1986 (38).

Antelope lipid is highly saturated (36) and comparisons indicate it has 1.5 times as much stearate and about two-thirds as much oleic as beef fat.

Breed and cattle type differences in distribution of fat also exist. In general, cattle selected for survival in cool-wet environments place a greater priority on subcutaneous fat (i.e., Angus, Hereford). Those selected for milk production preferentially deposit internal fat. This likely reflects the relative importance of the insulatory function of external fat in cold stress versus the ability to mobilize lipids rapidly from highly vascularized internal sites on demand to support high levels of milk production. Cattle also differ in their ability and priority to deposit intramuscular fat. Greater numbers of adipocytes are located near highly vascularized red muscle fibers than are found with anaerobic white fibers. Selection for muscle growth typically increases the ratio of white to red fibers,

reducing the ability and priority to deposit intramuscular fat.

Priorities for fat deposition increase with weight, age, rate of growth and proximity to maturity. Typical patterns of protein and fat deposition (Fig. 15-2) illustrate the increasing proportion of fat with weight and the effects of repartitioning with either endogenous or exogenous growth regulation. Rates of fat deposition increase at an increasing rate with rate of growth, while protein growth increases at decreasing rates and/or plateaus with rapid rates of growth. As a consequence the proportion of fat in gain increases rapidly with rate of gain. Repartitioning through endogenous (i.e., larger mature size) or through exogenous mechanisms (i.e., estrogens, zeranol) increases the extent of redirection of nutrients (37) from fat to protein (Fig. 15-3) with rapid growth rates. It is through this redirection in daily tissue growth that body composition over time is modified such that

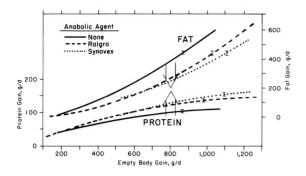

Figure 15-2. Impacts of endogenous and exogenous regulation on body composition vs weight.

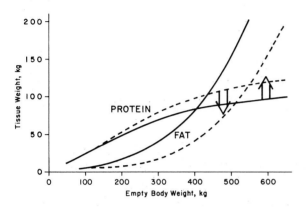

Figure 15-3. Repartitioning from fat to protein with respect to rate and composition of growth.

percent fat at any weight increases with rate of growth to that weight (29).

An understanding of these mechanisms through which animals control the priorities for and nature of lipids deposited that lead to the changes discussed should provide alternatives for desired tissue modification. With present concerns regarding both the amount as well as the types of fatty acids in meat products for human consumption, a concerted effort is needed to develop systems to regulate the locations, types and amounts of fat deposited in and with muscle tissues.

PRACTICAL USE OF ADDED FATS

Fats in Diets

Fat is present at relatively small levels in the basal forages and grains comprising rations commonly fed. Additional fat enters as oilseed fat in supplements or as some form of fat added directly for management and/or nutritional reasons. Ration characteristics are an important aspect associated with the addition of fat. Fat may be added to rations to reduce dust, eliminate fines, improve consistency and flow characteristics and to aid in processing such as in pelleting. The addition of 1-2% fat may improve ration and pellet characteristics while reducing pellet die temperature, lubricating the die and as much as doubling output of a pellet mill. However, there are limits to the amount of fat that can be added to rations for both feed management as well as nutritional management reasons. Feeds with more than 10% added fat are oily in warm climates, but have poor flow characteristics when cold, thus providing limitations in most feeding programs. These problems are essentially eliminated when the fat is provided in intact oilseeds such as cottonseed or soybean seeds; however, feeding whole unprocessed oilseeds can introduce other potential problems such as enzyme inhibitors or toxic compounds. Depending on the level of inclusion and the nature of the diet, these may or may not be real problems. Whole oilseeds are increasing in use in ruminant rations, especially in dairy cattle lactation diets, and provide the first real opportunity to increase the level of added fat beyond the traditional 5% limit in the total ration. The role of lipids in nutrition of ruminants becomes more apparent when one considers the large amount of lipid stored per day by finishing cattle (as much as 1 kg/d) and the amount secreted in milk by high-producing cows (as much as 2 kg fat). This is accomplished in spite of the fact that the diet typically provides less than half of this amount. Additionally, ruminants depend heavily on non-glucose metabolites in lipid-related metabolism because glucose levels provided through the diet are much lower than in non-ruminants.

Some forms of fat are much more desirable than others in providing these management related characteristics. Unsaturated fats may serve as an effective H sink in the rumen by consuming H, and coupled with a CH_4 inhibitor may enhance ruminal efficiency. This requires an unsaturated fat and would be best provided as a triglyceride to avoid impairing biohydrogenation. When ruminal fiber digestion is expected (normal case for cattle fed forages), the fat must be provided in a form that will not reduce activity of fiber digestion

310

by the microbes. Provided in the appropriate form, fat can be used effectively to increase diet energy density and total energy intake, and replace a portion of the readily fermentable carbohydrate that would otherwise be reducing fiber digestibility through negative associative effects. When an alteration in the fatty acid composition of depot or milk fat is desired, fat must be provided in a form that will escape rumen modification yet be degradable and absorbable in the small intestine. Any impact of the added fat on digestion and availability of other nutrients must be considered as well. Common interactions can include complexing of minerals and reductions in available levels of critical minerals to both the microbes as well as the animal.

Fats and Rumen Function

Fats can provide positive impacts on rumen function through reducing the level of readily available carbohydrate needed and thus enhancing fiber utilization, and through biohydrogenation can enhance energy recovery. However, fats historically have typically been implicated in negative rather than positive roles in rumen function. Traditional wisdom is to limit fats to less than 5% of the total ration in an attempt to prevent rumen fermentation problems. The nature and form of fat are very important, and along with levels of critical minerals, determine whether added fat will be an asset or a liability. Fat may impact rumen function in several ways.

Fiber digestion is sensitive to rumen fermentation conditions and fat reduces fiber digestion under common conditions through several mechanisms (2). Suggested mechanisms include physical coating of fiber with fat, toxic effects modifying some microorganisms, surface-active effects on microbial membranes and reduced cation availability through formation of soaps. A reduction in cation availability may also impact pH, as well as remove needed cations from microbial use. Adding fat as linseed oil has greatly decreased protozoal numbers in a number of studies, indicating their sensitivity to either direct or indirect effects of adding fat. Adding metal cations as alfalfa ash (5), Ca salts or limestone successfully prevented the depression in fiber digestibility caused by added fat. Ca forms insoluble soaps with fatty acids and prevents them from interfering with rumen microbes.

In recent research (4) complexing tallow or soy fatty acids as Ca-soaps through $CaCl_2$ or by adhesion to verxite, alleviated most or all negative effects of fatty acids on rumen fiber digestion.

Both the degree of unsaturation and esterification are of critical importance in determining the extent to which fat may impact fiber digestion. Poly-unsaturated fats are generally much more toxic to rumen microbes than saturated fats. Esterification is also a factor and, although microbial lipolytic activity is high, adding fat as esterified vs free fatty acids, especially at levels of 5% and above, has a greater detrimental effect on fiber digestion (2). However, addition of fatty acids (linoleic) in the free form inhibits biohydrogenation and must be a consideration.

MILK FAT CONCERNS

Factors critical to milk fat synthesis and mechanisms to increase milk fat production have been reviewed (2), and general concepts will be highlighted in this section. While conventional rations probably provide adequate fat to maintain milk production, the use of high-energy rations that divert nutrients from mammary to adipose tissue and result in low-fat milk have provided the opportunity for a considerable amount of research in the area of milk fat depression and mechanisms to enhance milk fat production.

Fats Present

Milk fat may come directly from absorbed dietary fat, from fatty acids synthesized in the mammary gland or from retrieval of adipose tissue fat, and usually reflects some combination of two or more of these sources. Milk contains a large proportion of short-chain fatty acids synthesized in the mammary gland. Fatty acids of C4 to C16 which typically represent 50% of the total milk fat, are synthesized in the mammary gland. C16 fatty acids can come either from mammary synthesis or from the blood. All C18 and longer fatty acids are derived from the blood, but may be of dietary or adipose origin. On the average, 40% of milk fat is derived directly from absorbed fat and 10% comes from adipose tissue, but these proportions reflect diet supply and metabolic priorities and change markedly depending on stage of production and level of lactation.

Fat Depression

Milk fat depression occurs in response to a reduction in absorbed acetate relative to propionate which usually occurs when fiber level or its digestibility is reduced. This induces a response in adipose tissue which then competes with the mammary gland for acetate and takes up dietary long-chain fatty acids with a concomittant reduction in mobilization of fatty acids from adipose tissue. These conditions cause the low milk-fat fat cow syndrome.

Dietary fats are transferred efficiently to milk fat (16), especially when adipose tissue storage is not extensive. Several studies indicate transfer efficiencies of 50-75% for dietary long-chain fat to milk. About two-thirds of the long-chain fat in milk comes from lipoprotein triglyceride with the remainder presumably from NEFA. The relative contribution of endogenous triglycerides is greatest in early lactation where extensive mobilization provides NEFA from which the liver synthesizes VLDL which are taken up by the mammary gland. In later lactation, when adipose tissue deposition is occurring, dietary contributions make up a much greater fraction of long-chain milk fat.

While it might seem that milk fat could simply be increased by feeding more fat, uptake of fat by the mammary gland inhibits de novo synthesis, effectively inhibiting any increase in total milk fat. It is interesting that as mammary short-chain fatty acid synthesis decreases and the proportion of long-chain fatty acids increases, oleic acid (C18:1) increases greatly. This is most likely a mechanism to maintain milk fluidity. In addition, the long-chain poly-unsaturates in fish oils reduce mammary uptake of lipids, perhaps through inhibition of mammary lipoprotein lipase. Probably the lone exception occurs when feeding protected fat which elevates plasma VLDL sufficiently to exceed the negative feedback of long-chain fats on mammary fat synthesis. In this case an increase in milk fat often results. However, milk protein is often then reduced, thus limiting the utility of this approach. Feeding supplemental niacin at 6 g daily has effectively increased milk fat and yield of fat-corrected milk in a number of studies (31, 32). Whether this occurs through a change in rumen fermentation or through metabolic effects reducing lipolysis and subclinical ketosis has not been clearly established.

SUMMARY

Herbivorous animals, because of the composition of their diet, consume only small amounts of a diverse group of lipids. Much additional lipid, primarily the VFA, is produced in the rumen. Rumen microorganisms have a marked effect on dietary lipids containing fatty acids. Esterified fatty acids are hydrolyzed from triglycerides and other compounds in the diet. Following hydrolysis, a majority of the unsaturated acids are hydrogenated, but a complex mix remains which contains mono- and di-unsaturated acids in which normal *cis* bonds have been altered to **trans** bonds, bonds have been moved, chain length may have been altered and odd-length and branched-chain acids have been added to the mix via microbial activities. Adequate amounts of required essential fatty acids (18:2, 18:3) apparently avoid alteration by passing through the rumen as components of phospholipids.

Free fatty acids pass into the intestine bound to particulate matter. They are emulsified, dispersed into micelles through the action of pancreatic lipase and bile salts, and diffuse into intestinal cells. In the intestinal cells the fatty acids are reesterified and transported via VLDL or chylomicrons through the lymphatic system. Short-chain VFA's go directly to the liver via the blood after absorption through the rumen wall. Tissue metabolism of fatty acids is similar to non-ruminants. Synthesis is minimal in the liver and extensive in adipose tissue. Precursors of fat synthesis are primarily acetate, butyrate and lactate. Butyrate is preferred by the mammary gland and acetate and lactate are principal precursors for adipose tissue. $NADPH^+$ is generated primarily through the pentose cycle or from oxidation of acetate via NADP-isocitrate dehydrogenase.

Adipose tissues in ruminants are important reserves of energy, but the fatty acid content

312

is known to vary with site in the body, by species, age, diet and other factors. Deposition of body fat or production of milk fat can be regulated by exogenous hormones.

In practical situations, fat is often used in ruminant diets, but the amount must be limited unless precautions are taken to reduce undesirable effects on the rumen microbial population. Milk fat depression in dairy cows is a common syndrome in cows fed heat processed grains in large amounts, particularly when accompanied by pelleted forages.

References

1. Wiseman, J. 1984. Fats in Animal Nutrition. Proc. 37th Nottingham Easter School. Butterworths, Boston.
2. Palmquist, D.L. and T.C. Jenkins. 1980. J. Dairy Sci. 63:1.
3. Gurr, M.I. 1984. In: Fats in Animal Nutrition, p. 1. Proc. 37th Nottingham Easter School. J. Wiseman, ed. Butterworths, Boston.
4. Jenkins, T.C. and D.L. Palmquist. 1984. J. Dairy Sci. 67:978.
5. Brooks, C.C. et al. 1954. J. Animal Sci. 14:210.
6. Latham, M.J. et al. 1972. Appl. Microbiol. 24:871.
7. Harfoot, C.G. 1981. In: Lipid Metabolism in Ruminant Animals, p. 25. W.W. Christie, ed. Pergamon Press, Oxford.
8. Steele, W. and J.H. Moore. 1968. J. Dairy Res. 35:371.
9. Moore, J.H. and W.W. Christie. 1984. In: Fats in Animal Nutrition, p. 123. Proc. 37th Nottingham Easter School. Butterworths, Boston.
10. Harrison, F.A. and K.J. Hill. 1962. J. Physiol. 162:225.
11. Yamamoto, A. and G. Rouser. 1967. Biochimica e Biologia Sperimentale 6:135.
12. Lennox, A.M., A.K. Lough and G.A. Garton. 1968. Brit. J. Nutr. 22:237.
13. Adams, E.P. and T.J. Heath. 1963. Biochimica et Biophysica Acta 70:688.
14. Thompson, A.B.R. and J.M. Dietschy. 1981. In: Physiology of the Gastrointestinal Tract, p. 1147. L.R. Johnson, ed. Raven Press, New York.
15. Noble, R.C. 1981. In: Lipid Metabolism in Ruminant Animals, p. 57. W.W. Christie, ed. Pergamon Press, Oxford.
16. Mattos, W. and D.L. Palmquist. 1977. J. Nutr. 107:1755.
17. Harrison, F.A., W.M.F. Leat and A. Forster. 1974. Proc. Nutr. Soc. 33:101A, 102A.
18. Palmquist, D.L. 1976. J. Dairy Sci. 59:355.
19. Puppione, D.L. 1978. J. Dairy Sci. 61:651.
20. Green, P.H.R. et al. 1979. J. Clin. Invest. 64:233.
21. Blum, C.B. 1980. Circulation. 62:181.
22. Palmquist, D.L. and W. Mattos. 1978. J. Dairy Sci. 61:561.
23. Palmquist, D.L. and W. Mattos. 1977. Fed. Proc. 36:1140.
24. Ballard, F.J., R.W. Hanson and D.S. Kronfield. 1969. Fed. Proc. 28:218.
25. Annison, E.F. et al. 1967. Biochem. J. 102:637.
26. Hood, R.L. 1982. Fed. Proc. 41:2555.
27. Emery, R.S. 1979. J. Animal Sci. 48:1530.
28. Swan, H. 1974. In: Thermo Regulation and Bioenergetics Patterns for Vertebrate Survival. H. Swan, ed. American Elsevier Pub. Inc., New York.
29. Byers, F.M. 1982. Fed. Proc. 41:2562.
30. Noble, R.C. 1984. In: Fats in Animal Nutrition, p. 185. Proc. 37th Nottingham Easter School. Butterworths, Boston.
31. Muller, L.D. et al. 1985. J. Dairy Sci. 68:163(Suppl. 1).
32. Horner, J.L. et al. 1985. J. Dairy Sci. 68:162(Suppl. 1).
33. Leat, W.M.F. 1977. J. Agr. Sci. 89:575.
34. Thompson, J.R., R.A. McClymont and M. Fenton. 1978. Agr. and Forestry Bulletin, 57th Annual Feeders Day Report, p. 37. University of Alberta.
35. Mattson, F.H., R.A. Field and J. Kunsman. 1973. J. Food Sci. 38:63.
36. Booren, A., R.A. Field and J. Kunsman. 1973. J. Food Sci. 38:63.
37. Lemieux, P.G. et al. 1984. Beef Cattle Res. in Texas 4227:32.
38. USDA. 1986. Composition of Foods. Agriculture Handbook No. 8-13.

16 VITAMINS IN RUMINANT NUTRITION

by J. Tal Huber

INTRODUCTION

At the tissue level, ruminants require all of the vitamins necessary for normal function in other mammals in the same approximate concentrations. However, rumen microorganisms possess the ability to synthesize the B vitamins and vitamin K which will be discussed later. Vitamins A, D and E are not synthesized by the microbes of the rumen and must be furnished in the diet of ruminants. The main thrust of this chapter will deal with these dietarily essential, fat-soluble vitamins, but discussion of important features on the B vitamins and vitamin K, particularly where they relate to modern production practices, will also be included. Additional information on symptoms, pictures illustrating deficiencies, and older literature are readily available (7).

VITAMINS ESSENTIAL IN RUMINANT DIETS

VITAMIN A

The main precursor to vitamin A found in plants and consumed by ruminants is β-carotene. Other common carotenoids (such as α carotene, γ carotene and cryptoxanthins) possess vitamin A potency, but in lesser amounts. Vitamin A functions in the animal body as the alcohol (retinol) or aldehyde (retinal). Many stereoisomers of vitamin A exist due to *cis-trans* stereoisomerism at its several double bonds. Greatest biological activity has been shown for the all-*trans* forms, with all other isomers being less active. The conversion of β-carotene to vitamin A occurs in the mucosal cells of the small intestine. This process appears much less efficient for ruminants than monogastrics. For rat growth, 1 mg β-carotene is equivalent to 1,667 IU of vitamin A, whereas the conversion estimate for ruminants is 400 IU vitamin A (or 24% of that in monogastrics).

Absorption and Storage

Both carotene and vitamin A are absorbed from the gut but other tissues such as the lungs are capable of cleavage of carotene to vitamin A. After IV infusions of carotene, sheep showed greater increases in vitamin A than calves, suggesting that sheep probably are more efficient in carotene conversion to vitamin A than cattle. Supporting a species difference within ruminants is the observation that sheep and goats have very little carotene in blood or milk; whereas, large amounts are secreted in milk of certain breeds of cattle (Guernsey and Jersey), but little in the Holstein, Brown Swiss or Ayrshire.

Absorption of vitamin A from the small intestine is energy dependent and transport to the liver is through the lymph as an ester of long-chain fatty acids carried by low density lipoproteins. At the liver the vitamin is stored in the Kupffer cells from which it is released as the free alcohol form to be transported to tissues by another lipoprotein. Liver turnover rates of vitamin A are highly variable depending on intake and function of the animals. Average times for 50% of the vitamin to exit the liver in several studies has ranged from about 90-320 d. Rapidly growing feedlot cattle and lactating dairy cows show most rapid turnover due to their high production state (7). Ample evidence shows that liver stores of vitamin A will be depleted completely in order to maintain a minimum concentration in the blood (27). Hence, blood or liver levels alone are often poor indices of the true vitamin A status of an animal, but using the two in concert gives a more reliable picture.

Functions, Deficiency Symptoms and Levels of Vitamin A

Basic functions of vitamin A include combining with the protein opsin to form rhodopsin in the retina of the eye. The rhodopsin (or visual purple) is a pigment contained in the rods which are receptors of dimlight vision. A second important metabolic role of vitamin A is in normal growth and maintenance of squamous epithelium cells. Vitamin A also affects bone growth, possibly through its influence in the synthesis of chondroitin sulfate.

314

Deficiency symptoms of vitamin A reflect insufficient amounts to maintain its normal functions, but they are manifested as a multitude of problems. Night blindness and a failure to discern objects in dim light are early symptoms and common for all animals. In cattle with moderate deficiency, there occurs a degeneration of the mucosa of many organs. Tissues usually damaged include the respiratory and urogenital tracts, the kidneys, the salivary and buccal glands and the eyes, making them much less resistant to infections. Deficient animals are also more susceptible to colds and pneumonia and other diseases of the respiratory tract. Supplementation of vitamin A rapidly restores mucosal integrity.

Reproductive disorders due to vitamin A deficiency are characterized in females by increased abortions, more retained placentas and birth of weakened, blind or dead calves. Young ruminants (particularly calves) are often born with a mild vitamin A deficiency because of low liver storage while in utero, even when supply of dams is adequate. The condition is worsened in deficient dams which will give birth to blind, deformed calves as shown in Fig. 16-1. Deficient males show impaired sexual activity and ability, abnormal sperm with decreased motility, degeneration of seminiferous tubules (Fig. 16-2) and general testicular injury. A low carotene diet with adequate vitamin A may cause abnormal sperm and a delayed maturation in the epididymis (30). Late symptoms of vitamin A deficiency include convulsions, total blindness and degenerative changes in the kidneys. An extreme deficiency during growth leads to cancellous, weak bones which are excessively thick.

The first and perhaps the most sensitive indication of a vitamin A deficiency in growing calves is increased cerebrospinal fluid pressure (CSFP) due to decreased absorption of cerebrospinal fluid. Values of CSFP above 120 mm saline suggest a vitamin A deficiency. Blood plasma concentrations of vitamin A of <10 μg/dl indicate a severe deficiency of vitamin A and suggest that liver stores have probably been depleted to critical levels (<1 μg/g). Even when plasma reaches below 20 μg/dl vitamin A, a mild deficiency is probably present. Eaton (9) reported that 50% of the calves tested had ocular pappiledema and 60% squamous metaplasia of the parotid duct

Figure 16-1. A blind calf born to a cow with a severe vitamin A deficiency.

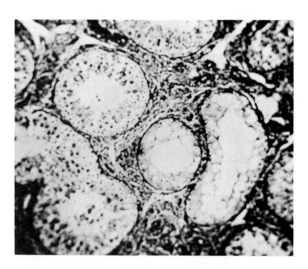

Figure 16-2. Histological section from a testis of a vitamin A deficient bull. The picture shows degeneration of the seminiferous tubules. Courtesy of J.F. Proctor, Nat. Dairy Prod. Corp.

when plasma vitamin A levels were <10 μg/dl. Respective values for calves at 5 μg/dl were 85 and 93%.

Toxic Levels and Symptoms of Vitamin A

Because of apparent degradation in the rumen, ruminants tolerate larger amounts of vitamin A without showing toxic symptoms than non-ruminants. Beef cattle have been fed 50-100 times the recommended allowance for 6 months without overt toxic effects. However, in younger calves feed intakes and body weights will be depressed when vitamin A is fed at about 100X requirement. Clinical signs of hypervitaminosis A are: greater liver,

315

heart and kidney weights, increased SGOT, decreased serum albumin and increased serum globulin. Perhaps the most sensitive sign of vitamin A toxicity is a decrease in CSFP at around 20X, probably due to a blockage between certain cavities in the brain.

Symptoms of acute vitamin A toxicity in humans include headaches, vomiting, diarrhea and giddiness, which are followed after about a week by desquamation of skin and loss of hair. Chronic toxicity from lesser amounts of vitamin A results in anorexia, scaly dermatitis, patchy loss of hair and pain in the skeletal system. Toxic problems in monogastrics have been noted at vitamin A intakes of 10-50X that recommended in normal diets, relatively lower than for ruminants.

Recommended Dietary Levels and Variability in Feeds

The recommended allowance of 10.6 mg β-carotene/100 kg bodyweight for growing dairy calves was based on early research, but still appears valid for most species of growing ruminants (25). At a conversion ratio of 400 IU vitamin A per mg of β-carotene, this would amount to 4,240 IU vitamin A/100 kg bodyweight. For animals in lactation or reproduction, the suggested allowance is almost doubled (19 mg β-carotene or 7,600 IU of vitamin A/100 kg of bodyweight). Furnishing vitamin A in large excess of suggested allowances is a common practice in formulation of dairy cow rations in the USA and results in increased concentrations of the vitamin in milk, but little apparent benefit to the animal.

The practice of supplementing ruminant rations with the minimum daily allowance of vitamin A is often recommended because of great variability in the potency of the vitamin in normal feedstuffs, particularly forages. When harvested at recommended maturity, legume hays are quite abundant in β-carotene, but biological availability is lost during storage or in the presence of heat. Hay stored in a barn for 6 months loses over 70% of its vitamin A activity. Silages which have undergone excessive heating or exposure to air are essentially devoid of the functional vitamin.

Factors Affecting Vitamin A Utilization in Ruminants

Vitamin A activity (from the vitamin or its precursors) is diminished in the rumen by 20-80%. This effect is probably more on high-concentrate than high-forage diets, so there may be a greater need of supplementing A in high-grain diets. This is often compounded by the fact that grains are lower than forages in β-carotene. Cattle consuming diets high in corn silage have also responded to vitamin A addition, even though the β-carotene present was calculated to be sufficient for their needs. Feeding of antioxidants (ethoxyquim) or 3% ethanol have reduced liver losses of vitamin A. On the other hand, low protein diets and aflatoxin have increased losses. Several other factors such as phospholipids, dietary P, chlortetracycline and stilbesterol have little effect on vitamin A status of animals.

Conditions of stress caused by parturition, abortion, cold weather or acute bacterial infections have been associated with an increased need for the vitamin. During such periods animals often respond favorably to supplemental vitamin. Heat stress was shown to cause greater losses of vitamin A resulting in a need for increased supplementation during hot weather (7).

Some studies suggest that the presence of high nitrate in ruminant diets (in forage, water or grain) interferes with vitamin A utilization (see Ch. 23). However, several other reports have discounted nitrate as being a problem in most practical feeding situations and the interaction of nitrate and vitamin A was not supported.

β-CAROTENE AND REPRODUCTION IN CATTLE

German workers (19) discovered sizable amounts of β-carotene (BC) in corpora lutea of dairy cows and followed with studies which linked high levels of plasma BC with improved reproductive performance, characterized by decreased days open, less services per conception and a reduced incidence of silent heats and cystic ovaries. A subsequent trial in the USA involving 4 farms (60 cows/treatment) showed that supplementation of 300 mg/d of BC (in excess of that normally contained in diets) resulted in improved reproduction. In contrast with these results, controlled studies at Kentucky (5) and Virginia (3) showed no benefit in reproductive efficiency from feeding 200-600 mg daily

316

of supplemental BC to cows in early lactation. However, one subsequent Virginia study (4) which included cows with poorer than normal reproductive performance did show a reduction in days open (116 vs 186) from supplementing with 600 mg/d of BC. Subtle differences in corpus luteum response to human chorionic gonadotropin were also attributed to BC ingestion. This amount of BC is 2-6X that recommended to supply vitamin A needs of the cow. The mechanism of its effect on reproduction has not been established and further controlled research to show efficacy and mode of action is needed before its use can be recommended.

VITAMIN D

Many compounds possess vitamin D activity, but only vitamin D_2 (ergosterol in plants) and D_3 (7-dehydrocholesterol in animals) are important dietary sources. Irradiation by sun or ultraviolet light which cleaves a carbon to carbon bond is essential for making both forms of vitamin D biologically active. Vitamins D_2 and D_3 were thought earlier to possess equal biopotency for ruminants and other mammals; while for birds, D_3 was considered superior to D_2 in Ca transport. However, recent evidence by USDA workers (12) shows that pigs and ruminants use D_3 more efficiently than D_2. For ruminants, the authors suggest that there might be a preferred degradation of D_2 by rumen microorganisms.

Prior to performing its function, vitamin D is changed to 25-hydroxycholecalciferol (HCC) and then to 1-25-dihydroxycholecalciferol (DHCC) in liver and kidneys, respectively. The HCC is 4-5X more effective than D_3 in curing rickets in rats and DHCC about 5X more effective than HCC. Recently, these more active forms of the vitamin have been synthesized by commercial laboratories and should become available for use in the field in the near future.

Functions of Vitamin D
The primary function of viatmin D (or DHCC as the active form) is to stimulate formation of Ca-binding protein (CBP) in the mucosa of the small intestine. Action of CBP is necessary for absorption of Ca into the bloodstream. Concentration of DHCC in the intestine is increased if blood plasma is marginal in Ca or P. This elevation in DHCC results from increased mobilization of HCC from the liver and is controlled by parathormone. Activated vitamin D (DHCC) is also involved in mobilization of Ca from the bones and in absorption of P through action of a vitamin D-dependent phosphate pump in the small intestine.

Deficiency Symptoms
Deficiency symptoms of vitamin D are related to poor bone mineralization. They commence with a thickening of the metatarsal and metacarpal bones. Bent forelegs, swollen and stiffened joints; humped backs and straightened pasterns will follow. In the latter stages, symptoms that may occur include paralysis of hind quarters, stiffness of gait, tetany, labored breathing and accumulation of synovial fluid in joints. The term characterizing these symptoms in growing ruminants is rickets, and in adults, osteomalacia. Rickets have been produced experimentally in young

Figure 16-3. A vitamin D deficient calf. Note the enlarged joints and crooked front legs. Courtesy of F.R. Spratling, U. of Cambridge.

Figure 16-4. Female shown in Fig. 16-3, now recovered from the deficiency and 22 mo. of age. She has a small stature, short legs and a narrow pelvis. Courtesy of F.R. Spratling, U. of Cambridge.

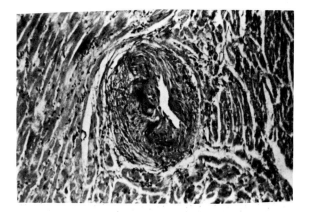

Figure 16-5. Hypercalcification of the kidney of a dog fed excessive vitamin D. Photo from author's collection.

calves (Fig. 16-3), but the deficiency is rare under most normal feeding regimes. Upon restoration of vitamin D to the diet of an animal with rickets, clinical symptoms disappear rapidly but a diminished bone structure may still persist (Fig. 16-4). Osteomalacia may occur in aged cows, but is often due to multiple factors and not only to a vitamin D deficiency. Some research indicates that low vitamin D intakes in calves inhibits estrus, while supplementary D often restores fertility of anestrus cows or causes earlier than normal estrus after calving (7).

Initial signs of low vitamin D intakes are lowered concentrations of blood Ca and/or inorganic P, accompanied by increased serum phosphatase. Direct measures of vitamin D or metabolite concentrations in plasma or tissues have not as yet been useful measures of the vitamin status of animals, but methods are being developed. Storage of considerable HCC occurs in the liver during periods of luxury intake and may provide the animals' needs for several weeks in the event of an absence of vitamin D in the diet.

Toxic Symptoms and Toxic Levels of Vitamin D

Vitamin D in large excess of requirements causes toxicity characterized first by increased calcification of bone, followed by greater resorption of Ca from the bones, a weakened skeleton, and calcification of soft tissues such as kidneys, joints, heart, lungs and arteries. Figure 16-5 shows

hypercalcification of a kidney which resulted from intake of excessive vitamin D. The kidney damage can be fatal due to uremia.

In one study, intramuscular (IM) delivery of a bolus of 17.5-20 million IU of vitamin D_3 to pregnant cows 30 d prepartum was lethal to 80% of the animals within a few days following parturition. Dosing with 2-5 million IU caused milk fever in 100% of the cows. On the other hand, oral administration of 20-30 million IU of D_3 daily to cows for up to 7 d before calving is a well known prophylactic treatment for milk fever and does not cause toxicity symptoms. The higher toxicity of the IM compared to the oral route for D_3 delivery confirms effective degradation of vitamin D in the rumen.

Recommended Feeding Levels

The literature is not clear as to the optimum amount of vitamin D needed in ruminant diets. Deficiency symptoms are prevented in adult cows at 5,000-6,000 IU/d. However, higher levels have been beneficial in some studies. One study showed a reduced incidence of milk fever by feeding 70,000 IU/d to cows susceptible to the disease (11a), and another showed increased Ca utilization and earlier estrus in cows provided with 300,000 IU of vitamin D weekly in a capsular form, but there were no differences in milk production or services per conception (28).

One reason it has been difficult to induce a vitamin D deficiency in cattle is that exposure to sunlight activates D_3 in the skin and it has been generally accepted that this would prevent deficiency problems. However, in some areas ruminants might be exposed to insufficient sun irradiation for vitamin D activation to occur during certain seasons because of cloud cover, housing practices or too acute an angle (35° or less) for sun rays to be effective. In New Zealand, Australia and Northern Europe, a high incidence of rickets which was vitamin D responsive has been reported in young sheep grazing cereal crops and good pastures.

Variability of Vitamin D in Feeds

Similar to vitamin A, vitamin D activity is highly variable in feeds, even though it is not as sensitive to heat as are vitamins A or E. Forages are generally good sources of vitamin D if they have been exposed to sun or ultraviolet light, but large variability in forages has been shown for vitamin D activity. For this reason and because it is cheap insurance against a possible deficiency, it is recommended to supplement in the feed of dairy cows an amount of vitamin D equal to the minimum daily allowance (or about 10,000 IU/d). Cattle reared in minimum sunlight also need added vitamin D as do baby calves raised in dark barns on milk replacers.

Vitamin D for Prevention of Milk Fever

Massive doses (20-30 million IU daily) of vitamin D will reduce the incidence of milk fever (16). This amount is close to the toxicity level, so feeding should begin 3-5 d before calving and not continue for over 7 d. Difficulty in predicting calving dates negates the effectiveness of this practice as a prophylactic measure. The hydroxylated metabolites (HCC and DHCC) have been shown effective in preventing milk fever without the potential danger of toxicity when fed or injected IM a few days prior to parturition (16). Further discussion of milk fever is presented in Ch. 24.

VITAMIN E

Similar to vitamins A and D, there are several forms in nature which possess vitamin E activity, the most potent being α-tocopherol (5,7,8-trimethyltocol) with β, γ and δ tocopherols being 50, 20 and 10% as bioactive as the α form. Vitamin E action was thought to be closely associated with reproduction in animals for many years. However, this was true only for a few species (rat, mouse, hampster, guinea pig, etc.), but not ruminants.

Metabolic Functions

It is generally accepted that the predominant metabolic function of vitamin E is to serve as an antioxidant, thus preventing peroxidative degradation of fats in animal cells and the consequent formation of free-radical peroxides which inhibit action of certain enzymes and damage cellular membranes. Supporting the antioxidant role is the discovery that other antioxidants furnish vitamin E-like protection to the animal. However, deficiency symptoms in some animals (such as encephalomalacia in chicks) are alleviated only by vitamin E and not by other antioxidants.

A relationship between the function of selenium (Se) and vitamin E has now been clarified. Earlier work showed that vitamin E deficiencies responded to dietary Se. The antioxidant effects of gluthathione peroxidase (Se is an integral part of this enzyme molecule) have been established (2) and is discussed in Ch. 18. Even though Se delayed death in ewes which were severely deficient in vitamin E, only the vitamin could prevent death, suggesting a need for vitamin E in the presence of a Se-adequate diet. Julien et al (17) found that injection of vitamin E (680 mg/d) and Na selenite (50 mg/d) for 20 d before calving reduced retained placentas in dairy cows. Se was thought the principal reason for the effect, and it was not determined whether through the antioxidant or some other action of the nutrients.

Deficiency Symptoms

Vitamin E deficiency symptoms in ruminants are characterized by dystrophic lesions in the muscle known commonly as "white muscle disease" because of the white striations of connective tissue which develop in muscle bundles. One early sign of vitamin E deficiency in calves is hypercellularity and scattered necrosis in muscle fibers as illustrated in Fig. 16-6. This is often accompanied by increased concentrations in the serum of several enzymes reflective of muscle damage. These are: glutamic oxaloacetic transaminase (SGOT), alanine transaminase and lactic dehydrogenase. Also, increased excretion of

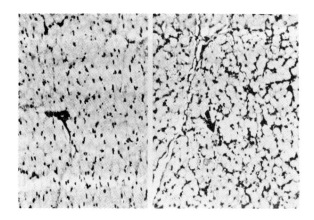

Figure 16-6. The picture on the left is the cross section of normal muscle of a calf fed a 20% protein diet of milk origin; that on the right shows hypercellularity in a cross section of muscle from a calf fed a 20% protein diet from dichloroethane-extracted fish. Occasional individual fibers exhibit increased eosinophilia (arrow). Photos from Michel et al (21).

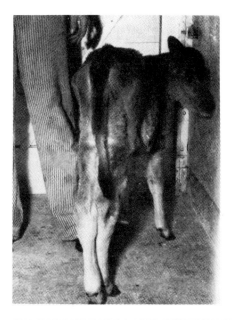

Figure 16-7. Top. Vitamin E-deficient calf. This calf shows a stance with the hind legs crossed, said to be typical of deficient calves. Bottom. Calf standing with lowered, extended head and illustrating the prominent suprascapula. Courtesy of Dept. of Animal Sci., Iowa State U.

urinary creatine (5-10 fold) has been noted in vitamin E deficient lambs. Overt deficiency symptoms, produced experimentally in calves and observed in the field, commence with a weakening of leg muscles causing the calf to walk with a crossing of the hind legs (Fig. 16-7). A relaxing of the pasterns, splaying of the toes and impairment of the calf's suckling ability (due to injury of the tongue musculature) have also been reported. Later stages include an inability of the animal to stand or control head movements.

Dietary Requirements

Need for vitamin E in pre-ruminants depends on the content and degree of unsaturation of dietary fats. Calves fed milk diets with no unsaturated fat will not develop white muscle disease at very low intakes of vitamin E. However, inclusion of unsaturated fats in milk-type diets greatly increases the amount of vitamin required to prevent the disease. Studies by the author and associates with baby calves showed that twice as much vitamin E was needed (92 vs 46 mg/d) to maintain normal blood serum levels of α-tocopherol when fish protein concentrate (with 5% fish fat which was highly unsaturated) replaced milk protein in milk replacer diets (21). A decrease in serum vitamin E of calves on a normal milk replacer containing emulsified lard oil as the fat was also shown,

suggesting the need for supplementation of vitamin E in some diets previously thought adequate.

Even though prolonged feeding of some milk replacers as the only feed might result in a poor vitamin E status of young calves and lambs, the early consumption of grain and hay offsets the development of deficiency problems in the field. After weaning, and with the advent of a functional rumen, vitamin E deficiencies related to ingestion of unsaturated fats disappears because of the biohydrogenation of fats by rumen microorganisms before they reach the tissues. Also,

320

intake of fats and oils is less on the typical ruminant than pre-ruminant diet.

Generally, commercial milk replacers for calves, kids and lambs contain, at most, 10-20 mg/lb of added vitamin E. This amount is usually sufficient when fats used are saturated animal fats (tallow, lard, butter) and herd replacement calves rapidly commence eating dry feed which causes rumen development. However, the author would prefer that supplemental vitamin E in milk replacers be increased to 25-30 mg/lb as insurance against possible deficiencies that may develop due to oxidative deterioration of the fat during storage and other possible problems.

There does not appear to be sufficient data available to establish a definitive vitamin E requirement for ruminants. Estimates of between 15 and 60 mg/kg dry matter have been proposed for beef cattle. This range should also meet the needs of dairy cattle, sheep and goats. Because of the various dietary factors which impinge on vitamin E needs in ruminants (such as Se, antioxidants, unsaturated fats, etc.), it is not surprising that the establishment of dietary requirements is difficult.

Supplementation of Vitamin E in Ruminant Diets

Most natural feeds for ruminants (grains and forages) contain adequate vitamin E, so supplementation is generally not needed and has not positively affected animal performance in several experiments. However, the vitamin is heat labile (as is vitamin A), so silages or hays which have undergone excessive heating or a lengthy storage period may be partially or totally devoid of vitamin E activity. One report (20) demonstrated that cows fed hay had lower blood tocopherols and higher SGOT than cows fed well-preserved corn silage. Calves of cows on the different diets were similar to their dams in vitamin E status and SGOT. Supplementation of vitamin E to animals consuming feeds suspected as being low in vitamin E activity as their main diet is advisable.

Most concentrate rations for dairy cows contain supplemental α-tochopherol at 5-25 mg/lb as an insurance against a possible problem due to variability in the feed. Heavy supplementation of vitamin E (400-1,000 mg/d) to dairy cow rations is effective in reducing

the oxidized flavor of milk (caused by peroxidation of fatty acids), but the cost of such a practice makes it prohibitive in normal situations unless the sale or a price reduction of milk is threatened.

Toxicity Levels and Symptoms of Excess Vitamin E

While no studies on vitamin E toxicity were found for ruminants, chicks fed 10,000 IU/kg of diet showed reduced Ca and P in blood plasma and in bone ash (24). The authors concluded that excessive vitamin E apparently interfered with Vitamin D utilization. Considering the relatively high cost of supplemental vitamin E and the large quantities probably needed for producing toxicity, it is unlikely that this would be a problem in ruminant diets. However, surveys of human intake suggest that 15-20% of the population is consuming 10X the RDA for vitamin E and that even though overt toxicity symptoms have not been observed, caution should be exercised against intake of such an excessive amount of the vitamin.

THE B VITAMINS

In ruminants an adequate supply of the B complex vitamins and vitamin K are as essential at tissue and cellular levels for proper body function as they are in monogastrics. However, synthesis of these vitamins in liberal amounts by rumen microorganisms usually negates the need for dietary supplementation. Hence, extensive study of B vitamins and vitamin K in diets for ruminants has not been conducted.

Table 16-1 shows the estimated rumen synthesis for riboflavin, niacin and pantothenic acid. As noted, they are all produced in

Table 16-1. Rumen synthesis of certain B-vitamins in relation to needs of animal.[a]

Vitamin	Needs, mg/d	Rumen synthesis, mg In 6 h	In 24 h	Rumen synthesis, % of needs
Riboflavin	32	35	140	440
Niacin	182	219	876	480
Pantothenic acid	117	43	172	150

[a]Needs were generated from (13), rumen synthesis data came from (1).

considerable excess of calculated requirements. Using calves fitted with rumen and duodenal fistulas, recent results (23) have generally confirmed potential rumen synthesis of thiamin, riboflavin and niacin. Moreover, they showed little inhibition of B vitamin synthesis when cattle were fed chlortetracycline (22) or monensin (23). Some differences in B vitamin synthesis were reported due to type of grain fed, with the synthesis of thiamin greater for sorghum than barley or corn, but grain had little effect on supply of thiamin available for intestinal absorption (23).

Generally, B vitamin requirements for ruminants at the tissue level have been extrapolated from those established for non-ruminating calves and lambs on all-milk diets.

Table 16-2. Suggested B-vitamin requirements for ruminants.[a]

	mg/100 kg body wt[b]	mg/700 kg cow
Thiamin	6.5	46
Riboflavin	4.5	32
Niacin	26	182
Pyridoxine	6.5	46
Biotin	.2	1.4
Pantothenic Acid	19.5	117
Folic Acid	3.3	23
Choline	2,100	18,200
Vitamin B_{12}	0.060	0.420

[a] Adapted by author from (13)
[b] This amount should be available for absorption, but because of rumen synthesis, an actual dietary requirement has not been established.

Estimated needs for ruminants, as adapted by the author (13), were mostly taken from studies conducted by B.C. Johnson and associates at the U. of Illinois which were published during the years of 1947 to 1955 and are given in Table 16-2 (see ref. 7 for applicable literature).

Only recently have there been investigations which focused on production responses to addition of B vitamins to ruminant rations. These responses will be reviewed, but it should be remembered that the levels of the vitamins given to induce such responses are usually for specialized production situations and do not necessarily reflect requirements for normal growth, reproduction or production. Table 16-3 lists clinical signs of deficiencies of the B vitamins observed in early experiments with calves and lambs.

Thiamin: Special Considerations of B Vitamins in Ruminant Rations

An apparent thiamin deficiency, called polyencephalomalaca (PEM) in the USA or cerebrocortical necrosis in Europe, which is often responsive to B_1 therapy (IV injection of 2.2 mg thiamin/kg BW), has been observed in cattle and lambs fed high concentrate or high sugar diets. In Fig. 16-8 are photos of 2 calves, one suffering from PEM and the other from acidosis and a thiamin deficiency, which symptoms are similar to the early stages of PEM. It has been theorized that PEM-inducing

Table 16-3. Clinical signs of deficiency of several B-vitamins observed in calves and lambs in early experiments.

B-Vitamin[a]	Deficiency
Thiamin	Polyneuritic, incoordination of forelimbs, arrythmia of heart, increased blood pyruvate and lactate
Riboflavin	Redness of mouth mucosa, lesions in the mouth, copious salivation and lacrimation
Niacin	Anorexia, diarrhea, dehydration
Pyridoxine	Epileptic fits characterized by thrashing of head and legs, and grinding of teeth
Pantothenic Acid	Scaly dermatitis around eyes and muzzle
Biotin	Paralysis of the hind quarters
Vitamin B_{12}	General emaciation, muscular weakness, white-spotted kidney condition
Folic Acid	Leucopenia (in lambs, not calves)
Choline	Extreme weakness and labored breathing

[a] Deficiency symptoms of most of the B-vitamins include a general emaciation often characterized by anorexia, weight loss and diarrhea. These lead to death if allowed to progress to the extreme conditions.

Figure 16-8. Upper. A calf affected with PEM. This animal shows symptoms of nystagmus and opisthotonus as a result of involvement of the central nervous system. Courtesy of C.K. Whitehair, Michigan State U. Lower. A fattening bull calf showing disturbance in balance after development of acidosis and a thiamin deficiency, presumably very similar if not identical to the early stages of PEM. Courtesy of A. Henning, U. of Leipzig, Germany.

diets (typical of those causing lactic acidosis) stimulate the synthesis of a thiaminase by rumen microbes that destroys the available thiamin. Problems with PEM are less frequent in dairy than beef cattle, probably because of higher levels of forage in dairy diets. PEM (non-infectious) is more prevalent in young than older animals, probably because of lower thiamin reserves in the young. It was characterized in lambs by high intercranial pressures resulting in blindness, muscle tremors, grinding of teeth, opisthotonus and convulsions. In the acute form, lambs die in 1-2 d if not corrected, and the sub-acute form leaves them blind, uncoordinated and weak.

A clear understanding linking thiamin deficiency and PEM has not been proposed. Total blood thiamin is similar in affected and unaffected animals, although the diphosphorylated form is greatly decreased in PEM. Symptoms similar to PEM are readily induced by amprolium, a coccidiostat which acts as an antagonist to thiamin, or by feeding the rhizomes from dried bracken fern, known for its high thiaminase activity.

It has been suggested that PEM is the result of thiamin being converted to pyrithiamin and other metabolites of the vitamin. Regardless of the mechanism of the development of PEM and the involvement of thiamin, it has been shown consistently that injection (IV or IM) of thiamin eliminates the symptoms of the disease if it has not progressed to an irreversible stage.

Niacin

The B vitamin most studied in ruminants in recent years has been niacin. Glucogenic and lipolytic effects of niacin had been observed in rats. In 1972 it was shown that pharmacological doses (100-400X the estimated requirement) of niacin administered to lactating cows with sub-clinical ketosis resulted in an initial decrease and then a rebound in plasma ketones and free fatty acids (29). Blood metabolites and appetite returned to normal with ketotic symptoms disappearing after the rebound phase, or about 3 weeks after treatment. Subsequent studies indicated some alleviation of subclinical ketosis by feeding 6-12 g niacin/d. Further study is needed to more clearly elucidate the conditions and levels that niacin supplementation might affect clinical or subclinical ketosis in lactating dairy cows. It has been postulated that niacin exerts an insulin-like effect which stimulated lipogenesis to a greater extent than lipolysis. A more detailed discussion of niacin and ketosis is given in Ch. 24.

Niacin Effects on Milk Production. The feeding of 6 g niacin daily or about 20X the previously recommended allowance increased milk production by 1-3 kg/d in early lactation dairy cows fed all natural protein (Table 16-4) (18, 26). However, niacin inclusion in rations containing NPN did not increase milk yields, nor were results positive with cows in mid or late lactation. In a field study,

Table 16-4. Influence of niacin and protein source on dairy cow performance.[a]

| | Treatment | | | |
| | Soy bean meal | | Urea | |
Item	(+Niacin)	(−Niacin)	(+Niacin)	(−Niacin)
Milk yield, kg/d[b]	26.7	25.4	26.0	25.5
Milk yield, weeks 9 & 10, kg/d[c]	25.5	23.0	24.3	24.5
Dry matter intake, kg/d	19.1	19.5	19.7	18.5
Feed utilization, milk/kg DM	1.44	1.34	1.37	1.44
Body weight change, kg/d	0.58	0.31	0.34	0.63

[a]Data from (18), means are for 32 cows (8/treatment) for 10 weeks of treatment. Cows were evenly divided into early and mid lactation groups. Positive response to niacin was greater in early lactation.

[b]Milk yields are adjusted for pre-treatment.

[c]Interaction of niacin by protein source, sig (P < .10).

supplementation of 6 g niacin/d did not result in an overall increase in milk yields, but production was increased compared to controls in the high-yielding group of first-calf heifers (15). No explanation was given as to why only this group responded positively to the vitamin.

The mechanism of the niacin effect on milk production has not been clarified. Some studies have suggested an increase in microbial protein synthesis (26), others proposed a positive effect on protozoal growth (8). A change in energy metabolism is an additional possibility for explaining the increased milk production elicited from supplemental niacin.

Niacin Addition to Growing Rations. Supplementation of niacin to growing steers has often yielded positive results in diets high in corn grain and corn silage (6). In contrast, other studies have not shown a benefit from adding niacin to growing and fattening rations. In one trial niacin enhanced the adaptation of growing calves to urea-type diets (6). As shown in Table 16-5, supplemental niacin supported more rapid adaptation of feedlot cattle. One study showed feed efficiencies were improved by niacin addition after 28 and 56 d on feed, but no differences due to the vitamin were seen at the termination of the study (112 d).

In summary, addition of 2-12 g of niacin to ruminant rations might be cost effective in production situations where milk yields or

Table 16-5. Influence of niacin on adaptation of feeder calves to a urea-containing ration.[a]

Item	Control	Niacin[b]
No. cattle	10	10
Initial weight, kg	198.6	193.3
Final weight, kg	216.0	219.0
Gain, kg	17.4	25.7
Days	29	29
Av. daily gain, kg[c]	0.60	0.89
Dry matter/d, kg		
Corn silage	4.20	4.50
Urea supplement	0.79	0.79
Mineral supplement	0.40	0.40
Total	5.39	5.68
Dry matter/gain	8.98	6.41

[a]From (6)

[b]Supplement provided 70 mg added niacin/kg of diet dry matter.

[c]Means differ, P < .01.

weight gains are stimulated, particularly in light of the inexpensive cost of the vitamin. However, further research is needed on niacin levels and their relationships to performance and physiological function. Rumen and systemic effects should also be clarified.

Choline

Quantitatively, choline is required in greatest amounts of all the B vitamins. It serves as a structural constituent of cells, aids in nerve impulse transmission, is important in fat metabolism and provides labile methyl groups for a number of metabolic reactions in the

324

Table 16-6. Effect of added choline on intake and milk production.[a]

| | Added choline chloride, g/kg concentrate | | | | | | |
| | Experiment 1 | | | Experiment 2 | | | |
Item	0	1.5	3.0	0	2	4	6
Dry matter intake, kg/d	19.7	20.1	19.7	13.7	14.3	13.6	13.6
Dry matter intake, % of BW	3.26	3.35	3.30	2.22	2.37	2.20	2.24
Choline intake, g/d	8.0	26.6	41.5	5.2	27.2	48.7	73.2
Milk production, kg/d	24.7	25.6	25.0	16.6	17.8	18.7	17.6
Milk fat, %	3.43	3.48	3.77	2.64^b	2.74^{bc}	3.41^c	2.86^b
Milk protein, %	3.33	3.36	3.35	---	---	---	---
Fat corrected milk yield, kg/d	22.5	23.6	24.5	13.1^b	14.7^{bc}	16.8^c	14.5^{bc}
Fat yield, kg/d	0.84	0.89	0.94	0.43^b	0.50^{bc}	0.62^c	0.49^{bc}
Protein yield, kg/d	0.82	0.86	0.83	---	---	---	---

[a]Data from (10). Exp. 1 used 18 cows with a 12-wk experimental period in a switchback design. Exp. 2 was a 4 X 4 Latin Square with 4 cows/trt.

[bc]Means in the same row with different superscripts differ (P < .1).

animal body. Several studies have supplemented choline to rations for growing-finishing cattle which generally increased choline intakes from about 1,000-1,500 mg/kg ration. These tests at several locations have been inconclusive, so choline is not generally added to beef cattle diets.

Action of choline in fat metabolism has led to investigation of effects of choline on milk fat synthesis in dairy cows. In one report 4 g/d of choline xanthate had little effect on milk fat content or milk yields, but in subsequent studies by Maryland workers (10), 3-4 g/d of supplemental choline chloride increased milk fat percent and FCM yields 10-30% above controls in cows on high-concentrate, low-forage diets (Table 16-6). Cows receiving 6 g of choline chloride daily did not increase in milk fat and were similar to controls. The authors hypothesized that choline facilitated transport of free fatty acids from adipose tissue, through the liver, to the mammary gland. Further study on this problem is warranted.

VITAMIN K

Vitamins K and K₂ are derivatives of naphthoquinone, are fat-soluble, and sensitive to light and oxidation. Either serves as a necessary blood clotting factor in animals. Vitamin K_2 is normally synthesized in liberal quantities in the rumen of ruminants and in the intestine of most animals, so there is little

chance for a deficiency to occur under normal feeding situations. One practical problem which has arisen with respect to vitamin K is the dicoumarol found in moldy sweet clover; it acts as a metabolic inhibitor to the vitamin, causing delayed blood clotting and generalized hemorrhaging in the body. This problem can be overcome by dosing with high levels of vitamin K.

CONCLUSIONS

Vitamins A, D and E must be furnished in ruminant diets, but the B vitamins and vitamin K are synthesized in apparently adequate amounts by the microbes in the rumen. Special situations where production responses have been elicited or metabolic problems corrected from supplementation of certain B vitamins, such as niacin for treatment of subclinical ketosis and for stimulating increased milk yields in high yielding dairy cows, or thiamin for treatment of PEM, have been mentioned.

Because of wide variations in content of vitamins A, D and E in normal feedstuffs for ruminants, particularly harvested forages, and because of the multitude of factors which affect their utilization and bioavailability, it is recommended to add equal to the minimum daily requirement of vitamins A and D to the diets for lactating dairy cows and growing beef cattle, even though calculated intakes of the vitamins from natural feedstuffs might appear sufficient. For other species of ruminants supplementation levels should bring diets up to at least minimum daily allowances.

Literature Cited

1. Agrawala, I.P., et al. 1953. J. Nutr. 49:631.
2. Ammerman, C.B. and S.M. Miller. 1975. J. Dairy Sci. 58:1561.
3. Bindas, E.M., et al. 1984. J. Dairy Sci. 67:1249.
4. Bindas, E.M., et al. 1984. J. Dairy Sci. 67:2978.
5. Bremel, H.D., et al. 1982. J. Dairy Sci. 65:(1)178.
6. Byers, F.M. 1981. Animal Nutr. Health. 36(6):36.
7. Church, D.C. 1979. (ed.). Digestive Physiology and Nutrition of Ruminants. Vol. 2, 2nd Ed. O & B Books, Inc. Corvallis, OR.
8. Dennis, S.M., et al. 1982. J. Dairy Sci. 65:1643.
9. Eaton, H.D., et al. 1970. J. Dairy Sci. 53:1775.
10. Erdman, R.A., et al. 1984. J. Dairy Sci. 67:410.
11. Fronk, T.J. and L.H. Schultz. 1979. J. Dairy Sci. 62:1804.
11a. Hibbs, J.W. and H.R. Conrad. 1966. J. Dairy Sci. 49:243.
12. Horst, R.L. and T.A. Reinhardt. 1983. J. Dairy Sci. 66:661.
13. Huber, J.T. 1975. Proc. Amer. Assoc. Bovine Practic., 7th Ann. Conv., July, p. 128.
14. Jaster, E.H., et al. 1983. J. Dairy Sci. 66:1039.
15. Jaster, E.H., et al. 1983. J. Dairy Sci. 66:1046.
16. Jorgensen, N.A. 1974. J. Dairy Sci. 57:933.
17. Julien, W.E., et al. 1976. J. Dairy Sci. 59:1960.
18. Kung, L., Jr., et al. 1980. J. Dairy Sci. 63:2020.
19. Lotthammer, K.H., et al. 1978. Roche Symp., London.
20. Lynch, G.P. 1983. J. Dairy Sci. 66:1461.
21. Michel, R.L., et al. 1972. J. Dairy Sci. 55:498.
22. Miller, B.L., et al. 1983. J. Animal Sci. 57(1):453.
23. Miller, B.L., et al. 1983. J. Animal Sci. 57(1):454.
24. Murphy, T.P., et al. 1981. Poultry Sci. 60:1873.
25. NRC. 1978. Nutrient Requirements for Dairy Cattle. Natl. Acad. Sci., Washington, DC.
26. Riddel, D.O., et al. 1981. J. Dairy Sci. 64:782.
27. Swenson, M.J. (ed.) 1977. Dukes Physiology of Domestic Animals, 9th Ed. Cornell Univ. Press, Ithaca, NY.
28. Ward, G., et al. 1972. J. Dairy Sci. 55:768.
29. Waterman, R., et al. 1972. J. Dairy Sci. 55:1447.
30. Weiss, R.R. 1977. Nutr. Abstr. Rvw. 47:487.

by Ron Kincaid

INTRODUCTION

The term "mineral" is used by nutritionists to refer to inorganic chemical elements, but is used by many other scientists to mean a homogeneous crystalline compound. Mineral elements are not inert materials. Mineral elements may change valence states and are transferred from one chemical compound to another. Minerals are active participants in enzymatic reactions, have specificity of function, and are critical to life.

The designation between major elements and minor or trace elements is a partial carry-over from the time when some elements in a sample could be analyzed qualitatively but not quantitatively. The term "trace element" now has come to refer to an element present in animal tissues in levels reported in parts per million or less. There are seven elements classified as major elements: calcium (Ca), chlorine (Cl), magnesium (Mg), phosphorus (P), potassium (K), sodium (Na) and sulfur (S). Silica, the most abundant element on earth, is classified as a trace element because of its low concentration in tissues.

The importance of the interaction of soil, plants and animals is much greater for ruminants than for non-ruminants because of the greater dependence of ruminants on forages and grazing activities for nutrients. Soil factors greatly influence the mineral content of plants upon which ruminants rely for most of their mineral intake. Fertilization of soils with K, Ca or P directly affects the mineral content of plants with increased concentration of these elements. The addition of limestone to soils can have an indirect effect on mineral levels in plants by elevating soil pH which generally increases plant uptake of molybdenum (Mo) and cobalt (Co) and decreases uptake of nickel (Ni), manganese (Mn) and copper (Cu). Soil type has a direct influence on mineral content of plants because certain parent soils are inherently deficient in certain minerals and the ability of plant roots to withdraw elements from soils is a partial function of the binding of elements to soil particles.

The species of plant, season of year and stage of maturity affects the mineral levels in plants. Legumes have greater concentrations of Ca, Cu and zinc (Zn) than grasses, but less Mn and Mo. As plants mature there tends to be a decrease in P and K while the silica and aluminum concentrations increase. Seasonal differences in mineral contents of plants become important in relation to K and grass tetany and the development of P and Cu deficiencies in beef cattle.

The term "biological availability" is an important concept in mineral metabolism. O'Dell (1) has defined biological availability as "that proportion of a nutrient in food, usually determined chemically, that can be absorbed by an animal and used by tissues to perform biological functions." Thus, biological availability refers to both the uptake and utilization of the element. An element can be absorbed but not utilized by the body. For example, Cu can complex with Mo in the blood and not be utilized by the body. The biological availability of mineral elements is affected by organic chelates and other inorganic elements which may be present in feedstuffs. However, ruminants are spared much of the detrimental effect of chelation to organic materials because many organic chelates are degraded in the rumen.

Blood serum values representative of normal macromineral values for sheep and cattle are shown in Table 17-1. These will be referred to from time to time.

CALCIUM

Dietary Sources

Most grains have deficient levels of Ca while forages contain levels of Ca in excess of ruminant requirements. Crops grown on sandy or acid soils have less Ca than crops from better soils. Legumes contain higher levels of Ca than most grasses. Alfalfa contains an average of 1.2% Ca but levels range

Table 17-1. Levels of major elements in serum.

	Ca	Pi	Mg	SO₄-S	K	Cl	Na
	. . . . mg/dl				. . . . mEq/ℓ		
Cattle & sheep	9.0-12	4.5-6.0*	1.8-2.3	2-4	3.9-5.8	97-111	132-152

*Higher in young

from 0.6% to >2%. Immature corn silage contains about 0.6% Ca, but this decreases to 0.3% in mature corn silage. Many by-product feeds, used extensively in cattle rations, are very low in Ca. For example, whole potatoes contain <0.1% Ca and cottonseed hulls, whole cottonseeds and brewers grains also are relatively low in Ca.

The main sources of inorganic Ca added to rations are ground limestone, dicalcium phosphate and defluorinated rock phosphate. Limestone often is the least expensive Ca source. Dicalcium phosphate contributes to the dietary Ca level, but may be added to rations to meet the P requirement. Bone meal is a good Ca source but is not normally added to rations because of costs.

The biological availability of Ca from various feedstuffs is commonly expressed as a biological value relative to reagent $CaCO_3$ standards. Dicalcium phosphate and bone meals have biological values >100 while limestone, alfalfa and orchardgrass have biological values of <100. Nearly a third of the Ca in alfalfa is present as Ca oxalate. Crystals of Ca oxalate are degraded by rumen bacteria (3) and Ca made available for absorption when the oxalate crystals are exposed to bacteria. The extent to which Ca oxalate crystals are protected from degradation may be a major determinant of the biological availability of Ca in alfalfa (4). Some Ca oxalates invariably escape degradation in the rumen. The ARC (5) assumes a bioavailability of 68% for dietary Ca. The NRC (6) allows a safety margin by using 45% bioavailability of Ca in feedstuffs. If the Ca bioavailability in alfalfa is <45%, a discount should be made in the alfalfa content of Ca when balancing rations. Recent work indicates the Ca bioavailability in high oxalate forages is 50% or less (7). In lactating cows with feed intakes of 3 times maintenance or more, a depression in Ca bioavailability may occur due to a decrease in the extent of digestion of the potentially digestible fraction of forages.

Absorption

Ca absorption occurs with the greatest efficiency in young calves and generally decreases with age in cattle. Deer also have a reduction in Ca uptake with age (2). Increased absorption in mature cattle occurs in response to increased Ca need. Added dietary fat decreases Ca utilization and fiber digestion in ruminants due to formation of Ca soaps. Ca has a low solubility in rumen fluid (8). Some Ca absorption occurs directly from the rumen into the bloodstream, but the net is small (9). Most absorption of Ca occurs from the small intestinal tract. Ca is absorbed from the lumen of the small intestine, through the mucosal cell, to the basolateral membrane in a process mediated by either a Ca-binding protein or alkaline phosphatase or Ca ATPase activity (10). The percent of dietary Ca absorbed from the lumen of the small intestine is generally regulated by Ca needs of the animal (11). Ca needs of the animal are increased by milk production, bone deposition and fetal growth. A drain on blood Ca increases parathyroid hormone release (12), which catalyzes hydroxylation of the 1 position of 25-hydroxycholecalciferol, Ca absorption is increased from the intestinal tract and Ca mobilization occurs from bone. Excessive administration of vitamin D_3 can partially overcome the regulatory system on Ca absorption with excess Ca being absorbed and deposited in soft tissues.

Metabolism

Ca is mobilized from bone under the influence of parathyroid hormone and vitamin D to maintain plasma Ca levels at about 9.5 mg/dl (13). Ca mobilization from bone becomes extremely important in cows immediately following parturition for Ca secretion into milk. Cows which develop parturient paresis apparently lack the ability to quickly mobilize Ca from bone. The appearance of hydroxyproline in blood or the excretion of hydroxyproline in the urine can be used as an indication of bone mobilization (13). Cows older than five years of age have a slower postpartum elevation in hydroxyproline. This indicates a decreased responsiveness of aged cows to stimulators of bone Ca mobilization.

Endogenous losses of Ca can occur via the milk, kidney and bile. The secretion of Ca into milk is an active process with Ca levels in milk being relatively constant (1.23 g Ca/kg milk). The excretion of Ca via the kidney is under the influence of parathyroid hormone and normally is only 2 or 3% of total loss. Factors which influence Ca secretion into the intestinal tract via the bile are not known.

Most of the Ca (99%) in the body is found in the hydroxy apatite matrix of bone and teeth. The other 1% of the Ca in the body is very important and functions in muscle contraction, nerve sensitization and blood clotting. Reduced blood levels of Ca cause tetany and convulsions in ruminants while excess Ca causes soft tissue calcification. Too rapid intravenous infusion of Ca can cause cardiac arrest. Ca is known to activate a protein called calmodulin. Ca binds with an inactive calmodulin molecule to form an active complex which regulates the intermediary metabolism within the cell. Calmodulin is found in all eucaryotic cells (14).

Deficiency

Diagnosing a Ca deficiency is not easy because of lack of signs prior to the development of broken bones and convulsions. Blood Ca levels are not responsive to Ca intake because Ca reserves in bone are mobilized to prevent a depression in blood Ca. Only when Ca stores in bone are no longer adequate to meet the demands of the body or when bones have been so demineralized that they become fragile is a deficiency obvious. In dairy cattle, metabolic problems have been reported when the Ca to P ratio is less than 1.1:1 (15). These metabolic problems have occurred independently of the usual signs of Ca deficiencies.

Excess

Toxicity due to dietary Ca is rare. Cattle, except for prepartum cows, can tolerate Ca to P ratios up to 6 to 1. Greater than a 6:1 ratio of Ca to P reduces feed intake (16). Thus, Ca toxicities are unlikely because most rations contain <6:1 ratios and high Ca levels are unpalatable. Excess dietary Ca does not reduce Zn absorption in cattle as in non-ruminants. The effect of Ca on Zn absorption is only apparent in the presence of phytate. In the rumen, P in phytate is metabolized to inorganic P. Therefore, Ca has no detrimental effects on Zn absorption in ruminants (17), but may affect young animals prior to the development of a functional rumen or when feedstuffs containing phytate are treated to bypass ruminal metabolism.

Requirements

Dietary Ca requirements (NRC) as a percent of ration dry matter:

Dairy cattle (6)

Growing heifers and bulls,	0.40%
Dry pregnant cows,	0.37%
Lactating cows,	0.43%-0.60%
Mature bulls,	0.24%

Beef cattle (18)

Growing and finishing cattle, not given as a percent of ration dry matter	
Pregnant heifers,	0.27%-0.33%
Early lactation,	0.27%-0.58%
Dry pregnant cows,	0.25%-0.27%

Sheep (19)

Fattening lambs,	0.26%-0.37%
Non-lactating ewes,	0.21%-0.30%
Early lactation,	0.48%-0.52%

Ca is sometimes added to ruminant rations to improve nutrient utilization (see later section on buffers). The addition of 0.5-1.0% limestone to corn silage at the time of ensiling increases lactic acid content, carotene and, in some instances, cattle performance. Responses of cattle in feeding trials to elevated dietary Ca have been mixed and is probably affected by forage and grain characteristics (20-22). A dietary Ca level of 1% or more will diminish the detrimental effects of fat on rumen fermentation (23).

CHLORINE

Dietary Sources

The Cl content of feedstuffs is variable (Table 17-2). Molasses contains large amounts

Table 17-2. Sodium and chloride levels of selected feedstuffs.[a]

Feed	Sodium	Chloride
	..... % of DM	
Barley	0.02 -0.06	0.13-0.20
Beet pulp, dried	0.17 -0.23	0.04
Corn, grain	0.003-0.03	0.03-0.06
Cottonseed meal	0.03 -0.06	0.04-0.05
Molasses, cane	0.15 -0.23	2.8 -3.7
Oat, grain	0.06 -0.18	0.10-0.12
Soybean meal, 44% CP	0.01 -0.30	0.01-0.10
Corn silage	0.005-0.02	0.10-0.18
Alfalfa	0.01 -0.05	0.03-0.64

[a]Adapted from Fettman et al (24)

of Cl, but corn grain has very little. Generally, Na is more limiting than Cl in the diet and the addition of NaCl (which has a Na:Cl ratio of 1:1.56) to the diet to meet the Na requirement will satisfy the Cl requirement. However, there is a potential for development of a Cl deficiency when NaHCO$_3$ is used to meet the Na requirement and no other Cl source is added to the diet.

Absorption

Limited work has been published on Cl absorption and metabolism. Presumably, Cl is well absorbed with few interferences in healthy animals. Cl can be absorbed across the rumen wall against an approximate 10-fold concentration gradient (25). Most Cl absorption occurs post ruminally. When dietary Cl is low, fecal and urinary losses of Cl are reduced as part of a homeostatic mechanism (26).

Metabolism

Cl functions in the regulation of acid-base balance and in electrolyte exchange. In the colon, Cl exchanges with bicarbonate to promote a reduction in blood pH. In the kidney, Cl also exchanges for bicarbonate ion but the effect is to increase blood pH and promote ammonium ion excretion. The addition of Cl to the diet affects the anion-cation balance and may affect animal performance. Dietary Cl may affect the response of heat-stressed dairy cows to supplemental K sources because cows responded favorably to KHCO$_3$ supplementation but not NaCl. Other work has

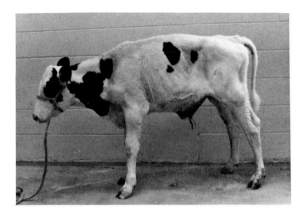

Figure 17-1. Chloride-deficient calf. The calf was emaciated and severely dehydrated. Notice the arched back and spraddled leg stance. The calf died 2 d after the photograph was taken. Plasma Cl was 32 mEq/ℓ just prior to death. Courtesy of M. Neathery, University of Georgia.

shown bicarbonate and Cl concentration in plasma to be inversely correlated. Cl levels are maintained in cerebrospinal fluid by an active transport mechanism (25).

Cl is present in substantial quantities in most body tissues and fluids. Milk contains about 0.11% Cl (24) and plasma 100 mEq/ℓ. Whole blood contains less Cl (61 to 72 mEq/ℓ) than plasma because red blood cells have only 55-64 mEq Cl/kg. Cl levels in rumen fluid are 10 to 30 mEq/ℓ (25). Overall, the body contains about 0.10 to 0.11% Cl (27).

Deficiency

Plasma Cl levels are reduced when cows are fed low Cl diets. Cl deficiencies have been produced in non-lactating ruminants by removal of gastric juices (28). Also, a defect in Cl reabsorption in the ascending limb of Henle's loop has been reported in man (Bartter's syndrome) and results in a Cl deficiency (29).

Consequences of Cl deficiency include hyponatremia, hypochloremia, hypokalemia, alkalosis and increased plasma rennin. Other signs include poor growth, decreased milk yield, reduced feed intakes, emaciation, dehydration and pica (24). Cl has a specific function with angiotensin. Angiotensin I is converted to Angiotensin II by a Cl-activated enzyme. Angiotensin II, a vaso-constrictor, is inactivated by a Cl-activated angiotensinase.

Accordingly, Cl may be implicated in the development of hypertension.

Requirements

The NRC does not give a specific Cl requirement for sheep, dairy cattle or beef cattle. The Cl requirement appears to be affected by lactation, stress and growth. A dietary chloride level of 0.04% is adequate for maintenance and some growth of calves for at least limited periods of time (26). However, 0.11% dietary chloride is inadequate for lactating cows causing reduced feed intakes, body weights, and milk yields within a few weeks (24). The NRC (12) gives a requirement for NaCl of 0.25% for dry, pregnant cows and 0.46% for lactating cows. Na requirements are listed as 0.10% and 0.18%, respectively. This suggests the Cl requirement for lactating cows is 0.28% or less, and for dry, pregnant cows, 0.15% or less. Recent results of trials with calves and lactating cows suggest the current NRC requirements for NaCl will meet the Cl requirements (24).

MAGNESIUM

Dietary Sources

Most forages have levels of Mg greater than the Mg requirement of ruminants. Early spring grasses, however, have low Mg levels and high levels of K which interfere with Mg absorption by the animal (30, 31). Corn, oats and barley have Mg levels of 0.13-0.19%, marginally adequate for cattle. The inorganic source of Mg most commonly used in rations is MgO. Both MgO and $MgSO_4$ have biological availabilities of about 50%. The bioavailability of Mg for dolomitic limestone is less, only about 25%. Mg sources tend to be unpalatable to cattle and intakes from Mg licks are small and erratic. Absorption of Mg in ruminants is higher in preserved than succulent forages, and higher from grains than forages.

Absorption

Mg absorption occurs from the rumen, omasum, small intestine and colon. Quantitatively, most Mg is absorbed from the rumen and omasum. Probably two mechanisms are operable for Mg absorption. One is an active, saturable mechanism, and the second is a passive, non-saturable mechanism (32, 33). The active mechanism is the primary route of absorption during low Mg intakes. Thus, the efficiency of Mg absorption improves when Mg intakes are low (30). The passive, non-saturable mechanism is the quantitative absorption route during periods of high or excessive Mg intake. This passive, non-saturable mechanism for Mg absorption explains the failure to greatly reduce Mg absorption with elevated intakes. Mg absorption from the rumen is reduced by high rumen ammonia concentrations (34), and may result in formation of insoluble Mg ammonium phosphate (8). Because Mg absorption is energy-dependent, low energy rations may decrease absorption (30).

The absorption of Mg is impaired by K, Ca, Mg, fat, sulfate, phosphate, citrate and trans aconitate (30, 41). Some fermentation products include NH_3, volatile fatty acids, lactic acid, CO_2 and long-chain fatty acids.

Metabolism

The amount of endogenous Mg recycled to the rumen via the saliva is relatively small. Saliva contains only 6-10 mg/ℓ (8). Mg levels in blood rarely exceed an upper threshold of 2.5 to 3.0 mg/dl. Perhaps this threshold reflects the capability for reabsorption of Mg in the ascending limb of the kidney. Urinary Mg is closely correlated with absorbed Mg. Mg also is endogenously lost via the bile, pancreatic intestinal juice and milk (35). The Mg level in milk is about 126 mg/kg and explains the greater incidence of grass tetany in lactating cows. Mg is present in sweat and during hot weather this loss represents approximately 25% of total daily Mg loss.

Deficiency

Signs of Mg deficiency include muscular twitching and tremor, vertigo, ataxia, nystagmus, muscle wasting and weakness, excitability, soft tissue calcification, hyperemia, convulsions, tachycardia, apathy, premature ventricular beats, ventricular trachycardia, and fibrillation, coma and death (11). Mg depletion in ruminants generally occurs only in milk-fed calves. However, Mg also is involved in the etiology of grass tetany (see Ch. 24).

Requirements

Mg requirements for cattle increase approximately 2 to 4 times with lactation.

Intestinal absorption of Mg is decreased by maturity and bone mobilization is reduced with age. Thus, the mature beef cow with a nursing calf is faced with a low Mg intake, impaired Mg absorption and mobilization, and elevated Mg requirements. The combination of these factors results in hypomagnesemia which reduces food intake. Daily intakes of 20 g Mg are needed to assure the lactating cow does not develop grass tetany.

Mg is required by rumen microorganisms. Most Mg is located intracellularly in bacteria. While low Mg levels in rumen fluid of cattle is probably not limiting to fermentation, in vitro media should contain 2-25 mg Mg/ℓ (8).

The dietary requirement for Mg is listed from 0.07 to 0.20% for most classes of livestock. The requirement level is affected by the physiological state of the animal and the bioavailability of the dietary Mg. Supplemental Mg is sometimes fed to increase milk fat percentage of cows consuming fat-depressing rations (30).

Dietary Mg requirements (NRC) as a percent of ration dry matter:
Dairy Cattle (6)
    Growing heifers and bulls   0.16%
    Dry, pregnant cows   0.16%
    Lactating cows   0.20%
Beef Cattle (18)
    All classes   0.05%-0.25%
Sheep (19)
    All classes   0.04%-0.08%

Mg is relatively non-toxic. Excess intake of Mg increases plasma Mg but causes a much larger increase in urinary Mg concentrations. Diarrhea results from large excesses of Mg intakes with intensity of the diarrhea closely related to the level of Mg in the diet (11). The poor palatability of most Mg sources limits the likelihood of toxic consumption by cattle.

PHOSPHORUS

Dietary Sources

After Na, P is the most common deficiency for grazing ruminants. Low P levels in pasture and roughages are widespread, particularly in arid and tropical regions. The P content of plants may be 0.3% (DM basis) in early spring, but may decrease to 0.15% with maturity (36). Deficiencies of P are prevalent in cattle subsisting on mature, dry forages. Most grains and natural protein supplements are good sources of P. Dicalcium phosphate is the major P supplement used in the USA. Defluorinated phosphate is the second major source of inorganic P. Except for ammonium polyphosphate and phosphoric acid used largely in liquid feeds, relatively minor amounts of other P sources are used in ruminant feeds. Fertilizer-grade phosphates should not be fed to cattle because of high levels of fluorides (37). Some phosphates mined in the Northwestern part of the USA have sufficient levels of vanadium to affect production. Bone meal now is a minor P source, constituting less than 1% of consumption of feed P sources.

Absorption

P is absorbed in the ortho phosphate form. Pyro and meta phosphates are less biologically available than ortho forms of inorganic P for ruminants. Excessive heating converts ortho phosphate to pyro and meta phosphates. Hydrated phosphate sources are more biologically available than the anhydrous sources of the same type, and the biological value of phosphate is reduced by driving off the water of hydration. The more water-soluble sources generally have higher biological values. Aluminum contaminants reduce the biological value of the phosphate. Dicalcium phosphate, ammonium polyphosphate, steamed bone meal and defluorinated phosphate have good biological availabilities, followed by low-fluorine rock phosphates and soft rock phosphate (38).

Digestion of dietary P differs in ruminants and non-ruminants. First, phytin P, which accounts for much of the P in plants, is largely hydrolyzed in the rumen (39). Therefore, the P in plants does not have to be discounted when balancing rations for ruminants. When rumen microbial degradation is bypassed such as with suckling, preruminants and protein treatment for rumen bypass, phytin P should be treated the same as for non-ruminants. The detrimental effects of phytate on the absorption of Ca, Zn and other mineral elements are much less in ruminants because the phytate is degraded. Secondly, significant amounts of P are released from microbes in the intestinal tract by the very high activities of RNAase and DNAase in ruminants. Nucleic acids are comprised of 10% P. In fact, there is a good correlation between the incorporation of P into microbial material and VFA formation (8). P absorption is about 90% efficient in young calves, 55% in cows, 95% in milk-fed lambs and 60% in mature sheep (5, 11).

Phosphate is probably transported across the small intestine by both passive and active transport mechanisms. Phosphate absorption is increased by vitamin D_3 which may either change membrane permeability, alter the configuration of a phosphate carrier, or stimulate production of pump sites. Alkaline phosphatase activity could function as a mediator in any of these roles and P absorption is proportional to alkaline phosphatase activity in some species.

Metabolism

Inorganic P levels in plasma are not under close homeostatic control. Thus, many factors will influence the levels of inorganic P in plasma. Dietary levels of Ca, P, Mg and vitamin D affect plasma inorganic levels. Similarly, factors such as age, season of calving, season of year, state of lactation, and pregnancy influence plasma inorganic P. Hourly or diurnal variations in inorganic P also occur (40). In general, inorganic P in plasma tends to reflect dietary P intake with levels less than 4 mg/dl indicating possible deficiency. Inorganic P is higher in calves (6-8 mg/dl) and declines with age in cattle (4.5-6 mg/dl) until maturity at 4-5 years of age (11). Plasma inorganic P tends to decrease with peak milk yield (40). Levels of plasma inorganic P decrease dramatically at time of parturition and also decline during onset of paturient paresis. In fact, the severity of paresis is related to the magnitude of the decline of both plasma Ca and inorganic P (see Ch. 24). Consumption of P in feed quickly increases plasma inorganic P. Likewise, exercise will cause an increase.

Bovine milk is closer in ionic composition to intercellular fluid than extracellular fluid. The concentration of inorganic P in milk (75 mg/100 ml) is about 11 times the concentration in plasma (41). Because the secretion of phosphate from plasma to milk is an active process, milk inorganic P does not reflect low blood P or low P intakes (40). The active transport system for P in the mammary gland probably operates at the basolateral membrane. Inorganic P may utilize the Na phosphate co-transport system to enter the alveolar cell. The movement of P through the alveolar cell into milk follows a concentration gradient enhanced by decreased P osmotic pressure in milk.

The ruminant recycles more P through saliva than non-ruminants. This may serve two purposes. First, saliva secretion supplies rumen microbes with an added source of P (58 g in a mature cow; 8) and, secondly, secretion of saliva contributes to total P homeostasis. Bovine saliva contains about 100 mg P/dl. This level is about 16 times the level of P in plasma. The saliva of sheep contains about 3 times the level of P as the saliva of cows. Apparently, secretion of P in saliva is stimulated by parathyroid hormone (42).

The availability of endogenous P from bone varies with the type of bone. Most P is incorporated into dense bone as hydroxy appatite crystals that are poorly available. Some P is believed to be adhered with Ca and several other minerals to bone surfaces and can be released rapidly (43). Parathyroid hormone and vitamin D are required for maximal bone reabsorption. Soft tissues also are a reserve of P. Intracellular fluids contain about 75 mEq P/ℓ. Strenuous exercise quickly increases plasma inorganic P.

Deficiency

Correction of P deficiency is made more difficult because of lack of a specific taste for P by the animal and the high cost of P supplements. P deficiency signs are non-specific and are often confounded by concurrent low energy intakes. Problems associated with P deficiencies in ruminants include reduced feed intake, pica, reduced rates of gain, low conception rates, reduced milk production, poor appearance (Fig. 17-2) and rickets. Osteomalacia, lameness and fractures of bones occur when bone ash is reduced due to long-term P deficiency (Fig. 17-3, 17-4). In severe deficiencies, cows may not calve for a couple of years (36). Recently, Call and others (44) found normal reproduction in heifers fed 66% of NRC recommended P.

P is required by bacteria for cellulose digestion. However, levels of P required for maximum cellulose digestion appear significantly less than levels required to maintain adult body stores of P (45). Durand and Kawashima (8) estimate the requirement level of rumen microbes for P as 3.7-4 g/kg digestible organic matter.

333

Figure 17-2. Phosphorus deficient (top) and adequately fed steer. The deficient steer received a ration with 0.12% P as compared to 0.18% for the other steer. Idaho Agr. Expt. Sta. photo. Courtesy of W.M. Beeson, Purdue Univ.

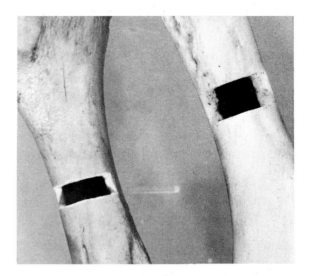

Figure 17-3. Femurs from phosphorus deficient (left) and normal animal (right). Note the big difference in the thickness between the two. Courtesy of M. Durand, Queensland Department of Primary Industries.

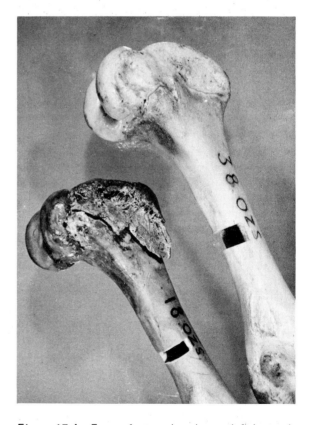

Figure 17-4. Femur from a phosphorus deficient animal (left) and a normal femur (right). The former is less than half the weight and the joint surfaces are grossly eroded. Courtesy of M. Durand, Queensland Department of Primary Industries.

Excess P

While ruminants are fairly tolerant of a high ratio of Ca to P, they are intolerant of ratios of unity or less. At Ca to P ratios of 1.1 to 1 or less, metabolic and other problems often occur. Excess P to Ca will cause urinary calculi in sheep (16). Ca to P ratios greater than 6 to 1 may reduce phosphate absorption and are most critical when P is deficient or marginally deficient. Lactating dairy cattle are more tolerant of high P intakes than feedlot cattle, possibly due to greater dietary requirements and concurrent large intakes of Ca. Dietary levels of 0.55% P have no detrimental effects on milk production in dairy cattle, yet may reduce rate of gain in feedlot steers.

Requirements

P can be supplemented by direct incorporation into the diet, by feeding free-choice, or indirectly by P fertilization of pastures. Soil fertilization is generally not practical for supplementing P to cattle grazing rangelands with sparse plant growth. When fed free-choice, dicalcium phosphate is often mixed with a trace-mineralized salt in a 1:1 ratio. Intakes of this mix vary with environmental conditions and with individuals, but is generally about 50 g/hd/d.

Dietary P requirements (NRC) as a percent of ration dry matter:

Dairy Cattle (6)

Growing heifers and bulls	0.26%
Dry, pregnant cows	0.26%
Lactating cows	0.31-0.40%
Mature bulls	0.18%

Beef Cattle (18)

Growing and finishing cattle, not given as a percent of ration dry matter

Pregnant yearling heifers	0.19-0.22%
Dry, pregnant mature cows	0.20-0.22%
Two-year-old heifers nursing calves	0.23-0.25%

Sheep (19)

Early-weaned lambs	0.24-0.27%
Finishing lambs	0.16-0.23%
Ewes, early gestation	0.21-0.25%
Ewes, late gestation	0.20-0.23%
Ewes, early lactation	0.34-0.37%
Ewes, maintenance	0.24-0.28%

POTASSIUM

Dietary Sources

K deficiencies occur in ruminants although under fairly specific conditions. Beef cattle fed mature, weathered roughages, large amounts of concentrates with poor quality roughages, or dairy cattle fed large amounts of concentrates with either corn silage or a poor quality roughage source are most likely to encounter a K deficiency.

The level of K in feedstuffs is extremely variable and heavily influenced by management of forages, season and soil types. Generally, grains have <0.5% K, molasses 4%, corn silage 0.5-3.0%, grasses 0.2-4.0% and legume forages 0.2-5%. The double sulfate of K and Mg contains 18% K while K_2SO_4 and KCl contain 41% and 50% K respectively.

Bioavailability and Absorption

K in feedstuffs is assumed to be nearly completely available to ruminants with nearly all dietary K absorbed (11). Analytically, 99% of the K in forages appears in the cell-soluble fraction (46) which indicates near complete bioavailability. Some response differences reported with K supplementation may be due to associative effects of Na or Cl. The main site of K absorption in sheep is the small intestine (47).

Metabolism

Most of the K in the body is located intracellularly. Serum K levels normally are 3.5-5.5 mEq/ℓ and intracellular fluid levels are 159 mEq/ℓ. Total body K is closely related to the lean body mass of animals and can be used to estimate body composition according to the equations: Protein % = [(K x 0.0011) – (BW x 0.0038) + 3.542] x 6.25 and Fat % = (BW x 0.099) – (K x 0.025) + 0.75 where K = total body K in g and BW = bodyweight in kg (48). Accordingly, males have greater percent body K than females of comparable weight. Most endogenous K is lost via the urine and excretion is promoted by aldosterone. Insulin causes a cellular uptake of K and a reduction in serum K. Likewise, increased serum K will cause a release of insulin (49). Concentrations of plasma K are depressed in late prepartum and early post partum cows (48).

K is exchanged for hydrogen or reabsorbed within the renal tubule (50). The effect of large K intakes are increased plasma K (this is an immediate effect), increased plasma Na, decreased plasma volume, increased frequency of urination, decreased blood pH and increased respiratory rate (16).

Deficiency

K depletion may occur due to loss of lean body mass (pseudo-K depletion). A true K depletion occurs when the loss of K is in excess of any loss of lean body mass. Other causes of K depletion include sweating, gastro-intestinal losses due to vomiting, diarrhea, inflammatory diseases of the bowel, or excessive aldosterone secretion.

A K deficiency causes reduced feed intakes, rough hair coats, pica, and cellular acidosis due to replacement of potassium ions with hydrogen ions in the cells. Reductions in feed intake, milk yield and plasma K occur within

Figure 17-5. A K-deficient lamb fed a semi-purified diet with 0.1% K. Note the listless and emaciated appearance. University of Missouri photo. Courtesy of R.L. Preston.

a few days of feeding a K-deficient diet (51). Blood changes include reduced plasma K and elevated hematocrit values (11). K depletion causes tetany conditions, cramps, muscle spasms, twitching, muscle pain, fatigue, muscle weakness, muscle atrophy, pica and death.

Excess

Large intakes of K are associated with grass tetany and may contribute to udder edema. Large intakes of K reduce Mg absorption (47) and stimulate insulin release (49), events involved in grass tetany. The effect of K on udder edema is less clear. There are field reports of persistent udder edema in cows consuming large amounts of K. This edema may occur in mid or late lactation as well as early lactation. Field observations of an association of K and udder edema have not been confirmed by research trials. Feed intakes of calves are reduced by 6% K in the diet (52).

Dietary K requirements (NRC) as a percent of ration dry matter:

     Dairy Cattle (6), 0.80% for all classes.
     Beef Cattle (18), 0.65% for all classes.
     Sheep (19), 0.5% for all classes.

K supplementation of ruminant rations may have three particularly useful purposes: (a) supplemental K is often included in rations of feedlot cattle after shipping (53). The stress of shipping often causes diarrhea and other gastro-intestinal upsets in cattle. The diarrhea depletes the body of K and supplemental K is given to replete the body K stores. (b) Supplemental K may help in heat-stressed animals. Heat stress increases respiration rate, elevates blood pH, and increases K lost via sweat (51). (c) Supplemental K to elevate dietary K above 0.8% for lactating cows during peak milk production may be beneficial. Cows in early lactation appear to respond to greater than 0.8% K with greater milk yields (54, 55). This may reflect increased K requirement because milk contains about 0.15% K and fecal K loss increases with greater feed intake (5).

SODIUM

Dietary Sources

Na is the mineral most likely to be deficient when ruminants receive no mineral supplementation. Forages and grains generally contain levels of Na below dietary requirements for ruminants. Most forages contain <0.1% and most grains <0.05% Na (see Table 17-2). The content of Na in forages can be increased by fertilization, but direct supplementation of the diet with Na is generally preferable. K fertilization reduces Na levels in forages (11). All dietary Na sources are thought to have good bioavailability.

Animals have a specific taste for Na (56). This is in contrast to other minerals. Because of this specific Na taste, self-feeding of Na sources to correct a dietary deficiency does work. Intakes of other elements are regulated by mixing with Na and allowing the Na to determine intake. There is considerable individual animal variation in Na intake when given free-choice. There also is variation caused by the type of Na supplement, whether NaCl, $NaHCO_3$, loose or block. Salt is mixed at 10 to 20% to limit self-feeding of energy or protein supplements. The level of salt necessary depends upon the intake desired, size of the animal, etc.

Absorption

Transfer of Na and water occurs across the rumen wall into the lumen of the rumen in response to osmotic pressure of the rumen fluid. Na has a net secretion in the small intestine and is nearly completely reabsorbed from the colon in sheep and cattle (27). Na uptake from the small intestine is influenced by the presence of sugars and amino acids. Active Na transport in the small intestine is linked to anion absorption. The absorption

336

of Na in the colon is predominantly electrogenic. Na enters the cells with an electrical gradient and crosses the basolateral membrane into blood against both chemical and electrical gradients. Na entry into the intestinal mucosal cells is a saturable process but a nonsaturable component may exist. A carrier mechanism for Na may exist or Na may simply diffuse through highly selective hydrophylic channels.

Metabolism

Endogenous losses of Na occur through the saliva, intestinal secretions, sweat and urine (5). Normally, a very large amount of Na is secreted into the saliva and helps to contribute to the total Na intake of the animal. When Na is limited in the diet, salivary secretion of K increases in response to reduce Na secretion. The Na to K ratio in saliva can be used as a test for adequacy of Na intake. Intestinal secretion of Na appears to be fairly constant, even when dietary Na is limited. When dietary Na is reduced, there is some depression in Na concentrations in serum but the correlation is not very good. The main organ regulating Na excretion is the kidney. When Na intake is limited, the kidney very effectively reduces Na excretion in the urine. Na conservation in the kidney is in response to aldosterone secretion. Aldosterone secretion rate appears to be above normal with pregnancy. In sheep, after rapid consumption of dry feed, there is an increase in plasma renin and a decrease in plasma volume. The saliva serves to affect a rapid transfer of Na and water from circulation to the rumen.

Na is the major cation in extracellular fluid. Na plays a major role in the transmission of nerve impulses and in muscle contraction. About 40% of the Na content of the body is located in the bone. The content of Na in bone increases with maturity and may contribute to bone hardness (11). This is in contrast to K which decreases in bone with age.

Deficiency

Na deficiencies in ruminants are most likely to occur during lactation or rapid growth, in tropical or semi-arid environments and in ruminants grazing pastures which have been heavily fertilized with K (36). Low dietary Na increases the animal's appetite for Na and causes pica. In a Na deficiency, growth, milk production, feed intake and body condition of the animal are all reduced. As the deficiency progresses, there is loss of body weight, shivering, incoordination, general weakness, cardiac arrythmia and death (11). Diarrhea causes a net secretion of Na into the intestinal lumen with a large loss of Na in the feces. Diarrhea is accompanied by less Na loss in urine. Na loss from the body also occurs with starvation and the loss is not prevented by Na supplementation.

Measurement of dietary levels of Na is the best way to detect a Na deficiency. When dietary Na cannot be estimated, the Na level in saliva and plasma will give an indication of Na status.

Requirements

Dietary Na requirements (NRC) as a percent of ration dry matter:

Dairy Cattle (6)
Lactating cows 0.18%
All others 0.10%
Beef Cattle (18)
All classes 0.06-0.10%
Sheep (19)
All classes 0.04-0.10%

Generally, 0.5% to 1% NaCl or a trace mineralized salt mix is added to ruminant rations. This amount is in excess of minimum requirements. When fed free-choice in loose salt form, the consumption of salt varies from 20 to 40 g/head/d for adult animals.

Excess

Salt levels up to 5% of the diet generally cause no problems. Four percent dietary salt will increase flow of fluid through the reticulo-rumen (57). Excess intake of salt causes severe anorexia, anhydremia, weight loss and collapse in cattle (16). Two percent salt in the water will reduce performance of sheep. Some dairymen restrict intake of Na prepartum in cows, particularly first-lactation heifers. This is in response to the belief that Na intakes contribute to development of prepartum udder edema in cows.

SULFUR

Dietary Sources

Feedstuffs with appreciable protein contents are good sources of S (Table 17-3). Forages generally contain 0.1-0.3% S, except for

Table 17-3. Sulfur levels in selected feedstuffs.[a]

Alfalfa hay	0.30%
Red clover, early bloom	0.17
Corn silage	0.08
Oat hay	0.30
Sorghum silage	0.10
Barley grain	0.18
Beet pulp, dehy	0.22
Brewers dried grains	0.34
Corn, grnd, dent yellow	0.14
Molasses, beet, sugar	0.61
Cottonseeds, whole	0.26
Cottonseed meal, 41% CP, solv-extd	0.23
Soybean meal, 46%, solv-extd	0.49

[a]Adapted from NRC (6)

corn silage which often has <0.1% S. Differences exist in the biological availability among organic and inorganic S sources. The bioavailability of L-methionine>Ca sulfate≥ammonium sulfate>DL methionine>Na sulfate≥K-Mg sulfate≥molasses≥Na sulfide≥lignin sulfonate≥elemental S (58). Sulfur bioavailability varies in forages with fescue having a lower biological availability than grass silage.

Absorption and Metabolism

Ruminants can effectively utilize dietary sulfate for amino acid synthesis because sulfate is reduced to sulfide in the rumen by bacteria as shown (58). The reduction of sulfate

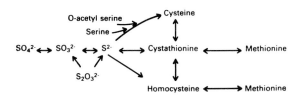

to sulfide occurs at maximum rate at pH 6.5. Incorporation of sulfate into cysteine occurs at a faster rate than into methionine. Microbial incorporation of sulfate into amino acids is faster with a concentrate substrate than with roughage. Dietary sulfide also is released by metabolism of protein and the sulfide can be incorporated into microbial protein. The ratio of N to S in microbial protein is 14.5 to 1 (58). Sulfide formation in the rumen adversely affects Cu bioavailability by the formation of insoluble cupric sulfide. S also affects the uptake of selenium (Se) by rumen

microbes (59) and high intakes of S increase Se excretion and reduce the effectiveness of Se in preventing white muscle disease (58). While S and Se form structural analogs, S has not been shown to replace Se for biological activity.

Sulfide can be absorbed directly from the rumen and is absorbed rapidly from the small intestine. Sulfate in the rumen is poorly absorbed across the rumen wall to the bloodstream.

Some sulfate is recycled from blood to the rumen via the saliva (60). Sulfate cannot be endogenously reduced to sulfide. In liver, sulfide can be oxidized to sulfate, a step inhibited by Mo. Excretion of sulfate is both via the urine and feces (27).

Deficiency

In a S deficiency there is emaciation of the animal, poor appetite and dullness. S-deficient sheep also have loss of wool (19). If not corrected, a S deficiency will lead to extreme emaciation and death.

S deficiency can be diagnosed by measuring dietary S or serum sulfate. Other blood changes reported include: increased serine, citrulline, alanine, cysteine, non-essential amino acids, decreased glycine, tyrosine and increased lactate (59, 61).

When S is deficient in the diet, changes occur in microbial fermentation. Utilization of NPN is impaired by low S levels in rumen fluid and microbial growth is retarded. S deficiency also either reduces use of the acrylate pathway or the number of lactate-utilizing bacteria, resulting in lactate accumulation. There is an appreciable reduction in cellulose digestion, possibly due to the reduced bacterial growth (27, 58, 59. 62).

Excess

Excessive intake of S in ruminants is often accompanied by an increase in the dietary Cu requirement. Excess S also can lead to large amounts of H_2S being formed in the rumen; this may inhibit motility. When this occurs, the rumen microbial population is reduced. Toxicity due to S can be from use of $(NH_4)_2SO_4$ as a N source, $CaSO_4$ as a Ca source, or to consumption of water high in S (>100 mg SO_4/ℓ). Many regions of the country have water supplies which have appreciable concentrations of S (63). Some deep

338

well irrigation water is high in S and toxicity has occurred in cattle drinking this water. Other signs of a S toxicity include anorexia, weight loss, possibly pulmonary emphysema and hepatic necrosis (64).

Requirement

The dietary requirement for S for sheep is 0.14 to 0.26%. For steers the requirement is 0.1% up to 0.15% sulfur and for lactating cows 0.20% S. Often, the S requirement for ruminants is expressed as a N to S ratio. This ratio is most often given as 15:1 for cattle and 10-12:1 for sheep. The biological availability affects requirement levels and N/S ratios.

Dietary S requirements (NRC) as a percent of ration dry matter:

Dairy Cattle (6)	
Growing heifers and bulls	0.16%
Dry pregnant cows	0.17%
Lactating cows	0.20%
Mature bulls	0.11%
Beef Cattle (18)	
All classes	0.08-0.15%
Sheep (19)	
Young lambs	0.18-0.26%
Mature ewes	0.14-0.18%

DIETARY BUFFERS

Buffers added to rations of sheep, beef cattle and dairy cattle will improve performance under certain conditions. The greatest benefit is realized when buffers are added to ruminant rations during the adaptation period of roughage to concentrate type diets. This adaptation period is about 3 weeks. Dietary buffers help prevent a decrease in ruminal fluid pH (65) and subsequent accumulation of lactic acid (66). For many beef feedlot and dairy operations, frequent ration changes occur. Routine use of dietary buffers is common under these conditions. Dietary buffers also are used to help prevent milk fat depression during hot summer weather. Frequently, the amount of grain consumed by dairy cattle is increased during summer. Salivary secretion and rumen buffering capacity decrease during hot weather. These have detrimental effects upon milk fat but can be partially overcome by dietary buffers.

$NaHCO_3$ is the most widely used dietary buffer. Normally, bicarbonate is included in the ration to provide for 0.5 to 1.5% of DM.

MgO may improve milk fat percentage, possibly by increasing fatty acid absorption by the mammary gland. MgO is added at 0.5 to 0.75% of the concentrate or 0.25-0.4% of the total ration. $NaHCO_3$ and MgO can be fed together successfully in rations. Both $NaHCO_3$ and MgO can increase digestion of acid-detergent fiber (67). They also have been shown to reduce propionate levels in rumen fluid (67). $NaHCO_3$ improves digestibility coefficients of sheep and milk fat in goats fed low-fiber diets (68).

Dietary limestone may act as an intestinal buffer to increase amylase activity in the small intestine. Pancreatic α-amylase has an optimal activity at pH 6.9. Limestone is ineffective in affecting ruminal fluid pH and VFA levels (69). While fecal pH is elevated by dietary limestone (70), fecal pH may not be a reliable index of starch digestion (67). When the total amount of added buffer exceeds 1.5% of diet dry matter, feed intakes generally are depressed. Also, excessive amounts of buffers fed to sheep will increase the incidence of kidney stones. Na bentonite is not a dietary buffer, but may have some cation exchange capacity. Bentonite is fed at 2.5-5.0% of the ration dry matter (69).

Rations which benefit least from the addition of dietary buffers are those high in fiber or those containing appreciable amounts of alfalfa. Alfalfa has a relatively high cation-exchange capacity (71) which may lessen the need for buffers. Rations containing a large percentage of corn silage and high-moisture corn are low in fiber, cation exchange capacity, and often benefit from added buffers.

The addition of buffers to rations affects the cation-anion balance. A large positive balance of Na and K to Cl and S may be needed to achieve maximum performance of ruminants. Several different formulas have been put forward to calculate this cation-anion balance. At this time a numerical relationship between cation-anion balance and animal performance has not been established.

DETECTION OF DEFICIENCY

The detection of dietary deficiencies in major elements is made much easier by analysis of both diet and blood. Dietary analyses are particularly helpful when representative samples can be obtained. For grazing animals a representative sample of the diet is not possible. Blood is the most commonly analyzed tissue but careful interpretations are needed. Blood analysis of several animals within a herd or flock is needed for a valid interpretation. Blood samples from only one or two animals may give misleading data. Changes in the mineral content of blood may be a secondary effect of a disease or metabolic disorder and not the primary cause. An example of this is the reduction in plasma inorganic P levels which occur during milk fever. Likewise, blood levels often do not decrease until after endogenous stores have been depleted. Thus, a current dietary deficiency may not become evident for weeks. Plasma levels of some elements are affected by fasting, feeding, gestation, milk yield and season of year. Table 17-4 lists the analysis of choice for determining deficiencies of the major mineral elements.

Table 17-4. Analyses of greatest value in assessing ruminant deficiencies of major minerals.[a,b]

Mineral	Diet	Blood plasma	Urine	Saliva
Ca	*Ca*			
P	*P*	P		
Mg	Mg,K,N	*Mg*	*Mg*	
Na	*Na*		Na	*Na,K*
K	*K*			
Cl	*Cl*			

[a] Adapted from Miller and Stake (72)
[b] Italics indicates greatest value.

SUMMARY

Ruminants increase or decrease intestinal absorption of P, Ca, and Mg in response to changes in dietary intake and metabolic needs. Ruminants also increase or decrease endogenous excretion of all the macro minerals in response to dietary intake. These homeostatic control mechanisms operate to maintain normal metabolic processes and to minimize deficiencies and toxicities. However, intake of the macro minerals must be within minimum and maximum levels. Generally, nutritional deficiencies of macro minerals are more likely to occur than toxicities. Conditions leading to deficiencies are becoming well-defined. Absorptive efficiency of a mineral from a dietary source can affect requirement levels: e.g., P in rock phosphate or Mg in dolomitic limestone are not well absorbed. Certain soil types and feedstuffs predispose animals to mineral deficiencies. Interactions occur between elements, e.g., Mg x F, Ca x P, S x Cu, and may cause problems in certain conditions. Diagnosis of deficiencies cannot be made easily in the field because of lack of obvious signs. Deficiencies of any of the major elements result in reduced performance of the affected animals. Dietary analysis is the best single measure when diagnosing a nutritional deficiency of a macro mineral. When this is not possible, blood analysis from several animals in the herd or flock should be performed and interpreted critically. Often, low plasma levels of a particular mineral may be of a secondary response to a health or diet problem and not the primary cause.

Literature Cited

1. O'Dell, B.L. 1972. Ann. N. Y. Acad. Sci. 199:70.
2. Stephenson, D.C. and R.D. Brown. 1984. J. Nutr. 114:1014.
3. Allison, M.J., H.M. Cook and K.A. Dawson. 1981. J. Animal Sci. 53:810.
4. Ward, G., L.H. Harbers and J.J. Blaha. 1979. J. Dairy Sci. 62:715.
5. ARC. 1980. The Nutrient Requirements of Ruminant Livestock. Agr. Res. Council, London.
6. NRC. 1978. Nutrient Requirements of Dairy Cattle. 5th Ed. Natl. Acad. Sci., Washington, DC.
7. Blaney, B.J., R.J.W. Gartner and T.A. Head. 1982. J. Agr. Sci. 99:533.
8. Durand, M. and R. Kawashima. 1980. In: Digestive Physiology and Metabolism in Ruminants. Y. Ruckebusch and P. Thivend, eds. AVl Publishing Co., Inc., Westport, Conn.
9. Yano, F., M. Sekiya, R. Kawashima and K. Kumada. 1978. Jap. J. Zootech. Sci. 49:680.
10. Wasserman, R.H. 1981. Fed. Proc. 40:68.
11. Miller, W.J. 1979. Dairy Cattle Feeding and Nutrition. Academic Press, New York.

340

12. Saeki, T. and M. Hayashi. 1981. J. Dairy Sci. 64:748.
13. Yarrington, J.T., C.C. Capen, H.E. Black and R. Re. 1977. J. Nutr. 107:224.
14. Cheung, W.Y. 1982. Sci. Amer. 246:62.
15. Carson, R.L., A.B. Caudle and H.E. Riddle. 1978. Theriogenol. 9:505.
16. NRC. 1980. Mineral Tolerance of Domestic Animals. Natl. Acad. Sci., Washington, DC.
17. Kincaid, R.L. 1979. J. Dairy Sci. 62:1081.
18. NRC. 1984. Nutrient Requirements of Beef Cattle. Sixth Ed. Natl. Acad. Sci., Washington, DC.
19. NRC. 1975. Nutrient Requirements of Sheep. 5th Ed. Natl. Acad. Sci., Washington, DC.
20. Kincaid, R.L., J.K. Hillers and J.D. Cronrath. 1981. J. Dairy Sci. 64:754.
21. Fernandez, J.A., C.E. Coppock and L.M. Schake. 1982. J. Dairy Sci. 65:242.
22. Nocek, J.E., D.G. Braund and J.E. English. 1983. J. Dairy Sci. 66:2533.
23. Palmquist, D.L. 1982. Proc. Pac. NW Animal Nutr. Conf., p. 67.
24. Fettman, M.J., et al. 1980. Proc. Cornell Nutr. Conf., p. 117.
25. Coppock, C.E. and M.J. Fettman. 1978. Feedstuffs 50(7):18.
26. Burkhalter, D.L., et al. 1979. J. Dairy Sci. 62:1895.
27. Church, D.C., G.E. Smith, J.P. Fontenot and A.T. Ralston. 1971. Digestive Physiology and Nutrition of Ruminants, Vol. II. 1st Ed. O & B Books, Inc., Corvallis, OR.
28. Neathery, M.W., et al. 1981. J. Dairy Sci. 64:2220.
29. Simopuolos, A.P. and F.C. Bartter. 1980. Nutr. Rev. 38:201.
30. Thomas, J.W. 1983. Magnesium in Animal Nutrition. In: Minerals, The Often Neglected Nutrients. Proc. Natl. Feed Ingredients Assoc. Nutrition Institute, Chicago.
31. Fontenot, J.P. 1972. In: Magnesium in the Environment. J.B. Jones, Jr., M.C. Blount and S.R. Wilkinson, eds. Taylor Country Printing Co., Reynolds, GA.
32. Martens, S.H. 1983. Brit. J. Nutr. 49:153.
33. Roth, P. and E. Werner. 1979. Int. J. Appl. Rad. Isot. 30:523.
34. Martens, S.H. and Y. Rayssiguier. 1979. Magnesium Metabolism and Hypomagnesemia. In: Digestive Physiology and Metabolism of Ruminants. Y. Ruckelbusch and P. Thivend, eds. MTP Press Ltd.
35. Miller, W.J., W.M. Britton and M.S. Ansari. 1972. In: Magnesium in the Environment. J.B. Jones, Jr., M.C. Blount and S.R. Wilkinson, eds. Taylor County Printing Co., Reynolds, GA.
36. McDowell, L.R., J.H. Conrad, G.L. Ellis and J.K. Loosli. 1983. Minerals for Grazing Ruminants in Tropical Regions. Fla. Agr. Exp. Stn. Bull.
37. Hillman, D., D.L. Bolenbaugh and E.M. Convey. 1979. J. Dairy Sci. 62:416.
38. Preston, R.L., et al. 1977. Phosphorus in Ruminant Nutrition. Natl. Feed Ingredients Association, Des Moines, Iowa.
39. Jacobson, N.L., K.D. Wiggers, M.H. Wiggers and G.N. Jacobson. 1977. Phosphorus in Ruminant Nutrition. Natl. Feed Ingredients Assoc., Des Moines, Iowa.
40. Forar, F.L., R.L. Kincaid, R.L. Preston and J.K Hillers. 1972. J. Dairy Sci. 65:760.
41. Cerbulis, J. and H.M. Farrell, Jr. 1976. J. Dairy Sci. 59:589.
42. Tomas, F.M. 1974. Quart. J. Exp. Physiol. 59:269.
43. Nordin, B.C. 1976. Calcium, Phosphate and Magnesium Metabolism. Churchill Livingstone, New York.
44. Call, J.W., et al. 1978. J. Animal Sci. 47:216.
45. Witt, K.E. and F.N. Owens. 1983. J. Animal Sci. 56:930.
46. Kincaid, R.L. and J.D. Cronrath. 1983. J. Dairy Sci. 66:821.
47. Greene, L.W., K.E. Webb, Jr. and J.P. Fontenot. 1983. J. Animal Sci. 56:1214.
48. Belyea, R.L., et al. 1978. J. Dairy Sci. 61:206.
49. Lentz, D.E., F.C. Madsen, J.K. Miller and S.L. Hansard. 1976. J. Animal Sci. 43:1082.
50. Meneely, G.R. and H.D. Battarbee. 1976. Nutr. Rev. 34:225.
51. Beede, D.K., et al. 1983. Proc. Sixth Annual International Minerals Conf., St. Petersburg Beach, Florida.
52. Neathery, M.W. 1980. J. Dairy Sci. 63:82.
53. Travis, J. 1979. Feedstuffs 51(10):17.
54. Dennis, R.J. and R.W. Hemken. 1978. J. Dairy Sci. 61:757.
55. Kincaid, R.L., et al. 1984. Nutr. Rep. Int. 30:571.
56. Denton, D. 1982. The Hunger for Salt. Spring-Verlag, New York.
57. Cheng, K.J., et al. 1979. Can. J. Animal Sci. 59:737.

58. Goodrich, R.D., T.S. Kahlon, D.E. Pamp and D.P. Cooper. 1978. Sulfur in Ruminant Nutrition. Natl. Feed Ingredients Assoc., Des Moines, IA.

59. Whanger, P.D. 1972. World Rev. Nutr. Diet. 15:225.

60. Kandylis, K. 1983. J. Dairy Sci. 66:2263.

61. Chalupa, W., R.R. Oltjen, L.L. Slyter and D.A. Dinius. 1971. J. Animal Sci. 33:278 (abstr.).

62. Bird, P.R. 1972. Aust. J. Biol. Sci. 25:1073.

63. NRC. 1974. Nutrients and Toxic Substances in Water for Livestock and Poultry. Natl. Acad. Sci., Washington, DC.

64. Bird, P.R. 1972. Aust. J. Biol. Sci. 25:1087.

65. Kilmer, L.H., L.D. Muller and T.J. Snyder. 1981. J. Dairy Sci. 64:2357.

66. Van Campen, D. 1975. Effects of Buffers on Ruminal Acids. In: Buffers in Ruminant Physiology and Metabolism. Ed. Weinberg and Sheffner Church and Dwight Co., Inc. New York.

67. Erdman, R.A., R.W. Hemken and L.S. Bull. 1982. J. Dairy Sci. 65:712.

68. Hadjipanayiotou, M. 1981. J. Dairy Sci. 65:59.

69. Fisher, L.J. 1983. Proc. Pac. NW Animal Nutr. Conf., Corvallis, OR.

70. Haaland, G.L. and H.F. Tyrrell. 1982. J. Animal Sci. 55:935.

71. McBurney, M.I., P.J. Van Soest and L.E. Chase. 1983. J. Sci. Food Agr. 34:910.

72. Miller, W.J. and P.E. Stake. 1974. Feedstuffs 46(28):24.

18   THE TRACE ELEMENTS

by J. K. Miller, Nancy Ramsey, and F. C. Madsen

Although traces of certain minerals were recognized in plant and animal tissues early in the 19th century, it was nearly six decades before significant biological importance was attached to some of them. More than 60 inorganic elements have been identified in tissues of man, animals, fungi, bacteria and dietary components and the importance of many of them in biological processes has been established. Dietary requirements or average concentrations in the whole body of animals for trace elements are less than 100 ppm (1G). The microminerals have been so designated on this basis rather than on amounts present in the biosphere. For example, Si and Fe, 2nd and 4th in abundance in the earths crust, are trace elements.

Underwood (2G) has arbitrarily divided the microelements into three groups:

Dietary essential—cobalt (Co), copper (Cu), iodine (I), iron (Fe), manganese (Mn), molybdenum (Mo), nickel (Ni), selenium (Se) and zinc (Zn).

Possibly essential—arsenic (As), cadmium (Cd), chromium (Cr), fluorine (F), silicon (Si), tin (Sn) and vanadium (V).

Contaminants—aluminum (Al), barium (Ba), boron (B), bromine (Br), cesium (Cs), lithium (Li), rubidium (Rb), strontium (Sr) and titanium (Ti).

Definite proof that a mineral element is required is not always easy to come by. Natural foods and feeds, soil and water supplies may have sufficient quantities of the elements to satisfy requirements. Purified diets have been most helpful in this respect. Even here, however, many laboratory reagent chemicals have traces of a variety of different elements other than the chemical compounds specified on the label. Consequently, a "pure" diet may be difficult to achieve. Even airborne dust, unless carefully filtered, may provide sufficient quantities of certain elements to prevent expression of a deficiency.

F has been recognized in the prevention of dental cavities and has shown other possibilities in animal metabolism. Studies with purified diets have indicated that As, Cr, Si, Sn

and V may be essential for specific physiological functions. However, Al, B, Br, Cs and Sr, which appear to be required by plants, have not been identified as being essential for animals.

With the exception of Fe in hemoglobin, myoglobin, and some storage compounds, I in thyroid hormone, Co in vitamin B_{12}, and Zn in biological membrane structure, most trace minerals seem to function as biological catalysts. Their roles may range from weak ionic effects to specific combinations with proteins to form metalloenzymes. A great volume of in vitro data on trace element-enzyme associations has been accumulated during the last 30 years. However, Underwood (2G) has pointed out that several pathological disorders cannot yet be explained in biochemical or enzyme terms, strongly suggesting either undiscovered metalloenzymes or other vital roles yet unknown for the microelements (i.e., non-enzymatic functionally active compounds). I and Co are two examples of this thesis. Some trace elements appear to play a role in the configuration of the RNA molecule, perhaps linking purine or pyrimidine bases or both through covalent bonds and, hence, bearing a functional relationship to protein synthesis and the transmission of genetic information.

Present knowledge is based on the work of many investigators too numerous to reference here, but most of this work has been covered in recent reviews (1G through 12G).

COBALT (Co)

Several disorders, known locally in various areas as coast disease, bush sickness, wasting disease, pining or salt sick have been recognized in ruminants for years. Prior to the 1930's, sheep and cattle could not be raised successfully on large areas because of these disorders. The problem was solved by discoveries first in Australia then in New Zealand and Florida (1, 2G, 3G) that these disorders could be treated or prevented by supplemental Co.

Identification of cyanocobalamin (vitamin B_{12}) as a Co-containing compound has provided an explanation of the biological function of Co. In ruminant nutrition, Co occupies a unique position among the trace elements, an element utilized solely as an integral part of a vitamin by animals which are dependent upon the symbiotic activities of their gastro-intestinal microorganisms for their supply of the vitamin (1).

Distribution of Tissue Co

Co is widely distributed throughout the body, without excessive accumulation in any particular organ or tissue, although concentrations are generally higher in the kidney, liver and bone than in other tissues (1). Livers of ruminants fed adequate diets typically contain 0.15 ppm or more of Co, although normal animals may be found with lower levels. Co concentrations in liver can be increased 10X normal by massive doses without increasing vitamin B_{12} synthesis and ruminants fed Co-deficient rations can be maintained in health by vitamin B_{12} injections without raising their liver Co to normal (2G). Liver Co concentration is, therefore, an unreliable criterion of the Co-vitamin B_{12} status of ruminants. Liver should contain at least 0.3 ppm of B_{12} in fresh tissue to be considered adequate. Liver B_{12} in sheep fed a low-Co diet (0.06 ppm) can be increased from <0.2 ppm to >0.7 ppm by IM injections with 200 μg B_{12} on alternate days for several weeks (2).

Co in normal cows' milk ranges from 0.4 to 1 μg/ℓ, depending on Co status of the cow's diet (1). Blood Co concentrations are low but vary widely, probably due to analytical inaccuracies or sample contamination. Rumen contents of adequately fed animals may contain 4-7 μg of Co/kg, much of which is taken up by the rumen microorganisms.

Function

Apparently, ruminants have a metabolic requirement for B_{12} rather than for Co by itself. Before the rumen becomes functional, the young also have a dietary requirement for vitamin B_{12}. Vitamin B_{12} is an essential component of methylmalonyl CoA mutase which is necessary for the metabolism of methylmalonic acid. Propionic acid, the primary gluconeogenic substrate in fed ruminants, is metabolized solely by the methylmalonate pathway in the liver. Since ruminants do not absorb appreciable amounts of glucose from the gastro-intestinal tract, they are dependent

on gluconeogenesis, particularly from propionate.

The vitamin is also necessary for normal hemopoiesis by facilitating the cyclic metabolism of folic acid which is essential for thymidine and thus DNA synthesis (3). Its methyl group transfer activity is also essential for a normally functioning nervous system.

Metabolism of Co

Absorption and Excretion. Feces is the primary excretion route of radiocobalt after oral administration to sheep and cattle. This is in contrast to approximately equal recoveries in feces and urine of Co from dietary sources. ^{60}Co excretions by sheep and cattle range from 80-85% in feces and <1-11% in urine after oral administration compared to 7-8% in feces and 65-78% in urine after I.V. dosing (4G). Recoveries of dietary Co from sheep fed fresh forage, however, average 35% in feces and 30% in urine (4). Chemical form of Co may contribute to these differences between radiocobalt and dietary Co.

Investigations with sheep fitted with rumen fistulae and re-entrant cannulae at the proximal duodenum or terminal ileum have shown Co to be secreted into the forestomachs and absorbed from the small and large intestines (4). Co appears to share with Fe at least part of the same intestinal mucosal transport mechanism (1). However, because Co functions primarily as a component of vitamin B_{12} which is produced by rumen microorganisms rather than in tissues of the host animal, absorption of the vitamin rather than the element should be considered. Absorption efficiency of vitamin B_{12} has been calculated to be $<3\%$ in sheep.

Co and Vitamin B_{12} Metabolism. Co. as an integral part of the B_{12} molecule, occupies a unique position among the trace elements. Although Co can be present in the tissues in bound forms other than B_{12}, no other physiological function has been demonstrated.

The need for oral intake of Co by ruminants has been shown by many studies, but the benefits of I.V. administration of Co have not been consistent. In theory, recycling of Co to the rumen (4), either through the saliva or across the rumen epithelium, should provide rumen microorganisms with Co for B_{12} synthesis. Either I.V. or oral dosing with Co

344

will increase liver concentrations of Co but the correlation between Co and liver B_{12} is not high when large doses of Co are given. The liver will take up only about 14% of labeled B_{12} given I.V.

The amount of B_{12} synthesis in the rumen is substantial as rumen contents may contain up to 10 μg of B_{12} activity/g of dry matter. Apparent synthesis in the gastro-intestinal tract of sheep fed natural rations is ca. 2-3 mg/d but only a fraction of this is true vitamin B_{12}. Rumen microorganisms synthesize a variety of Co-containing B_{12}-like molecules that are believed to have no physiological function for the host. Total B_{12} activity in rumen contents may be 10-20X greater than true B_{12} activity. Pseudo B_{12} compounds appear in the liver of calves but their function in the rumen is unknown, although some are growth-promoting factors for certain bacteria.

Vitamin B_{12} is much less effective when given orally than when given parenterally to ruminants. This may be due to its low (<3%) absorption. It is also possible that rumen microorganisms may convert part of the dietary or rumen B_{12} to some of the pseudo vitamins. At any rate, only a small portion of Co synthesized into B_{12} may be of use to the host. This may explain the greater Co requirement of ruminants compared to other species such as the horse, rabbit or quokka. These species not only utilize dietary B_{12} more efficiently than ruminants but also absorb B_{12} produced in the cecum or large intestine. The rabbit can also obtain additional B_{12} by coprophagy.

Other Nutritional Factors

A conditioned B_{12} deficiency in cattle has been caused by drinking water containing silicofluoride which is toxic to some rumen organisms known to synthesize B_{12}. It can be corrected by treatment with B_{12}.

Infusion studies with isolated sections of sheep jejunum suggest Co reduces motor activity of the gut. Co infused with other salts or organic compounds reduces absorption of Na, K, P, glucose, glycine and water but elevates Ca absorption and increases excretion of Na into the intestinal lumen (5).

High dietary Mo (200-400 ppm) changes the distribution of B_{12} in bovine liver and heart tissue, probably by reducing ruminal B_{12} synthesis. Synthesis of B_{12} can be restored by

addition of Co to such rations. Co can improve utilization of Cu and Fe in animals fed a low Mo diet and also improve utilization of Fe for blood hemoglobin formation in heifers receiving Mo in the diet. Co does not appear to modify the reduced liver Cu seen with addition of Mo, but injected B_{12} or oral Co will help prevent Cu deficiency in cattle (6).

Phalaris staggers, a disease observed in sheep and cattle in Australia, New Zealand, South Africa and the USA, occurs when these animals graze the perennial grass *Phalaris tuberosa.* It can be prevented by weekly dosing with Co. This function of Co does not appear to be related to its vitamin B_{12} activity. However, prior treatment with Co will not reduce morbidity or mortality of sheep ingesting toxic alkaloids from *Heliotropium europaeum.* Ruminants receiving adequate Co are less susceptible to Se toxicosis, perhaps due to the function of B_{12} in the formation of dimethyl selenide and other excretory products of Se.

Dietary Requirements

Young, growing sheep have the highest Co requirement followed by mature sheep, calves 6-18 mo of age, and mature cattle. Severe Co deficiency results when cattle and sheep are maintained on forage containing 0.02-0.05 ppm Co (dry basis). Plasma B_{12} concentrations progressively increase as dietary Co level is raised from 0.04 ppm to 0.34 ppm. Dietary requirements for Co by ruminants have been established at 0.1 ppm for dairy cattle and sheep and 0.05 to 0.1 ppm for beef cattle (3G).

Prevention of Co Deficiency

Co deficiency can be prevented by a regular intake of Co from supplemental sources. Co oxide, Co carbonate and Co sulfate are effective for ruminants (3G). Fertilization of pastures with about 140 g Co sulfate/acre will usually suffice up to 3 years. Spraying of plant foliage is also successful. Co can also be supplied by addition to supplemental feed or salt.

Drenching is a sure way of getting Co into animals where it may not be feasible to fertilize pastures. However, animals must be drenched at least once per week to maintain maximum gain. Concentrations of B_{12} and Co in the rumen drop rapidly after dietary intake is stopped and liver Co levels are depleted in 10-30 d.

One means of eliminating the laborious task of drenching is to use ruminal pellets prepared from cobaltic oxide and clay compressed to provide a dense long-lasting source of Co. This method is successful provided the animal does not regurgitate and lose the pellet. The pellet may also become encrusted with phosphatic salts, thus reducing the release of Co. This can be partially alleviated by inclusion of steel screws which serve to abrade off any coating (2G).

Co Deficiency

Co-deficient areas have been reported in Australia, New Zealand, East Africa, Norway and through Central and South America (3G). Deficient areas in the USA include portions of New England and the lower Atlantic Coastal Plain with sections of the Midwest and Great Lakes region yielding forages that are moderately low in Co. Degree of Co deficiency differs greatly from season to season and from year to year. Seasonal changes in pasture composition may contribute to severity of Co deficiency because Co content of grasses is less than that of legumes and forage Co content varies with season. Other factors affecting the mineral content of pastures are soil type, changes in pH due to fertilizer application and whether pastures are cut frequently or grazed. Co deficiency is more likely to develop on lightly grazed pastures because animals on heavily grazed pastures pick up more Co from the soil. In Australia, Co deficiency occurs in areas where the soil has largely been derived from shells of marine origin.

Cattle, sheep, goats and presumably wild ruminants are affected by Co deficiency. Lambs are particularly sensitive followed by mature sheep, calves and adult cows. The increased sensitivity of young animals may be due to a higher requirement for rapid growth and higher metabolic rate than adults. Severity of Co deficiency may vary from mild to acute. Time required to develop deficiency symptoms depends on dietary intake as well as tissue reserves of B_{12}.

Ewes may consume a Co-deficient diet throughout pregnancy with no overt changes other than decreased serum B_{12} (7). However, after lambing they begin to lose their appetites and serum B_{12} declines to very low levels (100-200 pg/ml). Lambs born to ewes with low serum B_{12} levels are unthrifty, gain poorly and have serum B_{12} as low as 25 pg/ml. If the period of B_{12} insufficiency extends for some time before pregnancy, signs of low B_{12} status become evident during pregnancy and perinatal mortality among the lambs is high.

Symptoms of Co deficiency include depressed appetite, listlessness, decreased growth or loss of weight, reduced milk production, rough hair coat, wool with low breaking strength in sheep and anemia resulting in pale skin and mucous membranes. Extreme or prolonged deficiency may result in emaciation (Figs. 18-1 and 2), muscle incoordination, stumbling gait and eventually death.

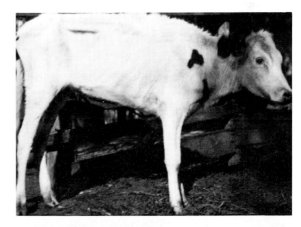

Figure 18-1. Co-deficient animal (top). Note the severe emaciation. Bottom. The same animal several weeks after Co administration. Courtesy of R.B. Becker, Florida Agr. Expt. St.

Figure 18-2. Co-deficient sheep. Note the severe emaciation and wool chewing that has occurred (right). The lamb on the left received an adequate diet. Courtesy of S.E. Smith, Cornell Univ.

Changes characteristic of severely affected animals include low plasma glucose and alkaline phosphatase, (Table 18-1) fatty degeneration of the liver and hemosiderosis of the spleen. There may be hypoplasia of the bone marrow and other bone marrow abnormalities. Red blood cells and hemoglobin levels are low but plasma proteins do not appear to be affected. Restoration of normal erythropoiesis by folic acid treatment, which has no effect otherwise, suggests the anemia is secondary.

Withdrawal of Co from a diet otherwise adequate results in a marked drop in B_{12} activity in rumen contents to only 4-12% of the previous level. When Co in the rumen falls to less than half the normal level of 40 μg/ℓ, synthesis of B_{12} falls from >600 to <50 μg/d. However, there may be no obvious impairment of physiological function until liver B_{12} falls below 0.15 ppm. Liver Co may drop from the normal level of 0.2-0.3 ppm to 0.04-0.06 ppm or less in deficient animals. The first clinical symptoms of Co deficiency appear when blood B_{12} falls from the normal range of 1-3 μg/ℓ to 0.3 μg/ℓ or less.

Weight loss in Co-deficient sheep is not due entirely to loss of appetite because deficient animals lose weight faster than pair-fed controls (8). Greater fecal N excretion and fasting energy expenditure in Co-deficient animals appear to be due primarily to insufficient B_{12} in the tissues. Metabolism of N or energy, methane production or roughage digestibility are not altered in sheep fed a Co-deficient diet as long as tissue reserves of B_{12} are adequate.

Because B_{12} is an essential component of methylmalonyl CoA mutase and a methyltransferase involved in methionine biosynthe-

Table 18-1. Biochemical changes due to Co deficiency in cattle and sheep.[a]

	Normal range	Co-deficient range
Cattle		
Hemoglobin, g/dl	9-12	5.2-7
Plasma glucose, mg/dl	70-90	38-66
Plasma alkaline phosphatase, IU/ℓ	30-60	10-30
Plasma vitamin B_{12}, pg/ml	400-800	53-132
Sheep		
Hemoglobin, g/dl	10-13	6-11
Packed cell volume, %	32-40	20-36
Plasma glucose, mg/dl	57-72	16-51
Plasma alkaline phosphatase, IU/ℓ	47-93	9-47
Plasma glutamic oxalacetic transaminase, S.F./ml	48-70	86-1490
Blood pyruvate, mg/dl	0.6-0.9	1.75-2.20
Plasma ascorbic acid, mg/ℓ	4-8	1.07
Plasma pyruvate kinase, mU/ml	40-80	1000

[a]MacPherson, A., et al (6)

sis, urinary outputs increase 5-12X for methylmalonic acid and more than 30X for forminoglutamic acid when Co (B_{12}) is deficient. The latter acid increases in the early stages more so than the former. Serum B_{12} concentration is inversely related to urinary forminoglutamic acid concentrations (9). Ruminants are dependent on gluconeogenesis from propionate so urinary loss of its primary metabolite, methylmalonic acid, can have serious physiological consequences.

Co-deficient sheep can metabolize formate normally but clearance from blood is delayed slightly for acetate and markedly for propionate (10). The livers of deficient animals can metabolize malate and succinate normally but cannot convert propionate to succinate. This leads to accumulation of the intermediate, methylmalonyl CoA. Addition of 5'-deoxyadenosylcobalamin, the B_{12}-containing coenzyme essential for the functioning of methylmalonyl CoA-mutase, restores the conversion of methylmalonyl CoA to succinyl CoA.

Unusually high proportions of odd-numbered fatty acids in adipose tissue of B_{12}-deprived lambs which die before or soon after birth may result from use of accumulated propionic acid as a primer unit for fatty acid synthesis (7). Failure to metabolize propionate at the normal rate may explain the depressed appetite in B_{12}-deficient animals.

Supplemental Co will stimulate the appetite of Co-deficient animals within a few days. Deficient animals will also respond to single injections of B_{12} (250-500 μg) and this response lasts 4 to 6 wk.

Co Toxicity

Toxic levels appear to be at least 300X the requirement so Co toxicosis is less likely than Co deficiency in ruminants under practical conditions (5G). However, accidental over-supplementation with Co is possible. Co toxicity may occur frequently in Australia when Co has been used in salt licks, in mixed rations or applied to pastures. Symptoms of Co toxicity in ruminants include loss of appetite, reduced water consumption, slower growth or weight loss, lacrimation, salivation, rough hair coat, muscular tremors, inco-ordination, increased hemoglobin, higher packed cell volume and increased liver Co (5G). Post mortem examination reveals liver degeneration, lung congestion and hemorrhaging in the small intestine.

Doses of 4.4 to 11 mg/kg of body weight are toxic to sheep and cattle, although up to 3.5 mg/kg can be tolerated for as long as 8 wk. Oral doses of 0.9 mg/kg or I.V. doses of 0.66 mg/kg are toxic to calves. Calves are more susceptible than sheep to Co toxicity. The maximum safe level of Co is 20 ppm for cattle and 50 ppm for sheep (11).

Ewes can develop signs of clover disease when grazed on pastures primarily of subterranean clover (*Trifolium subterraneum*) that have been heavily fertilized with Co. Symptoms include depressed fertility and cystic degeneration of the cervix and uterus. The administration of Se appears to reverse, to some extent, the adverse effects of the Co.

COPPER (Cu) AND MOLYBDENUM (Mo)

Essentiality of Cu for animals was established about 60 years ago by the demonstration that supplementation with both Fe and Cu was required to correct anemia in milk-fed rats. Mo was first recognized for its toxicity, but abnormalities may result in both ruminant and monogastric animals when dietary Mo is very low. Because of the close interrelationship between the two elements, Cu and Mo will be discussed together.

Tissue Cu and Mo

Liver, brain, kidneys, heart, pigmented part of the eye, and hair or wool are highest in Cu concentration in most species; pancreas, spleen, skeletal muscle, skin and bone are intermediate; and thyroid, pituitary, prostrate and thymus are lowest. Of ruminant tissues analyzed, the liver has the greatest concentration of Cu, ranging from 100 to 600 ppm (dry weight basis) in normal adults, although in the western parts of the USA liver Cu is usually 100 ppm or less. Liver Cu may fall below 10 ppm during Cu deficiency or exceed 600 ppm when dietary Cu is excessive.

Cu in plasma or whole blood is typically near 100 μg/dl but may increase to 165 μg/dl in sheep fed high dietary Cu, Mo and S (Table 18-2). Plasma Cu is low in the young lamb, but red cell Cu is more similar to that of adults (Table 18-3). Disease conditions, including arthritis, infected wounds, meningitis and abscessed feet, may increase plasma Cu (ceruloplasmin) in sheep. Elevated plasma Cu has also been noted in animals with

Table 18-2. Cu content of plasma and tissues of sheep fed a diet containing 80 mg Cu, 3.7 g S and 0.6-60 mg Mo/kg.[a]

| Item | Dietary Mo, ppm | | | |
	0.06	21.40	39.60	60.30
Plasma, mg/ℓ	0.95	0.96	1.25	1.65
Tissue mg/kg dry wt				
Liver	987.00	812.00	660.00	835.00
Kidney cortex	26.00	26.00	94.00	236.00
Kidney medulla	8.20	8.40	14.90	40.40
Lungs	11.50	11.50	12.50	17.40
Spleen	2.20	4.10	3.70	13.00
Heart	18.80	18.80	22.60	27.40
Skeletal muscle	5.00	4.60	5.60	6.10

[a]From Van Ryssen and Stielau (1)

Table 18-3. Distribution of blood Cu in sheep of different ages.[a]

Age	Whole blood Cu	Plasma Cu	Direct reading Cu[b]	Indirect reading Cu[c]	Red blood cell Cu
			μg/dl		
Adults	98	102	20	81	95
Fetus	45	26	17	11	78
Newborn	83	63	47	16	104

[a]From Church et al (4G)
[b]Equivalent to albumin-bound Cu
[c]Equivalent to ceruloplasmin Cu

348

hypocalcemia, hypomagnesemia and pregnancy toxemia, probably because of degenerative changes of the liver known to occur in these situations. Plasma Cu is of little value in predicting liver Cu although plasma Cu levels of 50 μg/dl are indicative of low liver Cu levels.

Ionic Cu is too toxic to exist free in the body in substantial amounts so it must be bound to organic molecules. In intestinal mucosal cells of most species, Cu is bound to S-rich proteins which are either identical or closely related to the thioneine moiety of metallothionein (2). Cu in sheep liver cytosol is present in three main proteins with approximate molecular weight of 150,000, 27,000 and 10,000 (3). Over half of the Cu in normal sheep liver cytosol is in the 10,000 molecular weight fraction (metallothionein). With excessive dietary Cu, the capacity of metallothionein and higher molecular weight proteins may be exceeded and excess Cu is bound to a low molecular weight protein not found in liver of normal or Cu-deficient sheep (4). Cu is found in the red blood cells in a nearly colorless protein complex called erythrocuprein, with a molecular weight of about 35,000 and containing about 0.34% Cu. A non-dialyzable Cu fraction in plasma which reacts with diethyldithiocarbamate has been termed direct reading (or direct-reacting) Cu. The Cu in this fraction, which normally constitutes 10% or less of the total Cu in plasma, is loosely bound to albumin and involved in Cu transport to the liver. The remaining Cu in plasma is firmly bound to ceruloplasmin, a globulin complex containing 8 atoms of Cu. Synthesis of ceruloplasmin in the liver and its role in transporting Cu to other tissues has been reviewed (2).

Deposition of Cu in the developing fetus increases constantly throughout gestation. The total amount of Cu accumulated daily by total products of conception in the ewe increases by almost 6 times between the first and second thirds of pregnancy and doubles again in the final third (5). The instantaneous rate of Cu deposition in the fetus increases exponentially between the 80th and 144th d of gestation (6). Cu concentrations in most tissues of near term ovine and bovine fetuses are similar to adult concentrations when dietary Cu is adequate. However, when the ewes' Cu intake is low, tissue Cu of newborn lambs may be much lower than in the ewe (7).

Table 18-4. Mo content of plasma and tissues of sheep fed diets containing 80 mg Cu, 3.7 g S and 0.6-60 mg Mo/kg.[a]

Item	Molybdenum, mg/kg diet			
	0.60	21.40	39.60	60.30
Plasma, mg/ℓ	0.06	0.12	0.54	0.92
Tissues, mg/kg dry wt				
Liver	2.50	5.60	11.00	21.20
Kidney cortex	1.70	6.50	54.70	136.50
Kidney medulla	1.40	2.30	7.10	24.10
Lungs	0.60	1.20	2.40	6.20
Spleen	0.20	0.80	3.40	11.30
Heart	0.10	0.40	1.20	1.70
Skeletal muscle	0.20	0.20	0.40	0.90

[a]From Van Ryssen and Stielau (1)

Cu averages near 10 μg/dl in bovine milk (8) and does not respond to dietary changes in Cu (9).

Blood levels of Mo vary sharply with Mo intake, increasing from 1-5 μg/dl in ruminants receiving normal rations to 160-280 μg/dl in sheep fed diets containing 4.5 ppm (10) and 700 μg/dl in cows fed 173-300 ppm Mo (11). Mo concentrations in other tissues also increase markedly with increasing Mo intake (Table 18-4). The Mo content of milk responds rapidly and directly to increases in Mo intake, but differences due to Mo intake in the normal range of 1-5 ppm can not be detected (9).

Functions of Cu and Mo

Cu is a constituent of several enzymes or is essential for their activity. It is involved in a broad range of biochemical functions in the animal body, including prostaglandin synthesis and formation of aortic elastin. The observation that binding of ADP is increased when mitochondrial membrane Cu content is increased and depressed by Cu-complexing agents susgests Cu is a component of adenine nucleotide binding sites of mitochondrial membranes (12). Erythrocuprein functions as a superoxide dismutase catalyzing the dismutation of monovalent superoxide anion radicals into hydrogen peroxide and oxygen. This is part of an important chain of reactions which protect cells from the highly reactive free radicals generated by cellular metabolism. Cerebrocuprein, a water-soluble protein containing 0.33% Cu isolated from bovine brain, also has superoxide dismutase activity (13).

Ceruloplasmin is a ferroxidase involved in Fe utilization and in promoting the rate of Fe saturation of transferrin in plasma. Ceruloplasmin also oxidizes epinephrine, norepinephrine, serotonin and melatonin and may function in controlling the plasma levels of certain amines. Monoamine oxidase, an enzyme with a molecular weight of 195,000 daltons, contains 4 atoms of Cu/molecule. It catalyzes the oxidative deamination of a variety of monoamines to the corresponding aldehydes and is involved in maintaining the structural integrity of both vascular and bone tissue. Bovine plasma amine oxidase has a molecular weight of about 170,000 and contains 2 atoms of Cu per mole of protein (14). Tyrosinase, which also requires Cu, is essential in the pigmentation process because it catalyzes the first two steps in the synthesis of melanin from tyrosine.

Cu toxicity in sheep has been associated with the lower extreme of dietary Mo intake. Other biochemical functions of Mo, apart from its reactions with Cu, are related to the formation and activities of xanthine oxidase, aldehyde oxidase and sulfite oxidase. Mo participates in the reaction of xanthine oxidase with cytochrome C and the reduction of cytochrome C by aldehyde oxidase. Mo is required for growth, cellular oxidation, purine metabolism and is possibly involved in Fe metabolism.

Absorption and Excretion of Cu

Feces is the primary route of Cu excretion in ruminants. Percentages of dietary Cu or orally administered ^{64}Cu excreted by sheep or cattle in most studies range from 80-92% in feces and 1-3% in urine. From 1-5% of ^{64}Cu given I.V. is usually recovered in urine. True availability of Cu, estimated from relative responses in blood of hypocupremic ewes to Cu given orally or intravenously, ranges from 4-11%. Absorption of Cu from various gastro-intestinal tract sections has been measured in sheep (15) and cows (16) fitted with rumen fistulas and intestinal re-entrant cannulas or by the Cr_2O_3 ratio technique in calves (17). In general, Cu is secreted anterior to the small intestine and absorbed from the rest of the tract.

Cu homeostasis is effected in most species by controlling the rate of absorption which in turn is regulated in part by mucosal metallothionein (2). Elevated metallothionein levels, induced by Cu as well as by Zn, Cd or Hg, reduce absorption of Cu. Absorbed Cu is excreted primarily via the bile and the intestinal tract. In sheep, unlike other species, Cu is not associated with metallothionein in intestinal mucosal cytosol and capacity to synthesize metallothionein in response to increased dietary Cu is limited (3). This may contribute to the sheep's susceptibility to Cu poisoning, especially if Cu is excreted in bile via sequestration of protein-bound Cu (metallothionein) by the lysosomes (18).

Absorption and Excretion of Mo

Excretion of Mo by ruminants is influenced markedly by both ration and gastro-intestinal site of dose deposition. When the diet is predominantly roughage, typical excretions of orally given ^{99}Mo are 90-95% in feces and 2-4% in urine. Relative ^{99}Mo excretions are somewhat lower in feces (60-80%) but higher in urine (10-20%) when a higher concentrate diet is fed. Urine becomes the primary route of ^{99}Mo excretion (27-50%) when the dose is delivered directly to the abomasum. Recoveries of ^{99}Mo following I.V. injection have ranged from 10-50% in urine and 7-30% in feces. Much of the variation undoubtedly is due to dietary differences.

Despite the marked effects of passage through the rumen on its excretion, Mo does not appear to be absorbed from the rumen or omasum. There is net secretion of Mo into the rumen but absorption occurs in the abomasum and small intestine (19). Uptakes of Mo from ovine small intestine sections incubated in vitro are highest in the distal ileum, intermediate in the mid small intestine and lowest in the proximal duodenum (20). Homeostatic control of Mo appears to be negligible since blood Mo changes sharply in response to changing dietary levels.

Factors Modifying Cu and Mo Metabolism
Effect of Mo on Cu. Cu-Mo antagonism is nutritionally significant when Mo in feed is either exceptionally low (<0.2 ppm) or high (>7 ppm) and may induce Cu toxicity at the lower and Cu deficiency at the upper extreme. Excess dietary Mo is frequently associated with increased concentrations of Mo in plasma and liver (Table 18-4), whereas Cu is increased in plasma (Table 18-2) but reduced in liver (Table 18-5).

350

Table 18-5. Kidney and liver Cu concentration in lambs fed diets containing 45 mg Cu 2, g S and 0.7 to 16.7 mg Mo/kg.[a]

Item	Dietary Mo, ppm				
	0.7	2.7	4.7	8.7	16.7
Tissue, mg/kg dry wt					
Kidney	250	21	22	20	20
Liver	1691	697	587	476	274

[a]From Suttle (21)

Contrasting responses of ruminants and non-ruminants to Cu-Mo antagonism are probably related to the influence of the rumen. Fecal excretions of both ^{64}Cu and ^{99}Mo are much higher when the radioisotopes are given orally (to the rumen) than when delivered directly to the abomasum. Although neither Cu nor Mo appears to be absorbed from the rumen, formation in the rumen of an insoluble complex which remains intact on passage through the gastro-intestinal tract could inhibit absorption of both Cu and Mo from the intestines. Administration of Mo in the diet and Cu by subcutaneous injection (22) or by continuous I.V. infusion (23) largely circumvents the antagonism.

Effects of S on Cu and Mo. Pasture containing relatively low sulfate (0.1-0.2%) allows Cu storage in the liver when forage Mo is high, but with elevated forage sulfate (0.4%), liver Cu may be depleted. A direct antagonism between Cu and sulfate appears to be due to formation of cupric sulfide which is relatively insoluble. Supplementation with ferrous sulfide will also reduce liver Cu markedly.

When sulfate is low, very little Mo is excreted in urine; when sulfate intake is increased, urinary Mo increases markedly and blood Mo falls. Both organic and inorganic forms of S reduce plasma Mo levels. Conversely, increasing Mo intake increases urinary excretion of sulfates. Interactions between sulfate and Mo appear to occur at several sites with different effects. Because Mo can inhibit sulfate reduction (24), it may decrease the amount of sulfide formed in the rumen, thereby increasing Cu availability to the animal. However, results of in vitro microbial systems suggest that the inhibitory effect of Mo on sulfide production can be decreased by formation of a non-available complex of Mo

with Cu (25). Sulfate and Mo may also interact antagonistically at the membrane transport level (26). A similar pattern for Mo and sulfate uptakes by sheep small intestine segments in vitro (20) suggests that sulfate inhibits uptake of Mo by competition for sites on a common transport system.

Cu-Mo-Sulfate Interactions. Interactions between Cu and either Mo or S separately do not account for all the changes described above. It has been recognized for years that Mo depletes liver Cu in sheep only when adequate sulfate is present. Both sulfate and Mo must be elevated for sheep to develop dystrophic wool; sulfate or Mo supplements added separately to diets otherwise low in these elements may reduce liver Cu storages but do not usually produce wool lesions. Examination of relationships among S and Mo within normal dietary ranges (0.1-0.48% S and 0.5-4.5 ppm Mo, dry basis) on Cu availability to sheep by multiple regression techniques (27) indicates that S exerts a predominant and independent effect on Cu availability, whereas Mo has a lesser and S-dependent effect. In addition, increments at the lower end of the normal ranges of S and Mo concentrations have relatively large depressing effects on Cu availability.

Effects of S and Mo on Cu availability have been investigated further in hypocupremic ewes by adding 6 to 8 ppm Cu to basal diets containing 0.1 or 0.4% S and 0.5 or 4.5 ppm Mo (10). Repletion of plasma Cu was unaffected by Mo alone, only slightly reduced by S alone and totally inhibited by Mo plus S. Plasma Mo was increased greatly by Mo, decreased slightly by S and unaffected by Mo and S given together. The Cu-Mo-S antagonism can be circumvented if either Cu or Mo supplements are delivered to a site other than the rumen.

Supplementation of ruminant diets with Mo and S can elevate plasma Cu without affecting ceruloplasmin (Table 18-6), the additional Cu occurring as direct reacting Cu, most of which is TCA-insoluble. Results when three groups of sheep were fed a diet containing 10 ppm Cu and 0.08% SO$_4$ alone or supplemented with 25 ppm Mo or 25 ppm

Table 18-6. Effect of adding Mo or Mo + sulfate to diets containing 10 mg Cu, 0.5 mg Mo and 0.8 g S/kg on plasma Cu components of sheep.[a]

Diet	Supplement		Total Cu	Direct reacting Cu	TCA soluble Cu	Ceruloplasmin, unit[b]
	Mo ppm	SO$_4$, %	. . . .	μg/dl	. . . .	
Control	0	0	89	19	94	15.6
+ Mo	25	0	110	16	106	15.8
+ Mo + SO$_4$	25	0.5	114	70	69	14.2

[a] From Bremner and Young (28)
[b] Amount catalyzing the transformation of 1 μmol substrate/min.

Mo plus 0.5% SO$_4$ suggest Cu and Mo are closely associated in a plasma protein fraction whose formation is dependent on increasing dietary SO$_4$ (28). Several mechanisms for the three-way interaction among Cu, Mo and SO$_4$ have been proposed. Blocking of Cu transport across membranes, competition for a common carrier system and lower Cu absorption due to formation of Cu sulfide or insoluble Cu-Mo complexes are all consistent with reduced liver Cu, but why is plasma Cu elevated?

Observations by Dick et al (29) may explain the three-way interaction among Cu, Mo and SO$_4$. They found that Mo, with or without SO$_4$, administered through a duodenal fistula to sheep, had no effect on blood Cu. However, preformed thiomolybdate administered post ruminally resulted in a marked rise in the TCA-insoluble fraction of plasma Cu. Cu in plasma from freshly drawn sheep's blood normally is all contained in the filtrate after protein precipitation with TCA. Thiomolybdate added in vitro to this plasma progressively increases Cu in the TCA precipitate with a corresponding reduction in that recovered in the filtrate. Thiomolybdate given I.V. to sheep also raises blood Cu and increases biliary Cu excretion which accounts for much of the total Cu lost from the liver (30).

These observations suggest the interactive effects of Cu, Mo and S occur first in the rumen and then in the tissues. Reduction of sulfate to sulfide by rumen microorganisms is followed by reaction of this sulfide with Mo to form thiomolybdate. In the rumen, thiomolybdate combines with Cu thereby limiting absorption of dietary Cu. Additional thiomolybdate not combined with Cu in the rumen is absorbed into the blood stream and mobilizes tissue Cu, resulting in the elevated plasma Cu. Apparently, plasma Cu in this thiomolybdate complex is poorly available for Cu metabolism.

Effect of Other Dietary Components. Although less important economically than the interaction with Mo and S, Cu is influenced favorably or unfavorably, depending on whether Cu deficiency or toxicity is of concern, by several other dietary components. Solubility of Cu in rumen and abomasal contents decreases proportionally with increasing dietary protein (31). Small oral doses of Se increase growth and Cu levels in various organs, blood and wool of lambs (32). Supplemental Mn may also improve Cu absorption by calves (17). In contrast, supplemental Co reduces gains and lowers liver Cu concentration in lambs with a history of Co deficiency and Mo/S induced Cu deficiency (33). Supplementation of sheep diets with Zn at 10X dietary requirement reduces likelihood of Cu toxicity and reduces liver total Cu (34) but increases Cu content of sheep liver metallothionein (3). Involvement of Cu in Fe utilization explains why plasma Fe of Cu-deficient lambs is often low (35). Excess dietary Fe (800 ppm), however, can reduce plasma ceruloplasmin in calves to levels indicative of severe Cu deficiency (36).

Requirements for Cu

Cu requirements of ruminant species cannot be defined clearly when various interfering factors are present in the diet. Forage containing <3 ppm of Cu in the dry matter

352

during the growing period is generally deficient, between 3 and 6 ppm are marginal, and with >6 ppm deficiency diseases are rarely encountered. Suggested dietary Cu requirements of ruminants are 4 ppm for growing-finishing steers, 5 ppm for all classes of sheep and 10 ppm for all classes of dairy cattle (3G). A Cu:Mo ratio no less than 4:1 should insure adequate Cu availability. Minimum dietary requirements of Mo for satisfactory growth and health have not been determined.

Prevention of Cu Deficiency. Cu deficiency among grazing ruminants is widespread and supplemental Cu must be provided in many areas of the world. There are several possibilities for relief where Cu deficiency is a problem. Fertilization of pasture with Cu has been successful where soil pH is low but not on alkaline soil in the western USA where Mo content of forages may be increased. Supplemental Cu can be provided, but in range areas it is difficult to supply Cu in either mineral mixes or supplemental concentrates. The problem is compounded where waters are naturally saline because the animals may not consume enough salt on a regular basis to provide adequate Cu.

Where Mo intake is high, Cu must be provided in relatively high and frequent amounts to obtain satisfactory animal production. As a result many livestock producers have used injectible Cu glycinate or Cu EDTA complexes which are absorbed slowly. Doses of 30-40 mg for sheep and 120-240 mg for cattle can be administered subcutaneously or intramuscularly without undue hazard. The frequency of required dosing is greatly reduced with this method as compared to oral supplementation.

If mineral supplementation can be used, a mix with 0.5-1% Cu sulfate will be consumed readily by cattle and sheep. Supplemental Cu sources, listed in order of biological availability, include Cu sulfate, Cu carbonate and Cu oxide (3G).

Cu Deficiency

Cu deficiency in ruminants results in a number of symptoms which depend upon a variety of factors, only some of which are known. Manifestation of Cu deficiency depends on species, age and sex; on the severity and duration of deficiency; and on the environment in which the animal is maintained. Cattle may be unable to maintain normal Cu status under conditions where sheep have no problems. However, calves generally have higher liver Cu levels at birth even when their dams are depleted, so except in extreme deficiency, the calf is protected in utero and for up to 2 mo after birth (37). In contrast, status of the fetal lamb parallels that of the ewe. Increasing prevalence of Cu deficiency in lambs and calves in Northern Ireland has been attributed to reduction in potato growing, replacement of Cu-based fungicides with non-Cu preparations and use of antihelmintics other than Cu sulfate (38).

Cu deficiency symptoms, in order of appearance in calves, include hypocupremia (<20 μg/dl), growth retardation, impaired feed conversion, rough hair coat, diarrhea and leg abnormalities. First generation Cu-deficient sheep develop low plasma and tissue Cu but appetite, growth and feed conversion efficiency are not always impaired. Regardless of clinical appearance, Cu-depleted cattle exhibit gross or microscopic lesions of the skeleton and cardiovascular system (39). Falling disease in cattle occurs in some areas (particularly Australia) with very low Cu levels in forage. It is characterized by sudden cardiac failure due, apparently, to fibrosis of myocardial muscles. Ultra structural changes in the myocardium of young Cu-deficient steers have been attributed to loss of cytochrome oxidase activity (40).

Blood and Biochemical Changes. Low serum ceruloplasmin activity is often used as an indicator of Cu status. Reduced hemoglobin and hematocrit levels may be accompanied by a high incidence of hemoglobinurea. Increased liver Fe deposition most likely results from reduced Fe utilization. Decreases in plasma ferroxidase 1, plasma monoamine oxidase and liver cytochrome oxidase activities can be detected before the first overt clinical signs of Cu deficiency in cattle (39). Cytochrome oxidase may also be reduced in brain, intestinal mucosa and myocardial muscle. Other changes in ataxic Cu-deficient lambs include decreased dopamine and norepinephrine but not seratonin concentrations in the anterior brain (41).

Bone Changes. Cu plays an essential role in the function of enzymes involved in crosslinking between collagen precursors. Because structural integrity of collagen and thus normal bone formation is dependent on these processes, Cu deficiency can result in

Figure 18-3. A pacing heifer. This condition is believed to be due to a Cu deficiency. Courtesy of R.B. Becker, Florida Agr. Expt. Sta.

fragile, easily broken bones in ruminants. Clinical signs include enlargement of ends of long bones, beading of the ribs and other rachitic changes in young calves and osteomalacia in older animals (42). Cu-deficient cattle may develop a pacing gait (Fig. 18-3) due to marked stiffness of the legs. Lesions associated with Cu deficiency include abnormal development of the distal growth plates of the metacarpus and metatarsus (Fig. 18-4 and 5) and faulty hoof keratinization accompanying incomplete S cross-linking of hoof keratin (43). Decreased osteoblast activity and osteoporosis may result in marked bowing of the forelegs of sheep (Fig. 18-6).

Figure 18-4. Copper deficiency caused by normal Cu and high S and Mo. The back is arched, pasterns are straight, and the distal metacarpal ephyseal region is enlarged. Courtesy of B.P. Smith, Univ. of California, Davis.

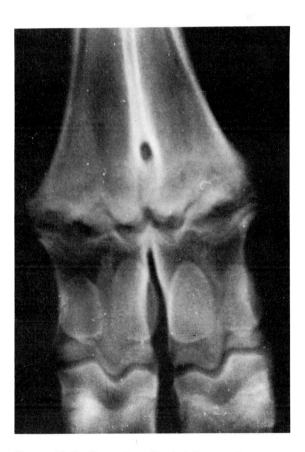

Figure 18-5. Secondary Cu deficiency. Anteroposteorior radiograph of distal metacarpal growth plate of severely affected calf, showing widened zone of cartilage and lipping of the medial and lateral areas of the growh plate. Courtesy of B.P. Smith, Univ. of California, Davis.

354

Figure 18-6. Osteoporosis in sheep. Note the marked outward bowing of the front legs of this lamb. This condition is apparently the result of too little Cu or too much Mo. Courtesy of W.J. Hartley, Univ. of Sidney.

Figure 18-7. Cu-deficient lamb showing the ataxia that sometimes occurs. Courtesy of W.J. Hartley, Univ. of Sidney.

Figure 18-8. Severe diarrhea produced by feeding 100 ppm of Mo to a heifer on an alfalfa ration. Courtesy of A.L. Lesperance, Univ. of Nevada.

Neonatal Ataxia or Swayback. This nervous disorder of lambs, and less frequently, of calves is characterized by incoordination and partial paralysis of hind quarters (Fig. 18-7). Muscular tremors, grinding of the teeth and dilation of the pupils of the eyes may also occur. Some of the lambs are paralyzed at birth and soon die; others develop the condition at a later date. Lesions in ataxic lambs include edema and cellular degeneration in the cerebrum and demyelination of nerve fibers in the cerebrum and spinal cord. Levels of Cu in blood, brain, liver and myelin are reduced and spinal cords are deficient in myelin lipid components such as cholesterol, cerebrosides and phospholipids (44). The first phase of myelination may be a critical time during pregnancy when an adequate supply of Cu from the ewe to the fetus is needed to prevent neonatal ataxia.

Diarrhea. A very severe diarrhea has been associated with Cu deficiency or Mo excess in cattle (Fig. 18-8) but only infrequently in sheep. Diarrhea in Cu-deficient steers has been correlated with mucosal atrophy in the small intestine, partial villus atrophy, elongation of crypts and goblet cell hyperplasia. These changes together with diminished cytochrome oxidase activity in the small intestine may produce a malabsorption syndrome resulting in decreased food conversion and diarrhea.

Depigmentation of Hair and Wool. Hair of cattle or wool of black sheep (Fig. 18-9) will not develop normal pigment (achromatrichia) due to insufficient tyrosinase activity. Pigment formation in black-fleeced sheep can be

Figure 18-9. Wool from normal and Cu-deficient sheep. On the left are typical normal black and white wools from sheep fed a basal diet. The other samples are from sheep on sulfate-Mo supplemented diets, showing banding of black wool, loss of definition of crimp and, in some, occurrence of secondary waves. From Church et al (4G).

Figure 18-10. Cu deficiency (left) induced by a low level of Cu and high levels of Mo and S. Note achromatricha (bleaching of hair) around eye and muzzle. Courtesy of N.F. Suttle, Moredun Institute, Edinburgh.

blocked within 2 d by raising Mo and sulfate in the diet. It is possible to produce alternating bands of dark and light wool (Fig. 18-10) by changing the diet frequently. Hair of Cu-deficient cattle may bleach, although there is a great deal of variation between individuals. Cu deficiency also reduces both quantity and quality of wool with loss of its characteristic crimp until the fibers resemble hair more than wool.

Effect on Fertility. Fertility may be reduced in Cu-deficient cows and ewes. There is no apparent association between libido and plasma Cu concentration in rams, but rams that induce pregnancy with the first service have higher Cu levels than those which are less successful.

Mo Deficiency. A deficiency of Mo, by itself, has not been described in ruminants. However, low dietary Mo (<0.2 ppm), insufficient to prevent adverse effects in sheep of Cu levels otherwise not excessive might be considered deficient.

Cu Toxicity

The range between inadequate and excessive dietary Cu levels for ruminants can be relatively narrow, although cattle are less susceptible than sheep to Cu toxicity. It is considered dangerous to exceed 10 ppm Cu for sheep for an extended period but the Cu requirement of calves appears to be near this level. The susceptibility of ruminants to Cu poisoning is partly due to continued Cu storage by the liver when intake is above that required in a given situation, no control mechanism being operative to restrict absorption and liver uptake. As a result, liver Cu concentrations may reach values exceeding 2,000 and even 4,000 ppm on a dry weight basis.

Causes of Cu poisoning of ruminants include administration of excessive Cu doses as antihelmintics or to correct Cu deficiency, accidental consumption of feed with high Cu content intended for swine, grazing too soon after application of Cu-containing fertilizer to pasture and exposure to Cu-based fungicides or insecticides. Hepatoxic plants such as *Heliotropium europaeum* or *Echium plantogineum* may make the liver more susceptible to accumulation of Cu. Prolonged feeding of concentrates to confined sheep can be dangerous, particularly if dietary levels of Mo and sulfate are low.

Symptoms Observed. Chronic Cu poisoning has three relatively distinct stages. During the first there is a gradual accumulation of Cu in the tissues, primarily the liver. No clinical symptoms are evident and blood Cu values are normal. This may occur over a period of 30 to 100 d. During stage 2, whole blood Cu may rise to about twice normal levels accompanied by increased plasma bilirubin,

356

decreased liver function and increased or decreased hematocrit, depending on route of Cu administration. Hematocrit increases if Cu is added to the diet or given orally but decreases following I.V. injection.

A variety of blood enzymes and metabolites may also increase. Gradual increases in plasma glutamic oxaloacetic transaminase (PGOT) and arginase occur during the clinically normal period as excessive amounts of Cu are stored in the liver. Both enzymes are thus useful as an aid in diagnosing Cu poisoning and for monitoring recovery. Of the two enzymes, arginase is the most useful for diagnosis because it is involved in the urea cycle and is found in large quantities only in the liver, whereas PGOT may indicate damage to tissues other than the liver (such as the heart).

The third stage is usually referred to as the hemolytic crisis. Clinical symptoms include accelerated breathing, elevated temperature, dullness, anorexia, dehydration, acute thirst, evidence of abdominal pain, jaundice and hemoglobinuria. The hemolytic crisis may be accompanied by an increased oxidative state of the blood, a sudden rise in serum creatine phosphokinase and erythrocyte distortion. Blood glutathione concentration falls drastically and whole blood Cu increases to 5-8 times normal. Total hemoglobin may drop as

much as 10 g/dl in 48 h (see Fig. 18-11), but methemoglobin increases and may account for as much as 60% of total hemoglobin. Elevated blood urea may indicate kidney damage, but changes in renal function and histology are not detected prior to the hemolytic crisis. These metabolic changes appear to result from degeneration of liver cells and sudden release of Cu into the blood. Animals generally die within 2-4 d after onset of clinical symptoms. Some breeds of sheep (Merino) are more resistant than others and may survive more than one crisis.

Post mortem findings indicate a generalized jaundice, including adipose tissue which may be a dirty-yellow color. The kidney has a distinctive black metallic sheen, the urinary bladder and gall bladder are apt to be distended with dark-colored fluids, and the spleen is enlarged, soft and dark. Outstanding histological changes include necrosis and fatty changes in liver, dilation and necrosis of renal tubules, petechial hemorrhages on the heart and splenic hemosiderosis. Added stress, change of environment, transportation, handling of animals, etc., are apt to trigger a hemolytic crisis.

Treatment or Prevention of Cu Poisoning. Hepatic Cu concentrations remain high and sheep may die months after withdrawal of excess Cu from the diet, so accumulated hepatic Cu must be reduced. Supplementation of feed with 0.1 g ammonium molybdate plus 1 g Na sulfate/sheep/d will prevent death losses in sheep with high and potentially lethal (45) Cu levels. Within 4 d after starting Mo-S supplementation, fecal Cu will increase but urinary Cu is not affected. Oral administration of 50 mg penicillamine/kg body weight/d induces cupriuresis but does not affect fecal Cu excretion (45).

Chronic Cu poisoning can be prevented by I.V. administration of thiomolybdate, a compound containing Mo and S (46). Amount of thiomolybdate must be adjusted to Cu intake because an excessive dose rate will cause diarrhea. Dietary Zn 5-10X the nutritional requirement may also have a protective effect against excess dietary Cu.

Mo Toxicity
The relationship between chronic high Mo intake and Cu metabolism has been discussed.

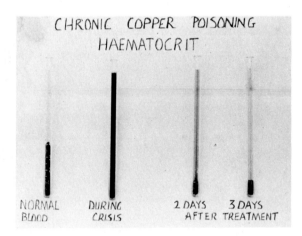

Figure 18-11. Hematocrits from sheep before, during and after the hemolytic crisis of acute Cu toxicity. Note in the second sample from the left (obtained during the crisis) that it is almost impossible to differentiate between plasma and cells. The amount of hemolysis that has occurred is shown by the two tubes on the right. Courtesy of J.R. Todd, Vet. Res. Lambs, Stormont, N. Ireland.

Mo is also acutely toxic, independent of its effects on Cu metabolism. It seems likely, however, that the great variety of problems that develop (i.e., swayback, falling disease, osteoporosis, achromatrichia and severe diarrhea) depend to some extent on the relative deficiency of Cu and the relative over-abundance of Mo. Severe acute Mo poisoning is unlikely due to refusal of poisoned feed. Mo in inorganic salts or as part of cured forage is less toxic than similar levels in grazed forages.

IODINE (I)

Goiter has been recognized since ancient times but it was not until the 18th century that its cause was linked to a deficiency of I. The metabolism of I has since been investigated intensively. These investigations have established much of the general knowledge on I metabolism in mammals and have suggested the most fruitful areas of study with ruminant animals.

Tissue Distribution

The primary physiological requirement for I is for synthesis by the thyroid gland of hormones which regulate the rate of energy metabolism. The thyroid gland concentrates I by an active process which is stimulated by thyroid stimulating hormone (TSH). The gastric mucosa, salivary glands, the placenta, and the mammary glands also transport I against a concentration gradient, but their uptake is not affected by TSH. Relative I concentrations in bovine tissues have been calculated from radioiodine data (1). The thyroid accumulates more I than the entire remaining body (Table 18-7). This is especially remarkable when it is considered that the thyroid of a 500 kg cow may weigh only 30 g. Nonthyroid tissue and fluid radioiodine concentrations, in descending order, are blood plasma, mammary gland, lung, kidney, lymph node, salivary gland, pancreas, adrenal, hoof, heart, spleen, liver and skeletal muscle. Swanson and Bacon (unpublished data, University of Tennessee) have recently analyzed bovine muscle and organ tissues for chemical I content (Table 18-8) and found thyroid gland to skeletal muscle ratios comparable to radioiodine ratios in Table 18-7. When cows receive adequate I, thyroid I

Table 18-7. Distribution of I in the bovine.[a]

Item	Relative weight	Relative I content
	. . . % of total body . . .	
Thyroid	0.006	55
GI tract contents	20	40
Muscle	37	I
Blood	7	1.2
Skeleton	15	0.7
Internal organs	15	1.3
Skin, hair, hoof, etc.	6	0.8

[a] From Miller et al (2). Based on radioiodine distribution after 6-8 daily doses.

Table 18-8. Mean I concentrations in blood plasma and tissues of Holstein cows fed a 0.9 ppm I diet supplemented with different levels of I as ethylenediaminedihydriodide.[†]

Tissue or fluid	Amount of I supplement, ppm			
	0	1	2	4
Blood plasma, ng/ml	114[a]	167[a]	192[b]	329[c]
Liver, ng/g	154[a]	175[a]	166[a]	213[b]
Heart, ng/g	168[a]	179[a]	194[a]	218[b]
Kidney, ng/g	195[a]	225[a]	243[b]	303[c]
Muscle, ng/g	162[a]	163[a]	170[a]	199[b]
Thyroid, μg/g	1672[a]	1653[a]	1915[a]	1936[a]

[†] Data from E.W. Swanson and J.A. Bacon, University of Tennessee (unpublished). Values in the same row with different superscripts are significantly different (P $<$ .05).

content is not altered by increasing dietary I by 4 ppm. Depletion of thyroid I in lambs grazing kale can be prevented, however, by supplemental I (3).

Inflamed or diseased tissues concentrate 24 to 218% more radioiodine (2) than corresponding healthy tissues, possibly because of infiltrating leucocytes. A microbicidal involvement of I by phagocytosing leucocytes (4) may be another important function of I in the body in addition to its role as a necessary component of thyroxine.

Thyroid Gland

The thyroid concentrates iodide from blood serum up to >100X. The active transport mechanism is dependent on TSH and also Na$^+$-K$^+$ATPase. In the gland, tyrosine bound to thyroglobulin is iodinated first in the 3-position (monoiodotyrosine), then in the 5-position (diiodotyrosine) under the

358

action of thyroid peroxidase. Thyroxine (T$_4$), still in linkage to thyroglobulin, is formed by oxidative condensation of two diiodotyrosine (DIT) molecules. T$_4$ is converted to 3,5,3' triiodotyronine (T$_3$) in the kidney and liver. T$_3$ also results from condensation of mono-iodotyrosine (MIT) with DIT. A small amount of 3,3',5' triiodotyronine (reverse T$_3$), which is without thyroid hormone activity, is also formed, probably by condensation of DIT with MIT (6G).

Peptide bonds between iodinated amino acids and thyroglobin are broken by proteases, liberating T$_4$, T$_3$, DIT and MIT into the cytoplasm. DIT and MIT are deiodinated by a microsomal dehalogenase which does not attack iodinated thyronines. T$_4$ and T$_3$ are released into the circulation and I from the deiodinated tyrosines is re-utilized.

The amount of I accumulated by the thyroid is partly a function of I status of the animal. Research with radioiodine has shown percentages of daily I consumption bound by the bovine thyroid to increase from 30% when I intake is near the minimum requirement to 65% or more with very low I intake. Intakes above the requirement, however, greatly reduce I uptake by the thyroid.

Thyroid secretion rates of cattle, measured by many investigators using different methods have been within the range of 0.2 to 0.3 mg/100 kg of body weight. Thyroxine

secretion rate is depressed by elevated environmental temperature and is influenced more by seasonal effects than by stage of lactation. Diet can markedly influence thyroid function. It is inhibited by a number of naturally occurring goitrogens, including those in plants of the genus *Brassica* and when large amounts of soybean meal are fed. Certain forages also contain factors which induce adjustments in thyroid activity when the forage fed is changed suddenly.

Absorption and Excretion

Results of many investigations have suggested the model for I metabolism in ruminants shown in Fig. 18-12. Between 70 and 80% of the daily I intake is absorbed directly from the rumen and an additional 10% from the omasum. Although some I is absorbed directly from the abomasum, re-entry of circulating I into the GI tract predominates here. Net absorption subsequently occurs from the small and large intestine, including the cecum, at a rate similar to that of other dry matter.

I is secreted by the chief and mucosal cells of the gastric mucosa, and its concentration in abomasal contents relative to blood plasma exceeds that of Cl by >15X in calves dosed daily with both ^{131}I and ^{36}Cl. Over 65% of a radioiodine dose given intravenously to mature cows can be recovered from the abomasum in 6 h (Table 18-9). More than

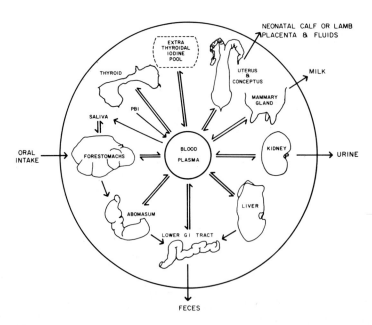

Figure 18-12. A model for the suggested metabolism of I. Church et al (4G).

Table 18-9. Thyroid uptake and recovery in bovine abomasal drainage of radioiodine during 6 h after intravenous ministration of ^{131}I-iodide or ^{125}I-thyroxine.[a]

Treatment and form of radioiodine dose	Material	
	Thyroid	Abomasal content
	. . . . % of dose	
Control, ^{131}I-iodide dose	1.7	66.7
Control, ^{125}I-thyroxine dose	0.22	3.9
100 mg I/d, ^{131}I-iodide dose	0.13	63.6
1000 mg I/d, ^{131}I-iodide dose	0.0002	69.6
10 g NaSCN/d, ^{131}I-iodide dose	0.57	26.0

[a]From Miller et al (1)

Table 18-10. Concentrations of I in milk and blood serum of cows fed increasing I levels.[a]

I intake, mg/d	Serum I, ng/ml	Milk I, ng/ml	Milk/serum, ratio
12	109	216	2.0
28	157	449	2.9
40	167	450	2.7
80	247	893	3.6
160	398	1559	3.1
400	1351	2036	1.5
800	1971	2393	1.2

[a]From E.W. Swanson and J.A. Bacon, University of Tennessee (unpublished) and Miller and Swanson (6).

17X more radioiodine administered as iodide than as thyroxine enters the abomasum, indicating iodide is the primary form concentrated by the gastric mucosa. High dietary I (10-100X normal intake), which effectively blocks thyroid uptake, does not reduce abomasal radioiodine secretion, but the goitrogen, thiocyanate, reduces radioiodine concentration by both the thyroid and abomasum. Because the kidney has essentially no threshold for I, recycling through the abomasum may promote conservation of I by transferring it from vascular to extravascular spaces, thereby preventing its excessive loss in urine.

Some of the thyroxine from plasma is constantly being degraded or conjugated in the liver and secreted via bile into the digestive tract where about 10% is reabsorbed. Major irreversible I losses from the body include urine, feces and milk (Fig. 18-12). I losses average 25% in feces and 40% in urine when daily I intake is normal (<20 μg/kg body weight/d). Urinary radioiodine excretion can be increased markedly with increasing dietary I and at daily intakes above 2 mg/kg body weight it may even exceed the daily dose for short periods. Elevated dietary I has little effect on the fraction of I intake excreted in feces and total fecal I increases in almost direct proportion to increased supplemental I (1).

Secretion in Milk

Important species differences exist in concentration of I into milk. Amounts of radioiodine secreted into milk of ruminant species average 8% of the dose for cows, 22% for goats and 39% for sheep. In the cow, unlike

the rat (5), entry of I into the mammary gland is not dependent on active secretion of milk. I enters milk primarily as iodide and as naturally secreted is <10% bound. Reabsorption of radioiodine from the udder, measured as that not recovered in milk 7 to 19 h after intramammary infusion, averages 82-94% in cows and goats. Balance between secretion and reabsorption thus determines net I content of milk.

Stable I content in milk varies linearly within the normal dietary range if other conditions are equal (Table 18-10). The capacity of the cow's mammary gland to secrete additional I appears to be reduced at I intakes between 160 and 400 mg daily. Massive I intakes (1-4 g/d) reduce ^{131}I concentration in milk by one-third to one-half.

Attempts to relate I concentrations in milk to stage of lactation, amount of milk produced and to seasonal effects have not been consistent. Effects of production or stage of lactation can be obscured by seasonal effects, which in turn are complicated by dietary variations. I concentrations are higher in colostrum than in normal milk (7) and may rise in normal milk with declining yield as lactation progresses (8). However, when the diet is deficient in I, depletion of I reserves may mask the normal tendency for I concentration to increase in milk with advancing lactation (9).

There is an inverse relationship between the amount of blood thyroxine and secretion of radioiodine into milk. Hypothyroid cows yield half as much milk that contains twice as much of a radioiodine dose as compared to

360

euthyroid cows. Treating the hypothyroid cows with exogenous thyroxine increases milk and reduces secretion of radioiodine into the milk (10). Goitrogenic substances in feed may also influence I concentrations in milk. One class of goitrogens, including perchlorate, thiocyanate and nitrate, blocks the uptake of inorganic iodide and reduces secretion of I into milk. In contrast, methylthiouracil, which is goitrogenic due to its inhibition of organic binding of I by the thyroid gland, increases milk I concentrations. Dairy cattle can adapt to low I intakes by reducing losses in milk, urine and feces (9) and when dietary I is adequate, lactation has little effect on the percentage bound by the thyroid (11).

Total I content of the developing bovine embryo is negligible prior to 60 d, but then increases in almost direct proportion to thyroid mass and body weight until day 138. Fetal thyroids contain more I than can be accounted for by increased thyroid mass by day 140, and reach I concentrations comparable to the adult level by 240 d of development (1). I turnover is more rapid in fetal than in maternal thyroids because the much larger maternal gland has been found to accumulate only about half as much radioiodine 24 h after dosing but about the same amount by 7 d.

I concentrations are usually 4-8X higher in bovine fetal plasma and amniotic fluid than in corresponding maternal plasma. Much of this is due to thyroxine which may be more than double the maternal concentration in second and third trimesters. Elevated circulating I and thyroxine in the neonatal calf clear rapidly during the first few days after birth, indicating the fetus may not be able to excrete I efficiently. After parturition, accumulated I is eliminated by normal urinary and fecal excretions.

Dietary Requirements

Theoretical dietary requirements for I can be based on feed intake, thyroid uptake efficiency, daily thyroxine secretion rate, and amount of thyroxine recycled. A daily thyroxine secretion rate of 0.2 to 0.3 mg/100 kg body weight would utilize about 0.7 mg I if the thyroid accumulated 30% of the dietary intake. Recycling of 15% of the thyroxine I would reduce the I requirement to 0.6

mg/100 kg body weight. At dry matter intakes of 2.5% of body weight, feed should contain 0.25 ppm I to supply this amount. This calculation indicates currently recommended I contents of 0.25-0.5 ppm (7G) in ration dry matter should be adequate for dairy cattle. Recommendations for other ruminant classes are 0.05 to 0.1 ppm for breeding beef cattle and 0.1 to 0.8 ppm for sheep (3G). Requirements may be somewhat higher during stress or lactation or when availability of dietary I to the thyroid has been reduced by goitrogenic feeds.

Utilization of Iodine Sources

The need for I supplementation to the diet of farm animals in certain areas has been well established. Many of the early positive responses to I supplementation were obtained with NaI or KI. Comparisons of other I compounds to iodide (Table 18-11) have shown Ca iodate, pentacalcium orthoperiodate (PCOP), K iodate, Na iodate and ethylenediaminedihydriodide (EDDI) to be comparable to NaI or KI in nutritional availability to ruminants (8G). Adequacy of an I source, however, depends on its physical as well as nutritional availability. Iodide and iodate, unfortunately, may be lost when mixed with other minerals or exposed to outdoor weather conditions. While physically stable, I from 3,5-diiodosalicyclic acid (DIS) is only about

Table 18-11. Thyroid uptakes by dairy cows and their neonatal calves of radioiodine following single prepartum doses with different radioiodine labeled compounds.[a]

| | Uptake, % of dose | |
Compound	Cows	Calves
Diiodosalicylic acid	2.2	1.9
Calcium iodate	17.1	14.5
Calcium periodate	17.6	13.8
EDDI	19.8	--
Sodium Iodide	17.3	13.8

[a]From Church et al (4G). ^{125}I-labeled compounds were compared with ^{131}I-labeled NaI by simultaneous within animal dosing in each experiment. Values from different experiments were expressed on a common basis by multiplying the ^{125}I/^{131}I ratio in each experiment by the ^{131}I average for all experiments.

20% as available to cattle as I from iodide and, when fed to ewes, it does not prevent subsequent I deficiency symptoms in their newborn lambs. Although rats utilize DIS efficiently, cows have much less ability to remove I atoms from the DIS molecule before it is excreted. PCOP combines physical stability with nutritional availability to cattle.

Deficiency

I deficiency may be a geographical problem where feeds and water are low in I or conditioned by presence of goitrogens. More than a year on low I diets may be required before deficiency symptoms are observed (9, 12). Usually, the first obvious sign is enlarged thyroid (goiter) in the newborn even though the dam may appear normal. Goiter results from changes in thyroid cells (Fig. 18-13) which enlarge the gland (Fig. 18-14). Deficiency during pregnancy may result in birth of hairless (or wool-less) weak or dead young, but only moderate goiter (hyperplasia of thyroid gland follicles without gross enlargement) may be observed in young animals with normal hair or wool.

Obvious goiter has been observed in adult sheep (Fig. 18-15) but usually is not seen in adult cattle. Other signs of severe or longterm I insufficiency include decreased wool growth (3), lower milk yield and reduced reproductive performance as evidenced by

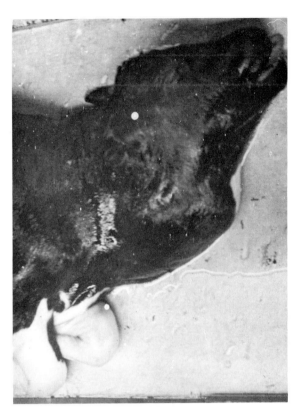

Figure 18-14. I-deficient calf. Note massive goiter. Calf was born about one month prematurely. Courtesy of J.H. Vandersall, Univ. of Maryland.

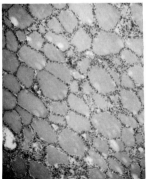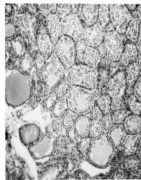

Figure 18-13. Microphotographs from thyroids of day-old lambs. That on the left is from a lamb whose dam had been supplemented with I. The picture on the right is from a deficient lamb. The section of the normal gland shows typical cells filled with colloid and flat epithelial cells. The deficient gland has few colloid filled cells and many high columnar-type cells. Courtesy of P.W. Aschbacher, N. Dakota State Univ.

Figure 18-15. Ewe showing a goiter due to I deficiency. Courtesy of W.W. Hawkins, Vet. Res. Lab., Montana State Univ.

irregular breeding intervals, low conception rate and retained placentas (13). Milk concentrations below 20 mg/ℓ are typical from cows in I-deficient areas (14). The observation that sheep can maintain normal T_3 levels

362

with dietary I inadequate for maximum T_4 production (3) suggests this may be an attempt to compensate for marginal I intake. This adjustment is advantageous because T_3 not only contains less I but also has higher biological activity than T_4.

Toxicity

EDDI has been fed to cattle at levels much higher than the nutritional requirement for prevention or systemic treatment of mycotic infections (15). Recommended daily I intakes range from prophylactic 40 mg to therapeutic doses of over 2,000 mg. All animals can tolerate I levels far in excess of their requirements, although species differ widely in susceptibility to I toxicity (5G). Pigs can tolerate 400 ppm I without adverse effects but toxic signs may appear in calves consistently fed 50 to 100 ppm. Young stock are more sensitive to excess I than are lactating cows. Toxicity signs include excessive salivation, watery nasal discharge, tracheal congestion which causes coughing, excessive lacrimation, and subnormal feed intake and growth rate. However, rapid recovery follows removal of the excess I from the diet.

IRON (Fe)

Fe, at 5% of the earth's crust, exceeds each of the essential major elements in abundance. Despite this fact, together with relatively low Fe requirements and ingenious mechanisms in the body to maintain Fe balance, Fe deficiency is one of the most common deficiency diseases in the world. In ruminants, Fe deficiency is unlikely in the adult but may occur in young animals fed milk for an extended period.

Fe in the Tissues

Whole body Fe content in both the ovine and bovine is near 60 ppm on fresh weight basis (1). Fe is present in all cells of the body and is involved in many biochemical reactions. Although the major portion of total body Fe is in hemoglobin (60-70%), myoglobin (3%) and in storage (26%), a small portion (<1%) is found in a number of enzymes. Catalases and peroxidases are heme enzymes which liberate oxygen from peroxides. Hemoglobin also has peroxidase action. The cyto-chromes are heme enzymes occurring in the cell mitochondria which provide a system for electron transfer through the capacity of the Fe atom to undergo reversible oxidation. Other Fe-containing enzymes include non-heme metalo-flavoproteins such as xanthine oxidase, succinic dehydrogenase and NADH reductase. The muscle proteins myosin and actomysin contain small amounts of Fe, the function of which remains to be shown.

Hemoglobin is a complex of globin and four ferroprotoporphrin moieties with a molecular weight close to 65,000 and an Fe content of about 0.35%. Hemoglobin functions as an oxygen carrier because the bonds between Fe and globin stabilize Fe in the ferrous state and allow it to be reversibly bonded to oxygen. When the Fe atom is oxidized to the ferric state (as in methemoglobin), it loses its capacity to carry oxygen. In ruminants, blood hemoglobin concentrations vary from about 12 g/dl in normal adults to half that concentration in young calves fed milk unsupplemented with Fe. Myoglobin, the heme-protein in muscle, has an Fe content of about 0.12%. Its structure is like that of hemoglobin, but it contains only one ferrous prophyrin group per molecule and has a molecular weight of only 16,500. Myoglobin has a greater affinity for oxygen than hemoglobin and thus can accept oxygen released by hemoglobin and serve as an oxygen reservoir.

Fe is present in blood serum in a non-hemoglobin form called transferrin or siderophilin. Transferrin is a glycoprotein which binds two atoms of ferric Fe per molecule and appears to serve as a carrier for Fe in the same way that hemoglobin acts as a carrier for oxygen. Transferrin may also participate in defense mechanisms of the body against infection. Normal plasma contains 240-280 mg transferrin per dl. Transferrins are also found in other extracellular fluids such as cerebrospinal fluid. Plasma transferrin is measured by the amount of Fe that plasma will bind before saturation. In normal individuals of most species only 30-40% of the Fe-binding capacity of transferrin in serum is utilized, the remainder representing an unbound reserve. Percentage saturation of plasma transferrin is much lower than this when dietary Fe is insufficient (Table 18-12). The sum of serum Fe plus the additional Fe required to reach the saturation limit is its total Fe-binding capacity.

Table 18-12. Fe concentrations in plasma and tissues of calves fed different levels of Fe for 12 weeks.[a]

	Dietary iron, ppm		
	10	40	100
Hemoglobin, g/ℓ	65	107	111
Plasma Fe, μg/dl	45	78	323
Transferrin saturation, %	5.5	9.1	39.7
Total Fe binding capacity, μg/dl	865	845	824
Tissue Fe, μg/g DM			
Liver	125	84	103
Spleen	850	936	1,191
Kidney	120	100	171
Heart	234	185	234
Muscle	31	25	41

[a]From Bremner and Dalgarno (2)

Table 18-13. Fe concentrations in serum and tissues of cattle of different ages.

Tissue and unit	Age, years			
	0.2[a]	1-3[b]	4-6[b]	7-9[b]
Blood serum, μg/dl	30	143	146	141
Liver, μg/g dry wt	60	128	235	223
Spleen, μg/g dry wt	309	3,067	20,614	30,740
Bone marrow, μg/g dry wt	--	28	62	100

[a]Milk fed calves
[b]From Blum and Zuber (6)

The reserve or storage Fe of the body occurs predominantly in two non-heme compounds, ferritin and hemosiderin. From two-thirds to three-fourths of total storage Fe in bovine and ovine livers is water soluble, presumably ferritin. Ferritin contains up to 20% Fe. Its central Fe nucleus is surrounded by a spherical protein shell of 24 subunits with a combined molecular weight of 445,000 (3). Hemosiderin consists mainly of ferric hydroxide in an essentially protein-free aggregate and may contain up to 35% Fe (2G). The ratio of ferritin to hemosiderin is determined by total level as well as by rate of Fe storage. In most mammals, ferritin is the primary Fe storage compound when the total level of stored Fe is low; at higher storage levels, hemosiderin may predominate. Serum ferritin is directly proportional to Fe stores under normal conditions and has been used as an index of Fe status. Concentrations of ferritin in bovine blood serum average near 4 μg/dl in cows (4) and <1 μg/dl in calves fed milk unsupplemented with Fe (5).

Much higher Fe concentrations are found in the spleen than in other tissues of the bovine (Tables 18-12 and 13). Fe concentrations in the spleen increase markedly with age but serum Fe remains relatively constant between 1 and 8 y of age (Table 18-13). Relative amounts of ^{59}Fe deposited in tissues 96 h after oral administration as ferric chloride to Fe-depleted calves were liver > spleen > kidney > heart > rib (7). Higher ^{59}Fe concentrations in liver than in spleen contrast with data in Tables 18-12 and 18-13, suggesting ^{59}Fe may not have achieved equilibrium with total

Fe in the body by 96 h. Time required for red blood cell uptake and deposition of ^{59}Fe in the spleen probably contributed to this difference.

Fe traverses the placenta of sheep and cattle at all stages of gestation and apparently is related directly to the amount of Fe actually required for incorporation into growing tissues (9G). Fe accumulation by ovine tissues, expressed either as the total amount or as a percentage of that in the whole fetal complex (fetus, fluids and placental membranes) increases almost exponentially between 47 and 141 d of gestation.

Mean uptake of intravenously administered ^{59}Fe by red blood cells ranges from 52 (8) to 72% (9) in sheep and 65% (10) in calves. Red blood cell lifespan averages 112 d (8). Half of intravenously injected ^{59}Fe clears sheep plasma in 2.5 h (8) which agrees with the first exponential component of the clearance curve for cows and goats (11). Plasma ^{59}Fe clearance rates can be analyzed into two exponential components with half times of 2-4 and 20-60 h in cows and 2.9-4 and 38-55 h in goats. ^{59}Fe administered intravenously to cows either as the Cl or specifically bound to transferrin is not distinguishable as separate pools by this technique. Fe deficiency in calves shortens half time of plasma Fe clearance, lowers plasma Fe concentration and red cell uptake of injected ^{59}Fe, and raises unsaturated Fe binding capacity (10).

While short-term ferokinetic studies are useful for comparative purposes, complete equilibration of ^{59}Fe with total body Fe during the relatively brief period monitored is unlikely. This problem has been avoided by using the long-lived isotope ^{55}Fe and allowing a prolonged period for it to become mixed with Fe in the blood and tissues (12). The

364

Table 18-14. Fe loss, turnover and physiological requirements of sheep and cows measured by [55]Fe clearance from blood.[a]

Measurement and unit	82 kg Sheep	468 kg Cows
Fe intake, g/d	1.6	4.2
Start of [55]Fe turnover slope, d	168.0	168.0
Red cell [55]Fe loss half-time, d	671.0	761.0
Estimated miscible Fe, mg/kg body wt	42.0	46.0
Body Fe turnover, mg/kg body wt/d	42.0	41.0
Total physiological Fe requirement, mg/d	4.0	19.0
Dietary Fe absorbed, %	0.2	0.4

[a]From Finch et al (12)

half time of red blood cell [55]Fe loss between 196 and 966 d after administration was 681 d in sheep and 761 d in cows (Table 18-14).

Absorption and Excretion

The amount of Fe absorbed is dictated by body needs, so absorption plays the determining role for the homeostasis of Fe metabolism. Fe in the intestinal lumen adsorbs to specific receptors in the brush border of the mucosal cell (13, 14). Mucosal transferrin, an Fe-binding protein similar to plasma transferrin, is thought to transport Fe across the brush border into the cytoplasm (15). Changes in amounts of transferrin in response to Fe status of an individual (16) undoubtedly contribute to regulation of Fe absorption. Upon release into the cytoplasm, Fe can be incorporated into ferritin or transported into the blood stream. At the serosal surface of the cell, Fe becomes attached to transferrin in the plasma. Ceruloplasmin, a Cu-containing serum protein, catalyzes the oxidation of Fe for binding to plasma transferrin (17). An intracellular pool of low molecular weight Fe compounds may act as an intermediate between extracellular Fe and a wide variety of intracellular processes.

The rate of erythropoiesis and the state of body Fe stores act to control absorption, particularly at the level of serosal transfer. Populations of receptors during mucosal cell formation may be controlled by homeostatic mechanisms within the body. Receptors on the brush border change slowly over several days in response to Fe status. Changes in transport across the serosal surface, which may be more responsive to changes in Fe status, occur with a somewhat shorter time

lag. Fe not transported to plasma is retained in the cell until it is sloughed off, thus returning to the lumen of the GI tract.

Movement through the GI tract and excretion of Fe have been measured in lactating cows fitted with rumen fistulae and re-entrant cannulae in the proximal duodenum (18). From an average daily intake of 5.9 g Fe, 5.2 g entered the small intestine, 6.3 g left the small intestine, and 5.4 g was recovered in feces. These results indicate net secretion of Fe into the small intestine, net absorption from the large intestine, and overall apparent Fe availability of 7.5%. Other daily recoveries of Fe were 33 mg in milk and 32 mg in urine. These data agree favorably with total recoveries of oral ^{59}Fe doses to sheep of 84 to 98% in feces and 0.04 to 0.05% in urine (Fig. 18-16), but indicate greater Fe absorption than estimated by dividing Fe turnover (assumed to equal the physiological requirement of Fe) by Fe intake (Table 18-14). Fe turnover from decline in specific activity of [55]Fe in circulating red cells may be less subject to error than balance data, but division of Fe turnover by dietary Fe would underestimate Fe absorption at high intakes. Most of the Fe in feces represents that unabsorbed from food. Fe once absorbed is tenaciously retained by the body.

Previously it was believed Fe was absorbed only in the ferrous (Fe^{++}) form because of the low solubility of ferric (Fe^{+++}) ions at neutral pH. Neither oxidation state of Fe exists in ionic form to any appreciable extent

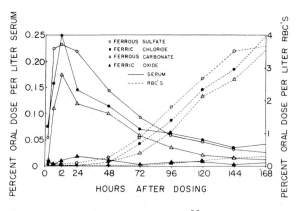

Figure 18-16. Effect of form of ^{59}Fe on uptake by red cells and serum by sheep following an oral dose. Note the negligible uptake from ferric oxide. From Church et al (4G).

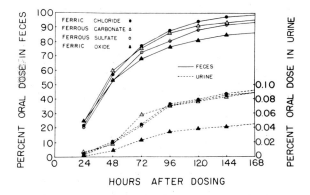

Figure 18-17. Accumulative fecal and urinary excretion by sheep of ^{59}Fe as influenced by form of Fe. Note the difference in urinary excretion of ferric oxide. From Ammerman et al (7).

under physiological conditions. Still the relationship between solubility in the digestive tract and absorption of Fe is important (Fig. 18-17). Chelates of ferric Fe are absorbed better than ferrous sulfate (19), the form once considered to be the most readily absorbed. Agents which form stable Fe chelates in the GI tract may prevent uptake of Fe by acceptor sites on mucosal cells, thus inhibiting absorption of Fe. However, weaker agents which form Fe chelates of lower stability may release their Fe to acceptor sites. These weaker agents may keep Fe available for absorption by reducing formation of poorly absorbed hydroxides and phosphates.

Sources of Fe

Leguminous plants are generally richer in Fe than grasses grown in the same sites. The normal range in legume forage is 200-400 ppm (dry basis), although values as high as 700-800 ppm have been reported for uncontaminated alfalfa. Grasses grown on sandy soils may contain 40 ppm or less. The level of Fe in pastures and forage can be affected greatly by contamination with soil and dust. Preservation and storage may influence availability of Fe in forage. Serum Fe and percentage transferrin saturation were higher in sheep fed formic acid-treated grass silage than in sheep fed hay from the same field (20). Cereal grains contain 30-60 ppm and oilseed meals 100-200 ppm. Most feeds of animal origin and some mineral supplements including ground limestone, oyster shell and many forms of Ca phosphate are excellent sources

of Fe. Milk is the one exception with an average Fe concentration of only 0.5 mg/ℓ.

Biological availabilities of various dietary Fe supplements have been compared on the basis of ^{59}Fe excretion and tissue deposition (7, 21), effectiveness in preventing hematological changes (2), or by regression of Fe balance on increasing Fe intake (22). Soluble sources such as ferric citrate, ferrous sulfate, ferrous carbonate and ferric chloride are comparable in availability to calves or sheep. In comparison with these compounds, Fe availability is higher for chelated sources such as Fe-EDTA, but much lower for ferric oxide or Fe phytate. As determined in moderately anemic calves, Fe from milk protein substitutes such as fish concentrate and soy flour is about 50 and 25%, respectively, as available as that from ferrous sulfate. Comparison of oral Fe supplements with injectible Fe-dextran sources suggest a much greater utilization of the injected compounds.

Fe Requirements

Determinations of dietary Fe requirement are influenced by age, growth rate, availability of source and criteria of adequacy chosen. Measurements are complicated further by homeostatic control mechanisms which reduce percentage Fe retention with increasing Fe intake. Fe requirements are defined more precisely for the young calf than for adult sheep or cattle. Decreases in serum Fe and blood hemoglobin in calves fed a milk substitute containing 19 ppm Fe for 12 wk were prevented by injection at 3 wk intervals with 800-900 mg Fe as Fe dextrin (10). These injections supplied less than one-fifth the daily dietary Fe requirement estimated from ferrokinetic data to be 160-180 mg for a 100-kg calf gaining 1 kg/d (10). Whole milk fed at 10% of body weight must be supplemented to contain 110-130 ppm Fe on a dry basis to provide this amount. Only 40 ppm Fe in milk on a dry basis prevented all but a very mild anemia in calves, but saturation of transferrin after 11 wk was less than one-fourth that in calves fed 100 ppm Fe (2). There was no difference in myoglobin content between calves receiving 10 and 40 ppm of Fe, but blood hemoglobin content was reduced at the lower intake (23). However, myoglobin content of veal from calves fed milk powder with 100 ppm of Fe was twice

366

that of veal from calves fed 40 ppm. Of course, calves raised for veal are intentionally kept in an anemic state because of the premium paid for their pale meat. Provided other complications do not affect performance, such anemic calves appear to grow almost as well as do Fe-supplemented animals.

From a practical point of view, Fe deficiency is usually not a problem in ruminants consuming food other than milk. Estimated Fe requirements for sheep and cows (Table 18-14) represent amounts required for growth and to replace turnover losses which, when divided by percentage Fe absorption, estimate dietary Fe requirements. Unfortunately, Fe turnover divided by what appears to be more than adequate Fe intake may underestimate apparent absorption (Table 18-14). This in turn would over estimate dietary Fe requirement. Fe requirements are probably modified to a considerable extent by other nutrients in the diet. For example, high levels of Mo will depress serum Fe as well as hemoglobin in lambs. An Fe level in the dry diet of 100 ppm should be adequate for calves to 3 mo of age with 35 ppm sufficient for other cattle (7G). Based on other data, these levels should also be adequate for sheep. If pale veal is of crucial importance, 30-40 ppm may be more desirable.

Deficiency

Fe deficiency in grazing sheep or cattle is unlikely unless there is chronic blood loss from parasites or disease. Anemia may develop in sheep infested with the parasite *Schistosomo mattheei* due to gastro-intestinal hemorrhage (24) because sheep are unable to re-utilize significant amounts of Fe from erythrocytes passed into the gut (9). *Trypanosoma congolense* infection in cattle is characterized by reduced hemoglobin and packed cell volume with initial hypoferremia, then hyperferremia following a hemolytic crisis (25). Although these may be exceptions, supplementation with Fe has corrected anemia in grazing cattle in some areas of Florida and helped to maintain milk yields on newly developed pastures.

Fe reserves of the neonatal calf are variable, but are usually sufficient to prevent serious anemia if dry feeds are provided within the first few weeks of age. It is when young animals are fed exclusively on a milk diet for

Figure 18-18. Lamb on right was fed 10 ppm Fe and developed symptoms of Fe deficiency. Normal lamb on left received 70 ppm Fe. From Church et al (4G).

several weeks as in veal production that Fe deficiency anemia develops. Hematological changes in calves fed milk diets unsupplemented with Fe may include reduced hematocrit, hemoglobin and serum Fe levels and lower saturation of transferrin (Table 18-12). Other changes include anorexia, lowered resistance to circulatory stresses, higher than normal pulse rate, labored breathing, reduced tissue concentrations of Fe and cytochrome C, and atrophy of the papillae of the tongue. Weight gains may or may not be reduced, depending on duration and severity of Fe deficiency. Symptoms in lambs include anorexia, depressed growth and emaciation (Fig. 18-18). In contrast to calves, hemoglobin, RBC count, and packed cell volumes tend to be higher in deficient lambs, suggesting hemoconcentration.

Toxicity

Excess dietary Fe can reduce feed consumption, weight gains and milk yield and cause diarrhea in ruminants. Measurable effects have been produced in lambs consuming 210-280 ppm but cattle can tolerate 1,000-2,000 ppm (5G). Undesirable effects of excess Fe are more likely when other nutrients, such as Cu or P, are near deficiency. Tissue Cu in calves fed 900 ppm Fe for 32 wk compared to controls fed 100 ppm Fe was reduced 95% in liver, 79% in plasma and 62% in RBC; plasma ceruloplasmin was only 11% of controls (26). However, feed intake and weight gain were not affected adversely and no symptoms of Cu deficiency such as skeletal lesions or changes in hair texture or color were found.

Toxicity of Fe is governed largely by its absorption because of the limited capacity of the body to excrete Fe. This may explain why more Fe from natural feed sources than from soluble compounds is tolerated. Toxic reactions can occur when plasma Fe is in excess of the physiological Fe-binding capacity. This loosely bound Fe is rapidly removed from the plasma but deposited premarily in the liver and spleen with little increase in kidney, heart or skeletal muscle. Maximum tolerable levels of dietary Fe have been set at 1,000 ppm for cattle and 500 ppm for sheep (5G). Higher levels can probably be tolerated when Fe is supplied from sources with low bioavailability.

MANGANESE (Mn)

Mn has been recognized as a required trace element for over 50 years and its deficiency can result in a wide variety of structural and metabolic defects (1). Much remains to be learned, however, about its specific biochemical roles. While Mn deficiency is a more serious practical problem with poultry than with sheep or cattle, ruminants are affected in some practical situations.

Tissue Mn

Mn is present in very small amounts in most tissues, averaging only 2.5 ppm (dry matter basis) in the total carcasses of lambs and calves (2). It is unevenly distributed with relatively higher concentrations in mitochondria rich tissues such as liver but low in muscle (Table 18-15). Heart, cartilage, gonadal tissues, hair and wool also contain appreciable amounts. The mitochondria are the principal sites for Mn uptake. In blood, Mn is transported in the trivalent form by a globulin protein called transmangin where one metal ion binds more than one protein molecule. Mn concentrations are about twice as high in RBC as in plasma.

Increasing dietary Mn increases soft tissue Mn concentrations but does not cause large accumulations if 2,000 ppm is not exceeded (3). Mn increases most in liver, a primary organ for Mn homeostasis, and bile, an important route of Mn excretion (4). As dietary Mn increases, uptake and specific activity of ^{54}Mn in ruminant tissues decrease (4, 5).

Turnover rates of ^{54}Mn differ widely among various tissues indicating a wide range in affinity for Mn. Radioactive Mn clears rapidly from calf blood following I.V. injection with only 0.3% or less remaining 30 min later (6). Liver initially accumulates most of the total body ^{54}Mn but releases it rapidly. Turnover of ^{54}Mn is also relatively fast in gall bladder, spleen, pancreas, small intestine and other visceral organs, but slower in muscle, bone and skin. The skeleton may contain 35% of the retained ^{54}Mn by 4 d after dosing (7). Most of the bone Mn is believed to be deposited in the inorganic portion, but a small portion is associated with the organic matrix.

Mn concentrations in the vagina are higher in cycling than in anestrous ruminants (8).

Table 18-15. Tissue Mn concentrations in sheep fed practical diets with different amounts of Mn added as MnO or $MnCO_3$.[a]

Sample	Amount and source of added Mn, ppm						
	Oxide					Carbonate	
	0	500	1,000	2,000	4,000	2,000	4,000
Serum, µg/dl	4.4	5.8	8.3	7.6	16.1	4.3	7.1
Tissue, ppm DM							
Liver	9.0	19.5	37.4	45.8	232.2	19.3	39.1
Kidney	4.2	6.4	19.5	16.4	34.8	12.8	20.7
Spleen	1.0	1.7	4.1	3.6	6.6	2.3	5.1
Heart	1.7	2.5	4.0	4.3	5.2	3.3	4.0
Muscle	0.4	0.7	0.7	1.0	1.0	1.0	1.0

[a]From Black et al (3)

368

Mn is higher in the corpus luteum on day 11 than on day 4 of the estrus cycle. The higher mobilization of Mn in the corpus luteum on day 11 is related to its abundance of mitochondria at this stage of the cycle. Mn content of reproductive tissues such as ovaries reflects dietary Mn intake, suggesting a relationship between availability of Mn and fertility (8). About 6% of absorbed ^{54}Mn is transferred to placental tissues, fluid and fetal tissues in pregnant sheep or cows (Fig. 18-19). Concentration of radioactivity in the placenta of pregnant ewes peaks 12 h after injection of ^{54}Mn when the placental concentration represents more than half of the total ^{54}Mn in the fetal compartment (9). By 168 h, placental concentration decreases to about 25% of the total fetal compartment but more than half of the ^{54}Mn is accumulated by the fetus, suggesting comparatively rapid transfer of Mn from ewe to fetus. Liver Mn concentrations are two fold greater in newborn lambs than in adult sheep, possibly reflecting inability of the gut and liver to regulate Mn absorption and excretion before birth (10). The enzyme manganese superoxide dismutase (MnSOD) accounts for less than 5% of total liver Mn in young lambs, but increases to approximately 30% in adult sheep. In contrast, MnSOD activity accounts for nearly all of the Mn content of heart tissue from both young lambs and adult sheep. Bovine milk normally contains about 0.03 ppm Mn, but the level can be increased 2-4 fold by feeding large amounts of Mn.

Functions

Mn functions biochemically either as a cofactor activating a large number of enzymes or as an integral part of certain metalloenzymes (11). Although many different enzymes can be stimulated by Mn, the effects are not specific for Mn in most cases, and the enzymes are not affected by Mn deficiency. A pathway specific for Mn, however, is activation of the glycosyl transferases which are required for synthesis of glucosaminoglycans (mucopolysaccharides). Mn is thus required for normal formation of skeletal cartilage.

Pyruvate carboxylase and MnSOD are Mn metalloenzymes. Pyruvate carboxylase catalyzes the first step of carbohydrate synthesis from pyruvate. Mn may not be specifically required for pyruvate carboxylase function because Mg, which is similar in chemistry, can replace Mn without changing enzyme properties (11). MnSOD belongs to a group of enzymes which catalyze the dismutation of superoxide free radical to hydrogen peroxide and water. These enzymes, in concert with glutathione peroxidase, chain-breaking antioxidants such as vitamin E and various other radical scavengers, minimize accumulation of reactive forms of oxygen which could damage cells.

Another superoxide dismutase from animal tissues contains Cu and Zn (Cu-ZnSOD). This enzyme functions primarily in the aqueous phase of the cytosol and plasma whereas MnSOD is present in cellular and subcellular membranes. Mn deficiency reduces MnSOD activity with concomitant increases in Cu-ZnSOD. Reduced MnSOD activity due to dietary deficiency of Mn is associated with higher than normal levels of lipid peroxidation in liver mitochondria (12). Adequate Mn during the development in utero may also be required for normal insulin synthesis and secretion in later life (1).

Absorption and Metabolism of Mn

Absorption of Mn by ruminants is low with <1% of an oral dose retained in the body after 13 d (13). Linear increases in fecal Mn account for essentially all of the additional Mn intake by sheep fed 0-4,000 ppm of supplemental Mn (14). Retention of oral ^{54}Mn

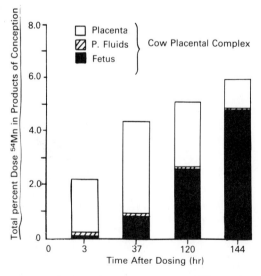

Figure 18-19. Partition of retained ^{54}Mn in the placental complex of gravid heifers after 270-d gestation. Church et al (4G).

by milk-fed calves can be reduced by almost 90% (from 18 to 2%) by addition of 15 ppm Mn to the milk (15). This amount of added Mn is sufficient to double liver Mn content and increase Mn concentration in bile 30 fold.

Comparison of amounts of Mn in the feed, entering the duodenum, leaving the ileum and appearing in feces reveal relatively little absorption or secretion of Mn in various sections of the ovine digestive tract (16). This procedure can only measure net absorption and does not differentiate between absorption and excretion occurring simultaneously at the same location. [54]Mn is absorbed rapidly following administration via duodenal catheters to calves, but its release back into intestinal contents is also rapid (17). More [54]Mn is absorbed in the cranial end of the digestive tract. The percentage of Mn excreted by feces is very high (Fig. 18-20), whether administered orally or by I.V. injection, but urinary Mn is negligible.

The bovine liver is capable of excreting 1.2 mg of Mn/min with Mn in bile reaching a maximum concentration of 20 mg/dl when Mn is infused intravenously at 4 mg/min (18). Parenterally administered [54]Mn, unlike [54]Mn absorbed from the digestive tract, is very sensitive to dietary Mn level. Biliary excretion may increase from 4 to 48% of an I.V. [54]Mn dose in calves fed 32 to 1,032 ppm Mn

but only 0.3% of a duodenal dose appears in the bile regardless of dietary Mn (19). Mn must be absorbed before it can be excreted in bile.

Upon absorption some of the ingested Mn may become bound to α_2-macroglobulin and possibly albumin (20). Most is removed by the liver and presumably excreted, while a small portion is bound to transferrin and released into the systemic circulation for transport to tissues. Opinions differ on the homeostatic control of Mn in ruminants. One opinion considers a small but constant fraction of Mn intake to be absorbed irrespective of its dietary concentration (20). The liver with its capacity to remove and presumably excrete excess Mn is considered to be the main homeostatic organ. The other opinion considers enterohepatic circulation of Mn, which plays a key role in homeostasis of injected Mn, to be less important in metabolism of fed Mn (19). If this is the case, changes in absorption as well as rapid endogenous fecal excretion are both major homeostatic control mechanisms for Mn (1G).

Interactions with Other Elements

Interactions between Mn and several other elements have been recognized. Dietary excesses of Ca or K can influence utilization of Mn by increasing fecal losses. Retention of Mn by calves can be depressed by excess Fe and enhanced by omission of Fe from the diet (4). Supplements of $CuSO_4$, $CoCl_2$ or KI also reduce Mn retention. Excessive dietary Mn is associated with decreased absorption of Fe and increased organ content of Zn but reduced Cu content of liver.

Dietary deficiency of Mn during pregnancy may cause biologically important alterations in utilization of certain minerals by both the dam and fetus (9). Mn deficiency increases Ca content in many tissues of pregnant ewes and increases Mg, P and Cu but reduces Ca in tissues of neonatal lambs. While the biological significance of some of the mineral changes is not readily apparent, Ca responses to physiological demands of fetal development can be impaired by a reduction in dietary Mn. Dietary Mn may be utilized to a greater extent when dietary Mg is low because Mn and Mg are similar in chemistry and can replace each other in several biological systems.

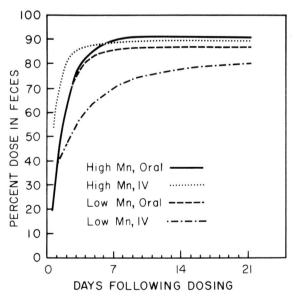

Figure 18-20. Accumulative excretion (% of dose) of [54]Mn in feces when administered I.V. or orally. From Church et al (4G).

370

Mn Requirements

Mn deficiency symptoms can occur in ruminants maintained on natural feeds containing <10 ppm of Mn. Mn-deficient pastures have been identified in several areas of the world. The majority of grains and forages generally contain adequate amounts of Mn (3G). Requirements for Mn appear to be greater for normal reproduction than for maximum growth (10G). Mn requirements have been set at 20 to 40 ppm for all classes of sheep, 10 ppm for growing and finishing cattle, 20 ppm for dry, pregnant beef cows and 40 ppm for all classes of dairy cattle (3G).

Availability of Mn

Mn content averages higher in forages than in corn grain, but variability within individual forages is extremely high. For example, ranges of 7-1,200 ppm in mixed grass and 1-29 ppm in shelled corn have been reported from the same laboratory (21). However, these analyses indicate that Mn is likely to be the least limiting of the various trace elements. Comparative studies on efficiency of utilization of supplemental Mn compounds by ruminants are limited, but Mn chloride and sulfate are both effective in preventing deficiency symptoms in cattle. High levels of Mn (1,200 ppm) from reagent grade $MnCO_3$ and $MnSO_4$ or from feed grade $MnCO_3$ and MnO are utilized comparably by lambs as indicated by fecal and urinary excretions. When tissue Mn level is the criterion for Mn availability, feed grade MnO is utilized more efficiently by sheep than reagent grade $MnCO_3$ (Table 18-15).

Mn Deficiency

Mn is less likely to be deficient than many other minerals because of its widespread occurrence in feeds. However, severe problems have been recognized in ruminants in several areas. Impaired reproductive performance has been noted in sheep, goats and cows maintained on feed low in Mn or containing substances reducing Mn utilization (9). Mn-deficient females are slower to exhibit estrus and require more services for conception. Rate of abortion is also increased.

Severe Mn deficiency has a pronounced effect on the newborn animal. Lambs or calves born to Mn-deficient dams exhibit low birth weights, reduced rate of gain, general weakness and nervous disturbances with irreversible paralysis developing later. The largest fetal reservoir of Mn is the bone and deformities due to Mn deficiency include enlarged joints, stiffness, twisted legs (Fig. 18-21) and shorter humeri and tibiae with reduced breaking strength. Bony excrescences (abnormal outgrowths) can also develop on the front tarsal joint (Fig. 18-22).

Figure 18-21. Mn-deficient calf born to a cow receiving 15 ppm of dietary Mn. Typical symptoms noted included enlarged joints, "knuckled-over" pasterns, and twisted forelimbs. Courtesy of Washington State Univ.

Figure 18-22. Malformations of forelegs of a Mn-deficient goat. Courtesy of Dr. A. Henning, Karl Marx Univ., Leipzig, G.D.R.

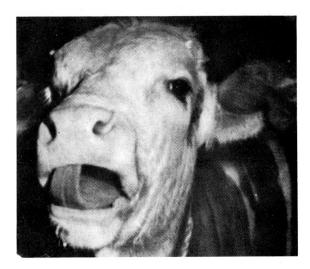

Figure 18-23. A Mn-deficient calf. This peculiar action of the tongue is said to be one characteristic of deficient animals. Courtesy of Dr. A. Henning, Karl Marx Univ., Leipzig, G.D.R.

Changes in calves maintained on low Mn diets include early development of a nervous tremor of the tongue (Fig. 18-23), later a general ataxia and trembling muscles appear, and after 14 wk changes are observed in the tarsal joints. Joint pain in deficient lambs is evidenced by reluctance to move voluntarily. When forced to exercise, they move with a peculiar gait described as rabbit hops.

Mn deficiency reduces concentrations of Mn in organs such as ovaries, liver, kidney, heart, spleen and bone. Reproductive problems appear when Mn content of the ovaries is low. Mn content of ovarian cortical stroma is lower in dairy cows with cystic ovaries than in cows that do not have cystic ovaries. Degenerative changes in the livers of Mn-deficient cows include fatty infiltration, abscesses and reduced bile volume.

Reduced activities of Mn-dependent enzymes could contribute to many of the changes seen in Mn-deficient animals. Bone abnormalities may result from reduced levels of glycosyl transferase which is required for synthesis of glycosaminoglycans. Defective synthesis of this component of cartilage can disturb development of the bone matrix. Excessive lipid peroxidation could contribute to degenerative changes in other tissues deficient in MnSOD.

Mn Excess

Excessive dietary Mn decreases growth, feed intake and efficiency of feed utilization by ruminants. Relatively low excesses (75-200 ppm) do not affect blood glucose, Ca or K but may depress serum Mg. Concentrations of hemoglobin and serum Fe have been decreased by as low as 45 ppm Mn. Up to 1,000 ppm Mn usually does not affect Ca or P retention, but may decrease Fe absorption, levels of Fe in liver, spleen and kidney, and reduce fiber digestibility. Liver Cu and Mn levels are increased by excessive Mn intake. Higher Mn levels (2,000 ppm) will also increase fecal excretion of both Ca and P. Cattle have consumed water containing 500 ppm Mn with no evidence of toxicity other than increased serum alkaline phosphatase and reduced Fe in plasma and liver. Most evidence indicates both sheep and cattle can tolerate 1,000 ppm Mn or more if the diet is otherwise adequate (5G, 10G).

NICKEL (Ni)

The presence of Ni in animal tissues and its in vitro biochemical functions have been known for years. More recently evidence for its essential physiological role in animals has been reviewed (1).

Absorption, Excretion and Tissue Concentration

Whether measured as stable Ni of dietary origin or as ^{63}Ni from single oral doses, feces accounts for 97% of total Ni excreted by ruminants regardless of dietary Ni content (2, 3). It is apparent that absorption of Ni is very low because urine is the primary route of excretion after intravenous injection.

Published tissue Ni concentrations range from 2.5 μg/g dry matter or lower in calves fed 64 ppm Ni or less (2) to 12-38 μg/g fresh tissue in lambs fed 65 ppb or 5 ppm Ni (3). Ni concentrations were similar in tissues of calves fed 1 or 64 ppm Ni, but increased when dietary Ni was raised to 251 ppm. Ni was not detected in blood serum of calves fed 1 or 64 ppm and was only 0.25 μg/ml in plasma of calves fed 251 ppm Ni, but was 12X greater when dietary Ni was increased from 251 to 1001 ppm. A Ni-metalloprotein called

372

nickeloplasmin containing 0.9 g atoms of Ni/mol has been isolated from human and rabbit serum (1).

Ni content of cows' milk is not increased measurably even by feeding over 1,800 mg of supplemental Ni daily (4). When special precautions are taken to prevent contamination from milking equipment, normal cows' milk contains <0.1 ppm Ni, the lower limit for reliable measurement.

Physiological Role

The specific physiological role(s) of Ni in the mammalian system has not been identified (1). Purification of RNA preparations increases their Ni concentration many times and Ni stabilizes the structures of RNA, DNA and ribosomes in vitro; thus, Ni may contribute to membrane and nucleic acid metabolism or structure. Addition of Ni to in vitro systems stimulates glucagon secretion, inhibits prolactin release and either inhibits or stimulates insulin release depending on Ni concentration. If physiological concentrations of Ni have similar effects in intact animals, these observations suggest Ni may be involved in carbohydrate metabolism and lactation. Reduced serum alanine transaminase activity in lambs fed only 65 ppb Ni (3) also suggests Ni may contribute to gluconeogenesis because alanine is a major gluconeogenic substrate for ruminants. Supplementation with Ni has partially alleviated changes associated with deficiencies of Zn and Cu.

Ni can activate numerous enzymes but has not been shown to be specifically needed for in vitro activation of any enzyme or to be required as an intrinsic component of any mammalian enzyme. Ruminal urease, an enzyme of bacterial origin, is much lower in lambs fed only 60 ppb rather than 5 ppm Ni (5). The bacterial enzyme seems to be specific for Ni because all other known trace elements were supplied in the diet. Although bacterial urease has not been isolated, jackbean urease has been identified as a Ni metalloenzyme containing 6 to 8 atoms of Ni/mole (1). In vitro addition of Ni to rumen fluid from Ni-deficient animals before assay does not increase urease activity, so increased urease activity after dietary Ni supplementation does not appear to result from activation of the enzyme by Ni.

Other beneficial effects of Ni have been demonstrated only in vivo; addition of Ni does not improve cellulose digestion by washed cell preparations and even very low levels (0.5 ppm) are toxic in vitro (6). Ureolytic bacteria adhere to the ruminal epithelial surface and urease appears to enhance transfer of N across the rumen wall by hydrolyzing urea to ammonia within the rumen mucosa (1). This may explain the greater responses to Ni supplementation when dietary protein is low or marginal because N recycling is more important under these conditions. An additional microbial function for Ni which may be of importance in ruminants is as a component of factor F_{430} which is present in methanogenic bacteria (1).

Interaction with Other Dietary Components

Ni may interact with or influence metabolism of a number of elements including Fe, Zn and Cu (1). Fe absorption is impaired during Ni deficiency, but Ni absorption is increased during Fe deficiency. Tissue Zn concentrations in goats and lambs decrease during Ni deficiency and supplemental Ni can improve performance of pigs and chicks fed Zn-deficient diets. Ni toxicity in chicks can be prevented by feeding high dietary levels of Fe or Zn. Ni supplementation may initially increase performance of Cu-deficient rats, but continued supplementation appears to exacerbate Cu deficiency symptoms. The antagonistic interaction between Cu and Ni may be influenced by level of dietary Fe.

Dietary Requirements

Ni requirements of domestic animals are not well established, but appear to be higher for ruminants than for other species that have been studied. The Ni requirement of young growing ruminants fed practical diets is approximately 1 ppm (1). Reported Ni contents of various feeds range from 0.04 to 3.9 ppm with seven of 14 feedstuffs analyzed containing <1 ppm Ni. Ni content is generally higher in forages than in grains and in legumes than in grasses. Forage Ni content is reduced by application of Ca carbonate to raise soil pH and decreases with advancing maturity. There is little evidence that Ni is likely to be deficient or that Ni supplements would be beneficial under practical conditions.

Ni Deficiency

Ni deficiency has been produced and described in rats, chicks, swine, lambs and goats (1). Deficiency symptoms in lambs and goats include reduced growth rate, increased mortality, decreased concentrations of protein in serum and total lipids and cholesterol in liver, lowered activities of serum alanine transaminase and glutamate oxaloacetic transaminase, decreased concentrations of Ni and Zn but increased uptakes of ^{63}Ni doses in tissues and reduced ruminal bacterial urease activity. Supplementation of a diet containing only 60-65 ppb Ni with 5 ppm Ni has increased N retention, total serum proteins, serum alanine transaminase and rumen bacterial urease in lambs (3, 5).

Ni Toxicity

Palatability of feed offered growing heifers is definitely reduced by 100 ppm Ni as the chloride or 500 ppm as the carbonate but not by half these amounts (4). Growth rate is not affected by 62.5 ppm Ni, but is retarded slightly by 250 ppm and markedly by 1,000 ppm (Fig. 18-24). Homeostatic control mechanisms for Ni in ruminants may break down differently in different tissues with increasing Ni intake (7). Dietary levels of Ni below 100 ppm have little effect on Ni levels in several tissues, but Ni concentration increases somewhat with 250 ppm and sharply when 1,000 ppm is fed (2). Lactating cows can be fed over 1,800 mg Ni as $NiCO_3$ per cow daily (corresponding to about 100 ppm Ni) without significantly affecting feed

Figure 18-24. Calf on right was maintained on normal ration to 12 wk of age. Calf on left received 1,000 ppm Ni daily for 8 wk. From Church et al (4G).

consumption (4). Ni is relatively non-toxic to ruminants, probably because of its very low absorption and tissue deposition (7). The maximum tolerable level for cattle has been set at 50 ppm (5G).

SELENIUM (Se)

Until 1957 the only nutritional signifiance for Se was thought to be related to its toxixity. More recently, attention has been focused primarily upon its nutritional value as an essential element. Se deficiency is recognized to be much more widespread and economically important than toxicity.

Tissue Distribution

The kidney has the highest concentration of Se followed by liver and other glandular tissues in the ruminant (Tables 18-16, 17, 18). Cardiac muscle contains appreciably more Se than skeletal muscles; intestinal and lung tissues can be relatively high, but nerve and adipose tissues are low.

Some of the variation reported for tissue Se concentration is due to chemical form of Se in the diet (Tables 18-16, 17). Tissue Se reaches higher concentrations in lambs or steers fed diets with natural Se (corn grown in S. Dakota) than when the same level of Se is supplied by supplementing low-Se diets (containing Michigan corn) with Na selenite. Concentrations of Se in liver and kidney increase up to 5-fold 1-14 d after injection of lambs and calves with commercial vitamin E and Se preparations, but return to baseline levels within 30 d (4G). Plasma Se of dairy cows initially fed low dietary Se (32 ppb) increases linearly up to 3-fold during supplementation with 25 to 75 ppb additional Se, but these levels are not maintained more than 20-40 d after withdrawal of added Se (Table 18-19). Levels of Se in serum at birth are higher in calves from Se-supplemented cows than from unsupplemented cows (5), demonstrating placental transfer in cattle. However, amount of Se crossing the placenta depends on chemical form of Se. Se in organic form (such as ^{75}Se-labeled selenocystine or selenomethionine) is transferred more readily across the placenta than ^{75}Se-selenite.

Se is secreted into milk of sheep and cows providing a source of Se to the suckling young in addition to that received during fetal

Table 18-16. Se concentrations in tissues of lambs and steers fed Se in natural and inorganic forms.[a]

| Tissue and source of corn in diet[b] | Animal and ppb Se added as selenite | | | | | |
| | Lambs | | | Steers | | |
	0	100	200	0	100	200
	. . . . ppb wet basis					
Serum						
Michigan	68	114	134	44	65	73
South Dakota	156	164	168	76	91	90
Muscle						
Michigan	88	92	110	70	86	100
South Dakota	167	159	167	135	136	158
Liver						
Michigan	242	380	533	258	384	435
South Dakota	618	656	756	498	499	524
Kidney						
Michigan	1,207	1,261	1,223	1,483	1,372	1,366
South Dakota	1,301	1,351	1,211	1,458	1,578	1,544
Subcutaneous Fat						
Michigan	38	47	37	21	33	29
South Dakota	36	37	48	48	50	55

[a] From Ullrey et al (1).

[b] Natural Se contents of diets were 85 ppb with Michigan corn and 199 ppb with South Dakota corn.

Table 18-17. Tissue and fluid Se concentration and blood glutathione peroxidase activity in beef cows maintained in a low Se area with or without intraruminal Se pellets.[a]

| Item | Treatment | |
	Se supplemented	Control
Tissue concentration, Se, ng/g or ml		
Liver	118[d]	47
Heart	126[d]	48
Lung	106[d]	26
Spleen	119[d]	58
Muscle	48[c]	20
Kidney	703[c]	628
Ovary	85	47
Plasma	48[d]	15
Milk	11	9
Blood GSX Px, EU/g Hb[b]	150[d]	20

[a] From Hidiroglou et al (2)

[b] One EU = decrease in log GSH of 10^{-3}/min.

[c,d] Significantly higher than control (c, $P < .05$; d, $P < .01$).

development. The proportion of dietary Se transferred to cows' milk decreases with increasing Se intake (6, 7). Se content of non-fat dry milk ranges from 27-240 ppb (3-40 μg/ℓ in liquid milk), depending on geographical origin (8). Se from natural sources, such as brewers grains, appears to be more available than selenite for secretion into milk. Milk Se content will rise from 10 to 37 μg/ℓ when dietary Se is increased from 47 to >770 ppb, but the response is not linear due to a decreasing fraction of dietary Se entering milk with increasing intake (6). This explains the narrower range in Se concentrations of milk than of grain samples collected worldwide (8). Even theoretically toxic Se levels supplied by 260 mg Na selenite per cow daily increase milk Se only from 28-80 μg/ℓ (9). Thus, unless Se is fed at levels toxic to the cow, its transfer to milk is too low to pose a potential hazard to human health.

Blood levels of Se are variable, depending upon dietary intake and possibly other factors as well (Tables 18-16, 17). The majority of

Table 18-18. Glutathione peroxidase activity and Se content in tissues of lambs fed low-Se artificial milk or practical type diets supplemented with different amounts of Se.[a]

Diet[b] and tissue	GSH-Px activity				Se concentration			
	0	50	100	500	0	50	100	50
	. . . . . EU[c]/ml or g fresh basis				. . . . ppb fresh basis			
Artificial milk								
Heart	130	295	1,470	1,240	40	90	134	256
Lung	289	815	1,720	1,870	45	99	131	220
Kidney	298	1,270	2,710	2,380	233	436	543	1,015
Liver	4	83	348	344	49	104	183	557
Pancreas	37	140	438	935	54	88	133	247
Muscle	14	33	150	149	21	31	44	80
Plasma	3	24	261	249	15	51	99	151
Packed RBC	7,810	14,400	21,700	30,700	206	348	492	760
Practical diet								
Heart	70	410	1,100	1,450	37	80	190	257
Lung	168	420	1,190	1,490	58	98	195	344
Kidney	--	--	--	--	574	804	1,140	1,270
Liver	126	190	204	427	49	96	181	575
Pancreas	179	362	1,100	1,660	162	190	264	401
Muscle	28	66	132	225	23	36	55	97

[a]From Oh et al (3)

[b]Se content by analysis was 10 ppb in artificial milk and 20 ppb in practical type diet.

[c]See Table 18-17, footnote b.

Table 18-19. Changes in plasma Se of dairy cows during and after addition of graded levels of selenite to a low-Se diet.[a]

Measurement and time of sampling	Amount of added Se, ppb			
	0	25	50	75
Dietary Se				
Before supplementation	32	32	32	32
During supplementation	32	57	82	107
Plasma Se				
Before supplementation	25	23	27	24
During supplementation				
+ 26 days	30	55	79	100
After supplementation				
+ 20 days	35	38	47	54
+ 39 days	35	29	48	42
+ 45 days	40	34	56	40

[a]From Conrad (4)

Se in plasma and erythrocytes of sheep is associated with the selenoenzyme glutathione peroxidase (GSH-Px) (10). The enzyme, with a molecular weight of 88,000, contains 4 atoms of Se per protein subunit of 22,000 molecular weight (11). Erythrocyte GSH-Px activity is highly correlated with Se concentration in whole blood. Thus, Se status of ruminants can be estimated in field studies by a simple test in which GSH-Px activity is measured by oxidation of NADPH via a coupled enzyme using a fluorescent spot procedure (12). Defluorescence occurs within 5 min with blood from a Se-adequate animal, but fluorescence is still present after 60 min when Se is deficient.

Tissue GSH-Px responds differently to various levels of dietary Se depending on the specific tissue and animal age or type of diet. This is illustrated by two experiments from the same laboratory (Table 18-17). GSH-Px activity was almost undetectable in livers of 8-wk-old lambs fed a basal artificial milk diet containing 10 ppb Se. Other lambs fed 50 ppb supplemental Se in the artificial milk diet still had lower GSH-Px activity in liver than 18-wk-old lambs born to ewes fed a practical type diet containing only 20 ppb Se. Kidney Se concentrations were also 2X higher in the older lambs fed a practical diet than in the young lambs fed artificial milk. It is not known whether these differences are due to age or diet. Both Se and GSH-Px activity of lamb enythrocytes and pancreas increase with each increment of dietary Se, but in lung, heart and plasma, GSH-Px plateaus at 100 ppb Se (the recognized requirement), yet Se concentration continues to increase. For this reason GSH-Px activity may be a better index of Se adequacy than is total tissue Se (11).

Physiological Role of Se

A metabolic function for Se was not established until 16 years after the first evidence for its essentiality when GSH-Px was shown to be a selenoenzyme (13). GSH-Px is a member of an important system for catabolism of reduced oxygen intermediates of both endogenous and exogenous origin (11, 14). Metabolic problems are not posed by molecular oxygen or its ultimate reduction product, water, but intermediates in this reduction pathway are extremely reactive with several organic compounds. Membranes of cells and subcellular organelles contain relatively high levels of polyunsaturated lipids which, if unprotected, are subject to peroxidation. Highly reactive forms of oxygen including hydrogen peroxide and fatty acid hydroperoxide can damage membranes, disrupt cellular functions and may adversely affect animal health, particularly under intensive management conditions. GSH-Px mediates oxidation of reduced glutathione to glutathione disulfide and utilizes the resulting reducing equivalents to convert hydroperoxides to the less damaging alcohols. GSH-Px is highly specific for the hydrogen donar GSH, but is very nonspecific for the peroxide substrate.

Along with GSH-Px, other links in the chain functioning to minimize excessive accumulation of reactive radicals include superoxide dismutase (SOD), chain-breaking antioxidants such as vitamin E and various other radical scavengers. Some components of this system function primarily in the aqueous phase of the cytosol and plasma (GSH-Px and Cu-ZnSOD), whereas others (vitamin E and MnSOD) are present in the membrane itself. Uncontrolled peroxidation and altered metabolism could result from a deficiency or malfunction in any of these mechanisms. White muscle disease (WMD) and retained placenta, which will be discussed later, are examples of resulting problems. The fact that these components function as a team may explain some of the varied results of Se deficiency. SOD activity measured in tissues of lambs before 1 wk of age is only half that of 16-wk-old adult sheep (see section on Mn). This delayed development of SOD activity may contribute to the greater susceptibility of very young animals to WMD.

Metabolism of Se

Absorption and Excretion. Se is absorbed primarily between the duodenum and ileum and is excreted into the duodenum. The amount of Se excreted in bile is small, averaging <2% of an intravenous ^{75}Se dose (15). Feces is the primary excretory route of orally administered Se in mature ruminants in contrast to monogastric animals in which urinary Se predominates. Before rumen function develops, young milk-fed lambs excrete more Se in urine and less in feces than older animals. In comparison with intraruminal doses, Se administered I.V. or subQ is generally excreted to a greater extent in urine and less in feces. Se absorption and retention are both linear for dairy cows fed Se levels between 50 and 260 ppb (Table 18-20), but Se retention by calves may be inversely related to intake when feed contains 300-1,300 ppb Se (17). Negative Se balance can occur when Se-deficient diets are fed without supplemental Se.

Se Metabolism by Rumen Microbes. Se content of rumen microbes in sheep fed various diets exceeds dietary Se by 46-fold on a dry matter basis, 11-fold on a N basis or 26-fold on a S basis (18). Rumen microbes can incorporate Se into selenoamino acids, but Se is more firmly bound in microbial protein when selenomethionine rather than selenite or selenate is the source of Se. Incorporation of ^{75}Se by rumen microbes is inversely proportional to previous dietary Se intake by the host animal. Se can also affect the metabolism of rumen microbes as evidenced by VFA content in rumen fluid (19) or S incorporation by microbes (20).

Table 18-20. Apparent absorption and retention of Se by non-lactating dairy cows fed different amounts of Se.[a]

Av. dietary Se, ppb	Av. Se intake μg/d	Se absorbed		Se retained		
		μg/d	% of Se intake	μg/d	% of Se intake	% of Se absorbed
53	468	152	32	95	20	68
71	685	192	28	130	19	67
128	1376	512	37	374	27	72
264	2918	1408	48	1088	37	77

[a]From Harrison and Conrad (16)

Availability of Se incorporated into microbial cells to the host animal appears to be low. Up to 40% of Se is converted to an insoluble form when rumen microbes are incubated with selenite in vitro. This conversion apparently is affected by chemical form because less of the Se becomes insoluble when the source is selenomethionine. Most of the Se excreted in feces is inorganic and insoluble in water or organic solvents. Pasture plants grown in the presence of ^{75}Se in ruminant feces accumulate <0.3% of the added radioactivity, demonstrating the poor availability of Se in feces. Thus, ruminant animals could contribute to a loss of this element from the Se cycle which may explain why Se deficiency is becoming a problem in heavily grazed areas of the USA where no known deficiency problems had been encountered in the past.

Interaction of Se with Other Dietary Components

Vitamin E and Se. Available data on influence of vitamin E on Se retention are conflicting (4G). Supplemental vitamin E has been associated with increases, decreases or no effect on Se retention by sheep in different reports. Conversely, serum vitamin E levels can be depressed in ewes treated with Se. This indicates a partitioning effect of Se on tissue vitamin E since decreased plasma vitamin E with increased dietary Se has been accompanied by increased deposition of vitamin E in tissues such as skeletal muscle, pancreas and kidney. This suggests involvement of Se in tocopherol transport from blood to certain tissues. However, other reports have shown very little effect of Se on tocopherol metabolism. Relative amounts of Se and vitamin E

given, route of administration, diets fed and age of experimental animals may have contributed to these differences.

A type of WMD produced when the diet is low in vitamin E and high in unsaturated fatty acids is responsive to vitamin E but not to Se. Occurrence of WMD is more likely, however, when diets are low in both Se and vitamin E. Se and vitamin E have a sparing effect on each other and a combination of both is more effective in prevention of WMD than either given alone. For example, Se supplementation may prevent clinical signs of WMD but not elevated serum glutamic oxaloacetic transaminase (GOT), susceptibility of red blood cells to hemolysis or microscopic lesions of WMD. Vitamin E alone or with Se restores GOT, lactic dehydrogenase (LDH) and creatine phosphokinase (CPK) activities to normal levels, whereas Se alone has only a transient effect (21).

Se, as a component of GSH-Px, in concert with vitamin E undoubtedly plays an important role in protecting biological membranes from peroxidative damage (11, 14). Both vitamin E and GSH-Px guard against excessive accumulation of organic hydroperoxides but by different mechanisms: vitamin E prevents formation of these highly toxic products; GSH-Px converts them to the less harmful alcohols. Thus, because both Se and vitamin E affect a common intermediate, their physiological effects would appear identical.

S and Se. Increased S intake, either by direct addition to the diet or by gypsum fertilization of pasture, has been implicated in increased incidence of WMD in some but not all reports (4G). Supplemental S may produce

378

pathological tissue changes similar to those seen in WMD, including cardiac calcification which can be prevented by Se. Conversely, S supplementation has been shown to delay development of WMD as indicated by plasma activities of LDH, GOT or malic dehydrogenase. Sheep fed a low-S diet (0.07%) maintain higher levels of Se in plasma and wool than when the diet contains 0.2% S, but Se balance is not affected by S intake within this range (22). At higher levels of dietary S there is little difference in tissue uptake of Se by sheep fed 0.28 or 0.62% S. In the reverse situation Se status of sheep has little effect on distribution of ^{35}S in their blood and tissues after dosing with ^{35}S-methionine (20).

Other Nutritional Factors and Se. Other trace elements are associated with Se utilization. When Se is excessive, several elements including arsenic, mercury, cadmium or Cu reduce its toxicity (23). Se also reduces toxicity of mercury and cadmium. Se administered together with Cu improves the performance of sheep even in the absence of clinical deficiency signs for either element. A beneficial interaction between Se and Cu seems reasonable because GSH-Px and Cu-ZnSOD have similar subcellular locations and are highly interdependent in controlling peroxidation. A synergism has also been observed between Se and Co in New Zealand but not in the United Kingdom.

Heat treatment of dystrogenic diets has reduced incidence of WMD, implicating the presence of a heat-labile factor. Occurrence of WMD is consistently higher in sheep fed legume hay rather than non-legume hay even when Se contents are the same (24). Interestingly, vitamin E content is higher in legume hay than in grass hay. Distrogenic feeds may contain an inhibitor of succinoxidase, one of the first enzymes affected by peroxidation of unsaturated lipids. The action of this enzyme inhibitor can be reversed by vitamin E. Even exercise can influence development of WMD. This is not surprising as exercise can increase the requirement for vitamin E and raise cytoplasmic levels of GSH-Px and other antioxidative enzymes in heart and skeletal muscle (25). Thus, a number of factors in addition to dietary levels of vitamin E and Se must be considered.

Se Requirement

The dietary Se level of 0.1 ppm recommended for domestic ruminants (3G) is adequate under many but not all conditions. The Se requirement for wild ruminants such as deer, however, does not appear to be over 0.04 ppm (26). Se requirements of sheep may be higher when legumes as compared to non-leguminous forages are fed. Hay grown in certain areas also appears to contain antagonistic factors against Se utilization. Data from Wisconsin (3) suggest the Se requirement for reproducing ewes and their lambs fed legume-grass silage plus pellets containing 60% corn and 40% hay may be closer to 0.12 ppm. Even 0.2 ppm Se is insufficient to prevent elevation of some of the WMD indicator enzymes in sheep fed legume hay in Oregon (18). Dystrogenic diets such as those containing raw cull kidney beans may also raise the Se requirement of sheep nearer 0.2 ppm. It is evident that Se requirement is influenced markedly by the diet and that vitamin E is not the primary difference. Further research will be required to determine which other modifying factors (S, trace elements, organic compounds, inhibitors, etc.) change the Se requirements.

Methods of Se Administration

Se has been supplied to ruminants by various means. Application of Se to soil is inefficient in terms of amount required to meet Se requirement of animals. Injections of Se in gravid ewes at 90, 60 and 30 d before estimated parturition or in calves at birth will prevent WMD in lambs (18) and increase both Se and GSH-Px in serum of calves (27). In certain areas sheep are drenched 4X per year to control gastro-intestinal parasitism. Administration of 10 mg Se with the anthelinintic should prevent Se deficiency under most management practices. Se can also be provided by slow release Se pellets implanted at the base of the ear, by intraruminal pellets containing elemental Se or by salt containing 30-65 ppm Se.

Injections and drenching provide known and desired amounts of Se but are time consuming. Se can be supplied at low labor cost by fortified salt, but individual intakes may vary considerably. Intraruminal pellets will provide physiological amounts of Se for

3+ years (2) if efficacy is not lost due to formation of Ca phosphate deposits or loss of pellets from the rumen. However, intraruminal pellets or Se fortified salt may be less effective than injection or drenching for preventing subclinical Se deficiency in sheep as indicated by elevated amino transferase or decreased glutathione peroxidase (28).

Se Deficiency

Nutritional Muscular Dystrophy. This condition, also known as WMD or stiff lamb disease, occurs in many different areas of the world, occasionally causing very severe losses in young animals. It is at least partially due to a deficiency of Se in the diet, although there are other complicating factors. Occurrence is frequently related to consumption of forage produced in irrigated areas or where rainfall is relatively high. The incidence is sporadic; outbreaks may be very severe one year but of little consequence the next. It has occurred on many soil types, but is probably more prevalent on soils of volcanic origin. WMD occurs primarily between 3-4 wk of age in lambs and 4-6 wk of age in calves, but older sheep, weaned lambs and wethers up to several months of age may be susceptible. It occasionally occurs in pregnant or lactating ewes, but is rare in adult cows.

WMD is characterized by a degeneration of the striated skeletal and cardiac muscles. In skeletal muscle there is a bilaterally symmetrical distribution of the lesions. In very severe cases

the muscle is bleached almost white (Fig. 18-25). Skeletal muscles most affected include those involved with movements of the legs and neck. Muscle degeneration causes stiffness and difficulty in locomotion. Animals tend to carry their rear feet farther foreward and the front feet farther back than normal (Figs. 18-26, 27). The most severely affected part of the heart is usually the right ventricle. In general, skeletal damage is more severe in lambs whereas cardiac involvement predominates in calves.

Muscle lesions apparently vary in different situations because they are sometimes but not always accompanied by mineralization. For example, affected muscles may have greatly elevated levels of Ca, P and Na and moderate

Figure 18-26. A calf with WMD which occurred on a range in central Oregon. Note the marked dystrophy of muscles of the forelegs. Courtesy of O.H. Muth, Oregon State Univ.

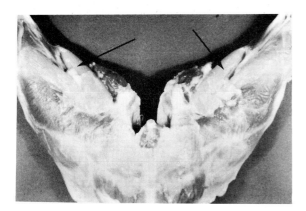

Figure 18-25. Rear quarters of a lamb carcass showing the marked bleaching of normal myoglobin color of some of the muscles that occurs in WMD. The arrows point to severely affected muscles. Courtesy of O.H. Muth, Oregon State Univ.

Figure 18-27. A lamb with WMD which was produced under experimental conditions. Courtesy of O.H. Muth, Oregon State Univ.

increases in Mg (Table 18-21). Degree of mineralization may indicate severity of the condition. An example of cardiac muscle calcification is shown in Fig. 18-28.

Growth is sometimes but not always depressed in Se-deficient lambs or calves, and Se supplementation will improve gain. Reduced wool quality (29) and production or

Table 18-21. Effect of white muscle disease in lambs on mineral composition of skeletal muscle.[a]

Mineral[b]	Adequate diet	Deficient diet[c]
Ca	25	25-4772
P	574	558-2391
Mg	123	93-332
Na	371	360-1237
K	1800	464-1773

[a] From Church et al (4G)
[b] Mg/100 g of fat-free dry matter
[c] Values shown are ranges in concentration

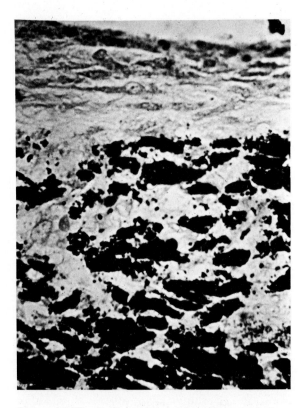

Figure 18-28. A microsection of cardiac muscle from a lamb with severe WMD. The black areas are stained with silver nitrate to show Ca deposits. Courtesy of O.H. Muth, Oregon State Univ.

a persistent diarrhea in older animals may respond to Se treatment.

Biochemical changes in lambs with WMD include increased GOT, CPK and LDH in plasma of which CPK appears to be the most reliable indication of muscle damage. Increases in lysosomal enzyme and colagenase activities in muscle presumably contribute to muscular degeneration. Glutathione content and total and protein sulfhydryl groups are reduced, but non-protein sulfhydryl groups increase in muscle of WMD lambs. Lower respiratory rates of mitochondria and changes in free plasma amino acid levels are also observed in lambs with WMD.

Se and Reproduction. Reduced fertility sometimes accompanies Se-deficiency in sheep and cattle, but reports have been contradictory (11G). Impaired fertility in Se deficiency is associated with embryonic loss (Fig. 18-29). In Se-deficient areas of New Zealand, oral administration of Se to ewes before mating has improved conception rate, reduced embryonic mortality and increased both lambing percentage and twinning rate. Even if prepartum injection of ewes with Se + vitamin E does not increase number of lambs born, preweaning survival of lambs may be improved (30). In contrast, Se supplementation in areas of Australia where WMD has been diagnosed has little or no effect on sheep fertility. Reports on Se requirement for maintenance of fertility in cattle has also varied.

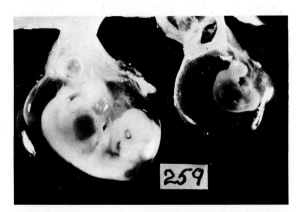

Figure 18-29. Embryos from sheep. The one on the right is from a ewe which was deficient in Se and was obtained 3 wk after breeding. The embryo on the left is a normal one. Courtesy of W.J. Hartley, Univ. of Sidney.

Seasonal fluctuations in forage Se and/or vitamin E may account for some of the conflicting observations (11G). Low tocopherol in forage or presence in feed of certain antagonists of vitamin E and Se may reduce fertility of ruminants in Se-deficient areas. Se-related infertility appears to be more prominent in sheep than in other domestic ruminants. Information concerning the influence of Se on fertility in male ruminants is limited, but Se does not appear to influence testosterone secretion in rams.

Se and Retained Placenta. High instances of retained placenta have been observed in dairy herds in areas with a history of WMD, so the possibility of Se deficiency alone or combined with vitamin E deficiency has been considered (31, 32). Unexplained placental retention is not always due to inadequate Se, because high instances have been reported in Nebraska (33) and South Dakota (34). Cows fed only stored forages for extended periods are more likely to have low vitamin E status than pastured cows because vitamin E content of forage declines during storage. However, no differences in incidence of retained placenta have been detected between pastured cows and cows fed only stored feeds for 4 years or longer (35).

Effectiveness of Se, vitamin E or both has not been consistent in different investigations (Table 18-22). Vitamin E alone fed daily during 2 mo before parturition did not reduce a 16% incidence of retained placenta (36). Se alone injected 3-4 wk before expected parturition has been partially effective in herds with 37-44% incidence of retained placenta in the United Kingdom (31, 32). In Ohio, 50 mg of Se given as a single I.M. injection 21 d before expected parturition had no effect on a 16% incidence of retained placenta in cows fed ensiled forage (36), but the same amount of Se fed divided over 60 d until calving reduced a 38% incidence to zero (37).

In areas of marginal to deficient Se intake, Se and vitamin E injected together 3-4 wk before expected parturition have markedly reduced or prevented retained placenta in many (31, 32, 36, 37, 38) but not all (39, 40) investigations. Se given as a single injection combined with vitamin E fed daily has also been an effective treatment (36). Additional Se may be ineffective where Se intake is

Table 18-22. Retained placenta in dairy cows given different combinations of Se and vitamin E.

Treatment, location and reference number	Incidence in control, %	Effect of treatment on placental retention
Se only		
Injection[a]		
Ohio (36)	16	none
United Kingdom (31)	37	reduced to 28%
United Kingdom (32)	44	reduced to 29%
Fed[b]		
Ohio (37)	38	reduced to 0
Vitamin E only		
Fed[c]		
Ohio (36)	16	none
Se plus vitamin E		
Injected[a,d]		
North Carolina (39)	18	slight to none[e]
Ohio (37)	38	reduced to 0
Ohio (37)	51	reduced to 9%
United Kingdom (31)	40	reduced to 0
United Kingdom (32)	44	reduced to 7%
Kentucky (38)	14	reduced to 3%
Virginia (40)	12	none
Nebraska (33)	28	none
South Dakota (35)	22	none
Se injected[a]; vitamin E fed[c]		
Ohio (36)	16	reduced to 0

[a] 15-50 mg Se injected intramuscularly 21-28 d before expected parturition.
[b] 12.5 mg Se fed to 5 d beginning 60 d prepartum, then weekly until parturition.
[c] 0.74 g vitamin E fed daily.
[d] 680 IU vitamin E injected intramuscularly 21-28 d before expected parturition.
[e] Treatment was effective only when dietary Se was deficient.

already adequate (33, 34) or when vitamin E is deficient. It also appears that Se and vitamin E together may be more effective when incidence of retained placenta is abnormally high than when it is relatively low.

Reduced GSH-Px activity as a consequence of Se deficiency (2) combined with inadequate vitamin E could allow excessive accumulation of reactive oxygen radicals (11). Resulting increases in cell and tissue alteration may contribute to a higher incidence of placental retention. For these reasons, both Se and vitamin E must be adequate during the critical period prior to parturition. Timing of a single Se-vitamin E injection is important. Several weeks lapse between Se administration and elevation of plasma GSH-Px (2). If Se is administered too early, plasma Se may return to preinjection levels (4) before parturition.

382

This may explain to some extent why Se fed divided over a 60 d period before parturition prevented placental retention (37) whereas the same amount of Se given as a single injection 21 d prepartum was ineffective (36).

Se Toxicity

Se Accumulation in Plants. Some plant species which require Se for growth have been termed indicator plants because they have been used in identifying Se-bearing soils. These plants are able to synthesize organic Se compounds including selenocystathionine, methylselenocysteine, selenocystine, selenomethionine and Se-wax complexes from forms of Se in the soil which are unavailable to most forage plants. Indicator plants have also been called converter plants because their organically bound Se is more readily taken up from the soil by other plants. Plants which do not require Se for growth, but are able to accumulate Se, are called secondary Se absorbers. The various indicator plants include *Xylorrhiga* spp, *Stanleya* app, and about 24 species of *Astrogalus.* The secondary accumulators include the Asters, *Atriplex* and others.

Indicator and other accumulator plants are less palatable to sheep or cattle when the Se content is high; thus, it is likely that animals will discriminate against potentially toxic plants unless forced to consume them. Most other plants, including native range plants, grasses, and crop plants such as barley, wheat and alfalfa, usually accumulate <30 ppm of Se. However, plants containing 5 ppm or more of Se are potentially toxic. The accumulator plants may, on occasion, accumulate up to 1% (10,000 ppm), but the secondary accumulators are more apt to contain up to a few hundred ppm of Se.

Acute Toxicity. Ingestion of a sufficient amount of seleniferous weeds, usually in a single feeding, will produce severe symptoms. Se affects movement and posture of the animal, which is likely to walk a short distance with an uncertain gait then assume a characteristic stance with lowered head and drooped ears. Other symptoms include elevated body temperature, diarrhea, weak, rapid pulse, labored respiration, usually bloating, prostration, and finally death, which is said to be due to respiratory failure. Post-mortem findings include congestion, hemorrhaging and degeneration of many organs and tissues. Consumption by mature sheep of 8-16 g/kg of body weight of plant material containing 400-800 ppm of Se may be fatal. The lethal dose is approximately proportional to the Se content of the plants.

Chronic Toxicity. A chronic form of intoxication results from the consumption of plant material, usually the cereals, grasses and hays, containing 5-50 ppm of Se, most of which may be protein-bound. This syndrome, also called alkali disease, is characterized by the loss of hair and malformation and sloughing of the hooves (Fig. 18-30). Generally, symptoms include anemia, reduced fertility, stiffness of the joints, lameness, loss of hair—particularly from the tail, and hoof lesions (Fig. 18-31). The feet may be so painful that animals are sometimes seen eating in a kneeling position. Consumption of excessive Se by pregnant ewes may result in production of lambs with malformed legs (Fig. 18-31).

A syndrome known as blind staggers can be produced in animals by several ingestions of sufficient amounts of plants to supply 2 mg of Se/kg of body weight. Affected animals wander in circles with apparent distortion of vision and develop anorexia, labored breathing, recumbency and death. Recent evidence suggests this disease is probably a result of toxic alkaloids (41), however, rather than Se as was once believed.

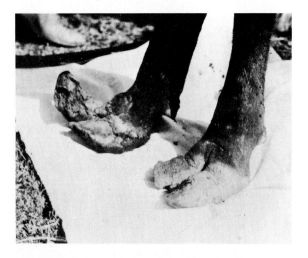

Figure 18-30. A close-up picture of the hooves of an affected bovine showing the marked deformation that occurs in the alkali disease syndrome. Courtesy of H.E. Eppson, University of Wyoming.

Figure 18-31. Top. A range cow showing typical symptoms of alkali disease type of Se toxicity. Note the loss of the switch of the tail, the deformed rear hooves and the poor condition. Middle. A steer with alkali disease. Painful feet cause the animal to kneel while eating. Bottom. Lambs born to a ewe consuming seleniferous forage. Note the deformed front legs. Courtesy of H.E. Eppson, University of Wyoming.

Se is one of the more toxic required minerals and there is potential for poisoning from Se compounds administered orally or parenterally to correct a deficiency if dosage is not controlled carefully. Prolonged ingestion of 2-5 ppm Se in the diet may reduce performance. Single oral or parenteral Se doses as low as 0.5 to 2 mg/kg of body weight (corresponding to ~25-200 ppm of a single days feed) have been acutely toxic to sheep and cattle with mortality exceeding 35% (5G). However, consequences of untreated Se deficiency in certain areas are equally as severe. The difference between a 0.1 to 0.3 ppm Se requirement and a potentially harmful level of 2 to 5 ppm seems rather narrow at first glance. However, it must be considered that toxic levels are 10 to 50 times greater than Se requirements. This range is considerably wider than the difference between requirements and toxic amounts of Cu for sheep.

ZINC (Zn)

Zn was established as an essential nutrient for mammals about 50 years ago, but the value of supplemental Zn in practical rations for farm animals was not recognized until much later. Positive proof that Zn is a required nutrient for ruminants was not published until 1960.

Tissue Distribution

The average total body concentration of Zn in ruminants, at 20 ppm on a fresh basis, is second only to Fe among the trace elements (1G). Cattle dosed with ^{65}Zn indicate relative decreasing concentrations in soft tissues in liver, pancreas, pituitary, kidney, adrenal, lung, heart and skeletal muscle. Bone, teeth, testicles, accessory sex glands of the male and digestive tract secretions also accumulate relatively high concentrations. Total Zn content of bovine tissues and organs appears to be under close homeostatic control and is reduced only slightly when a Zn-deficient diet is fed (Table 18-23). Zn content of liver, pancreas and bone is reduced 30-60% when clinical deficiency symptoms appear. Dietary Zn exceeding 600 ppm increases tissue Zn content, indicating a failure of the homeostatic control mechanism at this high level (1).

In calf and sheep livers, Zn is found with Cu in three major protein fractions with

384

Table 18-23. Effect of dietary Zn content on bovine tissue Zn concentrations.[a]

Tissue	Dietary Zn, ppm				
	2	17	33-40	233	633
	...... mg/kg dry wt				
Liver	84	109	114	213	870
Pancreas	--	80	108	228	1887
Spleen	--	93	90	--	--
Lung	72	88	80	--	--
Kidney	76	78	82	105	615
Heart	--	75	80	81	88
Skeletal muscle	78	109	95	75	84
Rib	62	71	76	97	125
Tibia	63	63	69	80	88

[a]From Church et al (4G)

molecular weights estimated at >75,000, 35,000, and 12,000 (2) or >150,000, 27,000 and 10,000 (3). Zn is usually absent from the low molecular weight fraction in Zn-deficient or high-Cu livers. Zn content of the 10,000 molecular weight protein, which has an amino acid analysis corresponding to metallothionein, increases with Zn supplementation of the diet.

One major and up to three minor metallothionein species have been isolated from tissues of both sheep and cattle (4). Excess Zn accumulates with metallothionein in the liver, kidneys, pancreas and small and large intestinal epithelia, but not with metallothionein in heart, testes, rumen papillae or abomasal mucosa in these species. The amount of Zn bound varies between the different species of metallothionein. Zn in hepatic metallothionein reaches a plateau of 270 µg/g of liver in cattle fed excessive Zn (2,000 ppm) and decreases with a half-life of 23 d when dietary Zn is reduced to basal levels.

Ruminant whole blood contains approximately 2 mg Zn/ℓ of which about half is in serum or plasma. Supplemental Zn has little effect on bovine blood serum Zn levels unless the dietary level is extremely high (300 mg/kg or above). Serum Zn of dairy cows may decrease with hyperthermal stress or ketosis but rise with advancing age or mastitis (5). Cow plasma Zn levels remain relatively constant from conception until late pregnancy and then begin a decline which becomes more marked during the periparturient period (6);

it may fall even lower in cows with dystocia. Unlike cattle, sheep with dystocia do not exhibit a fall in plasma Zn (7). Of the total Zn in lamb plasma, 66% is bound to albumin, 22% is bound to α_2 macroglobulin and 12% is unbound and presumably immediately available for physiological activity (8). During Zn deficiency bound Zn may decrease by half in albumin and by 83% in α_2 macroglobulin.

Gestation effects on fetal Zn accumulation are similar in cows and ewes (9G). Bovine fetal Zn increases by 13 times between the first and second thirds of pregnancy and by another 7 times during the final third. Total Zn accumulated by 270 d averages 135 mg in placenta, 3 mg in placental fluids and 551 mg in the fetus. Of the absorbed ^{65}Zn, 14% is transferred to the fetus, placenta and fluids. Gravid ewes transfer a similar percentage of the absorbed ^{65}Zn dose to the products of conception (Fig. 18-32), over half of which is deposited in the fetus. The total fetal burden of the ewe contains approximately 180 mg of Zn at 140 d. Ovine fetal liver Zn, as a percentage of total fetal Zn, decreases rapidly from 72 at 81 d to only 8 at 144 d of gestation (9).

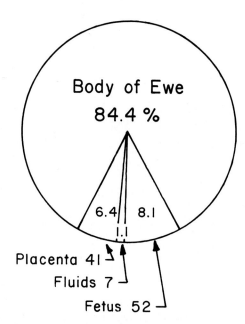

Products of Conception (15.6%)

Figure 18-32. Calculated partition of retained ^{65}Zn in the 140-d gravid ewe; 7 d after dosing. From Church et al (4G).

Although the Zn concentration of fetal bovine plasma is equal to or lower than maternal plasma at 270 d, samples from calves 24 h after delivery contained Zn at concentrations more than double that of their dams (6). Between the 85th and 140th d of gestation, fetal plasma Zn averages 65% higher than maternal in sheep and 41% higher in goats (10).

Lactation represents a major homeostatic demand for Zn in cattle despite the relatively low Zn content (4 mg/ℓ) of milk (11, 12). Colostrum contains 3-4 times more Zn than milk (2G). Milk Zn concentrations increase with high dietary Zn and decrease when Zn intake is low, but the percentage of the Zn intake appearing in milk declines rapidly as dietary Zn is increased (11). Most of the Zn in cows' milk is associated with high molecular weight protein fractions (13).

Functions of Zn

More than 200 enzymes in the six categories of the International Nomenclature are Zn metalloenzymes (14). A primary role of Zn in the animal body is related to its essentiality for the function of these enzymes (15). Carbonic anhydrase, alcohol dehydrogenase, glutamic dehydrogenase, lactic dehydrogenase and alkaline phosphatase are all Zn-containing enzymes. As a component of Cu-Zn superoxide dismutase, Zn is involved in protection of tissues against lipid peroxidation. Zn is also capable of activating a wide variety of enzymes in vitro, although many of these can also be activated by other divalent cations.

In addition to its critical role in enzymes, Zn has been associated with synthesis of DNA, RNA and protein and, thus, expression of genetic potential, cellular division, growth and repair (14, 15). Stabilization of membranes may also be a function of Zn. The cell mediated immune system may be adversely affected when Zn is lacking because of its critical role in the metabolism of nucleic acids and protein. Zn has also been related to the actions of insulin, glucagon, corticotropin and other hormones (4G). Actions of follicle stimulating and luteinizing hormones appear to be enhanced by Zn, and there is some evidence Zn plays a role in both keratinization and calcification. Zn content in protein fractions of bovine occular tissue is light dependent and is stoichiometrically related to rhodopsin. Furthermore, Zn has been associated with somatic and sexual development, taste acuity, vitamin A transport and utilization, sulfate metabolism and brain development.

Absorption and Excretion

The primary route of Zn excretion is through the feces and urinary excretion is very low (1G). Because absorption of Zn in ruminants is a dynamic process influenced by many dietary and physiological factors (16), selection of a figure representative of fecal excretion is difficult. The percentage absorbed increases with decreasing dietary Zn and is reduced with high Zn intake (Table 18-24). Clinically Zn-deficient animals will also absorb a higher percentage of their Zn intakes than normal animals. The higher percentage of dietary Zn absorbed by younger calves than by older ones may reflect deposition of large amounts of Zn in body tissue relative to intake rather than a reduced ability to absorb Zn with increasing age. Reduced Zn absorption and retention accompanying lower weight gain and N balances in calves during restricted energy and protein intake suggest

Table 18-24. Effect of zinc deficiency and dietary zinc concentration on fecal excretion of [65]Zn by ruminants.[a]

Species, age, Zn status and dietary Zn level	Method of dosing	
	Oral	Intravenous
	. . % of dose in 7 d . .	
Goats up to 6 months		
4-6 ppm, Zn deficient	24	4
4-6 ppm, normal	34	4
Calves up to 6 months		
3-6 ppm, Zn deficient	25	7
3-6 ppm, normal	37	--
8.5 ppm, normal	41	--
33-46 ppm, normal	52	10
240 ppm, normal	64	12
640 ppm, normal	77	13
Cows	. . . % of intake . . .	
6 ppm, Zn deficient[b]	25	--
17 ppm, normal	45	--
40 ppm, normal	65	--

[a] From Church et al (4G)
[b] Stable Zn measurements

Zn homeostasis is controlled at the tissue level and is closely related to protein deposition changes (17). Endogenous fecal Zn is also reduced by both low dietary Zn and Zn deficiency. These changes in Zn absorption are important for the homeostatic control of body Zn in accordance with needs.

The small intestine has been identified as the primary site of both absorption and excretion of Zn in ruminants. Data obtained with re-entrant cannulae in sheep (18) and cows (19) indicate net secretion of Zn into the forestomach and net absorption from the intestine. Absorption per unit of intestinal length of ^{65}Zn injected into various segments in calves is similar throughout the small intestine but negligible beyond the cecum (20). The appreciable Zn content of bovine saliva (0.5-1.0 mg/ℓ) undoubtedly contributes to apparent net secretion into the rumen. Apparently, Zn is secreted across the small intestinal mucosa because the cannulated pancreas accounts for one-fourth or less of the total endogenous loss in calves (21).

Zn is absorbed by an active process requiring aerobic conditions (15). The pancreas is thought to secrete a ligand (picolinic acid?) into the duodenum where the molecule complexes dietary Zn. The ligand-Zn complex is then transported into the epithelial cell where the Zn is transferred to binding sites on the basolateral plasma membrane. Finally, Zn is removed from the receptor sites by albumin and enters the portal circulation. The quantity of Zn entering the body is probably regulated by the quantity of metal-free albumin available at the basolateral membrane. Absorption of Zn is facilitated by cholecalciferol, leukocyte endogenous mediator and prostaglandin E_2. Metallothionein within the mucosal cell seems to be involved in controlling the amount of Zn available for movement into the circulation.

Interactions with Other Dietary Components

The well known antagonistic effects of Ca and phytate on Zn utilization in swine and poultry have not caused problems in ruminants. Zn content of sheep blood serum, rib, liver, brain and wool is not influenced by dietary Ca levels ranging from 1 to almost 4% of dry matter (22). The chelating agent EDTA partially overcomes the adverse effects of soybean meal on Zn absorption in non-ruminants, but does not affect absorption, secretion, reabsorption or tissue retention of ^{65}Zn in calves (4G). Isolated soybean protein, a source of phytate, reduces apparent absorption of Zn by calves only when the protein is deposited directly into the abomasum. These species differences probably result from events occurring in the rumen. Interdependence of phytate and Ca in forming a Zn-binding complex together with hydrolysis of phytate by rumen microorganisms may minimize effects of these dietary components on Zn availability to ruminants.

Zn in excess of dietary requirements interferes with Cu absorption and metabolism, possibly by induction of metallothionein. Cu can displace Zn bound to metallothionein because of the higher binding constant of Cu to thionein S. Association with metallothionein then prevents Cu from entering the circulation (23). Incidence of Cu toxicosis in sheep can be reduced by increasing their dietary Zn intake (24).

Cadmium is highly toxic to ruminants and its effects can be partially offset by feeding supplemental Zn. Cd combines with metallothionein which greatly reduces its toxicity and the amount of metallothionein increases with the amount of Cd absorbed (1G). However, Cd-induced metallothionein may reduce availability of other elements, including Zn. Dietary lead at 500 ppm also reduces absorption and tissue concentrations of Zn in calves (25).

Dietary Requirements

Ten ppm Zn in semipurified diets may be adequate for young ruminants as indicated by weight gain, feed consumption, testicle size, blood Zn content and clinical examination. However, Zn requirements are somewhat higher with more rapid growth rates than obtained in calves fed semipurified diets (17). Zn requirements of cattle under experimental conditions have usually been met by rations near 20 ppm (11), but deficiencies have occurred in the field with higher Zn levels (26). Gain of growing beef cattle fed basal diets containing approximately 20 ppm Zn has been increased by supplemental Zn in only 1 out of 7 experiments (27). The National Research Council has listed Zn requirements as 40 ppm for all classes of dairy cattle, 20-30 ppm for growing and finishing cattle, and 35-50 ppm for sheep (3G).

Sources of Zn

Plant species vary widely in Zn content, but relatively few are deficient except in areas where soil is very low in Zn (1G). Reported Zn contents of several feeds are 10-16 ppm in beet and citrus pulps; 17-24 ppm in alfalfa, Bermuda grass and clover hays; 16-21 ppm in barley, corn and grain sorghum; 30-43 ppm in oats, rye and wheat; 36-48 ppm in linseed, peanut, safflower and soybean meals; 106-124 ppm in brewers grains and wheat bran; and 400 ppm in bone meal. Zn content of forage may decrease with application of lime and as the plant ages.

Total Zn content in alfalfa or grass forage is associated 30% with neutral detergent fiber (NDF) and 24% with acid detergent fiber (ADF) and tends to decrease with declining forage quality (28). Zn in forage is found in three fractions with differing bioavailability to ruminants: a highly available soluble fraction, a potentially available fraction released by digestion of fiber (NDF) and protein, and a bound fraction of low availability (ADF). Apparent absorption of ^{65}Zn by calves is not affected by chemical form when given incorporated into immature hydroponically grown corn plants or as $ZnCl_2$ (29). However, greater uptake by metabolically active tissues of calves when ^{65}Zn is fed in the natural form in forage rather than as the chloride suggests the two sources are metabolized differently after absorption.

When fed at relatively high levels (380 ppm), Zn oxide or Zn sulfate do not differ appreciably in their effects on rate of wound healing or on tissue Zn content in calves. The sulfate, carbonate, oxide metal and several natural ores at levels more nearly meeting the dietary requirement are all relatively available sources of Zn (3G). A recent comparison indicates supplemental Zn reduces milk somatic cell counts in lactating cows and that Zn methionine is more effective than Zn oxide (30).

Zn Deficiency

Naturally occurring deficiency of Zn in ruminants was first reported in 1960 (4G). The deficiency was seen in grazing cattle on sandy soils in British Guinea where the predominant forage was Pangola grass (*Trachypagen polymorphus* or *Digitaria decumbens*). Naturally occurring deficiencies in ruminants have also been reported in Finland, the Netherlands, Greece and New Zealand. Numerous reports since 1960 have described experimentally produced Zn deficiencies in sheep, cattle and goats fed semipurified diets (1G, 4G).

A hereditary Zn deficiency in Dutch Friesian cattle apparently caused by a simple recessive gene has also been recognized in Denmark (31) and in the Netherlands (32). Calves appear normal at birth but characteristic skin lesions appear at 4 to 6 wk of age. The disorder is lethal if left untreated. Homozygous calves appear to have an unusually high requirement for Zn which can be met by oral supplementation if the dose is large enough. The disorder is analogous to acrodermatitis enteropathica in humans which appears to result from impaired Zn transport due to a defect in tryptophan metabolism proximal to synthesis of picolinic acid (15). When Zn intake is high enough, diffusion may allow sufficient Zn to pass without the transport mechanism.

Deficiency Symptoms. Experimentally induced Zn deficiency has been well characterized in ruminants (1G, 10G). Early deficiency symptoms in calves include decreased feed consumption and body weight gain and excessive salivation (Fig. 18-33). Calves develop a rough hair coat followed by swelling of the feet and legs, loss of hair on the rear legs and breaks in the skin around the hooves. Later symptoms include a stiff gait; swelling of the hocks and knee; red, scabby, creased skin (Fig. 18-34); inflamed skin with submucosal hemorrhages around the nose and mouth; parakeratotic changes in the skin, papillae of the rumen and of the esophageal mucosa; and in some cases, impairment of vision.

Similar symptoms have been reported for sheep (Fig. 18-35) and goats. Clinical Zn deficiency symptoms appear in lactating cows after 3 wk of dietary Zn depletion (33). Parakeratotic skin lesions, initially around the fetlock and pastern, spread over the hocks and inner surfaces of the shanks and finally the udder.

388

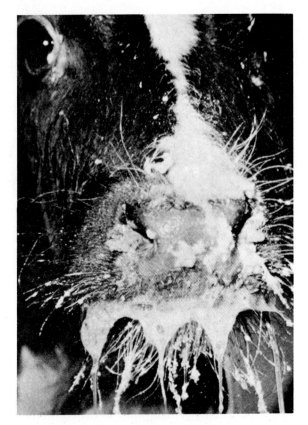

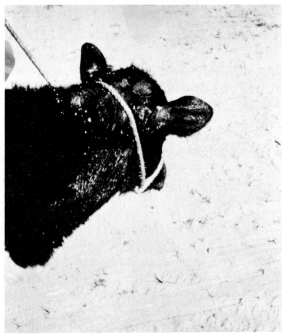

Figure 18-34. Zn-deficient lamb and calf. The deficient animals (on the left) received diets with 3 ppm Zn and the normals received 103 ppm. Courtesy of W.M. Beeson, Purdue Univ.

Figure 18-33. Zn-deficient calves. The (top) young calf shows excessive salivation, an early symptom; from Church et al (4G). The calf on the bottom shows the typical dermatitis seen about the head and neck in a deficiency of longer duration. Courtesy of W.J. Miller, Georgia Agr. Expt. Sta.

Figure 18-35. Zn-deficient Cheviot lamb on the left showing loss of hair and development of skin lesions around the eyes and mouth. The lamb on the right had the same ration plus a drench providing 0.7 mg of Zn/kg of weight/d. From Church et al (4G).

Naturally occurring symptoms in sheep include loss of wool and development of thick, wrinkled, pink skin (Figs. 18-36, 37). Zn deficiency may have been confused with mycotoxin poisoning in some of the early observations with cattle. Eczema, listed as a symptom of Zn deficiency in early reports, can also be caused by sporidesmin poisoning. Zn supplementation partially counteracts sporidesmin poisoning in cattle (34) and aflatoxin-induced changes in several Zn enzymes in calves (35).

Digestibility of the diet is impaired very little, if any (Table 18-25), but N and S retention may be reduced in deficient lambs due to increased urinary excretion of these elements, indicating a marked reduction in utilization of protein. Serum or plasma Zn may drop from normal levels of 0.8-1.2 mg/ℓ to very low levels of 0.15-0.2 mg/ℓ. Zn depletion reduces blood hemoglobin levels and activities of serum and bone alkaline phosphatase, liver alcohol dehydrogenase, muscle malate dehydrogenase, pancreatic carboxypeptidase A and B, and erythrocyte carbonic anhydrase. Liver Zn decreases rapidly, more so than in other organs, and mobilization of liver vitamin A is reduced. Liver alcohol dehydrogenase activity remains higher in control animals or in those which do not develop impaired vision when fed Zn-deficient diets.

Figure 18-37. A naturally occurring Zn deficiency in a Southdown ewe. Note the loss of wool on the belly, flank and quarter. From Church et al (4G).

Table 18-25. Effect of Zn deficiency in lambs on digestibility and retention of some nutrients.[a]

Item	Zn-deficient	Restricted-fed controls
Gain in 2 wk, kg	0.26	0.47
Dry matter intake, g	489	489
Dry matter digestibility, %	64.5	66.8
Nitrogen		
Intake, g	12.4	12.4
Fecal excretion, g	4.6	4.5
Urinary excretion, g	5.8	3.7
Balance, g	2.0	4.2
Sulfur balance, g	0.25	0.49
Zn intake, mg	1.17	15.8
Zn balance, mcg	70.6	1357

[a]From Church et al (4G)

Figure 18-36. A naturally occurring Zn deficiency in a young lamb. This 6-wk-old lamb shows loss of wool over the body, thick, wrinkled skin, and lesions around the mouth and eyes. From Church et al (4G).

Testicle size is reduced in calves and goats during Zn deficiency, but testicle size and activity and reproductive performance of initially Zn-deficient bulls can be restored after 43 wk on a normal ration (1G, 4G). Complete cessation of spermatogenesis in Zn-deficient lambs can also be reversed by feeding the lambs a diet with adequate Zn. Zn deficiency during pregnancy has more severe effects on the young than on the dam (36). Ewes that consume a diet containing 1 ppm Zn throughout pregnancy reabsorb, abort or deliver mummified or deformed lambs near term. Lambs born alive survive only a few days.

Zn Toxicity

The maximum safe level of Zn for ruminants is much higher than the minimum requirement (1G). Homeostatic control of tissue Zn concentration in cattle breaks down around 600 ppm dietary Zn, but decreases in rate of gain or body weight loss are first observed when dietary Zn reaches 990 ppm (5G). Lactating dairy cows tolerate up to 1,300 ppm Zn without measurably reduced performance.

High dietary Zn increases serum and tissue Zn particularly in the liver, pancreas and kidney. Cu is depressed but Fe is elevated in the liver. Elevated liver and duodenal Zn in the soluble cell fraction of calves fed 600 ppm Zn is associated with a 10,000 molecular weight protein (37). However, a comparable increase of dietary Zn does not affect organ Zn content or alter its intracellular distribution in mature cows, suggesting homeostatic control mechanisms regulating tissue Zn are much more effective in mature cows than in calves.

Susceptibility to Zn toxicity is greater in young animals than in more mature animals. Suckling lambs fed a milk substitute containing 840 ppm Zn (dry basis) for 4 wk developed symptoms of Zn toxicity including poor growth, low appetite and extensive renal damage (38).

Incorporation of Zn into the diet is more applicable to more intensive farming than to pastoral conditions such as in New Zealand where trace elements are often administered as drenches. Drenching with 60 mg/kg/d is fatal to wethers within 4 wk (34), but this amount is equivalent to about 3,000 ppm dietary Zn. Zn in a drench solution, similar to Cu salts, stimulates closure of the reticular groove mechanism and channels the dose directly to the abomasum where considerable damage to the mucosa can result.

The maximum tolerable Zn level has been set at 300 ppm for sheep and 500 ppm for cattle (5G).

OTHER MINOR AND TOXIC ELEMENTS

Evidence for the essentiality of arsenic (As), chromium (Cr), fluorine (F), silicon (Si) and vanadium (V) has been presented for rats and chicks. Essentiality of cadmium (Cd), lead (Pb) and tin (Sn) is controversial (1). Of the above elements, As is the only one for which evidence for essentiality has been obtained in ruminants. Goats must be fed an As-deficient (<50 ppb) diet for two generations before growth, body weight or number of young born are reduced (2). From 350-500 ppb dietary As appears to be adequate for goats. As may also be an important toxin in restricted areas when used in herbicides, insecticides or cotton defoliants. Cd, F, Pb and mercury (Hg) are recognized primarily for their toxicity (3, 4, 5, 5G, 7G) and are discussed later.

The significance of Cr for ruminants is unknown, but rats fed Cr-deficient diets exhibit hyperglycemia and elevated serum cholesterol. Si is required in chick and rat diets for normal bone and cartilage formation, however, in ruminants siliceous substances in plant tissues depress forage digestibility (6) and contribute to silica urolithiasis (7). Evidence of the essentiality of V is inconclusive, but in vitro studies indicate it has an insulin-like effect on phosphorylation of insulin receptors and activation of glycogen synthase (8), and V may have a specific physiological role as a regulator of Na-K ATPase (1).

At present, it is unlikely that any of these other minor elements might become deficient in ruminants under field conditions. However, the same sentiment was prevalent when Se essentiality was first demonstrated (8). Thus, all possible mineral deficiencies must be kept in mind regardless of how impractical they may seem.

Fluorine (F)

Fluorine is probably an essential element for all animals, but there is no evidence that a F deficiency would ever be of practical concern with ruminants (5G, 7G). Rather, F is more important in ruminant nutrition because of its toxic effects (4G).

Fluorine toxicity usually results from chronic fluorosis. Soil and water in some areas naturally contain sufficient fluorides to produce overt toxicity. Effluents from factories processing steel, aluminum or other raw ores may also cause local problems. Direct inhalation does not contribute significantly to fluoride accumulation in animals (5G), but these emissions may contaminate plants, soil and water. Raw rock phosphates and colloidal clays, often used as supplementary P sources for plants and animals, may contain toxic levels of F. Other sources of F may include insecticides or rodent poisons.

Toxicity of F-containing compounds appears to be related to their solubility. For this reason, NaF is more toxic than the same amount of F as CaF$_2$, raw rock phosphate, flue dust from an aluminum plant or F-contaminated soil. However, high-F hay grown on contaminated soil is about equally as toxic as NaF.

The soft tissues contain relatively little F, but under normal conditions F accumulates in the skeleton through life. Fluorine content varies with type of bone, location within a given bone, and between different bones of the same type in the same animal. Fluorine toxicosis has been associated with a F content in excess of 5,500 ppm (ash basis) in compact bone and 7,000 ppm in cancellous bone. Bone F may increase from 1,000 ppm in cows fed a control ration (12 ppm) to 10,400 ppm when dietary F is raised to 112 ppm. Dietary F has only minimal effects on concentrations of F in milk or in bones of unborn calves (5G).

Bone readily accumulates up to 96% of the total F in the body, so chronic F toxicity is manifested almost entirely by its effects on the teeth and skeletal system. Effects on digestibility, growth, milk production, or reproduction are usually negligible until obvious clinical symptoms appear. The first clinical signs of chronic fluorosis are manifested in the teeth of young animals (4G). An initial slight mottling of teeth enamel is followed by an increasing mottling, discoloration, appearance of patches of chalky enamel and some abrasion. More severe symptoms include a definite mottling, discoloration, hypoplasia, hypocalcification, pitted enamel and definite abrasion (Figs. 18-38 and 18-39). Teeth may be stained (vegetable stain) almost black. Severe fluorosis in bovine incisors can be caused by feeding F from 13-18 mo of age but there is little, if any, effect on teeth fully formed prior to exposure to F.

Increasing F concentration in tissues is followed after a time by periosteal hyperostosis (Fig. 18-40), intermittent lameness, reduced feed intake, and lower performance (milk production, gain, etc.). The skin tends to become dry, thick and non-pliable after long-term exposure to F. Bone lesions which develop are similar to porosis, sclerosis, hyperostosis,

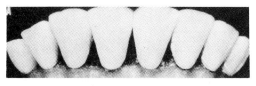
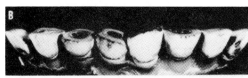
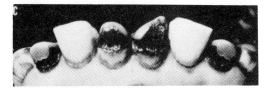

Figure 18-38. Fluorosis. A, normal teeth. B, dental fluorosis caused by continuous ingestion of high F levels. C, dental fluorosis caused by intermittent ingestion of high F levels. Note the bilateral lesions. Courtesy of J.L. Shupe, Utah State Univ.

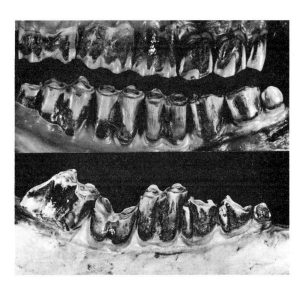

Figure 18-39. Fluorosis. Upper picture, normal molar teeth of bovine showing sharp grinding surfaces. B, dental fluorosis resulting in excessive erosion and loss of normal table surface. Courtesy of J.L. Shupe, Utah State Univ.

osteophytosis or malacia, depending upon interacting factors including the degree of fluorosis. Changes, which can eventually be diagnosed by palpation, are usually seen first in the metatarsae, mandible and

392

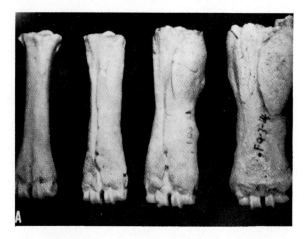

Figure 18-40. Fluorosis. Effect of excess F intake on the metatarsal bones. Left to right, normal bone and varying degrees of osteofluorosis. Courtesy of J.L. Shupe, Utah State Univ.

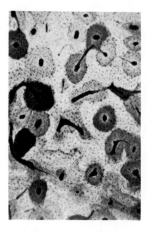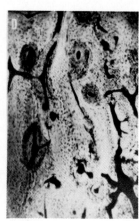

Figure 18-41. Effect of F on histology of the bone showing structure and various stages of remodeling activity. Right, abnormal bone structure with marked osteonal and interstitial changes. Courtesy of J.L. Shupe, Utah State Univ.

metacarpal bones and later in the ribs. Affected bones generally appear enlarged and chalky white and have a roughened, irregular periosteal surface (Fig.18-40).

Abnormal osteoblastic activity is thought to cause the formation of an abnormal matrix with disorderly, defective and irregular mineralization of the bones (Fig. 18-41). There can be spurring and bridging which eventually lead to marked rigidity and malfunctioning of th joints or spinal column. High incidence of arthritis is observed in dairy herds which also have characteristic tooth lesions.

Acute F toxicity may result when concentrated F sources are consumed in large amounts. This type of fluorosis is probably of much less economic importance than that which may result from chronic F intake. Symptoms appearing as early as half an hour after acute ingestion include: excitement, high F content of blood and urine, stiffness, anorexia, reduced milk production, excessive salivation, vomiting, spasmotic urination and defecation, weakness, severe depression and cardiac failure.

Compounds such as aluminum sulfate, aluminum chloride, calcium aluminate and calcium carbonate reduce toxicity of F in animals, probably by lowering solubility of F in the GI tract. Although these compounds may reduce F absorption, the best recommendation would be to reduce F intake if it is in a range likely to be hazardous.

Amounts of F tolerated are influenced by life expectancy and thus total lifetime exposure as well as by feed intake in relation to body weight. Long-term ingestion of F at a rate >30 ppm in the diet will result in symptoms of fluorosis after 2-3 years. Appreciably larger amounts (100 ppm+) can be tolerated for short periods (several months) without undue hazard. Maximum tolerable levels of F have been set at 40 ppm for young cattle and mature dairy cattle, 50 ppm for mature beef cattle, 100 ppm for finishing cattle, 60 ppm for breeding sheep and 150 ppm for finishing sheep (5G).

Lead (Pb)

Chronic Pb poisoning has only rarely been recognized in ruminants, although there is reason to believe it may be more of a factor than clinical reports suggest. Acute Pb toxicity is one of the most common causes of poisoning in cattle and has a mortality rate approaching 100%. Pica—resulting from situations such as a P deficiency—may be a predisposing factor because of the tendency of ruminants to chew and ingest a wide variety of foreign materials.

Peeling paint or discarded paint cans are common sources of Pb. Other major sources are waste from metal smelters and mining, contamination of forage from combustion of leaded gasoline along highways, motor oils and greases containing high levels of Pb after use in internal combustion engines, and discarded storage batteries. Sewage sludge usually contains considerable Pb and may contribute to soil Pb where used in large amounts. Pb toxicity should become less of a problem (at least in the USA) because few paints now contain any appreciable amount (if any) of Pb salts and also because of increasing use of non-leaded fuels in automobiles.

Pb is poorly absorbed by ruminants, but feeding Pb will result in accumulation in kidney, heart and skeletal muscles as well as other tissues such as bone and brain (4G). Blood levels of 0.35 ppm and clinical signs are satisfactory for diagnosis of toxicity. Moderate amounts (0.05-0.2 pmg/ℓ) of Pb can be found in milk of cows, but milk levels rapidly return to normal after withdrawal of Pb from the diet.

Clinical Pb toxicosis probably results through interference in normal metal-dependent enzyme functions and is characterized by hematological, neural, renal or skeletal abnormalities (5G). Pb poisoning causes severe brain lesions and irritation of the GI tract. It affects muscular coordination and red blood cell synthesis resulting in anemia. Signs of toxicity in cattle include a depressed appearance and poor performance, blindness, grinding of the teeth, muscular twitching and convulsive seizures. In sheep, Pb toxicity results in depression, anorexia, abdominal pain and (usually) diarrhea. Osteoporosis has been observed in young lambs and abortions in ewes. Young animals are generally more susceptible than older animals.

Treatment of Pb toxicity generally involves infusions of Ca-EDTA which forms a complex with the Pb and increases its excretion. Therapeutic doses of thiamin reduce tissue concentrations of Pb and may be of value in the prevention and treatment of Pb poisoning in cattle exposed to high environmental levels of Pb (9).

Cattle or sheep can be fed 10 ppm supplemental Pb in soluble form for extended periods without adverse effects but tissue Pb levels may increase significantly when 100 ppm is exceeded. Even 1,000 ppm dietary Pb has been tolerated by ruminants for several months with no visible signs of toxicity. The maximum tolerable dietary level for Pb is considered to be 30 ppm for most species (5G).

Cadmium (Cd)

Cd toxicity may occur when animals inhale Cd-containing dust or fumes or consume contaminated feeds, but Cd toxicity in cattle maintained under practical conditions has not been observed (7G). However, borderline toxicity is possible when ruminants are given feeds containing recycled animal waste or sewage sludge in which Cd may by concentrated. Ingested Cd, although poorly absorbed, is tenaciously retained by the body and concentrated in the kidney and liver. Very little of the retained Cd is found in muscle or secreted into milk.

General clinical symptoms of Cd toxicity include reductions in growth, feed intake, water consumption and milk production. Anemia, liver and kidney damage and increased mortality may occur. Other symptoms, similar to those of Zn deficiency, include retarded testicular development or degeneration, enlarged joints and scaly skin (7G). Some of the toxic effects of Cd can be diminished or prevented by Zn, Co, Se and thio compounds.

Cattle or sheep have been fed 3-5 ppm Cd for 3 mo with no changes other than increased Cd and reduced Cu and Fe concentrations in liver and kidney, but higher dietary levels are usually associated with some adverse health effect. A dietary concentration of 0.5 ppm is the maximum tolerable level (5G).

Mercury (Hg)

The most likely source of Hg for ruminants is treated seed grain used accidentally for feed. There is little reason to believe Hg is an important toxin for ruminants under practical conditions. Organic Hg compounds (especially methyl Hg) are more toxic than inorganic compounds due to higher absorption, greater retention and slower turnover rate in the body (7G). Conversion of inorganic Hg to methyl Hg in the rumen is negligible. Both chemical forms are deposited primarily in the kidney and liver, but muscle and brain also accumulate appreciable amounts of methyl Hg. Amounts of either chemical form secreted into milk are relatively small.

Cattle chronically ingesting inorganic Hg may develop depression, anorexia, emaciation and a stiff stilted gait (7G). Symptoms developing later include alopecia, scabby lesions around the anus and vulva, tenderness of gums and teeth and chronic diarrhea. Organic Hg compounds primarily affect the nervous system. Clinical symptoms include ataxia, neuromuscular incoordination, head pressing, twitching of eyelids, tetanus-like spasms on stimulation, excessive salivation, recumbency, and inability to eat or drink followed by tonic-clonic convulsions with opisthotonos and death. The suggested maximum tolerable dietary level of Hg is 2 ppm (5G).

SUMMARY

Information on the trace elements is too detailed to summarize in a paragraph or so. However, typical blood serum and liver concentrations of normal, adequately-fed animals are shown in Table 18-26. Information is also shown, where available, on site of absorption from and excretion into the GI tract, average excretions of oral or I.V. doses, and estimates of dietary requirements and probable toxic levels. It should be remembered that the values shown may vary widely. Dietary intake

of nearly every element will influence its concentrations in blood and liver as will many of the various interfering factors that have been discussed. Likewise, the relative amount that may be excreted via urine or feces can be influenced to a considerable degree by the dietary intake.

Most trace elements seem to function as integral components or activators of enzymes involved in numerous biochemical reactions on which life depends. Other functions of trace elements include Fe in hemoglobin, myoglobin and some storage compounds, I in thyroid hormone, Co in vitamin B_{12} and Zn as a component of DNA, RNA and biological membranes where it likely has a role in maintaining structure.

Superoxide radicals formed locally by the Fe-Mo enzyme xanthine oxidase may play important roles in phagocytosis and antimicrobial activity in the mammary gland (1). However, superoxide generated by cellular metabolism can also be harmful if uncontrolled. Reduced Fe can catalyze the reaction

Table 18-26. Summary of data on trace minerals-normal tissue levels, site of absorption, route of excretion, probable dietary requirements and toxic concentrations.

| Mineral | Tissue concentration | | Site of absorption and excretion in GI tract | | Excretion, % | | Probable dietary requirement, ppm | Toxic level, ppm |
	Blood serum, μg/dl	Liver, ppm	Absorption	Excretion	Oral dose via feces	IV dose via urine		
Co	0.1-0.3[a]	0.1-0.2	S.I., L.I.[a]	bile, gut	80-85	65-80	0.1	20[b] 50[c]
Cu	100	200±	S.I., L.I.	bile	80-90	1-5	10+	25[b] 100[c]
Fe	150	200+	S.I., L.I.	S.I.	80-98	?	35-100	500[b] 1,000[c]
I	5-10	<0.2	rumen, S.I., L.I.	abomasum, bile	30-50	30-60	0.1	>50
Mn	5	10-20	S.I.	bile, S.I.	90	<5	20±	1,000
Mo	1-5	2-4	abomasum, S.I.	saliva, rumen	60-80	10-50	<0.01?	5-10
Ni	10	30	?	?	65-75	25	1	>50
Se	10-20	0.5+	S.I.	bile	50-70	10-30	0.1-0.3	5
Zn	80-120	50+	S.I.	S.I.	50-95	1-5	40	500

[a]Vitamin B_{12}. Co functions as a component of vitamin B_{12} which is synthesized in the ruminant.
[b]Sheep
[c]Cattle

between superoxide anion and hydrogen peroxide which generates the hydroxyl radical, a potent inducer of lipid peroxidation. Unsaturated lipids in biological materials, particularly membranes, are subject to oxidation by free radicals generated in the presence of oxygen and certain transition elements (2). Conversely, these and other trace elements are involved in defense against potentially hazardous reactions initiated by oxygen metabolites. Similar symptoms of deficiency and toxicity have been described for several trace elements, and this may be partially explained through lipid peroxidation.

Lipid peroxidation in living cells is counteracted by systems for prevention, interception and repair working in concert (3, 4). These defense mechanisms include non-enzymatic radical scavengers and quenchers (α-tocopherol, ascorbate, flavonoids, β-carotene, vitamin A) and enzymatic systems (superoxide dismutase and various hydroperoxidases). Free superoxide radicals are converted to peroxides by Cu, Zn-superoxide dismutase in the cytoplasm and Mn-superoxide dismutase in the membranes. The cell is protected from deleterious effects of the resulting peroxide by glutathione peroxidase (Se), catalase (Fe) and other hemoprotein peroxidases.

Reducing equivalents required by these systems are provided by the reduced forms of glutathione (GSH) and NADPH. The ratio between reduced GSH and oxidized GSSG is influenced by Se (5). NADPH is generated via the hexosemonophosphate pathway. High dietary Zn has been shown to decrease peroxidation of hepatic fatty acids possibly by inhibiting the oxidation of NADPH (6).

Deficiencies as well as excesses of many dietary components undoubtedly disturb the cellular equilibrium between oxidation and antioxidant defense necessary for health and even survival of all aerobic organisms (7). Free radical damage may contribute to such livestock diseases as white muscle disease (WMD), retained placenta and even mastitis. Ruminants are born with an immature antioxidant defense system (8) which may explain the susceptibility of young lambs and calves to WMD. Trace element imbalances may be involved in a wide variety of veterinary and medical problems.

References Cited

General References
1G. Miller, W.J. 1979. Dairy Cattle Feeding and Nutrition. Academic Press, New York.
2G. Underwood, E.J. 1977. Trace Elements in Human and Animal Nutrition, 4th Ed. Academic Press, New York.
3G. Ammerman, C.B. and R.D. Goodrich. 1983. J. Animal Sci. 57(Suppl. 2):519.
4G. Church, D.C., et al. 1979. In: Digestive Physiology and Nutrition of Ruminants. Vol. 2—Nutrition, 2nd Ed. O&B Books, Inc., Corvallis, Oregon.
5G. NRC. 1980. Mineral Tolerance of Domestic Animals. Nat. Acad. Sci., Washington, DC.
6G. Ganong, W.F. 1981. Review of Medical Physiology, 10th Ed. Lange Medical Publ., Los Altos, California.
7G. NRC. 1978. Nutrient Requirements of Dairy Cattle. Nat. Acad. Sci., Washington, DC.
8G. Ammerman, C.B. and S.M. Miller. 1972. J. Animal Sci. 35:681.
9G. Hansard, S.L. 1983. Nutr. Abstr. Rev., Ser. B. 53:1.
10G. Miller, W.J. 1981. J. Dairy Sci. 64:1196.
11G. Hidiroglou, M. 1979. J. Dairy Sci. 62:1195.
12G. Nutrition Reviews. 1984. Present Knowledge in Nutrition, 5th Ed. The Nutrition Foundation, Inc., Washington, DC.

References on Cobalt
1. Underwood, E.J. 1984. In: Present Knowledge in Nutrition, 5th Ed., p. 528. The Nutrition Foundation, Inc., Washington, DC.
2. Peters, J.P. and J.M. Elliot. 1983. J. Dairy Sci. 66:1917.
3. Herbert, V. 1984. In: Present Knowledge in Nutrition, 5th Ed., p. 347. The Nutrition Foundation, Inc., Washington, DC.
4. Grace, N.D. 1975. Brit. J. Nutr. 34:73.
5. Li, V.V. and A.A. Abdrakhmanov. 1975. Nutr. Abstr. Rev. 46:825.

396

6. MacPherson, A., et al. 1973. Brit. Vet. J. 129:414.
7. Duncan, W.R.H., E.R. Morrison and G.A. Garton. 1981. Brit. J. Nutr. 46:337.
8. Smith, R.M. and H.R. Marston. 1970. Brit. J. Nutr. 24:879.
9. Russel, A.J.F., et al. 1975. Vet. Rec. 96:194.
10. Marston, H.R., S.H. Allen and R.M. Smith. 1972. Brit. J. Nutr. 27:147.
11. Neathery, M.W. and W.J. Miller. 1977. Feedstuffs. 49(38):22.

References on Copper and Molybdenum

1. Van Ryssen, J.B.J. and W.J. Stielau. 1981. Brit. J. Nutr. 45:203.
2. O'Dell, B.L. 1984. In: Present Knowledge in Nutrition, p. 506. Nutrition Foundation, Inc., Washington, DC.
3. Saylor, W.W., F.D. Morrow and R.M. Leach, Jr. 1980. J. Nutr. 110:460.
4. Harris, A.I. and P.D.G. Dean. 1973. Res. Vet. Sci. 4:106.
5. Moss, B.R., et al. 1974. J. Animal Sci. 38:475.
6. Williams, R.B., I. McDonald and I. Bremner. 1978. Brit. J. Nutr. 40:377.
7. Hidiroglou, M. and J.E. Knipfel. 1981. J. Dairy Sci. 64:1637.
8. Ho, S.K., et al. 1977. Can. J. Animal Sci. 57:727.
9. Ward, G.M. 1978. J. Animal Sci. 46:1078.
10. Suttle, N.F. 1975. Brit. J. Nutr. 34:411.
11. Huber, J.T., N.O. Price and R.W. Engel. 1971. J. Animal Sci. 32:364.
12. Gallagher, C.H. and V.E. Reeve. 1976. Aust. J. Exp. Bio. Med. Sci. 54:593.
13. Sharoyan, S.G., et al. 1977. Biochem. Biophys. Acta 493:478.
14. Ishizaki, H. and K.T. Yasunobu. 1976. Adv. Exp. Med. Bio. 74:575.
15. Grace, N.D. 1975. Brit. J. Nutr. 34:73.
16. Bertoni, G., et al. 1976. Zoot. Nutr. Animal 2:185.
17. Ivan, M. and C.M. Grieve. 1976. J. Dairy Sci. 59:1764.
18. Evans, G.W. 1973. Physiol. Rev. 53:535.
19. Miller, J.K., et al. 1972. J. Animal Sci. 34:846.
20. Mason, J. and C.J. Cardin. 1977. Res. Vet. Sci. 22:313.
21. Suttle, N.F. 1977. Animal Feed Sci. Tech. 2:235.
22. Suttle, N.F. and A.C. Field. 1974. Vet. Rec. 95:166.
23. Suttle, N.F. 1975. In: Trace Elements in Soil-Plant-Animal Systems. Academic Press, New York.
24. Huisingh, J., D.C. Milholland and G. Matrone. 1975. J. Nutr. 105:1199.
25. Bremner, I. 1975. Proc. Nutr. Soc. 34:10A.
26. Huisingh, J., G.G. Gomez and G. Matrone. 1973. Fed. Proc. 32:1921.
27. Suttle, N.F. and M. McLauchlan. 1976. Proc. Nutr. Soc. 35:22A.
28. Bremner, I. and B.W. Young. 1978. Brit. J. Nutr. 39:325.
29. Dick, A.T., D.W. Dewey and G.M. Gawthorne. 1975. J. Agr. Sci. 85:567.
30. Gooneratne, S.R. and D.A. Christensen. 1984. Fed. Proc. 43:790.
31. Ivan, M. and D.M. Veira. 1981. Can. J. Animal Sci. 61:955.
32. Awad, Y.L., et al. 1973. Zbl. Vet. Med. A, 20:742.
33. Whitelaw, A., et al. 1981. Animal Prod. 33:129.
34. Bremner, I., B.W. Young and C.F. Mills. 1976. Brit. J. Nutr. 36:551.
35. Bostedt, H., J. Pallauf and P. Pfeiffer. 1983. Fortschr. Veterinarmed. 37:190.
36. Humphries, W.R., et al. 1983. Brit. J. Nutr. 49:77.
37. Roberts, H.E. 1976. Vet. Rec. 99:496.
38. Todd, J.R. 1978. In: Proc. 3rd Int. Symp. Trace Element Metab. Man Animals-3. Freising-Weihenstephan, West Germany.
39. Mills, C.F., A.C. Dalgarno and G. Wenham. 1976. Brit. J. Nutr. 35:309.
40. Leigh, L.C. 1975. Res. Vet. Sci. 18:282.
41. O'Dell, B.L., R.M. Smith and R.A. King. 1976. J. Neurochem. 26:451.
42. Hidiroglou, M. 1980. Can. J. Animal Sci. 60:579.
43. Flynn, A., et al. 1977. J. Nutr. 107:1182.
44. Patterson, D.S.P., et al. 1974. J. Neurochem. 23:1245.
45. Hidiroglou, M., D.P. Heaney and K.E. Hartin. 1984. J. Animal Sci. 59(Suppl. 1):428.
46. Gooneratne, S.R., J. McC. Howell and J.M. Gawthorne. 1981. Brit. J. Nutr. 46:457.

References on Iodine

1. Miller, J.K., E.W. Swanson and G.E. Spalding. 1975. J. Dairy Sci. 58:1578.
2. Miller, J.K., E.W. Swanson and W.A. Lyke. 1973. J. Dairy Sci. 56:1344.
3. Barry, T.N., et al. 1983. Brit. J. Nutr. 49:241.
4. Pincus, S.H. and S.J. Klebanoff. 1971. New Eng. J. Med. 284:744.
5. Grosvenor, C.E. 1960. Amer. J. Physiol. 199:419.
6. Miller, J.K. and E.W. Swanson. 1973. J. Dairy Sci. 56:378.
7. Iwarsson, K. 1973. Acta Vet. Scand. 14:570.
8. Franke, A.A., J.C. Bruhn and R.B. Osland. 1983. J. Dairy Sci. 66:997.
9. Swanson, E.W. 1972. J. Dairy Sci. 55:1763.
10. Miller, J.K., B.R. Moss and E.W. Swanson. 1969. J. Dairy Sci. 52:677.
11. Blinco, C. 1975. J. Animal Sci. 40:342.
12. Hemken, R.W., et al. 1971. J. Dairy Sci. 54:85.
13. Hemken, R.W. 1970. J. Dairy Sci. 53:1183.
14. Alderman, G. and M.H. Stranks. 1967. J. Sci. Food Agr. 18:151.
15. Berg, J.N., et al. 1984. Amer. J. Vet. Res. 45:1073.

References on Iron

1. Suttle, N.F. 1979. Brit. J. Nutr. 42:89.
2. Bremner, I. and A.C. Dalgarno. 1973. Brit. J. Nutr. 29:229; 30:61.
3. Jacobs, A. 1977. Fed. Proc. 36:2904; Blood 50:433.
4. Furugouri, K., J. Miyata and K. Shijimaya. 1982. J. Dairy Sci. 65:1529.
5. Miyata, T., K. Furugouri and K. Shijimaya. 1984. J. Dairy Sci. 67:1256.
6. Blum, J.W. and U. Zuber. 1974. Res. Vet. Sci. 18:294.
7. Ammerman, C.B., et al. 1967. J. Animal Sci. 26:404.
8. Giles, R.C., et al. 1977. Amer. J. Vet. Res. 38:535.
9. Dargie, J.D. and J.M. Preston. 1974. J. Comp. Path. 84:83.
10. Mollerberg, L., et al. 1975. Acta Vet. Scand. 16:197,205.
11. Gibbins, R.A., et al. 1976. Biochim. Biophys. Acta 437:301.
12. Finch, C.A., et al. 1978. Proc. Soc. Expt. Biol. Med. 159:335.
13. Linder, M.C. and H.N. Munro. 1977. Fed. Proc. 36:2017.
14. Forth, W. 1974. In: Trace Element Metabolism in Animals-2. University Park Press, Baltimore.
15. Huebers, H.A., et al. 1983. Blood 61:283.
16. Savin, M.A. and J.D. Cook. 1980. Blood 56:1029.
17. Carver, F.J., D.L. Farb and E. Frieden. 1982. Biol. Trace Element Res. 4:1.
18. Bertoni, G., et al. 1976. Zoot. Nutr. Anim. 2:185.
19. Christopher, J.P., J.C. Hegenauer and P.D. Saltman. 1974. In: Trace Element Metabolism in Animals-2. University Park Press, Baltimore.
20. Overas, P. 1974. Nord. Vet. Med. 26:545.
21. Ammerman, C.B., et al. 1972. J. Animal Sci. 35:681.
22. Van Weerden, E.J., J. Huisman and J.E. Sprietsma. 1978. Z. Tierphysiol, Lierernahrg. Futtermittel. 40:209.
23. MacDougall, D.B., I. Bremner and A.C. Dalgarno. 1973. J. Sci. Fd. Agr. 24:1255.
24. Preston, J.M. and J.D. Dargie. 1974. J. Comp. Pathol. 84:73.
25. Tartour, G. and O.F. Idris. 1973. Res. Vet. Sci. 15:24.
26. Humphries, W.R., et al. 1983. Brit. J. Nutr. 49:77.

References on Manganese

1. Baly, D.L., et al. 1984. J. Nutr. 114:1438.
2. Suttle, N.F. 1979. Brit. J. Nutr. 42:89.
3. Black, J.R., C.B. Ammerman and P.R. Henry. 1985. J. Animal Sci. 60:861.
4. Ho, S.Y., et al. 1984. J. Dairy Sci. 67:1489.
5. Ivan, M. and M. Hidiroglou. 1980. J. Dairy Sci. 63:385.
6. Miller, W.J., et al. 1973. J. Animal Sci. 37:827.
7. Hidiroglou, M. 1980. Can. J. Animal Sci. 60:579.

398

8. Hidiroglou, M. 1980. Can. J. Animal Sci. 60:579.
9. Hidiroglou, M. and J.E. Knipfel. 1981. J. Dairy Sci. 64:1637.
10. Paynter, D.I. and I.W. Caple. 1984. J. Nutr. 114:1909.
11. Hurley, L.S. 1984. In: Present Knowledge in Nutrition, 5th Ed. The Nutrition Foundation, Inc., Washington, DC.
12. Zidenberg-Cherr, S., et al. 1983. J. Nutr. 113:2498.
13. Vagg, M.J. 1976. Proc. R. Soc. Med. 69:473.
14. Watson, L.T., et al. 1973. J. Animal Sci. 36:131.
15. Carter, J.C., Jr., et al. 1974. J. Animal Sci. 38:1284.
16. Ben-Ghedalia, D., A. Hasdai and E. Josef. 1983. J. Dairy Sci. 66:1298.
17. Miller, W.J., et al. 1972. J. Animal Sci. 43:460.
18. Hall, E.D. and H.W. Symonds. 1981. Brit. J. Nutr. 45:605.
19. Abrams, E., et al. 1977. J. Animal Sci. 45:1108.
20. Gibbons, R.A., et al. 1976. Biochem. Biophys. Acta. 444:1.
21. Adams, R.S. 1975. J. Dairy Sci. 58:1538.

References on Nickel
1. Spears, J.W. 1984. J. Animal Sci. 59:823.
2. O'Dell, G.D., et al. 1971. J. Animal Sci. 32:769.
3. Spears, J.W., et al. 1978. J. Nutr. 108:313.
4. O'Dell, G.D., et al. 1970. J. Nutr. 100:1447; J. Dairy Sci. 53:1266,1545.
5. Spears, J.W., C.J. Smith and E.E. Hatfield. 1977. J. Dairy Sci. 60:1073.
6. Martinez, A. and D.C. Church. 1970. J. Animal Sci. 31:982.
7. Miller, W.J. 1973. Fed. Proc. 32:1915.

References on Selenium
1. Ullrey, D.E., et al. 1977. J. Animal Sci. 45:559; 1978. 46:1515.
2. Hidiroglou, M., J. Proulx and P. Jolette. 1985. J. Dairy Sci. 68:57.
3. Oh, S.H., et al. 1976. J. Animal Sci. 42:977,984.
4. Conrad, H.R. 1977. In: Proc. Georgia Nutr. Conf., Atlanta, Georgia.
5. Weiss, W.P., V.F. Colenbrander and D. Cunningham. 1984. J. Dairy Sci. 67:416.
6. Conrad, H.R. and A.L. Moxan. 1979. J. Dairy Sci. 62:404.
7. Maus, R.W., et al. 1980. J. Dairy Sci. 63:532.
8. Varo, P., M. Nuurtamo and P. Koivistoinen. 1984. J. Dairy Sci. 67:2071.
9. Fisher, L.J., C. Hoogendoorn and J. Montemurro. 1980. Can. J. Animal Sci. 60:79.
10. Beilstein, M.A. and P.D. Whanger. 1983. J. Nutr. 113:2138.
11. Hoekstra, W.G. 1975. Fed. Proc. 34:2083.
12. Board, P.G. and D.W. Peter. 1976. Vet. Rec. 99:144.
13. Rotruck, J.T., et al. 1973. Science 179:588.
14. Combs, G.F., Jr., T. Noguchi and M.L. Scott. 1975. Fed. Proc. 34:2090.
15. Symonds, H.W., D.L. Mather and M.J. Vagg. 1981. Brit. J. Nutr. 46:487.
16. Harrison, J.H. and H.R. Conrad. 1984. J. Dairy Sci. 67:219.
17. Kincaid, R.L., et al. 1977. J. Animal Sci. 44:147.
18. Whanger, P.D., et al. 1978. J. Animal Sci. 46:515; 47:1157.
19. Hidiroglou, M. and J.R. Lessard. 1976. Intern. J. Vit. Nutr. Res. 46:458.
20. Hidiroglou, M. and C.G. Zakardas. 1976. Can. J. Physiol. Pharmacol. 54:336.
21. Whanger, P.D., et al. 1977. J. Nutr. 107:1288.
22. White, C.L. and M. Somers. 1977. Australian J. Biol. Sci. 30:47.
23. Hill, C.L. 1975. Fed. Proc. 34:2096.
24. Whanger, P.D., et al. 1972. J. Nutr. 102:435; Nutr. Rep. Intern. 6:21.
25. Quintanilha, A.T. 1984. Biochem. Soc. Trans. 12:403.
26. Brady, P.S., et al. 1978. J. Nutr. 108:1439.
27. Weiss, W.P., et al. 1983. J. Dairy Sci. 66:1101.
28. Horton, G.M.J., W.L. Jenkins and R. Rettenmaier. 1978. Brit. J. Nutr. 40:193.

29. Peter, D.W., D.J. Buscall and P.J. Reis. 1984. Proc. Australian Soc. Animal Prod. 15:529.
30. Kott, R.W., J.L. Ruttle and G.M. Southward. 1983. J. Animal Sci. 57:553.
31. Trinder, N., C.D. Woodhouse and C.P. Renton. 1969. Vet. Rec. 85:550.
32. Trinder, N., R.J. Hall and C.P. Renton. 1973. Vet. Rec. 93:641.
33. Ishak, M.A., et al. 1983. J. Dairy Sci. 66:99.
34. Schingoethe, D.J., et al. 1982. J. Dairy Sci. 65:2338.
35. Schingoethe, D.J., et al. 1978. J. Dairy Sci. 61:1582.
36. Harrison, J.H., D.D. Hancock and H.R. Conrad. 1984. J. Dairy Sci. 67:123.
37. Julien, W.E., et al. 1976. J. Dairy Sci. 50:1954,1960.
38. Hemken, R.W., et al. 1978. J. Dairy Sci. 61 (Suppl. 1):209.
39. Segerson, E.C., et al 1981. J. Dairy Sci. 64:1833.
40. Gwazdauskas, F.C., et al. 1979. J. Dairy Sci. 62:978.
41. Van Kampen, K.R. and L.F. James. 1978. In: Effects of Poisonous Plants on Livestock. Academic Press, New York.

References on Zinc
1. Miller, W.J., et al. 1970. J. Nutr. 100:893.
2. Bremner, I. and R.B. Marshall. 1974. Brit. J. Nutr. 32:283.
3. Saylor, W.W., F.D. Morrow and R.M. Leach, Jr. 1980. J. Nutr. 110:460.
4. Whanger, P.D., S.H. Oh and J.T. Deagen. 1981. J. Nutr. 111:1196.
5. Wegner, T.N., et al. 1973. J. Dairy Sci. 56:748.
6. Dufty, J.H., J.B. Bingley and L.Y. Cove. 1977. Australian Vet. J. 53:519.
7. McSparren, K.D. and P.P. Lorentz. 1977. Res. Vet. Sci. 22:393.
8. Parry, W.H. 1977. Nutr. Metab. 21(Suppl. 1):48.
9. Williams, R.B., I. McDonald and I. Bremner. 1978. Brit. J. Nutr. 40:377.
10. Lichti, E.L., et al. 1970. Amer. J. Obstet. Gynecol. 106:1242.
11. Neathery, M.W., et al. 1973. J. Dairy Sci. 59:98,212,1526; J. Animal Sci. 37:848.
12. Schwarz, F.J. and M. Kirchgessner. 1978. Z. Lebensm. Unters. Forsch. 166:6.
13. Eckbert, C.D., et al. 1977. Science 195:789.
14. Sandstead, H.H. 1985. Nutr. Revs. 43:129.
15. Sandstead, H.H. and G.W. Evans. 1984. In: Present Knowledge in Nutrition, 5th Ed. The Nutrition Foundation, Inc., Washington, DC.
16. Miller, W.J. 1973. Fed. Proc. 32:1915.
17. Stake, P.E., W.J. Miller and R.P. Gentry. 1973. Proc. Soc. Expt. Biol. Med. 142:494.
18. Grace, N.D. 1975. Brit. J. Nutr. 34:73.
19. Bertoni, G., et al. 1976. Zoot. Nutr. Animal 2:185.
20. Hampton, D.L., et al. 1976. J. Dairy Sci. 59:712;1963.
21. Stake, P.E., et al. 1974. J. Nutr. 104:1279.
22. Anke, M., et al. 1976. Naturwiss. 25:271.
23. Anonymous. 1985. Nutr. Rev. 43:148.
24. Bremner, I., B.W. Young and C.F. Mills. 1976. Brit. J. Nutr. 36:551.
25. White, F.D., et al. 1985. J. Dairy Sci. 68:1215.
26. Spais, A.G. and A.A. Papasteriadis. 1974. In: Trace Element Metabolism in Animals-2. University Park Press, Baltimore.
27. Beeson, W.M., T.W. Perry and T.D. Zurcher. 1977. J. Animal Sci. 45:160.
28. Kincaid, R.L. and J.D. Conrath. 1983. J. Dairy Sci. 66:821.
29. Neathery, M.W., et al. 1972. Proc. Soc. Exp. Bio. Med. 139:953.
30. Kincaid, R.L., et al. 1984. J. Dairy Sci. 67(Suppl. 1):103.
31. Andresen, E., et al. 1973. Lancet 1(808):839.
32. Kroneman, J., et al. 1975. Zbl. Vet. Med. A. 22:201.
33. Kirchgessner, M., W.A. Schwarz and H.-P. Roth. 1978. In: Trace Element Metabolism in Man and Animals-3. Freising-Weihenstephan, West Germany.
34. Smith, B.L., et al. 1977. N.Z. Vet. J. 25:124,310.
35. Wyatt, R.D., et al. 1985. J. Dairy Sci. 68:437.

400

36. Apgar, J. and J.A. Fitzgerald. 1985. J. Animal Sci. 60:1530.
37. Kincaid, R.L., et al. 1976. J. Dairy Sci. 59:552,1580.
38. Davies, N.T., et al. 1977. Brit. J. Nutr. 38:153.

Other Minor and Toxic Elements References
1. Nielsen, F. and W. Mertz. 1984. In: Present Knowledge in Nutrition, 5th Ed. The Nutrition Foundation, Inc., Washington, DC.
2. Anke, M., et al. 1978. In: Trace Element Metabolism in Man and Animals-3. Freising-Weihenstephan, West Germany.
3. Ammerman, C.B., et al. 1977. J. Animal Sci. 44:485.
4. Bremner, I. 1974. Quart. Rev. Biophys. 7:75.
5. Neathery, M.W. and W.J. Miller. 1975. J. Dairy Sci. 58:1767.
6. Smith, G.S., et al. 1975. J. Animal Sci. 41:882,891.
7. Bailey, C.B. 1981. Can. J. Animal Sci. 61:219.
8. Tamura, S., et al. 1983. Biochem. Biophys. Res. Comm. 113:80.
9. Bratton, G.R., et al. 1981. Tox. Appl. Pharmacol. 59:164.

Summary References
1. Farasch, E.D., et al. 1981. Cell 25:67.
2. Sevanian, A. and P. Hochstein. 1985. Ann. Rev. Nutr. 5:365.
3. Sies, H. 1985. In: Oxidative Stress. Academic Press, Orlando, Florida.
4. Chow, C.K. 1979. Amer. J. Clin. Nutr. 32:1068.
5. LeBoeuf, R.A. and W.G. Hoekstra. 1985. Fed. Proc. 44:2563.
6. Chvapil, M. 1976. Med. Clin. N. Amer. 60:799.
7. Wills, E.D. 1985. In: Oxidative Stress. Academic Press, Orlando, Florida.
8. Paynter, D.I. and I.W. Caple. 1984. J. Nutr. 114:1909.

19 DIGESTION, METABOLISM AND NUTRIENT NEEDS IN PRERUMINANTS

by Sidney J. Lyford, Jr. and J. Tal Huber

The preruminant is in a transition stage of life starting at birth when it is dependent principally on a highly digestible liquid diet and progressing to a point when it is a functional ruminant and uses the rumen, reticulum, and omasum for processing of herbage or other feedstuffs provided by man.

This chapter deals with development of digestive function of young ruminants from birth to the time when the animal is a functionally mature ruminant. The major changes occurring in the rumen-reticulum with respect to size, papillary growth and fermentative action will be mentioned, as well as those in digestive enzyme concentrations, metabolism of principal nutrients and salivary production. Our objective is to relate these changes to nutrient needs and utilization in this transition stage of the animal's life.

DEVELOPMENT OF DIGESTIVE FUNCTION

Motility

Muscular contractions occur in each of the forestomachs of the young suckling ruminant with regular contractions established when solid food is eaten. No stable rumen contractions are observed in calves fed milk only, even after 15 weeks of age, while adult level contractions are present by 3-5 weeks of age in calves fed hay and concentrates. The development of motility appears closely related to the development of an active rumen fermentation (see Ch. 4). Abomasal contractions seem limited to strong peristaltic contractions in the pyloric antrum. However, the normal pattern of contractions of the forestomach moves the abomasum extensively as well.

The first feeding results in hypermotility of the small intestine with the development of normal motility within 4-6 d if the tract becomes colonized by bacteria (1). During nursing an inhibition of motility occurs in the gastric antrum of both the calf and lamb, followed by an increase in total activity for the first 2 h post feeding. Spikes of activity are initiated on the smaller curvature of the fundus, being coupled to distinct peristaltic contractions of the pyloric antrum which are most pronounced at the opening of the pylorus for movement of abomasal contents into the duodenum. Peristaltic action in the small intestine is disrupted for 1-2 h following a meal (dependent on meal size), but the frequency of duodenal contractions doubles.

Reticular Groove Closure

Groove closure results from complex sensory stimuli including olfactory, visual, thermal and chemical (see Ch. 4). It is voluntary in action and the result of a conditioned pattern of behavior. When liquids are consumed by nursing, the lips of the reticular groove contract and rotate to form a tube for direct liquid passage from the esophagus through the cardia to the reticulo-omasal orifice.

However, the method of feeding liquids may alter the effectiveness of closure. Consistent closure of the groove is obtained by sucking milk or water. Drinking milk from an open pail results in large "gulps" and causes leakage from the groove into the rumino-reticulum (RR). However, losses of milk rarely exceed 20%.

Certain salts—NaCl, $NaHCO_3$ and to a lesser extent, $CuSO_4$, produce groove closure in cattle up to two years of age. Drenching liquids or involuntary consumption through coercion from a nipple bottle produces no/or only limited closure in older cattle. However, effective closure may be maintained for relatively long periods. Ruminant calves raised on a mixed diet of solid feed plus bucket-fed milk show efficient closure up to 12 months, after which some spillage into the rumen occurs.

Rumination

Ruminating behavior in the nursing neonatal is initiated with the consumption of solid fibrous feeds. Rumination is commonly

402

observed at 8-12 d of age in lambs and 11-14 d in calves given forages and concentrates from birth. By 2 weeks calves are ruminating an average of 3 periods/d, each about 15 minutes long. By 5 weeks rumination increases to 12 periods/d, 23 minutes in length. However, calves fed a finely ground and/or pelleted hay show a marked reduction in ruminating time.

The mature pattern of time spent in chewing and rumination is established by 3 months with an increase in the number of boluses, but a decrease in chews per bolus continuing to adulthood. Increased jaw strength in the developing ruminant increases efficiency of particle size reduction.

Rumination efficiency (cell wall constituents processed/d/$W^{0.75}$) varies with age and species. In calves it is about half that of mature cattle but equal to mature sheep. However, goats are more efficient than sheep (23.7 g vs 14.9 g/kg $W^{0.75}$), and similar to young heifers (see Ch. 5).

Salivary Secretion

There is little parotid salivary production in kids or lambs under 3 weeks of age, but secretion occurs soon thereafter and reaches adult proportions (with respect to gland weight) at about 12 weeks in goats and 6-10 weeks in lambs (2). The size of parotids but not submaxillary or inferior molar glands increases rapidly with consumption of fibrous feeds. Table 19-1 illustrates the stimulatory

effect of hay and pasture on parotid secretion rates and saliva buffering capacity in growing lambs. Removal of forage from the diet returns the parotid secretion and buffering capacity to preruminant levels.

INITIATION OF FORESTOMACH DIGESTION

Microbial Populations

Microbial colonization of the digestive tract takes place in the first few hours of life beginning with the animal's first contacts with the environment and non-sterile foods (see Ch. 7). In one study microbial analysis of the small intestine of newborn calves before feeding showed 8.6 X 10^7 bacteria/g tissue at 8-12 h after birth with *E. coli,* streptococci and *Clostridium welchii* predominating (3). After feeding colostrum and/or milk, lactobacilli are the main bacterial species colonizing the intestinal tract during early life (4) with numbers in excess of 10^8/g tissue observed.

Rumens of week-old calves exhibit bacterial species characteristic of, but in different proportions to, the adult. Cellulolytic bacteria are in surprisingly high numbers at 1 week and increase to adult concentrations by 2-3 weeks. Lactate fermentors are high during the first 3 weeks, dropping to adult levels by 9-13 weeks. Aerobic bacteria and coliform are higher in the calf rumen during the first few weeks than later. At about 6 weeks

Table 19-1. Development and secretory activity of the parotid gland in the lamb as affected by diet.[a]

Diet	Body weight, kg	Rumen mucosa, g	Parotid weight, g	Parotid secretion, g/g/min	Buffering capacity, meq/ℓ
Experiment 1					
Milk only	20.2	49	6.8	0.20	111
Hay	18.6	129	9.6	0.51	160
Shavings	19.9	161	9.6	0.50	143
Purified	18.8	146	8.0	0.27	130
Experiment 2					
Grazing	23.2	201	11.7	0.44	165
Grazing followed by milk only	25.9	54	10.2	0.26	127

[a]Experiment 1 ages 13-14 weeks at time of measurement. Experiment 2, lambs grazing with dams to 9 weeks of age with half of the lambs returned at this time to a milk only diet until reaching 19 weeks of age. Excerpted from reference 3.

bacteria characteristic of adults predominate, but some characteristics of calf patterns remain, which disappear by 9-13 weeks. Microbial activity, as measured by free rumen carbohydrase activities, are at adult levels in lambs and calves as early as 2-3 weeks of age.

Establishment of protozoa requires direct inoculation or intimate contact with mature ruminants. The first ciliates established are oligotrichs (*Endodinium* followed by *Diplodinium*), followed by the holotrichs (*Isotricha* and *Dasytrichia*). Protozoa are well-established by 10-12 weeks in calves. Flagellate protozoa have been reported as early as 3 weeks of age in calves on solid feeds, but ciliates were not observed before 11 weeks.

Microbial Digestion

Calves fed solid food show rumen VFAs and ammonia patterns similar to the adult by 3 weeks of age. In one study rumen fluid from 10 to 14-day-old calves digested cellulose and starch similar to that from 70-d-old feedlot lambs. In another experiment lambs restricted to milk only for 8 weeks and then given access to concentrates achieved a rumen fluid digestive capacity equal to feedlot lambs within 6 d. Numerous studies show adult VFA concentrations are attained by 6-8 weeks in lambs and calves.

When calves are abruptly weaned from milk to a solid diet, it takes several weeks for rumen digestion to increase to maximal levels —possibly as long as 8 weeks. Associated with these changes are increased production of microbial protein and greater rumen metabolism of dietary protein (5).

Rumen microbial protein production accounts for about 50% of the protein reaching the abomasum of 5-week-old calves given access to solid feeds from 1 week of age and weaned at 4 weeks. Microbial production of protein is delayed when weaning is delayed. Essential amino acid composition of digesta obtained by rumen and abomasal cannulas revealed little change with age in microbial composition.

GASTRIC DIGESTION

Pregastric and Gastric Secretions

The abomasum plays a major role in coagulation of milk and the initiation of protein and fat digestion. The first digestive enzyme added to ingesta is pregastric esterase, mainly secreted by the palatine glands and other regions of the oral cavity in calves (see Ch. 7). Quantities of pregastric esterase secreted are large and may be important at birth in balancing low pancreatic lipase. However, due to efficient digestion of fat in the small intestine, the overall importance of pregastric esterase to the neonatal calf is questionable.

Pepsin and chymosin are secreted by fundus glands of gastric mucosa as inactive precursors, but are rapidly activated by acidic conditions of the abomasum. These enzymes are present just prior to birth in the lamb and calf, with chymosin activity increasing in the lamb immediately after birth with a decrease during the next 2-4 weeks (Fig. 19-1). An increase in pepsin activity occurs upon introduction of solid food, and is roughly proportional to increased body weight.

After weaning, pepsin is the main abomasal enzyme secreted by lambs and calves. Chymosin decreases with age, but may increase if the calf is returned to a milk-type feed containing casein.

Secretion of HCl by parietal cells of the abomasum is low in the newborn but increases rapidly thereafter. Cell numbers are low at birth but increase 10-fold during the first 3 d of life. Consequently, the pH of abomasal fluid in lambs is ca. 5.8 soon after

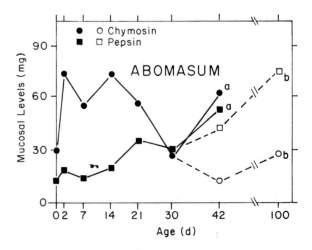

Figure 19-1. Abomasal mucosal levels of pepsin and chymosin from lambs (a) raised on milk replacer to 42 d of age or (b) given access hay + concentrates and weaned at 30 d. Solid lines indicate preruminant and broken lines ruminant status. From Guilloteau (6).

404

birth, but drops to ca. 3.0 after fasting for 2 d (13). The observed delay in acid production is important for protection of immunoglobulines from proteolysis just after birth.

Protein Coagulation and Digestion

Coagulation of milk occurs soon after entering the abomasum, primarily through the action of chymosin, though pepsin also has appreciable clotting activity. Firmness of the curd decreases with age as chymosin decreases (7). The pH of the abomasal contents prior to feeding is between 1 and 2, increasing to about 6.0 at the end of the meal, it then drops as acid secretion increases and as whey fluids exit, reaching prefeeding levels in about 5 h. The optimum pH for chymosin activity is 3.5 and that of pepsin is 2.0.

Outflow of digesta into the duodenum is the greatest during the first hour after milk consumption, and peaking in the jejunum at 4-5 h. The first material exiting the abomasum is whey fluids containing carbohydrate and soluble N compounds, followed 3-4 h later by thicker, more viscous materials (pH 1.5-3.5) from the breakdown of casein by pepsin and HCl. The casein clot is slowly digested over 12-18 h with the next meal usually incorporating remaining clot fragments from a previous feeding. Fat globules are dispersed throughout the curd matrix, the release of which presents the duodenum with a continuous supply of protein and fat (4).

Greater protease secretions occur in calves fed mildly heated skim milk powder compared to severely heated skim milk powder, fish protein concentrate (FPC) or solvent-extracted soybean flour (SF). Acid production was lowest when feeding SF, but the highest with FPC, even though feeding FPC produced no abomasal protein coagulation.

Protein Sources and Gastric Emptying Effects

Lack of coagulation accelerates gastric emptying of proteins and lipids normally retained by the denatured protein matrix, adversely affecting protein, lipid and mineral digestibilities. The increased passage rate of ingesta to the small intestine produces a rapid increase in plasma triglycerides, free amino acids and glucose, which are relatively constant if a normal clot forms. Gastric emptying may be retarded by high fat, glucose or amino acids, particularly glycine. However, the

primary factor influencing abomasal emptying is fill or tension on the abomasal wall. Replacement of milk proteins by whey, soybean or fish proteins increases abomasal emptying due to lack of coagulation.

Larger quantities of milk fed at a meal require a longer time for the whey fluids to leave the abomasum, delaying the drop in pH of the abomasal fluids and prolonging digestion of the casein clot. Increasing meal size with age or body weight is compensated for by increases in abomasal secretions, digestion and outflow rates. Type of dietary fat (replacement of milk fat with lard, tallow, soybean or corn oil) does not affect the rate of abomasal emptying, proteolysis or gastric pH in young dairy calves.

Abomasal Fat Digestion

Pregastric esterases (PGE) which preferentially hydrolyze C-4 to C-8 linkages are mixed with milk during swallowing. This produces a dispersion of the enzyme and fat globules throughout the curd matrix where it is closer to its optimal pH (4.5-6.0) than the 2.5 in abomasal fluid.

Hydrolysis of the C8-C12 acids occurs at equal rates for PGE and pancreatic lipase, but PGE is not able to hydrolyze fatty acids longer than C14. While the potential hydrolysis of milk fat by PGE may be 67-70%, data from the week-old calf suggest that only 1/3 of the dietary lipid leaves the abomasum as FFA and monoglycerides. Direct infusion of milk into the abomasum to avoid the addition of pregrastric esterase does not reduce milk fat digestibility in week-old calves even though abomasal hydrolysis is decreased.

PANCREATIC AND INTESTINAL SECRETIONS

Pancreatic Secretions

Qualitatively, pancreatic and intestinal secretions of the preruminant are like those of the adult ruminant and non-ruminant. All pancreatic secretions are present at birth (see Ch. 9). Proteolytic enzymes are secreted in inactive, zymogen forms and are activated by removal of a 7-amino acid residue from the N-terminus at a pH of 5.0. Optimal pH for the proteolytic enzyme activity is between 7.6 and 8.0.

Guilloteau et al (6) found that pancreatic tissue of lambs doubled in total nucleic acid during the first 2 d without an increase in tissue weight. This was followed by moderate hyperplasia during the next few days and slow growth into adulthood. The large secretory potential for protein digestion observed in the first 2 d probably reflects accumulation of zymogenic stores in late fetal life and limited release during the first few hours. Increased lipase activity with little fat in ruminant diets and increased amylase activity with limited starch escaping rumen breakdown suggests that age and weight may govern pancreatic enzyme secretion. Research suggests that, if adaptation to changing substrates occurs, it does so slowly.

Large increases in pancreatic amylase of calves occur with time (8.9, 46.8 and 269.2 mg/12 h at 7, 24 and 63 d of age, respectively, while trypsin remains relatively constant between the first and tenth week of life (18). Chymotrypsin may be less important because it hydrolyzes the same peptide bonds as pepsin and chymosin and the ratio of α-chymotrypsin:trypsin is usually lower in preruminants than ruminants. Ribonuclease is high in preruminants. Large doses of RNA given to milk-fed calves were digested and absorbed before reaching the ileum.

Pancreatic Secretion

Secretions of pancreatic enzymes are greatest 1 h after feeding even though the main outflow of N and lipid from the abomasum occurs at 5-10 h. Most secretion of trypsin and total protease occurs 0-1 h post feeding, coinciding with the outflow of whey N. There is little relationship between protease activity and N flow, or lipase activity and lipid flow after the first hour of feeding. In one study pancreatic fluid secretions for a 12-h period beginning with a meal, averaged 297, 441 and 602 ml for 7, 24 and 63-d-old calves, respectively. However, there was little effect of age on secretory capacity per unit of live weight (0.71, 0.85 and 0.80 ml/kg, respectively). Calves fed milk replacers with 50% of the protein from fish or soybean protein produce less trypsin, chymotrypsin, total protease and ribonuclease, but more lipase during 12 h post feeding than calves only fed milk protein.

Endocrine regulation of pancreatic secretions in young calves is similar to other young mammals, with secretin, cholecystokinin and pancreozymin increasing amylase, proteins, H_2O, Ca, Mg, P and Zn output. Somatostatin and glucagon inhibit these effects, while gastrin increases pancreatic flow, protein and amylase.

Intestinal Secretions

In the small intestine, young ruminants are high in lactase, low in cellobiase, maltase and trehalase but have no sucrase activity. Fructose is poorly absorbed and its presence in large amounts causes severe diarrhea. Calf intestinal lactase is high at birth but decreases 25% during the first 8 d of life while maltase activity, initially low, increases 40% during that time. These changes are related to renewal of the intestinal epithelium. In week-old lambs, epithelial cell replacement is said to occur within 50 h in the duodenum, 91 h in the jejunum and 94 h in the ileum.

Lactase activity continues to decrease with age, remaining more active in milk-fed calves than weaned ones, and may remain high even if starch replaces lactose in the diet. Maltase activity is much lower than lactase in young ruminants, and less than in the pig, rat and humans. Lactase and cellobiase are very low in adult ruminants, while maltase activity increases slowly, reaching adult levels by about 14 weeks.

Dipeptidase activity in the small intestine of sheep, pig, dog and humans increases successively from the duodenum to the mid ileum and decreases toward the distal ileum with 75-90% in the mucosa. Activities are highest in the apical and middle of the villi and low in the crypt region, similar to disaccharidases. These enzymes are fully developed at birth but a colostral factor acts as an inhibitor.

Intestinal Digesta Characteristics

The pH of the duodenal contents is essentially the same as abomasal contents, rising to about 4 immediately after feeding and dropping to about 2, afterwards. In the ileum the pH is not affected by a meal and has increased to 7-8. Volume of chyme entering the duodenum is about twice that consumed, due to the addition of saliva, digestive juices, bile and other fluids.

406

PROTEIN DIGESTION AND METABOLISM

Dietary Sources

Protein digestion in the preruminant is initiated by gastric secretions and continues throughout the length of the small intestine. Administration of free amino acids suggests maximal absorption 7-15 m distal to the pylorus. Protein digestibility of calves fed non-milk proteins in liquid diets is least during the first 2 weeks of life but gradually increases for about 2 months (Table 19-2).

Milk Proteins. In preruminants milk proteins have a high true digestibility which increases somewhat during the first 6 weeks (Table 19-2). Whey proteins may be better utilized if subjected to moderate heat; however, heat denaturation of milk and whey

proteins reduces digestibility, promotes diarrhea and poor performance of lambs and calves.

Soybean Proteins. Preparation of soybean protein concentrates for use in milk replacers should consider the removal of the indigestible soluble carbohydrates, raffinose, sucrose and stachyose which contribute to diarrhea. The several trypsin inhibitors present require inactivation. Calves develop blood antibodies against certain soybean proteins which may be removed by methanol or hot ethanol extraction, or by acid or alkali treatment. Other compounds such as phenolics, hemagglutinins and goiterogenic factors present in soybeans should also be removed.

The detrimental effects of feeding soybean flour are greatest in young preruminants. Marked morphological changes (partial

Table 19-2. Apparent nitrogen digestibility of diets containing different protein sources fed to calves at different ages.

Protein source	Proportion of protein supply, %	Age at time of determination and digestion coefficients			Ref. no.
		8 d	15 d	22 d	
Skim milk[a]	100	78.6	87.3	85.9	9
Pea protein isolate	50	64.8	77.4	83.9	
Pea protein conc.	50	43.4	44.8	53.3	
		8-13 d	15-20 d	22-27 d	
Skim milk[b]	100	73.3	80.0	85.8	10
Fababean conc.	25	72.5	78.1	86.8	
Fababean conc.	50	64.2	71.6	82.0	
Fababean conc.	80	60.5	68.2	81.6	
		10-15 d		30-35 d	
Skim milk	100	85.3		94.0	11
Soy concentrate	100	56.9		72.6	
Soy flour full fat	100	61.3		68.7	
Soy flour defatted	100	28.5		51.0	
		7 d	28 d	70 d	
Skim milk	100	86	94	92	12
Soy flour	36	61	84	84	
Soy flour	70	60	66	66	
Fish conc.	33	74	83	86	
Fish conc.	60	71	75	87	

[a]Calculated digestibility values; PPI, 66.8% and PPC, 11.0%.
[b]Calculated digestibility values; fababean conc. 56.8, 65.1 and 79.9% respectively for each age.

atrophy of the jejunal villi and crypt elongation) have been shown to occur when feeding heat-treated soybean flour or wheat gluten to preruminant calves. This effect has been attributed to antigenic proteins, glycinin and β-conglycinin. First exposure produces a slight effect, but successive exposures results in marked abnormalities and diarrhea. Restoration of normal morphology requires about 10 d after returning to a milk diet (13).

Partial replacement (up to 50%) of milk proteins with properly treated soybean protein extracts is common practice in the milk replacer industry in the USA for feeding replacement heifers, but not veal calves. Calves older than 3 weeks or over 45 kg may be raised successfully with complete replacement of milk by soybean protein sources.

Fish Protein Concentrates. Fish meals, fish protein hydrolysates (FPH) and fish protein concentrates (FPC) are potential replacements for skim milk for feeding calves and lambs. Quality depends on species of fish, freshness, the nature of the fish by-product, and processing and drying procedures. Oxidized fats found in fish wastes and products from oil species reduce nutritional quality, so stabilization or removeal of fat is required. Success of the solvent used for extraction of fat depends on efficiency of fat removal and absence of solvent residues. A high quality, low-fat liquid FPH (white fish with liver removed) has been used to replace up to 2/3 of the milk protein in the liquid diet for dairy calves to 6 weeks of age without loss of performance. More frequent feedings (4X/d) improved gains.

Production of FPH with bacterial rather than plant proteases is less nutritious for veal calves. Replacement of skim milk by FPH should be restricted to about 35% of the protein for veal, which is also the maximum FPC level suggested for calves younger than 3 weeks of age. Dried fish solubles are not recommended for inclusion in milk replacers at any level because of decreased gains probably due to poor EAA composition and low digestibility relative to milk.

Field Bean Proteins. Fababean (*Vicia faba L.*) protein is similar to that of soybean but higher in lysine and lower in methionine. Fababean concentrate, supplemented with

methionine, was used successfully to replace 25% of the skim milk protein of diets for calves between 3-30 d of age. Reduced digestibility and greater cecal fermentation occurred at higher levels (up to 80% of the protein), although there was substantial adaptation by 1 month of age (10). Mechanical processing of field beans by micronization improved digestibility over other processing methods.

Pea Protein Concentrates. Pea (*Pisum sativum L.*) protein concentrates (PPC) and isolates (PPI) have been fed to 3 to 23-d-old calves, replacing half of the skim milk protein. Protein digestibilities of 84.0 and 75.4 and 47.5% were observed for the skim milk, PPI and PPC, respectively. Starch and oligosaccharides made up over 20% of PPC and probably were responsible for its poor protein digestion, which improved with age (9). The PPI might be used to replace up to half the skim milk protein in replacers for older preruminant calves.

Single Cell Protein Sources. The amino acid composition of yeast grown on hydrocarbons is similar to that of milk except for lower methionine levels. Extraction with solvents may be necessary to remove residual oil. An alkane-grown yeast (*Candida tropicalis*) fed to supply 1/4 of the dietary protein has been used successfully in diets of fattening veal calves between 3-16 weeks of age. Higher levels did not affect calf health but significantly reduced weight gains. Similar results were obtained with preruminant lambs. Acid treatment of the yeast to break down the cell walls improved digestibility. Digestibilities of protein in lambs from raw or acid-treated yeast and skim milk were 67, 77 and 88%, respectively. One problem with yeast in milk replacers is the poor digestion of the carbohydrate fraction (22% consisting of mostly mannans and glycans) which resulted in reduced pH of large intestinal contents. Diets containing 50% of their protein from ethanol-grown bacteria, supplemented with methionine, approached skim milk diets in protein digestibility (88.8 vs 91.3%) when measured at the terminal ileum of calves.

In summary, the problems occurring with most alternative protein sources used in replacers to substitute for milk protein in

408

preruminant diets are related to lower protein quality, increased rate of gastric emptying, altered gastric and pancreatic secretions, reduced digestibility and digestive tract disturbances. Undesirable effects are more pronounced during the first month of life. When undigested residues are fermented in the large intestine, there is little amino acid contribution to the animal. Alternate protein sources might be used at low levels, providing consideration is given to characteristics causing digestive problems.

PROTEIN ABSORPTION AND METABOLISM

Many changes occur in the protein supply of the developing ruminant. In the fetus there is an active transfer of amino acids and ammonia from placental and maternal circulation. Postnatal supply is initially from monogastric digestion of high quality protein, which is gradually replaced by microbial digestion of lower quality plant materials, with microbial protein becoming the major protein source for maturing ruminants.

Fetal Amino Acid Metabolism

Comparison of amino acid (AA) concentrations across the placenta of sheep revealed a net accretion into the fetus, and a placental uptake of all AA tested (Fig. 19-2). Amount of placental transfer varies greatly with the different amino acids. Of the N entering sheep fetal circulation, about 60% is retained for growth during the last third of pregnancy. The utero-placental mass produces NH_3 which enters both uterine and fetal circulation.

Some functioning of the ovine fetal digestive system is shown by metabolic activity and protein turnover. This observation is consistent with swallowing of amniotic fluid by the fetus and absorption of contained nutrients. The fetal liver has a high synthetic capacity and turnover of protein which is exported to other tissues. Lungs were similar to liver in synthetic capacity with brain and kidney less, but greater than skeletal muscle. However, due to different tissue masses the contribution to whole body protein synthesis was as follows (%): muscles, 20.5; gastro-intestinal tract, 20.5; liver, 14.4; and lungs, 9.4 (15).

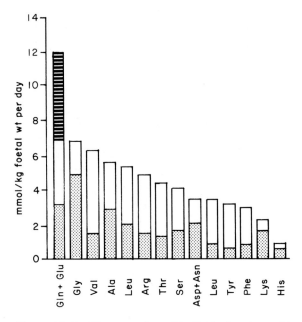

Figure 19-2. The accretion of individual amino acids in the fetal lamb during the latter part of gestation, umbilical uptake, and glutamate loss from fetal circulation. The open bar segment represents the uptake by umbilical circulation in excess of fetal accretion and for glutamine + glutamate, is the net excess accounting for both accretion and glutamate excretion. From Battaglia and Meschia (14).

Glutamate and Glutamine Metabolism

Glutamine and alanine are major substrates for rapidly growing tissues with glutamine having important roles in NH_3 detoxification, N conservation, N transport between gut, liver and kidney and gluconeogensis. The placenta is a major source of glutamine in the fetal lamb, providing more than half the supply near parturition. Two-thirds of the glutamine is synthesized by the placenta from glutamate and one-third comes from maternal circulation. About a third of the placental requirement for glutamate comes from fetal circulation with the rest from α-ketoglutarate or glutathione.

A postnatal increase in the gluconeogensis and glutathione metabolism occurs which redistributes cysteine from the kidney for protein synthesis. Glutamate and glutamine metabolism by the brain is complex, and depending upon the cell type, both synthesis and breakdown may be occurring simultaneously. Glutamine is possibly important in neurotransmission, AA transport, the development of the central nervous system and the blood-brain barrier.

Colostral Immunoglobulin Absorption

The intestine of the neonatal calf is permeable to colostral immunoglobulins for a short time after birth, but delay in the consumption of colostrum greatly reduces γ-globulin uptake. Matte et al (16) found 66% of ingested immunoglobulin G (IgG) in calf plasma when colostrum was fed 6 h after birth, but at 12, 24, 36, or 48 h, absorbed IgG dropped to 46.7, 11.5, 6.7 and 6.0% of that fed. Antibody absorption is rapid and by 5 h after feeding about 50% of maximum blood levels are reached.

The ileum is the primary site of γ-globulin absorption, with little absorbed from the duodenum but some from the jejunum. The γ-globulin uptake is greater in heavier than lighter calves, and increases per unit of intestinal length.

Reduction in antibody absorption with time appears related to renewal of the intestinal lining that occurs 40-48 h after birth. This renewal begins with the epithelial cells in the crypts of the villi and proceeds with their migration to villi extremities. In calves absorption occurs across all villi epithelial cells at 6 h of age, but is restricted to the tips by 53 h. Corley et al (17) found significant reductions in γ-globulin absorption by newborn calves first exposed to *E. coli* obtained from the duodenum of older calves. This was accompanied by intracellular penetration of *E. coli* into mesenteric lymph nodes by 2-6 h and exfoliation of microvilli. Colostrum feeding prior to exposure prevented *E. coli* attachment and penetration (Fig. 19-3).

Other evidence has been cited for competition of *E. coli* with immunoglobulins (IG) for the same receptor site on the surface of the intestinal epithelial cells, thus reducing IG transport across the intestinal mucosa. Selectivity of IG absorption appears more developed in humans, guinea pigs and rabbits than in ruminants where a wide variety of macromolecules are absorbed, though some selectivity may occur after passage through the absorptive cells. Receptors for IG have been identified in the intestine of rats and may protect IG from proteolytic digestion.

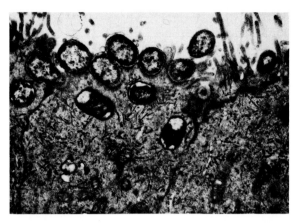
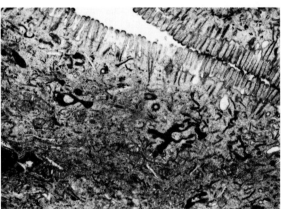

Figure 19-3. Electron micrographs of intestinal villi from two baby calves. The top photo shows apical ends of several ileal epithelial cells from an *E. coli* exposed calf which had received no colostrum. The microvilli were largely absent at the sites of *E. coli* attachment. *E. coli* were also within the apical cytoplasm (approx. 16,000X). The bottom photo shows that ileal epithelial cells from a calf which had received colostrum prior to *E. coli* were unaltered cytologically. Dark aggregations of colostral proteins were in the apical tubular system of the cells (approx. 14,000X).

Absorption of IgG and immunoglobulin A increase linearly with concentration in the colostrum, but immunoglobulin M absorption may be reduced by excessive colostrum or a delay in feeding after birth. Practical management of colostral immunoglobulins should include: feeding the first milking as early as possible to insure maximum IG absorption, and feeding a sufficiently high volume (4-6 ℓ by 6 h) to adequately protect the calf until it develops its own immunity. Administration of colostrum by nipple bottle to newborn

410

calves is often recommended because quantities suckled are quite variable.

Amino Acid Absorption

While little information is available, AA absorption in the preruminant undoubtedly is like that of adult ruminants and monogastrics. Uptake of AA from the small intestine is more rapid in the peptide form than as single AAs. Intracellular fluid of the mucosa appears to be the site of depeptide hydrolysis, which is followed by transfer of free AA into the plasma. Longer peptides (>2 AA) are probably broken down at the brush border, though gly-gly-gly and others usually resistant to mucosal hydrolysis may enter the portal blood where they are hydrolyzed readily by the liver, kidney or other tissues. Some data suggests L-leucine absorption rates for calves fed hay and concentrates are reduced compared to calves fed milk, but there was no difference in L-lysine absorption.

Protein Metabolism

In preruminants gluconeogensis from protein supplies precursors for up to 28% of the glucose synthesized. Most AA are found in portal plasma following a meal, but alanine, glutamic and aspartic acids are extensively metabolized in the gut wall to pyruvate, α-ketoglutarate and oxalacetate, respectively. In constrast, levels of plasma AA remain unchanged or decreased after meals in mature ruminants.

In preruminant lambs, either a deficiency or excess of EAA result in decreased protein synthesis and increased urinary excretion. Energy utilization also decreases due to urea synthesis; and inefficient conversion of some AA (especially phenylalanine, tyrosine, histidine and lysine) to energy occurs. This waste has been attributed to a heavy influx of AA into the metabolic pathways, resulting in an inability for proper use for protein synthesis. Best utilization occurs when EAA:NEAA ratios are in approximately equal proportions.

Plasma urea N (PUN), N-balance, apparent digestibility of N (ADN) and plasma lysine have been used to evaluate the lysine requirement in the preruminant calf and gave estimates of 8.5, 7.2, 7.5, and 7.6 g lysine/d, respectively, for lysine needed by 50-58 kg calves gaining 0.25 kg/d (18). The graphs in Fig. 19-4 illustrate the division of data into

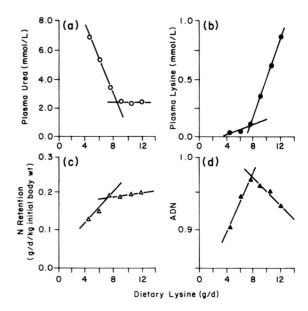

Figure 19-4. The use of 4 different methods used to determine lysine adequacy in calves. Graphs present dietary lysine supplementation as it affects plasma urea, plasma lysine, N retention and apparent digestibility of N (ADN). From Williams and Hewitt (18).

insufficient vs adequate levels of supplementation with the intersection of the two slopes used to estimate requirements. Because lysine goes almost exclusively to tissue synthesis, the relative proportion of EAA:lysine in the body can estimate the requirement for other EAAs. In most studies with preruminants, data from all these methods correlate highly with each other, but plasma EAA or N balance appear best because of many factors affecting PUN or N digestibility.

High starch diets produce an apparent protein sparing effect in calves, resulting in elevated levels of certain free amino acids in muscle tissue and increased N retention. However, it is unclear whether starch increases AA transport in association with higher insulin levels or reduces breakdown of muscle protein.

Razzaque et al (19) studied the metabolism of ^{14}C-labeled bacterial nucleic acids fed in a liquid diet to preruminant lambs. Extensive absorption occurred (58.3% in 12 h) with 38% of that absorbed exhaled, 34% excreted in the urine and 29% retained in tissues. Their data suggest that retention of the purine base may be more important than the nucleoside when salvaging dietary bacterial nucleic acids for tissue nucleic acid synthesis. Allantoin, excreted in the urine, appears to be the primary end product of microbial purine metabolism in calves and sheep (20).

FAT DIGESTION AND ABSORPTION

In preruminants fat hydrolysis is initiated in the abomasum by pregastric esterase, and continued by pancreatic lipase in the small intestine. The products, sn-2 monoglycerides and free fatty acids (FFA) are polar and act as an interface of emulsion particles around the fat droplets. These combine with biliary and pancreatic secretions to form the micelles, with little incorporation of di- and tri-acylglycerols. As a result, fat droplets are transformed from emulsified triglyceride particles 5,000 nm in size to micelles consisting of bile salts, FFA, 2-monoacylglycerol and other lipid soluble components which average of 3-5 nm.

Micelles facilitate transfer of lipids into intestinal epithelial cells. There is limited absorption of non-micellar FFA and mono-acylglycerol. Short and medium chain fatty acids may readily penetrate the mucosal layers and do not depend on micelle formation. After entering the intestinal mucosal cell, triglycerides are resynthesized, formed into chylomicrons and transported to the lymphatic system.

Phospholipids are hydrolyzed to either the sn-1 or sn-2 acyl lysophosphoglyceride and a FFA by position-specific pancreatic phospholipase A_1 or A_2. The latter is less sensitive to acid and is stimulated by the secretions of the Brunner's glands found in the proximal duodenum. This results in greater production of the sn-1 acyl lysophosphoglyceride for absorption. Phospholipids may be further cleaved by intercellular enzymes from sloughed off epithelial cells of the small intestine. Cholesterol esters are not incorporated readily into micelles, but first require hydrolysis by pancreatic sterol ester hydrolyase.

Digestibility of lipids is about 90% in the neonatal calf, increasing to 95% by 5 weeks of age. Milk fat is close to 100% digestible when fed to calves or lambs. However, other fats are not well digested (tallow, 91.8%; tallow FFA, 85.4%; and corn oil 76.4% in calves). Reduced digestibility may be due to the depressing effects of FFA on milk curd firmness in the abomasum (21). Increased ease of hydrolysis in the preruminant calf is found when fats contain shorter chain FA (51), or the sn-2 position is occupied by a shorter FA such as palmitic in lard vs stearic in tallow, or when fats like tallow are intraesterified with butyric acid.

In general, when used in milk replacers the digestibility and utilization of animal and vegetable fats are high in preruminants, providing they are emulsified to particle sizes less than 3-4 μm by homogenization. Low pressure dispersion of high fat (40%) diets may be more effective than homogenization and has resulted in greater weight gains. Interactions between sources and levels of dietary protein and fat in milk replacers showed that level and quality of protein were positively correlated with fat digestibility.

Emulsification of Dietary Fats
A lack of fat emulsification can lead to diarrhea and loss of hair in early life of calves. Emulsifiers, such as glycerol monostearate and lecithin, as well as antioxidants are generally added prior to homogenization and spray drying. The addition of lecithin improves the digestibility of tallow used in milk replacers, but has little or no effect on fats with normally high digestibilities. Addition of bile salts (in vitro experiments) markedly increases (8 fold) the effectiveness of pancreatic lipase to hydrolyze the C-18 acids, particularly stearic. Phospholipids added to the bile salts produce a marked increase in the solubility of FA, especially palmitic and stearic acids which are insoluble in water. Solubility also increases as acidic pH levels are neutralized. Lysolecithin, produced from the hydrolysis of lecithin, appears to be as effective as lecithin in solubilization of long chain saturated fatty acids.

FAT METABOLISM

Fetal Lipid Metabolism
Fetal lipid metabolism in ruminants is similar to other mammals in that lipids provide the main energy stores at birth, which are derived from both *de novo* synthesis in the fetus and maternal transfer of FFA. No direct transfer of triglycerides, phospholipids, or cholesteryl esters across the placenta has been shown. Fetal concentrations of phospholipids

in liver, kidney and brain are only half that in respective maternal organs and sphingomyelin in fetal brain is 16% of that of adults. Oleic is the main FA in fetal phospholipids, whereas linoleic and linolenic are higher in adults.

Neonatal Lipid Metabolism

In lambs large increases in plasma FFA (to 30 mg/dl) occur 2-5 h after birth due to mobilization of adipose tissue for energy. After 72 h, FFA drops to about one-third of original levels and account for only 5% of total plasma FA. Thermogenesis and brown adipose tissue contribute little to the plasma FFA. Brown adipose tissue is capable of extremely high metabolic rates, apparently within the cell which contains a large proportion of cytoplasm, many mitochondria and high phospholipids. High metabolic rates have been observed in lambs and young caribou (*Rangifer tarandus*) immediately after birth. Both have very high surface areas per unit birth weight. The newborn may be

capable of increasing metabolic rate 3 to 4 fold by shivering and non-shivering thermogenesis. Brown adipose tissue disappears by one month of age in the lamb and calf.

Lipid Transport

Transport of lipids in the young ruminant (8-week-old lambs) is similar to that of mature ruminants and other mammals. Transport of cholesterol by the mesenteric lymph of calves is increased when skim milk diets are supplemented with soybean oil, beef tallow or milk fat, compared to the other lipid sources. Milk fat supplementation resulted in the greatest cholesterol and the least triglyceride transport.

Plasma Lipids

Plasma lipids in lambs increase after birth with ingestion of ewe's milk, but remain below birth levels when fed milk replacers devoid of fat. Palmitic and oleic made up 67% of the fatty acids in plasma triglycerides

Table 19-3. The relative abundance of the major fatty acids in cholesteryl esters and phosphatidylcholine of blood plasma from preruminant calves fed different fat sources.[a]

Fatty acid	Tallow		Coconut oil[b]		Corn oil	
	Diet	Plasma	Diet	Plasma	Diet	Plasma
Content of diet or plasma cholesteryl esters						
14:0	2.8	0.6	16.5	8.7	0.1	0.2
16:0	29.5	7.4	8.5	6.4	13.9	8.0
18:0	3.8	1.0	2.4	0.3	2.6	0.2
18:1 n-9	25.7	10.4	6.6	3.8	28.8	2.0
18:2 n-6	3.8	67.9	3.2	68.7	52.7	87.4
18:3 n-3	0.6	5.8	0.2	3.6	0.7	0.7
20:2 n-6		0.04		0.02		0.04
20:4 n-6		1.2		1.3		0.4
Phosphatidylcholine						
14:0		0.2		1.0		0.1
16:0		15.0		19.2		20.0
18:0		31.5		29.0		15.1
18:1 n-9		22.1		12.3		10.3
18:2 n-6		18.8		30.3		44.3
18:3 n-3		0.9		0.8		0.2
20:2 n-6		0.3		0.4		4.6
20:4 n-6		1.4		1.9		0.6
Total 22 PUFA[c]		0.7		0.8		0.4

[a] Adapted from Jenkins et al (21)
[b] The other fatty acids present in coconut oil were: 8:0, 9.6%; 10:0, 6.8%; 12:0, 46.0%.
[c] PUFA = Polyunsaturated fatty acids.

which increased 179% at 2-3 h postfeeding. Cholesteryl esters and phospholipids increased 56% and 62% respectively; peaking 5 h post feeding.

Composition of plasma lipids at 28 d in pre-ruminant calves fed different fats averaged: cholesteryl esters, 50-57% (of the plasma lipids present); phosphatidylcholine, 20-25%; triglycerides plus FFA, (2-5%); cholesterol (5-8%) and sphingomyelin (3-5%). For fatty acid composition of these as affected by different dietary fats, see Table 19-3.

Essential Fatty Acid (EFA) Metabolism

In ruminants, highly selective incorporation of polysaturated fatty acids into phospholipids and cholesteryl esters insures their presence for special roles in membrane structure and function.

Efficient preservation of EFA was shown in starved sheep by very little oxidation of linoleic compared to palmitic and stearic acids after infusion of the ^{14}C-labelled forms. While in non-ruminants EFA may be used for energy, the ruminant fetus and neonate face problems of trying to obtain sufficient EFA from plasma FFA in maternal circulation or from colostrum where content is less than in other species. Hence, the amount of linoleic acid required to supply the EFA needs of the lamb and calf is less than in non-ruminants.

Most maternal bovine and ovine plasma levels are higher in linoleic than linolenic acid. However, preferential placental transfer of linolenic and its derivatives suggests a more important role of linolenic derivatives in fetal development.

Brain phospholipid content of 22:6w3 in the fetal calf, newborn lamb, and fawn are 4-8 times that of muscle phospholipids and arachidonic (20:4w6) acid is about twice as high. The higher brain levels of 22:6w3 in all species, particularly ruminants, suggests efficient conversion from linolenic acid. The constant level of arachidonic acid in tissues at all ages suggests it as the main essential fatty acid at the tissue level. Linoleic is stored and converted to other EFAs as needed.

Linoleic content of plasma FA in suckling lambs increases dramatically during the first 48 h or life (from 0.7-13.7%) with linolenic increasing some (from 0.2-3.5%). Both peak at 4-8 d of age. Linoleic content of plasma cholesteryl esters increases markedly during

the first week of life (from 5-25%). Feeding protected polyunsaturated fats to ewes 1 month prior to lambing significantly increased linoleic acid in milk and blood plasma, but did not affect linolenic. At birth lamb plasma EFAs were very low and were unaffected by the ewe's feed, were but rose significantly 1 d after nursing.

Adipose Tissue Metabolism

In contrast to the adult ruminant, biohydrogenation of unsaturated FA does not occur in the undeveloped forestomach of the preruminant. As a result, dietary lipid composition has a pronounced effect on the FA ratios present in the adipose tissue. The shorter chained FA consumed (8:0, 10:0 and 12:0) are elongated to C14 or longer, while the other FA reflect the composition of the dietary lipids.

In the developing ruminant, unsaturated dietary fats may bypass the rumen through the reticular groove or by escaping hydrogenation in the growing rumen. Hence, when corn oil was fed to lambs on a barley ration, linoleic acid in adipose tissue increased significantly. Similar results were found when feeding protected lipids, but not when barley was fed alone or corn oil was fed with pelleted alfalfa.

CARBOHYDRATE DIGESTION AND ABSORPTION

In the early neonatal calf and lamb there is efficient digestion of lactose, glucose and galactose, but only slight digestion of starch and maltose. Sucrose is not digested and fructose is poorly absorbed. Glucose or galactose fed alone are extensively absorbed in the duodenum but when fed together, glucose absorption takes priority. However galactose, whether fed with glucose or produced as the result of lactose hydrolysis, is absorbed efficiently posterior to the duodenum.

Starch Digestion

Post ruminal starch and maltose digestion increase considerably during the first 3 months but remain low in older pre-ruminants compared to monogastrics. In a study using duodenal and ileal cannulas in calves, only 43.0% of the maltose and 59.8% of the starch was hydrolyzed when the digesta reached the

414

distal ileum. No rise was seen in blood glucose, perhaps due to slow release and its concurrent metabolism by the mucosa and liver, or because of microbial fermentation in the ileum. The limited starch hydrolysis probably is not due to insufficient α-amylase as much as low maltase and the lack of an oligo-1,6-glucosidase.

Limited levels of partially hydrolyzed starch have been used successfully in the diet of neonatal lambs when starch replaced glucose and lactose at 17% of the gross energy. No significant differences in growth rates or utilization occurred. Increasing starch to 41% of the diet (33% of the gross energy) did not create adverse effects, but 49% depressed performance the first 15 d of life (23). The lower levels fed were 6-6.5 $g/kg^{0.75}/d$, well within the 14.2 $g/kg^{0.75}/d$ of gelatinized starch shown to be digested by 5-9 week old lambs.

Amylolytic and maltase activities increase with age in calves and lambs kept on liquid diets beyond 2 months, and also on normal diets. If starch escaping the rumen is not excessive, intestinal digestibilities of 80-90% have been observed and values have approached 100% for partially hydrolyzed starch. Starch which escapes intestinal digestion serves as a readily available substrate for microbial fermentation in the cecum and small intestine. The VFAs produced by such fermentation contribute energy to the animal, but the microbial protein is lost.

CARBOHYDRATE METABOLISM

In ruminants, four periods of carbohydrate metabolism have been suggested: (a) the intra-uterine stage with fetal glucose requirements supplied by maternal circulation, (b) the immediate post natal stage of 2-3 weeks with glucose supplied through milk by maternal lactose production, (c) a transitional period of developing rumen fermentation and diminishing milk supplies between 3-8 weeks of age, and (d) the fully ruminant stage at 8-12 weeks of age when rumen fermentation meets energy needs. Thus, carbohydrate metabolism in the neonatal ruminant is similar to monogastrics with a dependency on dietary carbohydrates for glucose, but in functional ruminants glucose sources are fermented and make the animal dependent mainly on non-carbohydrate compounds (gluconeogensis) for glucose supplies.

Fetal Glucose Metabolism

Prior to birth, glucose is the primary energy source for the fetus. In sheep, fetal glucose needs take precedence over those of the ewe and may result in pregnancy toxemia, during which the fetus maintains a relatively constant plasma glucose. Fetal plasma glucose during this time may also be partially maintained by breakdown of fetal glycogen stores, which are about 2X adult levels for liver and 5X for skeletal muscle.

Plasma glucose in fetal lambs (10-30 mg/dl) is lower than in ewes, and accounts for 50% of the O_2 uptake. Fructose is present in fetal circulation. Though its role is poorly understood, it may serve as a carbohydrate reservoir for the fetus.

Neonatal Glucose Metabolism

Within 2 h after birth plasma glucose increases in calves and lambs due to glycogenolysis. The glucose rise maximizes at about 100 mg/dl by 48 h after birth and is not dependent on feeding, although it may be enhanced by certain feeding regimes. During this time liver glycogen falls to 10% of fetal values and remains low for several days, rising to adult levels by 2-3 weeks of age.

The high plasma glucose observed in the neonatal calf gradually drops to adult levels (45-55 mg/dl) by 12 weeks of age. Decreases in blood glucose with age are independent of diet and may be explained in part by replacement of glucose-containing fetal red blood cells with the glucose-absent adult forms, though plasma glucose levels also show some decrease.

Plasma glucose in the early neonatal appears to be affected by feeding. Eales et al (24) found levels of 47 mg/dl in the 1-h-old lamb just prior to feeding colostrum, which increased to 131 mg/dl 3 h after feeding. Similar increases but of shorter duration were observed when lambs were fed bovine colostrum. Lambs given a milk replacer showed marked hyperglycemia (421 mg/dl) due to faster gastric emptying of a non-casein diet.

Typical of non-ruminants, and in contrast to adult sheep, fetal and neonatal ruminants respond to insulin injections with depressions in blood glucose, while high blood glucose levels stimulate insulin secretion. Infusions of glucose into fetal circulation increases insulin levels, suggesting fetal plasma levels control release of insulin in the fetus. Removal of large glucose loads is less important in the mature ruminants, and acetate metabolism in peripheral tissue is sensitive to both insulin and glucose levels.

Gluconeogenesis

Liver gluconeogenesis normally begins within minutes after birth, thus avoiding hypoglycemia. In the 3-8 week transition period from a preruminant to a ruminant, gluconeogenesis supplements the diminishing supply of glucose available from the digestive tract. Also, increasing propionate from rumen fermentation becomes an important precursor of glucose synthesis.

After 8 weeks of age blood glucose decreases to near adult levels (40-60 mg/dl), and at weaning gluconeogenesis becomes the primary source of glucose for body metabolism. In addition to propionic acid, amino acids provide between 15-35% of the substrates for gluconeogenesis with alanine and glutamine/glutamate providing 40-60% of these AA. Other AA that are readily gluconeogenic are aspartic acid, arginine, glycine, histidine, proline, serine, threonine, and valine. Glucose entry rates from hepatic gluconeogenesis are relatively constant over a 24-h period.

NUTRIENT NEEDS OF PRERUMINANTS

Nutrition of the dam can have a profound effect on the health and well-being of young animals. The mother will deplete herself (up to a point) of essential nutrients in order to furnish sufficient supplies for the growing fetus. However, severe maternal deficiencies can result in abortion and deformities of the newborn or a weakened condition at birth. Less severe deficiencies of the dam result in reduced size, lower body reserves of nutrients and a poorer chance of survival of the newborn.

Good reviews have been published on nutrition of preruminants. These include those dealing with calves (25, 26), with lambs (27, 28) and goat kids (29). Little has been reported concerning digestion and nutrition of other preruminants, but basic similarities have been shown to exist between the less common and the major domestic species.

Early Postnatal Needs

The fat-free body of calves and lambs contains about 19% crude protein at birth, and is more chemically mature than newborn rats and mice (11-13% CP) or many other species (30). While body protein at birth is relatively high, body lipid is very low in calves and lambs (2-4%) compared to humans (16%). The fat present in young ruminants at birth is brown fat and is higher in mitochondria and metabolic activity than white fat which accumulates rapidly after birth. Gains of young animals in fat are greater than in protein as shown for lambs which accumulated 2.5 times more fat than protein during the first 6 weeks after birth.

Although mother's milk may not be complete in all nutritional aspects, the mixture of protein and calories in milk are about optimum for growth of young ruminants. Compositional analyses of milk from cows, ewes and goats, as well as cow colostrum are shown in Table 19-4. Assuming normal energy values for the milk components, the percents of total calories in the milks furnished by fat, protein and lactose were 50-60, 20-25 and 15-25, respectively. An increase of nonprotein calories at the expense of protein to the extent of causing a protein deficiency will result in depressed growth and a shift of excess energy towards increased body fat. Conversely, excess dietary protein will be catabolized to energy through gluconeogenesis and result in increased energy expenditure to process excessive N for excretion.

Moderate shifts between calories from fat and carbohydrates in milk-type rations will usually not affect body composition, but gains in body weight might be diminished if fat and/or total calories are too low. There appears to be a limit as to amount of lactose preruminants can digest efficiently—about double that contained in milk when milk or milk replacers are fed at normal levels (8-10% of body weight of replacers containing 12-15% solids).

Energy Requirements

NRC energy requirements for calves from 45 to 90 kg body weight or approximately during the first 8 to 10 weeks of life are

416

Table 19-4. Composition of colostrum (first 24 hours) of a cow and of the milks of the cow, sheep and goat.[a]

Component	Cow		Ewe's milk	Goat's milk
	Colostrum	Milk		
Total solids, %	21.9	12.5	18.4	13.0
Fat, %	3.6	3.7	7.5	4.5
Protein, %	14.2	3.4	5.6	3.3
Casein, %	5.2	2.6	4.2	2.5
Lactose (anhydrous), %	3.1	4.6	4.4	4.4
Ash				
Calcium, %	0.26	0.13	0.19	0.14
Phosphorus, %	0.24	0.10	0.15	0.12
Magnesium, %	0.04	0.01	0.02	0.02
Sodium, %	0.07	0.06	0.04	0.04
Potassium, %	0.14	0.16	0.19	0.17
Chlorine, %	0.12	0.10	0.14	0.15
Iron, mg/100 g	0.20	0.05	0.05	0.05
Copper, mg/100 g	0.06	0.02	0.01	0.01
Cobalt, μg/100 g	0.50	0.05	---	---
Manganese, mg/100 g	0.016	0.003	0.006	0.004
Iodine, μg/100 g	0.03	0.01	---	---
Carotenoids, μg/g fat	35	7	---	---
Vitamin A, μg/g fat	45	8	8	9
Vitamin D, IU/g fat	4	2	---	2
Vitamin E, μg/g fat	125	20	20	14
Thiamin E, μg/100 g	60	40	70	50
Riboflavin, μg/100 g	500	150	500	120
Niacin, g/100 g	100	80	500	200
Pantothenic acid, μg/100 g	220	350	350	350
Vitamin B_6, μg/100 g	50	52	70	7
Vitamin B_{12}, μg/100 g	1.0	0.3	1.0	0.1
Biotin, μg/100 g	4	2	5	1.5
Folic acid, μg/100 g	1	5	5	0.2
p-Aminobenzoic acid, μg/100 g	--	10	--	--
Choline, mg/100 g	53	13	4	13
Ascorbic acid, mg/100 g	2.5	2.0	3.0	2.0

[a]From Walker (30)

shown in Table 19-5. These are estimates based on mixed diets of milk, grain and hay which represent the main system for feeding calves, lambs and kids in most developed countries. As is evident for all sizes listed, gains are increased 60-100% by an increase of 15-20% in energy intakes because of the fixed cost of maintenance regardless of amount of tissue accretion. This is an important principle to consider for all animal production systems.

As is evident when considering feed DM and energy intakes together, increased gains for a given weight are achieved mainly by increasing the energy density of the ration. The general practice at this age is to limit milk or milk replacer and provide solid feed (mostly concentrate) ad libitum. As age and weight increase more hay and fibrous feeds will be consumed. However, little hay is consumed before about 6 weeks of age and calves do not acquire a taste for silage and fermented feeds until 10-12 weeks.

Estimated requirements are given for the various energy systems due to the diversity in application in different areas. Body weights

Table 19-5. Daily energy and protein requirements of growing dairy heifers fed mixed diets of milk concentrate and hay.[a]

Body weight kg	Daily gain, g	Daily feed DM, kg	NEg,	NEg,	ME,	DE,	TDN, kg	Total CP, g	Dig. Protein[b] DE mg/Kcal
			. . . . Mcal						
45	270	1.23	1.35	0.52	3.65	4.16	0.94	141	27.0
	545	1.27	1.35	1.05	4.58	5.10	1.16	200	31.3
68	360	1.82	1.82	0.70	5.02	5.87	1.31	222	30.3
	635	1.86	1.82	1.24	6.07	6.85	1.55	291	33.9
90	450	2.45	2.26	0.92	6.50	7.53	1.70	295	31.3
	725	2.45	2.26	1.47	7.52	8.53	1.94	363	34.0

[a]Adapted from NRC (31)
[b]Assuming an average Dig. Protein of 80% for such diets.

only go to 90 kg because most calves on hand-feeding systems are completely weaned by this size, but under range or less intensive management, nursing may continue until 6-10 months of age.

Protein Requirements

As mentioned earlier, baby ruminants (during the first 2 to 3 weeks of life) are probably the most demanding of mammals for high quality protein. As rumen function commences, microbial and feed proteins complement that of milk, requiring less stringent demands for protein quality in the liquid ration.

Estimated needs for protein are given in Table 19-5 and are related to both size and growth of animals. These estimates are somewhat higher than those derived by Roy (32) for calves on milk rations, but similar to those suggested by Walker (30) which were estimated from DE requirements. A protein to calorie ratio (g protein/kg DE) within desirable limits is important for good utilization of protein furnished in the diet. As is evident, this ratio should be about 30. Many milk replacer diets with a low fat content (<12%) possess too wide a ratio and are wasteful of protein which is generally the most expensive major nutrient in the diet.

Even though milk protein is 90-100% digestible and has a biological value of 75 to 80 for preruminants, some evidence suggests a benefit in growth from supplementation of methionine and, in some cases, lysine, to milk diets fed calves and lambs. The response from

these amino acids is even greater on milk replacer diets comprised of large amounts of vegetable protein, particularly soybean products and has led to routine additions of methionine and lysine.

Non-protein N is of no value until development of a functional rumen. Several studies have shown beneficial effects from adding urea to concentrate diets for young calves and lambs, but full use of NPN should wait until rumen size reaches adult proportions (4-5 months of age).

Vitamin and Mineral Requirements

In Table 19-6 are given estimated vitamin and mineral allowances recommended for young calves on a liquid ration prior to significant contribution of the B-vitamins and vitamin K from rumen fermentation. Generally, cow colostrum is quite rich in several key vitamins (A, E, B_{12}, choline) compared to milk. This is nutritionally important, because vitamins A and B_{12} are marginally deficient in the newborn, and it gives tissues a chance to replenish early in life.

As noted, several of the vitamins and minerals are low or marginal in milk or milk products, and need supplementation in young ruminants maintained for extended periods on only milk or milk-type diets. However, introduction of concentrate, hay or pasture in early life precludes the need of vitamin and some mineral supplementation of liquid diets because solid feeds supply some of these nutrients and the microbes produce B vitamins and vitamin K in the rumen. Despite

418

Table 19-6. Suggested vitamin and mineral allowances for young calves (per 45 kg B.W.).[a]

Fat soluble vitamins	
A	2000 IU[b]
D	500 IU[b]
E	20 mg[b]
Water soluble vitamins	
Thiamin	4.0 mg[b]
Riboflavin	2.0 mg
Niacin	13.0 mg[c]
Pyridoxine	3.0 mg[c]
Biotin	0.2 mg[c]
Pantothintic acid	10.0 mg
Choline	1200 mg[c]
Folic acid	0.6 mg[c]
B_{12}	40 μg[b]
Macrominerals, % of ration DM	
Calcium	0.40
Phosphorus	0.30
Potassium	0.70
Magnesium	0.20[b]
Salt	0.30
Sulfur	0.15
Microminerals, ppm	
Iodine	0.6
Manganese	15.0[b]
Copper	6.0
Cobalt	0.1
Zinc	25.0
Iron	100.0[b]
Selenium	0.1

[a] From Huber (33)
[b] Deficient in milk and milk products.
[c] Borderline in milk and milk products.

lack of data indicating a beneficial response, supplementation of the concentrate mixture for young ruminants with vitamins A, D and E as well as Ca, P and trace-mineralized salt (containing Se) has been the common practice.

Water Requirements

During the liquid feeding period early in life of young ruminants, the mother's milk should normally furnish sufficient water for the young if milk is provided as the primary nutrient source. Milk from cows and goats contains 7.0 and 4.4 kg water/kg DM, respectively, and provide more water than the 3 to 3.5 kg/kg DM suggested for older ruminants living in moderate temperatures. However, many factors influence water requirements, such as ambient temperature, humidity, or salt, protein, fiber or dry matter in feed.

Milk replacers fed to preruminants often contain higher salt levels than mother's milk (because of addition of large amounts of whey, etc.), so feeding free choice water or higher dilution rates for replacers are suggested. Despite a wide range of dilution rates of milk replacers fed calves, data from one study suggest that maximum growth is obtained at about 15% solids, which is quite similar to that of mother's milk. Offering of water free choice in this study did not equalize water intakes. Results of the study suggest that daily water needs for the baby calf on a liquid diet are about 0.5 kg/kg $BW^{0.75}$. For baby lambs, estimates are 0.3 kg/kg $BW^{0.75}$.

As solid feed intakes increase during the transition from preruminant to ruminant, the need for water in addition to that furnished by the liquid diet increases. Animals on pasture or other succulent feeds during this period need less water, but it is generally recommended to offer clean, fresh water ad libitum.

Increasing ambient temperature within the thermal neutral zone (10 to 27°C) linearly increases water needs of ruminants, but rate of increase becomes much greater as temperatures approach the 37 to 40°C range. As humidity increases, transpiration rates decrease and so do water requirements.

NUTRIENT DEFICIENCIES

During pre- and post-natal growth, preruminants might be vulnerable to nutrient deficiencies. A classical example demonstrated experimentally is deficient vitamin A in the mother's diet resulting in blind, malformed or dead calves.

The status of preruminants at birth is tenuous for several nutrients. Their body reserves are very low in energy, vitamin A, B_{12}, Fe, etc. The abundance in colostrum of most of these critical nutrients (more so than milk) provides a buffer against deficits during this period. However, intake of colostrum is severely limited under many management situations.

Feeding normal amounts of milk to pre-ruminants until weaning will usually protect them from most nutrient deficiencies, particularly if solid feeds (such as grain, hay and pasture) are introduced simultaneously. However, some milk replacer formulations might provide insufficient energy because they are too low in fat or too high in indigestible carbohydrates; too little digestible protein because of unprocessed vegetable proteins or other poorly utilized sources; an imbalance or insufficiency of vitamins or minerals. B-vitamins or vitamin K might be of particular concern if rumen function is delayed and they are not being furnished by a viable microbial fermentation.

CONCLUSIONS

Preruminants begin life in a condition similar to young monogastrics in many aspects of digestion, absorption, and metabolism of major nutrients. However, their potential for small intestinal degradation of vegetable proteins, certain sugars, starch and other polysaccharides is inferior to monogastrics. Also, quality of protein appears more critical in young preruminants than monogastrics. During early life, the preruminants undergo a transition state where rumen fermentation commences the production of volatile fatty acids which replace glucose as the primary metabolites for cell oxidation and lipogenesis. Normal feeding of grain and hay will bring on this transition more rapidly and result in ruminants of mature proportions by 3 to 4 months of age.

Literature Cited and References for Further Reading

1. Titchen, D.A. and J.C. Newhook. 1975. In: Digestive Physiology and Metabolism in the Ruminant. Univ. of New England Publ. Unit, Armidale, Australia.
2. Church, D.C. 1976. Digestive Physiology and Nutrition of Ruminants. Vol. 1 — Digestive Physiology, 2nd Ed. O & B Books, Inc., Corvallis, Oregon.
3. James, R.E., C.E. Polan and K.A. Commings. 1981. J. Dairy Sci. 64:52.
4. Thivend, P., R. Toullec and P. Guilloteau. 1980. In: Digestive Physiology and Metabolism in Ruminants. AVI Publ. Co., Inc., Westport, CT.
5. Leibholz, J. 1975. Australian J. Agr. Res. 26:1081.
6. Guilloteau, P., et al. 1983. J. Dairy Sci. 66:2373.
7. McMahon, D.J. and R.D. Brown. 1985. J. Dairy Sci. 68:628.
8. Ternouth, J.W., J.H.B. Roy and S.M. Shotton. 1976. Brit. J. Nutr. 36:523.
9. Bhatty, R.S. and G.I. Christison. 1980. Can. J. Animal Sci. 60:925.
10. Whittenberg, K.N. and J.R. Ingalls. 1979. J. Dairy Sci. 62:1626.
11. Akinyele, I.O. and K.E. Harshbarger. 1983. J. Dairy Sci. 66:825.
12. Roy, J.H.B., et al. 1977. Brit. J. Nutr. 38:167.
13. Kilshaw, P.J. and H. Slade. 1982. Res. Vet. Sci. 33:305.
14. Battaglia, F.C. and G. Meschia. 1981. Proc. Nutr. Soc. 40:99.
15. Schaefer, A.L. and C.R. Krishnamurti. 1984. Brit. J. Nutr. 52:359.
16. Matte, J.J., C.L. Girard, J.R. Seoane and G.J. Brisson. 1982. J. Dairy Sci. 65:1765.
17. Corley, L.D., T.E. Staley, L.J. Bush and E.W. Jones. 1979. J. Dairy Sci. 60:1416.
18. Williams, A.P. and D. Hewitt. 1979. Brit. J. Nutr. 41:311.
19. Razzaque, M.A., et al. 1981. Brit. J. Nutr. 45:517.
20. Smith, R.H. 1975. In: Digestion and Metabolism in the Ruminant. Univ. New England Publ. Unit, Armidale, Australia.
21. Jenkins, K.J., J.G.K. Kramer, F.D. Sauer and D.B. Emmons. 1985. J. Dairy Sci. 68:669.
22. Richard, M.J., R.I. Thacher, A.D. McGilliard and N.L. Jacobson. 1983. J. Dairy Sci. 66:113.
23. Soliman, H.S., et al. 1979. J. Agr. Sci. 92:343.
24. Eales, F.A., L. Murray and J. Small. 1982. Vet. Rec. 111:451.
25. Roy, J.H.B. and I.J.F. Stobo. 1975. In: Digestion and Metabolism in the Ruminant. Univ. New England Publ. Unit, Armidale, Australia.

420

26. Appleman, R.D. and F.G. Owen. 1975. J. Dairy Sci. 58:447.
27. Treacher, T.T. 1973. Vet. Rec. 92:311.
28. Pearce, G.R. 1972. Australian Meat Res. Comm. Rev. No. 6:1.
29. Morand-Fehr, P. and D. Sauvant. 1984. In: Livestock Feeds and Feeding, 2nd Ed., p. 372. D.C. Church, ed. Prentice-Hall, Inc., Englewood Cliffs, NJ.
30. Walker, D.M. 1979. In: Digestive Physiology and Nutrition of Ruminants. Vol. 2 — Nutrition, 2nd Ed. D.C. Church, ed. O & B Books, Inc., Corvallis, OR.
31. NRC. 1978. Nutrient Requirements for Dairy Cattle. Nat. Acad. Sci., Washington, DC.
32. Roy, J.H.B. 1970. The Calf: Nutrition and Health, 3rd Ed. The Pennsylvania State Univ. Press, College Park, PA.
33. Huber, J.T. 1984. In: Livestock Feeds and Feeding, 2nd Ed. Prentice-Hall, Inc., Englewood Cliffs, NJ.
34. Milligan, L.P., W.L. Grovum and A. Dobson. 1986. Control of Digestion and Metabolism in Ruminants. Prentice-Hall, Inc., Englewood Cliffs, NJ.

20 NUTRIENT NEEDS DURING CRITICAL PERIODS OF THE LIFE CYCLE

by David J. Schingoethe, F. M. Byers, and G. T. Schelling

EFFECT OF NUTRITION ON FERTILITY, REPRODUCTION AND LACTATION

by David J. Schingoethe

The ruminant requires nutrients for many functions, but the amounts required increase during times of increased or impending production. Thus, nutritional needs are greater and more critical for fertility, maintaining reproduction, lactation and growth. In this chapter we will briefly point out nutritional needs to consider during each of these critical periods of the life cycle.

FERTILITY

Energy Status of the Animal

Insufficient intake of energy is probably the main nutritional factor affecting fertility. Inadequate energy intake results in delayed sexual maturity and lower conception rates, followed by smaller and weaker offspring at birth.

First estrus in cattle usually occurs at 10-11 months of age in large breed heifers and somewhat earlier in smaller breeds, but age at which it occurs can be affected by plane of nutrition. Weight appears to be a greater determinant of when heifers reach puberty than age, as heifers within a breed normally come into first estrus at similar weights. Swanson (1) predicted puberty for Holstein heifers at 10 months when gains are 0.82 kg/d, 11 months at 0.68 kg/d and at 14 months at 0.54 kg/d. This agrees with results of a 20-year study (2) on long-time reproductive efficiency of heifers fed at low (65% of standard nutrient allowances), medium (100%), and high (146%) planes of nutrition. All heifers reached puberty at about 275 kg body weight, but puberty occurred at 20, 11, and 9 months of age for heifers fed at low, medium and high planes of nutrition. The use of feed additives such as ionophores, which allow improved efficiency of growth in ruminants, offers promise in helping young ruminants achieve acceptable rates of gain with minimal amounts of feed (3). The type of diet fed may also affect age at puberty. Rhodes et al (4) observed delayed puberty in beef heifers fed large amounts of a protein-protected lipids. Nutritional effects on puberty in other species and in males are likely similar, with ages and weights varying with the corresponding species involved.

Fertility rates are higher when females are gaining than when losing weight. Even animals in poor nutritional status can have optimum fertility if gaining weight for 30 d before and after breeding.

The relationship between energy status and conception rates occurs not only in the young, first breeding ruminant, but also in the rebreeding of animals during concurrent lactation. The loss of body weight following parturition in response to energy needs for lactation has generally been considered to influence normal reproductive functions negatively. Conception rates are usually higher when cows are maintaining or gaining weight at time of service than if they are losing weight (5). In one study involving over 1,100 cows, those with a net gain in weight during 30-90 d postpartum had a first service conception rate of 64% while the conception rate was only 46% in cows which were losing weight. In another study, beef heifers fed maintenance, medium and high levels of energy had conception rates by 120 d postpartum of 64, 72 and 87%. Animals in negative energy balance also may not ovulate. Under experimental conditions there is only a minor relationship between milk yields and days to first ovulation, rate of uterine involution, first service conception rates, and days open. Contrary field reports are probably related to how high-producing cows are managed.

Flushing is a practice of increasing nutrient intake prior to mating as a means of assuring that the animal is gaining weight at breeding time. This practice is quite successful in ewes and in some other multi-ovulator species and may result in a 15-30% increase in lamb crop. Flushing is usually accomplished by providing

422

animals with fresh pastures, supplemental harvested forage, or up to 0.25 kg of grain daily. This practice usually begins 2-3 weeks prior to breeding and continues through the breeding season. In general, animals already maintained in a high nutritional state will benefit little, if at all, from flushing.

While excessively thin animals may have delayed puberty, irregular heat periods and poor fertility rates, excessively fat animals are sometimes sterile and often have reduced fertility and abnormal udder development (1, 2). A three-year Oklahoma study (6) found that obese beef cattle required more services per conception (1.7) than controls (1.43). Obese animals are more likely to have more long-term problems with reproduction and reduced production than are thin animals (1, 2).

Protein

Clinical signs of infertility associated with a protein deficiency include a delay in the onset of puberty, an increase in the number of days open, and a decrease in appetite. The latter sign makes it difficult to separate a protein deficiency from a concurrent energy deficiency; however, an energy deficiency generally has a much greater influence on reproduction than a protein deficiency. Methionine supplementation improved reproduction when diets contained 12.5% crude protein but not when diets contained 15.5% crude protein (5). This indicates that certain amino acids may become rate limiting at lower protein levels, and supplementing the limiting amino acid may be as effective as elevating total protein intake in alleviating the problem.

A summary of over 85,000 calving intervals showed no evidence of urea feeding affecting reproduction (5). A later study also showed no effects on reproduction when dietary urea intakes were <200 g/cow/d.

Vitamins

Vitamin needs of ruminants are frequently met by a combination of rumen and tissue synthesis and natural feeds. Commerical concentrates frequently contain supplemental vitamins. Thus, infertility due to a vitamin deficiency is reduced greatly in areas where intensive practices are utilized. Only the fat-soluble vitamins need to be supplied in ruminant diets and are thus the only candidates for causing deficiency problems (see Ch. 16).

Vitamin A. A deficiency may cause delayed onset of puberty, but most of its adverse affects are reflected later in gestation and during parturition. Deficient animals often have normal estrous cycles, ovulate and conceive with normal early fetal development.

Fresh green forages contain abundant supplies of β-carotene, the precursor of vitamin A, which are lost during time feed is in storage. In recent years decreased use of grazing, particularly in many dairy operations, probably has reduced the β-carotene intake of animals substantially. This is usually not considered a problem because diets can be supplemented inexpensively with vitamin A. However, recent studies indicate that β-carotene influences reproductive performance independent of vitamin A (7). Reproductive problems such as silent heat, reduced conception rates, ovarian cysts, and embryonic mortality may be associated with β-carotene deficiency.

Early studies in Germany indicated a definite benefit in cattle to supplemental β-carotene starting prepartum and continuing through 100 d postpartum. However, most recent studies, particularly in the USA, have demonstrated only minor improvements in reproductive performance. Because β-carotene supplementation is currently relatively expensive, the results of most studies to date indicate supplementation would not be economically beneficial. These less than dramatic results may point out that many diets are not sufficiently deficient in β-carotene to affect reproduction adversely.

Vitamin D. A deficiency of this vitamin reduces fertility by delaying puberty and by suppressing signs of estrus. Supplementing cows postpartum with high amounts (43,000 IU of D_3) resulted in earlier first estrus; however, uterine involution was delayed by the vitamin D supplementation (5). More research is necessary before supplementing diets with high levels of vitamin D can be recommended.

Vitamin E. Cows deficient in vitamin E reproduce normally. While vitamin E supplementation may improve fertility in laboratory rats, there is no evidence to indicate that vitamin E supplementation will benefit reproductive performance in ruminants. If vitamin E supplementation is beneficial, it is likely to occur only under Se deficiency conditions.

The two nutrients have independent biological functions which can result in a sparing affect on each other.

Minerals

Phosphorus. P deficiency is the mineral deficiency most frequently associated with infertility. Diets low in protein and energy are also frequently deficient in P. A severe deficiency can delay the onset of puberty and postpartum estrus while a moderate deficiency may be associated with poor conception rates (5).

Selenium. Reduced fertility is sometimes associated with Se deficiency in sheep and cattle; however, other factors may also be involved (8). Low tocopherol in the roughage or the presence of antagonists of vitamin E and Se may reduce fertility in animals raised or maintained in Se-deficient areas. Se-related infertility appears to be more prominent in sheep than in other domestic ruminants. The impairment has generally been due to embryonic or fetal loss at 20-30 d of pregnancy rather than to anestrus or infertility. Conception rates and lambing percentages were improved in several cases by Se supplementation starting one month before breeding and continuing throughout pregnancy. However, Se supplementation to sheep or cattle in Se-deficient areas has not always affected conception rates.

Se may have a role in normal ovarian function, which makes it effective in preventing cystic ovaries (9). Seventy-eight cows maintained on a Se-deficient diet had a lower incidence (19%) of ovarian cysts when injected with 0.1 mg Se/kg body weight 21 d prepartum than control animals (44% cysts) during the first 12 weeks postpartum. The feeding of 740 mg of vitamin E/cow/d during the prepartum period had no effect on the incidence of cystic ovaries.

Other Minerals. Other minerals have also been shown to be related to fertility, but relationships have not always been clear (8). The relationship between Cu deficiency and infertility in ruminants is difficult to ascertain because affects may be related indirectly through some general dysfunction caused by Cu deficiency. Inactive ovaries, delayed estrus and reduced conception rates have been attributed to Cu deficiency in cattle (see Ch. 18). Lower conception rates were also observed in sheep and goats fed Cu-deficient diets. In many cases fertilization occurred, but resulted in embryonic death, fetal death, abortion or mummified fetus. Cu administration to bulls improved semen quality through increased sperm motility and fewer dead spermatozoa. While the above mentioned symptoms of Cu deficiency have been noted, there are also many situations of severe Cu deficiency in which no reproductive problems were observed. There are also reports of impaired reproduction under hypercupremic conditions (10).

Co is required to insure fertility in ruminants. Reduced conception rates are the most common signs of Co deficiency in cattle, while sheep may not show signs of estrus. Irregular and silent heats are also common. In one study (8) a beef herd grazing a Co-deficient pasture had a first service conception rate of 53% compared to 67% when given Cu therapy, and 93% when given Co and Cu. In tropical areas such as central Africa and northern South America which are also deficient in Co, the calving interval is often 24 months instead of the usual 12-14 months. The reasons for this are not known, but may be partially attributed to slower rates of uterine involution. Uterine involution took 6.9 weeks in Co-deficient cows compared to 3 weeks in Co-treated cows. Sperm counts in male ruminants may also be reduced with Co deficiency.

Iodine influences reproductive functions because of its vital role in thyroid function (8). Thus, reproductive failure in cases of iodine deficiency are likely to be secondary manifestations of thyroid dysfunctions resulting in anestrus, irregular estrus, retained placenta, abortion and stillbirth.

Mn is necessary for normal fertility in ruminants (8). Silent heat, irregular estrus, infertility, abortions and birth of deformed offspring have been reported for cattle, sheep and goats with a Mn deficiency. Conception rates of only 35-40% are not unusual. Dairy cattle with a Mn intake of less than 40 ppm in the feed maintained high fertility when Ca and P content of the diet were adequate and balanced. Spermatozoa motility and sperm numbers were reduced in ejaculates from male goats fed Mn-deficient diets.

424

Zn deficiency in ruminants, as in other species, causes a more pronounced impairment of fertility in the male than in the female. The effect is severe and appears to be specific to the final stages of spermatozoa maturation. Delayed testicular development in the young male or atrophy in the adult are common indicators of Zn deficiency. Reduced conception rates and increased embryonic mortality also occur in female ruminants under Zn deficiency situations. Goats fed semipurified diets low in Zn had low conception rates and fewer kids per goat (8).

REPRODUCTION

Once the animal becomes pregnant, the next objective is to maintain that pregnancy to term with the production of normal, healthy offspring. Fetal requirements for nutrients become measurably significant only during the last trimester, but deficiencies of certain nutrients any time during the gestation may have an impact. Many nutrients impact gestation, some are the same as those which affect fertility.

Energy and Protein

Requirements of many nutrients increase in late gestation in proportion to the increased size and nutritional requirements of the developing fetus. Quantitatively, energy and protein requirements increase most noticeably, and are usually taken into account in most feeding systems. The energy requirements for a mature dairy cow during the last two months of gestation are 30% higher than for the same sized non-pregnant cow; protein requirements are 90% higher (10). Energy and protein requirements in pregnant animals of other ruminant species are also proportionately higher than for the non-pregnant animal.

Well-grown heifers can calve with a minimum of problems, while poorly grown heifers may have smaller calves and more calving difficulty (1). Conversely, fat animals have more difficulty in calving than those in more moderate condition, and are more likely to have problems associated with "fat cow syndrome" (discussed in Ch. 24).

Inadequate energy intake in late gestation can be especially costly to smaller ruminants such as sheep and goats carrying twins or triplets because the energy demand of the feti can become a proportionately large segment of the animal's total energy requirements. For instance, energy and protein requirements of the late gestation ewe may be twice as great as for a non-pregnant ewe (10). Sheep and goats receiving inadequate energy during gestation have fewer multiple births and smaller offspring. Resorption of the fetus or mummification of the fetus has been reported in wild ruminants such as deer under severe energy deficiency. In addition, those unable to meet the increased energy demands of the twin or triplet feti may develop pregnancy toxemia or ketosis. The symptoms are similar to symptoms of lactational ketosis in high-producing cows (Ch. 24). Lactational ketosis is precipitated by the high glucose demand for milk synthesis, whereas in the pregnant ewe, ketosis is caused by the high glucose demand for the developing fetus. Lactational ketosis by itself is seldom fatal because a drop in milk production reduces the glucose demand, correcting the situation. However, in pregnancy toxemia, the problem may be fatal because the glucose demand will be removed only by parturition or abortion.

Vitamins and Minerals

Vitamin A. A deficiency during gestation may result in abortion or birth of weak, blind, uncoordinated offspring, keratinization and degeneration of the placenta, retained placenta and metritis (5). Vitamin A and its precursor, β-carotene, both are effective in preventing these problems.

Vitamin D. A deficiency during gestation may result in offspring being born with rickets. Because of its role in Ca and P absorption, adequate vitamin D intake or massive doses of vitamin D around the time of parturition may reduce the likelihood of milk fever (Ch. 24).

Vitamin E and Se. Both of these nutrients have a role in preventing retained placentas. Se is an essential component of glutathione peroxidase, but the need for large amounts of glutathione peroxidase is reduced when the animal has adequate vitamin E. Vitamin E deficiency is not likely to occur in functionally mature ruminants (10), although the vitamin E status may be reduced when not consuming fresh forages or if consuming feeds stored for several months (12). However, Se deficiency is likely in areas of the world where feeds grown contain <0.1 ppm Se.

The incidence of retained placenta is often greater than 20% in cattle in Se-deficient areas instead of a more normal 7-10% incidence. British and Ohio researchers reduced the incidence of retained placentas by giving Se and vitamin E 20-30 d prepartum (9, 11). This vitamin E-Se therapy was also effective in other areas where Se is deficient, but not in situations of adequate dietary Se (12). Giving both Se and vitamin E is more effective than Se or vitamin E alone.

Most research has been conducted under Se deficiency conditions, and thus positive responses to Se therapy were observed. However, when Se intake was adequate, cattle consuming higher amounts of vitamin E had fewer cases of retained placenta and calving difficulty (11, 12). This is most apparent in cattle grazing fresh forages or fed recently harvested forages during the dry period as such forages contain more vitamin E, vitamin A and β-carotene than feeds stored for longer periods of time.

The usual method of administrating vitamin E and Se in many research experiments and in the field is an intramuscular injection of 5 mg Se and 68 units of vitamin E/45.4 kg body weight 20-40 d prepartum. One injection approximately 21 d prepartum is usually as effective as two injections at 42 and 21 d prepartum. Another approach is to feed sufficient amounts of supplemental Se to assure that the diet contains at least 0.1 ppm. If supplemental vitamin E is fed, it should probably be in amounts sufficient to provide 500 mg or more of vitamin E/cow/d, although the exact amount needed has not been established.

Ca. Problems with Ca absorption and/or mobilization affect reproduction indirectly via milk fever. Cows with milk fever are likely to have retained placentas and dystocia, followed by a higher incidence of cystic ovaries and reduced conception rates. Refer to Ch. 24 for more information on milk fever.

P. As mentioned earlier, the main affect of P deficiency is delayed puberty and infertility. P deficiency during gestation will not cause

abortions, but the offspring may be stillborn or weak.

I. Deficient or excessive amounts of I can both cause reproductive problems (5, 8). I deficiency in the diet of pregnant cows can cause premature birth of dead or weak calves affected with goiter. I toxicity can also result in abortions as exemplified in a Michigan dairy herd of 70 cows which received 12,000 mg of supplemental I daily for a month. This does of approximately 3,000 times the daily recommended allowance resulted in 13 abortions, most of which occurred in the first trimester of pregnancy.

Cu. Cu deficiency has been associated with an increase in calving difficulty and retained placentas; however, other studies have shown no benefit from Cu supplementation. Sheep that graze on Cu-deficient soils may give birth to weak lambs which are "swaybacked" (10).

Mn. A deficiency of Mn in diets of goats resulted in increased rates of abortion and reduced birth weights of kids (10). In cattle, abortions and birth of calves with deformed or twisted legs are clinical signs of Mn deficiency.

LACTATION

The change in nutritional requirements as an animal shifts from the pregnant to the lactating state varies substantially with species and production level (10). For the beef cow nursing one calf, nutritional needs may not increase at all, or at most her requirements may increase by one-third. The ewe nursing twins may have a 50-60% increase in nutrient requirements over late pregnancy, which may place her requirements during peak lactation at about 3 times her normal maintenance requirements. Many wild ruminant species would be in a similar category as the beef cow and ewe as their lactation period is relatively short and the amount of milk produced is only enough to maintain the offspring until weaning.

Nutritional requirements for dairy cows and goats of breeds bred for milk production increase greatly following parturition. The high-producing dairy cow or goat may require 3-6 times as much energy as required for maintenance and late pregnancy. These animals are producing much more milk than their offspring need, and these production levels are maintained for a longer period of time than the young would normally be fed milk.

Table 20-1 lists an example of nutrient needs for a high-producing dairy cow as compared to her needs for body maintenance or needs in late gestation. While the production level used in this example may seem high to some readers, many dairy cows today are producing that much or more milk. For instance, the current world record milk production leader, Beecher Arlinda Ellen, produced 22,250 kg of milk in 365 d. That was an average of 69 kg milk daily for a whole year, with a maximum daily production of over 88 kg of milk!

In order to produce large quantities of milk, a cow must consume large amounts of a nutritionally balanced diet. For instance, Ellen consumed in excess of 60 kg of feed dry matter daily, about 7 kg of dry matter/100 kg of body weight, while setting her world production record. Most cows are not likely to consume that much feed because the average cow consumes about 3-4% of her body weight as feed dry matter during mid lactation. But it illustrates that, under the right conditions, cows can be encouraged to eat more feed and produce more milk. It is a challenge for dairymen to help the cow adjust to the large nutritional demand following parturition by getting her to consume as much high quality feed as possible. In the following paragraphs, I will review several points to

consider in meeting the nutritional needs of high-producing dairy cows. Much of this same information is directly applicable to dairy goats, only on a smaller scale quantitatively.

Energy

The most critical period for a dairy cow is from parturition until peak milk production. Peak or maximum daily production for most cows occurs 6-8 weeks postpartum (Fig. 20-1). Each one kg increase in peak milk production usually means an additional 200 kg of total milk for the lactation (13). The persistency with which a cow maintains her production throughout the remainder of lactation can be influenced by many factors including nutrition, management, age and genetics. For most cows, production declines at a rate of about 5-7% per month, with two year-olds generally more persistent than older cows in maintaining production.

The nutritional demand for production during early lactation can be met by increasing the NE_L value of the diet as well as by increasing total feed intake. Although feed intake follows nutritional requirements somewhat, there is a lag in time between requirements and consumption (Fig. 20-1). While peak production occurs 6-8 weeks postpartum, peak feed intake doesn't occur until

Table 20-1. Daily energy, protein, Ca, and P needs of a 650 kg cow at maintenance, late gestation and peak production of 60 kg milk daily.[a]

| Nutrient | Status | | |
	Maintenance	Late gestation	Peak lactation[b]
Protein, kg	0.515	0.931	5.735
Energy, NE_L, Mcal	10.30	13.39	54.70
Calcium, g	22	39	184
Phosphorus, g	18	28	126

[a]Based on NRC for dairy cattle (10).
[b]Requirements for maintenance plus production of 60 kg milk containing 4.0% fat.

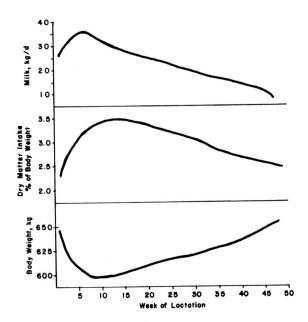

Figure 20-1. Milk production, dry matter intake and body weights during lactation.

12-15 weeks postpartum. The nutritional deficit must be made up by "borrowing" nutrients from the cow's body. If that source is not available, peak production and total lactational production will likely be less than optimal. For a high-producing cow to produce an additional 7 kg of milk (3.5% fat), she must mobilize either 1 kg of body weight or consume an additional 2-3 kg of concentrate mix. Cows in good condition often lose 90-135 kg of body weight during early lactation; this would support 700-900 kg of milk production.

The two nutritional factors most likely to limit milk production are energy and protein. Actually, getting the cow to consume enough energy is the more difficult problem. If a cow is consuming less than desired amounts of feed, one can simply formulate her diet to contain higher percentages of protein and minerals to assure that she gets her required amounts of those nutrients in the amount of feed she consumes. However, formulating the diet to insure adequate energy intake and at the same time maintain a normal rumen is more difficult.

To obtain maximum feed intake soon after parturition and to attain the highest peak milk production, the diet should be high in energy and yet contain sufficient fiber to assure normal rumen function. Roughage in the proper quantity and physical form is also necessary to maintain normal milk fat percentage (14). This usually corresponds to a minimum of about 17% crude fiber or 19% ADF in dietary dry matter. Higher amounts of fiber may be needed to maintain fiber effectiveness if forages are ground, pelleted or finely chopped.

Some ruminant nutritionists use the terms non-structural carbohydrates and structural carbohydrates when referring to carbohydrate portions of the diet. They are essentially talking about concentrates and forages because concentrates supply primarily non-structural carbohydrates such as starches and sugars while forages supply primarily structural carbohydrates such as cellulose and hemicellulose.

Optimum energy intake can usually be achieved with diets of 40-45% good quality forage and 55-60% concentrate. Feeding more than 60% concentrate, especially if total forage dry matter intake is less than 1-1.5% of body weight, increases the risk of having cows go off feed or having a reduced milk fat percentage.

The digestibility of energy in diets is often reduced at high levels of intake, especially for diets containing high proportions of concentrates. In the NRC publication on Dairy Cattle (10), the authors attempted to take this into account in that all NE_L values were reduced by amounts expected at a consumption rate of 3 times maintenance. This does not entirely account for some differences in apparent feeding values of feeds subject to different types of processing. Nutritional utilization of most feed grains is improved by coarse grinding, cracking or rolling the grains (10); however, quantitative data with lactating cows are limited. Data with beef cattle (10) indicate that steam processing and flaking of grains increased energy utilization as compared to feeding the grain whole or cracked. Other treatments such as micronizing, exploding, roasting and popping of sorghum can improve digestibility of starch to an extent similar to steam processing and flaking.

On a dry matter basis, high-moisture corn is at least equivalent and possibly better utilized than dry corn. Recent USDA (Beltsville) data (15) further illustrated some important considerations when shelled corn and ear corn, both dry and as high-moisture corn, were fed to lactating as well as dry cows. (A) DE, ME and NE/kg of dry matter were higher for high-moisture than for dry corn when fed to lactating cows. (B) NE values/kg of dry matter were lower for lactating cows than for dry cows, which agreed with previous statements included in NRC (10). (C) Ground ear corn was equal to ground shelled corn for lactating cows. This was contrary to results of digestibility studies conducted at near maintenance levels of intake upon which many feed composition values are based (10), but was consistent with many field reports. This response was likely due to the increased rate of passage through the gastro-intestinal tract with increased feed intake combined with the limited intestinal starch-digesting capabilities in ruminants (see Ch. 21).

Feeding Added Fat. Another way to increase the energy density of the diet is to

428

feed additional amounts of fat (16). Replacing portions of the concentrate in the diet with fat can allow an increase in energy of the diet while avoiding excessive starch or deficient fiber intakes. Most forages, grains and protein supplements fed to ruminants contain 1-3% fat. The amount of fat in the total diet can be increased to 5-6% of diet dry matter without adversely affecting feed intake or nutrient utilization. However, diets containing more than 8-10% fat may result in reduced feed intake, digestive upsets, and reduced fiber digestibility (16, Ch. 21). This is because many fatty acids are inhibitory to rumen microorganisms, especially fiber digesters, and because ruminants have limited fat digesting capabilities in the abomasum and small intestine. Providing additional Ca in diets which contain added fat improves nutrient utilization of the diet, presumably by forming insoluble soaps in the rumen so that the fatty acids do not interfere with ruminal fiber digestion (17). The soaps apparently dissociate post-ruminally, making the fatty acids available for absorption.

Feeding additional fat to cows during early lactation holds promise as a means of putting the cow in a more favorable energy status; however, the results of experiments to date are not as promising as one would hope for. Milk production has been increased only slightly when high-producing cows were fed additional fat during the first 3-4 months of lactation (16, 18). However, even if fat fails to increase milk production, it may be beneficial to the cow by reducing incidences of milk fat depression, ketosis, and reproductive inefficiency associated with postcalving weight loss.

The fat content of milk is usually unaffected when diets contain additional fat, although there are examples in which fat content is altered (16, 18). For instance, fat content of milk is usually unaffected when oilseeds such as cottonseed and soybeans are fed, but is greatly reduced when cows are fed soybean oil, partially hydrogenated oil, safflower oil or vegetable oils. Treating lipids with formaldehyde to protect them against hydrogenation in the rumen generally prevents this milk fat depression (16). Milk production may increase slightly when roasted or extruded soybeans are fed instead of unheated soybeans. Milk fat content is unaffected, but may be reduced if extremely large amounts of extruded soybeans are fed (19). Feeding whole sunflower seeds as a source of fat does not affect milk fat content, but milk fat percentages may be reduced slightly unless the diet also contains additional Ca (18).

The fatty acid composition of milk fat is altered only slightly when fed added fat in forms which can be altered by rumen microbes (16, 18), but may be greatly different when fed ruminally protected lipids (20). Changes in the fatty acid composition reflect changes in fatty acid composition of the diet as modified by rumen microbes. Great increases in polyunsaturated fatty acids in milk fat as when feeding formaldehyde-treated safflower oil can have undesirable affects on the flavor of milk and milk products, primarily increasing oxidized flavors. Feeding other sources of fat ordinarily have no substantial affects on flavor of milk or milk products (18, 21), although research data in this area are limited at this time.

Milk protein content is often reduced 0.1-0.2 percentage units when fed additional fat. Why this occurs and how to prevent it is currently unknown, although some theories have been proposed (16). This apparently minor reduction in milk protein content may be considered important to dairymen who sell milk to cheese plants that include protein percent or solids-not-fat percent in the milk as a factor in determining the price paid for milk.

Total feed intake is usually unaffected by added fat in the diet, although some cows may be slower to adapt to high fat diets. Cows may consume smaller but more frequent meals (22). This suggests that from a feeding management standpoint, a high-fat concentrate should not be fed under conditions where feeding time is restricted, such as in a milking parlor.

Optimizing Feed Intake During Lactation. Water content of the diet may be a factor to consider when attempting to achieve optimum intake. This is not important for diets containing primarily hay and concentrates, but can become a limitation for diets containing mostly ensiled or fresh forages, coupled with other high-moisture feeds such as high-moisture corn, wet brewers grains and liquid whey. The maximum water content of the total ration which will not restrict total dry matter intake is not known, but Minnesota researchers (23) observed reduced dry matter intake when diets contained less than 60-65% dry matter. Some research suggested that dry matter intake drops by 0.2 kg/100 kg of body weight for every 10 percentage unit increase in moisture content of the diet.

Frequency of Feeding. The number of times cattle are fed daily may influence total dry matter intake. A recent review by Gibson (24) indicated that feeding cows more frequently had a small positive effect on milk fat percent and, to a lesser extent, on milk yield. A minimum of four daily feed offerings, alternating between forages and concentrates, appeared to be the most desirable method of feeding ration components individually. Feeding a total mixed ration assures that all nutrients are always consumed in the intended ratio and eliminates possible concerns about feeding sequence. However, the frequency of feeding total mixed rations for optimal production is not clearly defined at this time.

Protein

Requirements for protein increase even more dramatically at the onset of lactation than energy requirements because milk solids contain about 27% protein (10). Using the example in Table 20-1, a cow producing 60 kg milk per day requires 11 times as much protein as for body maintenance alone, while she requires more than 5 times as much energy. Even a cow producing 30 kg daily will need 6 times as much protein as for body maintenance alone.

This increased demand for protein can be met by increased protein content of the diet coupled with increased feed intake. While 10-12% crude protein in the diet dry matter may be adequate for the dry, pregnant cow, this same cow will likely need 16% or more crude protein in her diet during the first few months of lactation. Energy needs are the major determinants of feed intake, but as indicated previously, high producing cows seldom consume enough energy to meet those needs during the first 2-3 months of lactation. The energy deficit can be made up with "backfat", but a cow's protein reserves are

quite limited. Cattle may store some protein in the blood, liver, and muscles, but these reserves may be used over a short-term period of protein deficiency and will soon become depleted (25). Chronic protein deficiency also reduces feed intake which results in a combined deficiency of protein and energy. To insure that cows receive adequate protein in early lactation, one may want to formulate diets to contain a higher percentage of protein than would be needed if the animal were consuming enough feed to meet her energy needs, because she probably will not be eating that much.

While ruminants can utilize both natural proteins as well as non-protein N (NPN) to meet crude protein requirements, the high-producing, early lactation cow will utilize protein more efficiently than NPN (26). In mid to late lactation both types of N sources may be essentially equivalent to each other because the cow may require only 12-13% crude protein in her diet at that time. In early lactation the cow's protein requirements are greater than rumen microbial protein requirements. For instance, a cow producing 30 kg of milk daily requires 25-150% more protein than can be supplied by rumen microbial protein synthesis (27). So if the cow is fed a lot of readily soluble N, much of the extra N may be lost from the rumen as ammonia before it can be incorporated into microbial protein (see Ch. 12). But, if the diet contains mostly or all natural proteins which are degraded more slowly in the rumen than is NPN, much of this excess protein may escape or bypass degradation in the rumen and still be available for digestion in the lower gut.

A number of experiments have indicated that NPN and natural proteins are equivalent to each other as crude protein sources in supporting milk production in diets containing up to about 11-13% crude protein (Fig. 20-2). At higher crude protein concentrations, feeding natural proteins support higher production than will be supported by NPN. More slowly degraded (bypass) proteins may support greater production than more rapidly degraded proteins.

The exact point at which natural proteins start supporting greater production than NPN varies with amounts of readily fermentable carbohydrates in the diet. For instance, the two crude protein sources may be equivalent

430

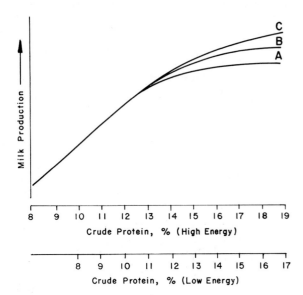

Figure 20-2. Milk production response to diets containing increasing amounts of crude protein from non-protein N (A), or from natural proteins of high solubility (B) or low solubility (C).

at up to 13% crude protein with an abundance of fermentable carbohydrates in the diet, whereas production responses may start separating at 11% crude protein and low energy. Recent research in the writer's laboratory (28) illustrated that increasing the amount of readily fermentable carbohydrates in the diet can improve NPN utilization. In those experiments, milk production by cows fed 15.5% crude protein diets which contained urea and dried whey—a source of readily fermentable carbohydrates— was greater than when cows were fed urea with corn as the main concentrate energy source and equivalent to production obtained when fed soybean meal as the supplemental crude protein source.

It is important to remember that for optimum animal production it is still best to maximize the use of the rumen, and bypass the rumen with nutrients only when that provides an additional benefit. Thus, when feeding bypass proteins one still wants to be sure to supply sufficient N and energy to the rumen for optimal microbial protein synthesis and fiber digestion. Two recent reviews discuss protein-energy interrelationships (25) in cows and give a summary of several protein evaluation schemes (29).

Bypass Proteins for Dairy Cows. The premise behind the use of bypass protein to increase milk production is based on results of earlier research which indicated that presenting more amino acids to the mammary gland increased milk protein synthesis. This was first shown with mammary secretory cells in culture media (30) and later with intravenous infusions of amino acids (31). These were followed by a number of experiments (including 32) which demonstrated that infusion of proteins or amino acids into the abomasum can result in increased milk production. Milk production was increased an average of 6.7% and milk protein production was increased 10.2% in 11 experiments in which casein was infused into the abomasum.

The above information indicates potential increased productivity but is of little value unless one can find a practical means of presenting more amino acids to the intestinal tract for absorption, and ultimately to the mammary gland for milk protein synthesis. Methods of achieving this goal have focused on two approaches: (a) selecting dietary protein ingredients which are degraded more slowly in the rumen, and (b) protecting proteins from ruminal degradation by chemical or physical treatment.

Proteins in various feed ingredients vary in solubility and degradability, thus it is possible to formulate diets which differ in the rate in which they will be degraded in the rumen (see Ch. 12). For instance, proteins in soybean meal are less soluble than proteins in some other protein supplements, although there is by no means a perfect correlation between solubility and degradability. Proteins in corn, milo, brewers grains, and distillers grains are less soluble than in ensiled forages, which in turn are less soluble than proteins in fresh grasses or legumes.

Several research trials evaluated milk production when cows were fed diets differing in protein solubility (33, 34). Production was increased in some but not in all trials. A summary of 11 experiments in which diets varied in protein solubility (33) showed an average of 6.8% more milk when dietary soluble N was reduced. In cases of no response, protein requirements may not have been much greater than what could be supplied by microbial protein synthesis and normal rumen bypass.

These data suggest a couple of precautions to consider in any attempt to increase milk protein production via increasing ruminal bypass protein. (a) Only high producing cows are likely to benefit from bypass proteins and even they will benefit the most only during the first 3-4 months of lactation. It is difficult to ascertain which production level should be considered as the point above which cows will benefit from bypass protein. We (35) suggest that, in many cases, cows producing more than 30 kg of milk daily will likely benefit from bypass protein, while those producing less than that may have little or no response. From a herd management standpoint this may indicate that herds averaging more than 7,000 kg milk/cow/year may benefit by using bypass proteins. (b) Some low solubility proteins may be so poorly solubilized in the rumen that microbial protein synthesis is lowered, due to a deficiency of N in the rumen. This could nullify any possible benefits of the bypass protein. This was exemplified in some experiments which obtained increased production by supplementing low solubility protein diets with NPN (33). (c) Some bypass proteins are severely deficient in certain essential amino acids. Thus, bypassing the rumen with such a protein has little or no benefit to the animal if the supply of limiting amino acids is not increased.

Many dairymen do not have the luxury of selecting ration ingredients that contain less naturally soluble protein. Forages and grain ingredients which they use may be limited to whatever is available, and the selection of protein supplements may be quite limited, also. In this situation solubility of proteins can be reduced by treating protein supplements with something which will reduce protein solubility in the rumen, but allow the protein to be digested in the gastro-intestinal tract. Chemicals such as aldehydes, alcohols, and tannins, as well as treatment with heat are methods available to reduce protein solubility (see Ch. 12).

Table 20-2 summarizes data from several experiments in which proteins treated with formaldehyde were fed to lactating cows. South Dakota State University research (33) indicated that formaldehyde treatment of a whey protein concentrate, one of the highest quality proteins available, resulted in

Table 20-2. Lactational response to diets containing formaldehyde-treated protein supplements.[a]

Treated protein	Number of experiments	4% fat-corrected milk	
		Average	Range
		. . . % of control	
Whey protein concentrate	1	113.5	--
Casein	6	105.5	105.5-110.0
Plant proteins	13	101.5	92.9-116.9

[a]Data summarized from several sources summarized by references 33 and 34.

about the greatest increase (+13.5%) in milk production of any formaldehyde-treated proteins evaluated. This increase was associated with a greater mammary uptake of essential amino acids. Feeding formaldehyde-treated casein usually resulted in small (2-10%), but consistent increases. However, formaldehyde treatment of plant proteins has not always been beneficial. When increased production was observed, the increases were modest (1-3%) except for one Canadian study with formaldehyde-treated rapeseed meal. Apparently, overprotection of the protein is especially likely to occur with plant proteins and may have been a problem in some of the above studies. The optimum formaldehyde-to-protein ratio is likely different for various protein sources. For instance, treating soybean meal with more than 0.5% formaldehyde may cause overprotection whereas more than 1.4% formaldehyde was necessary before overprotection occurred with sunflower meal (33).

Treatment of ensiled forages with formic acid or formaldehyde generally improves the feeding value of the silage (33, 34). Proteolysis is reduced during the ensiling process, thus reducing fermentation losses of N and preserving more of the forage proteins for consumption by animals.

Moderate heat treatment of proteins offers the possibility of reducing protein solubility without substantially decreasing overall protein quality and without the possible risk of chemical residues in milk or meat. Heat treatment of protein supplements such as soybean meal is a routine procedure via the toasting-desolventizing process of preparing soybean meal. This treatment provides a means of destroying several heat-labile anti-nutritional factors present in soybeans such as

432

trypsin inhibitors, lipase and urease that are not present in many other protein supplements. Subjecting soybean meal to additional heat, or the heat treatment of other protein supplements, may further improve protein utilization. However, when using heat treatments, one must be cautious to avoid damaging proteins by excessive heating which may reduce, rather than improve, the protein's utilization by animals.

Milk production was usually increased when lactating cows were fed heat-treated soybean meal (33, 35). Increases of 6-8% by high-producing cows during early lactation were common while little or no response occurred when fed to lower producing cows, especially if in mid to late lactation. Another interesting point was that in research by Huber and Kung (see 34) the greatest production was obtained when fed ammoniated corn silage and heated soybean meal. This illustrated the possible concern of bypass proteins not providing enough soluble N for optimal ruminal microbial protein synthesis.

The ratio of soluble N to non-structural carbohydrate content may also be a factor to consider in optimizing protein and energy utilization by the high-producing cow. As mentioned previously, increasing the amount of readily fermentable carbohydrates in the diet may allow the use of more soluble proteins in the diet without reducing production. The effectiveness of various sources of carbohydrates in achieving this goal is not well documented but likely varies. For instance, the starch in corn may be solubilized and fermented in the rumen at different rates than starch from other feed grains.

Vitamins—Special Considerations

Vitamin supplementation of diets usually has no direct affect on milk production, but there are situations in which supplementation of certain vitamins may be considered. Most nutritionists recommend supplying supplemental vitamins A and D to insure adequacy of the diet for the animal's health even though no response in production is likely to occur.

Vitamin E supplementation may be necessary if oxidized flavor of milk becomes a problem. Such a problem may occur when diets contain only stored feeds and/or when diets contain supplemental fats. If oxidized milk flavor problems occur, 400-1,000 mg of additional vitamin E/head/d may be needed to correct the problem (10).

The B vitamins are usually synthesized by rumen microorganisms in more than adequate amounts to meet the cow's needs. Thus, supplementation with B vitamins or microbial products such as yeast to supply B vitamins is usually unnecessary and will not show any benefit; however, recent evidence indicates that supplementation of certain B vitamins may occasionally be beneficial. Because niacin is involved intimately with energy metabolism, niacin supplementation may increase milk production by moderating effects of ketosis on energy-stressed, high-producing cows (36 and Ch. 24). Niacin supplementation is most effective if initiated either before or immediately after calving and continued for 4-10 weeks. Choline supplementation will not affect milk production when diets contain adequate forage, but may slightly increase milk fat percentages and fat-corrected milk when diets are low in fiber. Co and/or vitamin B_{12} supplementation will not likely be beneficial unless diets are deficient in Co.

Minerals—Special Considerations

Ca and P requirements increase substantially with the onset of lactation as milk contains substantial amounts of both minerals. The inability of a cow to adjust rapidly to this increased Ca demand can result in milk fever (see Ch. 24). Diets should be formulated with the intent of meeting the animal's requirements of these two minerals; however, considerable resorption of Ca and P from bones can occur to make up for short-term deficits. In fact, many cows may be in a negative Ca and P balance during the first 3-5 months of lactation. Ca requirements may increase slightly with high-fat diets due to increased fecal Ca losses.

The nutritional availability (true digestibility) of Ca may vary with different sources, so one may want to take this into account when formulating diets (10). Ca from inorganic sources may be more available than that from organic sources. Of the various organic sources, Ca from alfalfa is used less efficiently than from other sources due to the relative indigestibility of Ca-containing crystals such as Ca oxalate which may be up to one-third of the total Ca in alfalfa (37). The nutritional availability of various sources of dietary P may differ, although these differences are not likely to be of significance for ruminants.

Substantial amounts of Na and Cl are also secreted in milk so it is essential to supply adequate amounts in the diet. It is recommended (10) that diets for lactating cows contain 0.18% Na or 0.46% NaCl. These are about 80% higher concentrations than for dry pregnant cows. Because substantial amounts of Na may be included in the diet from buffers such as $NaHCO_3$, it may be necessary to evaluate the dietary adequacy of Cl. While Cl is seldom considered to be deficient in diets, a deficiency can occur when diets are formulated to meet Na requirements if substantial amounts of Na are supplied by ingredients other than NaCl. Cl deficiency symptoms, which included dramatic reductions in milk production, were demonstrated in Cornell University studies (38) in which cows were fed practical diets containing 0.1% Cl. Their research indicated that the Cl requirement for lactating cows is around 0.18-0.27% of diet dry matter. Most feeds are low in Cl, but some feeding programs may meet Cl requirements with lesser amounts of salt. For instance, molasses contains 2-3% Cl.

Lactating cows have high K requirements because of the large quantity of K secreted daily in milk. The requirement may be further increased by environmental heat stress. Decreased feed intake with a corresponding decrease in milk production can occur under K deficiency situations. While K deficiency was previously considered unlikely to occur, it is more likely to occur today because of several changes in recent years which tend to reduce the amount of K fed (38). Most forages contain considerably more K than required by cattle; however, many concentrates are deficient in K. Some forages (corn silage) and fiber sources (corn cobs and cottonseed hulls) are also low in K. Thus, feeding programs which include larger amounts of concentrates, more corn silage, and complete feeds using low K fiber sources are likely to be bordering on K deficiency.

Lactating cows may require more I than non-lactating cattle because about 10% or more of the I intake is normally excreted in milk (38). To insure adequate I intake for high-producing cows, diets should contain 0.5 ppm I. However, in some cases dairymen need to be cautious to avoid providing excess I. Overfeeding of organic iodides such as ethylene-diamine-diiodide (EDDI), which is often used to prevent foot rot, and misuse of sanitizers can boost milk I levels dramatically because excretion of I via milk is one of the cow's means of getting rid of excess I. In some situations the high I content of this milk could become toxic to humans.

Feed Additives

Buffers. Rations which contain higher proportions of concentrates, especially when coupled with ensiled and/or chopped forages, tend to create a more acidic condition within the rumen because of the larger amounts of readily fermentable carbohydrates and reduction in saliva secretion. This may make the cow more prone to go off feed, creating conditions which may lead to displaced abomasum, milk fever or ketosis. Such conditions in the rumen are also associated with changes in the VFA produced, particularly an increase in the proportion of propionate which is highly correlated with milk fat depression. Problems resulting from a lowered ruminal pH can be prevented or alleviated by adding buffering agents to the diet (39; see Ch. 17).

Products Which Alter Rumen Fermentation. Several products have become available in recent years and more will likely be available which alter rumen fermentation and improve the efficiency of feed utilization. Some of these products may be beneficial to lactating cows whereas other may be more appropriate only for growing ruminants.

The addition of ammonium salts of iso C-4 and C-5 acids (AS-VFA) such as isobutyric, isovaleric, and 2-methyl butyric, and the straight-chain valeric acid may be effective in increasing milk production when fed to lactating cows (40). These fatty acids are essential growth factors for some of the important cellulolytic bacteria present in the rumen. Increased production is apparently a result of increased feed utilization. Response to AS-VFA seems to be greatest when forage is primarily corn silage, although limited data with other forages usually produced positive responses.

Ionophores such as monensin and lasalocid as well as other propionate enhancers or methane inhibitors are effective in improving the efficiency of feed utilization in the rumen. However, such products are not appropriate to feed to lactating cows because the resulting increased propionate to acetate ratio in the rumen will translate into a marked depression in milk fat production. Preliminary research (41) suggests that a somewhat similar product, actaplanin, may be useful with lactating cows even though it may cause a slight reduction in milk fat percentages.

Products With Hormone Activity. The inclusion in dairy rations of materials with hormone-like activity for the purposes of increasing milk production has received periodic attention for many years. Feeding thyroprotein or other products having thyroxine-like activity has received the most attention. While the feeding of such products may stimulate an initial increase in production, removal of the product from the diet results in as great or greater decrease in production (10). Long-term use of thyroprotein can adversely affect a cow's health. There is some evidence that feeding low levels of estrogens and/or corticoids may stimulate milk production, but legal limitations in some countries preclude such use.

The hormone currently showing most promise for use in increasing milk production is growth hormone. The mode of administration currently in use in research is by injection, and will not likely ever be via feeding because this proteinaceous hormone would be destroyed in the digestive tract. Initial experiments with growth hormone are very encouraging (42). Increases in milk production of 10-40% were observed in short-term studies conducted at various stages of lactation. A recent long-term study in which high-producing cows were given daily injections of natural bovine growth hormone or recombinantly derived bovine growth hormone from 84 to 272 d postpartum resulted in production increases of 16.5 to 41.2% (Table 20-3). The recombinantly derived growth hormone was more effective than pituitary growth hormone.

Animals responded to the increased nutritional demand for milk production by increasing their feed intake. Daily dry matter intake of cows injected with 27 mg/d of recombinant growth hormone averaged 4.6% of body weight as compared to 4.1% for the controls (Fig. 20-3). These high-producing cows were able to replenish body reserves adequately during the treatment period. While some cows were in negative energy balance for as long as the first 10 weeks on the trial, all cows were in positive energy balance over the 27-week treatment period. This indicates that the use of growth hormone may be more beneficial when used with cows in mid to late lactation rather than in early lactation, although this premise has not yet been evaluated adequately. During the first two months of lactation, when cows are already in negative energy balance, they may not be able to

Table 20-3. Effect of exogenous growth hormone on lactation performance.[*]

Variable[**]	Control	Pituitary bovine somatotropin 27.0 mg/d	Methionyl bovine somatotropin 13.5 mg/d	27.0 mg/d	40.5 mg/d	SE
Cows/treatment	6	6	6	6	6	
FCM, kg/d	27.9[a]	32.5[ab]	34.4[bc]	38.0[c]	39.4[c]	1.8
Milk fat, %	3.6	3.3	3.8	3.6	3.6	0.1
protein, %	3.4	3.4	3.4	3.4	3.4	0.1
lactose, %	4.8	4.8	4.9	4.8	4.9	0.1
Net energy intake, Mcal/d	34.1	35.1	36.7	39.2	37.5	1.8
balance, Mcal/d	4.7[a]	2.9[ab]	3.7[ab]	2.8[ab]	1.7[b]	1.0
Gross efficiency						
Observed, kg FCM/Mcal NE intake	0.83[a]	0.90[ab]	0.93[abc]	1.00[bc]	1.03[c]	0.04
Corrected[†]	0.94[a]	1.04[ab]	1.03[ab]	1.10[b]	1.12[b]	0.03
Theoretical[‡]	0.96[a]	1.00[a]	1.03[ab]	1.07[b]	1.07[b]	0.02

[abc] Means within rows with different superscripts differ (P < .05).

[*] From Bauman et al (42). Treatment period was 188 d commencing at 84 ± 10 d postpartum.

[**] FCM = 3.5% fat-corrected milk; NE = NE_L.

[†] Corrected for body weight gain. Corrected efficiency = kg FCM [Mcal NE intake – (weight gain x 60.0 Mcal/kg)].

[‡] Calculated as kg FCM divided by NE requirements for maintenance and milk.

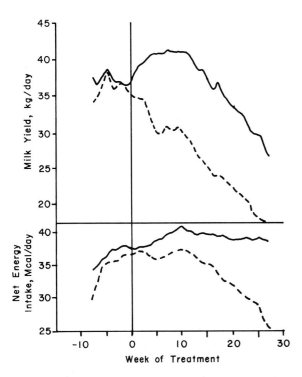

Figure 20-3. Effect of exogenous bovine somatotropin on milk yield and dry matter intake. Treatments commenced at week 0 (84 ± 10 d postpartum) and continued for 27 weeks. Methionyl-bovine somatotropin (27 mg/d) and control (excipient) treatments indicated by solid and dashed lines, respectively (42).

respond sufficiently to the increased nutritional demands by additional increased feed intake. The additional drain on body reserves at that time may make them more prone to ketosis and may reduce reproductive efficiency.

Growth hormone does not affect the efficiency of feed utilization, but simply redirects nutrients within the body to productive purposes such as milk production or muscle growth. Thus, productive efficiency is increased by dilution of costs associated with maintenance. This is the same mechanism observed in genetically superior cows and the basis for improvements which have been made through the use of genetic selection.

FEEDING MANAGEMENT FOR DAIRY CATTLE

Proper management of the dairy feeding program helps assure that cows receive the appropriate amounts of nutrients without causing metabolic or digestive upsets. Several key areas to consider in feeding management are discussed in following sections.

Dry Period

A cow should be dry 6-8 weeks between lactations for maximum lifetime production. This allows the mammary gland to involute and prepare for the next lactation. Cows with no dry period or short dry periods usually produce less milk than expected in the next lactation, sometimes as much as 25-40% less. However, giving cows more than 6-8 weeks is costly in that the cow is consuming additional feed while not producing milk. Maximum dry matter intake and milk production can be obtained if cows are fed during the dry period in a manner which gets them in good body condition without becoming excessively fat. Conditioning of the cow for the next lactation should start near the end of lactation because feed energy is converted to body tissue more efficiently by lactating than by non-lactating cows.

Precautions should be taken to prevent overly fat cows (see Ch. 24). Excessively fat cows are more likely to have calving difficulties, metabolic disorders such as ketosis, and infectious diseases (13). Fat cows often have reduced feed intake following parturition, possibly because of restricted gut capacity and because of the release of larger than normal amounts of free fatty acids into the blood which depress appetite. Decreased appetite following parturition may result in a serious shortage of nutrients which will reduce milk production and may cause ketosis.

In group feeding systems, dry cows should be fed separately from the milking herd. If fed with the milking herd, dry cows will consume too much energy and get excessively fat even when fed with the low production group. Cows that are in reasonably good condition when dried off can be maintained satisfactorily on forages alone. The amount of concentrate included in the ration should be determined by the quantity and quality of forage eaten and the body condition of the cow. Corn silage, if fed, should be limited during the dry period as free choice consumption will lead to excessive fattening. Also, cows receiving long stem hay during the dry period seldom have displaced abomasums in early lactation, while cows fed corn silage

436

during the dry period are more likely to have displaced abomasums.

Beginning about 10-15 d before expected parturition, the amount of concentrate fed should be increased to about 1% of body weight. This allows the cow to adapt to a higher energy diet thereby allowing for more rapid increases in feed intake following parturition. Several surveys of dairy practices indicated that increased concentrate feeding prepartum results in fewer cases of ketosis and milk fever. However, if this practice is overdone, there may be increased chances for displaced abomasum. Ketosis may be prevented via greater energy intake following parturition. Reduced incidence of milk fever may also be due to greater feed intake around parturition coupled with the fact that concentrates contain lower Ca to P ratios, thus helping to get the intake of these two minerals more in line with optimum recommendations for preventing milk fever. Composition of the prepartum diet also influences the incidence of milk fever (see Ch. 24). The prepartum diet should supply less than 100 g of Ca and adequate amounts of P.

Early Lactation

At the time of parturition a cow's nutritional needs increase suddenly. A cow genetically capable of high production will strive to produce as much milk as possible. The dairymen's role is to help her achieve this goal.

There are several things which can be done to help the cow increase feed intake as rapidly as possible. (a) Increasing concentrate in the diet the last couple of weeks prepartum helps the rumen microorganisms start adjusting to higher energy diets. (b) Avoid abrupt diet changes but gradually continue to increase the amount of concentrate fed as long as the cow responds. (c) Keep sufficient amounts of forage in the diet and preferably some long-stem hay. This will minimize the chances of a cow going off-feed and minimize the chances of milk fat depression. (d) Because the protein requirements are high at this time and the cow will likely not be consuming enough energy, the protein content of the diet should be formulated to be higher in protein than would be needed if consuming sufficient amounts of energy. (e) The crude protein should be supplied by natural proteins rather than NPN as the cow will utilize NPN less

efficiently in early lactation than she will be able to later on. (f) If buffers and vitamin supplements will be beneficial to the cow, they will most likely help her during early lactation.

Grouping Cows

Many larger herds handle cows in corrals or free stall barns with cows fed in groups. The herd can be handled as one group or, preferably, grouped by some means according to production and/or stage of lactation. The number of groups and how grouping is handled may vary with individual situations. However, a system of grouping cows according to production and/or stage of lactation usually results in more efficient utilization of feed resources and may improve labor efficiency.

One example of grouping of cows would be three groups for the milking herd plus a fourth group for dry cows. Group 1 would include all fresh cows and cows would remain in that group until dropping below a certain level of production or number of days postpartum. The rest of the milking herd would be divided into groups 2 and 3 according to production or stage of lactation. Some dairymen may wish to keep all cows in group 1 until they are bred. This minimizes the number of pens which have to be checked for heat. Because group 1 is also receiving the highest energy diet, conception rates may be higher than if fed lower energy diets. Two-year-olds may be grouped separately from other cows or kept in a group until lower production levels are reached than one would use for moving older cows. This would enable higher energy intake as allowance for their additional growth requirements.

The diets fed to each group would be formulated to meet the nutritional needs of the cows within that group. Some larger herds may formulate specific diets for each group whereas many dairymen may be able to feed all groups satisfactorily with one concentrate mix and simply vary the forage to concentrate ratios with each group.

Cows should be moved in small groups rather than one at a time to minimize fighting among cows as the group re-establishes their pecking order. Some reduced milk production often occurs when cows are moved, but one wants to minimize these drops in production.

Feeding Systems

Total mixed rations offer the advantage that every mouthful of the diet should be nutritionally balanced. However, the use of long-stem hay does not readily fit into many total mixed systems, so some dairymen have a modified total mixed system with the hay fed separately. Because a balanced blend of nutrients are always available for consumption, rumen fermentation patterns are usually more uniform than if concentrates are fed separately 2-3 times daily. Consequently, cows may be less prone to digestive upsets, may have fewer problems with milk fat depression, and may utilize NPN sources more efficiently than when concentrates are fed separately from forages.

Feeding concentrates separately from forages offers the opportunity to "fine-tune" feeding programs by feeding more concentrates to cows that need the additional nutrients. Feeding concentrates in the milking parlor is one method of providing concentrates; however, high-producing cows are not in the parlor long enough to consume all of the concentrate they need. Thus, additional concentrate also has to be fed elsewhere, or the highest producing cows will be limited in their producing ability. Several electronic concentrate feeding systems are currently on the market. Systems vary from simple models in which all cows with a magnetic-activating key can obtain all the feed they want to other systems which are computer controlled, can keep track of how much feed a cow is supposed to get, how much she consumed, and regulate how much she can consume within a given period of time.

Feeding sequence and feeding frequency can become factors to consider when concentrates are fed separately from forages. Limited research indicates a minimum of four daily feed offerings alternating between forages and concentrates appears to be the most desirable method of feeding diet components individually. While feeding animals more frequently may be thought to increase feed intake, limited research data indicate little benefit on increasing feed intakes and milk production. When feed is available continuously, cows spend about 3.5-4 h eating daily, with this time divided into 15-20 meals.

SUMMARY

The ruminant requires nutrients for many functions and these needs are greater than normal for fertility, maintaining reproduction, lactation and growth. Insufficient energy intake is the main factor limiting fertility, but deficiencies of some vitamins and minerals can also reduce fertility. Inadequate energy intake in late gestation can be especially costly to smaller ruminants such as sheep and goats carrying twins or triplets. Inadequate intake of vitamins A and E or of Se may increase the incidence of retained placentas; inadequate intake of several other minerals may be related to other reproductive problems. Nutritional needs greatly increase at the onset of lactation, particularly for modern breeds of dairy cattle and goats as they are capable of producing much more milk than their offspring require. The greatest challenge is to meet the energy requirements of the animal while maintaining sufficient fiber in the diet for normal rumen function. The protein requirement also increases dramatically and is best satisfied by natural proteins as the protein requirements of the high-producing animal often exceeds the rumen microbes' ability to synthesis protein. The addition of buffers and other feed additives to the diet offer an opportunity to further increase production of genetically superior animals but are likely of minimal help for less productive animals.

NUTRITION IN GROWTH

by F.M. Byers and G.T. Schelling

INTRODUCTION

Growth and development in ruminants represent complex issues with respect to nutrition. Growth is by nature a long-term and sometimes interrupted process, continuing in some form throughout an animal's life. The simplicity through which growth may be grossly estimated by changes in weight or stature provides an unwarranted degree of confidence in our ability to understand and predict requirements for animal function.

438

Nutrition for growth inherently includes a diversity of disciplines and integrates nutritional physiology with cellular function. It is, in fact, cellular function that establishes growth of specific tissues, and the coordinated expression of growth of all tissues results in what we measure as growth. Fortuitously, growth occurs in a reasonably predictable sequence with time, and weight and patterns of growth are similar across animals. Actual priorities for and limits to growth are established through both endogenous as well as exogenous regulation. Nutrition required reflects metabolic activity and turnover of tissues maintained as well as substrates required for net tissue growth. The profile and quantities of nutrients required depend on the summation of all tissue functions and mirror priorities and activity of respective animal tissues in any specific phase of growth.

BASIS OF GROWTH

All imaginable animal factors impact nutrition, some more directly than others, and most in ways that are only partially understood. The cornerstone of nutrition in growth and development is the physiological system through which growth and production functions are prioritized and regulated. Our limited understanding of growth and its regulation imposes restrictions on our ability to comprehend and project nutritional requirements for growth processes. With these limitations in mind, a variety of factors involved in growth processes can be identified.

Two very basic processes, homeostasis and homeorhesis, regulate all animal functions. Homeostasis allows for steady state regulation of physiological functions at established priorities. Growth would be simple if only homeostasis was involved. However, priorities for tissue function are forever changing. The underlying mechanisms governing priorities and modifying threshholds for tissue function involve a concept called homeorhesis. Homeorhesis, very simply put, is the directed and orchestrated establishment of new priorities for animal function. This occurs many times as an animal grows from birth to maturity. Repartitioning of nutrients from maternal tissue to fetal tissue and to milk requires setting new systemic priorities and is accomplished through homeorhesis. All factors that modify growth and productive functions operate through homeorhesis. Many times for our purposes we choose to modify animal function such as through castration of males and use of anabolic repartitioning agents including estrogenic compounds and growth hormone. It is through homeorhesis that we are able to impact priorities for tissue function and, as a result, animal growth.

Principal issues involved in nutrition for growth include growth functions which establish patterns for growth over time, priorities for orchestrated growth, physiological limits or ceilings for growth, the inherent efficiency of synthesizing and storing protein and fat in specific tissues and the net rates of growth relative to nutrients used for maintenance functions. Limits to net growth are invariably tied to the level of nutrition available relative to a variable entity called maintenance. Therefore, to establish nutritional needs for growth, the fraction or quantity of nutrients provided that will be directed for maintaining the animal—usually the first priority, must first be determined. Maintenance and growth are related, with maintenance actually increasing with level of intake and rate of growth, requiring a greater total quantity of nutrients in rapidly growing animals. As a result, maintenance is an important component of nutrition of growing animals, and factors germane to maintenance are also critical components of growth.

Irrespective of animal functions, it is convenient to separate nutrient needs for growing animals into maintenance and growth/production components. It is important to realize that while this is a partitioning of integrated functions that the animal makes little attempt to separate, requirements can be established more precisely to support desired growth. Maintenance requirements represent an important and many times the major portion of total nutrients used in growing ruminants. For this reason maintenance is of critical concern in understanding nutrition of growing animals. Factors affecting maintenance and growth include intrinsic animal as well as environmental (Ch. 22) and management components.

PHYSIOLOGICAL COMPONENTS OF NUTRITION IN GROWTH

The key physiological functions contributing to nutrient requirements include ion transport, protein synthesis and turnover, fat synthesis and turnover, and thermogenesis. The energy cost of ion pumping in maintaining cellular gradients probably accounts for 20-30% of total energy requirements for maintenance. Some tissue research indicates that ion pumping may account for as much as 60% of cellular oxygen consumption. Therefore, the requirement for ion transport could be much greater than 30% in animals with large fractions of metabolically active tissues. Ion transport and associated costs may be modified by external factors. A new family of compounds, ionophores, function through modifying ion transport across intact cell membranes and may impact both animal and microbial cell function, either reducing cellular requirements or increasing cellular efficiency.

Protein turnover also accounts for a large fraction of maintenance requirements. While protein synthesis is an inherently efficient process, net efficiency of protein storage is universally low. The relative contribution of protein turnover to requirements for maintenance vs net tissue growth depends on relative synthesis and turnover rates of tissues present. Fat, muscle and organ tissue are turned over at very different rates. In addition, not all organ tissues or all fat tissues turn over at the same rate. For instance, intestinal tissue protein turns over daily and liver protein turns over as rapidly as twice daily. Turnover rates for skeletal muscle are slower, averaging a turnover per week, and fat turns over even more slowly, with different rates for different depots. Increasing the fraction of metabolically active liver and intestinal tissues increases the contribution of protein turnover to animal requirements and reduces net growth possible with any given level of nutrition.

Fat turnover, while low, contributes to maintenance requirements depending on the metabolic activity of the storage location. Highly vascularized visceral and abdominal fat turns over more rapidly and, therefore, requires more energy. Fat stored as subcutaneous adipose tissue normally turns over more slowly, is less vascularized and requires less energy for maintenance. Depending on the environment, subcutaneous fat may reduce heat loss to a greater extent than the amount of energy required to maintain this tissue (1, 2), giving this tissue an effective negative maintenance requirement. Energy required to keep warm or cool contributes to thermogenesis (Ch. 13) and increases requirements for growing animals. Newborn animals depend on oxidative uncoupling in brown adipose tissue to generate heat in oxidative metabolism to maintain body temperature. Other animals may have similar abilities in normal adipocytes to generate heat. Thermogenesis becomes a larger component of nutrient requirements as a growing animal is maintained further from its thermoneutral zone (Chs. 13, 22).

Animal-Management Factors Effecting Nutrition in Growth

There are many animal factors involved in nutritional requirements. Some of these such as age and weight are somewhat related in that animals increase in weight as they grow concurrent with age. As a result, maintenance requirements (as a % of total requirements) decrease with time during growth, due both to increasing weight, age and fatness, and decreasing fraction of metabolically very active tissues. Requirements for net growth reflect composition of growth (protein, fat) along with composition of tissue maintained. As is evident, body composition is an important determinant of both maintenance and tissue growth, and also changes somewhat parallel to age and weight during growth from birth to maturity. As animals get older and heavier, composition of added tissue shifts primarily to fat which has a lower maintenance requirement but a greater energy density than protein.

The type of tissue, whether metabolically active precursor or less active user tissue, is a major factor in establishing requirements. Precursor tissues include GI tract and vital organ tissues involved in processing energy for systemic use which have very high requirements. User tissues, muscle and fat turn over more slowly than precursor tissues and have lower maintenance requirements. Cattle of different breeds differ as much as 50% (3, 4) in maintenance ME requirements, with higher

440

requirements for cattle of dairy background and with greater milk production potential (5). Cattle of larger mature size also tend to have greater maintenance requirements (6, 7). Sex class also has an impact on maintenance requirements, with requirements in the order of bulls > steers > heifers. Previous rate of growth is very important, and restricted growth reduces vital organ mass (7, 8) allowing for lower maintenance requirements during the subsequent period of growth. This allows more animal production for the same ME input and is likely the physiological basis of compensatory growth.

Several management factors also can modify maintenance requirements of growing animals. Ionophores function in part by reducing maintenance requirements (9, 10, 11) leaving more ME available for growth. Anabolic regulators (i.e., implants) repartition a portion of the energy from fat to protein deposition without reducing the efficiency of ME use as would be expected from the change in tissue deposition, indicating a possible effect on tissue efficiency.

Environment is an important contributor to nutrient requirements of growing animals (12). Many factors are included in environment such as season, photoperiod, temperature, relative humidity, pen conditions (i.e., mud), sky cover, radiation, air movement, precipitation, exercise, energy and water intake, parasites and diseases and nutrition per se. The interaction of the growing animal and these environmental factors are critical determinants of nutrient requirements for desired rates of growth. Animals of genotypes most adaptable to adverse environmental conditions (i.e., heat stress, parasites) will have lower nutrient requirements for any level of growth in that specific environment. This critical concept is commonly referred to as genotype-environment-interaction or GEI, and is an important determinant of nutrient requirements for growth. The nutritional environment, i.e., level of energy, protein and other critical nutrients is also affected by GEI, with lowest nutrient requirements for desired rates of growth when level, type and source of nutrients are optimally matched with animal characteristics and needs. Environment contributes substantially to nutrient requirements of growing animals across all phases of growth, and successful computer models of growing ruminants (13) include these factors.

Nutritional Efficiency of Tissue Growth

While fat is generally an energetically efficient tissue to deposit with an average efficiency of 70%, animal and storage location differences in efficiency exist. Protein deposition, conversely, is generally an inefficient process because most protein tissues turn over quite rapidly and must be redeposited many times during the life of an animal. Metabolically active precursor tissues are among the least efficient tissues to deposit (10% or less) while user tissues which turn over less rapidly are more efficient to deposit. Muscle tissue protein is still deposited with only a 30-40% efficiency (ME) and offers substantial opportunity for improvement. Because of the substantial differences in efficiency of depositing protein and fat, all factors that modify composition of growth automatically alter nutrient requirements for and efficiency of growth. In early stages of growth (fetal), nutrients, especially energy, are used very inefficiently (4, 9, 14, 15), reflecting both the type of tissue growing and the metabolic activity of support tissues. Additionally, animals with priorities for growth of precursor tissues (i.e., dairy breeds) will be less efficient, reflecting the type of tissue stored. Nutritional regulation of growth modifies the rates and fractions of protein and fat in tissue growth, also modifying efficiency of growth. Biological ceilings for growth establish the concept that availability of nutrients does not necessarily result in growth, an important concept for nutritionists attempting to establish minimal nutrient requirements for maximal growth of specific tissues, i.e., protein in muscle.

Because of these cellular limits for daily protein growth, increasing nutritional levels above needs for protein growth simply enhances rates of fat deposition (16) and, as a result, increases energetic efficiency. Nutrient requirements for growth reflect the summation of both support (maintenance) and specific tissue growth functions and thus are specific for an animal only with respect to stage, phase, rate and composition of growth. Phases of growth provide a useful mechanism for categorizing and discriminating nutrient requirements for growing animals, and are discussed in the next section. Regulation of growth is governed by several mechanisms, and these factors and their resulting impact on nutritional requirements of animals through stages of growth are addressed in successive sections.

NUTRITION FOR GROWTH-PHASES OF GROWTH

Four distinct phases of growth are present in feeding/management systems with domestic ruminants. These are fetal growth, birth to weaning, weaning to puberty or yearling age and finishing or growth to eventual maturity. Nutritional concerns differ between these stages, reflecting changing animal needs and desired growth rates. However, nutrition provided to the developing/growing animal during any stage has an impact on subsequent growth characteristics and nutritional demands. Because nutrition during gestation is covered in part in this chapter under reproduction and a part of pre-weaning nutrition is covered in nutrition of pre-ruminants (Ch. 19), only concerns specifically related to animal growth will be addressed in this section.

Nutrition and Fetal Growth

The fetal development phase, while perhaps the most critical period in an animal's lifetime, has, because of technical difficulties, been overlooked by most nutritionists. This is unfortunate because it is during this period that the pattern for a lifetime of growth is established. The number of muscle fibers is set sometime prior to birth and restriction of fetal growth prior to the time at which the total number of muscle cells have been developed will likely have a permanent effect on potential animal growth. Recent research (17) indicates that total DNA per fetus (cattle) increases throughout gestation, with most rapid rates of DNA growth at about 220 d, decreasing to near 0 by 280 d. A high percentage of the hyperplasia in later stages of prenatal development is muscle; thus restriction of growth during this phase would likely have its greatest effect on postnatal muscle development. Restriction of growth occurring through hypertrophy would not likely result in any permanent reduction in potential

muscle growth to maturity. The number of adipocytes is not set until some time after birth, and in some tissues hyperplasia may occur even near maturity (18). Because it is undesirable to limit total muscle in most ruminant species, provision of adequate nutrition to the fetus, by diet or from maternal tissues through the stage of muscle cell hyperplasia is very important.

Fetal nutrient requirements estimated from fetal tissue growth (15) provide a reasonable estimate of fetal demands and indicate that energy and protein requirements increase rapidly during the latter stage of gestation, and maximize between 240-280 d. Nutritional restriction during this critical period reduces birth weight by 10 (19) to 25% (20), depending on degree of restriction, and this reduced birth weight is reflected in parallel reductions in 205 d weaning weight as well. Efficiency of growth during this period is lower than in any other phase of growth, further amplifying nutrient requirements. Energetic efficiency of the dam and fetus is as low as 25% (4), and the efficiency of fetal growth is as low as 10% (9). Maternal restriction in fetal nutrient supply depends on dietary nutritional adequacy, maternal tissue stores, and maternal regulation of nutrient partitioning and of fetal blood flow. Fetal blood flow is reduced during heat stress and likely accounts for the reduced birth weight of lambs born shortly following summer heat stress. Maternal partitioning to maintenance, structural growth, survival or other functions may also reduce nutrients available to the developing fetus. Protein, energy and minerals are critical nutrients included in dam partitioning that may be restricted to the fetus. Obviously, the extent of maternal stores has a major impact on fetal nutrient supply because mobilization can occur only if sufficient reserves are available. Wild ruminants usually have the ability to cycle with seasons and develop reserves in anticipation of the fetal growth phase; this important function has disappeared in genetically superior domesticated and selected ruminants. Other consequences of nutritional restriction have been discussed in the reproduction section of this chapter. While maternal control regulates nutrient supply prior to birth, postnatal growth depends increasingly on nutrient supply from other sources.

442

Growth—Birth to Weaning

Growth during this stage actually encompasses several phases. The first phase immediately following birth lasts from several weeks to several months and is the period when the animal functions as a non-ruminant. Nutrition during this phase parallels that of non-ruminants (Ch. 19) until the animal begins to develop rumen function. Once a functioning rumen is established, nutrition becomes more complex. With advancing time after rumen development, the fraction of nutrients provided by milk decrease and from feed sources increase. Weaning may occur very early when young animals are fed milk replacers or after 6-8 mo as in beef cattle cow-calf enterprises. Nutrients may be provided via grazed forages, dry forages or silage, or a variety of grain-concentrate mixtures. Depending on the feedstuff base, energy, protein, minerals or all may be deficient to allow desired growth. Primary concerns include:

Milk production: level, composition and timing relative to needs of the offspring
Forage availability: quantity vs potential to use (timing)
Quality: energy density, protein level and type
Supplementation strategies: creep feeding, drylot
Weaning: age and strategies

Milk production may or may not be an important factor, depending primarily on weaning strategies. For most beef calves, lambs and offspring of wild ruminants, milk availability is a critical and often limiting factor. Young ruminants usually cannot consume all the milk the dam is capable of producing until they have grown for a period of time. Whether the level of milk produced can be increased in mid and later lactation as nutritional demands increase is a critical factor, and it is at this time that milk nutrients really become limiting. In common management systems the period of increasing offspring requirements coincides with a season of reduced forage availability (typically a summer dry period), and the dam's milk production level may be decreasing rather than increasing. Where possible with domestic ruminants, choice of a calving or lambing season such that forage quality is highest when the young ruminant can use it and the dam can also maximize milk production represents an optimal match. For the young ruminant, forage quality is more important than quantity because intake will be limited. With advancing time, forage consumption increases, milk intake decreases, and the quantity of forage available along with quality becomes important. Beef calves born in late winter and early spring (typical in many systems) are too small and too young to use the high quality forages available in late spring to early summer. When they reach the age where they can use significant amounts of forage—mid to late summer—forage quality and usually quantity are both declining or low. As a consequence nutrient requirements of the suckling ruminant commonly are not met when potential growth may be high, especially when requirements and forage production are out of phase. Several management alternatives may be used to circumvent this problem. Calves or lambs may be early-weaned and placed on the highest quality grazed or harvested forage available. Protein needs are high, and a natural protein supplement is usually required to provide needed protein unless very good quality legume forage is available. If weaning is not an option, calves or lambs can be supplemented separately by creep feeding or creep grazing. With appropriate feeders, gates, etc., a concentrate mix or better pasture may be provided when milk production becomes too limited. Advantages of meeting nutrient requirements of calves through creep feeding include: heavier weaning weight, economical gains, greater efficiency of feeding calf vs cow, allows expression of growth potential, reduces parasite incidence, improves cow condition, provides flexibility in marketing, establishes feeding behavior, and allows delivery of feed additives. However, creep feeding is not without problems, and some disadvantages limit its use in the industry. Creep feeding makes the dam's milk relatively less useful, is difficult under range conditions, and encourages fat deposition which causes heifers to get too fat and feeder calves to gain less rapidly in the feedlot. Benefits of creep feeding are usually diminished if calves are subsequently managed as stockers or are fed growing diets and backgrounded. As is evident, it is usually not advantageous to provide nutrition for maximum rates of growth of calves during preweaning growing stages because excessive fat deposition will usually occur. Nutritional programs during growth to weaning should be designed to provide nutrients required for near maximal daily protein growth but not provide energy to allow extensive fat deposition. In essence, nutrition must reflect maintenance and protein growth, and parallel growth potential of the animal. Calves with greater maintenance requirements and with greater potential for protein growth, whether because of mature size, sex class, growth regulation used, or priorities for growth, will need greater quantities of energy, preformed protein and macrominerals than calves with lesser potential for growth. Current Beef Cattle NRC requirements have begun to reflect these factors, however, more adjustment is usually required than is indicated.

Weaning to Yearling Age or Puberty

Nutritional requirements during this stage reflect both animal needs and management desires. This is simply because, if given the opportunity, most animals will consume sufficient nutrients to allow extensive fat deposition unless extensive redirection of growth toward protein deposition is provided. Additionally, the most desirable rate of growth during this stage depends also on what the subsequent phases will provide. Desired growth rates may range from little or no growth to 1.25 lb/d during a "wintering" holding period, to 1.25-1.75 lb/d on backgrounding programs, 1.75-2.25 lb/d on silage or limit-fed growing programs or maximum growth on high-energy feedlot diets. Cattle are commonly managed using all of these programs, and nutritional management must reflect program objectives to provide desired rates and composition of growth. The key concerns in nutrition of cattle in this phase involve matching feedstuff energy resources with cattle growth potential and providing optimal levels of protein, minerals, vitamins and feed additives to allow most efficient attainment of desired growth rates. Protein requirements reflect animal potential and priorities for growth as well as degree of growth regulation provided and restrictions in energy available for growth limiting protein deposition below animal limits. Energy sources used include grazed forages which range from vegetative-growing annuals to

dormant perennials and crop residues, similar forages fed dry or as silages and cereal grains.

Wintering or holding programs require protein and minerals for continued growth of protein through retrieval of fat and a basal energy source, i.e., crop residues or mature hay which will meet maintenance requirements and allow limited growth. This program requires the least nutritional management but also provides the slowest growth rates of any nutritional program.

Backgrounding and grazing programs sometimes have different objectives, but differ mainly in the length of time. In both programs, rate of gain is usually limited to less than 2 lb/d and excessive fat deposition is usually not desired. Therefore, energy requirements need to reflect maintenance and lean tissue growth, and protein of adequate quality must be provided to allow maximal protein growth at the target rate of growth. The basal forages are usually deficient in protein, and a source of protein that will provide amino acids for intestinal absorption must be provided. If sufficient readily fermentable carbohydrate is fed, a NPN source may provide a portion of this protein, provided a source of rumen escapable protein is included in the diet. For grazing animals the supplementation system may preclude optimal protein nutrition, especially if liquid supplements providing degradable protein and NPN are used where preformed protein is needed by the calf. Provision of minerals to balance the basal feedstuffs is essential, and limiting P or K may limit intake and result in less than desired growth. Cattle are commonly backgrounded in feedlots, where a forage such as silage is commonly used as the energy base. Recently developed programs also provide for backgrounding rates of growth on limit-fed grain diets. The level and type of protein provided must reflect the feedstuff base and rumen fermentation conditions prevailing such that adequate levels of amino acids are provided to the animal to allow maximal systemic protein growth with the energy available.

Growing programs differ from backgrounding programs in time and perhaps growth rate, although a distinction between these alternatives is not always obvious. Growing programs are designed to provide sufficient nutrition to allow the animal to deposit protein at

444

maximal rates while also allowing a nominal rate of fat deposition. Depending on cattle types and feeding systems, this phase may range from <100 to >200 d. Energy is usually provided by silage or a silage/grain combination, with requirements reflecting needs for maintenance, protein growth and also for some fat deposition. Daily protein and mineral requirements are as high in this sytem as in high-energy feeding programs, but energy requirements are lower due to lower rates of fat deposition expected. Protein is commonly provided by a combination of preformed plant protein and NPN, although NPN can provide a large fraction of the supplemental protein if rumen fermentation will support its use. Growing programs commonly become finishing programs, with a reduction of forage and an increase in the grain component, sometimes rapidly and in other programs gradually over a long feeding period. Associative effects of forage/grain combination diets (21) decrease efficiency of using forage and grain energy and increase dietary energy requirements, making a rapid switch from forage to grain feeding programs more desirable.

Finishing Phases of Growth

The finishing phase may be short or may cover nearly the total period of growth after weaning—which occurs very early in life for dairy calves. As a result, nutrient requirements vary with the physiological stage of the animal and the relative fraction of nutrients used for maintenance, protein growth and fat deposition. Because rates of growth commonly allow substantial levels of fat deposition, the fraction of nutrients used for fat deposition has a major impact on relative requirements for protein and minerals. It is very important to reliably predict rates of protein and fat deposition likely to occur to allow precision in estimating nutrient requirements for growth. Endogenous animal regulation of growth in concert with effectiveness of anabolic regulation imposed must be assessed to allow prediction of rates of protein or fat deposition at expected rates of growth. Mature size, rate of maturing, sex class, stage of growth and anabolic regulation used all impact the relationship of rate to composition of growth and modify priorities for growth at any rate of growth. Additionally, level of nutrition or energy source per se

(22) may also modify priorities for growth, with grain energy sources potentiating fat deposition.

Finishing usually refers to the stage of growth where fat deposition is both rapid and predominant. However, providing high energy levels in any phase of growth accentuates fat deposition, especially for animals with a limited capacity for protein growth. The relationship of rate of growth to composition of growth (Fig. 15-3) indicates the increasing fraction of fat in daily tissue growth with increasing rates of growth. Anabolic repartitioning agents including Ralgro® and Synovex® modify priorities for tissue growth, redirecting nutrients from fat to protein growth. The extent of this redirection is dependent on energy intake and rate of growth; with faster rates of growth and more rapid rates of fat deposition providing more opportunity for repartitioning. This increase in protein growth is also dependent on protein supply; inadequate protein intake limits the effectiveness of these growth regulators (23).

Limits for daily protein growth usually increase with mature size, with larger mature-size cattle placing a greater priority on protein growth at any rate of growth than smaller mature-size cattle at the same weight (24). Additionally, larger mature-size cattle have a greater capacity to respond to growth regulators, provided adequate energy and protein are available (25). However, in both large and small mature-size cattle, daily protein growth increases at a decreasing rate with increasing rate of growth (25). Intact males have the greatest propensity for protein growth, followed by steers receiving growth regulators, non-implanted steers and finally heifers. Sex class is, therefore, an important variable in animal growth and nutrient requirements for growth, and current NRC-Beef (26) guidelines consider each of these classes of cattle.

SUMMARY—RELATING GROWTH TO NUTRIENT REQUIREMENTS

Guidelines for nutrient requirements include a variety of animal factors (26, 27, 28, 29). Factors that increase protein content and reduce energy density of gain, also reduce energy requirements/unit of gain, while concurrently increasing protein and mineral

445

requirements/unit of gain. Mineral requirements are related to composition of growth, and mineral requirements in the 1984 NRC-Beef are, in fact, determined from predicted rates of protein growth. Therefore, prediction of composition of growth is required for estimation of most nutrients critical for growth, and it is for this reason that knowledge of type of growth occurring is so critical to assessment of nutrient requirements. While nutrient requirements are related to body composition and composition of growth in all stages of growth, growth becomes more flexible when priorities for protein growth begin to decline, and it is at this stage that prediction of growth becomes more interesting. During early stages of growth in animals receiving forage-based diets, protein growth normally predominates simply because only limited energy is consumed in excess of needs for maintenance and protein growth, and hence little fat deposition can occur. However, to achieve the desired final weight-composition endpoint, nutritional management is usually required to prevent large mature-size cattle from being too large or small mature-size cattle from being too small when the desired carcass composition is attained (30, 31). Nutrient requirements must be tailored to management objectives as well as animal needs to reach marketing goals efficiently. High-energy programs which provide rapid rates of gain are required beginning at an early age to promote sufficient fat deposition such that large size cattle and cattle with high priorities for protein growth will deposit sufficient amounts of fat to provide acceptable carcasses at desired slaughter weights. These same diets fed early in life to small mature-size cattle would result in very light carcasses when desired fatness is reached. Using nutritional regulation of growth to advantage allows development of feeding systems that will allow cattle of a wide range of types to produce acceptable carcasses at acceptable market weights. Usually, this entails use of high-energy diets beginning early in life for large size cattle and intact males, and high forage or low-energy diets for extended growing periods in smaller mature-size cattle and heifers.

Nutritional requirements for growth can therefore be considered to be more relativistic than absolute, with specific requirements appropriate only for a very specific set of conditions. Optimal requirements reflect nutritional management to achieve desired composition and rate of growth in specific stages of growth and are unlikely to allow maximal rates of growth across all phases. Establishing nutrient requirements on the basis of tissue growth allows prediction of requirements with a wide range of animal types or systems of growth regulation (endogenous or exogenous) and for animals in all stages of growth. With knowledge of composition of growth, prediction of nutrient requirements across several species of ruminant animals will be possible.

Literature Cited on Fertility, Reproduction and Lactation

1. Swanson, E.W. 1978. In: Large Dairy Herd Management, p. 494. C.J. Wilcox and H.H. Van Horn, eds. Univ. Presses of Florida, Gainesville, FL.
2. Reid, J.T., et al. 1964. Cornell Expt. Sta Bull. 987.
3. Bergen, W.G. and D.B. Bates. 1984. J. Animal Sci. 58:1465.
4. Rhodes, R.C., III, M.M. McCartor and R.D. Randel. 1978. J. Animal Sci. 46:769.
5. Morrow, D.A. 1980. Modern Vet. Practice, June, p. 499.
6. Arnett, D.W., G.L. Holland and R. Totusek. 1971. J. Animal Sci. 33:1129.
7. Hemken, R.W. and D.H. Bremel. 1982. J. Dairy Sci. 65:1069.
8. Hidiroglou, M. 1979. J. Dairy Sci. 62:1195.
9. Harrison, J.H., D.D. Hancock and H.R. Conrad. 1984. J. Dairy Sci. 67:123.
10. NRC. Nutrient Requirements of Domestic Animals. 1975, Sheep; 1978, Dairy cattle; 1981, Goats; and 1984, Beef cattle. Nat. Acad. Sci., Washington, DC.
11. Trinder, N., R.J. Hall and C.P. Renton. 1973. Vet. Rec. 93:641.
12. Schingoethe, D.J., et al. 1982. J. Dairy Sci. 65:2338.
13. Clark, J.H. and C.L. Davis. 1980. J. Dairy Sci. 63:873.

446

14. Davis, C.L. and R.E. Brown. 1970. In: Physiology of Digestion and Metabolism in the Ruminant, p. 545. A.T. Phillipson, ed. Oriel Press Ltd., Newcastle upon Tyne, England.
15. Tyrrell, H.F. and G.A. Varga. 1984. J. Dairy Sci. 67(Xuppl. 1):132 (Abstr.).
16. Palmquist, D.L. and T.C. Jenkins. 1980. J. Dairy Sci. 63:1.
17. Jenkins, T.C. and D.L. Palmquist. 1984. J. Dairy Sci. 67:978.
18. Finn, A.F., et al. 1985. J. Dairy Sci. 68:903.
19. Block, E., L.D. Muller, L.C. Griel, Jr. and D.L. Garwood. 1981. J. Dairy Sci. 64:1813.
20. Scott, T.W., et al. 1970. Australian J. Sci. 32:291.
21. Cadden, A.M., A. Urquhart and P. Jelen. 1984. J. Dairy Sci. 67:1414.
22. Heinrichs, A.J., D.L. Palmquist and H.R. Conrad. 1982. J. Dairy Sci. 65:1325.
23. Lahr, D.A., et al. 1983. J. Dairy Sci. 66:1891.
24. Gibson, J.P. 1984. Animal Prod. 38:181.
25. Oldham, J.D. 1984. J. Dairy Sci. 67:1090.
26. Satter, L.D. and R.E. Roffler. 1975. J. Dairy Sci. 58:1219.
27. Czerkawski, J.W. 1978. J. Dairy Sci. 61:1261.
28. Casper, D.P. and D.J. Schingoethe. 1986. J. Dairy Sci. 69:(in press).
29. Waldo, D.R. and B.P. Glenn. 1984. J. Dairy Sci. 67:1115.
30. Schingoethe, D.J., E.C. Hageman and B.L. Larson. 1967. Biochim. Biophys. Acta 148:469.
31. Fisher, L.J. 1972. Can. J. Animal Sci. 52:377.
32. Rogers, J.A., J.H. Clark, T.R. Drendel and G.C. Fahey, Jr. 1984. J. Dairy Sci. 67:1928.
33. Schingoethe, D.J. 1984. Application of rumen bypass proteins in ruminant diets. Animal Nutr. Res. Highlights, April. Amer. Soybean Ass'n., St. Louis, MO.
34. Huber, J.T. and L. Kung, Jr. 1981. J. Dairy Sci. 64:1170.
35. Sahlu, T., D.J. Schingoethe and A.K. Clark. 1984. J. Dairy Sci. 67:1725.
36. Dufva, G.S., E.E. Bartley, A.D. Dayton and D.O. Riddell. 1983. J. Dairy Sci. 66:2329.
37. Ward, G., L.H. Harbers and J.L. Blaha. 1979. J. Dairy Sci. 62:715.
38. Miller, W.J. 1981. J. Dairy Sci. 64:1196.
39. Thomas, J.W. and R.S. Emery. 1984. In: Proc. 39th Distillers Feed Conf., p. 43. Cincinatti, OH.
40. Peirce-Sandner, S.B., et al. 1985. J. Dairy Sci. 68:2895.
41. McGuffey, R.K., H.B. Green, R.P. Basson and E.L. Potter. 1983. J. Dairy Sci. 66(Suppl. 1):198.
42. Bauman, D.E., P.J. Eppart, M.J. DeGeeter and G.M. Lanza. 1985. J. Dairy Sci. 68:1352.

Literature Cited on Growth

1. Pullar, J.D. and A.J.F. Webster. 1977. Brit. J. Nutr. 37:355.
2. Thompson, W.R., et al. 1983. J. Animal Sci. 56:1241.
3. Solis, J.C., et al. 1984. J. Animal Sci. 59(Suppl. 1):430.
4. Warrington, B.G., et al. 1985. Proc. West. Sect. Amer. Soc. An. Sci. 36:449.
5. Ferrell, C.L. and T.G. Jenkins. 1984. J. Animal Sci. 58:234.
6. Byers, F.M. and R.E. Rompala. 1980. Proc. Eighth Symp. on Energy Metabolism. EAAP 29:92.
7. Koong, L.J., C.L. Ferrell and J.A. Nienaber. 1982. Proc. Ninth Symp. on Energy Metabolism. EAAP 29:245.
8. Rompala, R.E., et al. 1985. J. Animal Sci. 61(Suppl. 1):455.
9. Garrett, W.N. 1982. Proc. Ninth Symp. on Energy Metabolism. EAAP 29:104.
10. Byers, F.M. 1980. J. Animal Sci. 50:1127.
11. Byers, F.M. 1980. J. Animal Sci. 51:158.
12. NRC. 1981. Effect of Environment on Nutrient Requirements of Domestic Animals. Nat. Acad. Sci., Washington, DC.
13. Fox, D.G. and J.R. Black. 1983. J. Animal Sci. 57:717.
14. Rattray, P.V., et al. 1974. J. Animal Sci. 38:383.
15. Ferrell, C.L., W.N. Garrett, N. Hinman and G. Grichting. 1976. J. Animal Sci. 42:937.
16. Byers, F.M. 1982. Fed. Proc. 41:2562.
17. Prior, R.L. and D.B. Laster. 1979. J. Animal Sci. 48:1546.

18. Hood, R., et al. 1982. Fed. Proc. 41:458.
19. Warrington, B.G., et al. 1985. J. Animal Sci. 61(Suppl. 1): 458.
20. Byers, F.M., et al. 1984. J. Animal Sci. 59(Suppl. 1):66.
21. Byers, F.M., D.E. Johnson and R.L. Preston. 1982. Proc. Ninth Symp. on Energy Metabolism, EAAP 29:128.
22. Lemieux, P.G., et al. 1983. Fed. Proc. 42:533.
23. Byers, F.M. and P.E. Moffitt. 1979. Ohio Agr. Res. and Development Center. Dept. Series. 79-1, p. 75.
24. Byers, F.M., et al. 1985. Fed. Proc. 44:33.
25. Byers, F.M., et al. 1985. Proc. West. Sect. Amer. Soc. An. Sci. 36:440.
26. NRC. 1984. Nutrient Requirements of Beef Cattle. Nat. Acad. Sci., Washington, DC.
27. NRC. 1978. Nutrient Requirements of Dairy Cattle. Nat. Acad. Sci. Washington, DC.
28. NRC. 1985. Nutrient Requirements of Sheep. Nat. Acad. Sci. Washington, DC.
29. ARC. 1980. The Nutrient Requirements of Ruminant Livestock. Commonwealth Agr. Bureaux, England.
30. Byers, F.M. 1980. Ohio Agricultural Research and Development Center. Research Circular. 158:18.
31. Byers, F.M. 1984. In: Livestock Feeds and Feeding, 2nd Ed. p. 228. D.C. Church, ed. O & B Books Inc., Corvallis, OR.

21 NUTRIENT NEEDS OF RUMINANTS VERSUS MONOGASTRIC SPECIES

by David J. Schingoethe

Three major differences in nutrient needs of ruminants and monogastrics are readily apparent. (A) Ruminants can derive much of their energy from fibrous compounds such as cellulose whereas most non-ruminants can utilize only limited amounts of fibrous material. (B) Ruminants do not have a dietary amino acid requirement, only a N or crude protein requirement. (C) Ruminants do not have a dietary requirement for the B complex vitamins. All three of these differences are due to the microorganisms in the rumen which ferment cellulose and other complex carbohydrates for energy, synthesize microbial protein from a wide variety of N sources including non-protein N (NPN), and synthesize B vitamins. As a result of ruminal fermentation, ruminants are able to convert poor quality feed sources, which are unusable or poorly usable by non-ruminants, to high quality meat and milk which can be used by man and other non-ruminants.

While the differences cited in nutritional needs of ruminants versus non-ruminants are quite important, these are not the only differences between the two types of animals. Other differences become apparent when one attempts to bypass or eliminate the rumen from a role in digestion. Not all of the differences are understood, as illustrated in an experiment (1) in which researchers attempted to make "non-ruminant-ruminants" out of heifer calves by sewing the esophageal groove closed so that everything that the animal consumed went directly to the abomasum. Despite the fact that diets were formulated to meet nutritional requirements based on the best knowledge of nutrient requirements of non-ruminants and accounting for other known differences between ruminants and non-ruminants, those heifers did not live a normal life. After one heifer soon died from starvation from stuffing her abomasum with shavings that were used for bedding their pens, it was apparent that these animals still had a tremendous craving for roughage even

though their rumens were totally bypassed. The other heifers were maintained on concrete or rubber mats from then on. The researchers intended to breed these heifers and initiate lactation in them, but none of them lived that long. Growth rates were less than normal and the animals had several abnormal characteristics. When two heifers suddenly died of heart attacks at about 18 months of age, the experiment was terminated. Autopsies revealed extensive atherosclerotic plaques as well as several other abnormalities.

The above example illustrates that the rumen and its microbial population are not the only differences between ruminants and non-ruminants. Many, but not all of these other differences are known. Differences as well as similarities in nutrient needs between ruminants and non-ruminants will be discussed in this chapter.

ENERGY SOURCES

All animals derive energy from carbohydrates, fats and excess protein. Most of this energy is obtained from carbohydrates; however, the relative amount from carbohydrates vs. fats varies with species. Ruminants usually receive much less of their energy from lipids than do non-ruminants. Among carbohydrate sources there are also differences in forms and amounts of various carbohydrates which can be used by different species.

Carbohydrates

Ruminants can utilize, and in fact require, fibrous feeds in their diet for normal rumen function and rumen health. Inadequate fiber in their diet can lead to acidosis, rumen parakeratosis and other severe rumen dysfunctions. Ruminants can utilize cellulose because many strains of bacteria in the rumen produce cellulase enzymes which hydrolyze the β 1-4 linkages between glucose units in cellulose. Other microorganisms also produce enzymes capable of hydrolyzing the β 1-4 linkages in hemicellulose. All animals lack an enzyme to hydrolyze such linkages. Amylases present in pancreatic juice of all animals and present in saliva of non-ruminants hydrolyze the α 1-4 linkages of starch but not the β 1-4 linkages in cellulose.

Fiber. One generally thinks of non-ruminants as being unable to utilize cellulose and other fibrous compounds; however, that is not true of all non-ruminants. Some non-ruminants such as the hamster, vole, kangaroo and hippopotamus have considerable pregastric fermentation while others such as the horse and rabbit have considerable hindgut fermentation, which allows them to also utilize forages. Non-ruminants which can ferment much forage usually have sacculated portions of the stomach (e.g., kangaroo), cecum (e.g., rabbit), or colon (e.g., horse) where fermentation occurs. Thus, when considering nutrient needs of monogastrics, one has to further define the type of digestive system involved. If it is primarily gastrointestinal, with minimal pregastric or hindgut fermentation such as in swine, rats or humans, the carbohydrate needs are much different than for ruminants. However, if the digestive system includes considerable pregastric or hindgut fermentation, then carbohydrate requirements may be quite similar to those required for ruminants. Generally, when reference is made to non-ruminants in this chapter, the reference is to types such as swine, poultry, rats and humans, unless non-ruminant herbivores such as horses are specified.

Ruminants require a minimal amount of fibrous feeds for normal rumen function, but the exact amount required may vary with species, adaption to diets, and physical form of the fiber. As a guideline, dairy cows need a minimum of 1% of their body weight as dry matter from forages, which would be approximately one-third of their dry matter intake. Non-ruminants such as swine do not need fibrous feeds in their diet, but can tolerate some forages.

Hindgut digesters such as horses and rabbits cannot use as large a proportion of their dietary dry matter as forages as can ruminants because of limited gut capacity, although a faster rate of passage which allows more feed

to be consumed may partially compensate for this limitation. They are also usually less efficient than ruminants at digesting fiber. For instance, the same forage is usually only about 60-70% as digestible by horses as by sheep (2, 3). The horse is much more efficient in digesting fiber than the rabbit even though the rabbit practices coprophagy. The mule and onager or wild ass may be more efficient in fiber digestion than the horse (3).

Digestibilities of typical diets fed to ruminants are usually lower than digestibilities of typical diets fed to non-ruminants. This is because some fibrous components such as lignin are virtually indigestible. While cellulose and hemicellulose may be readily digested in the rumen, the digestion is less complete than digestion of starches and sugars. Fermentation losses such as CH_4 and CO_2 also reduce digestive efficiency. These fermentation losses also occur with nutrients such as starches and sugars which could be used directly by non-ruminants with no fermentation losses. Thus, while one of the advantages of ruminants is to make poorer quality feeds better via rumen fermentation, the digestibility of typical ruminant diets will never be as great as the digestibility of typical non-ruminant diets. This is not a total loss however, because ruminants are converting something (i.e., fiber) which cannot be used by non-ruminants such as humans to something (i.e., meat and milk) which can be used by man.

Fermentation in the large intestine of ruminants accounts from 4 to as much as 26% of the digestibility energy (4). Some of this is undoubtedly fermentation of cellulose which escaped ruminal fermentation, but can be due to considerable fermentation of starch when animals are fed high-starch diets. In contrast, hind-gut fermentation accounts for virtually all of the fiber digestion in non-ruminant herbivores such as the horse (5). However, there are some significant differences in fiber digestion between ruminants and hindgut digesters. The total stomach capacity of the horse is much smaller than in the ruminant, less than 20 ℓ vs. about 250 ℓ for a cow. As a result the horse's stomach is designed for almost constant intake of small quantities of feed, rather than large amounts at any one time. Fermentative digestion occurs after gastrointestinal digestion in the horse, whereas the

450

reverse order occurs in the ruminant, which dictates some differences in digestive efficiency and feeding strategy for the two species. Ingesta passes through the horse's digestive tract within 24 h while it may take three times as long—about 72 h—in ruminants. Thus, there is less time for hindgut fermentation than there is for ruminal fermentation, resulting in less complete fiber digestion. There is less microbial activity in the horse than in the ruminant which contributes to the lower fiber digestibility in hindgut digesters and restricts the amount of fiber than hindgut digesters can handle. The smaller capacity and less fermentation means a horse cannot handle as much forage as ruminants, and the fiber must be of higher quality; or, that the horse must have more rapid passage and eat more to compensate for lower digestibility.

Because of the lower microbial activity in the horse, only limited amounts of protein, B vitamins, and vitamin K are synthesized. Thus, little or no NPN should be fed to hindgut digesters and B vitamin supplementation may be necessary, whereas these are usually of little concern with ruminants.

The efficiency of absorption of fermentation products is probably less in hindgut digesters than in ruminants. This is because the small intestine of hindgut digesters, e.g. the horse, never gets a chance at the ingesta from the cecum and colon, whereas the small intestine, with its immense absorptive surface area, gets a chance to absorb ingesta from the rumen. Rumen microbial cells can be digested and absorbed in the abomasum and small intestine, whereas most microbial production in the hindgut is excreted in feces.

Starches and Sugars. There are several differences between ruminants and non-ruminants in the digestion of starches and sugars which merit consideration. Ruminants have no salivary amylase and much less pancreatic amylase than do non-ruminants. In addition, pancreatic amylase is apparently a non-inducible enzyme as there is little or no increase in amylase synthesis and secretion in ruminants fed high starch diets (6, 7). Limited data also indicate that ruminant pancreatic juice may have less buffering capacity than non-ruminant pancreatic juice. Thus, ruminant intestinal contents may be more acidic,

which would be a less than optimal environment for amylase to operate in.

Ordinarily, the limited intestinal starch-digesting capabilities of ruminants are of no major concern because most dietary starch is fermented in the rumen. Therefore, very little starch ordinarily reaches the small intestine. However, when high-grain (especially high corn) diets are fed at several times the maintenance requirement of the animal, as often occurs in high producing dairy cows, the increased rate of passage may result in more than normal amounts of starch escaping ruminal fermentation. This excess starch may "saturate" the intestinal starch-digesting capabilities of pancreatic amylase, resulting in some increase in microbial fermentation in the intestinal tract and increased fecal starch. Increased intestinal fermentation may partially explain the lower fecal pH often observed when fecal starch is elevated. The limited intestinal starch-digesting capabilities of ruminants may explain why feeds such as ground shelled corn and ground ear corn have equivalent feeding values when fed at high intakes, whereas the shelled corn has the greater feeding value when fed at maintenance levels of intake.

Adding Ca sources such as limestone to high starch diets sometimes reduces fecal starch and improves starch utilization by ruminants. Because fecal pH is often elevated, some writers have speculated that intestinal pH has been elevated sufficiently to improve the digestive efficiency of amylase in the intestinal tract. However, there are no direct data to substantiate this claim. It is more likely that the added Ca aided ruminal digestion by stimulating microbial fermentation and thus allowed more complete starch fermentation in the rumen. Fecal pH may have been elevated because of less intestinal fermentation.

There are also several differences between ruminants and non-ruminants in intestinal disaccharidase activity. This includes the disaccharidases lactase, maltase and sucrase.

Young mammals contain abundant lactase activity, but lose that activity as they get older (8). Loss of lactase activity occurs because most of the lactase activity is substrate induced with a minimal amount of constitutive lactase activity remaining. Thus, when animals are no longer consuming milk, no lactose is entering the small intestine and intestinal lactase activity decreases to very low levels. However, intestinal lactase is still inducible in functionally mature ruminants and non-ruminants as evidenced by increased intestinal lactase activity when lactose was presented to the small intestine of steers (9) and hogs (10). Ordinarily, insignificant amounts of lactose, if any, reach the small intestine of ruminants, even when fed large amounts of feeds such as liquid or dried whey. King and Schingoethe (11) observed that steers digested more than 98% of the lactose in the rumen when diets contained 60% of the dry matter as dried whey, indicating that the rumen microbes have a tremendous capability to ferment disaccharides such as lactose. A genetic deficiency of inducible lactase is extremely rare in ruminants although such a deficiency, which leads to lactose intolerance, occurs in some humans especially of negroid and oriental origin and in some breeds of swine.

Sucrase activity is very low, possibly totally absent (12), in the intestine of ruminants. Also, fructose is poorly absorbed from the intestinal tract of ruminants. Thus, milk replacers formulated for ruminants should not contain sucrose as digestive upsets and diarrhea will likely occur. There is no problem with feeding sucrose to ruminants once the rumen is functional because the sucrose is fermented readily in the rumen and little or no sucrose will enter the small intestine.

Intestinal maltase activity is also lower in ruminants than in non-ruminants. Maltase and isomaltase activities increase during the first 1-4 weeks of life, but thereafter the values are similar to those in adult animals (13). Much more maltase than isomaltase is usually present. Maltase activity is apparently non-inducible in ruminants (7). Because maltose and its precursor, starch, are normally fermented in the rumen, little maltose is usually presented to the intestinal tract for digestion. Thus, as was pointed out in the above discussion of starch digestion, when increased amounts of starch escape to the intestinal tract, the starch and maltose-digesting capabilities may become overloaded. Even if there is sufficient amylase activity to digest the starch, there may be inadequate amounts of maltase to digest the resulting maltose.

Lipids

Ruminants cannot utilize as much dietary fat as non-ruminants can, due to some differences between the two types of species in lipid digestion (see Ch. 15). Non-ruminants can often satisfactorily utilize diets containing 15-20% fat, whereas digestive upsets and feed refusals often occur when diets offered to ruminants contain more than 8-10% fat. This limited ability to utilize fat is usually of no consequence because diets typically fed to ruminants contain 2-4% fat. However, when one wants to increase the energy intake of animals such as high producing dairy cows, replacing carbohydrates with fats is one method of increasing the energy density of the diet. Ruminants can readily utilize diets containing 5-7% or more fat with no problems. This amount will increase energy density of the diet by 3-7% over the energy content of diets without added fat.

There are two reasons for limited fat utilization by ruminants: lipid inhibition of rumen microbial fermentation and limited pancreatic lipase activity. Fatty acids, particularly some of the unsaturated fatty acids, inhibit growth and fermentative activity of many species of rumen microbes. Unsaturated fatty acids are especially toxic to *Methanobacterium.* Unsaturated fatty acids increase surface activity, changing permeability of cell membranes. Hydrogenation changes these fatty acids to forms which are less surface active. Some species of bacteria and all species of protozoa are involved in hydrogenation.

Feeding high-fat diets often results in reduced digestion, reduced ruminal microbial cell numbers and reduced VFA production in the rumen. These adverse effects can be minimized or eliminated by providing additional Ca in the diet. The Ca apparently forms soaps with fatty acids which reduces their solubility in the rumen and reduces their likelihood of interfering with microbial activity.

The above mentioned problems with rumen microbial activity should not be interpreted to mean that rumen microbes cannot tolerate any fat. Some fat is necessary to provide microbes with lipogenic precursors, and microbial hydrogenation of fatty acids is slightly more favorable energetically for the host animal. The microorganisms ordinarily hydrolyze virtually all of the dietary

452

triglycerides, phospholipids and galactolipids consumed by the animal; ferment the glycerol and some of the fatty acids; and hydrogenate many of the unsaturated fatty acids.

The reduced pancreatic lipase activity in ruminants is usually no problem under normal husbandry conditions because most of the triglycerides are hydrolyzed in the rumen. However, when ruminants are fed lipids which have been protected against ruminal metabolism, such as by formaldehyde-protein treatment (14), or when fed additional fat such that some triglycerides escape to the abomasum and small intestine, the limited intestinal fat-digesting capabilities may be taxed. Carnivores secrete some lipase in their stomach, but abomasal lipase is virtually absent in ruminants. Ruminants secrete less pancreatic lipase than non-ruminants, although quantitative comparisons are limited (15). There are some hints that secretion of pancreatic lipase may be greater in lambs than in calves. This may indicate substrate induction of the enzyme because ewe's milk usually contains more fat than cow's milk. However, if lipase is an inducible enzyme, the ability to induce the enzyme is very limited. Otherwise, ruminants would be able to adapt to consumption of higher fat diets.

Despite some possible limitations in pancreatic lipase, young, nursing ruminants utilize milk fat quite efficiently. This is partially attributable to a group of oral lipases collectively known as pregastric esterase, which are present in the saliva of young ruminants, but absent in older animals (13). Pregastric esterase preferentially attacks short-chain fatty acids, particularly butyrate, on triglycerides. Hydrolysis is quite extensive; within 30 minutes of feeding about 50% of the triglycerides in the abomasum are hydrolyzed. Pancreatic lipase causes a greater release of long-chain fatty acids when milk fat has prior treatment with pregastric esterase.

Ruminal metabolism of dietary lipids is quite extensive. This results in a fairly uniform concentration of various fatty acids ultimately being presented for absorption into the bloodstream (see Ch. 15). Hydrogenation of unsaturated fatty acids is quite extensive. Thus, while the fatty acid composition of carcass and milk fat reflect the dietary fatty acid composition in non-ruminants, composition of carcass and milk fat in ruminants is altered

very little by large changes in dietary fat sources. Ruminant fat tends to be more saturated than non-ruminant fat, reflecting ruminal hydrogenation.

As a result of rumen metabolism, ruminant carcass fat and milk fat contain some branched-chain fatty acids, some *trans* isomers of unsaturated fatty acids, more saturated fatty acids, and more short-chain fatty acids than non-ruminant fat. The higher amounts of short-chain fatty acids are partially due to ruminal metabolism, but also due to extensive mammary gland synthesis of fatty acids from acetate.

Ruminants and non-ruminants both require small amounts of the essential fatty acids (linoleic, linolenic and arachidonic). Although dietary requirements are quite small, most feed sources contain more than adequate amounts and deficiencies are unlikely.

PROTEINS

All animals, both ruminants and non-ruminants, require amino acids at the tissue level for protein synthesis, with only minor species differences in specific amino acid requirements. But how these amino acids or their precursors are supplied in the diet can vary substantially between ruminants and non-ruminants. One major advantage of ruminants is that the rumen microbes can convert NPN and/or poor quality proteins to good quality microbial protein. Thus, one needs to be concerned only with the amount of N or crude protein fed to ruminants, whereas the amount of dietary essential amino acids is also a consideration with non-ruminants. Ruminants can use NPN as the only N source with substantial production, although it is generally recommended to supply no more than one-third of the crude protein requirements from NPN.

The ability of the rumen microbes to convert feed proteins to microbial protein can sometimes be a disadvantage, too. Namely, high quality proteins, i.e., proteins such as casein of higher biological value than rumen microbial protein, can be reduced in quality by being converted to microbial protein. To minimize this from occurring when high quality proteins are fed to ruminants, the proteins can be treated to minimize degradation in the rumen but still be digestible in the abomasum and small intestine.

NPN can be utilized by the animal only if it is converted to microbial protein in the rumen. For optimal NPN utilization the diet should contain sufficient amounts of readily fermentable carbohydrates, but not a large excess of crude protein. If there is insufficient energy available in the rumen to provide the carbon skeletons necessary for building new amino acids from the NPN, excess ammonia will be absorbed into the bloodstream. The ammonia in the blood will be converted to urea in the liver, unless there is a great excess—then some ammonia will enter peripheral blood and cause ammonia toxicity (see Ch. 23). Some of the blood urea is recycled to the rumen via saliva and reabsorption; however, much of it may be excreted via the urine and lost from productive purposes for the animal. Thus, while it is wasteful to feed excess crude protein to both ruminants and non-ruminants, feeding excess crude protein to ruminants—especially when much of the N is readily soluble in the rumen—can be especially wasteful.

In order to get around limitations of N metabolism in the rumen, it is sometimes advantageous to reduce solubility of feed proteins to assure that at least some feed protein escapes ruminal degradation (see Chs. 12, 20). This approach may be especially helpful for highly productive animals such as high producing cows during early lactation as they may require more protein than is required by the rumen microbes. However, one has to be sure that the bypass protein will be digestible in the lower digestive tract, and be of sufficiently good quality to provide the essential amino acids needed by the animal.

Protein digestion in the abomasum and small intestine of ruminants is the same as digestion in the stomach and small intestine of non-ruminants. Very few amino acids are absorbed through the rumen wall because only small amounts of free amino acids are usually present in the rumen. Thus, crude protein fed to ruminants cannot be used by the animal unless it is in the form of protein and/or amino acids as it enters the abomasum. The ingesta passing to the lower tract is a mixture of microbial protein and some undigested or partially digested feed protein. The mechanism of digesting these proteins is the same as

in non-ruminants. Because most feed crude protein is converted to microbial protein, the array of amino acids ultimately absorbed from the small intestine remains fairly constant in ruminants, regardless of the amino acid composition of the dietary protein. This amino acid array can be altered significantly only when large quantities of dietary protein of amino acid content substantially different from that of the rumen microbes bypasses the rumen. However, in non-ruminants the array of amino acids presented to the intestinal tract for absorption reflects the dietary amino acid composition.

VITAMINS

The fat-soluble vitamins A, D and E are required in diets of all animals. The only exception to this statement would be no dietary requirement of vitamin D for animals receiving substantial exposure to sunlight. The amounts required of various fat-soluble vitamins may vary somewhat with species and age. The requirements of vitamin E may vary significantly with species and age. Young ruminants and non-ruminants apparently require more vitamin E per unit of body weight than do mature ruminants. A vitamin E deficiency is almost impossible to demonstrate in functionally mature ruminants, whereas it can occur in young ruminants such as calves and lambs, and in non-ruminants.

Vitamin K and the B complex (water-soluble) vitamins are also required by the animal, but do not have to be provided in the diet of ruminants. This is because the rumen microorganisms usually synthesize more than sufficient quantities of these vitamins to meet the needs of the host animal. In fact, some of the B vitamins are synthesized in much greater amounts than are needed by the host animal simply because they are needed in larger amounts by some of the rumen microorganisms. Thus, diet formulation can be simplified greatly and can be cheaper for ruminants because additional B vitamins do not have to be included. When formulating diets for non-ruminants, a whole array of B vitamins must be included and in proper amounts for optimal animal growth and production.

Under some conditions ruminants may benefit from supplementation of certain B

454

vitamins. Increased ruminal microbial protein synthesis, milk production, weight gain and feed efficiency have been observed with niacin supplementation to cattle diets (17). Several studies indicated a greater response to niacin when diets contained urea, while others (17) obtained a greater response with all natural proteins—especially soybean meal—in the diet. Niacin and its metabolic derivatives are involved in energy metabolism of both microorganisms and the host animal, which may explain its role in improving NPN utilization. The greater response to niacin supplementation with soybean meal diets (17) may have been due to a shortage of niacin precursors in the rumen. Tryptophan often serves as the starting substrate for niacin synthesis by many microorganisms. But tryptophan is readily destroyed by heat, and apparently the heat treatment used routinely in preparing soybean meal may be sufficient to destroy some of the tryptophan. This would then reduce the amount of niacin which could be synthesized in the rumen to the point where a niacin insufficiency may occur in highly productive animals and in animals under stressing conditions such as ketosis.

Thiamin is usually synthesized in more than sufficient quantities in the rumen. However, when fed high energy rations such as often used in feedlot situations or when grazing certain plants such as *Kochia scoparia,* several things may occur which may create a thiamin deficiency for the host animal and result in polioencephalomalcia (PEM) (18). The thiamin deficiency may result from thiamin destruction by thiaminases of plant and/or microbial origin. Antagonists of thiamin such as pyrithiamin may also be produced which interfere with absorption and/or utilization of thiamin.

Choline supplementation is usually unnecessary for functional ruminants, although it may be needed by young ruminants and by non-ruminants. However, recent reports (19) indicate that choline supplementation of low forage diets of cattle may increase milk fat percentages. There are also a few reports of increased weight gains by cattle fed supplemental choline.

All animals require vitamin B_{12}; however, the vitamin does not have to be supplied in ruminant diets if there is adequate Co present. Ruminal microorganisms can synthesize sufficient amounts of vitamin B_{12} to meet the animal's needs unless the diet is deficient in Co. Supplying Co or the vitamin will alleviate the deficiency symptoms.

MINERALS

The requirements of all minerals are similar for all species at various stages of growth or productive cycles. Much of the P in grains may be present as phytates which are much less available to non-ruminants than are other forms of P. Inorganic sources of P are usually more available for non-ruminants than organic sources of P, but the P availability among various inorganic sources may also vary. The amount of Mg in the diet can also affect retention of Ca and P by non-ruminants.

SUMMARY

Dietary needs of ruminants are simpler and often cheaper than for non-ruminants even though nutrient requirements of various animal tissues are similar for most species. Because of microbial action in the rumen, ruminants can utilize fiber and, in fact require some fiber, as a source of energy; can utilize NPN and poor quality proteins; and do not need B vitamins in their diet. This enables ruminants to convert poor quality feed sources, which are useful in lesser amounts for non-ruminants, to good quality meat and milk. However, this same rumen fermentation can also cause less efficient use of high quality proteins and energy utilization is lowered by methane production. Ruminants cannot use as much dietary fat as non-ruminants because of adverse affects of fat on rumen microbial fermentation and of limited pancreatic lipase activity. Ruminants cannot digest as much starch, maltose and sucrose in the gastro-intestinal tract as non-ruminants can, but these nutrients will usually be digested in the rumen which eliminates the need for extensive intestinal digestion of these nutrients.

455

Literature Cited

1. Thomas, J.W. 1967. Proc. Symp. on Digestive Physiology in the Young Ruminant with Special Consideration to the Forestomach Bypass Calf. Univ. Maryland, College Park.
2. Jarrige, R. 1980. In: Digestive Physiology and Metabolism in Ruminants, p. 763. Y. Ruckebusch and P. Thivend, eds. AVI Publ. Co., Inc., Westport, CT.
3. Hintz, H.F., H.F. Schryer and J.E. Lowe. 1973. Feedstuffs 45(27):25.
4. Ulyatt, M.J., D.W. Dellow, C.S.W. Reid and T. Bauchop. 1975. In: Digestion and Metabolism in the Ruminant, p. 119. I.W. McDonald and A.C.I. Warner, eds. Univ. New England Publ. Unit, Armidale, N.S.W., Australia.
5. Stevens, C.E., R.A. Argenzio and E.T. Clemens. 1980. In: Digestive Physiology and Metabolism in Ruminants, p. 685. Y. Ruckebusch and P. Thivend, eds. AVI Publ. Co., Inc., Westport, CT.
6. Russell, J.R., A.W. Young and N.A. Jorgensen. 1981. J. Animal Sci. 52:1170.
7. Russell, J.R., A.W. Young and N.A. Jorgensen. 1981. J. Animal Sci. 52:1177.
8. Huber, J.T. 1969. J. Dairy Sci. 52:1313.
9. Huber, J.T., S. Natrajan and C.E. Polan. 1967. J. Dairy Sci. 50:1161.
10. Ekstrom, K.E., N.J. Benevenga and R.H. Grummer. 1975. J. Nutr. 105:1032.
11. King, K.J. and D.J. Schingoethe. 1983. J. Dairy Sci. 66:1675.
12. Dollar, A.M. and J.W.G. Porter. 1957. Nature 179:1299.
13. Roy, J.H.B. and I.J.F. Stobo. 1975. In: Digestion and Metabolism in the Ruminant, p. 30. I.W. McDonald and A.C.I. Warner, eds. Univ. New England Publ. Unit, Armidale, N.S.W., Australia.
14. Scott, T.W. and L.J. Cook. 1975. In: Digestion and Metabolism in the Ruminant, p. 510. I.W. McDonald and A.C..I. Warner, eds. Univ. New England Publ. Unit, Armidale, N.S.W., Australia.
15. Moore, J.H. and R.C. Noble. 1975. In: Digestion and Metabolism in the Ruminant, p. 465. I.W. McDonald and A.C.I. Warner, eds. Univ. New England Publ. Unit, Armidale, N.S.W., Australia.
16. Selner, D.R. and L.H. Schultz. 1980. J. Dairy Sci. 63:1235.
17. Riddell, D.O, E.E. Bartley and A.D. Dayton. 1981. J. Dairy Sci. 64:782.
18. Loew, F.M. 1975. World Rev. Nutr. Dietet. 20:168.
19. Erdman, R.A., R.D. Shaver and J.H. Vandersall. 1984. J. Dairy Sci. 67:410.

by B. A. Young

INTRODUCTION

The metabolic and nutrient needs of ruminants, as discussed in previous chapters, are for animals free from stress and disease. In practical situations there is invariably a complicated multitude of environmental factors impinging on animals which directly or indirectly influence their physical and psychological well-being and needs. Despite the general awareness of increased requirements or poorer animal performance during stress or disease, there are insufficient quantitative data to relate precisely many specific problems to the nutritional needs of ruminants. Because of these uncertainties and the virtual impossibility of creating animal environments completely free of stress, it is often necessary to slightly overfeed as a safety factor and/or to settle for less than maximum productivity. The capital investment and associated costs required to create an ideal, risk- and stress-free environment may not be justified by the anticipated improved animal performance (1, 2).

Stress related problems in ruminant production systems often occur at subclinical levels and may not be readily obvious, or occur during limited periods of the year and are associated with unusual weather conditions, seasonal variations or when the animals, such as the newborn, are particularly susceptible. The impact of environmental stress on ruminants is largely on food intake and the partitioning of ingested nutrients, particularly energy, among maintenance and productive functions of the animal (3). For these reasons a brief description is given below of a schematic representation of energy partitioning in ruminant animals before discussing the specific influences of stress. This chapter deals with environmentally related stresses while the subsequent chapter considers other forms of stresses and diseases which influence the well-being and nutrient needs of ruminants.

PARTITIONING OF NUTRIENTS

Feed is a major cost component of animal production and any factor affecting the efficiency with which feed is converted to saleable product directly influences the economy of the production system. Measures of biological energy are the basis for determining nutrient requirements of ruminants and heat energy is the currency of thermal balance (4). Energy, measured as calories or joules per unit time or as watts,* is a convenient common denominator to use when describing the effect of the environment on animals and these effects can be related to animal productivity and efficiency of utilization of feedstuffs.

Figure 22-1 illustrates schematically the partition of dietary energy intake of an animal. *Intake energy (IE)* is the combustible energy ingested per unit time (the usual time unit used in animal nutrition is one day) and is determined from the combustible energy density of the feed, its opportunity for ingestion and the appetite of the animal. The non-absorbed fraction of *IE* is voided in feces and its combustible energy is referred to as *fecal energy (FE)*. *Digestible energy (DE)* may be calculated as *IE – FE*. However, as feces also contain endogenous material, not all of the combustible energy of feces arises directly from the non-absorbed fraction of feed. Because of the endogenous component the calculated value is more correctly termed the apparent digestible energy. Similarly, *metabolizable energy (ME)* intake, which is the energy available for metabolism and production by the animal, may be calculated by subtracting from the intake energy the energy losses occurring in feces, *urine (UE)* and the *gaseous products* of *digestion (GE)*, viz., *ME = IE – FE – UE – GE.*

Maintenance functions involve the metabolism and ultimately oxidation of energy substrates. This oxidation occurs through (a) *basal metabolism (BM)* that is represented by the heat energy evolved in sustaining body integrity by the vital life processes; (b) *activity metabolism (AM)* including the voluntary muscular activity of seeking and obtaining

---

*1 calorie = 4.184 joules; 1 joule per second = 1 watt

457

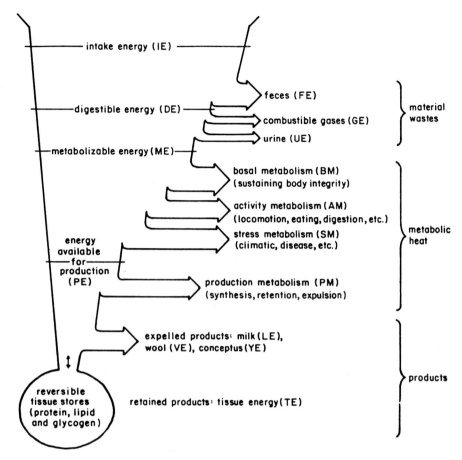

Figure 22-1. Partition of feed energy within a ruminant. After Young (5).

food, the processes of digestion, absorption, conversion of food into metabolizable forms, and the formation and excretion of waste products; and (c) *stress associated metabolism (SM)* arising from immediate and direct impingement of environmental abnormalities.

Energy is available for production after the maintenance needs of the animal are met (6). Because of the metabolic costs of product synthesis and retaining or expelling the product *[heat of product metabolism (PM)],* energy available for production is not entirely incorporated into animal products, be it retained in tissue growth or fattening *[tissue energy (TE)],* or expelled in a product, such as milk *(LE),* wool *(VE)* or conceptus *(YE).* Typically, animals retain energy as protein, lipid and glycogen when *ME* intake exceeds immediate needs. Conversely, retained energy is mobilized when the animal's demand is greater than the energy available from feed.

Overall Fig. 22-1 represents the intake of feed energy and its partition through the major routes of energy disposed of as material wastes *(FE+GE+UE),* as heat *(BM+AM+SM+ PM)* and as expelled *(LE+VE+YE)* or retained *(TE)* products. The *ME* oxidized for the various maintenance *(BM+AM+SM)* and productive *(PM)* processes is released in the animal as heat and is ultimately dissipated to the environment through physical avenues under the control of thermoregulatory mechanisms to prevent a rise or decline in body temperature. During cold stress, heat from maintenance and production metabolism may be of immediate value to the animal in maintaining body temperature, reducing the need of the animal to produce extra body heat by shivering or other cold-induced thermogenic processes. On the other hand, during heat stress thermoregulatory mechanisms are activated to dissipate excess heat from the body to

458

maintain homeothermy. Thus, these heats may be beneficial during cold exposure but a burden to the animal during heat stress.

Behavioral and physiological adjustments by the animal during stress or disease affect energy intake and its partition within the animal and therefore the amount of energy and nutrients available for production. These adjustments directly influence the level and efficiency of production.

THERMAL STRESS

Expressing the Thermal Environment

The thermal impact of the environment on animals is the consequence of the collective combination and interaction of animal and climatic variables (Table 22-1).

The conceptual index of *Effective Ambient Temperature (EAT)*, attempts to describe an environment in terms of equivalent thermal loads on animals and is expressed in temperature units of an isothermic environment without appreciable air movement, radiation or evaporation heat exchange (see refs. 3, 7). Attempts to formulate simple means of quantifying *EAT* have generally fallen short of expectations, usually because of the resourcefulness of animals in combatting thermal stress by physiological and behavioral reactions, which in turn influence the environmental demands. However, formulae for calculating *EAT* values for specific species and

Table 22-1. Variables influencing thermal impact of the environment on animals.

Environmental Variables

Air temperature
Air humidity and water in rain, snow, mud, etc.
Air velocity and direction (wind and forced convection)
Temperature of contact surfaces (floor, ground, etc.)
Thermal conductivity of contact surfaces
Solar radiation
Temperature, reflectivity and emissivity of surroundings
Water availability

Animal Variables

Metabolic heat production
Effective surface areas for conductive, convective, radiation and evaporative thermal exchange
Body surface temperature and temperature distributions
Thermal conductivity of pelage, skin and subcutaneous tissues
Body posture and movement
Reflectivity and emissivity of exposed surfaces
Wetted surfaces of respiratory tract and skin

animal type have been developed and combine the effect of selected environmental variables.

Wind-Chill. Wind-chill indices express the combined effect of air temperature and velocity on the environmental heat demand of dry environments. These indices are most useful in cool and cold environments where wind can have major detrimental effects. In warm to hot environments the cooling effect of air movement can be substantially beneficial in cooling an animal, but in extremely hot environments (when ambient temperature exceeds animal surface temperature) animals gain undesired heat convectively.

Increased air movement increases rate of convective and evaporative heat exchange (8). However, the net thermal effects are moderated by the thermal and moisture gradients between the animal surface and the environment. An increase in rate of heat loss or gain per unit increase in air velocity is greatest at relatively low air velocities because of the initial disruption of the boundary layer of still air at body surfaces.

Humidity. The air's moisture content influences an animal's heat balance markedly, particularly in hot environments where evaporative heat loss is crucial to homeothermy (9, 10). The higher the ambient vapor pressure, the lower the vapor pressure gradient from the skin or respiratory tract to the air, and hence the lower the rate of evaporation. An increase in ambient vapor pressure generally has less impact on the heat balance of species that depend more on panting (and less on sweating) to lose heat during heat stress. Hence, different weightings are given to dry-bulb and wet-bulb air temperatures in calculating temperature-humidity indices (THI) for different species.

A typical index for cattle in the USA is:

$$[(0.35) \, (\text{dry-bulb temperature}) + (0.65) \, (\text{wet-bulb temperature})]$$

Thermal Radiation. Thermal radiation received by an animal has two primary sources: solar radiation (infrared or short-wave) and terrestrial or long-wave radiation (emitted from surrounding surfaces). Long-wave radiation is gained by an animal when the surrounding surfaces are hotter than the surface of the animal but there is a net loss of heat when the surface of the animal is hotter than the surroundings. The net impact of thermal radiation on an animal depends on the sum of the combined solar and long-wave radiation received and the long-wave radiation emitted by the animal. Shades, nearby structures and other animals, ground cover, clouds, surface characteristics of the animal and the interior surfaces of housing are factors determining the net impact of thermal radiation; see reviews by McDowell (9), Fuguary (11) and Morrison (12).

For animals in hot climates the net gain of heat by thermal radiation from the sun can be substantial and very detrimental. In contrast, winter sunshine in cold climates tends to be sought and is apparently pleasurable to animals, although the net gain of body heat is of questionable importance. However, the net radiation from an exposed animal to a clear, cold night sky in winter may be a substantial route of heat loss.

In natural environments wild and domestic ruminants are often exposed to inclement weather. Many combinations of abnormal temperatures, humidity, wind, rain, snow and muddy conditions clearly have adverse affects on an animal's ability to maintain thermal balance, but to date no precise method has been developed to fully describe the total effective thermal environment over the wide range of naturally occurring conditions. The interaction of climatic and animal attributes makes this task most difficult and new approaches are needed to resolve this complex problem.

Thermal Balance and Transient Imbalances

Ruminants produce heat as a result of normal metabolic functions (see Fig. 22-1), and lose heat from their bodies at about the same rate to maintain homeothermy with a core (rectal) temperature of 37.5 to 39.5°C; peripheral and surface temperatures are usually considerably lower and more variable (10 to 35°C).

Shifts in metabolic heat production, consumption of food or water at other than body temperature, and fluctuations in the thermal environment result in transient heating or cooling of body tissues. The rate and amount of gain or loss of body heat depend upon the magnitude of the thermal load, the heat

capacity of the body, and the thermoregulatory responses of the animal. Body heat content is the product of the heat capacity of the body (mass x specific heat) and the mean temperature of the body. Any transient imbalance between metabolic thermogenesis and net heat loss to the environment causes a change in body heat storage and, where mass and composition of the body do not change, is reflected as a change in mean body temperature.

The change in body heat storage (ΔS, joules) can be estimated from the change in mean-body temperature (ΔTb, °C), body mass (W, gram) and the specific heat constant of body tissue (SpH).*

Mean body temperature (Tb) of cattle can be estimated from mean skin surface temperature (Ts) and body core temperature (Tc) by applying appropriate weighting factors.

$$Tb = 0.11\ Ts + 0.89\ Tc$$

and the change in body heat storage ΔS (joules) is then calculated as:

$$\Delta S = W \times \Delta Tb \times SpH$$

In natural environments animals are subjected to diurnal and seasonal fluctuations which change body heat content and, if of sufficient magnitude, may evoke thermoregulatory responses (see below). During transient periods of thermal stress, mammals tolerate some shift in stored body heat to reduce thermoregulatory effort. Large ruminants (cattle, buffalo, camel, etc.), because of their large size, have a high potential to use body heat storage as a buffer against sudden or transient thermal stress. For adult cattle a transient shift of 0.5°C in mean body temperature (not unusual for animals in a natural environment) represents an amount of heat equal to about 2% of the daily energy metabolism. In environments with cyclic thermal vairations the transient shifts in body heat storage can be substantial. This, of course, does not contradict the overall long-term need for a balance between heat production by animals and net heat loss to the environment.

---

*Specific heat of animal tissue is usually assumed to be 3.47 $Jg^{-1}°C^{-1}$.

460

Thermal Exchange

Heat is exchanged between animals and the environment by the same physical processes as heat is transferred in a non-biological system. These are the processes of *conduction (Hk), convection (Hc)* and *radiation (Hr),* which make up the so-called sensible (or Newtonian) heat flows, and the latent (insensible) heats of *evaporation (He)* of water from surfaces of skin or respiratory tract, and, in cold climates, the latent heat of melting ice or snow on an animal's back. The *net heat exchange (H)* of an animal, which may be a temporary gain but in the long-term is a net loss, is the sum of these physical processes so that

$$H = Hk + Hc + Hr + He$$

Overall the physical transfers of heat from an animal to the environment is largely dependent upon the size and direction of temperature and vapor pressure gradients, the velocity of air movement over the body surfaces and the temperatures of radiating surfaces of the animal and of the surrounding environment. The mass, temperature and physical state of materials entering (food and water) and leaving (milk, feces, urine, etc.) the body also affect the net heat content of the body and therefore its temperature. The principles of physical exchange processes are the same for animals and inanimate objects and are described in most handbooks of physics and appropriate texts (6, 7, 9, 13).

When confronted with changes in the physical attributes of the environment, animals alter their behavior, posture, and various physiological processes to modify the rates of transfer of heat from the body core to the body surface and from the body surface to the environment. These biological responses complicate any attempts to relate the rates of body heat loss to simple physical characteristics of an inanimate object. However, by making simplifications, relationships have been developed which provide practical means for estimating thermal exchange between an animal and its environment and the general influences of the environment on the productivity of the animal; see NRC (3), Young (5), Blaxter (6), Curtis (7) and Haresign et al (14).

Figure 22-2 is a representation for homeothermic animals between the evaporative and sensible components of heat loss, heat

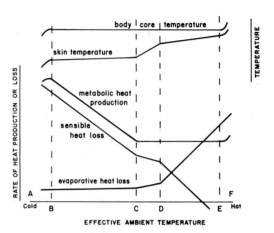

Figure 22-2. Diagrammatic representation of relationships between heat production, evaporative and nonevaporative heat loss and core-body temperature in a homeothermic animal. *A:* zone of hypothermia; *B:* temperature of summit metabolism and incipient hypothermia; *C:* lower critical temperature; *D:* temperature of marked increase in evaporative loss; *E:* temperature of incipient hyperthermal rise; *F:* zone of hyperthermia; *CD:* zone of least thermoregulatory effect; *CE:* zone of minimal metabolism; *BE:* thermoregulatory range. After Monteith and Mount (13).

production from metabolism and body core temperature. The latter represents the consequence of the net balance between heat loss and heat gain. Units and scale are purposely not included in Fig. 22-2 because of the large variation between animals and even within a single animal at different times of the day and annual seasonal cycles. The diagram is highly schematic, but serves to show the relationships between the major components influencing thermal balance and how animals achieve, over a *thermoregulatory range (BE),* a relatively constant body core temperature. The actual values and relative positions of the curves are very dependent upon the species, the age and weight of the animal, its physiological state, feeding and production level. It is also influenced by thermal and non-thermal environmental variables as well as the animal's adaptation to the environment (1, 3, 5, 6, 14).

Ruminant animals generally have a wide *zone of minimal metabolism (CE)* which is sometimes incorrectly referred to as the thermoneutral zone. The implication of thermoneutrality is that the animal is unaffected or neutral to the thermal environment. This is somewhat misleading as animals are continually adjusting to maintain thermal equilibrium by peripheral vasomotor control and by varying sweating or respiratory evaporatory heat loss. However, thermal stresses on animals are of practical concern only beyond the CE zone. There is increasing heat stress at effective ambient temperatures above E and cold stress at effective temperatures below *C*. The point *C* is referred to as the *lower critical temperature (LTc)*. It is defined as the effective temperature below which the animal must progressively increase metabolic heat production specifically to compensate for the increased thermal demand of the cold environment.

Heat Stress

At ambient temperatures in the zone of minimal metabolism and above, an animal becomes increasingly heat stressed and there is maximum vasodilation of skin capillary blood vessels. The physiological mechanisms of sweating and panting are activated to increase evaporative heat loss from the body surface and the respiratory tract. During severe heat stress there is a small increase in heat production by the animal because of the activity of panting. However, it is the increased body temperature with the environmental heat load which causes possible hyperthermia and may place the animal in a precarious position (13).

Because the opportunity for vaporization of water from the skin surface is reduced when the relative humidity of the air is high, a combination of high ambient temperature and high humidity may impose a serious stress upon an animal (see temperature-humidity index page 458). Such conditions can result in severe depressions in appetite and thus availability of nutrients for growth and production (9). However, with prolonged exposure to a hot environment, animals acclimate by lowering their resting metabolism as a consequence of reduced food intake and decreased thyroid hormone activity (11, 12). The discomfort of heat stress, therefore, may be relieved but high levels of productivity are usually not achieved.

Any adjustments to nutrient requirements for heat stress should be based on the severity of heat stress, which can vary considerably among animals depending upon breed, degree of physiological acclimatization, diet, level of productivity, and diurnal fluctuations in radiant heat load. For example, breeds of cattle with higher milk producing capacity tend to have a high metabolic intensity and, consequently, are affected by heat stress more than are the genetically heat-adapted *Bos indicus* breeds and crosses. Thus, productivity, albeit low, may be maintained in genetically adapted tropical cattle while genetically ill-adapted cattle with a higher milking potential are severely heat stressed (9).

During severe heat stress, maintenance requirements increase through the increased cost of panting and alterations in tissue metabolism because of increased tissue temperatures. The type and intensity of panting can provide an index for an appropriate diet adjustment. The percentage increase in metabolism, and thus maintenance dietary energy requirement, is about 7% while the animal is first-phase panting, i.e., rapid shallow panting, but 11 to 25% during second-phase open-mouth panting (see NRC, 3). However, with severe heat stress, appetite is usually depressed (see Table 22-4) and animals may not eat sufficient to meet their projected requirements. Marked reductions in productivity are, therefore, often observed.

High producing animals with the highest metabolic heat production tend to be the earliest and most severely affected by heat stress. However, in hot climates considerable relief can be achieved when there are cooler evening temperatures. With hot daytime temperatures, high radiation loads, etc., but nighttime cooling, animals shift their behavior patterns of grazing and eating mainly to the night period and maintain levels of productivity which are not possible when there is no diurnal relief in the heat stress (9, 12).

The availability of natural or artificial shade protecting animals from solar radiation is usually effective in reducing stress during hot summer temperatures. However, where high humidity is also a factor, simple solar shades are less effective because of the reduced opportunity for evaporative heat loss (9, 11, 12). Furthermore, shades in humid and high moisture areas can lead to the accumulation of mud where there is high animal density.

462

Acute Cold Stress

Lower critical temperature (LTc) is an important measure to have for animals in practical conditions for if extra ME is used to maintain body temperature such energy is not available for productive functions (see Fig. 22-1). Smaller animals tend to have higher *LTc* than large animals. Also, younger animals, partly because of their smaller size but also because of usually lower surface resistance to heat flux, have higher *LTc* than do adults (6,13). For example, a newborn calf has a *LTc* of about 10°C. An adult winter-acclimatized beef cow on a maintenance ration could have a *LTc* of –10°C, and a feedlot steer on a grain ration has a *LTc* of –25°C or lower (6, 15, 16). These values are for the European breeds of cattle which are normally those kept in the temperate or cooler agricultural regions. Of course, the tropical breeds and animals genetically adapted to hot environments would be expected to suffer from cold stress at temperatures considerably higher than those indicated above.

High producing animals on a high plane of nutrition tend to have low *LTc* (16). This occurs because of the substantial amounts of metabolic heat which arises as a consequence of synthesis of animal products (see Fig. 22-1).

Thermal insulation provided by wool or a thick hair coat, skin or subcutaneous fat layer, also tend to reduce *LTc*. A sheep in full fleece is likely to have a *LTc* well below 0°C whereas upon shearing the *LTc* is transformed to over 25°C (6, 17).

The slope of sensible heat loss line plotted against effective ambient temperature in zone *BC* shown in Fig. 22-2 represents total thermal insulation; the greater the thermal insulation the less is the slope of this line. As the heat loss rate rises with falling ambient temperature in zone *BC,* the animal progressively raises its metabolic heat production rate to maintain thermal balance. The rate at which heat production is increased with falling effective ambient temperature is the same as the rate at which the sensible heat loss rate increases, until *summit metabolism* (at point *B)* is reached. If the environmental temperature continues to fall beyond this point, the animal will not be able to produce sufficient metabolic heat to maintain body core temperature and, consequently, there is

hypothermia and, if not corrected, death of the animal (1, 13, 17).

Estimating Lower Critical Temperatures. It is desirable to know the approximate *LTc* of animals under practical conditions so that management or feeding strategies can be evaluated to minimize the detrimental effects on the animals and on production efficiency. By applying a couple of simplified equations, reasonable estimates can be achieved of *LTc* and the increase in energy needed to compensate for an acute cold stress. Of course, this increase in energy requirement would need to come from either the diet or from tissue energy reserves. Further details of these calculations and the derivation of the equations and tabulated values can be found in the reviews of NRC (3), Curtis (7) and Monteith and Mount (13). The *LTc* of an animal may be estimated as:

$$LTc = Tb - He \times Ie - Hm(It+Ie)$$

where

LTc = lower critical temperature (°C) expressed in terms of effective thermal environment
Tb = body core temperature (°C), 39°C a satisfactory assumption
It = tissue insulation, see Table 22-2
Ie = external insulation, see Table 22-3
Hm = metabolic heat when the animal is not cold stressed (MJ m^{-2} d^{-1})
He = evaporative thermal exchange (MJ m^{-2} d^{-1}), usually minimal in cold environments and 1.26 MJ m^{-2} d^{-1} a satisfactory assumption for ruminants.

Table 22-2. Estimates of tissue insulation (*It*).

Age, species	Tissue insulation[†]
Newborn	0.6
1-3 months old	1.0-1.75*
Adult cattle	1.2-2.75*
Adult sheep	1.0-1.5*

[†]Expressed as °Cm^2 dMJ^{-1}.
*Higher values in these ranges occur with increased body fatness, skin thickness and acclimation to cold.

Table 22-3. Estimates of external insulation (Ie; $^{\circ}Cm^2dMJ^{-1}$) in relation to coat depth F (cm). With increased air movement the hair coat of cattle is disrupted such that each 10 mph increase in wind velocity would reduce effective Ie by about 50%.

Newborn	Ie = 1.4 + 0.8 F
Adult cattle	Ie = 2.0 + 0.6 F
Adult sheep	Ie = 1.4 + 0.14 F

Hm can be estimated as the difference between the *ME* intake of an animal and the sum of energy in products *(NEp, net energy for production)*. This difference then needs to be expressed in terms of animal surface area (*A*).

$$Hm = (ME-NEp)/A$$

The surface area in square meters of a single standing animal (cattle) can be estimated from body weight (kg) according to the general formula

$$A(m^2) = 0.09\ kg^{0.67}$$

Changes in posture, lying down and huddling are normal thermally induced behavioral reactions and alter the animal's effective surface area. A surface area estimate based on the above equation must be adjusted appropriately.

The increase in dietary metabolizable energy or tissue energy required in an environment colder than the animal's *LTc* is given by the formula

$$Increased\ requirement\ (MJ\ d^{-1})$$
$$= A(LTc-EAT)/(It+Ie)$$

where *A, LTc, It* and *Ie* are as above and *EAT* is the effective ambient temperature expressed in terms of dry, still-air temperature (°C).

Such estimates of *LTc* express temperatures in terms of equivalent dry, still-air conditions and may not consider fully the consequence of wind, moisture, mud and radiation. Furthermore, variations in animal type, feeding level, time after feeding, behavior and prior thermal exposure also must be considered in the practical application of estimates of *LTc* values and increased nutrient requirements.

Coping with acute cold stress involves minimizing the risk and severity of the immediate effects of cold and pre- or early treatment of animals which are cold exposed in order to reduce the probability of development of secondary complications often associated with chilling (18). Provision of shelters, selection of appropriate calving, lambing or shearing times, and ensuring an adequate supply of feed can reduce such risks. Unfortunately, during acute inclement weather, animals tend to temporarily reduce their feed intake (Table 22-4) and become more susceptible to cold stress.

Chronic Cold

The ability of animals to cope with the cold improves during prolonged exposure to mildly cold conditions. Physiological acclimation changes occur in individual animals which increase their thermal insulation, appetite and basal metabolic intensity. These changes improve "cold hardiness" and reduce the risks of both acute and chronic cold stress (5, 16). These processes of physiological acclimation should not be confounded with genetic differences between animals and breeds and their ability to withstand thermal stress. Animals of the various genetic types may have very different basic levels of adaptation determined from genetic makeup from which to operate, but each also has an ability to physiologically adjust or acclimatize to stressful environments. This ability is more evident, for example, in European breeds of cattle than in the tropically adapted *Bos indicus* breeds (10, 14).

Insulation. Increased winter hair coat in cattle is apparently induced and retained by a shortening daily photoperiod and mild cold stress, respectively (15). Animals that are cold because of low ambient temperatures or because of reduced metabolic heat production, tend to retain hair in situations where animals with higher levels of heat production shed their hair coat. The hair coat of arctic ungulates, such as caribou and musk ox, is extremely well developed. The thermal insulation provided by the coat is their main protection from winter cold, especially in situations of limited feed supply. Increased thermal insulation, per se, reduces the *LTc* and the required cold-induced thermogenesis when animals are exposed to temperatures below their *LTc*. See discussion above on estimating *LTc*.

Metabolic Intensity. An elevated basal metabolic rate and not simply an acute metabolic response occurs as a physiological acclimation to cold (1, 15). Furthermore, with cold acclimation there is a higher potential *summit metabolism* (see Fig. 22-2). Cold acclimated animals, therefore, are able to survive and apparently suffer less in extreme cold than similar non-acclimated animals. The ability of sheep and cattle to withstand increasingly colder temperatures without shivering as winter progresses or during prolonged cold exposure is practical evidence of thermal acclimation and an illustration of the practical importance of this phenomenon (14). The situation with a large cold-region wildlife species is not as simple. In winter these animals are frequently faced with feed shortages and the feed which is available is usually of poor quality. An apparent survival strategy utilized by these species is to reduce activity and metabolic intensity during winter. With such a strategy they become greatly dependent on the thermal insulation of their hair coat for protection against cold stress.

Two forms of cold-induced metabolic responses which increase the nutrients required by animals are recognized: (a) an acute metabolic response at temperatures below *LTc* is essential to compensate directly for an increased rate of loss of body heat to the cold environment and (b) a chronic acclimation metabolic response. The former occurs only at temperatures below the *LTc* of the animal and is vital for survival of the animal in acute cold stress. The chronic acclimation metabolic changes most evident in small mammals and domestic livestock persist usually throughout the colder seasons of the year and contribute to the overall increased dietary energy requirement (3, 14). On the basis of currently available research, the change in metabolic intensity with cold acclimation represents a 0.91% increase in maintenance energy requirement for cattle for each degree below 20°C to which they have been adapted. Similar increases in metabolic intensity occur in sheep, but magnitude of the response is dependent upon the wool coat and external insulation; woolly sheep respond less than sheep with short fleece.

Appetite and Nutrient Value. It is well recognized that the thermal environment influences the appetite of domestic ruminants, increasing appetite with cold and decreasing appetite with heat stress (Table 22-4). Recent research reviewed by Christopherson and Kennedy (19) indicates that when domestic ruminants are exposed to cold there is also an increase in rumination activity, reticulorumen motility and rate of passage of digesta as well as a reduction in the volume of the reticulorumen. A consequence of these digestive changes is a reduction in digestion in the reticulorumen of roughage feeds associated with an increased rate of passage of digesta. These effects do not seem to be a problem with concentrate feeds, apparently because their digestibility is not influenced markedly by rate of passage.

Nutritional adjustments for the effect of thermal environment on the digestibility of roughage feeds has been suggested by NRC (3). For example, for the energy components of roughages given to cattle the following formula can be utilized:

$$X = Y + Y[0.0010(EAT-20)]$$

where X is the adjusted energy value, Y is the unadjusted value and EAT is the average effective ambient temperature (°C) to which the animal is exposed. The thermal influence on diet digestibility may be slightly greater for recently shorn sheep than for woolly sheep or cattle (19).

While an increase in rate of passage may decrease the biological value of feedstuffs because of reduced digestibility, there is an associated increased appetite (Table 22-4). Thus, in situations of abundant food supply, domestic ruminants may benefit more from the increase in appetite than the loss from the reduced ability to digest feed. However, the story is more complex with wild ungulates in that under natural winter conditions these species often reduce their feed intake despite the availability of feed.

Table 22-4. Estimates of variations in voluntary food intake as influenced by thermal and other stresses. After NRC (3).

Environmental stress	Response[†]
Severe heat stress *EAT*[*] 35°C	Marked depression in intake, especially with high humidity and/or solar radiation and where there is little night cooling. Animals on full feed — 10 to 35% depression. Animals near maintenance — 5 to 20% depression. Intakes depressed less when shade or cooling available and with low fiber diets.
Mild heat stress *EAT* 25 to 35°C	Intakes depressed 3 to 10%.
Cool environment *EAT* 5 to 15°C	Intakes stimulated 2 to 5%.
Mild cold *EAT* -5 to 5°C	Intakes stimulated 3 to 8%. Sudden cold snap or storm may result in digestive disturbances in young stock.
Cold stress *EAT* -15 to -5°C	Intakes stimulated 5 to 10%.
Severe cold stress *EAT* -15°C	Intakes stimulated 8 to 25%. Intakes during extreme cold (<-25°C) or during blizzards and storms may be temporarily depressed. Intake of high roughage feeds may be limited by bulk.
Rain	Temporary depression in intake of 10 to 30%.

Mud
  Mild, 10 to 20 cm deep
  Severe, 30 to 60 cm deep
	
	Intakes depressed 5 to 15%.
	Intakes depressed 15 to 30%. Mud effects are greatest when access to feed is limited and when there is a lack of a suitable bedded area.

Illness or disease (non-specific)	Usually accompanied with severe depression in voluntary intake.

[†]Estimates relative to intake of animal in a non-stressful environment.
[*]*EAT* — Effective Ambient Temperature

Other Nutritional Adjustments for Thermal Environment

While the energy requirements of domestic ruminants increase during cold weather, there is recent evidence that protein as a percentage of the diet can be reduced without affecting growth rate (20). However, any decrease in protein in the ration should only be proportional to the increase in food intake such that the absolute amount of protein intake is maintained. Any adjustment in ration composition in terms of protein, minerals or vitamins, should consider the economic and practical consequences of feeding excesses of some ration components. Protein fed in excess of immediate animal needs is catabolized and utilized as an energy source.

Increasing percentage roughage in the diet results in a slight increase in heat production because of greater heat increment associated with ingestion and digestion. Under hot environmental conditions this increased heat production can result in reduced voluntary food intake (9, 20). It is therefore advantageous to feed diets of low roughage content during hot weather. On the other hand, in cold environments an increase in roughage may at times be advantageous, particularly for animals such as overwintering beef cows on a restricted ration. However, for the high producing animal in cold conditions, substituting roughage for concentrate feeds may limit intake and reduce available energy and level of animal productivity (3).

NON-THERMAL STRESSES

Humidity and Moisture

The effects of humidity and moisture on animals are largely linked with the thermal influences of the environment (8, 9). In hot environments ruminants rely substantially on evaporative heat loss by sweating and panting to maintain homeothermy. High humidity reduces the capacity for evaporative heat loss and, consequently, with a combination of high ambient temperatures and high humidity there can be a substantial thermal stress on animals. In cold environments humidity is generally not important except when the dew point (100% saturation) is approached and moisture precipitates to wet surfaces and reduces the effective thermal insulation of the coat.

Natural or artificial additions of moisture to the animal's environment can have substantial influence. Water spray and sprinkler systems are used in hot, dry environments to achieve evaporative cooling in the animal's surroundings and coat. Similarly, water sprays are used to settle dust and other airborne particles which could cause respiratory disturbances (9, 11).

Excessive moisture additions from sprays, rain, snow or poor drainage can lead to muddy conditions, particularly in feedlots and where there are high animal densities. During periods of a rain or snow storm, there tends to be a temporary reduction in feed intake (see Table 22-4). Mud also may restrict animal behavior and motility, and if severe can also cause substantial reduction in feeding behavior and food intake. Of course, any reduction in food intake will have a direct consequence of reducing the level and efficiency of animal production. Snow or mud in the hair coat of animals not only reduces insulative value but as melting and evaporation occurs the required latent heat is a drain of body heat and may become an added cold burden to the animal.

Water requirements of ruminants are affected by the environment, increasing markedly as the ambient temperature increases because of the increased evaporation of water from the body surface and respiratory tract. Water requirements during heat stress are 3 to 4 times those for the non-stressed animal (3). This means that in hot environments animals need ready access to drinking water and, if available, animals will drink on 2 to 5 occasions daily. However, in extensive grazing systems in dry tropical areas water intake by ruminants will decline as the distance to the source of water increases; with a decrease in

water intake, food intake also decreases and productivity is lowered (9).

Cooling of drinking water has been reported in some studies to be beneficial for feedlot cattle in hot environments, but these results are not consistent across all studies (11). Heating of water in cold climates does not appear to be of practical benefit. In fact, over-wintering beef cows and other ruminants not at high levels of production can obtain their water needs by ingesting snow (21). The limits to this practice arise when animals are lactating or growing rapidly and have elevated water requirements. Also, snow as a source of water is only practical when animals have continuous access so that the snow can be consumed in small quantities throughout the day. Detrimental affects arise if animals are forced to consume large amounts of snow or cold water at one time (22).

Light

Animal behavior particularly relating to grazing times is influenced by daylight with peaks of activity and grazing occurring near sunrise and sunset. Furthermore, in hot tropical areas animals tend to avoid grazing during the heat of the day by moving their grazing activity to the cooler night period (9).

Addition of artificial lighting to intensive ruminant production systems has little or no direct beneficial effects on animal productivity. Of course, lighting of animal facilities can often be justified for management or other reasons independent of the direct effects on the nutritional requirements of the animals.

Sound

Information on the effects of sound on nutritional requirements of ruminants is generally lacking. Most reports that have examined this aspect of the environment indicate little or no effect of continuous music or sound (23). However, at levels of sound approaching 100 decibels feed intakes can be depressed (24). Also, intermittent sound or sonic booms cause marked responses in animals but generally there has been no long term effect on performance of ruminants. Animals near airports or on flight paths rapidly acclimate to the abnormal sounds and animal response declines.

467

Gaseous Environment

Gaseous contaminants such as NH_4, H_2S, CH_4, CO and CO_2 are problems usually only in intensive animal housing systems (1). Some of these gases have direct toxic effects on animals causing ill health and can be fatal. At subclinical levels there is generally a lack of information on their effects. However, some studies have shown detrimental effects on food intake and digestibility. For example, 75 ppm of NH_4 in air has a negative effect on feed intake and growth rate of lambs. With increased intensive ruminant production, especially with increasing use of liquid manure systems, there is greater risk of gaseous contamination and sub-clinical detrimental effects.

SUMMARY

In practical farming systems and in natural environments, environmental stress is unavoidable. Unless extreme, the ruminant animal readily overcomes by avoidance or some physiological mechanism most day to day stress, but there is often some nutritional cost involved. Hot conditions and heat-stress, especially if associated with high humidity or solar radiation, can reduce feed intake markedly and lower productivity. In contrast, under cold conditions food intake generally increases and there can be a reduction in digestive efficiency, but the main reason for the increased nutrient requirements of an animal is to compensate for the increased metabolic activity to keep the animal warm and the increased metabolic intensity associated with cold acclimation.

Other environmental conditions associated with high moisture (rain, snow, mud), unusual sound levels and gaseous contaminants can be stressful on ruminants and reduce productivity primarily through reducing appetite. However, some gaseous contaminants are highly toxic, causing ill health, and can be fatal.

Literature Cited

1. Clark, J.A. 1981. Environmental Aspects of Housing for Animal Production. Butterworths, London.
2. Hahn, L.G. 1981. J. Animal Sci. 52:175.
3. NRC. 1981. Effect of Environment on Nutrient Requirements of Domestic Animals. Nat. Academy Sci., Washington, DC.
4. NRC. 1981. Nutritional Energetics of Domestic Animals and Glossary of Energy Terms. Nat. Academy Sci., Washington, DC.
5. Young, B.A. 1975. Some Physiological Costs of Cold Climates. Missouri Agr. Exp. Stn. Spec. Rep. 175.
6. Blaxter, K.L. 1967. The Energy Metabolism of Ruminants. Hutchinson and Co., London.
7. Curtis, S.E. 1983. Environmental Management in Animal Agriculture. Iowa State Univ. Press, Ames, Iowa.
8. Thompson, H.J., et al. 1954. The Effect of Wind on Evaporative Cooling and Surface Temperature in Dairy Cattle. Missouri Agr. Exp. Stn. Bull. 548.
9. McDowell, R.E. 1972. Improvement of Livestock Production in Warm Climates. W.H. Freeman and Co., San Francisco.
10. Robertshaw, D. 1974. Environmental Physiology. Physiology series 1, Vol. 7. University Park Press, Baltimore.
11. Fuguary, J.W. 1981. J. Animal Sci. 52:164.
12. Morrison, S.R. 1983. J. Animal Sci. 57:1594.
13. Monteith, J.L. and L.E. Mount. 1974. Heat Loss from Animals and Man. Butterworths, London.
14. Haresign, W., H. Swan and D. Lewis. 1977. Nutrition and Climate Environment. Butterworths, London.
15. Webster, A.J.F., J. Chlumecky and B.A. Young. 1970. Can. J. Animal Sci. 50:89.
16. Young, B.A. 1981. J. Animal Sci. 52:154.
17. Armstrong, D.G., et al. 1959. Animal Prod. 1:1.
18. Webster, A.J.F. 1983. J. Animal Sci. 57:1584.
19. Christopherson, R.J. and P.M. Kennedy. 1983. Can. J. Animal Sci. 63:477.
20. Ames, D.R., D.R. Brink and C.L. Willms. 1980. J. Animal Sci. 50:1.
21. Young, B.A. and A.A. Degen. 1980. J. Animal Sci. 51:811.
22. Degen, A.A. and B.A. Young. 1984. Can. J. Animal Sci. 64:73.
23. Archart, L.A. and D.R. Ames. 1972. J. Animal Sci. 34:994.
24. Harbers, L.H., D.R. Ames, A.B. Davis and M.B. Ahmed. 1975. J. Animal Sci. 41:654.

by H. W. Essig, Gerald B. Huntington, Royce J. Emerick, and J. R . Carlson

BLOAT

by H. W. Essig

Acute tympanites (bloat) is a non-infectious disease which is common among ruminants in many parts of the world. Bloat in sheep and cattle is not a new disease, but it has increased markedly due to improvements in forage systems to include legumes and intensive pasture fertilization. Bloat was described by a Roman author in 60 A.D. in terms which indicate that the symptoms have not changed over the centuries. His treatment included, "pouring sour vinegar through the left nostril and putting 2 ounces of grease in the jaws." When we consider therapy of the condition today, little progress has been achieved. Much research has been conducted and there is a large volume of literature available. Of the numerous reviews the following are suggested for further reading (1, 2, 3, 4).

Production of gas (primarily CO_2) in the rumen is a normal result of the fermentation process. Bloat is characterized by an accumulation of this gas within the reticulo-rumen in sufficient quantity that normal pressure is exceeded and distension (bloat) occurs, because the animal is unable to remove the excess gas by eructation (belching). Swelling occurs first and greatest at the left flank above the rumen, then later on the right side of the animal (Fig. 23-1, 23-2). The degree of swelling may not always indicate the amount of animal distress. Other symptoms of bloat are: arched back with feet drawn under abdomen, kicking of abdomen, staggering gait, vomiting, frequent urination and defecation, labored breathing with nostrils dilated, tongue extended and eventual collapse, followed by death.

There are several kinds of bloat which may or may not be associated with each other. The following kinds are often discussed: (a) legume, (b) feedlot, (c) toxic [HCN and NH_3], (d) pathological (abcesses) and (e) obstructions (adhesions). The classification

of bloat employed by Cole et al (4) suggested the following:

A. Chronic bloat—a condition of tympany occurring irrespective of the qualitative nature of the diet (toxic, obstructive and pathological). B. Subacute bloat—a condition resulting from a specific dietary regimen, such as succulent legumes or a predominately concentrate diet, where ruminal pressure may vary from slightly above zero to 57 mm Hg.

Figure 23-1. A steer showing a moderate degree of bloat.

Figure 23-2. An example of the amount of ruminal distension which may occur in a severely bloated animal. Courtesy of E.E. Bartley.

C. Acute bloat—similar to subacute bloat except that the condition is further advanced and distressing symptoms appear. Ruminal pressure may vary from 45 to 69 mm Hg.

Bloat can be categorized as being caused by free gas or frothy (legume) conditions in the rumen. Free gas bloat is usually present in feedlot animals under the influence of toxic, pathological or obstruction conditions. Free gas in the rumen may also result from a failure of the mechanism for expulsion of fermentation gases. It is speculated that feedlot bloat may be a result of excessive consumption of dense feed which depresses the cardia below the fluid level thereby causing a gas buildup in the rumen. This phenomenon of overfilling has been demonstrated by filling the reticulo-rumen with liquid and elevating the hindquarters of the animal which resulted in inhibition of eructation with a gas buildup in the rumen. A small particle size diet of 61% ground corn, 22% alfalfa meal, 16% soybean meal and 1% salt fed twice daily for 19 d, at the Mississippi Experimental Station, to bloat-susceptible steers produced a high (90+%) incidence of gaseous bloat. Research (5) with fistulated cows fed either alfalfa hay or all-concentrate diets with either 0.5% or 4.0% salt indicated that the rumen fluid of those fed the low level of salt had lower pH and protozoal counts, and higher viscosity, soluble carbohydrate concentration and dry matter content than those given alfalfa hay or high-salt diet. They concluded that adding 4.0% salt to an all-concentrate diet implicated in feedlot bloat increased flow of material from the rumen and, in so doing, appeared to alter fermentation in such a way as to oppose development of conditions that lead to feedlot bloat.

Frothy bloat occurs in animals grazing lush legume pastures. It is generally accepted that a viscous, slimy mass is present that traps fermentation gases and prevents eructation even though the intraruminal pressure may be above normal (Fig. 23-3). Gas formation and accumulation is, without doubt, a factor associated with bloat. There is a question if frothy bloat is caused by an increased rate of gas production or simply an entrapment and accumulation of gas in the ingesta resulting in a failure of gas elimination. Recent research (6) indicated that chlorophyll concentration, buoyancy of particulate matter, and rates of

Figure 23-3. An illustration of the very foamy digesta in the rumen of a bovine with pasture bloat. Courtesy of E.E. Bartley.

gas production were significantly higher in bloated than non-bloated cattle allowed to graze alfalfa. It was suggested that the microbial colonization and retention of particulate matter provided active inocula for promoting rapid legume digestion with enhanced gas production and gas entrapment which produced a frothy mass resulting in bloat.

Many theories have been proposed as to the etiology of bloat. A theory has been proposed that "toxic factors" might cause rumen musculature to become immobile and eructation to cease. Toxic factors suggested have been hydrogen cyanide, hydrogen sulfide, flavone, histamine and unknown factors. None of these "toxic factors" have been conclusively shown to cause bloat in animals grazing legumes.

A physical deficiency theory has been proposed because in most cases of bloat on green legumes there is an absence of stimuli necessary to elicit primary contractions which are associated with the belching reflex. Because of this theory many livestock producers feed hay to animals grazing clover pasture. From a practical point of view it requires about 7.7 kg of grass hay/animal/d to prevent bloat; and lesser amounts may only temporarily reduce but not eliminate or prevent bloat.

The surface tension theory has been investigated by many researchers and has involved saliva secretion rate and composition, antibodies in saliva, saponin levels of legumes, slime production and S-18 protein (7, 8, 9, 10). The surface tension of saliva samples averaged 47.1 dynes/cm at 29 C whereas pure

470

water has a surface tension of 71.35 dynes/cm at 30 C. Saliva has a water content of 99%, consequently it must contain a surface-active agent. The quantity of saliva and its surface tension may well explain why certain animals bloat on a bloat provocative pasture and others do not. Saliva and more specifically the mucin in saliva may be the effective anti-foaming agent when associated with foaming rumen digesta. Research (3) has shown that when saliva is added to frothing rumen contents greater quantities of gas escaped than when no saliva was added. It has been postulated that bloat results when feeds containing foaming constituents fail to induce sufficient salivary secretions and may explain why some ruminants are more susceptible to bloat on young succulent legumes, while others may not bloat while consuming more mature legumes or hay.

Other investigators do not agree with the saliva-mucin theory. Leaf proteins have been considered to be involved in, if not totally responsible for, the production of froth. Workers in Canada (9, 10) put forth the idea that a single major protein constituent of alfalfa leaves, 18-S (Svedbergs) protein, was mainly responsible for bloat when alfalfa was used as a feed. Alfalfa that induced bloat contained about 4.5% 18-S protein whereas those that did not induce bloat contained less than 1%. Researchers in New Zealand (1) do not agree that 18-S protein (Fraction I) alone among leaf proteins is dominant in determining the properties of bloat foams. They suggest a Fraction II leaf protein is also involved in production of foam with a high persistence. The amount of slime from the rumen of cattle appears to increase with the onset and severity of bloat. Leaf protein is apparently a necessary ingredient in the complex mixture of rumen slime, plant protein and salivary mucoprotein for production of stable foam in the rumen.

Although proteins appear to be the most important plant factor associated with bloat, numerous other plant components have been studied. Saponins produce extremely stable foams and have been implicated in the bloat syndrome, however, some investigators indicate that bloat incidence and severity are not correlated with saponin levels in plant material (11). Plant pectins (15) and particulate

matter may act as foam stabilizers when foams are formed in the rumen.

Plant lipids and tannins are possible foam inhibitors. Plants with high tannin content have been found not to be bloat-provoking (1). In general, any plant constituent that decreases with increasing plant maturity correlated positively with incidence and severity of bloat. Also, any constituent that increases with maturity correlates well with the apparent absence of bloat.

In the grazing animal the incidence and severity of bloat appears to depend on a complex interaction of the grazing animal, grazed plant and rumen microorganisms (Fig. 23-4). The interrelationship of plant, animal and microorganism is necessary for bloat to occur, and the disruption of the influence of any of these factors will prevent the occurrence of bloat.

Plant Factor

It is commonly recognized that plants with a high protein content such as the temperate legumes white clover, red clover, persian clover and alfalfa (*Trifolium repens, T. protense, T. resupinatum L.* and *Medicago sativa*) are more bloat provocative than non-legumes. Sporadic outbreaks of bloat have been reported in animals grazing young succulent grasses such as ryegrass and wheat (12). Such grasses probably cause bloat because they usually contain high levels of froth-forming proteins. Immature legume growth with a high leaf-stem ratio is most likely to induce bloat. There is a decrease in bloat incidence and severity with increasing maturity and decreasing protein content of alfalfa plants. Analyses of alfalfa bloat foams indicated that the foaming constituents are primarily proteinacious. Soluble protein (18-S) from legumes, a foam stabilizing protein, has physical and chemical properties that makes it an ideal bloat-promoting agent. Soluble protein (18-S) content of legume leaves may be a good indicator of a plant's bloat-provoking potential.

The highly erratic incidence of bloat suggests that there is a strong influence of some environmental factors, especially rainfall and temperature to promote clover growth, on the bloat-producing potential of plants. Chemical composition of the plant, which is affected by maturity, influences the protein and

471

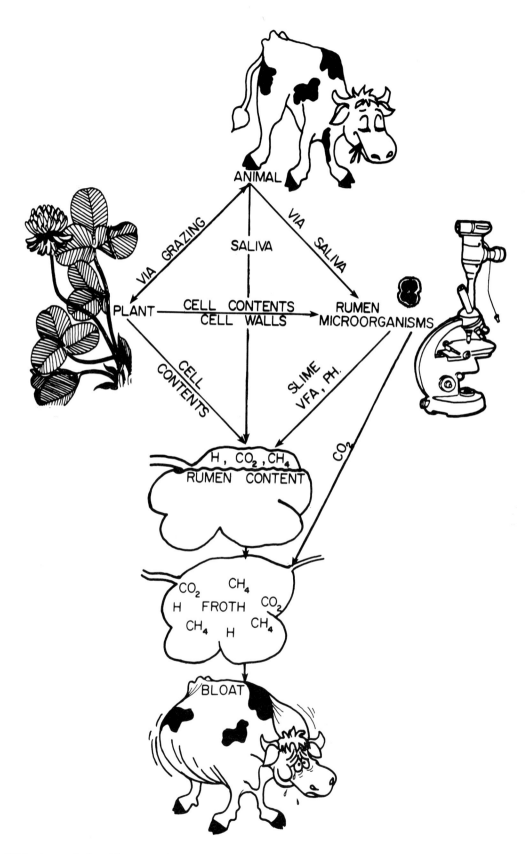

Figure 23-4. Interrelationship among legume plant, animal and microorganisms in bloat production in cattle.

472

carbohydrate utilization and production of slime, CO_2 and volatile fatty acids. The grazing animals as a part of the plant environment is probably extremely important in maintaining the plant in an immature state resulting in a highly bloat-provocative forage.

Animal Factor

There appears to be a genetic influence on occurrence of bloat in cattle. The use of sets of identical twin cattle on the same pasture has shown that similar susceptibility occurs in both members of a twin set. Evidence of breed differences is not clearcut, although there are bloat-susceptible animals in most breeds of cattle (13, 14, 15). Heritability estimates of bloat susceptibility are not known, but random groups of animals obtained for use in bloat research studies at the Mississippi Experiment Station showed that about 33% of the animals were highly susceptible to legume bloat, about 33% showed little or no bloat and the remaining 34% showed varying degrees of incidence and susceptibility to bloat.

There is no clearcut evidence of the role of age, sex or body condition on bloat susceptibility. Generally, animals do not become susceptible to frothy bloat until they have been allowed to graze bloat-provocative legumes for at least 3 or more days. A greater incidence and severity is evident after 5 to 7 d of grazing the forage. Usually a 3 to 7-d period of adjustment is required to cause shifts in populations and species of rumen microorganisms, and this appears to be highly correlated with incidence and severity of bloat.

Microbial Factor

Rumen bacteria and protozoa numbers and species are influenced by diet and are associated with bloat. There are few data available to show specifically how legumes influence microbial species and their metabolic activities which may result in bloat.

The rumen liquor, plant fragments, rumen fluid temperature and the microorganisms themselves, as predators and competitors, compose the environment which determines the relative number and metabolic activities of the microorganisms. The composition of rumen liquor is influenced by contributions of the animal via saliva and by plant cell

contents made available through chewing. The rumen microorganisms produce volatile fatty acids, lactic acid, NH_3, CH_4, CO_2 and bacterial slime. There is disruption of protozoal cells due to engorgement or pH changes that contribute to slime production through release of soluble protein, starches and lipids into the rumen liquor which may contribute to the nature and extent of bloat. Slime produced by rumen microorganisms may contribute frothing factors to legume or feedlot bloat. Kansas workers (3) postulated that mucin from normal salivary secretion, if sufficient in quantity, prevents bloat. If salivation is reduced during consumption of bloat-provoking diets, or if mucin is destroyed by excessive concentration of mucinolytic flora, bloat is likely to result.

Rumen microorganisms are a part of the bloat syndrome because oral administration of antibiotics such as penicillin, streptomycin, oxytetracycline, erythromycin, virginiamycin, monensin, lassolacid, salinomycin and tylosin singularly or in combination have reduced incidence and severity of bloat for limited periods of time (16, 17, 18). Prolonged use of antibiotics results in decreased efficacy of bloat control. The role of protozoa in fermentation appears to be similar to that of bacteria. When defaunation agents such as dimetridozole, copper sulfate and dioctyl sodium sulfosuccinate were administered to bloat-susceptible steers, both severity and incidence of bloat were reduced (13). Copper sulfate also influenced VFA concentrations, protozoa counts and CO_2 production. Protozoa appear to be important contributors to legume bloat in ruminants because they are able to rapidly assimilate soluble sugars and starches and to store these in the cytoplasm.

Bloat Prevention

Generally, the control of bloat is achieved through prevention. Numerous methods of prevention have been developed which control bloat for limited to extended time periods. Since legume bloat is a result of froth development in the rumen, a logical consideration of control would be physical control of foam by antifoaming agents. Several antifoaming agents like silicones, detergents, vegetable oils, animal fats, animal mucins and liquid paraffins have been used with some success. These materials have been administered through drinking water, sprayed on the forage, dosed by capsule, sustained release bolus (capsule), gel rings, gel drenches, grain supplements, molasses blocks and salt mixtures.

Criteria for effective, safe and practical bloat preventative agents have been described (3) as: (a) a single administration must effectively prevent bloat at least 12 h; (b) must act rapidly; (c) must be palatable; (d) must not deleteriously affect health, reproduction, rumen function, feed intake or quality and quantity of milk; (e) must not be eliminated in milk; (f) must not be in body tissue 5 d after administration; and (g) must be economical. Many compounds have been screened and do not meet all of these criteria.

The compound that meets the above criteria and is used widely in the USA for bloat prevention is the non-ionic surfactant poloxalene. It may be administered at a rate of 10 g/454 kg body weight daily in feed of animals fed a prepared diet or in molasses blocks for grazing animals (13, 16, 19, 20). The feeding of a corn-poloxalene mixture twice daily, immediately before grazing legumes, effectively prevents bloat. Molasses blocks containing poloxalene appear to be the most acceptable method of administration of poloxalene to beef cattle because it eliminates the necessity of daily feedings of supplements containing poloxalene. Animals fed poloxalene do not develop a resistance as is the case with antibiotics.

Methods of bloat prevention are many and varied. Antifoaming agents such as tallow and paraffin have been applied to the flank of the cow at milking and subsequently licked off during the day. Antibloat agents such as emulsified oil and pluronic type materials have been added to water sources to prevent bloat. Antifoaming agents such as tallow and paraffin have been sprayed on pastures for bloat control. Antifoaming agents and pluronic type materials may also be drenched, but this requires restraining the animal twice daily resulting in an unfeasible practice. The use of these compounds is potentially reliable, however failure to follow specific management recommendations along with unfavorable climatic conditions may lead to poor control of bloat.

A number of suggested animal and pasture management methods for prevention of bloat have been proposed. One of the most effective pasture management methods of bloat prevention is to maintain a grass-legume mixture with more than 50% grass in the forage system. A good animal management method is to cull all animals susceptible to bloat, but this has a disadvantage that high producers might be bloat susceptible. The suggestion is often made that legumes should not be grazed while wet with dew or rain. This is probably one of the most common beliefs about bloat prevention, and yet there is no experimental work to support this theory. In fact, most cases of bloat at the Mississippi Experiment Station have appeared to occur on clear, warm days with twice daily grazing. Another suggestion without merit is that cattle should graze legumes for short periods of time. This intermittent grazing and strip grazing is similar to the method used by researchers to experimentally produce bloat, where animals are grazed twice daily for 90 minutes then maintained in drylot when not allowed to graze. Fertilizing legumes with high levels of phosphorus or feeding of phosphorus compounds while grazing legumes has no effect on the incidence or the severity of bloat. The feeding of about 2.2 to 7.7 kg of hay before allowing animals to graze clover will give a temporary relief but will not eliminate bloat. It has been suggested that legume pastures not be grazed until they are in the bloom stage of maturity. This has little merit because it prevents use of legume pastures during their most productive portion of the growth cycle. Soilage (green-chopping) of the legume and feeding to cattle has been shown to produce less bloat than when grazed. This is probably due to animals being forced to consume the entire plant rather than leafy portions which may be more bloat inducive. New Zealand researchers (1) have sprayed legumes with a variety of oils to prevent bloat. Protection lasts for only a short time and has a high labor and management requirement to be successful.

Bloat Treatment

The best treatment of bloat is prevention. If the animal is severely bloated and can be placed in a chute with a minimum of excitement to the animal, a hose 2.54 cm (I.D.) may be inserted into the rumen to relieve some pressure in cases of free gas bloat, but little relief will be achieved in cases of frothy bloat. The hose may also be used to

474

administer such compounds as polaxalene, or antifoaming agents such as vegetable oil, mineral oil, paraffin, lard or turpentine. If the animal does not obtain relief from these anti-foaming agents, a trocar and cannula might be used, however, these instruments have limited usefulness in frothy bloat conditions due to their becoming plugged with froth and rumen mass. If the animal collapses the interior of the rumen can be exposed by making an incision about 15 cm long in the left paralumbar fossa area (Fig. 23-5, 23-6). Care should be taken when making this incision to make a quick opening and stand clear of the gushing froth that may go as high as 2.5 m into the air. Once the animal collapses, death is

Figure 23-5. An incision being made to relieve rumen gas pressure.

Figure 23-6. An animal resting after expelling most of its rumen contents through an incision into the rumen.

certain unless a rumenotomy is performed and artificial respiration is applied.

SUMMARY

Most clover and alfalfa, when grazed in the highly vegetative state, are capable of producing bloat in susceptible animals. Selection of animals against bloat susceptibility may be one method of control. Protozoa appear to be associated with legume bloat. Soluble protein (18-S) appears to be a contributor to slime production. The most practical method of bloat prevention is the use of poloxalene which may be fed in a block preparation to beef cattle or in the feed of dairy cattle. The use of antibiotics and other management practices provide only limited or short term bloat prevention.

ACIDOSIS

by Gerald B. Huntington

INTRODUCTION

Acidosis is defined as a condition of pathologically high acidity of the blood. In ruminants the term is expanded to include acidic conditions in the rumen (rumen acidosis). The condition can be acute, posing a life-threatening situation, or chronic (subacute), resulting in reduced feed intake and weight gain. Statistics are not available on incidence of acidosis, but lambs appear to be more susceptible than cattle to acute, fatal acidosis as evidenced by increased death loss in cases of grain overload. In general, death losses due to acidosis in any group of ruminants are probably small and sporadic. In wild species the disease probably exists; rumenitis has been identified in deer fed grain, but the deer did not die from high grain intake. The major physiologic and economic costs of acidosis result from chronic acidosis that goes undetected in large groups of cattle or sheep where feed intake and weight gain of the affected animals are masked until the group is slaughtered, when economic analyses and abscessed livers reveal the deleterious effects of acidosis. Dairy cows and goats are susceptible to acidosis, but common feeding practices and production criteria result in diets that are not conducive to acidosis. Various aspects of acidosis have been discussed in detail (1-5); these reviews are the basis for the present discussion.

ETIOLOGY

Etiology of acidosis has two major phases: (a) abrupt increase in ingestion of readily fermentable carbohydrates (RFC) followed by rapid ruminal fermentation to acids that alter the ruminal microbial population's profile and (b) absorption of the acids into the bloodstream resulting in acidosis. Sources of RFC include immature, rapidly-growing forages that have relatively high concentrations of intracellular carbohydrates, tubers or root crops that contain sugars, or cereal grains that contain starch. Cereal grains are the most common source of RFC that cause acidosis, both in ruminants that are adapted to high-grain diets as in feedlots, and unadapted animals that gain unplanned access to the corn field or grain bin. Thus, an abrupt increase in ingestion of RFC may be more than usual amounts of grain or be a change from an all-forage or high-forage diet. Fermentability in the rumen varies among grains, largely due to differences in fermentability of starch. Wheat is more conducive to acidosis than corn or milo, and is used for experimental induction of acidosis for that reason. Steam flaking, rolling, popping or other processing methods increase surface area or gelatinize starch and make RFC more fermentable, thereby increasing the potential for acidosis.

Increased RFC intake and resultant acidity causes lethal conditions for protozoa. In animals adapted to high-grain diets, protozoa, particularly entodinimorphs, are present until grain comprises 90% or more of the diet. Protozoa ingest starch as well as bacteria, and may play a role in ameliorating post-feeding acidity in grain-fed animals by at least temporarily removing substrate from bacterial access, or controlling to some extent bacterial populations. Cellulolytic bacteria that predominate in forage-fed ruminants have been found in rumens of grain-fed animals if ruminal fluid pH is 5.2 or greater (4).

Presentation of RFC to the rumen causes a rapid proliferation of amylolytic or sugar-using bacteria, particularly *Streptoccus bovis,* whose generation interval is measured in minutes under conditions of plentiful substrate. These bacteria produce VFA, which are normal fermentation products, and lactate, the product of *S. bovis. S. bovis* is ubiquitous in the rumen, as its name implies; it usually is present in grain-fed ruminants in greater numbers than lactobacilli, bacteria that frement RFC predominantly to lactate (4). However, reports of bacterial profiles of grain-fed ruminants vary a great deal, indicating the instability of ruminal bacterial populations associated with ingestion of RFC.

Ruminal lactobacilli proliferate in response to substrate (RFC) and produce either isomer of lactate. In forage-fed ruminants or in ruminants adapted to high-grain diets, lactate is not found or is present in trace amounts of ruminal fluid. Any lactate present in forage-fed ruminants is predominantly L-lactate. Abruptly increased intake of RFC causes accumulation of lactate in the rumen, and the isomeric ratio shifts to about 50:50 L-lactate: D-lactate. In the case of experimentally engorged ruminants, D-lactate may become the predominant isomer (1). Lactate produced in the rumen can be absorbed, passed from the rumen with ingesta, or provide substrate for bacteria; numbers of lactolytic bacteria such as *Megasphera elsdenii* increase immediately after ingestion of RFC, and ability of in vitro incubations of ruminal fluid to use lactate as substrate increases 6- to 8-fold over a period of 4 weeks of exposure to RFC as substrate (6). This time frame agrees well with usually recommended time

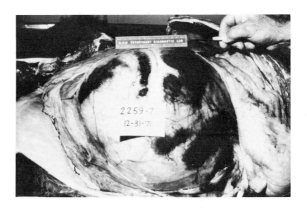

Figure 23-7. The exterior of the rumen showing inflammation and hemorrhaging in a rumenitis case. Courtesy of Don Helfer, Diagnostic Laboratory, Oregon State University.

476

sequence to adjust ruminants from forage to high-grain diets to avoid digestive disturbances. If lactate is produced at rates high enough to cause accumulation, then the opportunity for absorption of high amounts into the bloodstream is created, thereby contributing to systemic acidosis. Acute acidosis from engorgement with RFC causes proliferation of coliforms and clostridial species that may play a role in production of enterotoxins and contribute to diarrhea (4). Ethanol-producing species of bacteria and yeasts may proliferate as well; ethanol intoxication would explain some of the behavior of acidotic ruminants.

In acute cases of acidosis, ruminal fluid pH can approach the pKa of lactic acid (3.7). Low pH is instrumental in cessation of rumen motility. Normal fermentation is interrupted and production, if not concentration, of volatile fatty acids is reduced. Rumen epithelial tissue is damaged or destroyed by the acidic conditions (Fig. 23-7, 23-8), allowing opportunity for systemic invasion of bacteria responsible for liver abscesses, including *Sphaerophorus necrophorus* and *Corynebacterium pyrogenes*. In chronic cases, rumen acidosis is not as severe, but tissue damage does occur and rumen microbial environment is unstable, protozoal numbers are reduced, bacterial populations fluctuate, and potential for rapid proliferation of acid-producing amylolytic bacteria and lactobacilli is continually present.

The lower gastro-intestinal tract likewise is adversely affected by acid production. Inflammation of tissues in the small intestine is caused by acids from the rumen, and changes in substrate affect bacterial populations in the intestine, which contributes to diarrhea and loss of electrolytes. Although it is a rare occurrence, ruminants fed high-grain diets may vomit, indicating gastro-intestinal distress.

Acids produced in the rumen are absorbed into the bloodstream, where they accumulate and form the basis for systemic acidosis. Blood pH is lowered, there is electrolyte imbalance due both to loss to the lumen of the gut and to high acid concentrations. High osmolarity of chyme and diarrhea causes loss of water from blood and splenic release of erythrocytes in response to general physiological stress causes hemoconcentration. In severe cases acidosis interferes with renal function and oxygen transport. Peripheral arterioles rupture, particularly in the extremities which is manifested in laminitis, or founder (Fig. 23-9). Persistence of these physiological disturbances can cause death. In chronic cases the persistent acid in the blood and metabolic disorders associated with malfunction of abscessed livers results in loss of appetite or the "Thanksgiving dinner" syndrome, and weight gain and feed efficiency are subsequently affected (Fig. 23-10, 23-11).

Figure 23-9. A foundered heifer. Note the incomplete extension of the front leg and the elongation of the hoof on the left front foot. Courtesy of D.C. Church.

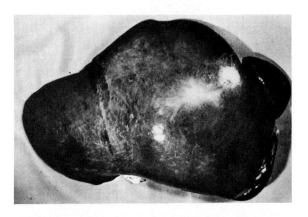

Figure 23-10. A beef liver with two large abscesses on the surface. Courtesy of Elanco Products Co.

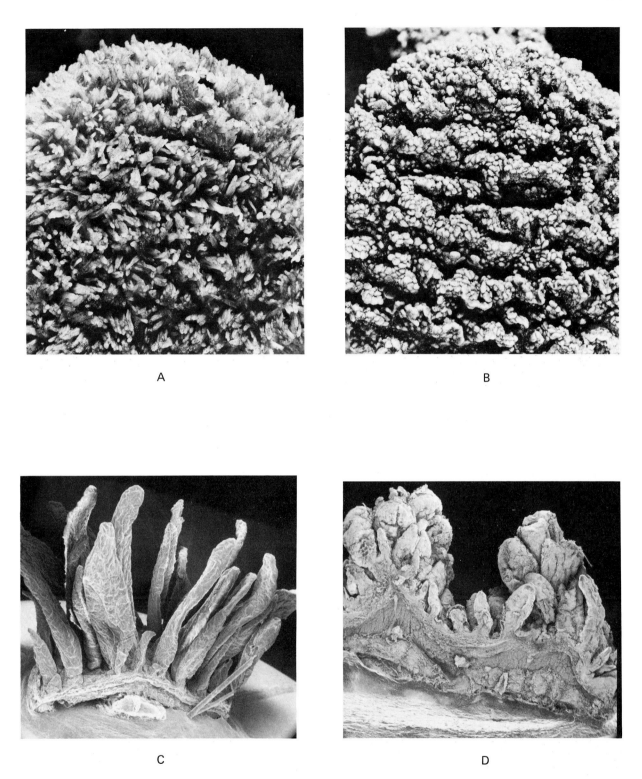

A

B

C

D

Figure 23-8. Abnormal papillary development in the rumen of calves 4-6 wk of age which were fed insufficient roughage. A, cranial sac with normal papillae. B, cranial sac showing clumping and a tendency to arrange in rows (1.5X). C, scanning electron microscope photos showing normal development and D, scanning electron microscope photo showing the abnormal rumen papillae (13-15X). Courtesy of M.D. McGavin and J.L. Morrill, Kansas State University.

478

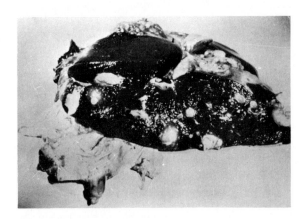

Figure 23-11. A cross-section of a liver showing severe abscesses deep in the liver tissue. Courtesy of Elanco Products Company.

SYMPTOMS

Gross symptoms of acidosis include marked reduction or cessation of feed consumption (anorexia), loose feces or diarrhea, a listless, depressed or distressed appearance, founder or sore feet and death. Other symptoms that can be measured or observed after the fact include decreased rate of gain and feed efficiency, high incidence of abscessed livers at slaughter, rumenitis in slaughtered or dead animals, altered blood metabolic profile and incidence of polioencephalomalacia. Abscessed livers are condemned at slaughter, are an economic loss to the meat processor and ultimately adversely affect the market price of live cattle. Fifty percent or more of beef cattle fed high- or all-concentrate diets may have abscessed livers, but 25% is a reasonable estimate of the average. Cattle with badly abscessed livers do not gain as rapidly or efficiently as unaffected animals.

Blood metabolic profiles have been used in research to document disturbances of acidosis in homeostatic mechanisms or metabolic function (7, 8). With acute acidosis, consistent disturbances include increased packed cell volume or hematocrit, decreased concentration of blood bicarbonate, decreased plasma or serum concentrations of minerals, particularly Ca, and increased concentration of lactate. Electrolyte concentrations and enzyme activities fluctuate, but responses vary with extent and severity of acidosis. Increased ruminal fluid and blood concentrations of histamine have been implicated as

contributory factors, but data on a direct role for histamines are inconclusive. These responses in blood metabolic profile have been found in buffalo, cattle and sheep that have ingested unusual amounts of RFC, either as grain, lush pasture or experimental engorgement. Data from lambs that consumed sufficient grain to become acutely acidotic (9) demonstrate the relationship between accumulation of lactate in ruminal fluid and disturbances in blood metabolic profile (Table 23-1). As ruminal fluid lactate accumulated, blood pH and bicarbonate dropped to life-threatening levels and serum Ca concentrations decreased. In other lambs that were fed increasing amounts of grain in a gradual fashion (Table 23-2), similar, but less dramatic, responses to ingestion of RFC were evident.

Production and subsequent absorption of lactate has long been implicated as factors in systemic acidosis. Ruminants as well as other mammalian species have well-established metabolic pathways to accommodate absorption of L-lactate because it is an intermediary metabolite. Until recently, D-lactate was considered the primary factor, giving rise to the name "D-Lactate acidosis" (1). However, recent research has shown ruminants can metabolize D-lactate and that they are not required to rely solely on renal clearance to eliminate an acid load of D-lactate (10). Research with forage-fed steers that were engorged with glucose or abruptly switched to a 70% concentrate diet demonstrates the close relationship between increased ruminal fluid concentrations of acids and absorption from portal-drained viscera, and emphasizes the contribution of all acids, not just D-lactate, to disturbance of acid-base status during acidosis (10).

Metabolic profiles of cattle that are adapted to high grain diets over a period of several weeks, the common industry practice, usually will not show effects of acidosis because causative factors have been minimized or eliminated. With careful management and strict attention to condition of the animals, feed intake, and diet preparation and mixing, some livestock feeders change to high grain diets in two weeks or less. If changes in metabolic profile are evident, they usually occur in the first two to three weeks of feeding high-grain diets (7, 8). On a practical basis, metabolic profiles are not very useful in

Table 23-1. Ruminal fluid lactate, blood pH, packed cell volume (PCV), and bicarbonate, serum calcium and lactate in acidotic lambs.[a]

| | Hours after receiving 90% concentrate diet | | | | | | | |
	0	4	6	16	24[b]	30	32	48
Ruminal fluid lactate, mM	<0.1	2.2		35.3	123.4		109.3	100.6
Blood pH			7.44			7.20		
Blood PCV, %			29.3			35.0		
Blood HCO_3^-, meq/ℓ			30.6			7.8		
Serum Ca, mg/dl			10.5			8.9		
Serum lactate, mM								
Total			1.56			9.84		
L-lactate			1.42			3.94		

[a]From Huntington et al (9)
[b]Lambs consumed feed equal to 6.6% of body weight by 24 h.

Table 23-2. Ruminal fluid lactate, blood packed cell volume (PCV) and bicarbonate, plasma Ca and L-lactate in lambs fed increasing levels of grain (concentrate).[a]

| | Day (% dietary concentrate) | | | | | | | | | | |
	0(0)	1(65)	2(65)	3(65)	4(65)	5(65)	6(85)	7(85)	8(85)	9(85)	10(85)
Ruminal fluid											
lactate, mM	7.3	5.1	5.0	3.0	8.8	6.2	6.8	7.5	3.8	7.7	11.2
Blood PVC, %	31.2	28.7	26.3	24.7	25.5	24.4	23.9	23.9	22.6	22.7	24.2
Blood HCO_3^-, meq/ℓ	27.2	20.7	22.7	25.0	24.0	23.9	22.3	19.0	19.8	18.3	17.4
Plasma Ca, mg/dl	10.0	9.9	9.1	8.8	8.8	9.3	9.6	9.8	9.5	9.7	10.2
Plasma L-lactate, mM	1.78	1.59	1.43	1.43	1.47	0.02	0.02	0.60	0.61	0.48	0.62

[a]From Huntington et al (6)

diagnosing acidosis; gross symptoms previously listed are reliable indicators when coupled with knowledge that animals had access to a source of RFC.

Polioencelphalomalacia (cerebrocorticonecrosis) is a disease associated with acidosis (5). The name refers to the brain lesions that result from acute thiamin deficiency; the deficiency results from production in the rumen of thiaminases that destroy thaimin or adversely affect absorption of thiamin from the gut (see Ch. 16). Polioencephalomalacia does not occur consistently with acidosis or feeding diets high in RFC, rather is better characterized as sporadic, localized outbreaks sometimes associated with acidosis. Ruminants that survive the disease are generally lethargic, "poor doers", and represent an economic loss due to poor weight gain.

THERAPY AND PREVENTION

As with most diseases, immediate therapy for acidosis is to remove the source of RFC and provide afflicted animals good quality forage or a diet low in RFC. In acute cases involving few numbers of animals, intravenous infusion of electrolytes may be practical; intravenous infusion of bicarbonate buffers may also help, if blood acid-base status is closely monitored to avoid "overkill" or induction of alkalosis. Antibiotics in the diets or by injection may aid in treatment of secondary involvements resulting from acidosis.

In spite of extensive and sophisticated research on etiology and prevention of acidosis, the most reliable prevention centers on management techniques, including gradual adaptation to diets high in RFC, close

480

monitoring of daily feed intake of diets high in RFC and of animals' condition, and provision of fresh feed and water daily. Most commercial feedlots have several diet formulations that vary in proportion of grain or other sources of RFC. These formulations are used to adapt ruminants initially and to respond to changes in intake after adaptation caused by a variety of factors, including incidence of disease, changes in weather or errors in feeding management.

Feed additives are commercially available that will reduce incidence of abscessed livers and effects of acidosis in large groups of animals, if used in conjunction with good management practices. These additives fall into three categories: antibiotics that have systemic effects; antibiotics that have rumen effects; and dietary buffers or neutralizers designed to ameliorate acidotic conditions in the gastro-intestinal tract (11). Antibiotics that have systemic effects, particularly in reducing incidence of abscessed livers, include chlortetracycline and tylosin; other antibiotics (erythromycin, zinc bacitracin) have been shown to reduce incidence of abscessed livers, but do not show consistent benefit in terms of feedlot performance of cattle. Antibiotics that have ruminal effects include the ionophores monensin and lascalocid; they alter feed intake and/or ruminal fermentation patterns in ways that facilitate microbial adaptation to increased concentrate intake. Other antibiotics (zinc bacitracin, penicillin, chlortetracycline) do not provide consistent ruminal effects. Dietary buffers or neutralizers (bicarbonates, hydroxides, silicates) have beneficial effects during initial phases of adaptation to high concentrate diets as evidenced by increased or more consistent feed intake, increased weight gain or decreased death loss during the first few weeks of feeding high concentrate diets. These additives do not provide consistent benefit in feedlot performance over the entire finishing period, however, and at levels that are beneficial during initial weeks may cause overall performance inferior to that obtained without additives. Most beneficial use of buffers or neutralizers appears to be addition to the diet during the first few weeks at 2 to 4% of the high concentrate diet, then removal to prevent potential negative effects on overall performance.

SUMMARY

Acidosis in ruminants is a diet-related disease caused by an abrupt increase in consumption of readily fermentable carbohydrates. Changes in ruminal microbial population and fermentation products result in absorption of large amounts of volatile fatty acids and lactic acid into the bloodstream which causes systemic acidosis. Prevention centers on gradual adaptation to diets high in readily fermentable carbohydrates and careful management while feeding such diets.

NITRATE AND UREA TOXICITIES

by R.J. Emerick

NITRATE TOXICITY

Nitrate (NO_3^-) sometimes occurs at high concentrations in forages consumed by ruminants. However, its occurrence in feedgrains is minimal. Accumulation of nitrate in plants is known to vary between species and to be influenced by several factors, generally those that tend to limit growth of plants while still allowing the uptake of nitrate by the roots. Among these factors, the most important is drought but others may include frost damage, herbicide treatment and shading.

Water represents another important carrier of NO_3^-, deriving it from soils, fertilizers, feedlots, municipal and private sewage disposal systems and industrial activities. Accumulation of NO_3^- in feed and water supplies, and problems associated with it, have been reviewed (1, 2). Only limited nutritional research concerning NO_3^- toxicity has appeared during the past decade.

Economic losses resulting from the ingestion of nitrate or its reduction product, nitrite (NO_2^-), are related to the total intake of these forms of N from all sources. However, water and forage may independently contain levels of NO_3^-, or NO_2^-, or both, that are toxic to livestock.

Among the forages most often involved, corn was the first to be recognized as having caused cattle deaths. However, the hay or straw of small grains, especially oats, as well as the green corn plant and corn fodder, sorghum, sudan grass and many weeds including wild sunflower (*Helianthus annuus*), pigeon grass (*Setaria virdis*), pigweed (*Amaranthus retroflexus*), kochia (*Kochia scoparia*) and thistle (*Salsola kali*) may be involved. Alfalfa, timothy and bromegrass, as well as native grasses, apparently are not important accumulators.

Following ensiling of plant material, the NO_3^- concentration can be reduced by the fermentive process with release of some of the NO_3^- N as gaseous N oxides. While gaseous nitric oxide and nitrogen dioxide are invisible, some of their polymers are often visible as a brown gas. These gases may accumulate in the silo and adjacent unventilated enclosures, and breathing them results in the often fatal malady commonly known as "silo filler's disease". NO_3^- content of silage cannot be assumed to have been reduced to safe levels by this phenomenon. The concentration remaining can be determined only by analysis.

Quantitative Expression of Concentrations

There are several methods for reporting the NO_3^- content of plants, rations or water. For the purpose of uniformity and the resulting greater ease in making comparisons, values are reported here in terms of N and are referred to as nitrate N (NO_3^- N), nitrite N (NO_2^- N), etc. Some laboratory and literature reports may use other methods including values based upon concentrations of the nitrate ion (NO_3^-) and nitrite ion (NO_2^-), or the K or Na salts of these ions. The following numerical relationships facilitate conversion from one term to another:

$1 NO_3^-$ N = 4.43 NO_3^- = 7.22 KNO_3 = 6.07 $NaNO_3$

$1 NO_2^-$ N = 3.29 NO_2^- = 6.08 KNO_2 = 4.93 $NaNO_2$

Physiology of Nitrate Toxicity

Of NO_3^- and NO_2^-, NO_2^- is the more toxic form, generally resulting from the microbial reduction of NO_3^-. This conversion may occur in the rumen, in moist feeds prior to consumption, or in water contaminated with organic matter capable of supporting extensive microbial growth. NO_3^- prior to reduction to NO_2^- is not particularly toxic for non-ruminants, but NO_2^- is similarly toxic for ruminants and non-ruminants. The primary toxicity of NO_2^- following absorption is manifested through oxidation of the Fe in hemoglobin from ferrous (Fe^{+2}) to the ferric (Fe^{+3}) form. The resultant methemoglobin is incapable of oxygen transport and death from anoxia may occur after 70 to 80% of the hemoglobin is converted to methemoglobin.

NO_3^- and its reduction products do not accumulate in the animal body; they are converted to other compounds or are excreted in the urine. To some extent they may be beneficial, serving as sources of N from which protein may be synthesized by rumen microbes. However, NO_3^- should never be used intentionally for this purpose.

Acute Nitrate Toxicity

Clinical signs of acute NO_3^- poisoning usually occur within 4 h following ingestion of a toxic amount of NO_3^-. These signs become apparent when methemoglobin levels approximate 30% or more of the total hemoglobin, and death may occur at methemoglobin levels in excess of about 80%. The usual signs of NO_3^- poisoning are those related to anoxia and include a rapid pulse rate and an increased respiration rate followed by labored breathing, muscle tremors and a general weakness. Forced activity increases severity of the signs. An afflicted animal may lie on its side with its mouth open. The membranes of the mouth, nose and eyes become a darker color due to the oxygen deficit, and the blood is a typical dark brown "chocolate" color. Death, if it occurs, can generally be expected within 12 h.

Maximum amounts of NO_3^- that may be consumed by ruminants without showing outward signs of illness are dependent mainly upon the type and quantity of diet, and the time period over which the dose is consumed. NO_3^- from fresh forages is released into the rumen more slowly than that from dry forage (2, 3), and cattle grazing pasture often tolerate higher intakes of NO_3^- than those fed dry forages (3, 4, 5). In addition, dietary sources of readily available carbohydrate have been shown to increase the tolerance of ruminants to NO_3^-. This is due to a more rapid utilization of NO_3^- and NO_2^- by rumen microbes with subsequently lower accumulations of NO_2^- being available for absorption.

A toxic dose of NO_3^- for ruminants on a poor quality, high forage diet, when administered as a single dose by drench, has most often been shown to be 75 to 90 mg NO_3^- N/kg body weight (2). Greater quantities are tolerated when administered over a longer period of time, as is generally the case with NO_3^- in the feed or water. Also, animals fed NO_3^- continuously tend to develop some degree of adaptation (6) due largely to changes in the rumen microbial population.

Although concern has sometimes been expressed about the possibility of urea-NO_3^- interaction that might increase the detrimental effects of dietary NO_3^-, available data (7, 8, 9, 10) indicate that the toxicity of NO_3^- is not intensified by the presence of urea. However, there is limited evidence that NO_3^- toxicity for ruminants fed diets suboptimum in energy may be increased by disproportionately high levels of readily available protein (11). Practical recommendations pertinent to various concentrations of NO_3^- in feedstuffs are as shown in Table 23-3.

NO_3^- related deaths in ruminants resulting from the consumption of waters containing less than 100 ppm NO_3^- N have not been documented. However, levels in excess of 300 ppm NO_3^- N in drinking water are considered potentially dangerous for ruminants. Maximum allowable concentrations of 100 ppm NO_3^- N and 10 ppm NO_2^- N recommended for livestock waters (13) allow a reasonable margin of safety. However, these concentrations are 10 times higher than the recommended limits of 10 ppm NO_3^- N and 1 ppm NO_2^- N for public water supplies which allow a larger margin of safety.

Treatment

NO_3^- toxicity is generally not recognized until some deaths have occurred. Occasionally, however, when animals are lost and the cause is immediately recognized as NO_3^-, other animals stricken but still alive may be saved by prompt action. A 4% solution of methylene blue injected intravenously (100 ml/450 kg body weight) generally results in the rapid reduction of methemoglobin.

Subacute Effects of Nitrate

Reproductive Performance. A non-significant negative correlation coefficient of only −0.18 between NO_3^- level in the forage and fertility based on non-return of artificially inseminated cattle was reported for 58 cattle herds (14). However, abortions among pregnant survivors of animals poisoned with high NO_3^- hay were reported in very early descriptions of NO_3^- poisoning and have been produced experimentally (15, 16, 17) under conditions that resulted in fatal methemoglobinemia in some of the animals. Smaller doses than those that were acutely toxic to some of the animals have failed to cause abortions even though maximum methemoglobin values of the dams approximated 50% of the total hemoglobin. An association between abortions in dairy cattle and exposure to lowland pastures having high weed populations was postulated to have been due to NO_3^- (17, 18), but the direct involvement of NO_3^- was not substantiated. Available data strongly suggest that NO_3^- or NO_2^--induced abortions in ruminants occur only under conditions approaching those required for manifestation of near fatal methemoglobinemia in the dam.

Nitrate-Vitamin A Interrelationships. Under acidic conditions, NO_2^- or gaseous oxides formed from it are capable of destroying carotene and vitamin A (19, 20). Non-ruminant animals in which orally administered NO_2^- and vitamin A were immediately exposed to the acidic medium of the gastric stomach have shown reductions in vitamin A storage (21, 22). Storage of vitamin A given by injection was not similarly reduced. For ruminants, NO_3^- and NO_2^- appeared to cause no

Table 23-3. Practical recommendations pertinent to various concentrations of NO_3^- in feedstuffs.

Nitrate nitrogen content (moisture-free basis)	Comment
0.0-0.15%	This level is considered safe to feed under all conditions.
0.15-0.45%	Feeds in this range vary from those safe to feed under most conditions to those for which the risk of poisoning is great. Feeds containing 0.15-0.3% nitrate N can be fed safely by limiting their daily use to ½ of the total dry matter in the ration. Feeds in the range of 0.3-0.45% should be limited daily to less than ¼ of the total dry matter in the ration. Hay, straws, and fodders in this range should not be fed when damp.
Over 0.45%	Forages containing over 0.45% nitrate N are all potentially toxic. It is recommended that they not be fed.

483

appreciable destruction of carotene in rumen fluid either in vitro (19) or in vivo (23). NO_3^--vitamin A interrelationships have been difficult to demonstrate in ruminants under experimental conditions, possibly because of the limited and varied amounts of NO_2^- reaching the acidic medium of the abomasum. However, such effects, while limited in number, have been reported to occur during periods of experimental high NO_3^- feeding (24, 25). Levels of NO_3^- required to achieve this effect were potentially toxic levels in the range of 0.4 to 0.5% NO_3^- N in the diet. Reports of no effect of a range of dietary NO_3^- levels on vitamin A status of ruminants have been more common.

Effect of Nitrate on Feed Intake and Weight Gain. A reduction in feed intake with a concomitant decrease in weight gain has sometimes been observed as a consequence of adding NO_3^- and NO_2^- salts to diets of ruminants (26, 27). Reductions in feed intake attributed to NO_3^- have generally been associated with levels of NO_3^- salts equivalent to 1% (0.15% NO_3^- N) or more of the total diet. Although NO_3^- at levels above 0.1% NO_3^- N has been circumstantially implicated in lowering milk production in dairy cattle (28, 29), researchers were unable to confirm this in controlled experiments utilizing dietary NO_3^- levels ranging from 0.1 to 0.5% NO_3^- N (15, 30, 31). However, NO_3^- levels in this range have, as discussed above, reduced feed intake in some ruminants, and lowered milk production accompanying reductions in feed intake could be expected.

Thyroid Function. Increased thyroid weights of experimental animals fed high NO_3^- or NO_2^- diets have been observed in some instances (8, 32, 33) but not in others (34, 35). Several monovalent anions including NO_3^- have been shown to be capable of interfering with normal iodine uptake of the thyroid gland (36, 37). Thyroid function appears to return to normal following a 2- to 4-week adaptation to NO_3^- (38, 39) and the interference of monovalent anions with iodine metabolism is overcome by adequate iodine in the diet (36).

UREA TOXICITY

Urea cannot be considered to be a substance foreign to ruminants in view of the cycling of important quantities of urea to the rumen via saliva. Urea has come into common usage as an economical source of crude protein in ruminant diets. It undergoes hydrolysis in the rumen, through the action of microbial urease, to ammonia and carbon dioxide (see Ch. 12). The ammonia is subsequently available for incorporation into microbial protein or, when present in excess, absorption into the blood stream through the rumen wall. Urea toxicity appears to be most directly attributable to physiological conditions related to the absorbed excess ammonia. Non-ruminants do not have a system for converting urea to ammonia and thus exhibit a low susceptibility to urea poisoning although they are highly susceptible to poisoning by ammonium salts.

Physiology of Urea Toxicity
The rapid release of ammonia from hydrolysis of potentially toxic amounts of urea in the rumen contributes to a rise in rumen pH (40, 41, 42, 43, 44). Under conditions of rumen alkalosis, ammonia absorption is increased. An alkaline rumen pH appears to be the most important factor contributing to high blood ammonia concentrations and related toxicity in animals consuming urea. Compared to urea, ammonium salts have less effect on rumen pH (45), and an elevated ruminal ammonia concentration can exist without toxicity if rumen pH remains below approximately 7.4 (41). Liquid urea supplements have been made less toxic through the addition of phosphoric acid (42, 46), and coating of urea particles with lipid materials (47) or extrusion processing of grain-urea mixtures (42) slow the release of ammonia and reduce toxicity.

Absorbed ammonia may be excreted in the urine as ammonium salts, used in transamination to form glutamine or converted to urea in the liver. Urea formation with subsequent recycling via saliva or excretion in the urine is the predominant means by which excess blood ammonia is handled. When the

484

ammonia-urea conversion capacity of the liver is exceeded, blood ammonia levels increase. Concentrations approximating 2 to 4 mg NH_4-N/dl of blood are generally associated with urea-induced deaths (48, 49). However, the chance of toxicity occurring has been found to be high when blood NH_4-N concentration exceeds 0.8 mg/dl in 60 min following urea consumption (41). Absorption of free ammonia logically leads to systemic alkalosis. While elevation of blood pH has been associated with high blood ammonia concentrations (41), subsequent inhibition of the citrate cycle with compensatory anaerobic glycolysis may cause a drop in blood pH at the time of urea-induced death (50). Higher concentration of ammonia in carotid blood compared to jugular blood indicates a rapid uptake of ammonia by brain (43), and central nervous system derangements are probably an important factor in the toxicity (44). The precise cause of death in ammonia toxicity, while not well defined, appears to involve respiratory arrest (51).

Acute Urea Toxicity

Clinical signs are usually apparent within approximately 20 to 30 min following ingestion of a toxic amount of urea, and death generally occurs in less than 4 h. Signs of urea poisoning include rapid breathing, tremors and slight incoordination followed by severe incoordination, excessive salivation and labored breathing. Eventually, afflicted animals lose the ability to stand and tetany becomes increasingly apparent (40, 48). Bloat, generally occurring to varying degrees, is consistent with a decrease and eventual cessation of rumen motility (40).

Urea toxicity is generally the consequence of inadequate mixing of urea-containing supplements into the ration, feeding of urea to animals not previously adapted to non-protein N, allowing free access to palatable sources of a high-urea concentrate particularly during periods of inaccessibility to other feeds, and the use of urea in low energy rations.

Cattle fed a complete dairy ration (concentrate + hay) died following single dosages of urea amounting to 0.27 to 0.50 g urea/kg body weight (48). Death generally occurred within 2.5 h. On the other hand, 0.18 g urea/kg body weight had no apparent effect. Cattle under the same dietary regimen showed

no signs of toxicity when urea in the diet was increased stepwise to 1.5 g/kg body weight daily, allowing adaptation. However, after deletion of urea from the diet for a period of 3 to 7 d, prior adaptation was lost.

Successful feeding of urea requires the presence of readily available dietary carbohydrate in amounts adequate to support rapid growth of ammonia-utilizing rumen microbes. The presence of preformed protein as well as certain amino acids have also been reported to increase tolerance to urea under experimental conditions (52, 53). Cattle fed a poor quality hay diet were poisoned by a single feeding providing 0.18 to 0.20 g urea/kg body weight while counterparts accustomed to an additional concentrate allowance showed no reaction to this level (48). Also, cattle and sheep deprived of feed for periods of 24 to 48 h were more susceptible to urea poisoning than were those on a regular daily feeding schedule (40, 48). Problems of toxicity are generally not encountered when the feeding of urea is restricted to an amount providing the equivalent of one-third or less of the crude protein (1 urea = 2.92 crude protein) in the concentrate portions of rations fed in quantities not exceeding protein requirements.

Treatment

A 5% solution of acetic acid administered orally in sufficient quantities (ca. 4 ℓ of common vinegar will suffice for a 450 kg cow) to neutralize the excess rumen ammonia is effective if administered before tetany becomes severe (48, 49). Additional quantities of cold water given orally may be beneficial in slowing down hydrolysis of urea to ammonia and will dilute the ammonia already present, lowering the concentration available for absorption (48). This treatment is effective only in the early stages of tetany and is rarely feasible if a number of animals are affected at one time. Emptying the rumen through a stab incision in the paralumbar fossa area, as is sometimes done in emergency treatment of bloat, may be more beneficial than other procedures if tetany has become severe (41, 43).

SUMMARY

NO_3^- and urea toxicities have independent bases, but both involve microbial conversion to the toxic forms, the toxic forms being

NO$_2^-$ and ammonia, respectively. Thus, poisoning from NO$_3^-$ or urea is a greater hazard in ruminant than in non-ruminant animals. NO$_3^-$-induced death in ruminants is the direct result of the conversion of an inordinately high proportion of hemoglobin to methemoglobin, a form incapable of oxygen transport. Subacute effects of NO$_3^-$, including abortion, reduction in vitamin A storage and reduced feed intake, appear to occur only with levels of dietary NO$_3^-$ that have the potential of being acutely toxic.

The cause of urea-induced death, while dependent upon a high blood ammonia concentration, is less clearly defined but appears to involve multiple metabolic alterations. Susceptibility of ruminants to NO$_3^-$ and urea toxicities are decreased by readily available carbohydrate in the diet, uniform mixing of ration ingredients, regular feeding schedules, and prior adaptation to the toxic compound.

ACUTE PULMONARY EDEMA AND INTERSTITIAL EMPHYSEMA IN CATTLE

by James R. Carlson

THE NATURALLY-OCCURRING DISEASE

Acute bovine pulmonary edema and emphysema (ABPE) is a naturally-occurring disease that causes respiratory distress and death in cattle after an abrupt pasture change. Similar clinical signs and pathological lesions are also caused by furan derivatives found in moldy sweet potatoes and in *Perilla frutescens,* a common weed in the United States. This brief review is limited to the disease which occurs after abrupt pasture change. Recent comprehensive reviews of these diseases are available (1-4).

Beef producers throughout the world use a variety of pastures and rangelands for grazing. In the summer months, these pastures and rangelands often become dry and over-grazed which requires removal of the cattle from these areas. A common practice involves abrupt transfer of cattle from the sparse, dry grazing conditions to irrigated meadows or other pastures which contain lush green forage. When abrupt pasture change occurs in late summer or early fall, the new pastures often contain young, rapidly growing grass or other forage as regrowth after hay removal. Within about 2 to 10 d after abrupt pasture change, cows may develop clinical signs of respiratory distress and die from acute lung disease.

Although the specific circumstances surrounding the disease outbreak may vary, abrupt exposure to improved grazing or feeding conditions is the most consistent observation associated with the onset of ABPE. The disease occurs on many types of forages including rape, kale, alfalfa, turnip tops, small grains, rye grass, Bermuda grass, mixed meadow grass and others. No specific species of lush forage has been implicated as the cause of ABPE. It is conceivable that temperature and light intensity in late summer or early fall influences forage composition and the incidence of ABPE, but these relationships have not been confirmed.

Outbreaks of ABPE have been reported in the spring and throughout the summer, but the highest incidence is in late summer and early fall. The time of occurrence is primarily related to when abrupt grazing transitions occur. The highest incidence of ABPE is in mature cows and they may often be nursing calves. The disease has been reported in bulls and younger animals, but the incidence is usually low. There is no evidence for breed differences in susceptibility to ABPE. Suggestions to the contrary may reflect greater numbers of cattle of some breeds at risk in particular areas.

The geographical distribution of ABPE is widespread. It is most common in the western USA, Canada and Great Britain. In Great Britain the disease is called "Fog Fever" because of its occurrence in cattle grazing lush regrowth (foggage) pasture, and it is one of the most prevalent diseases of adult grazing cattle in that country. ABPE also occurs in the southern and midwestern USA, as well as in other parts of Europe and other countries where cattle are managed intensively.

Clinical signs of ABPE usually occur within 2-10 d after pasture change and death may follow within 2-4 d. ABPE seems to occur more often on particular ranches and in localized areas, and the absence of ABPE on nearby ranches with apparently similar conditions cannot always be explained. The reasons may be related to subtle differences in animal management. When ABPE occurs the

486

morbidity may be as high as 50%, but is usually about 30% of affected animals. Cattle with ABPE have increased respiration rate, labored breathing and an apparent increase in expiratory effort. The clinical signs are progressive and within one or two days the cattle may exhibit an "expiratory grunt", frothing at the mouth, and breathing with mouth open with the head extended and lowered (Fig. 23-12). Cattle with these severe clinical signs may die.

Pathological lesions are limited to the lungs which are inflated, heavier than normal, firm and rubbery. The airways are filled with frothy edema fluid and the lungs contain interlobular gas bullae. The alveoli and small airways contain edema, hyaline membranes and cellular infiltration. Animals that die 3 d or more after onset of clinical signs have thickened alveolar septa resulting from diffuse alveolar epithelial cell hyperplasia.

CAUSE OF ABPE AND MECHANISM OF TOXICITY

The occurrence of ABPE has been recognized for over 150 years and many theories on the cause and prevention have been proposed. Until recently, none of these theories has resulted in a way to reproduce the disease experimentally or to reduce its incidence. In 1966, cattle that were given a large oral dose of tryptophan (TRP) died of acute lung injury and the clinical signs and pathological lesions were identical to those of naturally-occurring ABPE. Research has continued using this experimental model and the results have established the cause, mechanism of action and possible prevention strategies of ABPE.

Only intraruminal doses of TRP cause lung injury in cattle, indicating that ruminal fermentation of TRP is a prerequisite for the onset of ABPE. Ruminal bacteria ferment TRP to indoleacetic acid (IAA) with subsequent decarboxylation to 3-methylindole (3MI) (Fig. 23-13). Administration of 3MI by both intraruminal or intravenous methods and in much smaller doses than when TRP is given reproduces the acute lung injury caused by TRP and observed in naturally-occurring ABPE.

TRP can also be fermented to a number of other intermediates and end products, including indole, but the primary product is 3MI.

Several ruminal bacteria have been shown to convert TRP to IAA. The decarboxylation of 3MI has been shown to be catalyzed by a *Lactobacillus* sp. recently isolated from ruminal fluid (Fig. 23-14). This organism is a gram-positive, non-motile, non-spore-forming

Figure 23-12. Cow with severe clinical signs of TRP-induced acute lung injury.

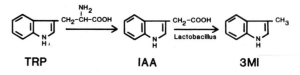

Figure 23-13. Two step fermentation of TRP to 3MI by ruminal bacteria.

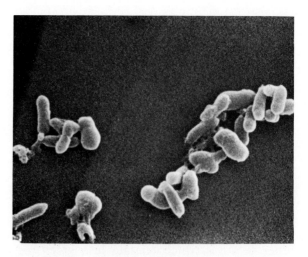

Figure 23-14. Electron micrograph of ruminal *Lactobacillus* sp. responsible for decarboxylation of IAA to 3MI (Ref. 5).

rod. It is an obligate anaerobe that ferments a limited number of sugars to D-(-)-Lactic acid. It is clear that ruminal fermentation conditions can influence the amount of 3MI produced from TRP, but a complete understanding of these factors is not yet available. The optimum ruminal pH for 3MI formation is approximately 6.5-7.0.

In cattle subjected to abrupt pasture change, the concentration of 3MI in the rumen increases for a period of a few days and then gradually declines as cattle become adjusted to the new grazing conditions. The time course of increase in ruminal 3MI concentration is compatible with the time of onset of ABPE and may also explain why cattle usually do not develop ABPE after the ruminal fermentation adapts to the new forage.

Ruminal 3MI is rapidly absorbed from the rumen and reaches body organs via the blood. Following direct infusion of a solution containing 3MI into jugular blood, the plasma concentration decreases with a half-life of approximately 20 to 30 minutes, indicating rapid clearance. At least 10 metabolites appear in the urine and the majority of these compounds are excreted within a few hours after dosing. These metabolites represent at least two metabolic pathways and the end products include 3-methyloxindole and/or derivatives, indole-3-carboxylic acid, and smaller quantities of hydroxyskatole and other compounds. Synthesis and administration of 3-methyloxindole or indole-3-carbinol, a precursor of indole-3-carboxylic acid, does not cause lung injury; indicating that these compounds or their subsequent metabolic products are not responsible for 3MI-induced lung injury.

The effects of 3MI on the lung are rapid. Within 30 minutes after beginning infusion there is ultrastructural damage in the alveolar Type 1 and non-ciliated bronchiolar epithelial (Clara) cells. Changes include swollen vesicles and mitochondria, and alveolar edema. After a few hours, sloughing of alveolar Type 1 and non-ciliated bronchiolar cells is apparent followed by proliferation of smooth endoplasmic reticulum (SER) in surviving cells after 24 to 48 h. Proliferation of SER suggests the involvement of mixed function oxidase (MFO) enzymes in metabolism of 3MI.

It is well known that the MFO system results in biotransformation of foreign compounds yielding products that are generally more polar and less toxic than the parent compound. Contrary to this general rule, there are many examples of metabolic activation of non-toxic parent compounds to reactive intermediates with cytotoxic, carcinogenic or mutagenic effects. These effects may be mediated by electrophiles which covalently bind to cellular macromolecules. The presence of covalently bound radioactivity is used as evidence that a reactive intermediate is involved in the mechanism of chemically-induced cytotoxicity. The binding must be proportional to dose and severity of injury as well as be species and organ specific. Conjugation of the reactive intermediate with sulfhydryl compounds or other detoxifying agents is expected to reduce the concentration of the reactive intermediate and the severity of cytotoxicity.

The formation of reactive intermediates from 3MI was investigated both in vitro and in vivo according to established criteria. Both crude and purified microsomal systems metabolize ^{14}C-3MI to activated intermediates that covalently bind to cellular macromolecules. This binding is dose dependent and it is highest in the lung compared to other organs and tissues. In fact, autoradiographic studies have shown localization of silver grains over the alveolar Type 1 cells and non-ciliated bronchiolar epithelial cells in goats and in only the non-ciliated bronchiolar epithelial cells in horses. Localization of binding in these specific cell types agrees precisely with the sensitivity to 3MI-induced cellular injury in these species. Increasing or sustaining tissue glutathione and/or cysteine concentrations reduces binding and protects goats from the effects of 3MI infusion, while depletion of tissue glutathione concentrations results in higher binding and more severe lung injury. Glutathione and cysteine conjugates of 3MI have been isolated from in vitro microsomal systems and purified by high pressure liquid chromatography. The production of these conjugates is dependent on MFO metabolism and inversely proportional to glutathione and cysteine concentration and covalent binding in this system. Glutathione transferases appear to play a partial role in the formation of the glutathione conjugate. There are

488

significant organ and species differences in the conjugate formation suggesting the possibility of cytotoxicity in other organs and species of animals under particular metabolic conditions of low glutathione concentrations. Mass spectroscopy has confirmed that a 3MI-glutathione conjugate is formed with a molecular weight of 436.

The conclusions drawn from these studies clearly establish the mechanism of 3MI-induced lung injury (Fig. 23-15). After absorption from the rumen, 3MI is metabolized by MFO enzymes in the lung resulting in the formation of a reactive intermediate. This reactive intermediate covalently binds to cellular macromolecules in alveolar Type 1 cells and in non-ciliated bronchiolar epithelial cells resulting in cytotoxicity. The reactive intermediate is inactivated by conjugation to glutathione and/or cysteine. The extent of conjugation of the reactive intermediate with sulfhydryl compounds may have some relationship to organ and species susceptibility to 3MI exposure.

PREVENTION OF ABPE

Knowledge of the cause and mechanism of action provides a logical approach to the prevention of ABPE. Similarly, evidence of the rapid metabolism and irreversible nature of the covalent binding suggests that treatment of animals with ABPE may have limited benefit. In fact, previous attempts at treatment have not been effective.

There are three potential approaches to prevent ABPE: (A) alter animal management and grazing conditions to eliminate abrupt change and excessive consumption of lush forage; (B) alter ruminal fermentation to reduce or eliminate 3MI production after abrupt pasture change; (C) intervene in the systemic metabolism of 3MI to block its effects on the lung.

The effects of 3MI can be blocked experimentally by using MFO inhibitors or by enhancing glutathione concentration, but these methods are unlikely to be practical. The most promising prophylactic methods involve approaches A and B above.

The primary focus of management changes should be to minimize the abrupt pasture change and limit intake of lush forage for the first 10-14 d. A more gradual transition to new forage will facilitate ruminal adaptation and reduce 3MI production. Ranchers have found that a variety of management changes usually reduce the incidence of ABPE. Unfortunately, it has not been possible to eliminate the disease through these procedures. Examples of some possible management practices that may reduce ABPE follow.

Cows should be moved to new pasture before grazing conditions have seriously deteriorated on existing pasture. Avoid giving hungry cows immediate access to lush pasture by prefeeding with hay or pregrazing lower-quality forage. Supply supplementary hay or other feed during the first 10 to 14 d after pasture change. Gradually expose cattle to lush pasture by movable electric fence and supplementary hay feeding. These and other management practices often reduce ABPE, particularly if they are combined with attempts to reduce 3MI production using antibiotic supplementation.

The second approach to prevention of ABPE involves inhibiting 3MI formation in the rumen. A large number of antibiotics representing a variety of classifications and other metabolic inhibitors and antagonists were screened in vitro to test their ability to inhibit ruminal conversion of TRP to 3MI. The ionophore antibiotics were the most potent class of inhibitors tested. Two of these antibiotics, monensin and lasalocid, were selected for in vivo experimental evaluation and field testing.

Groups of cows were given 200 mg/head/d of monensin beginning 1 d before and continuing until 4 d after a TRP dose was given to induce ABPE. Cows given monensin had

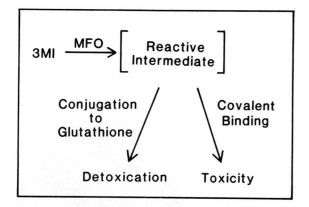

Figure 23-15. Schematic representation of mechanism of 3MI-induced acute lung injury in ruminants.

significantly lower ruminal 3MI concentrations and did not develop lung disease. Control cows given TRP, but without monensin, had higher ruminal 3MI and several died from acute lung disease.

A number of field trials have been conducted in which monensin has been given to cows just before and immediately after pasture change. Monensin was administered in gelatin capsules, protein supplements and in energy supplements. Monensin reduced ruminal concentrations of 3MI after pasture change in all experiments. Lower ruminal 3MI in monensin-treated cows would be expected to prevent ABPE in field trials as it did in experimental animals. Unfortunately, outbreaks of ABPE did not occur in either control or monensin-treated groups, so proof that monensin prevented ABPE was not possible. In one field study, changes in animal management were combined with monensin supplementation and compared to groups of control cows and cows given monensin. Supplemental feeding of dry hay along with 200 mg monensin/head/d resulted in the lower ruminal 3MI concentrations than in any other group of cows in the experiment. Combined management changes and antibiotic supplementation are expected to be the most effective means of prevention.

Experiments have also been conducted in which graded doses of lasolacid, up to 600 mg/head/d, have been given to cows before and after TRP dosing. Ruminal 3MI concentrations were well correlated with lasalocid dose with nearly complete inhibition of 3MI production at 600 mg lasalocid. Lasalocid also prevented ABPE at all doses used compared to cows given TRP without lasalocid. We anticipate that lasalocid will prove to be effective in preventing ABPE under field conditions, but field trials have not been conducted to date.

The results of these studies hold promise for reduced incidence of ABPE. More research is needed in order to devise the most effective and practical recommendations for prevention of ABPE. Higher doses of lasalocid, and perhaps monensin, result in greater inhibition of 3MI production. The most effective dose of these compounds must be established. The effective dose must be balanced by palatability considerations so that the dose will be ingested by cattle. More work is needed to determine the best method of antibiotic administration. Free choice supplements have been used, but these probably do not result in uniform consumption among all cows. Also, it is important that cattle begin consuming the antibiotic at the time of pasture change. Incorporation of antibiotics into different supplements or blocks are being considered. Development of a slow release bolus may also be a convenient and effective method of dose administration. If all of these problems are solved, the legal use of monensin and lasalocid cannot be assured until FDA approval for use of these or equally effective antibiotics for adult breeding cattle is granted. Hopefully, studies that are currently underway may aid in gaining approval for the use of these antibiotics for the prevention of ABPE.

SUMMARY

ABPE is an acute respiratory disease of cattle that often results in death of mature cows within a few days after abrupt change to lush pasture. The disease is caused by excessive consumption of lush forage resulting in abnormal ruminal fermentation and the production of 3MI from TRP in the green forage (Fig. 23-16). 3MI is absorbed from the rumen into the blood where it exposes the lung and other organs. The mixed function oxidase enzymes in the lung metabolize 3MI to a reactive intermediate which covalently binds to lung cells. The alveolar Type 1 and non-ciliated bronchiolar cells are most severely affected and these cells undergo sloughing. Cattle may die within a few days from acute edema, interstitial emphysema and/or the effects of alveolar cell hyperplasia. Treatment of the disease has not proven effective and control lies in prevention. Management changes to eliminate abrupt change from poor quality to lush green

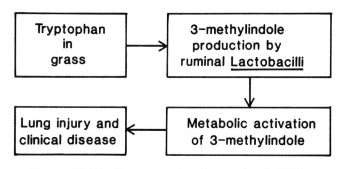

Figure 23-16. Summary of pathogenesis of ABPE.

490

pasture can reduce the incidence of ABPE by providing a more gradual adaptation of ruminal fermentation to new forage conditions. Ionophore antibiotics such as monensin or lasalocid inhibit ruminal convertion of TRP to 3MI and prevent experimentally-induced ABPE. An effective and practical means of prevention of ABPE will probably involve both management changes and antibiotic supplementation. These results promise to reduce or eliminate a disease that has affected cattle throughout the world for over 150 years.

Literature Cited on Bloat

1. Leng, R.A. and J.R. McWilliam. 1973. Proceedings of a Symposium held at the University of New England, Armidale, N.S.W., Australia.
2. Ayre-Smith, R.A. 1971. Aust. Vet. J. 47:162.
3. Bartley, E.E. 1967. Agr. Sci. Rev. 5:5.
4. Cole, H.H., et al. 1956. NAS-NRC. Pub. 388.
5. Cheng, K.J., C.B. Bailey, R. Hironaka and J.W. Costerton. 1979. Can. J. Animal Sci. 59:737.
6. Majak, W., R.E. Howarth, K.J. Cheng and J.W. Hall. 1983. J. Dairy Sci. 66:1683.
7. Cheng, K.J., D.E. Akin and J.W. Costerton. 1977. Fed. Proc. 30:193.
8. Horacek, G.L., L.R. Fina, H.S. Tillinghost and R.L. Gettings. 1977. Can. J. Microbiol. 23:100.
9. Howarth, R.E., et al. 1977. Can. J. Animal Sci. 57:345.
10. McArthur, J.M. and J.E. Miltimore. 1966. Proceedings of the International Grasslands Congress. pp. 518-521.
11. Majak, W., R.E. Howarth, A.C. Fesser, B.P. Goplen and M.W. Pedersen. 1980. Can. J. Animal Sci. 60:699.
12. Horn, G.W., B.R. Clay and L.I. Croy. 1977. Animal Sci. Res. Rept. Okla. Agr. Exp. Sta. MP-101:26.
13. Davis, J.D. and H.W. Essig. 1972. Can. J. Animal Sci. 52:329.
14. Stockdale, C.R., K.R. King and I.F. Patterson. 1980. Aust. J. Exp. Agr. Animal Husb. 20:265.
15. McIntosh, J.T. and F.R.M. Cockrem. 1977. N. Z. J. Agr. Res. 20:263.
16. Essig, H.W. 1967. Proceedings "New Horizons in Legume Bloat Control", A.E. Staley Mfg. Co. Schiller Park, IL. pp. 55-69.
17. Fitzgerald, R.D., E.C. Wolfe, R.H. Laby and D.G. Hall. 1980. Aust. J. Exp. Agr. Animal Husb. 20:688.
18. Bartley, E.E., et al. 1983. J. Animal Sci. 56:1400.
19. Graham, C.A., C. Pern and K.L. Lineham. 1977. Aust. J. Exp. Agr. Animal Husb. 17:555, 17:562.
20. Barr, D.A. and C.A. Graham. 1978. N. Z. Vet. J. 26:117.

Literature Cited on Acidosis

1. Dunlop, R.H. 1972. Adv. Vet. Sci. Comp. Med. 16:259.
2. Elam, C.J. 1976. J. Animal Sci. 43:898.
3. Huber, T.L. 1976. J. Animal Sci. 43:902.
4. Slyter, L.L. 1976. J. Animal Sci. 43:910.
5. Brent, B.E. 1976. J. Animal Sci. 43:930.
6. Huntington, G.B., R.A. Britton and R.L. Prior. 1981. J. Animal Sci. 52:1376.
7. Bide, R.W., W.J. Dorward and M.E. Tumbleson. 1973. Can. J. Animal Sci. 53:697.
8. Suber, R.L., J.F. Hentges, J.C. Gudat and G.T. Edds. 1979. Amer. J. Vet. Res. 40:1005.
9. Huntington, G.B. and R.A. Britton. 1979. J. Animal Sci. 49:1569.
10. Harmon, D.L. 1983. D(-)lactate metabolism in beef cattle. Ph.D. Dissertation. University of Nebraska, Lincoln.
11. Preston, T.R. and M.B. Willis. 1974. Intensive Beef Production. 2nd. Ed. Pergamon Press, Oxford, England.

Literature Cited on Nitrates and Urea

1. Emerick, R.J. 1974. Fed. Proc. 33:1183.
2. NAS. 1972. Accumulation of Nitrate. Nat. Acad. Sci., Washington, DC.
3. Geurink, J.H., et al. 1979. Neth. J. Agr. Sci. 27:268.
4. Phipps, R.H. 1975. J. Br. Grassland Soc. 30:45.

5. Dickson, I.A. and A. MacPherson. 1976. J. Br. Grassland Soc. 31:129.

6. Sokolowski, J.H., U.S. Garrigus and E.E. Hatfield. 1960. J. Animal Sci. 19:1295.

7. Hatfield, E.E. and G.S. Smith. 1963. J. Animal Sci. 22:1122.

8. Hoar, D.W., et al. 1968. J. Animal Sci. 27:557.

9. Carver, L.A. and W.H. Pfander. 1973. J. Animal Sci. 36:581.

10. Carver, L.A. and W.H. Pfander. 1974. J. Animal Sci. 38:410.

11. Takahashi, J., et al. 1980. Japanese J. Zootechnical Sci. 51:626, 649.

12. Olson, O.E., R.J. Emerick and E.I. Whitehead. Undated. South Dakota Ext. Ser. Fact Sheet 420.

13. NAS. 1972. Water Quality Criteria. The Environmental Protection Agency, Washington, DC.

14. Bennet, R.C., D.M. Seath and D. Olds. 1968. J. Dairy Sci. 51:629.

15. Davison, K.L., et al. 1964. J. Dairy Sci. 47:1065.

16. Davison, K.L., K. McEntee and M.J. Wright. 1965. J. Dairy Sci. 48:968.

17. Simon, J., et al. 1959. J. Am. Vet. Med. Assoc. 135:311, 315.

18. Simon, J., et al. 1958. J. Am. Vet. Med. Assoc. 132:164.

19. Olson, O.E., D.L. Nelson and R.J. Emerick. 1963. Agr. Food Chem. 11:140.

20. Pugh, D.L. and G.B. Garner. 1963. Agr. Food Chem. 11:528.

21. O'Dell, B.L., et al. 1960. J. Animal Sci. 19:1280.

22. Emerick, R.J. and O.E. Olson. 1962. J. Nutr. 78:73.

23. Mitchell, G.E., Jr., C.O. Little and B.W. Hayes. 1967. J. Animal Sci. 26:827.

24. Goodrich, R.D., R.J. Emerick and L.B. Embry. 1964. J. Animal Sci. 23:100.

25. Hoar, D.W., L.B. Embry and R.J. Emerick. 1968. J. Animal Sci. 27:1727.

26. Hale, W.H., F. Hubbert, Jr. and R.E. Taylor. 1962. Proc. Soc. Exptl. Biol. Med. 109:289.

27. Weichenthal, B.A., et al. 1963. J. Animal Sci. 22:979.

28. Case, A.A. 1957. J. Am. Vet. Med. Assoc. 130:323.

29. Stewart, G.A. and C.P. Merilan. 1958. Missouri Res. Bull. 650.

30. Crawford, R.F., W.F. Kennedy and K.L. Davison. 1966. Cornell Vet. 57:3.

31. Jones, I.R., et al. 1966. J. Dairy Sci. 49:491.

32. Sell, J.L. and W.K. Roberts. 1963. J. Nutr. 79:171.

33. Welsch, C., et al. 1961. J. Animal Sci. 20:981.

34. Jainudeen, M.R., W. Hansel and K.L. Davison. 1965. J. Dairy Sci. 48:217.

35. Tollett, J.T., et al. 1960. J. Animal Sci. 19:1297.

36. Wyngaarden, J.B. and B. Wright. 1952. Endocrinol. 50:537.

37. Bloomfield, R.A., et al. 1961. Science 134:1690.

38. Bloomfield, R.A., et al. 1962. Proc. Soc. Exptl. Biol. Med. 111:288.

39. Arora, S.P., et al. 1967. J. Animal Sci. 26:1485.

40. Clark, R., W. Oyaert and J.I. Quin. 1951. Onderstepoort J. Vet. Res. 25:73.

41. Bartley, E.E., et al. 1976. J. Animal Sci. 43:835.

42. Davidovich, A., et al. 1977. J. Animal Sci. 45:1397.

43. Davidovich, A., et al. 1977. J. Animal Sci. 44:702.

44. Bartley, E.E., et al. 1981. J. Animal Sci. 53:494.

45. Crickenberger, R.G., et al. 1977. J. Animal Sci. 45:566.

46. Bartley, E.E. 1981. Kansas State University Report of Progress No. 394.

47. Owens, F.N., et al. 1980. J. Animal Sci. 50:527.

48. Davis, G.K. and H.F. Roberts. 1959. Univ. Florida Agr. Exp. Station Bull. 611.

49. Buck, W.B., G.D. Osweiler and G.A. Van Gelder. 1973. Clinical and Diagnostic Veterinary Toxicology. Kendall/Hunt Publishing Co., Dubuque, IA.

50. Lloyd, W.E. 1970. Ph.D. Thesis, Iowa State Univ., Ames, IA.

51. Edjtehadi, M., M. Szabuniewicz and B. Emmanuel. 1978. Can. J. Comp. Med. 42:63.

52. Payne, E. and L. Laws. 1976. Brit. J. Nutr. 35:45.

53. Koenig, J.M., N.W. Bradley and J.A. Boling. 1982. J. Animal Sci. 54:426.

492

Literature Cited on ABPE

1. Carlson, J.R. and R.G. Breeze. 1983. Cause and Prevention of Acute Pulmonary Edema and Emphysema in Cattle. In: Plant and Fungal Toxins, Vol. 1:85-115. R.F. Keeler and A.T. Tu, eds. Marcel Dekker, Inc., NY.

2. Breeze, R.G. and J.R. Carlson. 1982. Chemical-Induced Lung Injury in Domestic Animals. In: Adv. Vet. Sci., Vol. 26:201-231. D.L. Dungworth, ed. Academic Press, NY.

3. Carlson, J.R. and T.M. Bray. 1983. Nutrition and 3-Methylindole-Induced Lung Injury. In: Adv. Nutritional Res. Vol. 5:31-55. H.H. Draper, ed. Plenum Press, NY.

4. Wilson, B.M. and L.T. Burka. 1983. Sweet Potato Toxins and Related Toxic Furans. In: Plant and Fungal Toxins. Vol. 1:3-41. R.F. Keeler and A.T. Tu, eds. Marcel Dekker, Inc., NY.

5. Yokoyama, M.T., J.R. Carlson and L.V. Holdeman. 1977. Isolation and characterization of a skatole producing *Lactobacillus* sp. from the bovine rumen. Appl. Environ. Microbiol. 34:837.

24 METABOLIC PROBLEMS RELATED TO NUTRITION

by L. H. Schultz, H. F. Mayland, and Royce J. Emerick

MILK FEVER, KETOSIS AND THE FAT COW SYNDROME

by L.H. Schultz

The high producing dairy cow is forced to make major metabolic adjustments following calving. She goes from a dry and pregnant period during which there is a need only for maintenance and fetal growth to a sudden demand for a large supply of all the nutrients needed to make a large volume of milk. Although she has a remarkable ability to mobilize body reserves and eventually to increase intake to reach homeostasis, intake lags behind requirements and usually does not reach maximum for about 12-14 weeks. During this period it is not surprising that metabolic disorders occur. The most common are milk fever and ketosis. Others which often complicate these two primary diseases are retained placenta or metritis, fat cow syndrome (where all problems are accentuated by overconditioning when dry) and displaced abomasum (where problems of adjustment of the digestive tract to the space vacated by the fetus are accentuated by high concentrate feeding). The discussion of milk fever and ketosis will stress the role of nutrition, but it is obvious that other factors, particularly hormonal changes involved in metabolic adjustment, are also important and will be considered.

MILK FEVER

Milk fever was first reported in Germany in 1793 and many theories regarding its etiology have developed over the years. Relatively recent reviews include those of Littledike (1), Jorgensen (2) and Littledike et al (3). The relationship of vitamin D metabolism to milk fever was reviewed by Horst and Reinhardt (4).

Occurrence

Data on the overall incidence of milk fever in the USA are lacking. The statistical reporting service in Wisconsin in 1982 indicated that 9% of the animals were affected and 71% of all herds had the problem. Reports from England give an incidence of 3.5% with 5%

mortality in those affected. It was also suggested that the productive life of affected animals was reduced 3.4 years. A number of reports suggest breed differences, with the Jersey and Swedish Red breeds having a higher incidence. There is no obvious explanation for this difference.

Incidence is related also to age. It occurs rarely if at all in first-calf heifers, seldom at second calving, with progressively higher incidence with increased age. Incidence is greater in cows with a previous history of milk fever. Canadian studies reported that about half of the field cases were in cows with a previous history.

Milk fever has been commonly associated with high production. The problem is rare in the beef breeds where milk production is lower. Although there appears to be a general relationship to high production, many cows which are not outstanding producers develop milk fever. It is also a common belief there may be a greater incidence at times of low barometric pressure and at certain seasons of the year, but conclusive evidence for these relationships is lacking.

The timing of the problem in relation to parturition is well known and documented. Canadian studies (5) found that 75% of the cases of milk fever occurred between 1 and 24 h after calving. Only 3% occurred before calving, 6% at the time of calving, 12% between 25 and 48 h after calving, and 4% later. Although some cows go down, with symptoms resembling milk fever, at other stages of lactation, the etiology of these cases appears to be different.

Symptoms

One of the earliest general symptoms is lack of appetite. The digestive tract is inactive. Defecation often occurs following treatment, indicating a return to more normal activity. Most commonly the cow is dull and listless. Cold ears and a dry muzzle are characteristic. The first specific symptom is incoordination when walking. Hind legs may be spraddled in an attempt to brace herself. If made to turn, she may stagger and fall. In later stages of paralysis, the cow lies down and is unable to rise and may struggle in attempting to stand. It is not uncommon for muscle injury and hemorrhage to occur as a result of struggling. This may result in failure to rise after treatment, even though she is alert and blood minerals are normal. It is common for the head to be turned to the side in the sternal recumbancy position. Canadian workers (5) have divided the progress of the disease into three stages: (I) standing, but hypersensitive and wobbly; (II) down on chest, drowsy, muscles flaccid; (III) on side, comatose, advanced muscle flaccidity. Field cases appeared in these stages in a 1:2:1 ratio.

Physiological Changes

Contrary to the common name, milk fever, body temperature is not elevated. In fact, a decrease in body temperature is very common. In one study the lower the body temperature the higher the incidence of "downers" and death. The decrease in muscle activity, decreased appetite and, possibly, a decreased metabolic rate are suggested as likely causes of the decreased temperature.

Decreased gut motility is commonly suggested as a contributing factor to milk fever. Feed intake, fecal output, rumen sounds and the frequency and strength of rumen contractions are reduced at calving. Studies do not seem to be available comparing normal to milk fever-prone cows, however. Depression of neuromuscular transmission was concluded to be the major cause of the paresis associated with the hypocalcemia of milk fever by Bowen et al (6).

Although changes in some urine constituents have been noted by some workers, 24-h urine Ca excretion is similar, both prepartum and postpartum, in normal and milk fever cows. Very little P is excreted in the urine prepartum.

Blood Changes

The major changes in the blood of milk fever cows are a decrease in Ca and P with an increase in Mg. Both total Ca and ionized plasma Ca decrease. The characteristic low blood Ca and excellent response to Ca therapy suggest that a more appropriate name for this condition would be parturient hypocalcemia. Table 24-1 shows the changes in blood components of normal and milk fever cows.

Table 24-1. Blood serum concentration of cows in various metabolic states.[a]

State	Blood serum (mg/dl)		
	Calcium	Phosphorus	Magnesium
Normal	9.4	4.6	1.7
Normal at parturition	7.7 ± 0.9	3.9	3.0 ± 0.5
Milk fever			
Stage I	6.2 ± 1.3	2.4 ± 1.4	3.2 ± 0.7
Stage II	5.5 ± 1.3	1.8 ± 1.2	3.1 ± 0.8
Stage III	4.6 ± 1.1	1.6 ± 1.0	3.3 ± 0.8

[a]Values taken from Jorgensen (2), Willoughby et al (5) and Horst et al (7).

In addition to the above blood mineral changes, a number of other changes in blood components occur. These represent changes that occur to some degree in all cows at parturition as a response to homeostatic mechanisms. Because of the inappetence and other accentuated changes in the milk fever cow, the magnitude of the changes is greater. For example, plasma free fatty acids (FFA) are elevated at parturition in non-paretic cows but elevated still more in paretic cows. Because of the significant negative correlation between FFA and Ca, it has been postulated that there was an increased "uptake" of Ca by adipose tissue as a result of increased lipolysis, and that this may be a causative factor in milk fever. However, Horst et al (7) were unable to demonstrate increases in subcutaneous fat Ca at parturition in either paretic or non-paretic cows. In fact, there was a positive correlation between plasma Ca and subcutaneous fat Ca, along with a highly significant negative correlation (–0.66) between plasma Ca and plasma FFA. It is likely that the elevated FFA levels at calving are simply a reflection of stress plus inappetence. Elevated glucocorticoids cause an increase in FFA and lack of adequate feed intake accentuates the FFA response.

The glucose and insulin situation also changes in the parturient cow, with an accentuated response in the milk fever cow. The usual positive relationship between glucose and insulin when the cow is in a stable condition is reversed at parturition and accentuated in milk fever. Blood glucose is high at parturition due to increased stress and the resulting elevation in glucocorticoids. But the cow does not respond with elevated insulin levels, presumably because the low Ca level inhibits insulin secretion by the pancreas. This also reverses the usual inverse relationship between blood glucose and plasma FFA, with the low insulin tending to accelerate mobilization of FFA from adipose tissue.

The significance of other blood changes in the paretic cow, such as decreased K, decreased citric acid, increased lactic and pyruvic acids, and increased Cl have not been clarified (1).

Hormone Changes

Low insulin and high glucocorticoid levels at parturition have already been mentioned. The adrenal glucocorticoids are considered to be important regulators of receptor binding and subsequent response to other hormones by their target tissue. Excessive glucocorticoid production at parturition has been suggested as a causative factor in milk fever (4). Ca absorption is decreased in glucocorticoid-treated animals, possibly because of a decreased concentration of $1,25(OH)_2D_3$ receptors in the intestinal mucosa. The role of glucocorticoids on bone cell function is less clear. Although cortisol-treated goats mobilized bone Ca better than control goats, the response was not immediate. Milk fever cows often do not show increased bone resorption until 2 to 3 d postpartum.

The two hormones associated with Ca homeostasis have also been widely studied in relation to milk fever. When it was found in earlier work that a high Ca diet during the dry period increased the incidence of milk fever, it was postulated that the parathyroid gland responsible for secreting parathyroid hormone (PTH) to increase Ca mobilization became "lazy" and failed to secrete adequate PTH at parturition. However, the availability of radioimmuno-assay procedures to measure circulating PTH has resulted in considerable data showing an increase in PTH levels in milk fever cows, with very high levels when the blood Ca was very low (8). There was no apparent increase in resistance to development of hypocalcemia with higher concentrations of PTH. A likely explanation of this apparent paradox is that there is a significant lag time involved in developing the capacity to mobilize large quantities of Ca from bone and gut.

Calcitonin produced by the thyroid gland is involved in reducing blood Ca in response to elevated Ca levels. Littledike (1) and others have reported elevated levels of calcitonin in the plasma of some cows prior to parturition. However, as hypocalcemia developed, calcitonin levels decreased to levels as low as or lower than during the dry period. However, in most cows calcitonin increase before parturition was small or non-existent. No relationship could be found between increased calcitonin levels prior to calving and the development of parturient hypocalcemia. In fact, the thyroid of cows with milk fever appears to be depleted of calcitonin (4). Thus, the role of calcitonin in the development of milk fever is not well understood at this time.

Because there is a marked increase in circulating estrogens a few days before calving, along with a marked decrease in progesterone, it has been tempting to associate the elevated estrogens with the milk fever problem. Some workers have reported hypocalcemia after estrogen administration. Some workers have reported elevated estrogen in paretic cows while others have shown no differences (4). Although estrogens may inhibit bone resorption in the rat, there is evidence to suggest that they may increase it in dairy cows. Estrogen reduced dry matter intake, which would reduce the amount of Ca consumed and available for absorption.

Interrelationship of Vitamin D to Milk Fever

It has long been known that vitamin D is involved in Ca and P balance. The preventive effects of vitamin D on milk fever have been investigated for over 40 years. Ohio workers found that feeding massive doses of vitamin D (20 million units daily) for 3-5 d before calving gave about 80% protection from milk fever if calving date was predicted accurately. However, there was difficulty in predicting calving date and concern over toxic effects when these levels were fed longer than 7 d. Later work with continuous feeding of high levels of vitamin D (100,000-500,000 units/d) showed some protection in cows with a previous history of milk fever, but none in cows without a previous history. Research on the mechanism of action of vitamin D suggests that the sites of action of pharmacological amounts of vitamin D are both the gastrointestinal tract and the bone. Some data indicate that vitamin D increased the net absorption of Ca and P from the gastro-intestinal

496

tract of pregnant cows. Rowland et al (9) found that feeding 30 million units of vitamin D daily increased bone resorption with no hypercalcemia in cows fed a Ca deficient diet, but hypercalcemia in cows fed a diet with normal amounts of Ca and P. Evidence of toxicity in cows of 30 million units of vitamin D fed daily for extended periods of time has been presented.

Vitamin D must be metabolized to active forms before it can produce its well-known physiologic effects of curing rickets, initiating Ca absorption, and influencing the mobilization of Ca from bones (see Ch. 16).

In studies to determine whether milk fever was the result of insufficient synthesis or secretion of the active metabolite $1,25$-$(OH)_2D_3$, Horst et al (10) studied the levels of this metabolite in the blood of paretic and non-paretic cows. Plasma $1,25(OH)_2D_3$ increased sharply in the paretic cows during the day preceding calving, reached a maximum of 200 picograms/ml at parturition, and maintained this level for 2.5 d. The non-paretic cows showed a slight depression the day before calving, and then a gradual increase up to a maximum of about 100 picograms/ml of plasma 2 d post calving. These results suggest that milk fever is not the result of insufficient synthesis or secretion of $1,25(OH)_2D_3$. It does suggest that the target organs of this compound as well as parathyroid hormone are not responsive at calving time in paretic cows.

The effects of the administration of large doses of vitamin D to pregnant cows near calving have been varied depending upon level, site of administration and timing in relation to calving. The feeding of 20-30 million units for up to 7 d before calving reduced milk fever without signs of toxicity. Feeding 5 million units or less of D_2 per day for 2 to 4 weeks prepartum did not prevent milk fever. Much more vitamin D is required if given orally than parenterally to prevent milk fever or induce toxicity, presumably due to degradation or modification in the rumen.

Parental administration of 2.5 to 5 million units of D_3 for 2 to 4 weeks prepartum induced milk fever, possibly by interfering with the normal $1,25(OH)_2D_3$ production during the early postpartum hypocalcemic period. Injection of 10 million units of D_3 about one week prepartum reduced the incidence of milk fever in cows with a previous history. Injection of more than 10 million units during the last 10 d of parturition may result in toxicity. There was 80% mortality within a few days after parturition in Jersey cows given injections of 15 to 20 million units of vitamin D in divided doses 20-3 d prepartum.

Studies on the effects of massive parenteral doses of vitamin D on plasma $1,25(OH)_2D_3$ levels show an increase about 2 weeks after administration, persisting at least 1 to 3 weeks depending upon dosage. Maximum hypercalcemia and bone resorption (indicated by plasma hydroxyproline) were greatest about 4 to 5 weeks after injection. Although injecting 10 to 20 million units 30 d prepartum minimized postpartum hypocalcemia, it maximized toxicity (20).

With the isolation of the vitamin D metabolites, it was logical to test their efficacy in milk fever control. The natural metabolites (25-OHD_3 and $1,25$-$(OH)_2D_3$) (2, 11, 12) or a synthetic analogue ($1\alpha OHD_3$) (13, 14) have been used with some success and avoidance of toxicity problems. The exact site of their action (bone or gut) is not known. The fact that hyroxyproline (bone resorption marker) increases in plasma of cows treated with $1,25(OH)_2D_3$ suggests that there is increased bone resorption prior to parturition. Use of vitamin D metabolites to prevent milk fever would be limited by the same factors that limit the use of vitamin D, such as timing of administration, dosage level, site of administration or carrier and dietary history. Ultimately an ideal combination for practical use should be worked out.

Prepartum Feeding Effects

Considerable evidence has accumulated suggesting that dry period feeding has a significant effect on the incidence of milk fever. Excessive Ca was implicated as far back as 1954. Other work suggested that inadequate dietary P was involved. Gardner (15) suggested that Ca:P ratio was important and that a ratio of 2.3 to 1 was ideal. However, most workers now seem to agree that absolute amounts of Ca and P are more important that ratio (2). Iowa workers (16) demonstrated rather clearly that milk fever could be prevented with a prepartum Ca-deficient diet. They fed less than 15 g of Ca/d. One problem with this procedure is to find a practical ration which will supply such a low Ca intake. Their diet (dry basis) was 50% corn silage and 50% shelled corn plus a low-Ca supplement. It was also necessary to limit intake to 14 lb of dry matter for a 1,000-lb cow daily. There is also a need for some concern regarding the effect of the Ca deficiency on subsequent milk production.

Evidence is accumulating that milk fever can be kept under reasonable control by controlling Ca and P intake during the dry period at levels near NRC requirements. Jorgensen (2) concluded that feeding <100 g of Ca/cow/d and keeping the Ca:P ratio <2 to 2.5 to 1, appeared to give the best results. It would appear that if adequate P is fed during the dry period (18 to 35 g/d), Ca intake may vary from near requirements (23 to 40 g) to 100 g/d without markedly influencing the incidence of milk fever. Jorgensen (2) reviewed a number of experiments with varying intakes and ratios of Ca and P and concluded that intake was more important than ratio. High Ca intake (>100 to 125 g/d) in most instances was accompanied by a high incidence of milk fever. Attempts to counteract an excess of Ca with an excess of P have generally been unsuccessful. Ohio workers (17) have demonstrated that an excess of P as well as Ca increased the incidence of milk fever. They conducted a field experiment and divided the cows into three groups on the basis of their Ca and P intake during the dry period. Cows in Group 1 with normal intake (approximately 0.5% Ca and 0.25% P) had a milk fever incidence of 9.5% (4 out of 42). Cows in Group 2 with a high Ca and high P intake (>0.5% Ca and >0.25% P) had an incidence of 35.2% (38 out of 108). In cows with a previous milk fever history the incidence was 60%. In Group 3, cows were fed low Ca and high P (<0.5% Ca and >0.25% P). Milk fever incidence was 18.8% (6 out of 32). Again the incidence was higher in cows with a previous milk fever history. Regression equations relating milk fever incidence to dietary Ca and P, blood P, and age of animals were calculated. For each increase of 0.1% of dietary Ca over 0.59% incidence of milk fever increased by 14%. For every increase in dietary P of 0.1% above 0.35%, incidence of milk fever increased by 19%. Increases in dietary P were reflected in blood P and for

every increase in blood P of 1 mg/dl above 5.8, incidence of milk fever increased by 20%. These data all suggest the rather critical importance of both Ca and P intake during the dry period in the control of milk fever. The daily requirements of a 1,430-lb pregnant dry cow are about 36 g of Ca and 28 g of P. These can be met by feeding about 21 lb (DM) of mixed hay or 30 lb (DM) of corn silage, provided absorption remains at 40% and 50% for Ca and P, respectively.

Other dietary factors may also have some influence on milk fever. It has been suggested that a high proportion of alkaline components (Na + K + Ca + Mg) in the diet in relation to acid components (Cl + P + S) was conducive to milk fever and that feeding of silage preserved with mineral acids reduced the incidence. The feeding of NH_4Cl has also been reported to increase acidity of the ration and Ca absorption. Neither of these procedures seems to have practical potential for milk fever control. Palatability of NH_4Cl apparently is a problem. Grain feeding levels during the dry period have also been studied in relation to milk fever with conflicting results. In one case increased grain feeding reduced milk fever while in another high prepartum grain feeding increased the incidence. Possibly the difference may have been related to condition of the cows. Theoretically, heavier grain feeding should tend to increase absorption of Ca because of a depressing effect on rumen pH. However, if cows become too fat, increased stress at calving and reduced feed intake would tend to increase milk fever.

Prevention
In order to recommend a control program, a rationale regarding the cause of the problem is needed, with preventive measures designed to counteract causative factors. Although there is neither complete agreement on optimum control procedures nor complete success on their adoption, enough information and consensus seems to be available to develop a rationale and make suggestions for prevention.

Rationale. There seems to be reasonable agreement that the sudden Ca drain imposed by initiation of lactation at parturition is the basic underlying cause of milk fever. There is a drain of about 5 to 8 g of Ca daily for the

498

fetus compared to 15 to 30 g of Ca secreted in colostrum on day 1 after calving. This difference can be greater than the total amount of Ca in the plasma and tissue fluids, the readily available body stores. The difference must be offset by an increased flow of Ca from absorption of dietary Ca from the gut or mobilization from bone. The fact that the amount of Ca excreted in the colostrum of paretic and non-paretic cows was not different (18) suggests variation in the ability of cows to compensate for the Ca drain. Mastectomy of milk fever-prone cows will prevent milk fever at the subsequent calving.

If the cow is relying heavily on the alimentary tract as a source of Ca to supply the demands imposed by initiation of lactation, any change in dietary supply caused by decreased appetite or a switch to a low Ca or high P diet would lead to hypocalcemia. If the cow is relying primarily on bone mobilization (as when underfed on Ca prior to calving), inappetence would have a lesser effect, but factors influencing bone mobilization would become more important. There is apparently a significant lag time in creating the capacity to mobilize large quantities of Ca from bone and gut, particularly bone. When cows were underfed Ca prior to calving, a severe hypocalcemia developed within 24 h of the dietary change, but it was corrected rapidly (1-2 d) and resulted in the cows being able to meet the entire lactational Ca demand from bone sources of Ca without developing milk fever at calving (16). Ramberg et al (19) suggested that in the normal cow the initial response to the lactational Ca drain is an increase in absorption from the digestive tract and that appreciable levels of bone resorption are not apparent until about 10 d after the onset of lactation. This presumably occurs in spite of elevated levels of both parathyroid hormone and $1,25(OH)_2D_3$, both of which stimulate bone resorption.

Specific Preventive Procedures. (I) Milking techniques. The common practice of incomplete milking after calving has not been effective in milk fever control. The likely reason is that once the demand for Ca occurs and it moves into the udder, it is out of the system, whether it is removed from the gland or not. Prepartum milking has also been ineffective. The apparent reason is that, although the Ca

drain is more gradual, there is still a large drain at parturition when target tissues involved in Ca mobilization lag in responsiveness.

(II) Vitamin D. Use of pharmacological doses of vitamin D_3 (20-30 million units/d for 2-7 d prior to calving) has been beneficial in prevention of milk fever, but timing and toxicity problems are great enough to eliminate this as a practical approach. Year around feeding of high levels of vitamin D (100,000-500,000 unit/d) has some beneficial effect in cows with a previous history of milk fever, but again the practicality is questionable. Julien et al (17) also found that 10 million units of vitamin D_3 injected prior to calving reduced milk fever in cows with a previous history, but again the risks seem to outweigh the gain with these massive doses.

Use of vitamin D_3 metabolites shows promise of being effective and practical, particularly in herds where excessive Ca is being fed during the dry period and Ca intake is difficult to reduce because of the feeding of legume forage. It also appears that control of P intake (adequate but not excessive) is important for maximum effectiveness. Factors such as which metabolite or analogues to use, timing of administration, carrier and site of administration still need to be optimized.

(III) Dietary approaches. Feeding dietary Ca according to NRC during the dry period, particularly, seems the most effective and practical way to keep the incidence of milk fever at a reasonable level. Excesses of either Ca or P have been shown to increase the incidence. Although feeding a Ca-deficient diet prior to calving may be the surest way of minimizing milk fever, it is difficult to manage and effects on the subsequent lactation have not been clarified. Assuring that adequate vitamin D is fed according to or slightly exceeding normal requirements would also be desirable to assure formation of adequate amounts of the active metabolites. Avoiding excessive fatness at calving would aid in milk fever prevention by tending to avoid excess stress and inappetence during the calving period. All management factors which tend to keep the cow on feed at calving, such as avoidance of stress, clean comfortable calving quarters and provision for exercise should be helpful.

Treatment. Regardless of preventive procedures, 100% freedom from milk fever is unlikely. Fortunately, treatment is very effective if initiated in time, and response is rather spectacular. A cow that is down may be up and eating within an hour or two. The method of choice for treating milk fever still remains the intravenous administration of Ca gluconate (25-100 g). Usually, 500 ml of a 20% solution is given. Slow administration is needed to prevent a heart block. Response is rapid but relapses are common (about 30% of cases). Presumably, this is due to an elevation of blood Ca above normal, triggering mechanisms to reduce it, such as calcitonin release, along with a continued lag in the ability of the cow to mobilize adequate gut and bone Ca. It has been suggested that $1,25\text{-}(OH)_2D_3$ or $1\alpha\text{-}D_3$ may be useful in reducing the incidence of relapse after treatment (3).

Inflating the udder with air is also effective, but generally is not used because of danger of udder infection or injury. Prior intramammary infusion of antibiotics and use of a pressure gauge to control pressure tends to prevent these problems. There is also evidence that relapses are reduced with udder insufflation compared to Ca gluconate treatment. The insufflation technique has been shown to have a definite inhibitory effect on milk production with a 35-50% reduction during the 24-h period after insufflation.

SUMMARY

Milk fever or parturient paresis (calving paralysis) usually occurs within 48 h of calving in older cows. Ca and P in the blood are reduced to about half of normal. Intravenous Ca gluconate is the most satisfactory treatment. The likely cause of the problem is the rapid movement of Ca into the milk when lactation is initiated. Although the hormone $1,25(OH)_2D_3$, a major stimulator of increased Ca absorption from the gut, and parathyroid hormone, a major stimulator of increased mobilization from bone, are high in the blood of the milk fever cow, the response of the target tissue is delayed. A major cause of this delay appears to be excess dietary Ca during the dry period. Recommended preventive procedures include avoiding excess Ca and P in the dry period diet as well as avoiding excessive fatness at calving.

KETOSIS

Ketosis of varying degrees can occur in all animal species with many different causes, but in the farm animals it is a practical problem primarily in the lactating dairy cow, the ewe in late pregnancy and the goat in either late pregnancy or early lactation. Thus, it is restricted to the ruminant species and associated with the energy drain imposed by advanced pregnancy (usually multiple births in sheep and goats) or high milk production in early lactation. Ketosis which occurs in the diabetic human is similar in certain respects but the cause, rather than a glucose drain for productive purposes, is the inability to utilize glucose due to a lack of insulin. No reports of diabetes in farm animals have come to the attention of the author. Since the major problem is in dairy cows, this discussion will deal primarily with lactation ketosis in dairy cows.

The term "acetonemia" was first used to characterize this disorder and is still used occasionally in the field. Technically, it is a less correct term since it means an increase in acetone in the blood, and other ketone bodies also increase. Reviews on this subject include Bergman (1), Kronfeld (2), Schultz (3, 4), Littledike et al (5) and Baird (6).

Identification of the Problem
Definitions. Ketosis is defined as a metabolic disorder in which the level of ketone bodies in body fluids is elevated. These ketone bodies are β-hydroxybutyric acid (βHBA), acetoacetic acid and acetone. Acetone is of minor importance to the animal unless the ketosis is severe and prolonged. It is poorly utilized but does cause the peculiar acetone odor of the breath, urine and milk of ketotic animals. Acetone is formed from acetoacetate at a rate of about 5%/h.

At low blood ketone concentrations found in normal animals, the ratio of β-HBA to acetoacetate plus acetone is about 7 to 1. As the animal becomes ketotic, the ratio decreases to as low as 1 to 1. In the non-ruminant the ratio increases as the animal becomes ketotic. It is not clear whether the ketone bodies are

500

responsible for the symptoms of ketosis, although it is known that high levels of aceto-acetate and acetone can depress the central nervous system (1).

Occurrence. Information is lacking on the incidence of pregnancy disease in sheep. Baird (6) suggests that the incidence in dairy cows in the USA and Western Europe lies in the range of 2 to 15%. Incidence in individual herds may be much higher. These figures obviously would be influenced by diagnostic criteria and the extent to which subclinical cases and cases complicated by other disorders were included. It is estimated that in approximately one-third of cows showing elevated ketone bodies the ketosis is secondary to other problems such as retained placenta, metritis, hardware, etc.

The incidence is higher in older cows, and certain cows tend to repeat, but the problem also occurs at first calving. In northern climates the incidence is higher in the winter and early spring, but this is likely due to more calvings during this period rather than a seasonal effect. Although problems can occur on pasture, recovery has often been observed when barn-fed cows with ketosis were turned out to pasture.

Primary ketosis in dairy cows almost always occurs during the first 8 weeks after calving, when there is peak lactation drain and energy intake has not caught up with output. About 3 weeks after calving is the most critical period. Complicating factors are common when problems occur within a few days of calving.

Symptoms. Visible symptoms of ketosis are not very specific and could indicate a number of different ailments. Fig. 24-1 shows a ketotic cow and Fig. 24-2 shows the same cow after recovery. The ketotic cow shows the typical gaunt and dull appearance. Occasionally, cows may be highly excitable, but this is not common. Usually, rumen contractions are not as regular, the rumen contents are firmer and the feces are rather dry. There is inappetence, with grain usually being refused first, then silage, while the cow may continue to eat some hay. Sometimes there may be incoordination, particularly of the hind legs. Some cases exhibit a curvature of the spine. Decreased milk production and

Figure 24-1. Cow with ketosis. Note gaunt appearance and dullness.

Figure 24-2. Cow in Fig. 24-1 after recovery from ketosis.

loss of weight are obvious consequences of the reduced feed intake. There is a distinctive acetone-like odor of the breath and fresh milk. Milk fat percentage is increased, even in subclinical ketosis. Usually the cow progresses into this condition gradually. Very seldom does a cow die from ketosis, and when death occurs the only obvious finding on post-mortem is a fatty liver. Although an acidosis develops in diabetic ketosis in humans due to the acid ketone bodies, this seldom occurs in the ketotic cow because the alkali reserve usually remains adequate (2).

Blood Changes. Table 24-2 illustrates the typical changes occurring in the blood of

Table 24-2. Blood changes in clinical ketosis.[a]

Component	Normal	Ketosis
	. . . . . mg/dl	
Blood		
Glucose	52	28
Ketones, total	3	41
Plasma		
Free fatty acids	3	33
Triglycerides	14	8
Free cholesterol	29	15
Cholesterol esters	226	150
Phospholipids	174	82

[a]Taken from Yamdagni and Schultz (7).

Table 24-3. Comparisons of blood and milk ketones.[a]

Qualitative milk test	Blood			Milk	
	Glucose	βHBA	AA+A	βHBA	AA+A
	. . . . mg/dl				
Negative	44	4.3	1.1	1.7	0.8
Trace	40	8.8	2.8	2.3	1.7
One plus	30	11.0	4.0	3.1	2.5
Two plus	35	14.7	7.0	2.8	5.5

[a]Taken from Schultz and Myers (8). βHBA, β-hydroxybutyric acid; AA, acetoacetic acid; A, acetone (all expressed as acetone).

cows with ketosis. The elevation of ketone bodies is characteristic. Normal levels could be considered anything below 10 mg/dl. Above this the cow progresses into subclinical ketosis. The ketone level of milk is about half the blood level, whereas the urine level exceeds the blood level by about four times. This makes the urine test somewhat overly sensitive for diagnosis, with most high producing cows showing positive urine tests in early lactation, often without need for treatment. The milk test is more conservative but more accurate than the urine test in indicating when there may be a problem. Milk starts to become positive with an alkaline Na nitroprusside powder at about 10 mg/dl total blood ketones. Since the mammary gland utilizes βHBA for milk fat synthesis, the level of this component in milk is markedly lower than in the blood. It appears at a rather constant level in milk of 2 mg/dl. Levels of acetoacetate and acetone in blood and milk tend to be similar. The qualitative tests for ketone bodies based on the development of a purple color with Na nitroprusside do not measure βHBA.

The second major change in the blood accompanying elevated ketones is a decrease in blood glucose, as shown in Tables 24-2 and 24-3. Normal levels in ruminants are about 50 mg/dl. Values below 40 can be considered subnormal. Ketotic animals may have levels as low as 25.

Although the emphasis in the name of the disorder and in the qualitative blood tests is on the elevated ketones, depressed blood glucose is the initial change likely responsible for subsequent changes in other components. Under unusual conditions (thyroxin administration, fat cow syndrome, certain infections, diabetes, etc.) it is possible to have normal or elevated glucose along with elevated ketones, but this is not typical or primary ketosis. The causative factor(s) are different and the animals do not respond to the usual treatments.

The third blood change is an increase in free fatty acids (FFA) which are a measure of the extent of lipolysis of adipose tissue or mobilization of body fat. They are transported as a FFA-albumin complex. The sequence of events involves reduced glucose (and reduced insulin) which triggers increased lipid mobilization and elevated blood FFA. These are in turn converted to ketone bodies in the liver. In the normal cow about 40% of the ketones come from FFA while in clinical ketosis, when a cow is not eating, 100% may come from FFA. The other major source is rumen butyrate, which would not be produced when the cow is not eating. Under ketotic conditions, within-cow correlations between blood glucose and ketones were negative (−0.68) while there was a significant positive correlation between FFA and ketones (+0.85).

The other blood lipids shown in Table 24-2 (triglycerides, cholesterols, and phospholipids) all decrease. The reason for this decrease is not completely understood. Less lipids are consumed so there is a reduced need for transportation of absorbed lipids. In nonruminants, elevated FFA result in increased production and secretion of lipoproteins into the plasma. This does not appear to be the case in the ruminant. Either less triglycerides are formed in the liver because of reduced

502

glycerophosphate resulting from low blood glucose, or there is some problem in lipoprotein release from the liver. The latter seems possible because in advanced ketosis a fatty liver may develop. Some writers have suggested that inadequate protein nutrition may result in reduced availability of the protein moiety of the lipoprotein, reducing lipoprotein release. Attempts to produce experimental fatty livers in ruminants by the author have generally been unsuccessful. Only under conditions where glucose availability is markedly reduced, such as alloxan diabetes or fasting of lactating or pregnant animals, has significant fat accumulated in the liver (9).

Other blood components also change in ketosis and likely are again a consequence of the reduced glucose. Blood acetate is usually elevated. Normal levels are about 6-10 mg/dl in the ruminant, the primary source being rumen fermentation, with absorption through the portal system with little metabolism in the liver. Acetate is non-ketogenic in the ruminant and may be beneficial to the ketotic cow through a glucose-sparing action. It is likely that there are two reasons for its elevation in the ketotic cow. One is increased endogenous acetate production, although some difference of opinion exists on the extent and importance of endogenous acetate in the ruminant (see Ch. 15). The other more likely reason is a decrease in acetate utilization as a result of low glucose and insulin levels. Fed alloxan diabetic goats showed increases in blood acetate to as high as 40 mg/dl while fasted diabetic goats stayed at about 5 mg/dl (9). This suggests that a reduction in utilization is the major cause of the elevation. Acetate levels in subclinically ketotic cows rose to about 20 mg/100 ml at the time of peak ketones and minimum glucose about 3 weeks after calving (10). The latter work also showed a decrease in insulin levels corresponding with decreases in glucose and increases in FFA and ketones.

Figures 24-3 and 24-4 show changes following parturition in the blood components of normal cows and cows with subclinical ketosis. No treatment was required in the subclinical animals. The marked drop in triglycerides at calving in both groups likely reflects the use of triglycerides for milk fat synthesis. The increases in cholesterol in both groups likely reflects increased lipid intake with increased grain feeding.

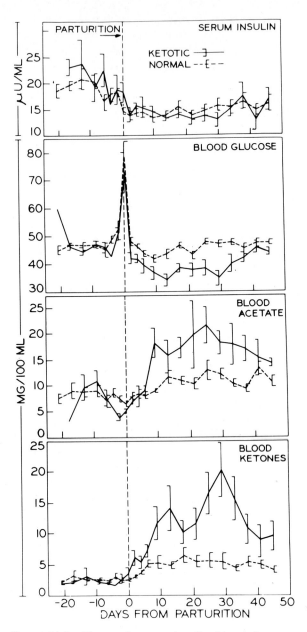

Figure 24-3. Changes in serum insulin, blood glucose, acetate and ketones in normal and ketotic cows before and after calving.

Diagnosis

The symptoms of ketosis have been described but they are not very specific, so care in diagnosis is needed. A distinction should be made between primary or spontaneous ketosis, where no apparent pathological condition other than the true ketotic syndrome exists, and secondary ketosis, in which other factors are involved. Because primary ketosis is a metabolic disorder, there is no elevation of body temperature, thus elevated

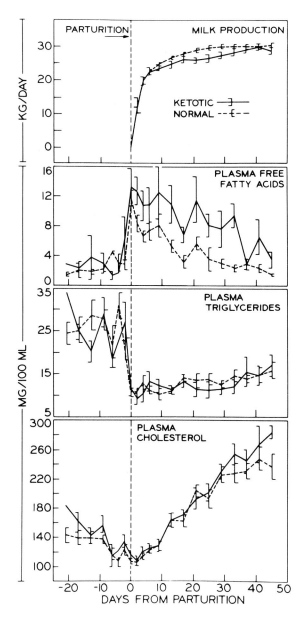

Figure 24-4. Changes in milk production and free fatty acids, triglyceride, and cholesterol in plasma of normal and ketotic cows before and after parturition.

temperature immediately implicates other factors. An elevated blood glucose level accompanying elevated ketones also suggests other complications.

The best field diagnostic procedure would involve a measurement of body temperature along with both a urine and milk test for ketone bodies. A negative urine test rules out ketosis. A positive urine test and negative milk test (a common finding) suggests some body fat mobilization but, without other

symptoms, no need for treatment. When the milk test becomes positive, even though the cow has not gone off feed, use of an oral glucose precursor such as propylene glycol, fed daily, is indicated. With more severe reactions and/or other symptoms, treatment is indicated. In one study in the writer's laboratory, 300 cows were tested with a commercial alkaline Na nitroprusside test powder designed for diabetics which becomes positive (trace) at 4-6 mg/dl milk ketones representing 10-15 mg/dl blood ketones. During the first 8 weeks after calving, 14% were positive. Of 42 positive cows, 22, or about half, were considered to require treatment by the herdsman or veterinarian.

A satisfactory test powder can be prepared using a base mixture of 75% granular Na_2CO_3 and 25% granular $(NH_4)_2SO_4$ to which enough fine granular Na nitroprusside (about 1%) is added to insure some of the small purple crystals in the material used for each test. A small mound of the powder about the size of a dime is placed on a white surface and moistened with a few drops of milk or urine. Development of a pink color indicates the presence of ketone bodies. With increasing ketones the color changes from pink to purple. Sensitivity decreases after several months, so new material should be prepared on a regular basis. Most of the ketone tests for human diabetics do not work well on milk.

In herds with ketosis problems, a simple weekly milk test for the first 6 weeks after calving would identify cows with beginning ketosis. Corrective action could be taken with oral materials before the cases became severe.

RELATIONSHIP TO GLUCOSE METABOLISM

Glucose is a critical metabolite for the high producing dairy cow. Not only is it absorbed in much smaller amounts from the digestive tract than in the non-ruminant, but it is needed in larger amounts for the synthesis of lactose in milk. Blood glucose levels are about half those of non-ruminants and must be maintained at 40-60 mg/dl to maintain normal function in many body tissues (see Chs. 14, 20). Both the glucose and galactose of the lactose in milk are derived largely from blood glucose in both cows and goats. This suggests that slightly more glucose on a weight basis than there is lactose in milk would need to be removed from the gland daily just to make the lactose. Thus, a cow producing 40 kg of milk containing 5% lactose would need over 2 kg of glucose daily just for lactose synthesis, in addition to that needed for oxidation for energy and for synthesis of glycerol. When blood glucose drops in ketosis, it is not surprising that milk production drops because the cow needs to make milk of relatively constant lactose content to maintain osmotic equilibrium with blood.

The main source of glucose for the ketosis-prone ruminant is propionic acid produced in the rumen. Although diets high in grain produce more propionic acid and thus may benefit the ketosis-prone cow, care needs to be taken when using such diets to feed enough roughage to keep the cow on feed and prevent other problems such as milk fat depression. The cow with milk fat depression is in an opposite metabolic state from the cow with ketosis and she tends to be depositing rather than mobilizing body fat. A second source of glucose is hydrolysis in the lower tract of starch which by-passed the rumen. Estimates of this contribution vary from none to a modest amount on rations high in grain. Increased starch by-pass would be helpful to the ketosis-prone cow. Protein can also be a source of glucose, but the contribution is relatively low in the normal animal. Although most amino acids are glucogenic, some are ketogenic (tyrosine, isoleucine, leucine, and phenylalanine). The metabolic intermediate of leucine, isovaleric acid, is markedly ketogenic. Glycerol is another minor source of glucose.

In summary, it appears that the major dietary sources of glucose would be propionate, protein and absorbed glucose from by-passed starch. During fasting, when liver glycogen is depleted, the major precursors would be amino acids from tissue protein and glycerol from mobilized fat.

Because oxalacetate plays a central role in the TCA cycle in the synthesis of glucose from propionate and many amino acids, and because adequate oxalacetate would favor fatty acid oxidation through the TCA cycle rather than formulation of ketone bodies in the liver, some have suggested oxalacetate deficiency as a cause of ketosis. Baird (6) suggests that ketogenesis might be regulated at the point of entry of acetyl-CoA into the TCA cycle, with high levels of oxalacetate in the mitochondrion favoring oxidation in the cycle rather than ketone body formation. A lack of precursors such as propionate may deplete oxalacetate in the ruminant.

It is tempting to use the simple explanation that hypoglycemia and ensuing ketosis in dairy cows is due to the glucose drain imposed by high milk production coupled with an inadequate supply of glucose precursors. It is likely that these are the major predisposing causes. However, if these were the only factors, it should be possible. to produce the condition simply by reducing the feed of the high producing cow. Fasting does produce similar blood changes of lesser magnitude but usually homeostatic mechanisms prevent the typical ketosis. Resumption of feeding usually causes recovery. It appears that in certain cows or under certain conditions at calving, such as excessive fatness, the homeostatic mechanisms do not function properly.

ROLE OF LIPID METABOLISM

Because the ruminant is particularly susceptible to ketosis, it was logical for researchers to explore the role of the VFA produced in the rumen in this condition. Although the ketotic cow has a reduced level of total VFA and the proportion of acetate was increased while propionate decreased, the same results could be obtained by fasting, so this is simply a reflection of reduced feed intake. Administration of propionic acid increased blood glucose and decreased ketones as expected. This information led to the development of oral Na propionate and later propylene glycol for treatment and prevention. Acetate caused little change in blood glucose or ketones, suggesting that it was neither glucogenic or ketogenic. It can be considered a glucose sparer, however, and could have some beneficial effects on ketosis. The fact that acetate is elevated in the blood of the ketotic cow may be related to the low level of insulin, which would reduce acetate utilization. Butyric acid is definitely ketogenic. Thus, butyrate in excess would be undesirable from the standpoint of ketosis. It is unlikely that butyrate production in the rumen would increase to amounts that would elevate blood ketones significantly. The possible ketogenic effects of normal butyrate production are counteracted by the antiketogenic effects of propionic acid. High-moisture hay crop silage can contain significant amounts of butyric acid and this could accentuate the ketosis problem. Fortunately, corn silage and most good quality wilted hay crop silages contain little butyric acid.

Lipolysis in Adipose Tissue

When blood glucose and insulin are reduced, adipose tissue lipolysis is increased and free fatty acids (FFA) are released into the blood to become the major source of ketones in the ketotic cow. The FFA appear to be taken up by the liver in a rather constant percentage, regardless of level, so lipolysis is an important part of ketosis. The importance of glucose in control of lipolysis is emphasized by the high negative correlation between glucose and FFA (-0.92) (11).

Pharmacological doses of niacin to ketotic cows markedly inhibited lipolysis and ketogenesis for about 36 h, but this was followed by a rebound to initial or higher levels in about 48 h (12). Later work has shown that niacin also affects carbohydrate metabolism, causing elevation of insulin levels and extended glucose tolerance curves.

Lipid Transport and Utilization

The sequence of events occurring in ketosis could be outlined as follows: (a) Blood glucose level decreases. (b) Hormone sensitive lipase activity in adipose tissue increases, presumably in response to decreased insulin and possibly other hormonal changes, resulting in elevated tissue levels of cyclic AMP. (c) Free fatty acids (FFA) are released in increased amounts into the blood, where they are carried as a FFA-albumin complex. (d) Liver uptake of FFA is increased. About 25% of circulating FFA are taken up by the liver (1) so elevated levels mean increased uptake. (e) Mammary uptake of FFA increases. Under normal conditions there is no net uptake of FFA by the mammary gland but appreciable uptake occurs in the ketotic cow. These FFA contribute to the FFA pool for milk fat synthesis. Triglyceride uptake by the mammary gland is reduced in ketosis but the decreased contribution of triglycerides to the FFA pool is more than compensated for by increased uptake of FFA. Therefore milk fat percentage is elevated in the ketotic cow. (f) The pathways of FFA metabolism in the liver change. Possible pathways are: esterification to triglycerides and some phospholipids, oxidation to CO_2, and partial oxidation to ketone bodies. Bergman (13) suggests that about 30% of the FFA uptake by the liver of normal fed sheep is converted to ketone bodies, but this increases to 81% in ketotic animals. This means a reduction in percentage esterification and oxidation to CO_2. (g) The lipid content of the liver increases. Although the percentage of FFA esterified is reduced, total esterification may be increased because uptake may be increased 5-10 times. Lipid accumulation would be expected unless release was accelerated. (h) Blood triglyceride levels decline. The fact that the lipid content of the liver is higher and that of the blood is lower supports the idea of an abnormality in release from the liver.

The mechanisms responsible for the shift in FFA pathways in the liver are not well understood. The increased FFA levels present more to the liver for processing and a relative oxalacetate deficiency would tend to decrease oxidation, forcing them into ketogenesis and esterification.

Fatty Livers

Cows with advanced ketosis or those that die from ketosis have fatty livers. Levels above 10% fat (wet basis) are considered abnormal. Early studies reported total liver fat levels in the early stages of ketosis of 7.4% and in later stages 21.5%. The author has found levels as high as 30% (68% on a dry basis). Recent studies by Fronk et al (14) showed that the primary lipid deposited was triglyceride, with significant elevations in overconditioned cows 2 d after calving compared to control cows. The other major lipid, phospholipids, went down, so the triglyceride:phospholipid ratio of liver fat went from 1.1 in the control cows to 3.4 in the overconditioned. It appears that there is gradual accumulation of lipid in the liver—thus making treatment increasingly difficult as the case progresses. The usual recovery pattern with milder ketosis suggests that there is not irreversible fatty degeneration, except possibly in older, chronic repeater cases.

The "fat cow syndrome" occurring in extremely fat cows shortly after parturition is characterized by an extremely fatty liver. In practically all instances it is complicated by infections such as metritis or mastitis, and disease resistance is low. Although this condition is characterized by excessive fat mobilization and liver deposition, along with high ketones, the condition is different from ketosis. Usually, blood glucose is elevated, so it appears that the hormonal response to stress triggers somewhat different metabolic changes.

Origin, Regulation and Utilization of Ketone Bodies

The principal precursors of ketone bodies in the ruminant are FFA from mobilized body fat and butyric acid produced in the rumen or ingested in silage. In the fed animal about half of the βHBA and one-fourth of the acetoacetate came from butyrate, with the rest from FFA. In the ketotic animal that is not eating, essentially all come from FFA.

The major sites of ketone body formation in the ruminant are liver and ruminal (and abomasal) epithelium. Both βHBA and acetoacetate (AA) are produced by these tissues but βHBA is the predominant one produced in the rumen wall. Other tissues in lung, kidney, mammary gland, and sometimes muscle can interconvert ketone bodies (βHBA and AA) but this does not represent net production. The overall effect in these tissues is utilization. Although βHBA may be a more desirable transport form because it is more stable, it has to be converted to AA before it is utilized in the tissues.

Most tissues can utilize ketone bodies. The pathway involves conversion to acetoacetyl-CoA, which can form acetyl-CoA and then be oxidized through the TCA cycle, or it can be used for fat synthesis or the formation of other compounds. The brain and nervous tissue of normal animals presumably do not utilize ketone bodies, but there is evidence of adaptation after a week or so of starvation so that ketone bodies are used. Such adaptation might explain the "nervous" cases of ketosis in that rapidly developing cases might exhibit nervous symptoms because adaptation had not occurred.

The present prevailing concept is that ketone body utilization is not significantly impaired in ketosis, but as the case advances production exceeds utilization. Maximum utilization of ketones apparently occurs at a blood level of about 20 mg/dl. Beyond this point, utilization cannot keep up with production and large increases in blood levels are seen.

Excretion of ketone bodies occurs in urine and milk of lactating cows, with urine excretion far exceeding that in milk. Excretion represents a loss of energy, but it is unlikely that excretion would ever exceed 10% of the amount produced.

When insulin secretion is not impaired, the influence of blood glucose on ketones has been demonstrated clearly. Administration of glucose decreases FFA and ketones quickly. The glucose influence could occur through a direct effect, for example on pathways of FFA metabolism in the liver, or indirectly through reducing FFA release from adipose tissue. A statistical path analysis of changes in these components suggested that about 75% of the variation in blood ketone level could be accounted for by these two effects of blood glucose level, with the indirect effect, via FFA levels, being relatively much greater than the direct effect.

Studies on factors affecting the ketogenicity of butyrate have shown that intravenous glucose, intravenous propionate, or oral propionate are equally effective in suppressing ketogenesis from butyrate in experimentally ketotic animals. Because circulating FFA did not change, it seems likely that there is a direct antiketogenic effect of glucose at the rumen wall as well as the liver.

It is likely that hormones play an important role in ketogenesis through endocrine changes involved in homeostasis. However, aside from the important role of insulin in lipolysis, little is known about the importance of hormones in the development of ketosis. The next section discusses the general hormonal relationships to ketosis.

Hormonal Relationships

One of the early concepts was that bovine ketosis was due to an adrenocortical insufficiency. This was based on the observation that glucocorticoids were beneficial for treatment and the presence of histological abnormalities in the adrenals of ketotic cows. However, the fact that responses were also obtained with ACTH suggested that the adrenal was still responsive because the action of ACTH was to stimulate glucocorticoid release. Response to glucose or glucose precursors would also argue against degenerative changes in the adrenal as a primary cause.

Thyroxine has been used in the experimental production of ketosis, but the unphysiological conditions used make it doubtful if thyroxine excess is a cause of field ketosis. Implants of triodothyronine at calving time increased either the severity or the incidence of ketosis in one study.

A number of hormones have been shown to influence glucose, ketones, and FFA when injected. Growth hormone, ACTH, and the catecholanines increased FFA, with glucocorticoids causing a slight increase. Glucagon caused a biphasic response in FFA, a decrease followed by an increase above normal, with opposite responses in blood glucose. In fed animals, ketones did not change despite rather large increases in FFA. Insulin caused an initial depression of FFA, along with decreases in glucose, presumably reflecting increased glucose utilization. Convincing evidence of abnormal secretion of any of these hormones as a direct cause of ketosis is lacking.

Nutritional Aspects

Energy Intake. Because there is good evidence that ketosis is accentuated by excessive fatness at calving and by a negative energy balance after calving, the ideal feeding program for ketosis control from an energy standpoint would be low to moderate feeding before calving with a high level after calving. There are some practical limitations in this program, however. Although feed can be offered, maximum intake is delayed until about the 12th week after calving because of unknown physiological factors. This is after the peak ketosis problem. In addition, at least one-third of the diet needs to be coarse roughage in order to keep cows on feed and maintain a normal fat test. This limits the amount of energy that can be fed. The feeding of fat would increase energy concentration, but levels above about 5% of the total diet tend to reduce nutrient utilization and may put an undue load on lipid transport mechanisms. However, feeding liberal quantities of high quality feeds within these

limitations should definitely aid in ketosis control. Gardner (15), using various concentrations of energy levels designated as low and high before and after calving found the optimum combination from the standpoint of both production and freedom from ketosis was low prepartum (115% of requirements), and high postpartum (fed to maintain body weight).

Kronfeld (16) has proposed that a lack of lipogenic nutrients may be involved in ketosis because they provide precursors for milk fat and make milk fat synthesis more efficient. As already indicated, added fat may help prevent a negative energy balance in early lactation and indirectly spare glucose, but there is considerable evidence for a beneficial effect of glucogenic nutrients in ketosis prevention and treatment.

Protein. Early research in the USA indicated that there was little evidence that feeding either high or low protein was conducive to ketosis. European workers have suggested that high protein rations create problems similar to ketosis, but evidence for this is lacking in the USA. Although it has been proposed that a shortage of methionine might be an important cause of ketosis, possibly because it played a special role in the formation of lipoproteins in the liver, administration of methionine analogue at a level of 40 g daily for 7 d to cows with subclinical ketosis had limited beneficial effect (3). It is concluded that although adequate protein nutrition is desirable, there is a lack of specific evidence that either a deficiency or excess of protein is a primary cause of field ketosis in the USA.

Minerals and Vitamins. There is a lack of convincing evidence of the direct involvement of mineral deficiencies in the development of primary ketosis. Control by supplementation would be easy if such were the case. Blood levels of K, P, Cl, Ca and Mg are not altered in ketosis. Co deficiency could be suggested as a contributing factor since Co-containing vitamin B_{12} is required as an essential co-factor in the conversion of propionate to glucose. There is evidence that blood and liver levels of vitamin B_{12} are lower in early than late lactation. However, there is no evidence that Co beyond that in trace mineral salt is beneficial.

Most herds with ketosis problems have adequate Co in the diet.

The vitamin which has received the most attention in relation to ketosis is niacin. Original work involved the already mentioned effect of pharmacological doses in inhibiting lipolysis and elevating glucose. More recent work has suggested possible beneficial effects of more physiological levels. For some time rumen synthesis of B vitamins has been considered adequate to meet the needs of ruminant species. Recent work has raised the question as to whether this is adequate for high producing cows in early lactation. A beneficial role of niacin supplementation through stimulation of rumen organisms as well as alleviation of ketosis has been suggested (17).

Fronk and Schultz (17) showed some beneficial effects of 12 g of nicotinic acid daily for cows with subclinical ketosis. Bartlett et al (18) showed reduced urine ketones and a lowering of the incidence of clinical ketosis from 4.8 to 1.5% in a field study of nine herds with 508 cows when 6 g of niacin was fed daily for the first 10 weeks of lactation. Dufva et al (19) showed some benefit in milk production, higher blood glucose and lower blood ketones and free fatty acids with the feeding of 6 g of niacin daily during early lactation. The 6 g daily dosage seemed to be adequate while 3 g was not. Other studies with the feeding of supplemental niacin in early lactation have not shown consistent results in terms of production response (14, 17). There seems to be an interaction with condition in that thin cows showed decreases in milk and increases in fat test, while cows in normal condition showed a positive response in milk production. It may be that only cows with subclinical ketosis show response, and thin cows are not likely to have ketosis. Nicotinamide coenzymes were low in mammary biopsy samples of ketotic cows in one study, possibly indicating a reduced synthesis of milk fat from acetate. Although more definitive evidence is needed, existing evidence suggests that herds with a high incidence of ketosis may benefit from niacin supplementation in early lactation.

Therapy

Many treatments have been suggested for ketosis, but only a few have stood the test of time. The following are the most commonly used and most effective (20).

A. **Intravenous Glucose.** Commonly, 500 ml of a 40% glucose solution is given. This is the most rapid way to provide an outside source of glucose. The disadvantages are: (a) some may spill over in the urine and be lost; (b) presumably it triggers insulin release, is used up rather rapidly, and blood glucose falls below normal levels within 2 h. Therefore, the animal has to make rather rapid homeostatic adjustments to return to normal. Slow, continuous intravenous drips of glucose (2,000 ml) represent a rather ideal type of therapy, but this is too cumbersome under field conditions.

B. **Hormones.** Glucocorticoids or ACTH have been used for ketosis treatment for many years. The beneficial effect of glucocorticoids appears to be due to increases in blood glucose through stimulation of gluconeogenesis from amino acids. ACTH stimulates release of glucocorticoids from the adrenal cortex. The effect lasts several days. The glucocorticoids cause decreased peripheral utilization of glucose in muscle and adipose tissue, which may initially cause some increased mobilization of body fat and elevation of ketones. The major disadvantages appear to be possible changes in hormonal balance and depletion of body protein through use as a glucose source. Repeated treatment with glucocorticoids may reduce adrenal activity and reduce disease resistance. ACTH may be indicated in cases that have been repeatedly treated with glucocorticoids in order to stimulate the by-passed adrenals. Fox (20) suggests dosage levels for glucocorticoids equivalent to 1 g of cortisone intramuscularly or intravenously, or 200-800 units of ACTH intramuscularly.

C. **Oral Glucose Precursors.** Two oral materials have been commonly used. Na propionate was used initially but has gradually been replaced by propylene glycol because of advantages in cost, handling, palatability and absence of Na. The usual dosage level of these materials is 250-500 g/d, preferably in two administrations/d. It is usually continued for 5-10 d. Drenching may be needed in cows that are not eating. Propylene glycol is converted to glucose in the liver via pyruvate and oxalacetate.

The advantage of the oral materials is that an exogenous source of glucose is provided at a modest level over a prolonged period. Often, the oral materials are used as a follow-up of glucose or hormone treatments. Sugar or molasses fed or given as a drench is not an effective treatment because it is not absorbed as glucose but converted to VFA in the rumen.

D. **Miscellaneous Treatments.** Co (at least 100 mg/d as sulfate or chloride) may be added to propylene glycol if a Co deficiency is suspected. Chloral hydrate (28 g twice daily for 3-5 d) is sometimes used to quiet nervous cases and occasionally in other special circumstances.

Prevention

It is not possible to give a set of recommendations which will prevent all ketosis. However, procedures which will maximize energy intake, provide adequate glucose precursors and minimize body fat mobilization have made it possible to keep this metabolic disorder under reasonable control. Specific recommendations include the following: (a) Avoid excessive fatness at calving. It is recommended that cows be in reasonable condition at drying off and that they be fed only enough to maintain that condition while dry. (b) Either eliminate or limit concentrate feeding while dry, but increase concentrates to modest levels in the late dry period, and then rapidly after calving, using care to prevent the cow from going off feed. (c) Feed high quality forage at a minimum of one-third of total dry matter intake after calving to keep the cows on feed and avoid a drop in fat test. (d) Do not make abrupt changes in the ration after freshening, particularly to low quality feeds. (e) Feed recommended levels of energy, protein, minerals and vitamins to meet current standards. (f) Avoid feeding high-moisture hay crop silage with elevated levels of butyric acid. (g) Maximize intake by providing palatable feeds fed at reasonable frequency along with optimum comfort, exercise and freedom from stress. (h) In problem herds, monitor the ketotic state with weekly milk tests for 6 weeks after calving. Feed propylene glycol at a level of 125-250 g daily to problem cows. (i) Production being equal, select for cows with good capacity and appetite.

SUMMARY FOR KETOSIS

Ketosis is a metabolic disorder of dairy cows occurring within about two months of calving and characterized by lack of appetite, listlessness, reduced milk production and weight loss. Most high producing cows have borderline ketosis when lactation peaks. The level of glucose in the blood is low and ketones are elevated. The ketones appear in increased amounts in the milk and urine and are used for diagnosis. About one-third of ketosis cases are secondary to other problems such as hardware, displaced abomasum, retained placenta and milk fever. The major cause of primary ketosis is the heavy glucose drain for milk lactose synthesis, combined with insufficient intake of feed to supply adequate precursors for glucose. Successful treatments include intravenous glucose, glucocorticoid injection, and oral propylene glycol, a glucose precursor not destroyed in the rumen. Preventive procedures include avoiding excess fatness at calving combined with liberal feeding of a palatable balanced ration after calving, or, in special problem cows, daily feeding of propylene glycol during the susceptible period.

PREGNANCY TOXEMIA IN SHEEP

This condition is sometimes called lambing sickness or twin lamb disease (21). It is pregnancy ketosis in late gestation in ewes carrying multiple fetuses. Increased emphasis on multiple births would tend to increase the potential for this problem.

Occurrence

Pregnancy toxemia (PT) occurs in all breeds of sheep in the second and subsequent pregnancies. Both thin and obese ewes carrying multiple fetuses develop the disease during the last month of pregnancy.

Cause

The cause is a combination of rapid growth of multiple fetuses and inadequate ewe nutrition, particularly low energy intake. Special stresses at this time may be an initiating or

510

accentuating factor. Experimental PT cannot always be produced by fasting alone, but superimposing a stress condition on fasting is quite effective. Transport, fasting, change of feed, inclement weather, and disease can all initiate the problem. The hypoglycemia resulting from the above appears to be the primary initiating factor, as in lactation ketosis.

Symptoms

The affected ewe usually isolates from the flock and shows inappetence, weakness, incoordination and may elevate the head. Eventually she lies down and rises only with assistance, often showing accelerated breathing and discharges from the nose. In the advanced stages there is progression to neurologic signs such as blindness, muscular tremors, convulsions, coma, and finally death. These are usually attributed to the hypoglycemia. Blood analyses will show the same changes as in lactation ketosis, namely low glucose and high ketones. The ketones are excreted in the urine and result in positive qualitative tests. Postmortem shows a fatty liver.

Treatment and Prevention

Treatment is not as effective as in lactation ketosis because the glucose drain continues to accelerate with growth of fetuses. Mortality rate of affected ewes may reach 80%. Recovery often results from parturition, either from natural birth or by surgery. The course may vary from about 2-10 d. The treatment of choice appears to be about 4 oz (i.e., 112 g) daily of propylene glycol by drench. Intravenous glucose in a single administration will give temporary benefit, but a prolonged glucose source is needed to keep pace with the fetal glucose drain. Reports vary on the ACTH and glucocorticoid relationships in pregnancy toxemia, some indicating low and others high glucocorticoid levels. In addition, the abortive effects of these hormones complicate their use for treatment (22).

Prevention involves proper nutrition and management during pregnancy. Extremes of condition (either too thin or too fat) should be avoided. Dietary energy and protein should be increased during the last 2 months of pregnancy. An 11% protein ration and about 1/2 lb of grain daily is usually suggested. In special problem situations, addition of about 2 oz. daily of propylene glycol

to the ration may be a useful preventative. Management practices which stimulate appetite, such as mild exercise, and which avoid stress are important parts of an overall control program.

FAT COW SYNDROME

In recent years the term "fat cow syndrome" has been coined to describe a condition occurring within a few days of calving in dairy cows that are excessively fat at calving time (23, 24). It is characterized by depression, lack of appetite and general weakness. Although it has some characteristics similar to ketosis, it is a somewhat different phenomenon. Almost invariably it is associated with other problems at calving, such as milk fever, displaced abomasum, retained placenta, metritis or mastitis. Often there is an elevated temperature due to the associated infection. Although the blood ketones and free fatty acids are usually high, the ketosis is usually secondary to another problem. Blood glucose may be high or low. Treatment is not very effective, usually consisting of intravenous glucose or oral propylene glycol, and antibiotics to combat the infection. Obviously, if blood glucose is high, the usual ketosis treatments will be of little benefit.

The cause appears to be a grossly excessive energy intake in late lactation and during the dry period. Long dry periods due to breeding problems aggravate the problem when the energy intake is high. It is often a herd problem where dry cows are kept in groups and fed all corn silage diets or are not separated from lactating cows fed high energy diets. This results in obese animals. Some experiments have shown that if these fat cows can get through the calving period without complications, they may be able to adjust to the mobilization of large amounts of fat (14). But they have an increased susceptibility to these problems and a reduced capacity to adjust. Optimum management at calving is more critical for the fat cow.

When the animal does not eat, the liver is flooded with mobilized free fatty acids, a fatty liver develops and recovery is difficult (25). Cows that die have fatty livers, but the exact time of onset of hepatic lipid accumulation has not been determined and the etiology is only partially understood. Preliminary results on the use of inositol as a lipotropic agent have not shown a beneficial effect (26). Niacin feeding after calving showed some reduction in weight loss (14), but niacin has not been evaluated specifically as a preventive for fat cow syndrome.

GRASS TETANY

by H. F. Mayland

INTRODUCTION

Grass tetany (hypomagnesemia) is a major health problem of cattle and sheep in temperate climates. It is caused by a deficiency of utilizable magnesium (Mg). This nutritional disorder includes a number of clinical diseases known as grass tetany, grass staggers, crested wheatgrass poisoning, wheat pasture poisoning, winter tetany, transport tetany, pasture flush staggers, and in calves, a disorder called milk tetany. The problem occurs in the United Kingdom, western Europe, South Africa, Argentina, New Zealand and the USA.

Animal losses vary from year to year. In the United Kingdom it is estimated that clinical cases occur in about 1% of the animals and that one-third of these die (50). Losses may be similar in other countries where dairy cows are maintained on pasture with little or no supplemental feeding. Beef-cattle losses probably occur at a lower rate, because milk production and subsequent Mg losses are less than for dairy cows.

In the USA grass tetany is more common in beef cows and less common in dairy cows because many of the dairy animals are dry

lotted or stall fed with high quality forages and concentrates. Significant losses to grass tetany occur in sheep and may be similar to, or less than, losses in beef cattle under comparable conditions. Few attempts have been made to evaluate the effects of hypomagnesemia on production. However, increased milk production has been measured after oral Mg supplementation in New Zealand dairy herds where average blood Mg levels were previously 10 to 14 mg/ℓ (47, 52).

Grass tetany has been investigated extensively, but the complex etiology is not well understood. Excellent reviews are available on the effects of soil, climate, forage, and animal interactions leading to hypomagnesemia. Of special interest are the two volumes dealing with broad aspects of grass tetany edited by Rendig and Grunes (33) and Fontenot et al (7).

ROLE OF Mg IN ANIMALS

Magnesium is essential for both animals and plants. It is the metal cofactor of many enzymes involved in the metabolism of carbohydrates, lipids and proteins. In animals it also exerts a strong influence on neuromuscular function. While Mg is essential to animals, it appears that there is no regulatory mechanism. Nevertheless, problems of Mg metabolism are rare in simple-stomached animals. However, Mg deficiency is common to ruminants.

The bodies of domestic ruminants contain about 0.05% Mg by weight (Fig. 24-5). Of that amount, about 65-70% is in bone, 15% in muscle, 15% in other soft tissues and 1% in extracellular fluids (8, 13, 23).

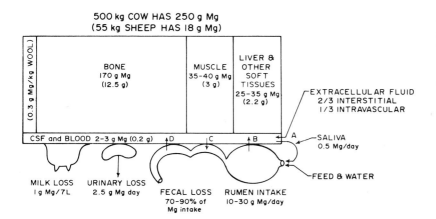

Figure 24-5. Model illustrating the distribution and movement of Mg in the cow (values for sheep are in parenthesis) including: (A) about 0.5 g returning in saliva, (B) primary absorption occurring from the rumen, (C) a small amount of resorption occurring in the small intestine, and (D) a small amount of absorption occurring from the large intestine.

512

Table 24-4. The amounts of Mg associated with the urinary and fecal endogenous loss, growth, pregnancy and lactation in sheep and cattle.[a]

	Sheep	Cattle
Endogenous loss (Inevitable loss)	3 mg Mg/kg liveweight	3 mg Mg/kg liveweight
Growth	0.41 g Mg/kg gain	0.45 g Mg/kg gain
Lactation	0.17 g Mg/kg milk	0.12 g Mg/kg milk
Pregnancy (Daily increment - early in conceptus)	0.01 g Mg/d	0.12 g Mg/d
-mid	0.03 g Mg/d	0.21 g Mg/d
-late	0.05 g Mg/d	0.33 g Mg/d

[a]From Grace (8)

Grace (8) summarized the absolute amounts of Mg needed for various production functions in sheep and cattle (Table 24-4). The data were developed from balance studies, isotope experiments and slaughter data.

The amount of Mg required by ruminants also depends upon animal age, size, stage of pregnancy, level of lactation and weather conditions (46). For example, mature pregnant beef cows fed a dry semipurified diet required 8.5, 7.0 and 9.0 g Mg/d to maintain the blood serum Mg level at 20 mg/ℓ at 155, 200 and 255 d gestation, respectively (30). These cows then required 21, 22 and 18 g Mg/d during early, mid and late lactation to maintain the blood-serum Mg level at 20 mg/ℓ, respectively (31). These experimentally derived values are greater than those that would be calculated from the information in Table 24-4, thus illustrating the low availability of Mg from these particular diets. Therefore, to calculate the Mg requirement on a dietary basis requires information on the availability of ingested Mg and its subsequent utilization by the animal.

FACTORS AFFECTING UTILIZATION OF Mg

Grass tetany occurs when animals do not ingest a sufficient amout of available Mg. This may occur when animals are on nutritionally poor diets, especially those low in Mg and Ca. However, grass tetany generally occurs when the dietary intake of total Mg is not particularly low, but factors exist (Fig. 24-6) which increase the animal's requirement for Mg or reduce the availability of dietary Mg to the animal. Most commonly, grass tetany occurs during early lactation in older animals that have been turned out to spring pasture.

Forage quality may vary from pasture to pasture. Jolley and Leaver (16) reported that pasture on which grass tetany occurred (prone) contained lower concentrations of Mg, Ca and Na and higher concentrations of K than pastures on which tetany had not occurred (free).

Pasture	Mg	Ca	K	Na
	. . . . mg/g			
Prone	1.8	4.9	25	1.2
Free	2.2	5.3	22	2.8

They also noted that the grass tetany-prone pastures had a lower proportion of legume in the grass-legume mix.

Grass tetany is often associated with intensively managed cool-season grasses. Grasses have lower concentrations of Mg and Ca and higher concentrations of K than do legumes or forbs. This is illustrated by data obtained by the author from a large number of native and introduced plants sampled in Idaho, Nevada and Utah during midspring.

Plant Type	Mg	Ca	K
	. . . . . mg/g		
Grasses	2	4	25
Legumes	3	14	20
Forbs	7	15	15

Grass tetany may occur on grass-legume mixed pastures, but does so in early spring when average air temperatures are <14°C (57°F). At that time the forage mixture is still mostly grass, because legume growth is limited by cool air temperatures. Cool soil temperatures can also result in forage Mg levels that are lower in spring than later when soil temperatures are warmer (Fig. 24-7).

Potassium

The Mg concentrations in forage and subsequantly in the blood serum of cattle are influenced strongly by high amounts of fertilizer K and, to some extent, fertilizer N. This is illustrated by the following blood serum Mg

513

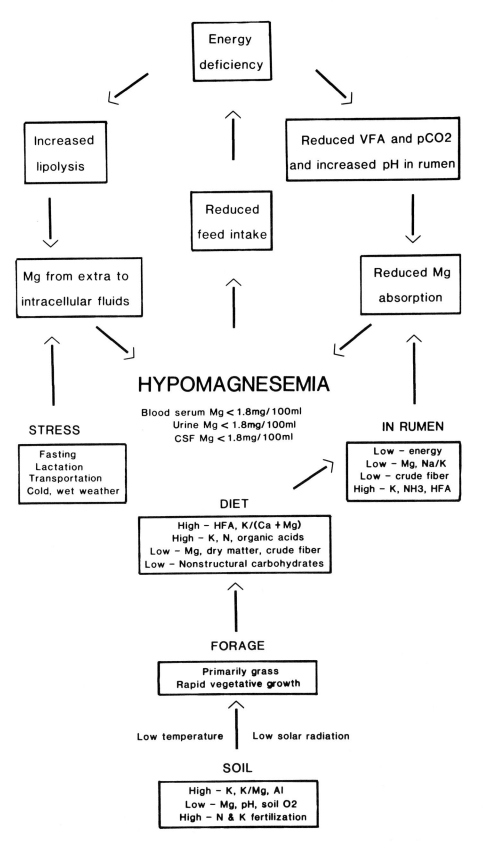

Figure 24-6. Schematic of the etiology of hypomagnesemia.

514

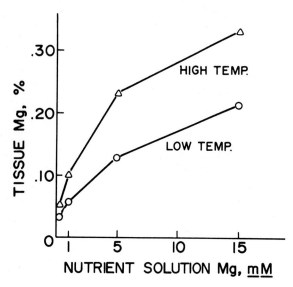

Figure 24-7. Tissue Mg levels in perennial ryegrass grown at 20°C day, 14°C night (low temp.) or 26°C day, 23°C night (high temp.) in sand culture containing given levels of Mg. Adapted from Grunes et al (11).

values in four dairy cows that grazed a series of differentially fertilized pastures (51). Similar findings have been reported for sheep.

Low N — low K   24.3 mg Mg/ℓ
High N — low K   21.5 mg Mg/ℓ
Low N — high K   17.4 mg Mg/ℓ
High N — high K   14.1 mg Mg/ℓ

Mg absorption by plants is reduced by high soil-K levels (24). Mg absorption by ruminants is also reduced by a high intake of K. Newton et al (29) fed wether lambs either a low-K (0.6%) or a high-K (4.9%) diet. Apparent absorption of Mg was depressed by the high-K relative to the low-K diet during eight consecutive 3-d trials (Fig. 24-8).

Sodium:Potassium

The Na concentration of immature grass is often insufficient to meet the requirements of the animal. This reduction (from dry winter diets) in dietary Na results in a compensatory increase in the K concentration in saliva and subsequently in the rumen fluid and a reduction in Mg absorption. Feeding high levels of Na may increase Mg absorption, but the excessive Na supply also increases urinary excretion of both Na and Mg (28). In the

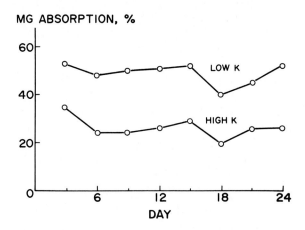

Figure 24-8. Effect of dietary K levels on apparent Mg absorption in wether lambs. Adapted from Newton et al (29).

latter case hypomagnesemia was observed despite the increased Mg absorption. Thus, the Na:K value may be more important than the absolute concentration of either Na or K (23).

The actual mechanism by which Na:K affects Mg absorption has not been identified. Martens and Kasebieter (22) suggested that, at least under in vitro conditions, Mg passes across the rumen wall by a transport system depending on the activity of the Na/K ATPase and that this activity can be reduced by high K concentrations.

Water

Martens (21) measured the Mg efflux from artificial rumen fluid in heifers 10-12 months old. He reported a near linear increase in Mg desorption from the rumen fluid at increasing Mg concentrations up to 13 mmol/ℓ. The Mg efflux changed very little at Mg concentrations greater than that. He calculated from this study that Mg absorption was saturated when rumen fluid contained a concentration of 11 mmol/ℓ. He noted that this value and one of 4 mmol/ℓ previously determined for sheep, differed from results of others and attributed this to improved methodology in his studies (21).

Animals often consume large amounts of water when grazing low dry matter forage. This could present conditions (Fig. 24-6) where the free or ionized Mg concentration in the rumen fluid is much less than the

515

Nitrogen

Grass tetany occurs most frequently when animals graze succulent forages containing high concentrations of N. Dutch, and later, New Zealand, workers reported that Mg availability decreases with increasing concentrations of N in the forage (Fig. 24-9).

The incidence of grass tetany is often accentuated by N fertilization which increases the N concentration in the forage. However, N fertilization alters the growth of forage plants and further exaggerates the levels of other dietary constituents that have been implicated in the etiology of grass tetany. These factors (Fig. 24-6) include low concentrations for dry matter, readily fermentable carbohydrates and crude fiber, and high concentrations of higher fatty acids (HFA, C12 through C18), K/(Ca + Mg) expressed on an equivalency basis, and organic acids.

The direct involvement of forage N in grass tetany may result from an interaction of high N and low fermentable carbohydrate concentrations. The rumen organisms, confronted with a rich protein and low-energy diet, metabolize the excess N into nitrogenous materials like ammonia (NH_3). The NH_3

concentrations may then rise to levels of 30-70 mmol/ℓ in the rumen fluid, Ruminal NH_3 production correlates well (r = .92) with the ratio of forage N to forage water-soluble carbohydrates in cows grazing ryegrass (48). It appears that an acute rise in NH_3 concentrations has at least a temporary effect on reducing Mg absorption from the rumen (23).

Energy Deficiency

Grass tetany frequently occurs when animals graze forage that is high in digestible protein (25-30% CP), but low in digestible energy (8-12% water-soluble carbohydrates, TWSC). Grass tetany coincides with the period during which the N/TWSC values are elevated (25). If animals were able to consume a sufficient amount of the tetany-prone forage to meet their energy requirement, they would ingest up to five times their crude protein requirement much of it as non-protein N. Such animals would likely suffer from NH_3 toxicity and reduce their feed intake, leading to a lower dry matter intake and further energy deficiency. These effects reduce the formation of VFA and CO_2 and the capacity to synthesize microbial protein, leading to further elevations in rumen fluid NH_3 concentrations (23).

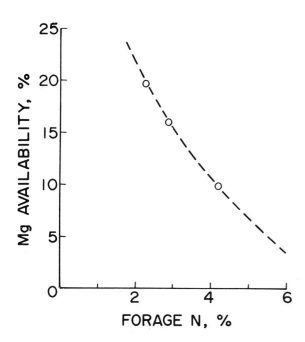

Figure 24-9. Relationship of "Mg availability" to forage N. Adapted from Metson et al (26).

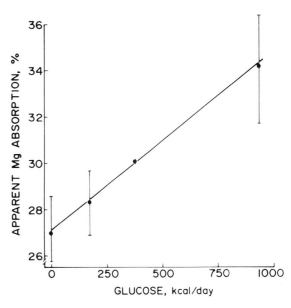

Figure 24-10. Apparent Mg absorption in sheep fed red clover-orchardgrass hay and supplemented with given levels of glucose. From Madsen et al (19).

516

Energy supplementation (Fig. 24-10) not only results in a higher production of VFA and CO_2, but provides more energy for the synthesis of microbial protein. This, in turn, reduces the concentration of NH_3 and removes the inhibitory action on Mg absorption.

Higher Fatty Acids (HFA)

Forages likely to produce grass tetany in animals contain 100-200 mmol HFA/kg, largely as unsaturated palmitic, linoleic and linolenic acids. These unsaturated HFA are not absorbed in significant amounts from the rumen, but are hydrogenated and the esterified fatty acids are liberated by hydrolysis before passing with the rest of the digesta into the intestine. However, Mg and Ca may form water-insoluble soaps with the HFA, pass through the animal via the feces and thus reduce the availability of the divalent cations.

Wilson et al (53) measured blood-plasma Mg concentrations in dairy cows grazing perennial ryegrass containing 180 mmol

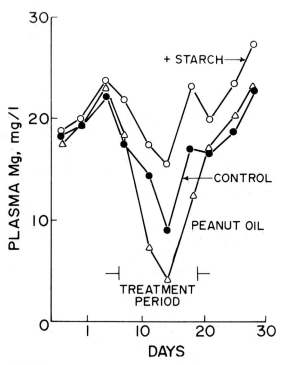

Figure 24-11. Plasma Mg concentrations in mature cows grazing a tetanigenic perennial ryegrass forage during the treatment period and not supplemented (control), or supplemented with 454 g starch or 220 ml peanut oil/d. Adapted from Wilson et al (53).

COOH/kg (Fig. 24-11). Cows on the control treatment suffered a significant depression in blood plasma Mg which was depressed further in cows supplemented with 50-70% additional HFA as peanut oil. A starch supplement, which served as an energy source, produced plasma Mg levels higher than those in the control group. These authors also noted that the oil supplement lowered plasma Mg concentrations more in mature than in young animals.

Organic Acids

Significant concentrations of organic acids, especially *trans*-aconitate and citrate, were measured in forages coincident to the large outbreaks of grass tetany in the 1960's. These acids were suggested as being capable of complexing Mg (10). Further animal investigations showed that drenching with KCl and either citrate or *t*-aconitate would induce tetany-like signs in animals. Drenching with only the KCl or either of the acids was ineffective (2).

It is possible that the presence of high K levels increased the absorption of the organic acid and that there may have been some complexing of Mg. However, citrate and *t*-aconitate are fermented quite rapidly in the rumen (38), and other workers have discounted the effects of these acids on Mg complexation (24). More recent research has shown that *t*-aconitate is metabolized rapidly to tricarballylate which is fermented very slowly (38). Based on its stability constant for Mg ($K_{eq} = 115$), tricarballylate could be a factor in hypomagnesemia (37), but in vivo verification is still needed.

Aluminum

The frequent association of high aluminum (Al) concentrations in forage and rumen samples with the incidence of hypomagnesemia has led some investigators to believe that Al could be involved with the development of grass tetany. Robinson et al (36), however, discounted the role of Al in grass tetany and reported that a large part of the Al intake was associated with soil contamination of ingested feed, and this did not affect Mg or Ca nutrition of dairy cows.

Mineral Indices

Several indices have been used to characterize the grass tetany potential of forage. The

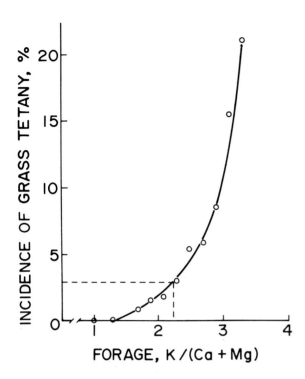

Figure 24-12. Relationship between the incidence of grass tetany and the K/(Ca + Mg) in forage; calculated on an equivalence basis. Adapted from Kemp and t'Hart (17).

first and most commonly used is the K/(Ca + Mg) ratio (Fig. 24-12) expressed on an equivalent basis. This ratio accounts for the antagonism of forage K and benefits of forage Mg and Ca on Mg absorption by the animal (24).

Another index, known as the Dutch Nomograph, is available in several references, including Mayland and Grunes (24). The Nomograph uses data on Mg, K and N concentrations in the forage. It is apparently useful in predicting the tetany hazard to dairy cows in areas where forage Ca levels are generally adequate (A. Kemp, personal communication). It is not as useful where forage Ca availability may be limiting. Under these conditions the K/(Ca + Mg) ratio seems to be more useful.

Magnesium Activity

The contrast in Mg availability from winter dry feeds and that from spring forage is typified by the data presented by Rendig and Grunes (33). They reported that of 20-25 g Mg ingested with winter rations, 72-75% was excreted in feces. However, of the 12 g Mg ingested with spring forage, 82% was excreted

in feces. The cows on the dry feed had an apparent absorption of 6 g Mg compared with only 2 g Mg for those on the spring forage.

There is uncertainty in how Mg is bound in feedstuffs. Mg and Ca may be bound to forage particles and be relatively unavailable for adsorption by the rumen organisms or the animal. Rumen microorganisms have a much higher requirement for Mg than Ca. The washed organisms may contain 6 mg Mg/g dry matter, but only 0.1 to 0.3 mg Ca/g dry matter (5). In addition, much Mg is also adsorbed to the surface of the microorganisms. This amount increases with increasing Mg levels in the media, but decreases when rumen fluid Ca values are high. The amount of adsorbed Mg and Ca is greater at pH values ranging from 6.5 to 7.5 than in more acid conditions, which is similar to data shown in Fig. 24-13. The adsorbed Mg and Ca can be released by washing the cells in an acid solution of pH 2.5 to 3.0.

Research since 1970 (23) has shown that net Mg absorption occurs in the digestive tract proximal to the duodenum. In sheep and adult cattle most of the absorption occurs from the rumen. A small amount of Mg is absorbed from the large intestine and a small amount is secreted into the small intestine. Thus, Mg absorption occurs largely from the same section of the gastro-intestinal tract wherein the digesta is immediately exposed to several of the factors that may reduce its availability. Perhaps some of the apparent inconsistencies in treatment effects are related to pH of rumen fluid that may be made less acidic because of changes in one or more of the components like an increase in forage N/TWSC values.

The solubility and/or ultra filterability (UF) of Mg in the rumen fluid is very sensitive to pH. Smith and Horn (43) reported that under in vitro conditions the portion of UF Mg in the strained fluid was greater than 80% at an acidity less than 6.0 pH, but the portion of UF Mg was less than 20% at pH values greater than 8.0 (Fig. 24-13). The stoichiometric point is at pH 7. Thus, very small shifts in pH to less acidic conditions might well be interpreted as reducing Mg availability. Such shifts could occur by several of the factors identified in Fig. 24-6. Horn and Smith (14) found that rumen pH after feeding was as high as 7.2 when animals were fed forage

518

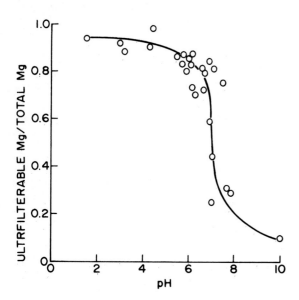

Figure 24-13. Relationship between Mg ultrafilterability and pH in rumen contents to which varying amounts of H_2SO_4 or NaOH were added in vitro. From Smith and Horn (43).

and that Mg absorption proximal to the duodenum was negatively correlated with the rumen pH.

Another factor possibly affecting Mg metabolism is the ionophore which is being used more commonly to increase growth rate of ruminants including those on pasture. Serum Mg concentrations have been reduced significantly by several of these growth promotants. The ionophore may serve as a carrier of various ions across the lipid bilayer (44), but it is not known if these molecules will affect overall mg metabolism.

Another aspect of Mg activity within the lactating ruminant is its effect on milk production. Wilson (52) conducted a 3-week study with dairy cows grazing a mixed ryegrass-clover pasture. One group was drenched with 10 g Mg/d as $MgCl_2$. A second group was infused rectally with 10 g Mg/d (as $MgCl_2$) during week 1 or injected subcutaneously with 2 g Mg/d as $MgSO_4 \cdot 7H_2O$ during weeks 2 and 3. The third group served as a control. Oral, rectal and subcutaneous treatments increased (P < .05) plasma Mg levels about 40% above that in the control animals. Nevertheless, all animals were considered hypomagnesemic during the study. Oral supplementation, but not rectal or subcutaneous infusion, increased milk fat yield and milk

yield about 12%, leading the authors to conclude that the benefits of Mg supplementation on production were effective in the rumen fermentation process.

CLINICAL SYMPTOMS

Normal, Chronic and Acute Hypomagnesemia

Based on blood serum or plasma Mg levels, animals may be normally magnesemic (18-30 mg/ℓ), chronically hypomagnesemic (5-18 mg/ℓ) or acutely hypomagnesemic (<5 mg/ℓ). Animals that are chronically hypomagnesemic may have reduced feed intake, be somewhat more nervous than usual and, if lactating, have reduced milk production. In general they do not show any visual symptoms. Acutely hypomagnesemic animals will likely exhibit visually detectable symptoms as described below. However, serum Mg levels as low as 6 mg/ℓ in cattle have been reported without visual evidence of hypomagnesemia (12).

As with chronic hypomagnesemia, acutely hypomagnesemic animals may be normocalcemic or more often hypocalcemic. Thus, visual symptoms may be a mixture of both Mg and Ca deficiency responses. This may occur because hypomagnesemia reduces the rate of Ca mobilization (4, 39). Various stresses may alter the Mg status of the animal in a way that it progresses slowly from normal to chronic, and sometimes to acute hypomagnesemia, or that it progresses rapidly to acute hypomagnesemic tetany followed by death.

Hypomagnesemia in Cattle

Hypomagnesemia can occur in all classes of cattle, but occurs most frequently in older lactating cows. Hypomagnesemic cows exhibit signs of nervousness, reduced feed intake, reduced milk production, and may show slight muscular twitching along the face, shoulder and flank. Animals may also display some spasticity of limb muscles when walking.

In progressive clinical tetany the cows stagger and fall on their sides with their heads thrown back, salivate profusely and grind their teeth. The disorder may progress quickly to paddling with front and hind feet, fluttering of eyelids, eyeballs rolled inward, convulsions, coma and death (Fig. 24-14). There are

Figure 24-14. Lactating beef cow that has died from grass tetany. Courtesy of J.A. Stuedemann, USDA-ARS, Watkinsville, GA.

no known characteristic postmortem lesions that can be used for diagnostic purposes.

Hypomagnesemia in Sheep

In sheep there is considerable variation between animals. Generally, hypomagnesemia occurs within 2-4 weeks after sheep have been moved to improved pasture or oat forage. Ewes with twins are more susceptible to grass tetany than are ewes with single lambs (15, 49). Severely hypomagnesemic ewes are depressed, stand with their heads down, are often separated from the flock and are reluctant to move.

In progressive clinical tetany the sheep stagger, collapse on their sides with heads thrown back and some froth may be present about the mouth. They may at this time have an increased heart and respiratory rate and elevated temperature. The disorder progresses quickly to paddling with all feet, grinding teeth and generalized muscular tremors, convulsions and death. Sometimes the clinically recognizable symptoms will precede death by only a few minutes, especially when animals are chased (15). There are no known characteristic postmortem lesions, although subendocardial hemorrhages may occur because of the severe tetanic convulsions.

PREDISPOSING CONDITIONS FOR HYPOMAGNESEMIC TETANY

Spring Tetany or Lactation Tetany

This is the *most common* situation in which hypomagnesemia occurs. The disorder appears within 2-4 weeks after cattle or sheep have been turned out to rapidly-growing pasture. It may also occur under conditions of

autumn regrowth. Older, lactating females are at greatest risk, but the problem may occur in other classes of ruminants.

Considerable variability may exist in the blood serum Mg levels among animals in the same herd. While a few animals may have >20 mg Mg/ℓ, the others will be evenly divided with 50% having values 11-20 and the others being <11 mg/ℓ. Of these, two-thirds may also be hypocalcemic.

Hypomagnesemic tetany occurs in sheep grazing young perennial grass or oat forage, especially if either has been fertilized with N and/or K. Grazing such lush pastures during frosty or cold weather within 2-4 weeks after lambing seems to predispose ewes to hypomagnesemia, often with accompanying hypocalcemia (49).

Mg and many times Ca deficiencies are basic to the condition. Yet a number of factors are peculiar to the spring tetany situation including high levels of forage N, K, HFA, and organic acids and low levels of forage Na, dry matter, fiber and soluble carbohydrates. Forage Mg may sometimes be lower during this period than at later times, but in other cases Mg levels appear normal. Animals may be stressed because of lactation, cool weather, inadequate dry matter intake, estrus and high water intake.

Wheat Pasture Tetany

Animals grazing wheat pasture or other lush cereal forage may be exposed to several problems, including frothy bloat, nitrate toxicity and grass tetany. The tetany may be primarily hypocalcemia with secondary hypomagnesemia (3).

Eng (6) noted that the 10-20% death loss in cattle grazing wheat pasture in 1982-83 could be attributed to grass tetany, bloat, nitrate toxicity or enterotoxemia. The chemical composition of the forage associated with the enterotoxemia losses was 24% dry matter, 31% CP, 14% fiber, 3.4% K, 0.15% Mg and 0.68% NO_3. This profile also typifies a highly tetanigenic forage.

Winter Tetany or Seasonal Tetany

Hypomagnesemia occurring under these conditions often involves beef cattle and out-wintered dairy cattle. These animals are grazing dry, mature grass, or are being fed poor quality fodder or grass that is very low in total Mg and other nutrients. It may also occur in stall-fed cattle on a low plane of nutrition (42). Animals may have serum Mg levels as low as 5 mg/ℓ and varying degrees of hypocalcemia. The low serum electrolytes are often associated with adverse weather conditions.

Hypomagnesemia occurs in over-wintering cows maintained on largely straw diets and occasionally supplemented with energy and/or protein. Mg, as low as 0.6 mg/g, could limit intake and reduce performance (20). Generally, winter tetany is accompanied by few or no visual symptoms. Stress of any type may result in symptoms ranging from moderate incoordination to paresis or tetany.

The author observed winter tetany in a group of 550 pregnant beef cows pastured on corn stalks (ears removed) and supplemented with a minimal amount of poor quality grass hay. This occurred in early winter and animals were outside with no protection. Stress resulting from a period of cold windy days, parturition and very early lactation resulted in 23 deaths from hypomagnesemic tetany. The tetany stopped when high quality alfalfa hay was fed and Mg supplementation provided.

Underfeeding, Fasting or Starvation Tetany

Underfeeding associated with reduced grazing time, reduced dry matter intake, and reduced rumination time may lower serum Mg of ruminants. This may often occur when animals that are turned out to spring grass are unable to eat enough dry matter because of the short growth and low dry matter content.

Milk Tetany

This generally chronic hypomagnesemic disorder appears in calves raised on whole milk or milk replacer (unless fortified with Mg). The problem is also reported to occur in bucket-fed calves 3-4 months of age that have access to lush green spring pasture (15). Visual signs are like those reported for adult cattle.

Transportation Tetany or Transit Tetany

This condition of hypomagnesemia occurs in sheep and cattle that have undergone long periods of fasting. It is a common metabolic disease of feeder lambs that usually occurs within 10 d after arrival at the feedlot (18). The problem also occurs after prolonged transport of cows and ewes in late pregnancy. This transportation stress may result in several disorders, including hypocalcemia, ketosis and hypomagnesemia. In the hypomagnesemia type (this may also include hypocalcemia) animals are restless, nervous and weak and have a staggering unsteady gait (Fig. 24-15). There may be partial paralysis of the hindquarters, muscular spasms, excitability, frothing at the mouth and champing of the jaws. The animal may be unable to stand and falls or lies down. It may quickly become laterally recumbent and paddle with all feet, then progress into tetanic convulsions and death.

Lucas (18) reported serum Mg, Ca, and P values (mg/ℓ) of 14, 73 to 78 and 102 to 108, respectively, in a group of lambs where transportation tetany was occurring. He reported normal values for these minerals as 20, 110 and 70 mg/ℓ, respectively. Repeated parenteral injections of large volumes of electrolyte solutions are recommended in addition to Mg repletion (1).

CHEMICAL SYMPTOMS

Blood serum Mg values in ruminants are normally 18-30 mg/ℓ. Chronic hypomagnesemia is associated with serum levels of 5 to 18 mg/ℓ and acute hypomagnesemia is associated with serum levels <5 mg/ℓ. However, these threshold values are somewhat arbitrary (35). Levels of Mg in both blood serum and blood plasma are similar. Higher blood levels of Mg (140 mg/ℓ) induce anesthesia, while even higher levels (200 mg/ℓ) are toxic (42). Hypomagnesemic animals may also be normocalcemic or hypocalcemic. Blood samples drawn postmortem will have elevated Mg levels because of the release of Mg from tissues during the muscle spasms associated with the tetanic convulsions.

Urine Mg concentrations range from 0 to 280 mg/ℓ and are curvilinearly related to blood serum Mg levels, but values approach zero as animals become increasingly hypomagnesemic. Urinary Mg levels of 20-100 mg/ℓ are given as inadequate and <20 mg/ℓ as indicative of severe deficiency and danger of tetany. Urine samples taken directly from the bladder within a few hours postmorten, in connection with blood samples from several

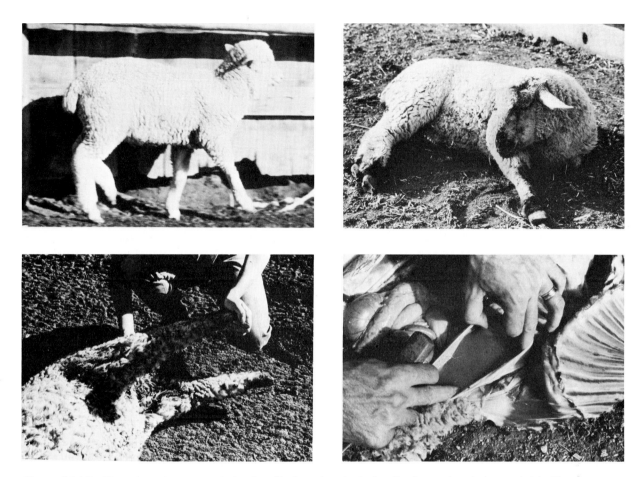

Figure 24-15. Transportation tetany in lambs. Earliest signs include stilted, atarcic gait (upper left). The next stage is lateral recumbency (upper right). Post-mortem signs include "tetany" of hind legs (lower left). The rumen may be bloated, but upon necropsy is found to be filled with fluid and empty of roughage or concentrate (lower right). Photos courtesy of R.E. Pierson (retired), Colorado State Univ., Ft. Collins, CO.

other animals in the herd, may provide a useful diagnosis.

DIFFERENTIAL DIAGNOSIS

Hypomagnesemia has often been confused with enterotoxemia. This latter condition typically occurs in calves, young cattle and sheep (15), although it has been diagnosed as occurring in adult cattle. It is caused by the toxins produced by *Clostridium perfringens* or *C. welchii* infections in the gut. It often occurs when animals are grazing lush pasture and symptoms may include staggering, salivation, convulsions and death. Death losses may be sporadic in cattle, but are often massive in sheep. Enterotoxemia can be confirmed by presence of the toxin in urine or in

gut tissue. Serum Mg levels should be determined on live animals in the herd to check the Mg status.

Grass tetany may also be confused with nitrate toxicity because both may occur on lush pastures, especially those heavily fertilized with N. The most useful indication of nitrate toxicity is the brownish discoloration of blood and tissues. Deaths from both problems have occurred together in some instances.

Some symptoms of grass tetany in high producing dairy cows may be confused with ketosis. About one-fourth of the cases will show nervous signs, stagger, froth at the mouth, have a high-stepping gait and occasionally have convulsions. Animals suffering from ketosis will have an acetone odor in

522

their breath and milk. The presence of ketone bodies in the urine will verify the ketosis (see earlier section).

Verification of the Mg status of ruminants is best done by measuring the Mg in blood serum obtained from at least several live animals in the herd. The Mg concentration in urine could also be used as a diagnostic test, because Mg levels decline rapidly to zero as the degree of hypomagnesemia increases. The urine sample should be carefully collected to avoid contamination with fecal material. Schneider et al (40) have proposed a quick test for evaluating the urinary Mg status of animals, but details of this procedure were not yet available to the author. This quick test may be an improvement on a semiquantitative indicator paper that has been used in Europe (41) to evaluate urine Mg levels.

TREATMENT OF ACUTE HYPOMAGNESEMIA

Treatment of tetany cases can be successful if given early and without excessive handling of the affected animals (1, 9). The safest general recommendation is to slowly inject, intravenously, 500 ml of a solution (50 ml for sheep) containing 25% Ca borogluconate and 5% Mg hypophosphite (or 15% Mg gluconate). The injections should be given slowly because there is danger of heart failure if given too rapidly. Serum Mg levels rise quickly, but return to preinjection levels within 3-6 h. A second dose may be required if the animal again exhibits acute signs. For optimum results the intravenous injection should be followed with a subcutaneous injection of 200 ml of a saturated solution of $MgSO_4$ (50%). Unfortunately, Mg drenches have not been effective in initially treating tetany because too much time is required for the Mg to be absorbed.

Rectally infused enemas containing 60 g of $MgCl_2 \cdot 6H_2O$ in 300 ml water have been useful in treating acute cases. Reynolds et al (34) reported that this procedure increased plasma Mg within 5 min and increased CSF-Mg levels within 30 min in calves that previously had CSF-Mg levels <18 mg/ℓ. Administering the Mg as an enema may be easier for many livestock operators than giving intravenous or subcutaneous injections and also allows the use of non-sterile equipment.

After the initial treatment, animals should be separated from the predisposing conditions and given high quality dry hay and, if possible, energy supplements. Also 30 g Mg (2 oz calcined magnesite containing 85% MgO) should be given daily. The Mg may be administered in a drench if necessary, but the amount can be reduced after a week. Cows that get tetany are likely to get it again later in the season or in subsequent years.

PREVENTION

Animal Management Techniques

Supplementing Mg in the animal's diet is recommended. Commercial grade MgO, $MgCl_2$, $MgCO_3$ and $MgSO_4$ are good sources. Dolomitic limestone and magnesite are only slightly available to the animal and are not recommended.

Animals can be fed high-Mg blocks or mineral salt mixtures. Licking wheels or licking belts are sometimes used to dispense $MgSO_4$ in molasses. Producers should check that the Mg remains in suspension. Avoid using crude protein-enriched supplements when cattle are grazing lush green grass.

Epsom salts ($MgSO_4 \cdot 7H_2O$) added to the drinking water is helpful if the trough is the sole source of water. $MgCl_2$ or Mg acetate may also be used. The author is familiar with a beef cow-calf producer who grazes about 800 mother cows on crested wheatgrass. Fifteen to 30 animals died annually from grass tetany until Mg supplementation was initiated during the tetany period. Except for a few rain puddles, these cows rely on a single source of water which is pumped into a 5,000 gallon holding tank from which it is piped to water troughs. For several weeks prior to and during the grass tetany season he daily adds 100 lb of $MgSO_4 \cdot 7H_2O$ to the water tank. This provides an average of 5 g Mg/cow/d and has reduced his losses to only a few animals during a 13-year period.

Spraying a water slurry of 10% MgO and 1.5% bentonite on forage is an effective way to increase Mg intake by animals grazing the treated forage. This procedure is not practical where forage yields are low.

Another practice that may be useful in preventing grass tetany is to use pastures that have been rested the previous year or have a lot of old growth present. This dry forage tends to dilute the negative effects of the lush, green new growth.

Mg boluses, when placed in the rumen-reticulum, may be useful in some circumstances in reducing grass tetany losses. Stuedemann et al (45) reported that the type they tested dissolved at a rate of 0.66 to 1.33 g Mg/d in rumen-fistulated steers. The boluses were also placed in some mother cows. Grass tetany occurred in one control cow and in one bolus-treated cow. The authors concluded that the Mg release appears too slow to be completely effective in preventing grass tetany.

Grunes and Mayland (9) recommend that throughout the high risk period beef cattle receive 8-10 g Mg/d and that lactating cows receive 20-25 g Mg/d. They recommend that dairy cows receive 30 g Mg/d, calves receive 4-8 g Mg/d, and lactating ewes receive about 3 g Mg/d. Mg supplements should be started several weeks before the tetany period to get the animals accustomed to them. The producer should check consumption. Because the mobile Mg is lost quickly from the bodies of adult ruminants, it is necessary to supplement on a daily basis during the tetany period (35).

Agronomic Management Techniques

Agronomic steps that will reduce the incidence of tetany include: (a) grazing forage having a higher level of available Mg, (b) applying moderate amounts of N and K fertilizer and then in split applications, (c) applying dolomitic limestone rather than calcitic limestone, if liming is required and (d) using mixed grass-legume pastures where possible.

Selection and breeding work is underway to develop tall fescue and crested wheatgrass cultivars that impose a lower risk of tetany (author's laboratory). Some selection work has already been conducted on Italian ryegrass. Moseley and Griffiths (27) fed sheep two experimental populations of Italian ryegrass. The one has 1.7 mg Mg/g and 4.6 mg Ca/g, while the other had values of 2.4 and 5.6, respectively. Concentrations of other minerals and IVDMD were not different between the two selections. Mg intake, apparent availability and retention were significantly greater with the high-Mg selection. Rumen fluid from animals fed the high-Mg

selection had a higher proportion of soluble Mg and a higher Na:K ratio in the supernatant liquor.

Reid et al (32) evaluated the effect of Mg supplementation of sheep when fed timothy grass. The grass was grown on a coarse textured acid soil that was either not fertilized or received 390 kg Mg/ha. Magnesium fertilization increased forage Mg concentration from 0.8 mg/g in the control to 1.5 mg/g. Supplemental feeding of Mg to sheep increased the intake of unfertilized as well as fertilized timothy by 13 and 15%, respectively. In this study, IVDMD of the Mg fertilized grass was less than that of the unfertilized grass. The Mg fertilization and the Mg supplementation of sheep increased Mg availability and serum Mg concentrations.

SUMMARY

Grass tetany is a major problem of cattle and sheep in temperate climates. It results from an inadequate supply of available Mg. This occurs when either actual intake of Mg is limited or, more often, because factors in the diet reduce the Mg availability. Grass tetany may also occur because of a need for increased amounts of Mg during parturition and early lactation.

Although grass tetany occurs in all classes of ruminants, older lactating animals are at greatest risk because of a reduced ability to mobilize body reserves of Mg. Chronic hypomagnesemia results in reduced feed intake and milk production. It may progress quickly into acute hypomagnesemia which terminates in convulsions, coma and death. Acutely stricken animals should receive Mg via enema or, preferably, by intravenous or subcutaneous injection. Chronically hypomagnesemic animals should receive daily supplemental Mg. Hypomagnesemic animals are frequently hypocalcemic.

URINARY CALCULI

by R. J. Emerick

Urinary blockage by calculi is an important cause of deaths in cattle and sheep. Occasional reports of the disease in other ruminants indicate that they are similarly

524

susceptible. Calculi may be formed at any location in the urinary tract. While the mere presence of small calculi in the kidney or urinary bladder is generally of no consequence, translocation into the ureters or urethra may result in urinary blockage. Urinary calculi appear to be formed equally in both sexes (1, 2), but urinary blockage is an important problem only in males because of the more constricted nature of their urinary tract.

Two types of urinary calculi predominate in cattle and sheep. The phosphatic type formed under feedlot conditions consists principally of Ca and Mg phosphates, and the siliceous type occurring mainly in range animals has silica (SiO_2) as its principal mineral component. Other types, including calculi composed principally of carbonates or oxalates, occur infrequently in ruminants (3, 4, 5). Non-ruminants, including man, most commonly form urinary calculi composed of phosphates, oxalates, urates or carbonates. All urinary calculi contain varying amounts of organic matrix materials.

CLINICAL SIGNS

At first, animals afflicted with urinary calculi may appear restless with frequent straining in an unsuccessful attempt to urinate. They may repeatedly stamp their feet and kick at the abdomen. In some cases when urinary blockage is not complete, urine may dribble slowly from the sheath. Upon failure to pass the stone and after complete blockage of urine flow, the bladder or urethra ruptures releasing urine into the body cavity or surrounding tissues resulting in a condition referred to as "water belly". At this stage the animal may show a complete loss of appetite and stand quietly or lie down, being very reluctant to rise. Death follows. Post-mortem examination generally reveals blood-tinged fluid in the body cavity, inflammation of the urinary tract and a hemorrhagic condition at the point of rupture.

PHOSPHATIC URINARY CALCULI

Phosphatic urinary calculi, depending upon the severity of conditions favoring their formation, may be formed in a majority of some groups of feedlot sheep and cattle. Losses from obstructive urolithiasis reach 10 to 30%

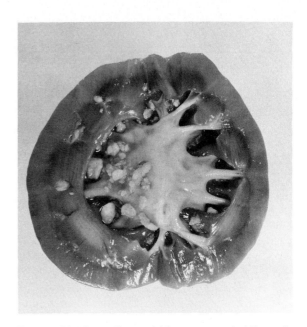

Figure 24-16. Sheep kidney opened bilaterally exposing phosphatic urinary calculi. Courtesy of R.J. Emerick, S. Dakota State University.

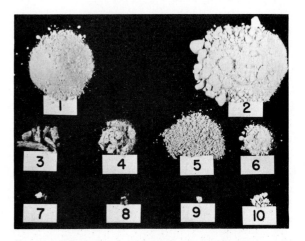

Figure 24-17. Urinary deposits showing variations in size and shape. (1) steer bladder deposit; (2) wether bladder deposit; (3) steer urethra deposit; (4) steer sheath deposit; (5) sheep bladder and urethra deposit; (6) sheep bladder deposit; (7) steer urethra deposit; (8) sheep kidney deposit; (9) steer urethra deposit; (10) sheep bladder deposit. Courtesy of R.J. Emerick, S. Dakota State University.

in severe cases. In addition to Ca and Mg phosphates, phosphatic urinary calculi contain varying amounts of organic matrix materials. These organic materials, largely proteins, probably play only a secondary role in phosphatic calculi formation (6, 7, 8). Co-precipitation with the Ca and Mg phosphates has been proposed as the method for incorporation of urinary proteins into the phosphatic urinary calculi. However, urinary proteins may play a more important role in the formation of siliceous urinary calculi as discussed later.

Major Causative Factors

High Urinary P Levels. Phosphatic urinary calculi appear to be caused by nutritional conditions that promote formation of urine that is alkaline and has a high P content. Since early observations that high urinary P levels were involved (9, 10), dietary P levels of 0.5 to 0.6%, representing about a two-fold increase over normal levels, have been used repeatedly for the experimental production of approximately a 50% incidence of urinary calculi in ruminants (8, 11, 12, 13, 14, 15, 16). However, practical lamb diets having normal P levels have been devised that promote high urinary P levels and are notably calculogenic (7, 17). In addition to the level of P in the ration, its nutritional availability and Ca-P ratio greatly influence the extent to which P is excreted in the urine (18).

Concentrate feedstuffs such as grains, oil meals, etc., fed to feedlot cattle and sheep, generally provide levels of P in excess of those required for optimum gains. By comparison, Ca concentrations in the concentrate feedstuffs are low, requiring the addition of legume forages and/or Ca supplements to obtain recommended Ca-P ratios.

Urine Alkalinity. The feeding of alkali-forming salts to ruminants increases alkalinity of the urine with a corresponding increase in incidence of phosphatic urolithiasis. With 2% of $NaHCO_3$ in the diet, phosphatic urinary calculi were produced in sheep fed a concentrate diet providing only 0.28% P (8). The extent to which a given feed will contribute to urine alkalinity cannot be surmised from the initial acidity or alkalinity of the ration ingredients. Most organic acids associated with the acidity of plants and plant fermentation products (such as silage, natural vinegars, etc.), are metabolized in the body and do not reach the urine except in the form of degradation products. When quantities of alkali-forming elements (Na, K, Ca and Mg) are

Table 24-5. Average calcium and phosphorus contents of some common feedstuffs (19).

Feedstuff	Calcium, %	Phosphorus, %
Grains and grain products		
Barley	0.08	0.42
Corn	0.03	0.27
Linseed meal	0.40	0.83
Oats	0.10	0.35
Sorghum	0.04	0.31
Soybean meal	0.32	0.67
Wheat	0.05	0.36
Wheat bran	0.14	1.17
Dry roughages		
Alfalfa hay	1.48	0.23
Bromegrass hay	0.39	0.25
Oat hay	0.23	0.21
Prairie hay	0.38	0.11
Timothy hay	0.32	0.17
Silages*		
Alfalfa	0.49	0.12
Corn	0.08	0.06
Sorghum	0.10	0.06

*As fed; approximately 67% moisture.

compared with quantities of acid-forming elements (S, P and Cl) in feedstuffs, the net result is that most forages contribute toward an alkaline urine, cereal grains have little influence and feeds having a high content of natural protein contribute some degree of acidity. In the later instance, the acid-forming effect is due mainly to the S released during biological oxidation of the S-containing amino acids. On the other hand, molasses contains much of the soluble alkali-forming mineral constituents of the plant from which it was processed and contributes strongly to the alkaline constituents of urine.

Low Urine Volumes. Variations in urine volume inversely influence the concentration of minerals and other excretory products in the urine. Urine volume is largely a reflection of water consumption. A lower water consumption and a subsequently greater concentration of urinary constituents occurring in animals on feed during the winter is believed to be an important reason for the higher urinary calculi incidence associated with that

526

season. It is worthy of mention that water hardness is not a cause of phosphatic urinary calculi. Further, the minerals (Ca and Mg) contributing to water hardness are among the factors found to protect against this type of calculi.

Prevention

Urine blockage due to urinary calculi in growing-finishing wethers or steers may occur at any time during the feeding period, but most losses occur after the animals have been on feed for at least 3 weeks. Preventive measures taken after outbreaks of calculi have occurred may appear to be only partially effective in that the stones already formed may lodge in the urethra and cause urine blockage at a later date. Most materials and practices offering some degree of protection against phosphatic urinary calculi appear to involve at least one of the following mechanisms: a lowering of urinary P levels; acidification of the urine; an increase in urine volume.

Urine P may be maintained at acceptable concentrations by avoiding an excess of dietary P and by maintaining a Ca-P ratio in the range of 1.5 to 2 parts Ca to 1 part P (11, 13). The P requirements of feedlot lambs and cattle are normally met by the amount of P inherent in high-concentrate diets, but Ca supplementation is generally required to obtain desired Ca levels. Ground limestone (37-39% Ca) is most commonly used for this purpose. Figure 24-18 shows the relationship of dietary Ca levels with urinary P concentrations and the incidence of urinary calculi reported for sheep.

If past experience with a given diet indicates that a phosphatic urinary calculi problem may be expected even with use of recommended levels of Ca and P, acidification of the urine should then be given consideration. Ammonium chloride (NH_4Cl) has been shown to be effective for this purpose (11, 15). NH_4Cl fed daily at a rate of 7.1 g to sheep or 28.4 to 42.5 g to fattening cattle has been approved by the Food and Drug Administration for prevention of urinary calculi. These amounts are equivalent to approximately 0.5% NH_4Cl in the total diet. $CaCl_2$ fed at levels approximating 1% of the diet has also been reported to be effective in reducing urine alkalinity and the incidence of

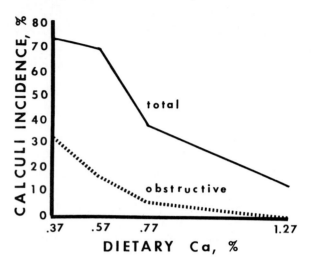

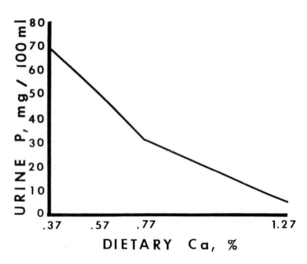

Figure 24-18. Phosphatic urinary calculi incidence (top) and urinary P concentrations (bottom) in lambs fed diets containing 0.55% P and various levels of Ca. Adapted from Bushman et al (13).

phosphatic urinary calculi (10, 11, 12). Use of $CaCl_2$ requires that its Ca contribution be given consideration when calculating the ration.

Urine volume can sometimes be increased by including NaCl in the diet at a level higher than normal. Levels equivalent to 4% to 10% of the total diet have been used for this purpose (15, 21). An increase in urine volume is dependent upon an increase in water consumption and the importance of an adequate supply of good quality water cannot be overemphasized. Feeding high levels of NaCl may be the least satisfactory of the methods for prevention of phosphatic urinary calculi because of the high dietary levels required and the potential for a reduction in ration palatability.

SILICEOUS URINARY CALCULI

Urinary calculi having silica (SiO_2) as their main mineral constituent are known to occur frequently in ruminants grazing the ranges of North America, Australia, the USSR and India. They may also occur in cattle and sheep fed high-Si feeds in drylot. Non-obstructive SiO_2 urolithiasis has been found in 50% or more of some groups of animals (22, 23). This type of urinary calculi occurs in non-ruminants only with daily ingestion of Si compounds such as Mg silicate used as an antacid (24) or tetraethylorthosilicate used for the experimental production of SiO_2 urinary calculi in laboratory animals (25, 26). The subject of Si metabolism and SiO_2 urolithiasis in ruminants has been reviewed by Bailey (27).

Major Causative Factors

The source of Si for formation of SiO_2 urinary calculi in ruminants appears to be the range grasses on which they graze or that are harvested for winter feeding. Oats, especially the hulls and straw, may also contribute important amounts of Si to the diet. Plants increase in Si content with maturation and subsequent leaching of soluble constituents. Native grasses collected over a period of two years from western South Dakota increased in SiO_2 content from about 5% of the dry matter in June to 8% in November (28).

Approximately 20% of plant Si may be due to wind-deposited soil particles (29). Up to 14% of the annual dry matter intake of sheep and cattle may come from soil under certain conditions (30). However, soil-born Si is of doubtful importance in the etiology of SiO_2 urinary calculi because of its low solubility.

A greater incidence of SiO_2 urinary calculi occurring in ruminants in North America during winter months may be due to the higher Si content of the forages as well as lower water consumption occurring during that season. Likewise, short water supplies may be a factor favoring a high incidence of SiO_2 calculi such as that occurring in Australia during summer (27).

Attempts to experimentally promote SiO_2 urinary calculi formation through the feeding of inorganic Si sources, principally sodium silicate (10, 31) and bentonite (32), have been futile. However, SiO_2 calculi have formed readily in rats fed diets containing an organic Si compound, tetraethylorthosilicate, that is readily hydrolyzed under acidic conditions to yield monomeric SiO_2. It has been suggested that maximum urinary output of Si is attained in ruminants when soluble SiO_2 is ingested in amounts adequate to saturate the reticulo-rumen fluid (33). A saturation concentration at body temperature is about 170 ppm SiO_2 (34).

Less than 1% of the Si in calculogenic diets is absorbed. Maximum daily urinary excretions of SiO_2 have been placed at approximately 1.5 g for cattle (35) and 0.25 g for sheep (33, 36, 37). Urinary SiO_2 concentrations for animals fed calculogenic diets are generally in the range of 400 to 1,000 ppm, these being about two to six times saturation concentrations. Polymerization of SiO_2 in solution proceeds at a rate proportional to the square of the concentration during the time that unpolymerized SiO_2 exceeds saturation, and rate of polymerization in pure solutions is most rapid at a pH of 5 to 7 (38). However, SiO_2 calculi have been observed to occur under either acidic or alkaline urinary conditions.

Aggregates of polymerized SiO_2 do not form readily in pure solutions at the SiO_2 concentrations found in urine. However, polymerization of SiO_2 is facilitated by the presence of electrolytes (39), and proteins present in urine will combine with polysilicic acids to form insoluble complexes (40). Bailey (27) describes how aggregation of micelles composed of these materials may be a first step in formation of nuclei for further SiO_2 deposition.

Prevention

Measures effective in the prevention of SiO_2 urinary calculi, having practical application at present, are those that reduce urinary Si concentrations. Attempts to reduce Si absorbtion through the feeding of aluminum compounds have been unsuccessful (43). Substitution of low-Si feeds for a portion of those having higher Si contents reduces SiO_2 urinary calculi. Feedstuffs that may be used

528

for this purpose include alfalfa and other legume forages and low-fiber cereal grains such as corn and milo.

Increasing water consumption is also effective in lowering urinary Si concentrations through an increase in urine volume. High levels of NaCl in the diet have been used for this purpose (41, 42). A grain-based supplement containing 12 to 20% of NaCl in a creep-feeder located near an adequate water supply has been suggested to be an effective vehicle for administering NaCl to range-based calves (27). A daily intake of about 1 g of NaCl/kg body weight was considered to increase water intake sufficiently to eliminate calculi formation.

Research with laboratory animals indicates that adequate P nutrition may also be an important deterrent to formation of SiO_2 calculi (26). While this observation has not been confirmed with ruminants, high Si range grasses often provide P at levels considered to be suboptimum for young ruminants and it would be prudent to provide P-containing mineral supplements under these conditions.

TREATMENT

Attempts to treat recognized cases of urinary calculi usually meet with limited success. Surgery represents the most effective treatment when urine blockage occurs. When examination shows the point of blockage to be the filamentous urethral process of rams or wethers, the process and the accompanying stone may be removed surgically. A procedure often used with steers involves a urethrotomy in which the urethra is surgically bisected at a point above the sigmoid flexure, and the urethral stump is secured through a skin incision forming a new urinary opening that bypasses the more constricted portion of the urinary tract. Steers treated in this manner often make acceptable weight gains for the remainder of the feeding period.

When obstruction is only partial, the use of muscle relaxants or, in the case of phosphatic calculi, materials for urine acidification may

occasionally meet with success. However, a stone removed or passed from an animal may represent only a portion of the precipitate present in the bladder; thus, the chance of re-occurrence is great.

NH_4Cl in the feed is commonly used for urine acidification. Administration of NH_4Cl in a drench or capsule should be approached with caution in that single dosages somewhat greater than amounts recommended daily in the feed for phosphatic calculi prevention may approach toxic levels under some conditions. (Readers are referred to the discussion concerning ammonium toxicity under the heading Nitrate and Urea Toxicities, Ch. 23.) Urine acidification used as a treatment of recognized cases of phosphatic urolithiasis requires urine flow for solubilization of stones, and solubilization can generally not be obtained in time to provide relief. The relative ineffectiveness of available treatments helps to emphasize the importance of following a program for calculi prevention.

SUMMARY

Phosphatic urinary calculi occurring in feedlot cattle and sheep and SiO_2 urinary calculi occurring in range animals are the most important types of urinary calculi found in ruminants. The lack of satisfactory treatments for urolithiasis gives emphasis to the importance of methods for its prevention. Principal causes of phosphatic urinary calculi appear to be nutritional factors that contribute toward high urinary P concentrations and an alkaline urine. Methods for prevention of phosphatic calculi include avoiding the feeding of excessive P, maintaining a Ca-P ratio of 1.5 to 2 parts Ca to 1 part P, and the feeding of acid-forming materials. Increasing urine volume through the feeding of high levels of NaCl is less effective than other methods for phosphatic urinary calculi prevention. However, with the exception of avoiding high-Si feeds, this is the only prophylactic measure currently having practical application for the prevention of SiO_2 urinary calculi.

Literature Cited on Milk Fever

1. Littledike, E.T. 1974. In: Lactation, Vol. 2, p. 355. Academic Press, New York.
2. Jorgensen, N.A. 1974. J. Dairy Sci. 57:933.

3. Littledike, E.T., J.W. Young and D.C. Beitz. 1981. J. Dairy Sci. 64:1465.
4. Horst, R.L. and T.A. Reinhardt. 1983. J. Dairy Sci. 66:661.
5. Willoughby, R.A., D.G. Butler, C.F. Cote and R.A. Curtes. 1970. In: Parturient Hypocalcemia, p. 237. Academic Press, New York.
6. Bowen, J.M., D.M. Blackmen and J.E. Heavner. 1970. Amer. J. Vet. Res. 31:831.
7. Horst, R.L., J.H. Thornton, N.A. Jorgensen and L.H. Schultz. 1976. J. Dairy Sci. 59:88.
8. Mayer, G.P. 1970. In: Parturient Hypocalcemia, p. 177. Academic Press, New York.
9. Rowland, G.W., C.C. Capen, D.M. Young and H.E. Black. 1972. Calcif. Tissue Res. 9:179.
10. Horst, R.L., J.A. Eisman, N.A. Jorgensen and H.F. DeLuca. 1977. Science 196:662.
11. Gast, D.R., R.L. Horst, N.A. Jorgensen and H.F. DeLuca. 1979. J. Dairy Sci. 62:1009.
12. Hoffsis, G.F., C.C. Capen, M.E. Packe and A.W. Norman. 1979. Bovine Pract. 13:88.
13. Marquardt, J.P., et al. 1974. J. Dairy Sci. 57:606.
14. Sachs, M.A., et al. 1977. Amer. J. Vet. Res. 38:2039.
15. Gardner, R.W. and R.L. Peck. 1973. J. Dairy Sci. 56:385.
16. Goings, R.L., et al. 1974. J. Dairy Sci. 57:1184.
17. Julien, W.E., H.R. Conrad, J.W. Hibbs and W.L. Crest. 1977. J. Dairy Sci. 60:431.
18. Hibbs, J.W., L.A. Muir and H.R. Conrad. 1970. In: Parturient Hypocalcemia, p. 35. Academic Press, New York.
19. Ramberg, C.F., J.M. Phang and D.S. Kronfeld. 1970. In: Parturient Hypocalcemia, p. 119. Academic Press, New York.
20. Littledike, E.T. and R.L. Horst. 1982. J. Dairy Sci. 65:749.

Literature Cited on Ketosis, Pregnancy Toxemia and Fat Cow Syndrome

1. Bergman, E.N. 1970. In: Dukes' Physiology of Domestic Animals, 8th Ed., p. 596. Cornell Univ. Press, Ithaca, NY.
2. Kronfeld, D.S. 1970. In: Physiology of Digestion and Metabolism in the Ruminant, p. 566. A.T. Phillipson, ed. Oriel Press, Newcastle upon Tyne, England.
3. Schultz, L.H. 1971. J. Dairy Sci. 54:962.
4. Schultz, L.H. 1974. In: Lactation, Vol. II., p. 317. Academic Press, New York.
5. Littledike, E.T., J.W. Young and D.C. Beitz. 1981. J. Dairy Sci. 64:1465.
6. Baird, D.G. 1982. J. Dairy Sci. 65:1.
7. Yamdagni, S. and L.H. Schultz. 1970. J. Dairy Sci. 53:1046.
8. Schultz, L.H. and M. Myers. 1959. J. Dairy Sci. 42:705.
9. Schwalm, J.W. and L.H. Schultz. 1976. J. Dairy Sci. 59:262.
10. Schwalm, J.W. and L.H. Schultz. 1976. J. Dairy Sci. 59:255.
11. Schwalm, J.W., R. Waterman, G.E. Shook and L.H. Schultz. 1969. J. Dairy Sci. 52:915.
12. Waterman, R. and L.H. Schultz. 1972. J. Dairy Sci. 55:1447.
13. Bergman, E.N. 1971. J. Dairy Sci. 54:936.
14. Fronk, T.J., L.H. Schultz and A.R. Hardie. 1980. J. Dairy Sci. 63:1080.
15. Gardner, R.W. 1969. J. Dairy Sci. 52:1973.
16. Kronfeld, D.S. 1982. J. Dairy Sci. 65:2204.
17. Fronk, T.J. and L.H. Schultz. 1979. J. Dairy Sci. 62:1804.
18. Bartlett, C.A., C.G. Schwab, J.W. Smith and J.B. Holter. 1983. J. Dairy Sci. Suppl. 66:175 (Abstr.).
19. Dufva, G.S., E.E. Bartley, A.D. Dayton and D.O. Riddell. 1983. J. Dairy Sci. 66:2329.
20. Fox, F.H. 1971. J. Dairy Sci. 54:974.
21. Jensen, R. 1974. Diseases of Sheep. Lea and Febiger, Philadelphia.
22. Patterson, D.S.P. and N.F. Cunningham. 1969. Proc. Nutr. Soc. 171.
23. Morrow, D.H. 1976. J. Dairy Sci. 59:1625.
24. Morrow, D.H., D. Hillman, A.Q. Dade and H. Kitchener. 1979. J. Amer. Vet. Med. Assoc. 174:161.
25. Reid, I.M. 1980. Vet. Rec. 107:281.
26. Gerloff, B.J., T.H. Herdt, R.S. Emergy and W.W. Wells. 1984. J. Animal Sci. 59:806.

530

Literature Cited on Grass Tetany

1. Blood, D.C., J.A. Henderson and O.M. Radostits. 1979. Veterinary Medicine. Lea and Febriger, Philadelphia.
2. Bohman, V.R., A.L. Lesperance, G.D. Harding and D.L. Grunes. 1969. J. Animal Sci. 29:99.
3. Bohman, V.R., F.P. Horn, E.T. Littledike, J.G. Hurst and D. Griffin. 1983. J. Animal Sci. 47:1364.
4. Contreras, P.A., R. Manston and B.F. Sansom. 1982. Res. Vet. Sci. 33:10.
5. Durand, M. and R. Kawashima. 1980. In: Digestive Physiology and Metabolism in Ruminants. Y. Ruckebusch and P. Thivend, eds. AVI Publ. Co., Westport, CT.
6. Eng, K. 1983. Feedstuffs 25:10.
7. Fontenot, J.P., G.E. Bunce, K.E. Webb, Jr. and V.G. Allen (eds.). 1983. Role of Magnesium in Animal Agriculture. John Lee Pratt Animal Nut. Pro., Virginia Polytechnic Institute, Blacksburg, VA.
8. Grace, N.D. 1983. The Mineral Requirements of Grazing Ruminants. N. Z. Soc. Animal Prod. Occasional Publ. No. 9.
9. Grunes, D.L. and H.F. Mayland. 1984. USDA Leaflet No. 561.
10. Grunes, D.L., P.R. Stout and J.R. Brownell. 1970. Adv. Agron. 22:331.
11. Grunes, D.L., J.F. Thompson, J. Kubota and V.A. Lazar. 1968. Ninth Intl. Congr. Soil Sci. Trans. II:597.
12. Hidiroglu, J., B.K. Thompson, S.K. Ho and J.G. Proulx. 1981. Can. J. Comp. Med. 45:124.
13. Hjerpe, C.A. 1967. Southwest. Vet. 21:33.
14. Horn, J.P. and R.H. Smith. 1978. Brit. J. Nutr. 40:473.
15. Hungerford, T.G. 1975. Diseases of Livestock, 8th Ed. McGraw-Hill Book Company, Sydney.
16. Jolley, L.C. and D.D. Leaver. 1974. Aust. Vet. J. 50:98.
17. Kemp, A. and M.L. t'Hart. 1957. Neth. J. Agr. Sci. 5:4.
18. Lucas, M.J. 1983. Mod. Vet. Prac. 64:213.
19. Madsen, F.C., D.E. Lentz, J.K. Miller, D. Lowrey-Harnden and S.L. Hansard. 1976. J. Animal Sci. 42:1316.
20. Mathison, G.W., R.T. Hardin and B.E. Beck. 1981. Can. J. Animal Sci. 61:375.
21. Martens, H. 1983. Brit. J. of Nutr. 49:153.
22. Martens, H. and H. Kasebieter. 1983. Zbl. Vet. Med. A, 30:1.
23. Martens, H. and Y. Rayssiguier. 1980. In: Digestive Physiology and Metabolism in Ruminants. Y. Ruckebusch and P. Thivend, eds. AVI Publ. Co., Westport, CT.
24. Mayland, H.F. and D.L. Grunes. 1979. In: Am. Soc. Agron. Publ. 35, p. 123. V.V. Rendig and D.L. Grunes, eds. Madison, WI.
25. Mayland, H.F., D.L. Grunes and D.M. Stuart. 1974. Agron. J. 66:441.
26. Metson, A.J., W.H.M. Saunders, T.W. Collie and V.W. Graham. 1966. N. Z. J. Agr. Res. 9:410.
27. Moseley, G. and D.W. Griffiths. 1984. Grass and Forage Sci. 39:195.
28. Moseley, G. and D.J.H. Jones. 1974. Proc. Nutr. Soc. 33:87A.
29. Newton, G.L., J.P. Fontenot, R.E. Tucker and C.E. Polan. 1972. J. Animal Sci. 35:440.
30. O'Kelley, R.E. and J.P. Fontenot. 1969. J. Animal Sci. 29:959.
31. O'Kelley, R.E. and J.P. Fontenot. 1973. J. Animal Sci. 36:994.
32. Reid, R.L., B.S. Baker and L.C. Vona. 1984. J. Animal Sci. 59:1403.
33. Rendig, V.V. and D.L. Grunes (eds.). 1979. Grass Tetany. Am. Soc. Agron. Publ. 35. Madison, WI.
34. Reynolds, C.K., M.C. Bell and M.H. Sims. 1984. J. Nutr. 114:1334.
35. Ritter, R.J., J.A. Boling and N. Gay. 1984. J. Animal Sci. 59:197.
36. Robinson, D.L., O.J. Hemkes and A. Kemp. 1984. Netherlands J. Agr. Sci. 32:73.
37. Russell, J.B. 1985. Appl. Environ. Microbiol. 49:120.
38. Russell, J.B. and P.J. Van Soest. 1984. Appl. Environ. Microbiol. 47:155.
39. Sansom, B.F., R. Manston and M.J. Vagg. 1983. Vet. Record 112:447.
40. Schneider, E., P. Tschudi and W. Leuenberger. 1985. Schweizer Archiv fur Tierheilkunde. 127:9.
41. Simesen, M.G. 1968. Medlemsblad Danske Dyrlaegeforen. 51:848.
42. Simesen, M.G. 1970. In: Clinical Biochemistry of Domestic Animals, 2nd Ed., Vol. 1:353. J.J. Kaneko and C.E. Cornelius, eds. Academic Press, New York.
43. Smith, R.H. and J.P. Horn. 1976. In: Nuclear Techniques in Animal Production and Health. IAEA. Vienna.
44. Spears, J.W. and R.W. Harvey. 1984. J. Animal Sci. 58:460.
45. Stuedemann, J.A., S.R. Wilkinson and R.S. Lowrey. 1984. Amer. J. Vet. Res. 45:698.
46. Terashima, Y., et al. 1984. Nutr. Rep. In. 29:869-875.

47. Turner, M.A. and V.E. Neall. 1978. N. Z. J. Agr. Res. 21:583.
48. Verite, R., B. Remond and M. Journet. 1984. Can. J. Animal Sci. 64 (Suppl):328.
49. West, D.M. and A.N. Bruere. 1981. N. Z. Vet. J. 29:85.
50. Whitaker, D.A. 1983. Outlook on Agr. 12:77.
51. Wilkinson, S.R. and J.A. Stuedemann. 1979. In: Am. Soc. Agron. Publ. 35, p. 93. V.V. Rendig and D.L. Grunes, eds. Madison, WI.
52. Wilson, G.F. 1980. Animal Prod. 31:153.
53. Wilson, G.F., et al. 1969. N. Z. J. Agr. Res. 12:467.

Literature Cited on Urinary Calculi

1. Emerick, R.J. and L.B. Embry. 1964. J. Animal Sci. 23:1079.
2. Nottle, M.C. 1982. Aust. Vet. J. 58:256.
3. Nottle, M.C. 1976. Res. Vet. Sci. 21:309.
4. Huntington, G.B. and R.J. Emerick. 1984. Amer. J. Vet. Res. 45:180.
5. Walter-Toews, D. and D.H. Meadows. 1980. Can. Vet. J. 21:61.
6. Finlayson, B., C.W. Vermeulen and E.J. Stewart. 1961. J. Urol. 86:355.
7. Packett, L.V. and S.D. Coburn. 1965. Amer. J. Vet. Res. 110:112.
8. Hoar, D.W., R.J. Emerick and L.B. Embry. 1969. J. Animal Sci. 29:647.
9. Lindley, C.E., et al. 1953. J. Animal Sci. 12:704.
10. Emerick, R.J., L.B. Embry and O.E. Olson. 1959. J. Animal Sci. 18:1025.
11. Emerick, R.J. and L.B. Embry. 1963. J. Animal Sci. 22:510.
12. Bushman, D.H., R.J. Emerick and L.B. Embry. 1965. J. Animal Sci. 24:671.
13. Bushman, D.H., R.J. Emerick and L.B. Embry. 1965. J. Nutr. 87:499.
14. Bushman, D.H., L.B. Embry and R.J. Emerick. 1967. J. Animal Sci. 26:1199.
15. Bushman, D.H., R.J. Emerick and L.B. Embry. 1968. J. Animal Sci. 27:490.
16. Hoar, D.W., R.J. Emerick and L.B. Embry. 1970. J. Animal Sci. 31:118.
17. Packett, L.V. and J.P. Hauschild. 1964. J. Nutr. 84:185.
18. Godwin, I.R. and V.J. Williams. 1982. Aust. J. Agr. Res. 33:843.
19. N.R.C. 1964. Joint United States-Canadian tables of feed composition. Nat. Acad. Sci., Washington, DC.
20. Crookshank, H.R., et al. 1960. J. Animal Sci. 19:595.
21. Elam, C.J., W.E. Ham and B.H. Schneider. 1957. Proc. Soc. Expt. Biol. Med. 95:769.
22. Connell, R., F. Whiting and S.A. Forman. 1959. Can. J. Comp. Med. 23:41.
23. Keeler, R.F. 1963. Annals N. Y. Acad. Sci. 104:592.
24. Herman, J.R. and A.S. Goldberg. 1960. J. Amer. Med. Assoc. 174:128.
25. Emerick, R.J., E.E. Kugel and V. Wallace. 1963. Amer. J. Vet. Res. 24:610.
26. Emerick, R.J. 1984. J. Nutr. 114:733.
27. Bailey, C.B. 1981. Can. J. Animal Sci. 61:219.
28. Fransen, S.C. 1982. Ph.D. Thesis. South Dakota State Univ., Brookings, SD.
29. Bailey, C.B. 1967. Amer. J. Vet. Res. 28:1743.
30. Healy, W.B. 1973. Nutritional aspects of soil ingestion by grazing animals. In: Chemistry and Biochemistry of Herbage, Vol. 1. Academic Press, London.
31. Schneider, B.H., E.D. Tayson and W.E. Ham. 1952. Wash. Agr. Exp. Sta. Cir. 203.
32. Huntington, G.B., R.J. Emerick and L.B. Embry. 1977. J. Animal Sci. 45:119.
33. Jones, L.H.P. and K.A. Handreck. 1965. J. Agr. Sci. 65:129.
34. Scheel, L.D., E. Fleischer and F.W. Klemperer. 1953. Ind. Hyg. and Occupational Med. 8:564.
35. Bailey, C.B. 1976. Can. J. Animal Sci. 56:213.
36. Nottle, M.C. 1966. Aust. J. Agr. Res. 17:175.
37. Nottle, M.C. 1966. Aust. J. Agr. Res. 17:183.
38. Iler, R.K. 1955. The Colloid Chemistry of Silica and Silicates. Cornell Univ. Press. Ithaca, NY.
39. Merrill, R.C. and R.W. Spencer. 1950. J. Phys. and Colloid Chem. 54:806.
40. Bailey, C.B. 1972. Can. J. Biochem. 50:305.
41. Whiting, F., R. Connell and S.A. Forman. 1958. Can. J. Comp. Med. 22:332.
42. Bailey, C.B. 1967. Science (N.Y.) 155:696.
43. Bailey, C.B. 1977. Can. J. Animal Sci. 57:239.

25 THERAPEUTIC NUTRITION

by J. H. Ternouth

Therapeutic nutrition is concerned with the correction of nutritional deficiencies or excesses (malnutrition), the replacement of nutrients to ameliorate a disease or disorder which does not have a nutritional cause and the feeding of drugs or nutrients to aid in the inhibition of diseases. Thus, therapeutic nutrition is the treatment of disease by regulation of the type or amount of food eaten or the parenteral or oral provision of some nutrient or substance. Some of these diseases may be evident to the trained observer but others are not. Many are only diagnosed by thorough investigation and laboratory examination of samples. Therapeutic nutrition, by definition, implies that a disease has been diagnosed and preferably that the degree of nutrient deficiency or excess recognized so that appropriate qualitative and quantitative therapy can be instituted.

Although there is a very large amount of information available on various aspects of nutrient requirements of healthy animals, much less research has been completed on the nutrition of animals suffering from diseases, except for certain discrete metabolic diseases, nutrient deficiencies and digestive tract disorders. It is unfortunately true that the lack of popularity and research in this aspect of animal diseases is due to the inability of commercial companies to make adequate profits from the sale of therapeutic diets. This can be contrasted with the popularity of chemical therapeutics.

THE EFFECT OF NUTRITION ON DISEASE

Chronic food restrictions commonly result in the increased appearance of human and animal diseases; in addition, certain diseases may appear in a more malignant form during a period of malnutrition. A considerable body of information has been accumulated that shows that nutrient deficiencies increase the susceptibility of man and monogastric animals to bacterial, rickettsial and viral diseases (1).

However, the effect of malnutrition upon the immunity of farm animals is only now being clarified (2). Conversely, well-fed animals are generally more resistant to bacterial and parasitic diseases (1, 3).

Sprunt and Flanigan (4) have proposed that there are two environmental influences in any particular ecological niche which affect the equilibrium between host and the microorganism. These are the nutrient supply to the microorganism and the potential antagonism to the microorganism of the host. Only when the nutrient supply is adequate or high and antagonism low does the microorganism become virulent and the host susceptible to the disease. Whitehair (5) has listed tissue integrity, antibody production, detoxification ability of the liver and kidneys and maintenance of the reticulo-endothelial system as antagonistic factors which are of considerable importance in limiting the virulence of diseases.

Energy and Protein (N) Deficiencies

An acute energy deficiency, as observed in ruminants as ketosis, is normally of too short a duration to allow time for infectious agents to be involved in the pathogenic process. A prolonged energy deficiency has been shown to decrease the resistance of mice to several species of bacteria, including *Staphylococcus aureus*, *Klebsiella pneumoniae* and *Shigella flexmeii*. In ruminant animals, the effects of prolonged energy deficiency are insidious (3) and commonly result in: reducing the size of the neonates of energy deficient dams with an increased risk of neonate mortality; inadequate colostrum production, especially from heifers; retarding the growth and delaying the onset of puberty of young animals; and reducing the milk yield and delaying the return to estrus of lactating animals.

Unfortunately, these are not clear signs of energy deficiency and the energy deficiency may be secondary to some other deficiency (for example, protein deficiency). Chronic energy deficiency and starvation, as observed in drought situations, result in emaciation, unthriftyness and weakness, and if uncorrected, eventually in death.

N or protein deficiency occurs commonly in rangeland situations in many countries, especially in the dry season. The effect of the deficiency is to depress nutrient (especially energy) intake so the effect of the deficiency is hard to distinguish from a primary energy deficiency (6).

Mineral and Vitamin Deficiencies

Specific mineral and vitamin deficiencies may have a marked effect upon the susceptibility of animals to infection as well as upon animal production (3). Co deficiency is known to cause diarrhea in cattle and sheep and a high incidence of infectious diseases are known to be a sequela of Fe deficiency. In cattle, the relationship between P deficiency, pica and botulism is well known. Many mineral and vitamin deficiencies (including P, Mg and S) result in significant reductions in food (energy and protein) intake so that concomitant energy-protein deficiencies occur.

Nutrient Excesses

Whilst nutrient deficiencies are commonly predisposing causes of disease, this is not invariably the case. A number of diseases caused by *Clostridial* sp. bacteria cause death among the best fed animals; enterotoxemia *(Clostridium perfringens)* commonly occurs in the lambs and calves which are the fattest in the group. Well-fed animals are more susceptible to some viral infections (4); the incidence of foot-and-mouth disease is greatest in well-fed cattle and occurs in a milder form during periods of food shortage. Hemonchosis causes death more frequently when the nutrition is high and the environmental conditions result in massive infestations (3). Anaplasmosis infection has been observed to cause considerable weight-loss in well-fed cattle but not in cattle losing weight.

Excessive ingestion of grain may result in non-infectious acute indigestion, bloat, parakeratosis and hepatic foci of *Sphaerophorus necrophorus,* the bacteria reaching the liver from the primary lesion in the ruminal wall along the ruminal veins.

Under hygienic conditions, calves may be fed liquid diets ad libitum without diarrhea occurring. However, under less hygienic conditions, the feeding of similar quantities of milk may result in the appearance of fermentative or putrefactive diarrhea (7).

THE EFFECT OF DISEASE UPON NUTRITION

The effects of stresses and diseases on the nutrition of any animal is dependent upon the type of tissue affected and on the severity and duration of the stress or disease. Some diseases and stresses have an effect upon a single tissue, which may in itself be diagnostically significant, but most influence a number of tissues or have secondary effects which are evident in other tissues.

Food Intake

Voluntary food intake is used by many veterinarians and animal scientists as a sign of health. Most forms of stress and disease result in some reduction in food intake while an improvement of food intake after a period of inappetence generally indicates that the animal is recovering from the disease or stress. The reduction in food intake may be a reduction in roughage intake or concentrate intake or both depending on the nature and severity of the condition.

There are many reasons for reduced food intake associated with disease or stress. Just as the control of food intake is a multifunctional control mechanism (6), so the disease and stress processes may modify the regulatory mechanisms in a variety of ways. Fever (hyperthermia) which occurs as part of many acute diseases may modify the thermoregulatory control mechanisms. The thermoregulatory control mechanisms are involved in the control of food intake. Changes of environmental temperature or body insulation are known to affect food intake. These are made in an apparent attempt to maintain energy balance. It appears that toxins produced by infectious agents and circulating metabolites released by damaged tissue cells, may reduce food intake either directly or possibly by the resultant hyperthermia.

Dehydration is known to reduce food intake in monogastric and ruminant animals. Diarrhea, by causing massive losses of nutrients in the feces (7, 8), results in a complex series of changes in the bloodstream so that dehydration, change in osmolality, ion concentration, acid-base balance, pH or increased

534

circulating metabolites or toxins may be the cause of the reduced food intake.

Artificial infection with large numbers of nematode larve have resulted in marked depressions in food intake of sheep. Similarly, Berry and Dargie (9) have reported depressions in food intake when sheep were artificially infected with metacercariae of *Fasciola hepatica.*

The reason for a reduced food intake is easy to understand when the animal lacks teeth or areas of the gastro-intestinal tract are inflamed, e.g. gingivitis or pharyngitis. Lesions in the oral cavity occur in a number of viral diseases including rinderpest, foot-and-mouth disease, vesicular stomatitis, bovine malignant catarrh in cattle and blue tongue in sheep. Food intake is reduced in animals suffering from non-infectious diseases such as simple or vagal indigestion, ruminal acidosis (grain overfeeding), traumatic reticulitis, and abomasal displacement (3, 10).

The effect of a reduced food intake will depend upon the size of available body reserves of the animal and the amount of consumed nutrient in most limited supply (11). When the stress or disease is chronic, then the reduced food intake will result in the appearance of one or a number of nutrient deficiency signs, unless some form of therapeutic nutrition is instituted. If the animal is anorexic for an extended period of time, some means (e.g. feeding by stomach tube or by parenteral administration) must be found for supplying the essential nutrient requirements, to allow the animal to recover, and to allow any therapeutic drugs to have an optimal effect upon the disease. Whitehair (5) points out that adequate nutrition will promote the effectiveness of other therapeutic agents. If the animal is consuming some food, increasing the concentration of nutrients in the diet may be a sufficiently large dietary change to insure that the maintenance nutrient requirements of the animal are met.

The normal order in which nutrients may become deficient in the animal during a period of inappetence is energy, protein, vitamins and minerals (11). It has been shown that blood proteins decline rapidly and there is ample evidence in man and laboratory animals to indicate that a protein deficiency results in reduced ability to form antibodies (2). Fell (11) concluded muscle and fat

catabolism in starved animals tends to make them edematous. In diseased or fasting animals there is almost invariably a negative N balance.

Energy reserves are depleted rapidly in the anorectic young animal, particularly liver glycogen, largely because they have very limited reserves of fat. Vitamin reserves, even the fat-soluble vitamins, are low in the young, although the hepatic reserves of the fat-soluble vitamins may be sufficient for some months in older animals. The water-soluble vitamins are rapidly depleted, particularly in the pre-ruminant animal or in an animal with impaired rumen function.

Gastro-Intestinal Motility

Motility is the result of the interaction of the stimulation of sympathetic and parasympathetic parts of the autonomic nervous system with the intestinal intrinsic nervous plexuses and musculature. Autonomic imbalance may result in hypermotility or hypomotility. The effects of various excitatory and inhibitory influences on the motility of the rumeno-reticulum have been tabulated (3). Gastro-intestinal nematodes, trematodes and cestodes, bacteria, protozoa, fungi and viruses cause diarrhea, either by causing an inflammatory response in the gastro-intestinal wall or by the production of toxins. However, this is not an invariable result as experimental parasitic infections have not been observed to cause any change in the rate of passage of water-soluble markers (12), and have reduced the rate of passage of stained particles. When diarrhea was produced artificially in calves using *Salmonella bovis-morbifans,* antibiotics and a water-soluble marker passed through the large intestine much faster than in healthy calves. Non-infectious stresses, toxins, laxative foods, cathartics and other drugs may have similar effects. When the integrity of the gastro-intestinal wall is damaged by any type of infectious agent, body fluids and electrolytes (or in severe cases whole blood) pass into the intestine (13), greatly increasing the quantity of abnormally watery feces produced by the animal (8). When the losses include significant amounts of protein and occur from the upper portions of the gastro-intestinal tract, partial digestion of the proteins by endogenous and microbial enzymes may result in a putrefactive (foul smelling, gaseous) diarrhea (7).

There is an appreciable amount of information relating the effect of stresses such as bloat to rumen function, but there is much less information relating infectious diseases to rumen function. Abnormal ruminal motility (secondary indigestion) is associated with a wide variety of causes; disturbed function may develop as a result of bacterial or parasitic disease—such as respiratory tract infection, anthrax, malignant catarrhal fever, coccidiosis, and severe infestations of stomach worms or liver flukes (3). Secondary indigestion may be associated also with febrile response to inflammatory involvement of a non-gastro-intestinal organ (acute mastitis, endometritis), with dislocations of the abomasum or intestinal tract, with milk fever or grass tetany, ketosis, a variety of plant toxins, and with peritonitis and pericarditis arising from traumatic reticulitis.

Digestion and Absorption

The degree of digestion and absorption occurring at any particular site in the gastro-intestinal tract is dependent upon the suitability of the microenvironment for digestion and absorption and the length of time the nutrients remain in that environment. Thus, hypermotility, by reducing gastro-intestinal transit time, results in reduced food digestibility and absorption.

There are over 100 species of anaerobic bacteria, protozoa and fungi present in significant numbers in the rumeno-reticulum. The condition of ruminal acidosis results in a massive change in the ruminal microflora and the disappearance of protozoa which must influence ruminal digestion. The synthesis of cellulase by ruminal microorganisms and its activity upon plant cellulose is suppressed at low pH levels. Rumenitis, hyperkeratosis, parakeratosis and ruminal stasis may all be expected to reduce the absorption across the rumeno-reticular wall.

In ruminant animals there is massive secretion of water, minerals and nitrogenous compounds into the gastro-intestinal tract. Na and P are secreted in large quantities in saliva, Cl by the abomasum and Na and bicarbonate by the liver and pancreas. These minerals are secreted in isotonic aqueous solutions to aid the process of digestion and any failure of the reabsorption portion of the cycle results in severe body losses. In addition, there is massive bidirectional diffusion of fluids in normal healthy animals, particularly across the ruminal wall. Thus, many of the losses associated with diarrhea are due to failure to reabsorb endogenous secretions rather than to absorb dietary nutrients. The hypoproteinemia and osteoporosis observed in lambs artificially infected with nematode larva may be the result of chronic plasma protein and inorganic P losses (14, 15).

In calves, secretion of abomasal acid and pepsin and pancreatic fluid and enzymes are reduced by a variety of non-infectious stresses and may in turn reduce the apparent digestibility of milk diets (16). Infections of the liver (including ketosis and *Fascioliasis*) which reduce bile production, or infections of the abomasum and small intestine which reduce gastric and enteric enzymes, acid and bicarbonate secretion must also depress digestion and hence absorption of nutrients. Coop et al (17) have found a depression in the lactase and maltase activity of the intestinal mucosa of sheep following artificial *Nematodirus battus* infection.

In young animals with less nutrient reserve in body tissues, water is a major limiting "nutrient" (8, 11), in conditions such as diarrhea where fluid loss is very high. Likewise, blood electrolytes such as Na, may be depleted rapidly because they are stored to a very limited extent in the tissues.

Non-Fecal Losses of Nutrients

An increased quantity of water and some nutrients may be lost by non-fecal routes in animals affected by certain stresses or diseases. In the healthy animal there is an obligatory loss of fluids associated with respiration and a loss in the urine. Polyuria (increased urinary flow) occurs when there is nephrosis or nephritis (damage to the renal glomeruli or tubular epithelium). The polyuria is accompanied by a variable loss of blood constituents including protein and electrolytes, depending on the severity of the renal damage. Hyperthermia, fevers and heat stress increase the respiration and sweating rates resulting in increased water and, in the case of sweating, electrolyte loss.

536

Tissue Metabolism

Many diseases disturb tissue metabolism so that nutrient reserves in cells are mobilized or metabolized and metabolic pathways are stimulated or depressed either directly or due to some neural or humoral control. For example, hepatitis, hepatosis and diseases such as ketosis, which result in derangement of liver function, interfere with the storage of vitamins and trace minerals in the liver. In addition the utilization of glycogen and fatty infiltration of the hepatic cells occurs in ketosis. Following periods of high Cu intake, the ingestion of hepatotoxins or acute starvation have resulted in Cu poisoning due to the release of Cu stored in liver cells.

The subject of acid-base balance is complicated (3, 18) and beyond the scope of this chapter. Metabolic acidosis occurs most commonly following sudden excessive grain feeding, ketosis or due to excess loss of plasma bicarbonate due to diarrhea. Respiratory alkalosis is caused by hyperventilation associated with fever, hyperthermia and heat stress.

EVALUATION OF THE NUTRIENT FLUX AND STATUS

Before any form of therapy can be instituted, a diagnosis of the cause of the disease or stress must be made. This diagnosis should include an estimation of the etiology, pathogenesis and prognosis of the disease or stress. It is beyond the scope of this chapter to enter into a discussion of differential diagnosis; such information may be found in the standard veterinary texts (3, 10).

Diagnoses are commonly made upon a clinical examination of the patient and the whole flock or herd. A clinical examination normally includes a visual and physical examination of the patients, reviewing the history of the appearance of the disease, the present and previous management, including the dietary management, of the animals and an examination of the environment. This clinical examination may then indicate the need for further nutritional, pathological, microbiological, hematological or other laboratory type examinations. The difficulty with these laboratory examinations is that they commonly involve a time delay which results in the diagnostician having to make a tentative

diagnosis and to institute immediate therapy based upon that tentative diagnosis.

As this chapter is concerned with therapeutic nutrition, the dietary treatment is based upon an evaluation of the food requirements of the healthy animal, the existing feeding regimen and the modifications to this regimen necessary to ameliorate the effect of the disease or stress. However, if it is to be successful, the proposed dietary treatment must be one which the animal will ingest, digest and metabolize. For instance, in adult and young animals with gastro-intestinal disorders, the initial diet may supply just the maintenance requirements.

Visual Appraisal of the Animal

It is possible to make a general evaluation of an animal's condition from visual observations. If such an examination is to be meaningful, it is axiomatic that the person making the evaluation be cognizant of normal body size, condition and conformation of that species, breed and type of animal. For example, a normal Jersey cow may look emaciated compared to an Angus bull.

An experienced herdsman or caretaker will perceive general skeletal and growth aberrations as well as poor conditioning of animals. Skeletal malformations in ruminants are often due to altered metabolism of, or imbalances or deficiencies of, minerals. Rickets is most evident as bowing of the legs and enlargement of the carpal and tarsal joints. Fluorosis, usually due to ingestion of minerals or forages high in F, causes lameness and exostoses of the long bones.

Young bovine animals suffering from generalized chronic starvation often have concomitant stomach worm infections, have rough hair coats and appear thin or emaciated. The size of their heads, length of tails and volume of their abdomens or bellies will often seem exaggerated. Older animals suffering from generalized starvation may appear weak, emaciated and thin. The hair of cattle will usually lack luster and the wool covering of sheep will appear dry with occasional missing patches. If starvation is prolonged, animals will appear depressed and with their eyes sunken in their orbits. This condition is common in herds on overgrazed rangelands and on continuously grazed grain stubbles. Starvation in sheep may be difficult to evaluate by visual observation, due to the wool covering, and physical palpation is desirable.

A protein deficiency in cattle or sheep may be due to a dietary deficiency *per se* or may be due to infections of blood-sucking internal and external parasites, e.g. gastro-intesintal worms or sucking lice or ticks. Hypoproteinemia (low blood serum protein) is the usual result. A common sign of this condition is a generalized edema, most evident as a watery swelling of the throat and neck area, frequently called "bottle jaw". Sheep heavily infected with *Haemonchus contortus* often appear depressed and anemic on superficial examination.

The state of exercise or excitement should always be considered when observing animals. Rapid or difficult breathing may be due to this cause or as an indication of disease of the lungs or air passages or a toxemia, anemia or alkalosis.

Animals which have excess saliva may be suffering from infections of the mouth or tongue. Animals should be observed for signs of diarrhea which, if prolonged, results in serious dehydration and correction of this dehydration is of utmost importance to the survival of the animal. Diarrhea of various types is observed as a common sign of many infectious diseases, such as Johne's disease, bovine virus mucosal-diarrhea disease, salmonellosis, coccidiosis, colibacillosis and gastro-intestinal parasitic infections. In addition, diarrhea is a common sign of various forms of indigestion or toxemias.

The general posture and movement of animals should be observed. Those that appear stiff or tucked-up may be suffering from diseases of the digestive tract, such as traumatic reticulitis, peritonitis, rumenitis or severe enteritis. These signs are common to several nutritional, metabolic, toxicological or infectious disease conditions.

Physical Examination of the Animal

The physical examination of the animal follows automatically after the initial visual examination. It involves inspecting in more detail the signs of abnormality initially observed from a distance. During the examination, rectal body temperature, pulse rate and rhythm, and respiration rate and rhythm are checked as indicators of pathological processes. Examination of skin texture and elasticity, as well as palpation, percussion, ballottement, fluid percussion and auscultation of the underlying tissues and organs are other important techniques. Virtually all these techniques are useful in diagnosing gastro-intestinal abnormalities. Rectal examinations, again by palpation and ballottement, are also useful for aiding in diagnosis of abnormalities present in the more caudal portions of the abdominal cavity of the bovine.

At this stage, a definite diagnosis may be made. Frequently however, it may be necessary to examine the environment of the animal (plants or other foods, soil etc.) or collect samples from the animal or the environment so that a definite diagnosis can be made. Ideally, this diagnosis should be quantified so that quantitative therapy can be instituted.

Qualitative Evaluation of the Food

Qualitative examination of the available forage may provide a guide to the nutrient status of the animal. The value of forages is dependent upon the plants present and their stage of growth. These factors are in turn influenced by the availability of nutrients from the soil and the rainfall and temperature patterns. There are significant differences in the intake and digestibility of various species and cultivars of forages at any particular stage of growth. In addition, stage of growth of the pasture has a considerable effect on intake and digestibility of pastures (19). When grasses are young, food intake and digestibility are both higher than when the grass is mature. Thus visual assessment of the types of forage and their stage of growth is an important guide to their value for the animal.

It is important to recognize that there is no simple direct method by which the food intake of grazing ruminants can be assessed. As the variation in the food intake of ruminant animals is the most important single nutritional factor affecting animal productivity, this is a major deficiency in the diagnosticians armory.

Assessment of the food intake of penned animals is normally available. However, unless the animals are individually penned, the

538

Quantitative Examination

The nutrients required by an animal on any particular day may be obtained from the consumed food or from a body reserve. Considerable quantities of some nutrients are stored in the body, for example, energy as fat, Ca and P as bone, Na and water in the rumen, vitamin A in the liver. Other nutrients are not stored in any quantity, for example, Mg, K and the B group vitamins. The quantity of nutrients in a reserve may be estimated by various techniques. When a diagnostician judges the "condition" of an animal, he is judging the health of the animal and the fat reserves or energy status. The quantities of some nutrient reserves may be judged by the concentration in the blood because there is a very close relationship between the body reserves and blood concentration. The use of such blood tests has been widely used in human and animal medicine. Other techniques are available for judging the status of the animal in terms of some other nutrient reserves, for example, X and γ ray absorption for Ca status of bones, bone biopsy and neutron activation for bone P, liver biopsy cores for vitamin A, Cu and Fe, Na/K ratios in saliva for Na.

The truest simple estimate of the flux (as distinct from the status) of a metabolite through the ruminant animal is the ratio of short to long-chain fatty acids in milk for energy (20). This is a measure of whether the energy in the fat is derived directly from dietary energy or from the catabolism of body reserves. When dairy cattle are fed restricted quantities of energy, the molar percentage of short-chain fatty acids (C4-C16) decreases from 72 to less than 60% while the quantity of oleic acid increases from 15 to 26%. The molar percentage of stearic acid also increases although there is no change in the blood glucose levels.

Laboratory Animal Profiles

The concept of "Metabolic Profiles" has been developed as a branch of preventative nutrition and represents the most comprehensive advance in this direction. The original aim of metabolic profile testing was to provide advice to dairy farmers on the need for nutrient supplementation to achieve optimal nutrient intake for milk production. Instead of waiting for signs of nutrient deficiency to occur in the most susceptible individual members of a herd, representative cattle from three production groups (non-lactating, medium and high producing cows) on a farm are monitored on a regular basis to attempt to detect the occurrence of sub-clinical nutrient deficiencies. Twelve blood metabolites or ions (blood packed cell volume, hemoglobin and glucose and serum urea, Ca, Mg, inorganic P, Na, K, total protein, albumin and globulin) were measured in the initial studies (21). Theoretically, there are no limits to the number of metabolites which can be included in the profile. However, in practice the numbers of metabolites included will depend upon the convenience, reliability and cost of the analytical techniques, the reliability of a result based upon single samples taken from a limited number of animals in a production group and the ability to interpret the results of a profile. The diagnosticians aim to be able to provide corrective nutrient supplementation for the cattle, but this supplementation is less precise if the nutrient input and production indices are unknown.

A number of factors may interact which complicate both the diagnosis and resultant treatment of the animals from a metabolic profile. The concentration of a number of blood metabolites and ions are influenced by a number of non-nutritional factors which cause changes which may be confused with nutrient deficiencies. Handling stress before sampling, the site of sampling and the time of sampling in relation to feeding time have effects upon the concentration of energy and protein metabolites. Season of the year, chronic parasitism and even calving may influence blood metabolite levels. Various authors (22) have provided a broader perspective of the use and function of profiles in the grazing animal industry and research.

The number of metabolites which may be usefully included in a profile as *indicators* of actual or impending limits to animal production will vary depending on the practical situation. The inclusion of other metabolites or ions (β-hydroxybutyric acid, ketone bodies, Fe, Cu, Zn, Mn) may be important in some situations; estimation of serum enzymes and hormones may be valuable in particular circumstances. The overall monetary and labor cost of profile testing has to be measured against the average improvement in production which can be expected from correcting the nutrient deficiencies revealed by the technique. Blowey (23) has used a limited profile (involving measuring glucose, urea and albumin only) to provide information on the energy and N status of cattle. Blowey emphasizes that such blood analyses are *an aid* in the investigation of some aspects of nutrition and from frequently repeated analyses useful *normal* standards have been developed. The interpretation of abnormal profiles needs careful differential diagnosis and an interdisciplinary approach involving the veterinarian, nutritionist and farmer.

PRINCIPLES OF PREVENTATIVE AND THERAPEUTIC NUTRITION

Whilst the principles of preventative and therapeutic nutrition can be derived from a knowledge of physiology and nutrition, information in the literature is quite sparse and some of the suggestions may or may not have a foundation of experimental or practical knowledge. Hopefully, this deficit will be remedied.

Preventative Nutrition

The need for preventative nutrition will be diagnosed from the occurrence of a nutrient deficiency in one or more members of a group of animals, from the results of a clinical examination, quantitative examination or from profile testing. The therapy will consist of adjusting the amount of the nutrient ingested for a primary deficiency or correcting the primary or secondary causes of the disease in the case of a secondary deficiency. For instance, Co deficiency may be corrected by the use of Co bullets, drenching with Co, vitamin B_{12} injection, or less directly by distributing Co sulfate on the pasture in a fertilizer. When iodine deficiency (goiter) in sheep is due to the effects of goitrogens, a change of diet to reduce the intake of goitrogens is necessary as well as feeding extra iodine. Thiouracil, thiourea sulphonamides and L-5-vinyl-2-thioxazolidone, the latter found in a number of plants in the *Brassica* spp., are known to be goitrogenic. The complex interrelationships between Cu, Mo and S

are well known (24). Although an observed Cu deficiency may be due to high levels of Mo and S reducing the absorption of the Cu, the Cu deficiency may have to be corrected as though it were a primary deficiency.

Therapeutic Feeding

Nutrients may be supplied by voluntary or involuntary feeding or by various parenteral routes. When the ruminant animal will voluntarily ingest food, the therapeutic nutrients may be added to its diet. Extra protein supplement may be added to grain when the protein content of the pasture falls. Similarly, extra P may be added to the grain fed to cattle grazing on P-deficient pastures. In some cases, an attractant may be needed to encourage the cattle to consume the supplementary nutrient. Molasses, molassine meal, grains and dried fodders are widely used attractants which may have the effect of disguising certain unpalatable nutrients.

Involuntary feeding involves the use of drenching guns or esophageal tubes. Many supplementary nutrients fed by tube are given as liquids. Cattle and sheep are commonly drenched or injected with vitamin A and D emulsions in the middle of the dry season of the year in Australia.

Parenteral nutrition may involve complete, total or supplementary feeding (25). Complete parenteral nutrition involves feeding the animal its *entire* nutrient requirements by intravenous injection. There are no reports of this being attempted in ruminant animals, although complete intravenous feeding of dogs throughout a pregnancy has been successful. Complete intravenous feeding of pre-ruminant calves has been described (26, 27). Total parenteral feeding involves feeding the animals' total requirements of some nutrients by a parenteral route. Total parenteral feeding is a short-term alternative to oral feeding and the aim is to cover the basal requirements of the most immediately necessary nutrients and to compensate for increased losses or deficiencies due to disease or stress. For example, when a calf has severe diarrhea with dehydration and the veterinarian decides to use total parenteral feeding, intravenous infusions of isomolar fluids containing Na, K, bicarbonate, P and glucose are used for 1-3 d. During this time no milk is fed and the animal is dependent upon the parenteral infusions for energy. No attempt is made to supply supplementary amino acids, other minerals or vitamins for the short period of the parenteral feeding. It is assumed that the calf has sufficient reserves of these other nutrients to last through the parenteral feeding period.

Slow Release Therapy

This is not a new field of therapy but it is one which is developing rapidly in recent years. A considerable range of micronutrients, drugs and hormones are combined with an adjuvant for administration using a variety of routes (24). A well known example of slow release therapy is the Co bullet, used to supply Co to the microflora in the rumeno-reticulum of cattle and sheep. Because of their high specific gravity, these bullets lodge in the reticulum and have been reported to last 1-3 years as determined by serum vitamin B_{12} concentrations. The bullet represents a slow release device which is valuable in grazing animals where supplementary feeding is not practiced and it is not possible to add the micronutrient to a fertilizer. Recently, various other gastro-intestinal devices have been developed including Cu needles, Se pellets (24), phosphate glass bullets for Cu, Co, Se, Zn, and I (28) and plastic barrels with wings to release a range of micronutrients, certain anthelmintics, anti-foaming agents for bloat and even Cr_2O_3 as an experimental gastro-intestinal marker (29).

Parenteral injection of tablets (pellets) or suspensions have been used for a variety of micronutrients, vitamins and hormones. The suspensions include Cu Ca EDTA, Cu methionate and various other Cu compounds, Ba selenate in beeswax, Na_2SeO_3 with hydrogenated peanut oil (24).

These forms of slow release therapy are generally used when it is not possible to provide adequate supplementation to all animals by an alternative feeding regimen. Feeding animals in groups on a supplementary feed or using self-feeding blocks or licks is not always satisfactory because of the variable intake of particular animals.

Oral Fluid Therapy

Parenteral fluid therapy is used as a treatment for dehydration in humans and small animals but is rarely used in cattle due to the sheer volume of sterile fluids necessary to provide effective therapy. Replacement fluids are given orally by stomach tube in relatively mild dehydration (<5%) and by the intravenous route only when the degree of dehydration is severe. One problem that has been recognized recently is that electrolyte solutions are poorly absorbed from the gastrointestinal tract of calves with diarrhea. This occurs even though there is evidence showing that colonic absorption is increased. It has been reported that the addition of glycine to glucose-electrolyte solutions enhances the absorption of water and Na from the intestine of the diarrheic calf. Quickest and most effective recovery of calves from experimentally induced diarrhea occurred when a glucose-glycine-electrolyte solution containing 21.6g glucose, 3.5g glycine, 4.8g NaCl, 2.3g KH_2PO_4 and 0.07g K citrate/ℓ were given orally with an antibiotic for 4 d (30).

Dalton's formula (31) for oral replacement fluids for calves recognizes the need to replace Na and P losses, to combat the acidosis and to supply K and glucose which are depleted largely by the associated anorexia. Prolonged anorexia results in hypokalemia because cattle, in particular, are inefficient conservers of K and ruminant diets commonly have a high K content. However, some caution is necessary in the inclusion of K in parenteral infusions for fluid replacement resulting from diarrhea as the animal is initially hyperkalemic. The hypokalemia may be exacerbated by hemolysis, severe tissue destruction and diarrhea.

Ruminant animals do have mechanisms for precisely regulating water and Na intake. As the animal starts to recover from the acute phases of a disease, provision of measured amounts of clean water and electrolyte solutions may be left in separate containers. Animals which are not drinking should be given further intraruminal infusions of isomolar solutions at least once daily. The electrolyte solutions should contain the equivalent of 80g NaCl and 20g KCl in 10 liters of water. The quantities of water and electrolyte solution consumed are monitored throughout the animals' recovery.

CORRECTION OF FEEDING AND DIGESTIVE ABNORMALITIES

Anophagia, aphagia (anorexia), polyphagia and allotriophagia (pica) all occur in ruminant animals. In veterinary medicine it is important to overcome the reason for the abnormality in feeding behavior as well as to correct the nutrient deficiency or imbalance which results from the abnormality. When animals are aphagic for several days, fluid therapy may be used to supply essential nutrients (see above).

A general recommendation for stressed and diseased animals (3) that have been "off feed" for some days or for those that have had extensive treatments with oral antibiotics or sulfa drugs, is that transplantation of fresh rumen fluid from a normal animal to the diseased animal is valuable (except for the milk-fed young). There are numerous examples where this type of treatment has been considered to hasten recovery. Many European veterinary practitioners routinely carry fresh rumen ingesta which may be fortified with trace minerals in areas where deficiencies are common. It would seem likely that many large feedlots or dairies could very well afford to maintain a rumen-fistulated animal to serve as a donor.

Making general recommendations on the most palatable type of food to offer to aphagic ruminants is not easy as the palatability of feeds is a sensation which is subjective to the animal. If the aphagia is diagnosed as being due to inflammation of the oral cavity, pharynx or esophagus, the most acceptable feeds will be soft, low in fiber and free from spines and awns. Should the aphagia be due to grain engorgement, hay should be offered. Generally speaking, it takes at least 2 weeks for the digestive tract of ruminants to completely adapt to a substantial change in a feeding program (32). Conditions which involve diseases which compromise the digestion or absorption of dietary nutrients in the diets result in corrective nutrition being required for this time.

Rumen pH generally varies between 5.0 and 6.5 in healthy animals. Lower pH values are associated with high grain rations and the higher pH values are experienced with high roughage (especially poor quality) and high protein rations, particularly if urea is included. The carbohydrates are fermented with the production of excess amounts of lactic acid. The pH may drop to the range of 3.5 to 4.5. Ruminal stasis, acidosis and dehydration then follow (10). On the other hand, fasting animals may have ruminal pH readings of 6.8 to 7.3 Despite this, anorectic animals,

especially those with diarrhea, may have a metabolic acidosis. Because of this, concentrates should be limited in rations of stressed and diseased animals. Moreover, these animals nearly always prefer to eat forages or bulky rations. Fine grinding of grains should be avoided and hays are best fed whole (not chopped). Whole rolled oats and wheat bran are useful in convalescent rations since they are palatable and do not depress rumen pH greatly. Hay and grass pastures can and should be fed ad libitum. Feeding a dry ration containing 55 to 70% TDN (2.0-2.5 Mcal ME/kg) at the daily rate of 1% of liveweight will usually maintain a morbid or convalescing animal.

Proteins are important in replacing normal N losses. The need for proteins undoubtedly increases when there is accelerated loss of body tissue and serum proteins. Diarrheas, especially hemorrhagic, deplete plasma proteins. Diets containing non-protein-N probably should be avoided in convalescent rations. If they are fed, supplementary S is indicated because the S-containing amino acids are important in healing processes. Generally speaking, a protein level of 120 to 140g/kg is probably adequate for diseased older animals.

Vitamins are necessary for ruminant metabolism, but supplementation with water-soluble vitamins is usually not considered important in adult ruminants. Vitamin A is associated with resistance to infection, especially of epithelial tissues. Thus it is important in the prevention and treatment of diseases of the respiratory and gastro-intestinal tracts. If vitamin A stores are low or the nutritional status of vitamin A is unknown, each animal should receive daily 20,000 to 50,000 IU/head for 5-7 d to aid in the prevention or recovery from the disease.

The requirements for non-electrolyte (elements other than Na and K) minerals are not generally believed to be critical in animals afflicted with non-nutritional diseases. Trace mineralized salt should be fed ad libitum in most situations, as should Ca and P.

Animals severely affected with internal parasites may suffer from a reduced food intake coupled with energy, protein, Ca, P, Mg, Fe, Co and vitamin A deficiencies. In addition, there may be some impairment of digestive and absorptive function. Therapy

542

therefore should include supplementation with minerals and vitamin A, the feeding of readily digested carbohydrate and protein. Perhaps milk proteins should be considered even though their general use in ruminant animals is expensive and wasteful. In addition, appropriate anti-parasitic drugs will be administered.

The frequency of feeding of animals during disease and stress convalescence is important. All too frequently animals are allowed to eat large meals which expand the gastrointestinal tract to an unnecessary degree and overtax the digestive and absorptive function of the tract, especially if the animal is hungry. Feeding little and often should be the preferred technique. When the animals are being fed 1% of liveweight daily (see above), this should be split into four meals spaced out as evenly as possible during the day.

CONCLUSIONS

In conclusion, it can be said that therapeutic nutrition regimens must be tailored to the individual disease or stress situation observed and diagnosed in the animal. The success of any therapy is dependent upon accurate diagnosis, a quantitative knowledge of the nutrient imbalances and encouraging the animal to consume adequate quantities of the therapeutic diet.

Literature Cited

1. Gross, R.L. and P.M. Newberne. 1980. Physiol. Rev. 60:188.
2. Sheffy, B.E. and A.J. Williams. 1982. J. Amer. Vet. Med. Assoc. 180:1073.
3. Blood, D.C., J.A. Henderson and O.M. Radostits. 1979. Veterinary Medicine. 5th Ed. Bailliere Tindall, London.
4. Sprunt, D.H. and C. Flanigan. 1960. Adv. Vet. Sci. 6:79.
5. Whitehair, C.K. 1970. In: Bovine Medicine and Surgery. Amer. Vet. Publ., Inc.
6. Baile, C.A. and J.M. Forbes. 1974. Physiol. Rev. 54:160.
7. Roy, J.H.B. and J.H. Ternouth. 1972. Proc. Nutr. Soc. 31:53.
8. Blaxter, K.L. and W.A. Wood. 1953. Vet. Rec. 65:889.
9. Berry, C.I. and J.D. Dargie. 1978. Vet. Parasitol. 4:327.
10. Whitlock, R.H. 1980. In: Veterinary Gastroenterology. Bailliere Tindall, London.
11. Fell, B.F. 1980. In: Scientific Foundations of Veterinary Medicine. Heinman, London.
12. Roseby, F.B. 1977. Aust. J. Agr. Res. 28:155.
13. Mylrea, P.J. 1968. Res. Vet. Sci. 9:5,14.
14. Brown, M.D., D.P. Poppi and A.R. Sykes. 1984. Can. J. Animal Sci. 64(Suppl.):197.
15. Sykes, A.R. and R.L. Coop. 1976. J. Agr. Sci. 86:507.
16. Roy, J.H.B. 1980. The Calf. 3rd Ed. Butterworths, London.
17. Coop, R.L., A.R. Sykes and K.W. Angus. 1976. Res. Vet. Sci. 21:253.
18. Michell, A.R. 1983. Irish Vet. J. 37:94.
19. Various authors. 1982. Nutritional Limits to Animal Production from Pastures. Commonwealth Agr. Bureau, London.
20. Stobbs, T.H. and D.J. Brett. 1974. Aust. J. Agr. Res. 25:657.
21. Payne, J.M. 1973. In: Production Diseases in Farm Animals. Bailliere Tindall, London.
22. Various authors. 1978. The Use of Blood Metabolites in Animal Production. Brit. Soc. Animal Prod. Occ. Publ. 1.
23. Blowey, R.W. 1975. Vet. Rec. 97:324.
24. Various authors. 1983. Trace Elements in Animal Production and Veterinary Practices. Brit. Soc. Animal Prod. Occ. Publ. 7.
25. Shenkin, A. and A. Wretlind. 1978. World Rev. Nutr. Diet. 28:1.
26. Sherman, D.M., G.F. Hoffsis, D.A. Gingerich and R.R. Bruner. 1976. J. Amer. Vet. Med. Assoc. 169:1310.
27. Hoffsis, G.F., D.A. Gingerich, D.M. Skerman and R.R. Bruner. 1977. J. Amer. Vet. Med. Assoc. 171:67.
28. Telfer, S.B., G. Zervas and G. Carlos. 1984. Can. J. Animal Sci. 64(Suppl.):234.
29. Laby, R.H., C.A. Graham, S.R. Edwards and B. Kautzner. 1984. Can. J. Animal Sci. 64(Suppl.):337.
30. Bywater, R.J. 1977. Amer. J. Vet. Res. 38:1983.
31. Dalton, R.G. 1967. Brit. Vet. J. 123:237.
32. Kronfeld, D.S. 1980. In: Veterinary Gastroenterology. Bailliere Tindall, London.

SUBJECT MATTER INDEX

Abdominal cavity, 52
Abdominal position, 51
  of digestive organs, 52
Abdominal topography, 23, 25
  of adult roe buck, 39
Ability to utilize fat, 451
Abnormal papillary development in rumen of calves, 476
Abomasal acid secretion, 97
Abomasal and intestinal cannulas, 97, 194
Abomasal cannulas, 167
Abomasal contents, 98
Abomasal contractions, 401
Abomasal distension, 65, 81, 99
Abomasal emptying, 96, 98, 101
Abomasal fat digestion, 404
Abomasal fistula, 68
Abomasal functional disturbances, 98
Abomasal growth, 56
Abomasal motor activity, 95
Abomasal motor patterns, 97
Abomasal mucosa, 35
  levels of pepsin and chymosin, 403
Abomasal pH, 173
Abomasal pouches, 174
Abomasal secretions, 404
Abomasal volume and outflow, 98
Abomasum, 25, 26, 44, 45, 46, 47, 50, 51, 52, 56, 66, 68,
  95, 98, 99, 100, 172, 173, 179
Absorption, 327
  and excretion
    and tissue concentration of Ni, 371
    of Co, 343
    of Cu, 349
    of Mo, 349
    of Se, 376
    of Zn, 385
  and metabolism, 337
    of Mn, 368
  and storage of vitamin A, 313
  coefficients, 180
  efficiency of vitamin B_{12}, 343
  from gastro-intestinal tract, 176
  from rumen, 330
  of amino acids from small intestine, 179
  of ammonia
    from reticulo-rumen, 177
    from rumen, 231
  of eructated gas, 93
  of lipids, 178, 179, 303
    from small intestine, 178
  of monosaccharides from small intestine, 178
  of Na, K, and P, 344
  of propionate and butyrate by sheep liver, 280
  of VFA, 150, 156
    from reticulo-rumen, 176
  through rumen epithelium, 279
Access to drinking water, 222
Accretion of individual amino acids in fetal lamb, 408
Accumulative fecal and urinary excretion by sheep of Fe, 365
Acetate utilization, site of, 279
Acid composition of duodenal digesta, 228
Acid concentrations, 156

Acid detergent fiber, 291
Acid-insoluble ash, 186
Acid production in rumen, 157
Acidity of abomasal contents, 173
Acidosis, 138, 139, 157, 294, 474
  and thiamin deficiency, 321
Active absorption of amino acids, 179
Active Na transport, 335
Acute acidosis, 477
Acute bloat, 469
Acute bovine pulmonary edema (ABPE) and emphysema, 485
  cause of, 486
Acute cold stress, 462
Acute F toxicity, 392
Acute nitrate toxicity, 481
Acute toxicity of Se, 382
Acute vitamin A toxicity, 315
Adaptation
  of microbial population, 138
  period of roughage to concentrate diets, 338
  to urea, 232
Adaptive seasonal changes of ruminal mucosa, 29
Adherent populations, 140
Adipose tissue
  composition and function, 306
  metabolism, 413
Ad libitum intake of food, 205
Advantages of chromic oxide as a marker, 187
Afferent limb of reflex closure of reticular groove, 65
Age
  effect of, 402
  of bacteria in rumen, 166
Agronomic management techniques, 523
Aldohexoses, 269
Aldopentoses, 269
Alimentary hyperglycemia, 289
Alkali disease, 383
Alkali disease syndrome, 382
Alkaloids, 285
Allantoin in urine, 182
Alpha-tocopherol, 318
Aluminum, 516
Amino acids
  absorption, 179, 410
    from small intestine, 179
  degradation in rumen, 233
  profile of feces, 181
  synthesis, 337
  transport, 179
  uptake by liver, 289
Ammonia, 177
  absorption, 230
  concentration in rumen, 229
  fixation, 230
  in rumen, 123
  intoxication, 230, 232
  -N concentrations, 235
  odors, 232
  -producing bacteria, 128
  toxicity, 231
  treatment, 295
Ammoniation of forage, 232

544

Amount digested in rumen, 151
Amount of digesta, 207
Amount of dry matter ruminated, 152
Amount of electrolyte excreted, 181
Amount of urine excreted, 181
Amylase levels, 117
Amylases, 178
Amylolytic and maltase activities, 414
Amylolytic bacteria, 128
Amylopectin, 271
Amylose, 271
Anabolic regulators, 440
Anaerobic fungi, 132, 154
Anaerobic microbes, 145
Anal canal, 41
Analyses of major minerals, 339
Analyses of milk, 415
Analyses of ruminant feces, 180
Analysis of stained particles, 187
Analytical techniques for lignin, 186
Anatomical differences of mid- and hindgut, 38
Anatomical terminology, 15
Animal factor, 472
Animal-management factors affecting nutrition in growth, 439
Animal management techniques, 522
Animal production efficiency, 228
Anorexia, 104
Antagonism between Cu and sulfate, 350
Antagonism between protozoa species, 137
Antibiotic feed additives, 258
Antibiotics effects, 139
Anti-frothing properties of saliva, 121
Antiperistaltic contraction, 86, 104, 105
Antiperistaltic wave of esophageal contraction, 75
Antral inhibition, 98
Anus, 41
Aorta, 36
Apparent absorption and retention of Se, 377
Apparent absorption of N, 243
Apparent costs for milk production, 265
Apparent costs of milk synthesis, 264
Apparent digestibility, 182
    example of calculations, 184
    methods of measurement, 183
    of energy and starch in rumen, 195
Apparently digested energy (DE), 251
Apparent Mg absorption in sheep, 515
Apparent thiamin deficiency, 321
Apparent vs. true organic matter digestion, 164
Appetite
    and nutrient value, 464
    and palatability and control of feed intake, 202
Archeological findings, 7
Aromatic acids in urine, 182
Aromatic growth factors, 135
Arteriodactyla, 1
Ascending colon, 40
Associative effects, 185, 191, 198, 257, 283
ATP, 164
    generated, 276
    generation, 157
    yield, 161, 163
Attachment
    of amylolytic bacteria, 140

of cellulolytic bacteria, 140
of rumen bacteria to rumen protozoa, 141
of rumen microorganisms, 140
of rumen protozoa, 140
to particulate matter, 140
to rumen wall, 140
Auerbach's plexus, 80
Autonomic nervous system, 42
Availability of nutrients
    for microbes, 157
    post-ruminally, 242
Availability of P from bone, 332

Backflow from omasum, 77
Bacteria, 276
    and protozoa, sources, 133
    attachment of protozoa, 141
    counts from cecum, 141
    development of population, 133
    in cecum, 142
    in rumen, 167
    isolated from lower intestine, 141
    number in rumen, 125
Bacterial polysaccharides, 285
Bacteriophages, 132
Balance of bacterial species, 138
Balance studies, 253
Basal metabolic rate, 205
Basis of growth, 438
Batch incubation, 169
Beef cattle, 212
    calculations to estimate energy requirements, 266
Behavior influences, 114
Beta-carotene, 315, 422
    and reproduction in cattle, 315
Bicarbonate and phosphate buffers, 121
Bile, 174, 179
    and pancreatic ducts, 39
    composition, 175
    ductules, 41
    pigments, 174
    salts, 174
Biliary secretions, 181, 302
    and pancreatic secretions, 411
Bioavailability
    and absorption of K, 334
    of Na, 335
Biochemical changes
    due to Co deficiency in cattle and sheep, 346
    in lambs with WMD, 380
Bioenergetics, 251
Biohydrogenation, 302
    and production of fatty acid isomers, 300
    of fats by rumen microorganisms, 319
Biological availability, 315
    of Ca, 327
    of Fe supplements, 365
    of Mg, 330
Biological ceilings for growth, 440
Biological function of Co, 343
Biological value (BV)
    of feedstuffs, 464
    of MCP, 228
    of phosphate, 331
Biphasic contraction, 75

Bite size, 110
Bloat, 95, 468
    prevention, 472
    treatment, 473
Blood
    ammonia, 483
    analysis, 339
    changes
        biochemical, 352
        due to ketosis, 500
        due to milk fever, 494
        in clinical ketosis, 501
    clotting factor, 324
    flow, 255
        to papillae, 57
    glucose, 289
        at parturition, 494
        level, 286, 503
    levels of Mo, 348
    metabolic profiles, 478
    thiamin, 322
    tocopherols, 320
    urea concentration, 230
Body
    composition, 439
    energy content, 255
    fat and food intake, 213
    size, 114
        and rumination capability, 108
    water pool, 217
Bolus, length of chewing time, 111
Bone changes, 352
Bone meal, 8
Bovidae, 2, 4
Bovine fetus, 44
Brain-gut axis, 99
Branched-chain amino acids, 135
Branched-chain fatty acids, 135
    sources of, 234
Branched fatty acids, 151
Breed differences, 493
Brunner's glands, 40, 102, 174, 176
Buffering activity of saliva, 67, 121
Buffering capacity, 157
    of rumen liquor, 294
Buffers, 433
B vitamins, 320
    requirements, 321
Bypass proteins, 430
    for dairy cows, 430
Bypass treatments, 240

Cadmium, 393
    toxicity, 393
Calcium, 326, 425
    absorption, 327, 344
    -binding protein, 316
    deficiency, 328
    mobilization, 328
        from bone, 327
    needs of the animal, 327
    solubility in rumen fluid, 327
Calculation of digestibility of feedstuff by difference, 184
Calculations to estimate energy requirements of beef cattle, 266

Calf affected with PEM, 322
Calf with WMD, 379
Calorimeter, 254
Calorimetry, 253
Calorimetry trials, 264
Camelidae, 3, 6
Cannulas, 193
    salivary, 118
Cannulation, 166
Capacity of ruminoreticulum, 25
Carbohydrate content of rumen protozoa, 286
Carbohydrate digestion, 280, 284
    and absorption, 413
    in small and large intestine, 285
Carbohydrate metabolism, 290, 414
    metabolism in neonatal ruminant, 414
Carbohydrate nutrition of ruminants, 269
Carbohydrates, 448
    consumed by ruminants, 276
Carboxpeptidase, 176
Cardia, 23, 27, 85, 86
Cardial collections, 119
Carotenoids, 313
Carrier mechanisms, 180
Cation-anion balance, 338
Cattle used to haul carts, 11
Caudal mesenteric artery, 42
Caudal view of intrathoracic abdominal organs of roe deer, 41
Cecal dilatation, 105
Cecal motor activity, 105
Cecocolic junction, 39
Ceco-colon, 40
Cecum, 40, 105
Celiac artery, 36
Cell, 217
Cellulase, 128
    and amylase activities at various pH values, 156
Cellulolytic activity, 133
Cellulolytic bacteria, 126, 276
Cellulosans, 273
Cellulose, 273
    degraded by protozoa, 277
    digestion, 153, 283
Cell wall material, 273
Cervidae, 2, 3
Cessation of growth, 56
Cessation of normal stomach motility, 76
CH$_4$ production, 135, 141
Changes
    in carbohydrate and lignin content with maturity of four
        grass species, 275
    in carbohydrate metabolism, 290
    in duodenal pH values of chyme, 67
    in fermentation pattern, 158
    in form of primary contractions, 73
    in microbial efficiency and yield with various rates of
        digestion and passage, 168
    in ovine stomach with age, 51
    in ruminal pH, ammonia and VFA concentrations, 229
    occurring in basal cells, 55
Cheek teeth, 21
Chemical composition of saliva, 120
Chemical stimulus, 82
Chemical symptoms of hypomagnesemia, 520
Chemical treatment

Chemical treatment (continued)
  and physical treatment, 240
    of carbohydrate-containing feedstuffs, 282
    of forages, 294
Chemostatic and thermostatic factors, 211
Chemostat systems, 167
Chewing, 19, 108
  behavior, 108
  during eating, 111
  during ruminating, 86, 111
  effect on parotid secretion, 122
  efficiency, 109, 114
  rate, 112
  time, 113
Chews
  per bolus, 112
    and hay intake, 112
  per minute, 87
Chloride-deficient calf, 329
Chlorine, 328
  absorption and metabolism, 329
  deficiencies, 329
  requirements, 330
Cholesterol and cholesterol esters, 179
Choline, 323
  action in fat metabolism, 324
  effect on intake and milk production, 324
Chromic oxide, 187
Chromium mordanted fiber, 188
Chronic bloat, 468
Chronic cold, 463
Chronic Pb poisoning, 392
Chronic protein deficiency, 429
Chronic toxicity
  of Se, 382
  of vitamin A, 315
Chylomicrons, 179, 304
Chyme delivered to duodenum, amount of, 96
Chymotrypsin, 176
Ciliate genera differences in substrate specificity, 130
Ciliate protozoa, 130, 146
Ciliates, 130
Circadian distribution, 87
Circadian pattern, 88
  of maintenance activities in sheep, 88
Classification
  and importance of ruminant animals, 1
  of fats, 298
  of nutritionally important carbohydrates, 269
  of species, 2
Cleavage of carotene to vitamin A, 313
Climatic conditions, 87
Clinical signs
  of ABPE, 485
  of deficiency of several B vitamins, 321
  of urea toxicity, 484
  of urinary calculi, 524
Clinical symptoms, 518
Coagulation of milk, 95
Cobalt, 342
  and vitamin B_{12} metabolism, 343
  deficiency, 345, 423
    and increased sensitivity of young animals, 345
  -deficient animal, 345
  -deficient sheep, 346

  dietary requirements, 344
  metabolism, 343
  nutritional factors, 343
  toxicity, 347
CoEDTA, 188
Cold exposure, effect on digestibility and ruminal turnover
  times, 199
Cold-induced metabolic responses, 464
Cold stress, 207, 458
Cold-stressed animals, 199
Collection bag for complete collection of feces, 183
Collection of feces, 183
Collection period, 183
Colon, 40
Colonization of starch, 155
Colostral immunoglobulins, 173
  absorption, 409
Commensalism, 134
Comminution of feed during eating and rumination, 86
Common amylolytic and dextrinolytic bacteria, 276
Common hepatic duct, 42
Comparative development, 49
Comparative slaughter, 254
  procedures, 255
  studies, 266
Comparative species responses, 208
Comparative water metabolism, 220
Comparison of blood and milk ketones, 501
Compensatory fiber digestion, 153
Components of cell maintenance, 259
Composition
  of barley straw and its undigested residue, 281
  of bile, 174
  of colostrum of cow and of milks of cow, sheep and goat,
    416
  of ether extract from forage leaves, 298
  of gas, 125
  of gastric juice, 172
  of microbes, 165
  of microbial cells, 164
  of pancreatic juice, 175
  of saliva, 120
Compounds
  biosynthesized by bacteria, 136
  required by bacteria, 136
  with vitamin D activity, 316
Concentrate diets, 168
Concentrate passage rate
  versus roughage passage rate, 149
  with various intakes of concentrate and roughage, 149
Concentrations
  of iodine in milk and blood serum, 359
  of marker, 165
  of bacteria, 141
  of NH_3, 177
  of soluble protein, 238
Conditioned B_{12} deficiency, 344
Conditioned rumination in goat, 90
Conditioning of cow, 435
Consequences of nutritional restriction, 441
Content of Na in forages, 335
Continuous or discontinuous culture, 169
Contractions, 68
  of omasal body, 78
  of reticulum and rumen, 52

Contractions (continued)
propagated along duodenum, 105
Control of energy intakes with mixed and high concentrate
diets, 204
Control of lower esophageal sphincter, 94
Controls over roughage intake, 203
Conventional digestion trial, 183
and basic procedural considerations, 183
Copper, 425
and molybdenum, 347
content of plasma and tissue, 347
deficiency, 344, 352, 353, 423
effect on fertility, 355
symptoms, 352
-deficient lamb, 354
deposition in the fetus, 348
in plasma, 348
-molybdenum antagonism, 350
-molybdenum-sulfate antagonism, 350
-molybdenum-sulfate interactions, 350
poisoning cause, 355
toxicity, 355
symptoms observed, 355
transport across membranes, 351
Cornified epithelium, 30
Correction of feeding and digestive abnormalities, 540
Corrections for feeding level, 266
Cow with ketosis, 500
Cow with spontaneous traumatic peritonitis, 77
Cracking or grinding of cereal grains, 192
Cranial and caudal esophageal sphincters, 32
Cranial mesenteric artery, 36, 42
Cranial pillar contractions during rumination and feeding, 89
CrEDTA, 188
Critical period for dairy cows, 426
Cross-feeding of intermediates, 134
Crowding of abdominal cavity, 147
Crypts of Lieberkuhn, 40
Currently recommended feeding systems, 265
Cutin, 285
Cyclical activity, 77
Cyclical motility of ovine omasum, 78
Cyclical motor activity of small intestine, 101
Cystic duct, 41

Daily flow rates and marker recoveries, 100
Daily water needs for baby calf, 418
Dairy cows, 211
Decerebrate preparations, 76
Decrease in blood glucose, 501
Defaunated animals, 132
Defaunation, 169
Defecation, 105
Deficiencies of P, 331
Deficiency symptoms
of vitamin A, 314
of vitamin D, 316
of vitamin E, 318
Deficient animals, 314
Degradation of D_2 by rumen microorganisms, 316
Degradation of wheat straw cellulose, 281
Dense materials, 150
Density of digesta, 208
Density of foodstuffs, 207
Depigmentation of hair and wool, 354

Depot fat in ruminants, 306
Depression in apparent digestibility, 257
Depression in Ca bioavailability, 327
Depressions in digestibility, 190
Descending colon, 39, 40
Detection of mineral deficiency, 338
Determinants of roughage intake in ruminants, 203
Development
and control of motility, 80
and secretory activity of parotid gland, 402
in embryo, 80
of bacteria population, 133
of digestive function, 401
of protozoa population, 134
of rumen, 289
of rumen function, 228
of rumen microbial population, 133
of rumen motility, 82
of salivary secretion in young ruminants, 123
Dextrinization, 272
Diagrammatic representation of digesta flow through a
re-entrant cannula, 194
Diaphragm, 26, 36, 42, 51
Diarrhea, 354
Dietary and hormonal control of glucogenesis, 289
Dietary approaches for prevention of milk fever, 498
Dietary buffers, 338
Dietary deficiencies in major elements, 338
Dietary fiber, 59
Dietary habits, 2
Dietary influences, 59
on ruminal motion, 82
Dietary N intake, 123
Dietary NPN, 231
Dietary nucleic acids, 241
Dietary requirements, 319
Ca, 328
essential microelements, 342
iodine, 360
K, 335
Na, 336
Ni, 372
vitamin B_{12}, 343
Zn, 386
Dietary sources
Ca, 326
Cl, 328
K, 334
lipids, 298
Mg, 330
Na, 335
P, 331
for protein digestion, 406
S, 336
Dietary starch, 178
Dietary Zn effect on tissue Zn concentrations, 384
Diet
composition, 155
effects, 137
on composition of depot fat, 307
on salivary secretion in young ruminants, 123
influence on digestive tract development, 46
modification, 241
Differences between ruminants and non-ruminants, 450
Differences between species, 49

548

Differences in pH and passage rate of digesta, 137
Differential diagnosis of hypomagnesemia, 521
Differential passage, 148
Different methods used to determine lysine adequacy in
    calves, 410
Digesta
    amount, 100, 207
    bolus, 86
    flow, 79, 104
        characteristics, 103
    k_p and microbial efficiency, 167
    movement in reticulo-rumen, 69
    texture, 89
    transfer, 79
        from reticulo-rumen, 78
    volume, 53, 101
Digestibility, 211, 257
    and BV, 243
    and feed intake, 169
    and metabolizability, 256
    coefficients, 182, 338
    depression, 282
    of energy, 427
    of feedstuffs, 191
    of lipids, 411
    of mixed diet, 184
    of starches, 272
    of typical diets, 449
    within species, 256
Digestible or metabolizable energy, 210
Digestion, 256
    absorption and excretion in ruminants, 172
    and absorption, 535
    definition of, 172
    in cecum, 153
    in intestine, 301
    means of expression, 151
    models, 151
    of dietary lipid, 178
    of dietary P, 331
    of microbial nucleic acids, 242
    of plant tissues, 154
    rate, 151
        and extent, 282
    trial, 253
Digestive and absorptive capacity, 242
Digestive function development, 401
Digestive organ development, relative change, 53
Digestive organ growth in lambs, 46
Digestive secretions, 173
Digestive system relative growth, 46
Digestive tract, 196
    compartments, 197
Dilution rate of fluid digesta, 195
Direct flow rate measurements, 64
Disaccharidases, 176, 178
Disaccharide, 271
Disappearance rate, 148
Displaced abomasum, 294
Disposition of gas, 98
Distension, 96, 210
    of abomasum, 77
    of reticulo-rumen, 202
    of reticulum, 204
        and cranial sac, 205

of rumen, 211
Distribution
    of blood Cu, 347
    of I in bovine, 357
    of nerves and blood vessels, 37
    of nitrogenous components in urine of sheep, 182
    of tissue Co, 343
Diurnal variations, 100
    of microbial population, 137
Diversity in types of microbes, 137
Diversity of ruminants, 1
Domestication, 7
Dorsal and ventral curvatures of rumen, 26
Draft animals, 9, 11
    buffalo, 9
    camel used to transport reeds, 10
    cattle providing power, 9
    Zebu cattle used to pull a plough, 10
Drinking, 109, 115, 221
    frequency, 115
    jaw motion during, 115
    water, 223, 224, 225
Dry matter, 147, 152
    and nitrogen balance at various efficiencies of microbial
        growth, 163
    content of feces, 180
    digestibility, 285
    digestion rates, 282
Dry period, 435
Duodenal acidification, 97
Duodenal digesta, flow patterns, 100
Duodenal hormones, 99
Duodenal infection, 99
Duodenal juice, 176
Duodenal papilla, 41
Duodenal pH, 174
Duodenal ulceration, 98
Duodenum, 41, 51, 102, 103, 175
Duration of rumination, 89

Early lactation, 436
Early postnatal needs, 415
Earth's surface, 7
Eating, 89, 108, 121
    and rumination, 152
        time, 113, 157
    habits, 108
    patterns, 111
    resting phase, 74
    time spent, 110
        factors which influence, 110
Ecological niche, 136
Effective ambient temperature (EAT), 458
Effectiveness of reticular groove closure, 401
Effect
    of age, 402
    of diet, 73, 307
        on dry tissue of stomach compartments, 82
    of disease upon nutrition, 533
    of exogenous growth hormone on lactation performance,
        434
    of feeding, 71
        on cecal motility, 105
    of hormones and additives on protein metabolism, 245

Effect (continued)
    of nutritional treatment on organ weight and fasting heat
        production, 260
    of nutrition on disease, 532
    of proteins, 285
    of rumen fistulation, 70
    of rumination without regurgitation on rumen motility
        patterns, 83
    of S on Cu and Mo, 350
    of species and type of ruminant on eating and ruminat-
        ing, 74
    of stresses, 535
    of VFA, 74, 91
        on growth, 158
    of Zn deficiency
        in lambs on digestibility, 389
        on fecal excretion, 385
Efficiency
    for glucose absorption, 286
    of animal production, 228
    of depositing protein and fat, 440
    of fat accretion, 263
    of ME, 253
    of Mg absorption, 330
    of microbial growth (MOEFF), 162, 234
        and protein escape, 236
        and influencing factors, 162
    of microbial N synthesis, 234
    of muscular work, 265
    of protein accretion, 263
    of tissue energy gain, 264
    of utilization, 261, 265
        of body tissues, 264
        of energy, 256, 264
        of feed energy, 250
        of ME, 262
Electrolyte concentration, 120
Electromyogram, 95
    of sheep reticulum wall, 75
Electromyographic changes, 103
Electromyography, 64, 101
Electron micrographs
    of intestinal villi from two baby calves, 409
    of some important rumen bacterial species, 127
Electron microscopy, 292
Elements identified in tissues of man or animals, 342
Elevation of ketone bodies, 501
Elimination of gas, 94
Elk antlers, 13
Emulsification of dietary fats, 411
Endangered species, 6
Endocrine factors, 204
Endogenous losses
    of Ca, 328
    of Na, 336
Endogenous urinary N, 182
End-products, 134, 170
    of fermentation, 145, 164
Energy, 426
    accretion curve, 264
    accretion in tissues, 267
    and protein, 424
        (N) deficiencies, 532
        requirements in pregnant animals, 424
        requirements of growing dairy heifers, 417

    balance techniques, 251
    deficiency, 515
    density of diet, 211
    expenditures, 254
    intakes, 211
        and ketosis, 507
        in relation to digestibility, 210
    loss, 258
    lost as urine (UE), 253
    metabolism, 250, 255
        definitions and abbreviations, 250
    requirements
        of beef cattle, 266
        of preruminants, 415
    reserves in form of lipids, 299
    retention, 261
    sources, 448
    status of animal, 421
        effect on conception rates, 421
    values of feeds, 265
Ensiling high moisture grains, 293
Enterogastric inhibitory reflex, 103
Entric nervous system, 80
Environmental factors affecting growth, 440
Environmental stress effect on nutrient needs, 456
Environmental temperature, 192, 199, 223
Enzymes, 176
    involved in hydrolysis of alpha-linked glucose polymers,
        286
Enzymic activity of saliva, 121
Epiglottis, 19
Epithelial development, 59
    of stomach, 53
Epithelial hyperplasia, 61
Epithelium, 22, 27
Eructated gas, 19, 86
Eructation, 22, 64, 70, 76, 81, 92
    and regurgitation reflexes, 84
    events associated with, 76
    inhibition of, 469
    reflex, 93
Esophageal fistula, 209
Esophagus, 22, 36, 65, 86
    anatomy of, 22
    cervical part, 22
    portions of, 22
    thoracic part, 22
Essential amino acids, 244, 410
    requirements, 233
Essential fatty acids (EFA), 303, 306
    metabolism, 413
Essential vitamins in ruminant diets, 313
Establishment of gastro-intestinal microbial population, 133
    of mature type rumen population, 133
    prerequisite for early development, 134
Establishment of protozoa, 403
Esterified cholesterol, 304
Esterified fatty acids, 179
Estimated rumen fermentation characteristics, 278
Estimates
    of external insulation, 463
    of ruminal degradation of protein, 238
    of ruminal escape of protein from common feedstuffs,
        237
    of tissue insulation, 462

550

Estimates (continued)
    of voluntary food intake as influenced by thermal and
        other stresses, 465
Estimating lower critical temperatures, 462
Ether extract (EE), 298
Etiology
    of acidosis, 475
    of bloat, 469
    of hypomagnesemia, 513
Evaluating nutritive value of dietary carbohydrates, 291
Evaluation of nutrient flux and status, 536
Evaporative cooling, 117
Evaporative heat loss, 254
Events associated with regurgitation, 74
Evolution, 2
Evolutionary development, 37, 80
Ewe showing a goiter, 361
Excess amino acids, 241
Excess dietary Ca, 328
Excess dietary Cu, 348
Excess dietary Fe, 366
Excess dietary Mn, 371
Excess P, 333
Excretion
    and composition of feces and urine, 180
    of endogenous waste products, 181
    of MFN, 190
    of microbial N in feces, 181
    of sulfate, 337
Existing ruminant and pseudo-ruminant species, 1, 2
Expected and observed nutrient digestibilities, 191
Expressing thermal environment, 458
Expression and measurement, 162
Extent of digestion, 282
Extent of hydrolysis, 300
External markers, 185
Extracellular glycoprotein coat, 140
Extra feed requirement for pregnancy, 267
Extra-reticular contractions, 74, 78
Extrinsic contractions, 68
Extrinsic vs. intrinsic motor activity of reticulum, 84

Facilities used for milking sheep or goats, 8
Factorial method, 246
Factors
    affecting maintenance and growth, 438
    affecting rumen digestion, 151
    affecting site of digestion, 193
    affecting vitamin A utilization, 315
    influencing apparent digestibility, 190
    involved in growth processes, 438
    modifying Cu and Mo metabolism, 349
    most likely to limit milk production, 427
Fat content of milk, 428
Fat cow syndrome, 294, 510
Fat
    deficiency symptoms, 306
    digestion and absorption, 411
    flavor, 151
    location in body, 307
    metabolism, 411
    and rumen function, 310
    in diets, 309
    turnover, 439
    utilization, 451

Fats present in adipose depots, 307
Fats present in milk fat, 310
Fatty acids, 277
    absorbed in small intestine, 303
    composition
        of commonly used feedstuffs, 299
        of fats from different species, 308
        of lipid from four body sites, 308
        of milk fat, 428
    in plasma, 214
    synthesis, 263
Fatty livers, 505
Febrile episodes, 76
Fecal energy losses, 183
Fecal excretion
    and composition, 180
    curve of pulse-dosed marker in feces, 197
    for Mn, 369
Fecal losses, 256
Fecal pellets, 40
Fecal pH, 338
Fecal recoveries of lignin, 186
Feed, 8
    additives, 258, 433, 480
    amount ingested, 115
        environmental and social effects on, 115
    intake, 154
        levels, 147, 283
    physical texture and moisture content, 121
    processing, 191, 292, 427
Feeding
    added fat, 427
    and recommendations for correcting digestive abnormali-
        ties, 541
    concentrates and stimulatory effects, 72
    frequency, 138, 429
    level, 99
        corrections for, 266
    management for dairy cattle, 435
    or lactation trials, 246
    strategies, 110
    systems, 265, 437
        tables of requirements, 267
    timing, 111
Feedlot cattle, 212
Feedlot diseases, 212
Feedstuff processing and conservation, 292
Femurs from phosphorus deficient and normal animal, 333
Fermentation, 148, 158
    and digestive capacities, 150
    balance, 160
        sample calculations, 161
        with various monensin levels, 161
    end products, 126
    in large intestine, 449
    of glycerol, 179
    pattern, 155
Fermented feeds, 246
Fertility, 421
Fetal amino acid metabolism, 408
Fetal development, 44
Fetal glucose metabolism, 287, 414
Fetal lipid metabolism, 411
Fetal nutrient requirements, 441
Fetus, 102

Fiber, 449
    digested in large intestine, 283
    -digesting ruminal bacteria, 153
Fibrous carbohydrates, 281
Field bean proteins, 407
Filiform ruminal papillae, 31
Fill or distension, 208
Finishing periods, 212
Finishing phases of growth, 444
Fish protein concentrates, 407
Flagellated organisms, 132
Flagellates, 130
Flow diagram of water-flow in vertebrates, 219
Flow
    from rumen, 167
    of digesta, 79, 104
        and cyclical motor activity, 103
    of energy through animal, 251
    of parotid saliva during mastication, 122
    patterns of duodenal digesta, 100
    to omasum, 148
Fluid and particulate digesta, 199
Fluid dilution rates, 198
Fluid passage rate, 148
Fluid turnover, 199
Fluorine, 390
Fluorosis, 391
Flushing, 421
Foamy digesta, 469
Food intake, 33, 203, 205, 533
Food selection, 110
Forage
    fiber analyses, 291
    maturity, 192
    particles, 195
    particle size, 294
    processing, 195
    to concentrate ratio effect on VFA ratios, 278
Forestomach, 23, 51, 84, 92, 192
    capacity, 80
    compartments, 23
    development, 45, 47, 49, 50, 62, 64
        factors affecting, 56
    epithelial surface, 55
    growth, 48, 56, 83
    mucosa, 27
    of lambs at birth and calves raised on different diets, 58
Formation of pelleted feces, 104
Fossil records, 1
Fossil remains, 1
Foundered heifer, 476
Fractional rate of protein synthesis, 262
Free cholesterol, 304
Frequency of defecation, 180
Frequency of feeding, 99, 138, 429
Frothy bloat, 94, 469
Functional organization of gastric centers, 84
Functions
    and deficiency symptoms and levels of vitamin A, 313
    of cobalt, 343
    of trace elements, 342
    of Cu and Mo, 348
    of vitamin A, 313
    of vitamin D, 316
    of Zn, 385

Fundic mucosa, 172
Fundic pouches, 97
Fungal activity, 155
Fungal enzyme methods, 292
Future for ruminant animals, 11

Gains and losses of water, 219
Gall bladder, 174
Gas, 92
    expulsion in cattle fitted with tracheal tube, 93
    pressure in rumen, 93
    production, 149
Gaseous energy loss (GE), 253
Gaseous environment, 467
Gastric digestion, 403
Gastric emptying, 96, 97
Gastric enzymes, 403
Gastric glands, 35
Gastric juice, 172
Gastric motility, 96
Gastric outflow, factors affecting, 96
Gastric secretion, 97
Gastrin, 96
Gastro-colic reflex, 105
Gastro-intestinal hormones, 204
Gastro-intestinal microbial population, 133
Gastro-intestinal motility, 534
Gastro-intestinal trace, 195, 196, 198, 208
    anatomy of, 14
    esophagus and stomach, 22
    head and associated glands, 15
    hindgut, 40
    specialization and adaptation, 14
Gelatinization, 272
    of starch, 195
Genetic influence on occurrence of bloat, 472
Geographical distribution of ABPE, 485
Gestation, 102, 263
Giraffidae, 2, 4
Glandular abomasal mucosa, 27
Glandular gastric mucosa, 35
Glandular mucosa, 23
Gland weight and anatomy, 117
Gluconeogenesis, 244, 273, 286, 288, 343, 415
    after feeding, 289
Gluconeogenic pathways, 286
Glucose
    absorption, 178
    metabolism by young ruminants, 290
    requirements
        for basal metabolism, 286
        for lactation, 287
    synthesis, 289
        from amino acids, 287
    tolerance, 290
    transport, 178
Glutamate and glutamine metabolism, 408
Glutathione peroxidase activity and Se content in tissues, 375
Glycerol, 288
Glycogen, 272
Goblet cells, 40
Goiter, 361
Goitrogenic substances in milk, 360
Goitrogens, 361
Grain, 195

Grain (continued)
    processing, 152, 153, 195
        treatments, 293
Grass tetany, 335, 511
Grazers and browsers, 110
Grazing
    and ruminating patterns, 111
    and searching for food, time spent, 111
Greater omentum, 39
Grinding and pelleting, 191, 195, 210
Grinding of forage and level of intake effect on digestibility
    and retention times, 198
Grinding or rolling, 293
Gross energy, 250
    intake, 251
Gross symptoms of acidosis, 478
Grouping cows, 436
Growth
    and development of ruminant digestive system, 44
    birth to weaning, 442
    efficiency of ruminal microbes, 235
    environmental factors, 440
    limits to, 437
    of digestive tract, 45, 47
    of stomach, 50
        of calves, 49
    rate for bacteria, 169
Gut capacity, 146, 151

Hard palates, 16
Head and associated glands anatomy, 15
Heat
    increment, 253, 263
    loss, 254
    production during gestation, 264
    stress, 207, 335, 457, 461
Heats of combustion, 161, 261
Hemicellulolytic and pectinolytic bacteria, 128
Hemicelluloses, 273
Hemolytic crisis, 356
Hepatic duct, 41
Hepatic enzymes concerned with gluconeogenesis, 290
Hepatic portal vein, 36, 42
Hepatic veins, 41
Herbage intake, 110
Hereditary Zn deficiency, 387
High-concentrate diets, 158
High-energy phosphate bonds, 261
Higher fatty acids (HFA), 516
High escape proteins, 240
    sources, 234, 239
High-grain diets, 475
High starch diets, 155
High urinary P levels, 525
Hindgut, 40
    fermentation, 449
    intestinal blood, lymph and nerve supply, 42
    motility, 64
Histological examination of rumen papillae, 60
Honeycomb, 32
Hormonal control, 289
    of carbohydrate metabolism, 290
Hormonal factors, 104
Hormonal relationships, 506
Hormones, 204, 508

    and ketosis, 508
    changes due to milk fever, 495
Host-microbe synergism, 145
Humidity, 458
    and moisture, 465
Hydrogenation, 178, 301
    and desaturation of fatty acids, 132
Hydrolysis, 178, 299
    of fiber, 158
    of starch, 269
    of urea, 229
Hyperactivity phase, 105
Hypergastrinemia, 99
Hyperglycemia, 77
Hyperkeratosis, 61
Hypervitaminosis A, 314
Hypocalcemia, 77
Hypoglycemia, 287, 291
Hypomagnesemia, 331
    in cattle, 518
    in sheep, 519
    prevention and treatment, 522
Hypothalamus, 205

Identification of ketosis, 499
Ileocolic junction, 40
Ileum, 39
Illustration of foamy digesta, 469
Implications of attachment of rumen microorganisms, 140
Importance of domestic ruminants as food source, 11
Importance of ruminants in world agriculture, 7
Importance of VFA, 279
Inadequate energy intake, 421
Incidence of grass tetany, 515
Incidence of milk fever related to age, 493
Incomplete digestion of starch, 191
Incomplete recoveries of any marker, 186
Increase in free fatty acids, 501
Index of efficiency of fermentation, 168
Index of starch digestion, 338
Indicators of markers, 185
Indigestible compounds or markers, 148
Indirect calorimetry, 254
Individual animal differences, 137
Induced rumination, 91
Inefficiencies of nutrient metabolism, 261
Infertility associated with protein deficiency, 422
Influences over roughage intake, 205
Influences over throughput and intake of roughage, 206
Infrared reflectance, 292
Ingestion of bacteria, 132
Ingestion of feed and water, 108
Inhibition
    of B vitamins synthesis, 321
    of digestive enzymes, 285
    of eructation, 469
    of fiber digestion, 153
    of gastric motility, 103
    of reticulo-ruminal cyclic contractions, 66
    of rumino-reticular contractions, 65
Initiation of forestomach digestion, 402
Initiation of forestomach growth, 56
Inorganic P in milk, 332
Insulation, 463
Insulin, 175

Insulin:glucagon ratio, 289
Intake effects on diet digestibility, 190
Intake levels, 190, 197, 257
    and feeding frequencies, 137
Intake of dietary N, 123
Intake of steers fitted with face masks to prevent rumination, 114
Interactions
    of Ni with other dietary components, 372
    of Se with other dietary components, 377
    of Mn with other elements, 369
    of Zn with other dietary components, 386
Intermediate acid-utilizing bacteria, 128
Intermittent pattern of flow of digesta, 101
Internal iliac arteries, 42
Internal markers, 185
Internal ruminal relief
    of concentrate selectors, 29
    of grass and roughage eaters, 30
Interorgan transport of amino acids used for glucogenesis, 288
Interrelationship of vitamin D to milk fever, 495
Interspecies hydrogen transfer, 135
    effect on rumen fermentation, 135
    end-products produced, 135
Intestinal digesta characteristics, 405
Intestinal digestion, 178, 242
    and absorption, 301
Intestinal fat-digesting capabilities, 452
Intestinal glands, 102
Intestinal mucosa, 174, 180
Intestinal pH, 174
Intestinal secretions, 405
Intestinal starch-digesting capabilities, 450
Intestine, 37
    large, 46, 104, 141
    length
        and relative size, 37
        of small and large, 46
    lymph nodes, 42
    mucosa, 39
    small 45, 46
    villi, 40
Intragastric nutrient infusion influence on gastro-intestinal motility, 74
Intragastric nutrition, 74
Intravenous glucose, 508
    and ketosis, 508
Intrinsic contractions, 68
Intrinsic reticulo-ruminal motility, 85
Intrinsic versus extrinsic contractions, 84
Inventories of domestic animals, 7
In vitro dry matter disappearance, 169
In vitro systems, 169
In vitro technique, 292
In vitro tissue preparations, 255
Iodine, 357, 425
    absorption and excretion, 358
    accumulated by thyroid, 358
    content of milk, 359
    deficiency, 361
    -deficient calf, 361
    losses from body, 359
    recycling, 359
    toxicity, 362

turnover, 360
Ionophores, 157, 259
    effect of, 139
Ion transport, 439
Iron, 362
    absorption and excretion, 364
    chelates in GI tract, 365
    concentrations in plasma and tissues, 363
    deficiency, 366
        in calves, 363
    in blood serum, 362
    in tissues, 362
    loss, turnover and physiological requirements, 364
    requirements, 365
    reserves of neonatal calf, 366
Irregular spiking activity, 98
Isotope dilution techniques, 287
Isotope markers, 165

Jacobson's organ, 17
Jaw motion, 108
    during drinking, 115
    patterns, 109
Jejunal coils, 39
Jejunum, 39, 103, 176
Joule, 250

Ketone bodies, 499
Ketosis, 499, 532
    diagnosis, 502
Kidney and liver concentration in lambs, 350

Laboratory animal profiles, 538
Laboratory procedures, 169
Laboratory techniques, 291
Lactation, 264, 425
Lactose intolerance, 451
Lag time, 282
Lamb with WMD, 379
Laminae, 33
Laminitis, 294
Lands
    Alpine communities, 7
    coastal marshes, 7
    deserts, 7
    forests, 7
    natural grasslands, 7
    non-productive, 7
    rangelands, 7
    savannas, 7
    shrublands, 7
    tundra, 7
    wet meadows, 7
Large intestine, 56, 104, 141
Latency time, 90
Lead, 392
Length of small and large intestines, 46
Lesser abomasum, 26
Level of feed intake, 99, 190, 194, 197, 282
    effect on rumen volume and kinetics of digesta passage, 197
    influence of, 147
Level of K in feedstuffs, 334
Levels of major elements in serum, 327
Light, 466

554

Light micrograph of rumen papillae epithelium, 61
Lignification of plant material, 284
Lignin, 185, 273, 291
   -carbohydrate complexes, 284
   content of forages, 284
   and phenolics, 283
Limits of microbial protein synthesis, 233
Limits to growth, 438
Lining of forestomach, 54
Lipids, 298, 451
   absorption, 179, 304
   inhibition of rumen microbial fermentation, 451
   metabolism, 504
   metabolized in rumen, 300
   transport, 412
     and utilization, 505
Lipolysis in adipose tissue, 505
Lipolytic bacteria, 128
Lipoprotein synthesis, 303
Lipoprotein triglycerides, 305
Lips, 15
Liquid digesta, 195
Liver, 174
   abscesses, 61, 157, 477
   and pancreas, 41
   Cu concentrations, 355
   lobules, 41
   stores, 314
   turnover of vitamin A, 313
Llama outfitted with back pack, 13
Local nervous system, 80
Long-term controls, 202, 203, 205
Losses of energy, 257
Loss of dry matter and protein, 239
Lower critical temperature, 462
Low pH, 134
Low recoveries of lignin in feces, 186
Low urine volumes, 525
Lymph, 179
Lymph vessels and nodes, 37

Macro elements for ruminants, 326
Magnesium, 330, 425
   absorption, 330
     in digestive tract, 517
   activity, 517
   availability from dry feeds, 517
   concentration in urine, 522
   deficiency, 330
   desorption from rumen fluid, 514
   level in milk, 330
   requirements, 330, 512
   utilization, factors affecting, 512
Maintenance, 258
   and growth, 438
   costs of microbes, 167
   requirements, 259
Major anions found in urine, 181
Major causative factors of phosphatic urinary calculi, 525
Major causative factors of siliceous urinary calculi, 527
Major differences in nutrient needs, 448
Major elements, 326
Management alternatives, 442
Mandibular gland, 19
Manganese, 367

   availability, 370
   deficiency, 370, 423
   -deficient calf, 370, 371
   -deficient goat, 370
   functions, 368
   requirements, 370
Manipulation of reflex, 66
Markers, 53, 149, 165, 166, 195, 196, 253
   administration, 193
   concentrations, 197
   procedures, 244
     specific to protozoa, 169
Mastication, 22, 152
   and salivation, 15
Mathematical modeling, 256
Mathematical models of protein metabolism, 245
Maximized intake, 213
Maximized nutrient intake, 211
Maximum excretion time, 99
Maximum feed intake, 427
Maximum rates of secretion, 173
Maximum safe level of Co, 347
Maximum tolerable levels of dietary Fe, 367
Maximum tolerable Zn level, 390
MCP
   biological value of, 228
   synthesis and outflow, 228
   synthesis in rumen, 235
Measurement, 92
   of digesta flow, 193
   of MCP production, 233
   of protein status and quality, 243
   of ruminal output, 166
   of amino acid status, 244
Meat meal, 8
Meat, wool and milk, 8
Mechanical activity of gastroduodenal junction, 98
Mechanical and electrical activity of duodenum, 102
Mechanics of eating, 108
Mechanics of rumination, 85
Mechanisms and significance of rumination, 90
Megacalorie, 250
Mercury, 393
Metabolic body size, 210
Metabolic disorders, 294
Metabolic energy for bacteria, 278
Metabolic function of vitamin E, 318
Metabolic functions, 318
Metabolic intensity, 464
Metabolic problems related to nutrition, 493
Metabolism, 327, 330
   crate used for collection of both feces and urine, 183
   of bacterial nucleic acids, 410
   of carbohydrates by young ruminants, 289
   of VFA, 151
Metabolizable energy (ME), 150, 251
   requirement, 261
Methane
   generation, 278
     quantity of, 279
   -inhibiting compounds, 258
   -producing bacteria, 128
   production, 278, 286
Methanogenesis, 258
Methanogenic bacteria, 159, 279

Methodology for use of markers, 185
Methods
    for partitioning digestion, 193
    for starch determination, 291
    of bloat prevention, 473
    of measurement of apparent digestibility, 183
    of measuring retention time, 195
    of Se administration, 378
    of structural carbohydrate analysis, 291
    to predict protein escape, 239
    used to measure stomach volume, 52
Methylindole (3MI), 485
    effects on lung, 486
Methylmalonic acid, 343
Micoplasmas, 132
Microbes
    and acidity, 157
    location in rumen, 146
    numbers of, 152
Microbe-substrate adherence, 153
Microbial activity, 111, 450
Microbial biosynthesis, 178
Microbial characteristics, 125, 141
Microbial colonization, 154
Microbial crude protein (MCP), 227
Microbial degradation of dietary protein, 229
Microbial digestion, 403
    in reticulo-rumen, 178
Microbial efficiency, 162
Microbial factor, 472
Microbial fermentation, 22, 92, 110, 337
    of carbohydrates, 276, 286
Microbial growth rates and efficiency, 154
Microbial hydrogenation of fatty acids, 451
Microbial interdependence and other interactions, 134
Microbial lipolysis, 179
Microbial lysis in rumen, 162
Microbial maintenance costs, 163
Microbial mass, 165
Microbial populations, 402
Microbial protein, 337
    recycling, 132
Microbial protein synthesis, 163
Microbial type-substrate interactions, 153
Microbial yield, 161
Microbiology of rumen and intestine, 125
Microorganisms, 55
    of intestine, 141
Microstructure of absorptive ruminal papilla, 31
Midgut, 37
Migrating motor complexes, 101
Migration among digesta particles, 187
Milk
    diet, 81
    fat
        concerns, 310
        depression, 311, 504
        fats present in, 310
    fever, 493
    production, 8
        apparent costs of, 265
        and dry matter intake and body weights during lac-
            tation, 426
        factors most likely to limit, 427
    proteins, 406

    replacer, 319, 320, 416, 418, 419, 451
        diets, 417
    secretion and concentration of I, 359
    synthesis and apparent costs, 264
    tetany, 520
    zinc concentrations, 385
Milking techniques for preventing milk fever, 498
Mineral and vitamin deficiencies, 533
Mineral indices, 516
Mineral salts, 198
Minerals, 326, 423, 425, 454
    and special considerations, 432
    and vitamins, 507
        relationship to ketosis, 507
    of N content, 122
    supplementation, 352
Minor and toxic elements, 390
Miscellaneous treatments for ketosis, 509
Mixing stomach contents, 64
Model for metabolism of I, 358
Model of VFA transport across rumen epithelia, 177
Models of digestion, 151
Models of protein digestion, 239
Modifying effects on microbial population, 137
MOEFF, 162, 163, 164, 165, 166, 167, 168, 169, 235, 236,
    237
    measurement in vivo, 165
Molar proportion of VFA, 278
Molybdenum
    content of plasma and tissues, 348
    deficiency, 355
    effect on Cu, 349
    toxicity, 356
Monosaccharides, 269, 275
    composition of certain ruminant feedstuffs, 275
Morphophysiological feeding types, 14
    concentrate selectors, 14
    evolutionary system of, 14
    grass and roughage eaters, 15
    intermediate, mixed feeders, 15
Motility, 103
    of gastro-intestinal tract, 64
    of GI tract, 401
    patterns, 71, 74, 83
Motor activity, 98
    of cecum, 104
    of omasum, 77
    of reticulum, extrinsic vs. intrinsic, 84
Motor effects of acute distension of rumen, 94
Mucosal crests, 32
Mucosal relief, 27
    of abomasum, 36
    of omasum, 33, 35
    of reticulum, 32
Mucosal surface relief, 28
Mucosal transport mechanism, 343
Multiple controls over intake, 202
Muscle fiber arrangement of reticular groove, 27
Muscular activity, 265
Mutualism, 134

Nasolabial glands, 117
    secretions, 71
Naturally occurring Zn deficiency, 389
NDF, 291

Negative associative effects, 191, 257
Negative pressure in trachea, 85
Neonatal ataxia, 354
Neonatal glucose metabolism, 414
Neonatal lipid metabolism, 412
Neonatal ruminants, 173, 290
Net absorption of Mn, 369
Net efficiency, 263
Net energy (NE), 252
    requirement for maintenance, 252
Net protein utilization, 228
Net secretion of Fe into the small intestine, 364
Neural influences, 105
Neural stimulation from drinking, 66
Neurohormonal control, 103
Neuropeptidergic regulation, 202
Neurotransmitter, 99
NH$_3$ toxicity, 178
Niacin, 322
    addition to growing rations, 323
    and protein source influence on dairy cow performance,
      323
    effect on milk production, 322
    influence on adaptation of feeder calves, 323
Nickel, 371
    deficiency, 373
    toxicity, 373
Nitrate and urea toxicities, 480
    effect on feed intake and weight gain, 483
    effects on reproductive performance, 482
    toxicity, 480
    -vitamin A interrelationships, 482
Nitrogen, 515
    balance of retention, 244
    balance trials, 243
    recycling to rumen, 230
    requirements, safety margins and economics, 245
    retention, 243
Nitrogenous components of ruminant urine, 182
Nitrogenous compounds found in urine, 181
Nocturnal grazing, 111
Non-carbohydrate components, 281
Non-fecal losses of nutrients, 535
Non-protein nitrogen utilization, 231
Non-structural carbohydrates, 280, 285, 291
Non-structural polysaccharides, 271
Non-thermal stresses, 465
Normal, chronic and acute hypomagnesemia, 518
Normal reticulum contraction, 76
Normal ruminal proteolysis, 235
Normal swallowing, 86
No spiking activity, 98
NPN and natural proteins, 429
NPN toxicity, 232
NPN utilization, 430
Number of extinct and living genera, 1
Numbers of microbes, 152
Nutrients
    deficiencies, 418
    digestibility, 285
    excesses, 533
    limitation, 138
    needs for high-producing dairy cow, 426
    needs of preruminants, 415
    requirements, 445

Nutritional aspects of ketosis, 506
Nutritional availability of Ca, 432
Nutritional demand for production, 426
Nutritional effects on puberty, 421
Nutritional efficiency of tissue growth, 440
Nutritional manipulations, 260, 262
Nutritional muscular dystrophy, 379
Nutritional problems related to gastro-intestinal tract, 468
Nutrition
    and fetal growth, 441
      for growth-phases of growth, 441
      in growth, 437
Nutritive quality of microbial protein, 228
Nutritive value of dietary carbohydrates, evaluation of, 291
Nylon bag methods, 292

Objectionable tastes or smells, 209
Occurrence of ketosis, 500
Occurrence of milk fever, 493
Occurrence of pregnancy toxemia, 509
Odd-chain length fatty acids, 151
Odor of feces, 181
Oligosaccharides, 269
Omasal absorptive capacity, 34
Omasal anatomy, 33
Omasal and large intestinal weight, 46
Omasal body, 77
Omasal canal, 32, 33, 51, 77
Omasal contractions, 77, 79
Omasal fermentation, 167
Omasal groove, 32, 79
Omasal horn papillae, 35
Omasal laminae, 33, 34, 78
Omasal orifice, 66, 78
Omasal pillar, 33
Omasum, 23, 26, 41, 44, 47, 48, 52, 56, 77, 86, 99
Opioid peptides, 204
Optimal level of NDF, 211
Optimal NPN utilization, 453
Optimal pH for ruminal amylase, 156
Optimal ruminal microbial protein synthesis, 432
Optimizing feed intake during lactation, 428
Optimum amount of vitamin D, 317
Optimum energy intake, 427
Optimum pH, 404
Oral cavity, 15, 20
Oral glucose precursors, 508
    and ketosis, 508
Organic acids, 516
Origin of ruminant stomach, 44
Origin, regulation and utilization of ketone bodies, 506
Osmolality, 98
    and pH of chyme, 97
    and pH and redox potential, 146
Osmotic pressure, 121
Osteoporosis in sheep, 354
Ostertagia circumcincta, 99
Other nutritional adjustments for thermal environment, 465
Outflow of digesta into duodenum, 404
Output of microbial organic matter, 162
Oxidation-reduction potential, 125
Oxidized flavor of milk, 320

Palatability, 202, 203, 204, 208, 209
    and effects of vision, smell and texture, 208

Palatability (continued)
of Mg sources, 331
Palate, 17
Pancreas, 42, 174
Pancreatic amylase, 175
Pancreatic and intestinal carbohydrases, 286
Pancreatic and intestinal proteases, 179
Pancreatic and intestinal secretions, 404
Pancreatic duct, 42
Pancreatic enzymes, 405
Pancreatic islets, 42
Pancreatic juice, 175
Pancreatic lipase, 179
Pancreatico-biliary secretions, 101
Pancreatic proteases, 176
Pancreatic secretions, 174, 302, 404, 405
Papillae, 30, 33, 47
development, 59
growth, 56, 82, 83
Parakeratosis, 59
Parasitism, 134
Parasympathetic fibers, 42
Parenteral nutrition, 539
Parotid duct, 17
Parotid gland, 19, 71
Parotid papilla, 19
Parotid saliva, 17, 19
Parotid secretion, 122
Particle floatation, 150
Particle production, 207
Particle size, 149, 150, 151
comparison, 86
of forages, 198
reduction, 154
Particulate digesta, 195
Particulate matter, 188
Partitioning of nutrients, 456
Partition of dietary energy intake of animal, 456
Partition of digestion in gastro-intestinal tract, 192
Partition of energy, 251
Passage of ingesta, 99
Passage rate, 155, 168, 196, 282
of ingesta to small intestine, 404
Pathways for synthesis, 277
Pathways for VFA production from pyruvate, 159
Pathways of fiber degradation in cecum and large intestine, 286
Pattern of ruminal digestion and regulation, 155
Patterns of feeding and rumination, 104
Pea protein concentrates, 407
Pectic substances, 274, 275
Pectin hydrolysis, 277
Pelleted ration, 213
Pelleting, 294
Pepsin, 174
secretion, 97
Peptides, 180
as a N source, 234
Perinatal development, 102
Period of transition in rumen microbial population, 138
Periods of rumination, 87
Peripheral receptor mechanisms, 205
Peristaltic action in small intestine, 401
Peristaltic contraction, 104
Peyer's patches, 40

pH, 125, 156, 157
of digesta, 179
of ingesta, 301
of ruminal fluid, 153
optimum for proteolytic enzymes, 241
Pharmaceutical products, 8
Pharynx, 17, 20
and larynx, 19
function of, 19
Phenolic acids, 285
Phenolic compounds in urine, 182
Phosphate absorption, 333
Phosphatic urinary calculi, 523
Phospholipids, 179
Phosphorus, 331, 423, 425
absorption, 331
deficiency, 332
deficient and adequately fed steer, 333
metabolism, 332
requirements, 334
Photoperiod, 205
Physical examination of animal, 536
Physical form of forages, 198
Physical regulation, 202
Physical texture and moisture content of feed, 121
Physiological changes due to milk fever, 494
Physiological components of nutrition in growth, 439
Physiological role of Ni, 372
Physiological role of Se, 376
Physiology of nitrate toxicity, 481
Physiology of urea toxicity, 483
Placental uptake of amino acids, 408
Plant factor, 470
Plant lignins, 284
Plasma
amino acid concentrations, 244
B_{12} concentrations, 344
concentrations of vitamin A, 314
gastrin, 102
glucose, 414
in fetal lambs, 414
inorganic P, 332
lipids, 412
urea N, 410
VFA, 289
Polyencephalomalaca (PEM), 321, 479
Polyethylene glycol, 188
Polysaccharides, 269, 271
Poor quality roughages, 210
Positive associative effects, 191
Possibly essential microelements, 342
Post-feeding changes, 152
Postruminal digestion, 175
and absorption of N compounds, 241
of protein, 179
Potassium, 334, 512
deficiency, 334
-deficient lamb, 335
depletion, 334
excess, 335
metabolism, 334
supplementation, 335
Potential approaches to prevent ABPE, 488
Power from ruminants, 8

Practical use of added fats, 309
Precursor for lipogenesis, 279
Precursor of milk fatty acids, 279
Precursors for fatty acid synthesis, 305
Predation by protozoa, 131
Predation of protozoa by other protozoa, 137
Predisposing conditions for hypomagnesemic tetany, 519
Predominant bacteria, 142
Predominant rumen bacteria, 133
Preference of protozoa for bacterial species, 131
Preferential placental transfer, 413
Pregastric and gastric secretions, 403
Pregastric fermentaion, 449
Pregnancy toxemia
   cause of, 509
   in sheep, 509
Prehensile organs, 15
Prehension, 15
Preliminary period, 183
Premolars, 17
Prepartum feeding effects, 496
Preruminant, 95, 319, 401
Preruminant stage, 101
Preruminant state, 81
Pressure changes
   in reticulum of young calf, 83
   in reticulum of cow at rest, 77
Pressure events in reticulo-rumen, 71
Pressure in llama stomach, 72
Pressure recordings
   in reticulum of deer, 75
   of cow starting to eat hay or ruminating, 75
Pressure waves in rumen, incidence of, 68
Preventative nutrition, 539
Prevention
   of ABPE, 488
   of Co deficiency, 344
   of Cu deficiency, 352
   of hypomagnesemia, 522
   of ketosis, 509
   of milk fever, 497
   of phosphatic urinary calculi, 526
   of rumination, 114
   of siliceous urinary calculi, 527
Primary and secondary ruminal contractions, 69, 71
Primary contractions, 68, 70, 85
   frequency, 93
Primary ketosis, 500
Primary peristalsis, 76
Primary reticulo-ruminal contractions, 68
Principles of preventative and therapeutic nutrition, 539
Priorities for fat deposition, 308
Processing of grains, 195
Process of hydrogenation, 301
Production from ruminants, 7
Production of VFA, 158
Products which alter rumen fermentation, 433
Products with hormone activity, 434
Progressive clinical tetany, 518
Propionate absorbed from rumen, 287
Propulsive waves, 102
Protein, 422, 429, 452
   absorption and metabolism, 408
   and fat contents of body, schematic representation, 262
   and ketosis, 507

   coagulation and digestion, 404
   degradation in rumen, 237
   deposition, 262
   digestion, 453
      and metabolism, 406
      models, 239
   effect of, 285
   escape, methods to predict, 239
   expenditures and estimated requirements, 247
   metabolism in lactating cow, 227
   metabolism in preruminants, 410
   requirements, 242, 429
      of preruminants, 417
   solubility, 238
      and degradability, 430
   sources, 179
      in rumen, 132
      and gastric emptying effects, 404
   synthesis, 244, 410
      in rumen, 286
   turnover, 439
Proteolytic bacteria, 128
Protozoa, 156, 277
   effect on rumen fermentation, 132
   in rumen, number of, 130
   predation of bacteria, 167
   role in rumen, 132
Proximal colon, 104, 105
Pseudoruminants, 6
Pseudorumination, 74 , 83, 90, 91, 109, 112
   as observed in sheep, 90
Pure cultures, 134
Purified diets, 234
Purines or pyrimidines for growth, 235
Pyloric region, 51
Pylorus, 172

Qualitative evaluation of food, 537
Quantitative examination, 538
Quantitative expression of concentrations, 481
Quantity of fecal dry matter excreted, 180
Quantity of gastric juice secreted, 172
Quantity of N recycled to rumen, 230

Range in saliva production, 122
Rare-earth elements, 187
Rate
   and extent of degradation of wheat straw cellulose, 281
   of absorption, 178
      of VFA, 176
   of ammonia release, 232
   of digestion, 148, 195, 282
      and extent, 256
   of gain by feedlot cattle fed various protein levels, 246
   of glucogenesis, 287, 289
   of hemicellulose degradation, 277
   of nutrient solubilization, 154
   of passage, 149, 194, 198, 208
   of protein deposition in tissue, 246
   of salivation, 152
Rationale of milk fever, 497
Ration physical form effect on rumen parameters, 61
Ratio of body length to intestinal length, 37
Readily fermentable carbohydrates, 137, 138
Receptive relaxation, 95

Recommended allowance, 315
Recommended dietary levels and variability in feeds, 315
Recommended feeding levels, 317
Reconstitution of grains, 294
Recreation, 7
    bull riding, 12
    game ranching, 11
    rodeo cowboy, 12
    use of ruminant animals, 11
Rectum, 40
Recycled sulfate, 337
Recycling
    of Co to rumen, 343
    of N to rumen, 229
    of urea, 244
Reduced fiber digestibility, 428
Reduced food intake, 534
Reduced milk fat percentage, 294
Reductions in tissue weights, 56
Re-entrant cannulas, 167
Re-entrant duodenal cannulas, 96
Reflex control of saliva secretion, 120
Reflex mechanisms of reticular groove, 65
Reflex rumination, 90
Regular spiking activity, 98
Regulation
    of fermentation, 158
    of urine flow, 219
Regurgitation, 19, 64, 71, 76, 81, 83, 109
    contractions, 75
    of digesta, 85
Relationship
    between pathways of gluconeogenesis and glucose precursors, 276
    between proportion of grain in the diet and digestibility, 190
    between retained energy and gross energy intake, 256
    between Se and vitamin E, 318
    of ketosis to glucose metabolism, 503
    of "Mg availability" to forage N, 515
    of retained energy to food intake, 252
    of ruminal pH, saliva production and rumination time to diet composition, 156
    of ruminal pH to ruminal acids, 155
    between fermentation products, substrate and other end-products, 160
Relative change in wet tissue organ weights, 49
Relative sizes of different parts of stomach in newborn calf, 95
Relative volume of cecum, 40
Release of energy from fermentation, 152
Rennin, 174
Reproduction, 424
    performance, 315
    problems, 422
Requirements
    for maintenance, 258
    during peak lactation, 425
    for Cu, 351
    for essential amino acids, 233
Reserve polysaccharide, 131
Residence time of feed residues, factors affecting, 197
Resting phase of eating, 74
Resynthesis and transport of lipids, 303
Retained energy and gross energy intake, 256

Retention and mixing of ingesta, 67
Retention time, 195, 197
    in rumen, 294
    of feed residues in the gastro-intestinal tract, 195
Reticular contractions, 70, 74, 77, 78, 80, 87
    during sham feeding, 73
Reticular groove, 32, 33, 34, 44, 51, 64
    closure, 64, 67, 401
        and activation of reticular groove reflex, 67
        and intraruminal drug delivery, 67
        and teat versus bucket feeding, 67
    contractions, 65
Reticular mucosa, 32
Reticular myoelectric activity, 80
Reticular pressure patterns, 77
Reticulo-omasal orifice, 32, 33, 34, 65, 78, 79, 80, 148, 150
Reticulo-rumen, 68, 81, 85, 95, 99, 194, 195, 199, 204, 205, 207, 208, 209, 213
    activity of bison, 88
    contents, 207
    contractions, 67, 70, 84
    fold, 68
    motility, 104
    motility patterns, 87
    movements, 67
    pressure in calves, 81
Reticulum, 23, 44, 48, 68, 70, 80, 86
    contraction, 87
    motor activity of, extrinsic vs. intrinsic, 84
Rhodopsin, 313
Roles
    of dietary carbohydrate in nutrition, 269
    of fat in intake control, 213
    of lipid metabolism, 504
    of metabolic water, 222
    of Mg in animals, 511
Rosettes of bacteria, 154
Roughage diets, 155, 158, 168
Roughage intake, influences, 205
Roughage passage rate with various intakes of concentrate and passage, 149
Route of Cu excretion, 349
Route of Zn excretion, 385
Rumen, 23, 39, 44, 48, 80, 148
    ammonia
        and nitrogen recycling, 229
        concentrations, 230, 483
    and 3MI, 487
    and acidosis, 535
    anaerobic mycoplasma, 132
    artery, 36
    bacteria, 125, 128, 475
        species, grouping according to type of substrates fermented, 126
        methods of classification, 126
        number, 125
        shapes, 126
        size, 126
        structures, 126
    buffering capacity, 338
    cannula, 66
    capacity, 48
    characteristics, 125
    contents, 95
    contractions, 72, 81, 82, 150, 401

560

Rumen (continued)
  crossfeeding, 235
  degradation of protein, 241
  digesta
    positioning, 149
    sub-fractions, 150
  digestibility, 194
  digestion, 148, 156, 168, 194, 237, 245, 280, 285, 293
    overview, 145
  distension, 93, 204
  dry matter, 147
    and ruminal volume and lignin passage rate, 147
    with various intakes of concentrate and roughage, 147
  ecosystem, 125
  environment, 279
    characteristics, 146
  epithelial and muscular growth, 57
  epithelium, 56, 61
  fermentation, 145, 176, 178, 227, 450
    and host metabolism, 150
    patterns, 198
  function development, 228
  gas pressure, 70
  grooves, 26, 27
  incubation, 281
  inflammation and hemorrhaging in rumenitis case, 475
  in newborn, 47
  liquid volume, 146
  liquids and solids, 150
  metabolism of dietary lipids, 45
  microbes, 227, 241, 299
    as protein source, 227
  microbial action, 152
  microbial biomass, 169
  microbial metabolism, 299
  microbial population, 133, 337
    limitation in geographical distribution, 136
  microbial protein production, 403
  microbial protein requirements, 429
  microorganisms, 269, 290, 343
    influence of various factors on, 137
  microvasculature development, 45
  mucosa, 28
  motility, 72, 100, 294
  osmotic pressure, 114
  papillae, 28, 29, 36, 48, 157
    development, 45
    growth in calves, 82
    parakeratosis, 294
  papillation in response to nutritional changes, 29
  particulate contents, 198
  passage rate, 147
  pellets, 345
  pH, 114, 155, 158, 176, 229, 240
    effects of, 139
  pillars, 27
  propionate production, 287
  proteases and peptidases, 238
  protein degradation, 239
  proteolysis, 238
  protozoa, 130, 276
    classification and identification of, 130
    different genera, 131
    size of, 130
  retention time, 150, 168, 169, 198, 283

  sampling errors, 166
  specific gravity, 112
  stratification, 150
  sulfur deficiencies, 235
  synthesis, 321, 324
    of certain B-vitamins, 320
    of lipids, 301
  temperature, 125
  ureolysis, 232
  veins, 30
  VFA concentrations with two levels of dietary concentrate, 157
  volume, 53, 59, 146, 147, 151, 153, 196
    with various intakes of concentrate and roughage, 147
  wall
    fully developed cross section, 55
    and transfer across, 230
Ruminants
  families, 2
  importance in world agriculture, 7
  production from, 7
  source of power, 8
Ruminant stomach, relative weights, 45
Ruminated bolus, 86
Ruminated polypropylene particles, 113
Rumination, 15, 22, 64, 71, 74, 83, 85, 91, 92, 108, 109, 111, 112, 113, 117, 146, 149, 155, 207, 401
  duration, 84, 87
  efficiency, 114, 402
    factors affecting, 88, 114
  periods, 22
  time, 84, 87, 109, 206
    of sheep, 88
Ruminoreticular digesta, weight, 53
Ruminoreticular fold, 30
Ruminoreticular growth, 46
Ruminoreticulum, 56
  capacity of, 25
  relative size, 49
  volume and contents, 54

Safe levels of toxic elements and ions in water, 224
Safety signals, 205, 211
Saline drinking water, 225
Salinity influence on water requirements, 223
Saliva, 207, 230, 294, 330, 332
  amounts, 120
  and surface tension, 470
  as aid in mastication and swallowing, 121
  collecting, 118
  excretion of K, 336
  function, 121
    and production, 117
  -mucin theory, 470
  production, 155
    by cattle consuming different types of feed, 122
    and methods used to measure, 117
  types, 117
Salivary glands, 15, 26, 117, 118
  names of, 117
  relative sizes, 119
Salivary lipase, 121
Salivary protein, 120
Salivary secretion, 100, 134, 338, 402
  in young ruminants, 123

Salivation rate, 152
Sampling from duodenum, 167
Sampling of ruminal microbes, 165
Satiety, 202, 204, 206, 207
    center(s) in brain, 202
Sausage casings, 8
Schematic of protein metabolism in lactating cow, 227
Seasonal adaptations, 29
Seasonal changes
    in pasture composition, 345
    in rumen papillation, 30
Seasonal differences in mineral contents of plants, 326
Secondary compounds which may affect carbohydrate diges-
    tion, 285
Secondary contractions, 68, 71, 73
    frequency, 93
Secondary Cu deficiency, 353
Secondary factors affecting digestion and utilization, 283
Secondary fermentation, 138
Secondary ketosis, 499
Secondary peristalsis, 76
Secondary ruminal contractions, 69, 76, 92
Secretin, 175
Secretions
    amount, 117
    during eating and rumination, 122
    of bovine muscle at sight of food, 72
    of I in milk, 359
    rate, 117, 173
    into digestive tract, 172
    into small intestine, 174
    with age, 123
Secretory activity, 173
Segmentary contractions, 105
Selection of particles for passage, 86
Selective feeders, 110
Selenium, 373, 423
    absorption and retention, 376
    accumulation in plants, 382
    and reproduction, 380
    and retained placenta, 381
    concentrations in tissues of lambs and steers, 374
    deficiency, 379
    metabolism, 376
        by rumen microbes, 376
    requirement, 378
    supplementation, 423
    toxicity, 382
    toxicosis, 344
Sensitivity to pH, redox potential and osmolality of bacteria,
    137
Sequence of events involved in eructation, 92
Sequential fermentation of alfalfa components, 155
Sequential microbial digestion, 154
Serum K levels, 334
Severity of Co deficiency, 345
Sham feeding, 73, 210
Sheep, 212
Short-term controls, 202, 203, 205
    of intake, 214
Sialic acid, 120
Sigmoid loop, 39
Signs of low vitamin D intakes, 317
Signs of Mg deficiency, 330
Silica, 186, 285

Siliceous urinary calculi, 527
Simple sugar-utilizing bacteria, 128
Single cell protein sources, 407
Sites
    and rate and extent of carbohydrate digestion, 280
    and end-products of digestion, 193
    in which digestion and absorption occur, 192
    of absorption, 409
        of K, 334
        of Mn, 369
    of acetate utilization, 279
    of action in digestion and absorption, 280
    of digestion, 194, 199
    of fermentation, 141
Situations in which markers are useful, 188
Skull of red deer, 21
Slime produced by rumen microorganisms, 471
Slow release therapy, 540
Small intestine, 45, 56, 64, 103, 173
    description, 39
    motility, 101
Smell, 115
Smooth muscle cell response via enteric nervous system, 80
Sodium, 335
    absorption, 335
    and chloride levels of selected feedstuffs, 329
    content of body, 336
    deficiency, 336
    excess, 336
    excretion, 336
    loss from body, 336
    metabolism, 336
    :potassium ratios, 514
    uptake from small intestine, 335
Solubility of Cu in rumen and abomasal contents, 351
Soluble carbohydrates, 153, 283
Soluble material released during chewing, 110
Soluble proteins, 239
Soluble sugars, 178
Sound, 466
Sources
    of branched-chain fatty acids (BCFA), 234
    of inorganic Ca, 327
    of Fe, 365
    of ME, 263
    of NPN, 232
    of S, 336
    of vitamin D, 318
    of Zn, 387
Soybean proteins, 406
Special considerations of B vitamins in ruminant rations, 321
Species, 1
    breed and age differences, 307
    comparisons, 70
    differences, 359
        in eructation, 93
        within ruminants, 313
Specific gravity, 86, 149
    of ruminant urine, 181
Specificity and distribution in rumen microbial population,
    136
Specific preventive procedures for milk fever, 498
Spike burst potentials, 105
Spiking activity, 102
Spiral colon, 40, 104, 105

Spiral colon (continued)
    and pelleted feces, 105
Spiral folds, 35
Spleen, 42
Splenic and pancreatic attachment, 26
Sporangia of rumen fungi, 132
Sprint tetany or lactation tetany, 519
Squamous epithelium, 33
Stained feeds, 186
Starch, 450
    and sugars, 450
    digestibility of corn silage and corn diets, 191
    digestion, 194, 413
        and utilization by ruminants, 280
        in small intestine, 280
    from various sources, 272
    intake and digestion in reticulo-rumen and total gastro-
        intestinal tract, 293
Starvation, 203
Starvation conditions, 138
State of the art, 202
Steam flaking, 195, 293
Stimulatory effects of feeding concentrates, 72
Stomach, 23
    abnormal development, 25
    blood and nerve supply, 36
    capacity of, 25
    gross anatomy, 26
    interior surfaces of compartments (mucosal relief), 26
    motility, miscellaneous factors, 76
        patterns, 64
    muscle layers of, 27
    of bovine fetus, 44
    of newborn calf, diagram, 48
    outer surface, 26
    repair periods, 29
    shape and proportions, 24
    size, 49
        and capacity, 23
    spatial relationship and internal structure, 28
    volume, 52
Storage Fe of body, 363
Storage lipids, 299
Stratification of rumen contents, 140
Stress related problems, 456
Structural carbohydrates, 275, 280, 286, 291
Structural formulae for starch, cellulose and pectin, 272
Structural lipids, 298
Structural polysaccharides, 273, 281
Subacute bloat, 468
Subacute effects of nitrate, 482
Sub-clinical ketosis, 322
Sublingual floor of lower jaw, 18
Sublingual gland, 19
Subspecies, 2
Substrate cycles, 259, 261, 263
Substrates bacteria will attack, 126
Substrates fermented and end-products produced by rumen
    ciliate protozoa, 130
Sucking behavior, 64
Suggested B-vitamin requirements for ruminants, 321
Suggested vitamin and mineral allowances for young calves,
    418
Sulcus abomasi, 35
Sulfide formation in rumen, 337

Sulfur, 336
    and Se, 377
    deficiency, 337
    excess, 337
    in parotid saliva, 123
    levels in selected feedstuffs, 337
    requirement, 338
    toxicity, 338
Summit metabolism, 462
Supplemental amino acids, 244
Supplemental beta-carotene, 422
Supplemental vitamin E, 320
Supplementation of NPN diets, 231
Supplementation of vitamin E in ruminant diets, 320
Supplementation with amino acids, 246
Surface to volume ratio, 152
Surgical sutures, 8
Survival time of microorganisms, 138
Swallowed ruminated boli, 86
Swallowing, 19, 152
Swayback, 354
Sympathetic nerves, 36
    fibers, 42
Symptoms
    of acidosis, 478
    of bloat, 468
    of Co deficiency, 345
    of ketosis, 500
    of milk fever, 493
    of pregnancy toxemia, 510
Synergistic relationship between ruminant microbes, 145
Synthesis and interconversions of VFA in rumen, 159
Synthesis and metabolism of lipids, 305
Synthesis by rumen microorganisms, 320
Synthesis of ceruloplasmin, 348
Synthesis of intracellular polysaccharide, 235
Synthesis of thiaminase by rumen microbes, 322
Synthesis of triglycerides, 304

Tactile stimulation, 89
Tannins, 285
Taste, 115
    and smell, 121
    for Na, 335
Tastebuds, 17
Techniques for study of energy metabolism, 253
Techniques of calorimetry, 253
Teeth, 15, 207
    and masticatory muscles, 20
    canines, 20
    deciduous dentition, 22
    enamel, 21
    formula for dentition, 20
    hardness, 21
    incisors, 17, 20
    molars, 21
    premolars, 21
    wear and loss, 21
Tension receptors, 204
Terminal ileum, 101, 104, 105
Tetany-prone pastures, 512
Theories on development of rumination, 91
Therapeutic feeding, 539
Therapeutic nutrition, 532

Therapy and prevention, 479
Therapy for ketosis, 508
Thermal balance and transient imbalances, 459
Thermal exchange, 460
Thermal radiation, 458
Thermal stress, 458
Thermogenesis, 439
Thermoregulatory range, 460
Thermoregulatory stresses, 203
Thiamin, 321
    deficiency, 322
        and PEM, 322
Thiaminase activity, 322
Thyroid gland, 357
    dysfunctions, 423
    function, 483
    secretion rates, 358
    uptake and recovery of radioiodine, 359
    uptakes by dairy cows and their neonatal calves, 360
Timing of feeding, 111
Tissue Cu and Mo, 347
Tissue distribution
    of I, 357
    of Se, 373
    of Zn, 383
Tissue energy, 259
Tissue gain, 261
Tissue metabolism, 305, 536
Tissue Mg levels, 514
Tissue Mn, 367
    concentrations, 367
Tissues which require glucose, 286
Tissue weight of glands, 117
Tissue weights and capacity of stomach organs, 57
Tolerance of livestock to salt, 224
Tongue, 17
    function, 17
    papillae, 17
Topographic relations in abdomen, 25
Total alimentary tract tissue, 45
Total body water, 218
Total microbial yield, 168
Total requirement for N, 246
Total tract digestibility, 194, 198
Toxicity
    levels and symptoms of excess vitamin E, 320
    levels and symptoms of vitamin A, 314
    signs, 362
    symptoms, 317
        of vitamin D, 317
Trace elements, 326
    function of, 342
Tragulidae, 3, 6
Transfer across rumen wall, 230
Transfer of protozoa, 134
Transportation tetany or transit tetany, 520
    in lambs, 521
Transport mechanisms, 332
Transport of lipoproteins, 304
Transport system for P, 332
Transpyloric flow of digesta, 99
Transverse sections of omasum, 34
Traumatic peritonitis, 76
Treatment
    and prevention of pregnancy toxemia, 510

of acute hypomagnesemia, 522
of acute nitrate toxicity, 482
of milk fever, 498
of Pb toxicity, 393
of urea toxicity, 484
of urinary calculi, 528
or prevention of Cu poisoning, 356
to reduce protein solubility, 431
Tricarboxylic acid cycle, 279
Triglycerides, 179, 303
Trisaccharide, 271
True digestibility, 183
    for total amino acids, 180
True vs. apparent digestibility, 189
Trypsin, 176
Tryptophan (TRP), 486
Turnover of microbial cells, 166
Turnover of protein, 263
Turnover rates of Mn, 367
Two-choice preference test, 209
Type and size of protozoa, 156
Type of grain and grain processing, 195
Types of isolated organisms, 142
Types of tannins, 285
Typical energy accretion curve, 264

Udder edema, 335
Ultradian variations, 100
Ultrastructure of epithelia, 56
Underfeeding, fasting or starvation tetany, 520
Unguiculiform papillae, 33
Ungulates, 1
Unsaturated dietary fats, 413
Urea, 232
    feeding, 422
    toxicity, 483, 484
Urinary calculi, 333, 523
    incidence, 526
Urinary deposits, 524
Urinary excretion, 410
    and composition, 181
    of SiO_2, 527
Urinary Mg, 330
Urine
    alkalinity, 525
    color, 181
    Mg concentrations, 520
    volume, 526
Utilization
    of absorbed amino acids, 243
    of dietary buffers, 338
    of iodine sources, 360
    of markers to measure digestibility, 185
    of ME, 258
    of NPN, 417
    of structural carbohydrates, 294

Vagotomy, 103
    of sheep, 84
Vagovagal reflex, 84
Variability of vitamin D in feeds, 318
Variables affecting the quality or quantity of saliva, 121
Variable secretion, 118
Variables influencing thermal impact of environment on animals, 458

Variation
  between animals, 519
  from animal to animal of bacteria, 137
  in bacteria, 137
  in minerals of N content, 122
  in MOEFF, 235
  in protozoa, 137
  in rumen microbial population, 136
Veins, 36
Vena cava, 41
Ventral buccal gland, 17
Ventricular or gastric groove, 35
Ventricular or reticular groove, 32
VFA, 150, 173, 261, 277, 286, 290
  absorption, 176, 177
    and metabolism, 279
    from reticulo-rumen, 176
  concentrations, 105, 133, 229, 403
    vs. production rates, 158
  effects on growth, 158
  in rumen, 202
  in rumen fluid, 204
  production, 158, 278, 286
  ratios and uses, 158
  relative production rates, 161
    example of calculations, 161
  requirement of bacteria, 135
  transport, 61
    model of, 177
Viable counts from digesta, 142
Visual appraisal of animal, 536
Vitamin A, 313, 422, 424
  deficiency symptoms, 314
  functions, 313
  needs, 316
Vitamin B_{12}-like molecules, 344
Vitamin B_{12} synthesis in rumen, 344
Vitamin D, 316, 422, 424
  concentrations in plasma or tissues, 317
  deficiency, 317
  -deficient calf, 316
  for prevention of milk fever, 318, 498
  metabolites, 496
Vitamin E, 318, 422
  and Se, 377, 424
  deficiency, 319
  -deficient calf, 319
  -deficient lambs, 319
  requirement, 320
Vitamin K, 324
Vitamins, 422, 424, 453
  and mineral requirements, 417
  in ruminant nutrition, 313
  required by bacteria, 136
  and special considerations, 432

Volume
  of chyme, 405
  of pancreatic juice, 175
  of reticulo-rumen contents, 205
  of urine, 220
Voluntary feed intake, 285
Voluntary intake, 210
Voluntary roughage intakes, 207

Water, 513
  and adaptation, 220
  and intermediary metabolism, 218
  and its functions, 217
  as a coolant, 218
  availability, 221
  comparative use, 220
  conservation, 220
  consumption, 115
    by livestock, 222
  content of carcass components, 217
  content of diet, 428
  excretion, 220
  functions and regulations, 218
  in feces, 221
  in forage, 221
  in rumen, 66
  quantitative requirements, 222
  requirements, 221, 223
    effect of increasing ambient temperatures, 223
    of preruminants, 418
    of ruminants, 466
  -soluble markers, 188
  turnover, 217, 223
    rates, 220
Watering behavior, 221
Weaning to yearly age or puberty, 443
Weight gain, influence on protein need, 247
Wet tissue weights, 59
Wheat pasture tetany, 519
White muscle disease, 318
Whole animal glucose requirements, 287
Wind-chill, 458
Winter tetany or seasonal tetany, 519
Wool, mohair and leather, 8

X-ray use, 64

Young ruminants, 314

Zinc, 383
  contents of several feeds, 387
  deficiency, 387, 424
    symptoms, 387
  -deficient lamb and calf, 388
  toxicity, 390
Zone of minimal metabolism, 460